Harnessing AutoCAD®

DRAW FROM EXPERIENCE!

Also available for Release 13 of AutoCAD®
from Delmar Publishers

AutoCAD r13 Update Guide for DOS and Windows, by Sham Tickoo
ISBN 0–8273–7433–X

The Illustrated AutoCAD Quick Reference for DOS, by Ralph Grabowski
ISBN 0–8273–6645–0

The Illustrated AutoCAD Quick Reference for Windows, by Ralph Grabowski
ISBN 0–8273–7149–7

The AutoCAD Tutor for Engineering Graphics, by Alan Kalameja
ISBN 0–8273–5914–4

Using AutoCAD r13 for DOS, by James Edward Fuller, edited by Ralph Grabowski
ISBN 0–8273–6824–0

3-hole punched binding ISBN 0–8273–6972–7

Harnessing AutoCAD r13 for DOS, by Tom Stellman, G.V. Krishnan, Robert Rhea
ISBN 0–8273–6822–4

3-hole punched binding ISBN 0–8273–6971–9

Harnessing AutoCAD r13 for Windows, by Tom Stellman, G.V. Krishnan, Robert Rhea
ISBN 0–8273–7199–3

3-hole punched binding ISBN 0–8273–7224–8

AutoCAD: A Problem-Solving Approach r13 DOS, by Sham Tickoo
ISBN 0–8273–6015–0

AutoCAD: A Problem-Solving Approach r13 Windows, by Sham Tickoo
ISBN 0–8273–7432–1

AutoCAD: A Visual Approach r13 DOS/Windows—Series, by Steven Foster and others
(Call for individual module ISBNs)

Call your local representative for more information and a complete listing of all that Delmar Publishers offers the AutoCAD user!

Harnessing AutoCAD®

Release 13 for Windows

**Thomas A. Stellman
G. V. Krishnan
and
Robert A. Rhea**

elmar Publishers Inc.™

I(T)P™ ernational Thomson Publishing Company

Albany • Bonn • B • Cincinnati • Detroit • London • Madrid
Melbourne • Mexico Cit   • w York • Pacific Grove • Paris • San Francisco
Singapo kyo • Toronto • Washington

NOTICE TO THE READER

Publisher does not warrant or guarantee any of the products described herein or perm any independent analysis in connection with any of the product information contained herein. Publisher does not a me, and expressl disclaims, any obligation to obtain and include information other than that provided to it by the manu turer.

The reader is expressly warned to consider and adopt all safety precautions that ght be indicated by the activities described herein and to avoid all potential hazards. By following the instructions tained herein, t e reader willingly assumes all risks in connection with such instructions.

The publisher makes no representations or warranties of any kind, including but not nited to, the warranties of fitness for particular purpose or merchantability, nor are any such representations implied with spect to the mate al set forth herein, and the publisher takes no responsibility with respect to such material. The publ er shall not be liole for any special, consequential or exemplary damages resulting, in whole or in part, from the readers' e of, or reliance upo, his material.

Trademarks

AutoCAD® and the AutoCAD® logo are registered trademarks of Autodesk, Inc.

Windows is a trademark of the Microsoft Corporation.

All other product names are acknowledged as trademarks of their respective ow ers.

Cover Design: Michael Speke

Delmar Staff:

Publisher: Robert Lynch
Acquisitions Editor: Mary Beth Ray, (CompuServe 73234,3664)
Project Development Editor: Jenna Daniels, (CompuServe 76433, 1677
Production Coordinator: Andrew Crouth, (CompuServe 74507,250)
Art and Design Coordinator: Lisa L. Bower
Publishing Assistant: Karianne Simone, (CompuServe 76433,1702)

Library of Congress Cataloging-in-Publication Data

Stellman, Thomas A.
  Harnessing AutoCAD for Windows release 13/Thomas A. Stell
G.V. Krishnan, and Robert A. Rhea—[2nd ed.]
    p. cm.
    ISBN 0-8273-7199-3
    1. Computer graphics. 2. AutoCAD for indows. I. Krishnan
II. Rhea, Robert A. III. Title.
T385.S754 1995
620'.0042'02855369—dc20

43755
CIP

BRIEF CONTENTS

CONTENTS

Chapter 4 Fundamentals III 4-1

Chapter 5   Fundamentals IV 5-1

Chapter 8   Hatching and Boundaries 8-1

Chapter 9   Blocks and Attributes 9-1

Chapter 18 AutoLISP 18-1

INTRODUCTION

HARNESSING THE POWER OF AUTOCAD

Writing a book on AutoCAD® is much like reining in a team of spirited horses, with each new release bringing greater design and graphics power. *Harnessing AutoCAD®* Release 13 for Windows is a book written to give you skills to rein in and master this seemingly boundless program so that AutoCAD® is working for you.

Now in its 2nd edition, *Harnessing AutoCAD®* Release 13 for Windows was written and updated as a comprehensive tool for the novice and the experienced AutoCAD user, both in the classroom and on the job.

Release 13 offers powerful new features—annotation, hatching dimensioning, 3D solid modeling, editing, improved interface and interoperability—and *Harnessing AutoCAD®* Release 13 for Windows was written specifically to provide help where needed to harness the power of AutoCAD.

The book opens with an overview of all aspects of AutoCAD® so that the user can establish a basic understanding of how CAD works. Users immediately gain a broad range of knowledge of the elementary CAD concepts necessary to complete a simple drawing. We do not believe the user should be asked to wade through all components of every command or concept the first time that command or concept is introduced. Therefore, we have set up the early chapters so that fundamentals are covered and practiced extensively to better prepare the user for the more advanced topics covered later in the book.

HIGHLIGHTS AND FEATURES OF THIS NEW EDITION

- Competency-based objectives begin each chapter to keep you on track with the new CADD Skill Standards

- Toolbars, dialog boxes and menu illustrations completely redone to match AutoCAD Release 13 interface

- Expanded coverage of AutoCAD fundamentals

- New, expanded chapter covering all dimensioning topics

- Expanded coverage of hatching and boundaries

- Exercises in each chapter reinforce skills just learned

- All new step-by-step project exercises at the end of the chapters help the user master key AutoCAD commands.

- End-of-chapter questions provide a test of key chapter concepts

- An option for SIMPLE FLEXIBILITY: Each chapter of *Harnessing AutoCAD* is written to take you step-by-step through many features of AutoCAD. However, not everyone follows the same path when learning the software. We offer a separate, non-bound, 3-hole punched alternative of this edition. Chapter page numbering is self-contained, so you may "customize" the direction this text takes by arranging the chapters in the order that suits you best.

RELEASE 13 ENHANCEMENTS AND WHERE TO FIND THEM

New AutoCAD Release 13 Feature	Inside the revision of *Harnessing AutoCAD*
Advanced geometry, including free-form NURBS and ellipses, as well as construction lines and rays.	**Expanded Fundamentals chapters (2-5)** Chapter 2 covers the ELLIPSE command, while Chapter 5 expands on drawing construction lines and rays, and the SPLINE command. A section in Chapter 4 teaches the use of grips.
New construct and modify commands.	**Expanded Fundamentals chapters (2-5)** Chapter 4 includes coverage of the GROUP and LENGTHEN commands and additional options of the Object Snap modes. Chapter 9, Blocks and Attributes, covers the abilities of the EXPLODE command.
Editing of multiple lines of text, and a new spell checker.	**Placing Text (Chapter 5)** This section covers the new MLINE command and the spell checker.
Associative hatching that automatically updates when boundaries or hatch patterns change.	**Hatching and Boundaries (Chapter 8)** An expanded chapter covers the new commands and enhancements of hatching boundaries.
Special linetypes with shapes and text.	**Utility Commands (Chapter 12)** **Customizing AutoCAD (Chapter 17)** Coverage of the LINETYPE command appears in chapter 12, while the more advanced user can learn to create custom linetypes in Chapter 17.
Dimensioning	**Dimensioning (Chapter 6)** This all-new chapter covers the full range of dimensioning commands and utilities to enable the user to comply with the conventions of most disciplines.
Integrated solid modeling	**AutoCAD 3D (Chapter 14)** This expanded chapter covers the commands of solid modeling, now a standard feature.
Built-in, high-quality rendering	**Rendering (Chapter 15)** With coverage of the new lighting features and file formats, this chapter explores Release 13 rendering enhancements.

HOW TO USE THIS BOOK

Overview

The first chapter of this text provides an overview of the AutoCAD program, its interface, the commands, special features and warnings, and Release 13 enhancements. This chapter is only an introduction to the program, not a lesson in using the commands, which are described in detail throughout the book.

Fundamentals

Harnessing AutoCAD contains four chapters devoted to teaching the fundamentals of the program. Fundamentals I introduces some of the basic commands and concepts, such as beginning a drawing, coordinate systems, and basic draw, modify and text commands. Fundamentals II covers the commands necessary to for more involved drawings, including modify and construct commands, as well as object snap applications. Fundamentals III teaches additional draw, modify and display commands, as well as providing coverage of Object Selection modes. Fundamentals IV covers drawing construction lines and rays, multilines, placing text, inquiry commands, and setting system variables.

Intermediate

After mastering the fundamentals, the user moves on to more intermediate topics including dimensioning, plotting and printing, hatching and boundaries, blocks and attributes, external references and drawing environments. Other chapters are introduced that teach students to make the most of AutoCAD, including utility commands, scripts and slides, 3D commands, rendering, and use of the digitizing tablet.

Advanced

For the advanced AutoCAD user, this book offers two chapters: Customizing AutoCAD, which includes customizing of toolbars, (Chapter 17) and AutoLISP (Chapter 18). These two chapters teach the user to make AutoCAD more individualized and powerful, tailored to special needs.

Appendices

There are nine appendices in the back of this book. Appendix A is an introduction to hardware and software requirements of AutoCAD. Appendix B provides information on file handling. Appendix C is a quick reference of AutoCAD commands with a brief description of their basic functions, while Appendix D gives a visual reference of AutoCAD menus and toolbars. A description of file types used by AutoCAD can be found in Appendix E. Appendix F and G provide information of common error messages and the recovery of damaged drawings. Appendix H gives information in table form about AutoCAD system variables. To see the hatch and fill patterns, fonts, and linetypes provided with the AutoCAD program, refer to Appendices I, J, and K.

STYLE CONVENTIONS

In order to make this text easier for the user, we have adopted certain conventions that will be used throughout the book.

Convention	Example
Command names appear capitalized	the MOVE command
Pull-down menu names appear with the first letter capitalized	pull-down menu Draw
A key icon appears when you should respond by striking a key on your keyboard	[Enter] ENTER or RETURN [Shift] Shift [Esc] Escape [Ctrl] Control
Command sequences are indented. User inputs are indicated by boldface. Instructions are indicated by italics and are enclosed in parentheses.	Command: **MOVE** Select Objects: **G** Enter group name: *(Enter group name)*

DRAW FROM EXPERIENCE

After learning to use AutoCAD with our text, you must have some drawings of which you are especially proud. Would you like to share your experience with the next generation of *Harnessing AutoCAD* users? Send us your drawing files with your name, affiliation, address, phone number, and a brief description of your "experience" harnessing AutoCAD to create this drawing. With your permission, we'll incorporate as many as we can into the next edition of *Harnessing AutoCAD*.

WE WANT TO HEAR FROM YOU!

Many of the changes to the look and feel of this new edition were made by way of requests fromusers of our previous editions. We'd like to hear from you as well! If you have any questions or comments, please contact

The CADD Team
c/o Delmar Publishers
3 Columbia Circle
PO Box 15015
Albany NY 12212

ABOUT THE AUTHORS

Thomas A. Stellman received a B.A. degree in architecture from Rice University and has over 20 years of experience in the architecture, engineering, and construction industry. He has taught at the college level for over ten years and has been teaching courses in AutoCAD since the introduction of version 1.4 in 1984. He is the author of *Practical AutoLISP* (Delmar Publishers, 1990), and conducts seminars covering both introduction to AutoLISP and advanced AutoLISP. In addition, he develops and markets third-party software for AutoCAD. He is currently a CADD consultant, AutoLISP programmer, and project coordinator for Testengeer, Inc. in Port Lavaca, Texas.

G. V. Krishnan is director of the Applied Business and Technology Center, University of Houston—Downtown, a Premier Autodesk Training Center. He has used AutoCAD since the introduction of version 1.4 and writes about AutoCAD from the standpoint of a user, instructor, and general CADD consultant to area industries. Since 1985 he has taught courses ranging from basic to advanced levels of AutoCAD, including customizing, 3D AutoCAD, solid modeling, and AutoLISP programming.

Robert Rhea is an associate professor in the Engineering Technology Department at the University of Houston—Downtown. He is the coordinator of the Process and Piping Design program, the only four-year B.S. degree in Piping offered in the United States. He is a co-author of *Using Intergraph MicroStation, PC* (Delmar Publishers, 1990) and has taught AutoCAD in professional development programs and regular CAD courses at the college level since 1987.

The authors would like to thank Charles "Captain CAD" McAuley of the CAD Institute, Phoenix, Arizona, for contributing material to Chapters 12 and 17.

CHAPTER

1

OVERVIEW

INTRODUCTION

Since its beginning in the early 1980s, AutoCAD has grown into one of the most powerful computer-aided, drafting/design programs available at any price. Release 13 brings major innovations in interaction with the program. If this is your first time using AutoCAD, then the "look and feel" will be learned in its new form. If you are experienced with AutoCAD, it may take some time to get used to some of the new mouse/puck button actions. It is like taking up the reins of a powerful Arabian stallion again after it has been trained to be more responsive and sensitive to your bidding.

What's New in AutoCAD Release 13 for Windows can be characterized by the terms "Usability" and "Interoperability". "Usability" has been enhanced by bringing AutoCAD Release 13 for Windows closer to the look, feel and flexibility that users expect to find in other popular Windows programs. "Interoperability" in AutoCAD Release 13 for Windows means that AutoCAD and other Windows programs are now on better "speaking terms." Graphics and data created in one can be more easily exchanged with the other(s). In addition, AutoCAD Release 13 for Windows device drivers maintain compatibility with peripherals purchased for Release 12 and are broadened for the latest new peripherals such as graphics and printer/plotter devices.

For better "Usability" or "User Interface", the new Windows oriented Graphical User Interface being applied to Release 13 incorporates the following features:

- Customizable Toolbars
- Optional Toolbar anchor locations
- Floating Toolbars in different shapes and with flyouts
- Scroll bars are available to move around the drawing
- Dialog boxes have tabbed sections where applicable
- Icon options and control
- Keyboard assignment
- Floating Command window
- Aerial View window
- Drawing preview
- More powerful On-Line Help

For better "Interoperability," the new Windows-oriented graphics and data exchange features being applied to Release 13 incorporate the following features:

- Windows OLE is supported
- AutoCAD SQL Environment (ASE) enhancements
- AutoCAD SQL Interface supports the SQL2 ISO standard

- Release 13 drawings can be saved in Release 12 format for backward compatibility
- AutoCAD Runtime Extension (ARX) provides a C++ interface
- Application Integration Guidelines (AIG) ensures compatibility between applications
- Broadening Peripheral support includes security of existing along with accommodating new peripherals

The beginning of this chapter describes how to get into the AutoCAD screen. If you need to set up the AutoCAD program on the computer and you are not familiar with computer operating systems (files, drives, directories, operating system commands, etc.), you may wish to review the Appendix on Disk Operating System (DOS), refer to the Installation & Performance Guide that comes with the program, and/or consult the dealer from whom you purchased AutoCAD. Once the computer is set up (which may be the case if you are using this book in the classroom), you will have at your disposal a powerful design/drafting tool that continues to grow in power with each new release.

The balance of this chapter is a brief overview of the basic concepts, commands, and skills that can help you use AutoCAD to its fullest. These concepts, while not specifically tied to a particular command, are the "tools of the trade" for all drafters and designers and the backbone of a Computer-Aided Drafting and Design (CAD) program. Detailed explanations and examples are provided for the concepts and commands throughout the chapters that follow.

AUTOCAD COMMANDS

Commands are divided into related categories as much as possible by AutoCAD. For example, Draw is not a command, but a category of commands used for creating primary objects such as lines, circles, arcs, text (lettering), and other useful objects that are visible on the screen. Categories include Modify, View, and another group listed under Data for controlling the electronic drawing environment. The commands under Data are also referred to as "Tools," "Drawing Aids," and "Utility Commands" throughout the book. Learning the program can progress at a better pace if the concepts and commands are mentally grouped into their proper categories. This not only helps you find them when you need them, but also helps you grasp the fundamentals of computer-aided drafting more quickly.

GETTING STARTED

Design/drafting is what AutoCAD (and this book) is all about. So, how do you get into AutoCAD? First, start Windows by typing **Win** at the operating system prompt and pressing ⏎. When the

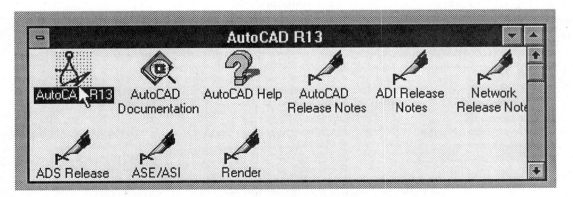

Figure 1-1   AutoCAD for Windows icon in the Windows Program Manager

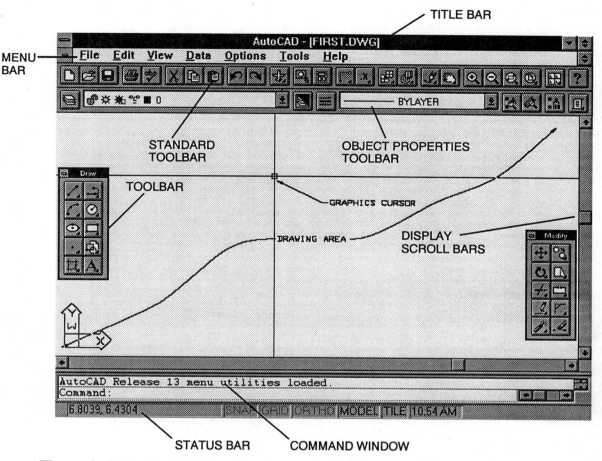

Figure 1-2 The AutoCAD Screen

Program Manager appears, double-click the left mouse button with the cursor on the AutoCAD for Windows icon (see Figure 1–1). AutoCAD's screen is displayed as shown in Figure 1–2.

When you start AutoCAD, you immediately view a drawing plane of an "unnamed" drawing. You may invoke commands to have AutoCAD create lines, arcs, circles, text, or other objects. You may even change the environmental parameters such as linear and angular units, the area being "looked" at, layers, and others. You may either save the "creations" under a drawing name of your choice or exit AutoCAD, abandoning the work you have done.

AUTOCAD SCREEN

The AutoCAD Screen consists of the following:

Drawing Window The drawing window is where AutoCAD places the objects you create. In this window, AutoCAD displays the cursor, indicating your current working point. As you move your pointing device (usually a mouse or puck) around on a digitizing tablet, mouse pad, or other suitable surface, the cursor mimics your movements on the screen. The cursor is in the form of cross-hairs when AutoCAD prompts you to select a point. It changes to a small pick box when you are required to select an object on the screen. AutoCAD uses combinations of cross-hairs, boxes, dashed rectangles, and arrows under various situations so you can quickly see what type of selection or pick mode to use.

Status Bar The status bar at the bottom of the screen displays important information about the current layer, the status of various modes, and the cursor's coordinates.

Title Bar The title bar displays the current drawing name for the AutoCAD application window.

Toolbars The toolbars contain tools that represent commands. Click a toolbar button to start the command, then select options from a dialog box or follow the prompts on the command line. If you position your pointer over a toolbar button and wait a moment, ToolTips displays the name of the tool, as shown in Figure 1–3. In addition to ToolTips, AutoCAD displays a very brief explanation of the function of the command on the status bar.

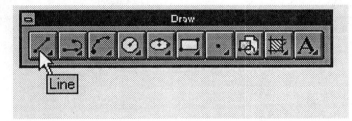

Figure 1-3 Toolbar with a display of ToolTips

Some of the toolbar buttons have a small triangular symbol in the lower right corner of the button indicating there are "flyout" buttons underneath that contain subcommands. Figure 1–4 shows the circle flyout located in the Draw toolbar. When you pick a flyout option, it remains on top to become the default option.

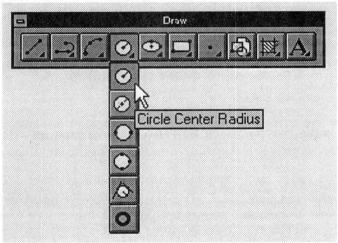

Figure 1-4 Display of the circle flyout located in the Draw toolbar

You can display multiple toolbars on screen at once, change their contents, resize them, and dock or float them. A docked toolbar attaches to any edge of the graphics window. A floating toolbar can lie anywhere on the screen, and can be resized.

To dock a toolbar, position the cursor on the caption, and press the pick button on the pointing device. Drag the toolbar to a dock location to the top, bottom, or either side of the drawing window. When the outline of the toolbar appears in the docking area, release the pick button. To undock a toolbar, position the cursor anywhere on the border of the toolbar and drag and drop it outside the docking regions. To place a toolbar in a docking region without docking it, hold down `Ctrl` as you drag. By default, the Standard toolbar and Object Properties toolbar are docked at the top of the drawing window (see Figure 1–2). Figure 1–5 shows docking of the Standard toolbar and Object

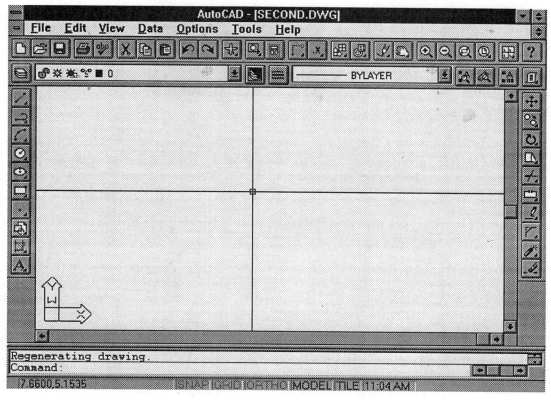

Figure 1-5 Docking of toolbars in the drawing window

Properties toolbar at the top of the drawing window, the Draw toolbar on the left side of the drawing window, and the Modify toolbar on the right side of the drawing window.

If necessary, you can resize a floating toolbar. To resize a floating toolbar, position the cursor anywhere on the border of the toolbar and drag in the direction you want to resize. Figure 1–6 shows different combinations of resizing of Draw toolbar.

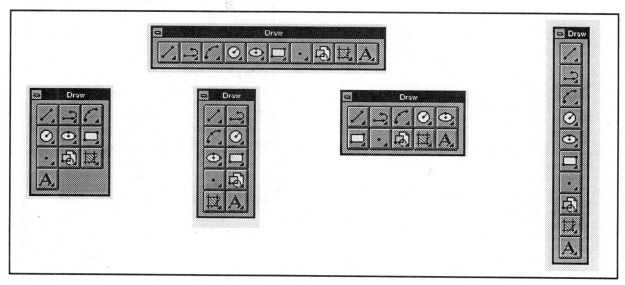

Figure 1-6 Draw toolbar in different resizing positions

Figure 1–7 Positioning the cursor to close a toolbar

To close a toolbar, position the cursor on the top left corner of the toolbar, as shown in Figure 1–7, and press the pick button on your pointing device. The toolbar will disappear from the drawing window.

To close all the toolbars that are displayed in the drawing window, select the **Close All** option available in the cascading submenu Toolbars from the pull-down menu Tools.

AutoCAD for Windows Release 13 comes with 17 toolbars. They are listed in the popdown menu of Toolbars from the Tools pull-down menu. You can open any of the available toolbars by selecting the name of the toolbar from the submenu Toolbars from the Tools pull-down menu, as shown in Figure 1–8.

The Standard toolbar contains frequently used tools, such as the Redraw, Undo, Redo, and Zoom commands. The Object Properties toolbar contains commands related to layer, inquiry, and modify.

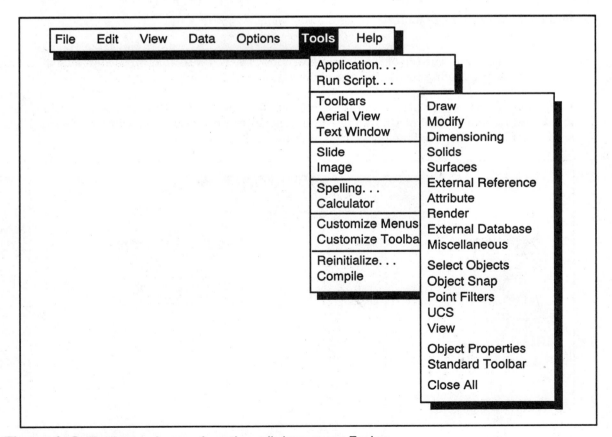

Figure 1–8 Toolbars submenu from the pull-down menu Tools

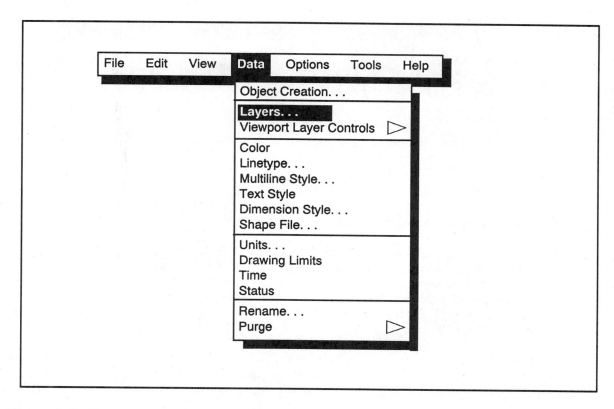

Figure 1-9 Example of a pull-down menu

Pull-down Menu The pull-down menus are available from the menu bar at the top of the screen. AutoCAD provides only utility commands in the pull-down menus and almost all of the drawing and modifying commands are provided in the way of toolbars. To select any of the available commands, move the cross-hair cursor into the menu bar area and press the pick button on your pointing device, which pops that menu bar onto the screen (see Figure 1–9). Selecting from the list is a simple matter of moving the cursor down until the desired item is highlighted and then pressing the designated pick button on the pointing device. If a menu item has an arrow to the right, it has a cascading submenu. To display the submenu, move the pointer over the arrow and press the pick button. Menu items that include ellipses (...) display dialog boxes. To select these, just pick the menu item. See Appendix D for the hierarchy of the pull-down menus.

Command Window The command window is a dockable window where you enter commands and AutoCAD displays prompts and messages. By default, the command window is a floating window with a caption and frame. You can move the floating command window anywhere on the screen and resize its width and height with the pointing size.

There are two components to the command window: The single command line where AutoCAD prompts for input and you see your input echoed back, and the command history area which shows what has been going on in the current drawing session.

The command history area can be enlarged like other windows by picking the top edge and dragging it to a new size. You can also scroll inside the enlarged area to see previous command activity by using the scroll bars (see Figure 1–10).

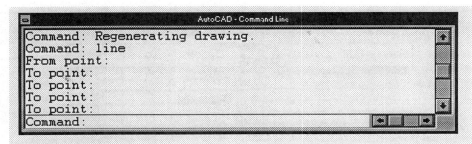

Figure 1-10 Command history

By default, the ⬛ function key allows you to switch between text mode and graphics mode. The text mode will allow you to scroll through the command activity.

When you see "Command:" displayed in the Command Window, it signals that AutoCAD is ready to accept a command. After you enter a command name or select a command from one of the menus or toolbars, the prompt area continues to inform you of the type of response(s) that you must furnish until the command is either completed or terminated. For example, when you pick the LINE command, the prompt displays "From point:" and after selecting a starting point by appropriate means, you will see "To point:" asking for the end point of the line.

Each command has its own series of prompts. The prompts that appear when using a particular command in one situation may differ from the prompts or sequence of prompts when used in another situation. You will become familiar with the prompts as you learn to use each command.

When you type the command name or give any other response by typing from the keyboard, make sure to press ⬛ or spacebar. The ⬛ sends the input to the program for processing. For example, when you type LINE you must press ⬛ or spacebar in order for AutoCAD to start the line drawing part of the program. If you type in LIN and press ⬛ or spacebar, you will get an error message, unless someone has customized the program and created a command alias or command named "LIN". Likewise, typing in LINEZ and pressing ⬛ or spacebar is not a standard AutoCAD command.

The spacebar has the same function as ⬛ except when you are typing in strings of words, letters, or numbers in response to the TEXT command.

You can press ⬛ or spacebar at the "Command:" prompt to repeat the previous command. When repeated in this manner, a few commands skip some of their normal prompts and assume default settings.

Terminating a Command

There are three ways by which you can terminate a command.

1. Complete the command sequence and return to the "Command:" prompt.

2. Use the ⬛ key to terminate the command before it is completed.

3. Invoke another command from one of the menus which automatically cancels any command in progress.

INPUT METHODS

There are several ways to input an AutoCAD command.

Keyboard

To enter a command from the keyboard, simply type the command name at the "Command:" prompt and then press [Enter] or the spacebar ([Enter] and the spacebar are interchangeable except when entering text).

Toolbars

The toolbars contain tools that represent commands. Click a toolbar button to start the command, then select options from a dialog box or follow the prompts on the command line.

Pull-down Menus

The pull-down menus are available from the menu bar at the top of the screen. AutoCAD provides only utility commands in the pull-down menus and almost all of the drawing and modifying commands are provided in the way of toolbars. AutoCAD Release 13 for Windows comes with two menu files ACAD.MNU and ACADFULL.MNU. These are located in "C:\ACADR13\WIN\SUPPORT" directory, assuming AutoCAD is installed in the C: drive and ACADR13 is the sub-directory. If your location is different, substitute your drive and path location for your case. The ACADFULL.MNU has additional pull-down menus, Draw, Construct and Modify menus and is intended to ease the transition for AutoCAD 12 users until they become familiar with the Toolbars. To load the ACADFULL.MNU menu, at the "Command:" prompt, type **menu** and press [Enter] or spacebar. AutoCAD displays the Select menu file dialog box, as shown in Figure 1–11. Select the **acadfull.mnu** file from the file list box and click the OK button.

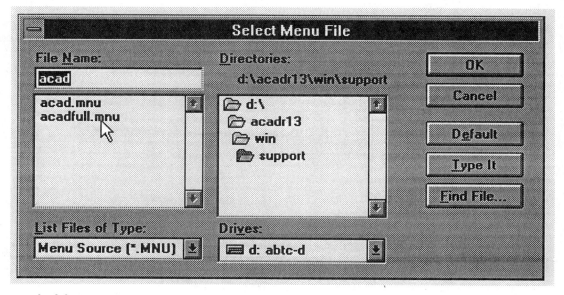

Figure 1-11 Select Menu File dialog box

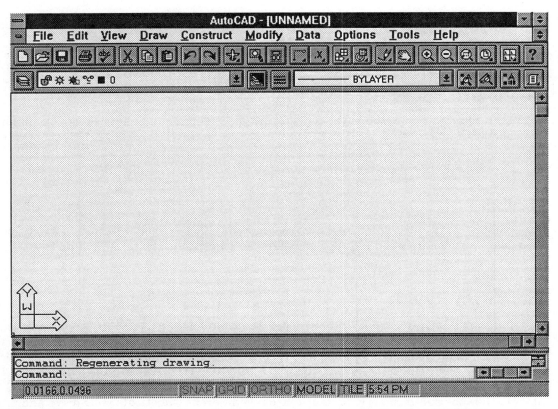

Figure 1-12 AutoCAD screen with available pull-down menus after loading ACADFULL menu file

AutoCAD loads the menu file and displays all the available pull-down menus in the menu bar, as shown in Figure 1–12.

Side Screen Menu

The side screen menu provides another, older way to enter AutoCAD commands. By default, the side screen menu is turned off in the Windows version of AutoCAD Release 13. While this book does not refer to the side screen menu, traditional DOS users of AutoCAD may be more comfortable using it. To display the side screen menu, type **preferences** at the "Command:" prompt and press Enter or spacebar. AutoCAD displays the Preferences dialog box, as shown in Figure 1–13.

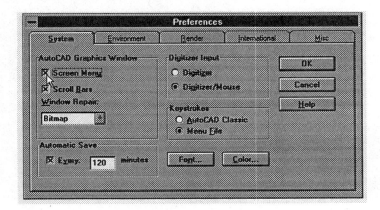

Figure 1-13 Preferences dialog box

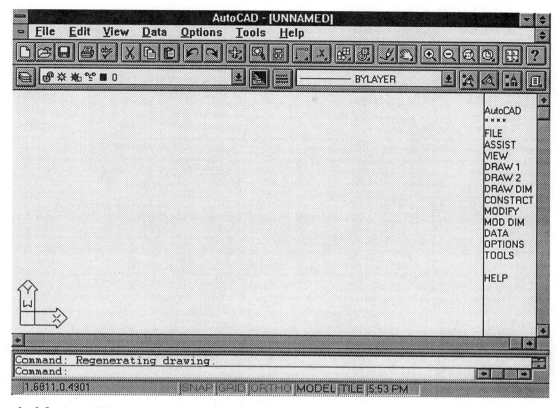

Figure 1-14 AutoCAD screen window with side screen menu

Select the System page, as shown in Figure 1–13, turn on the toggle button Screen Menu located in the AutoCAD Graphics Window, and click the OK button. AutoCAD displays the side screen menu, as shown in Figure 1–14.

Moving the pointing device to the right will cause the cursor to move into the screen menu area. Moving the cursor up and down in the menu area will cause selectable items to be highlighted. When the desired one is highlighted, you may choose that item by pressing the designated pick button on the pointing device. If the item is a command, it will either be put into action or the menu area will be changed to a list of actions which are options of that command. The screen menu is made up of menus and submenus. At the top of every screen menu is the word "AutoCAD." When selected, it will return you to what is called the root menu. The root menu is the one that is displayed when you first enter AutoCAD. It lists the primary classifications of commands or functions available.

At the bottom of every menu are the SERVICE and LAST items. The SERVICE menu provides various object selection modes and utility commands. The LAST menu, when selected, returns the previous menu to the screen.

When you select a menu item whose name is all uppercase and does not end with a colon (example: DRAW1) AutoCAD displays a submenu when selected. A menu item whose name ends with a colon (example: LINE:) not only displays a submenu, but cancels execution of any command in progress and invokes the named command. Subcommands and options are lowercase or a mixture of uppercase and lowercase (example: Window) and work properly only when picked in appropriate sequence responses. See Appendix D for the hierarchy of the screen menu.

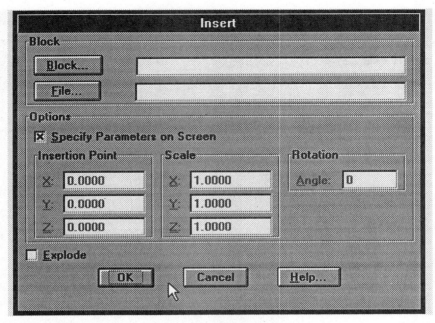

Figure 1-15 Dialog Box invoked from the DDINSERT Command

Dialog Boxes

Several commands, when invoked, cause a dialog box to appear. These dialog boxes cover the screen with lists and descriptions of options, long rectangles for receiving your input data, and, in general, a more convenient and more user-friendly method of communicating with the AutoCAD program for that particular command.

AutoCAD Release 13 has a notable increase in the number of commands and responses that can be input through dialog boxes. The commands that include ellipses (. . .) such as PLOT. . . and HATCH. . . display dialog boxes. In addition, you can type at "Command:" prompt the commands that begin with "DD" (for Dynamic Dialog) to cause a dialog box to appear when invoked. Figure 1-15 shows the dialog box that appears when you invoke the DDINSERT command. Setting the System Variable FILEDIA to zero permits most commands to be operated through keyboard/prompt interaction instead of dialog boxes. For detailed explanation on different dialog box components, see the section on Using Dialog Boxes.

Cursor Menu

The AutoCAD cursor menu (see Figure 1-16) appears at the location of the cursor by pressing the third button on a three-or-more button mouse. On a two button mouse you can invoke this feature by pressing [Shift] + (the second button). The menu includes the handy object snap mode options along with the X,Y,Z/Filters. The reason for the OSNAP/FILTERS being in such ready access will become evident when you learn the significance of these functions.

Digitizing Tablet

After the mouse, the digitizing tablet is the most common input device. It combines the screen cursor control of a mouse with its own printed menu areas for selecting items. The most

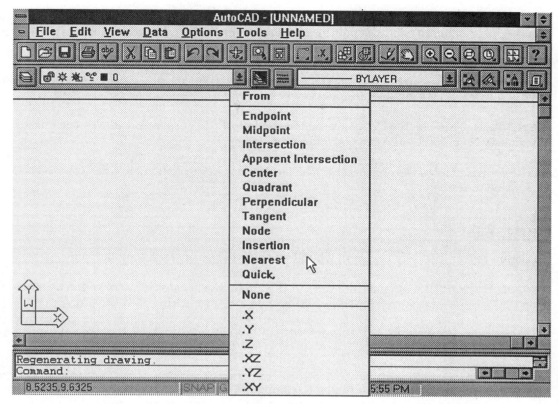

Figure 1-16 Cursor Menu

significant feature of tablet menu selection is that you can select from pictures in addition to words. Another powerful feature of the tablet (not related to entering commands) is that it allows you to lay a map or other picture on the tablet and trace over it with the puck (the specific pointing device for a digitizing tablet), thereby transferring the objects to the AutoCAD drawing.

USING DIALOG BOXES

When a dialog box appears, the cross-hair cursor changes to an arrow, pointing up and to the left. You can use the arrow keys on your keyboard to make selections in the dialog box, but it is much easier to use your pointing device. Another way to make selections in a dialog box is to use keyboard equivalents. You can move the cursor from one field to another by using the [Tab] key when the cursor is not in the edit box.

Edit Box

An edit box is an area that accepts one line of text entry. It is normally used to specify a name such as a layer name or even file name including the drive and/or directory path. Edit boxes are often used as an option to selecting from a list of names when the desired name is not in the list box. Once the correct text is keyed in, enter it by pressing [Enter].

Moving the pointer into the edit box causes the text cursor to appear in a manner similar to the cursor in a word processor. The text cursor, in combination with special editing keys, can be used to facilitate changes to the text. You can see both the text cursor and the pointer at the same time, making it possible to click the pointer at a character in the edit box and relocate the text cursor to that character.

Right and Left Arrows < > This moves the cursor right or left (respectively) across text without having any effect on the text.

Backspace This deletes the character to the left of the cursor and moves the cursor to the space previously occupied by the deleted character.

[Delete] key This deletes the character at the location of the cursor causing any text to the right to move one space to the left.

Buttons

Actions are immediately initiated when you click on one of the dialog buttons.

Default Buttons If a button (like the **OK** button in most cases) is surrounded by a heavy line, then it is the default button and pressing [Enter] is the same as clicking that button.

Buttons with Ellipses (. . .) Buttons with ellipses display a second dialog box, called a sub-dialog or child dialog box.

> **NOTE:** When a sub-dialog box appears, you must first respond to the options in the sub-dialog box, before the underlying one can continue.

Screen Action Buttons Buttons that are followed by an arrow (<) require a graphic response, such as selecting an object on the screen or picking/specifying coordinates.

Disabled Buttons Buttons with action that is not currently acceptable will be disabled. They appear grayed out.

Character Equivalents A button with a label that has an underlined character can be activated by pressing that character + [Alt] combination on the keyboard.

Radio Buttons Radio buttons are used when only one of two or more selections can be active at a time (see Figure 1–17). Pressing one will deactivate any other in the group, like selecting a station button on the radio.

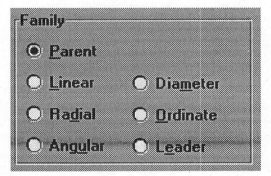

Figure 1-17 Radio Buttons

Figure 1-18 Check boxes

Check Boxes

A check box acts as a toggle. When clicked, the check box switches the named setting between ON and OFF, as shown in Figure 1-18. An X in the check box means the option is turned on; a lack of an X means the option is turned off.

List Boxes and Scroll Bars

List boxes make it easy to view, select, and enter a name from a list of existing items such as filenames and fonts. Use the pointer to highlight the desired selection. When you click on the item, it appears in the edit box. You accept this item by clicking OK or by double-clicking on the item. For example, Figure 1-19 shows the list box from the Standard File dialog box.

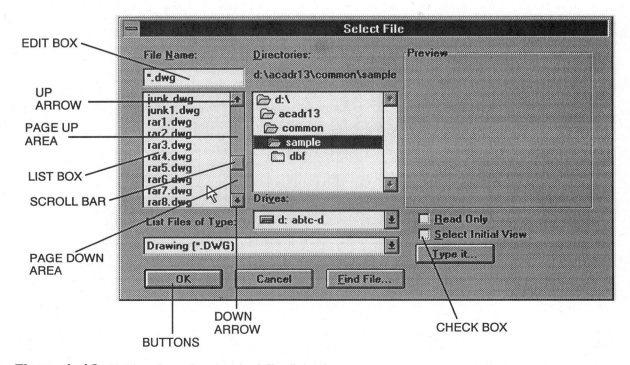

Figure 1-19 List box from the standard file dialog box

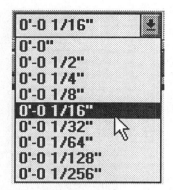

Figure 1-20 Display of the expanded list

List boxes are accompanied by scroll bars to facilitate moving long lists up and down in the list box. The scroll bar has the following components.

1. **Slider box** — When you point and hold onto the slider box, you can move it up and down to cause the list to scroll down and up.

2. **Page up/down areas** — The space above the slider box is the page up area. Picking anywhere above the slider box scrolls up one page at a time. The space below the slider box is the page down area. Picking anywhere below the slider box scrolls down one page at a time.

3. **Up/down arrows** — When picked, these arrows cause the list to scroll up or down one item at a time.

Some buttons that have multiple options available are really just unexpanded list boxes. They will have a down arrow on the right side. Selecting the down arrow displays the expanded list as shown in Figure 1-20.

Alert Messages

Alert messages appear when certain errors are made. The message reports the error along with a verification button such as **OK, YES, NO,** or another message similar to the one shown in Figure 1-21.

Figure 1-21 Alert Messages

> **NOTE:** Many dialog boxes have a **Help. . .** button. If you are not sure how to use the feature in the dialog box, pick the **Help. . .** button for a brief explanation of the dialog box.

GETTING HELP

When you are in the graphics window, AutoCAD provides a context-sensitive help facility to list its commands and what they do. The HELP command provides a limited amount of on-line assistance within AutoCAD. When an invalid command is entered, AutoCAD prints a message to remind you of the availability of the help facility.

Whenever you need help, at the Command: prompt type **help** or ? and press the spacebar or Enter and AutoCAD displays the HELP window similar to the one shown in Figure 1–22.

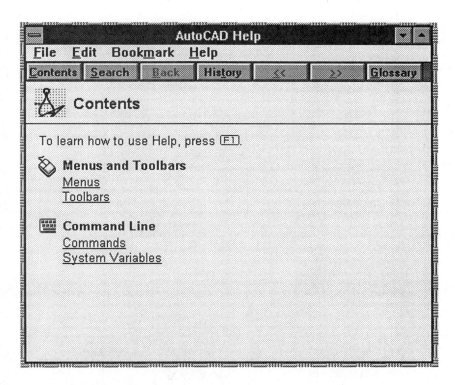

Figure 1-22 The Help table of contents

The HELP command is one that can be used while you are in the middle of another command. This is referred to as a "transparent command." To use a command transparently (if it is one of those that can be used that way), simply prefix the command name with an apostrophe. For example, to use HELP transparently type **'help** or **'?** in response to any prompt that is not asking for a text string. AutoCAD displays help for the current command. Often the help is general in nature but sometimes it is specific to the commands current prompt.

As an alternative, press function key F1 to bring up help. When you ask for help in the middle of a command, AutoCAD displays context-sensitive help. For example, if you press F1 in the middle of the LINE command, AutoCAD automatically selects the help information describes how to use the LINE command, as shown in Figure 1–23.

Help flips to an independent window, so you probably will need to press the switch-task key Alt + Tab or press F2 to switch back to the AutoCAD graphics window.

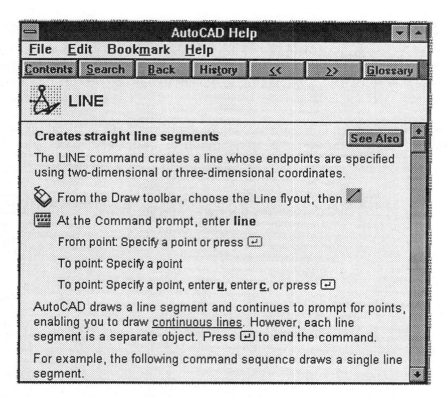

Figure 1-23 Context-sensitive help for the LINE command.

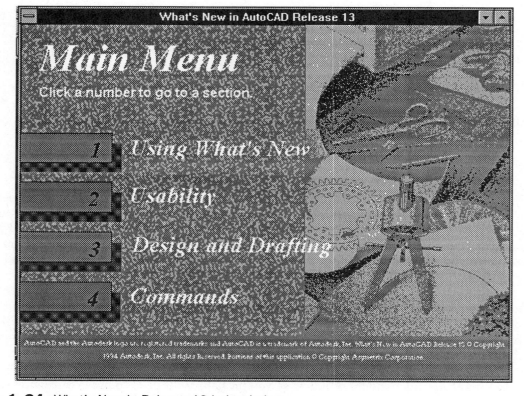

Figure 1-24 What's New in Release 13 help window

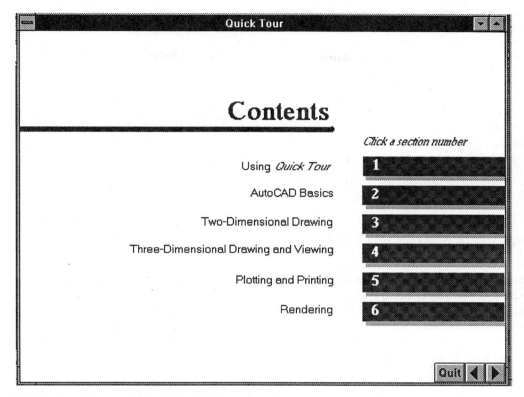

Figure 1-25 Quick Tour of AutoCAD R13 functionality help window

In addition, you can view an interactive presentation of "What's New" in AutoCAD Release 13 for Windows by selecting **What's New in Release 13...** from the pull-down menu Help. AutoCAD provides a quick overview of the new features by categorizing them into four sections as shown in Figure 1–24.

You can also view an interactive presentation of a "Quick Tour" of AutoCAD R13 functionality by selecting Quick Tour... from the pull-down menu Help. AutoCAD provides a quick tour of AutoCAD R13 functionality by categorizing into six sections as shown in Figure 1–25.

DRAWING SETUP

One drawing unit can correspond to whatever form of measurement your drawing requires. It can be inches, feet, millimeters, or whatever units you require. This allows you to draw with real world values and eliminates the possibility of scaling errors. Once the drawing is complete you may plot it at whatever scale you like. As mentioned earlier, drawing in real world is an advantage of AutoCAD that some overlook. If a drawing is done with this principle, you can plot it at several different scales, which eliminates the need for separate drawings at different scales.

AutoCAD allows you to choose from several formats for the display and entry of the coordinates and distances. For example, you can choose feet and fractional inches for architectural drafting; other options include scientific notation and engineering formats. Similarly, you can select the format used for display and entry of angles. Degrees in decimal form are the most common choice, however, you might also select gradient, radians, degrees/minutes/seconds, or surveyor's units.

AutoCAD provides a rectangular drawing area referred to as the limits, with lower left and upper right corners expressed in X and Y coordinates. You may set the limits to accommodate your drawing. For example, if you are drawing a printed circuit board that is 6 inches high by 8 inches wide, you can choose a drawing unit to be in inches and place the lower left corner of the circuit board at coordinates (2,2). You can then set your lower left coordinates for the limits (drawing area) at 0,0 and upper right coordinates at 10,8.

If your drawing exceeds your original plans or the drawing limits become too restrictive, you can easily increase the drawing limits.

For additional information on LIMITS and UNITS commands, see Chapter 2.

DRAWING ENVIRONMENTS

In AutoCAD, you have the option to work on your drawing in two different environments, model space or paper space. Most of the drafting and design work done in model space. You use paper space to arrange, annotate, and plot various views of your model. While model space is a 3D environment, paper space is a 2D environment for arranging views of your model. Prior to AutoCAD Release 11, the drawings were created entirely in the model space. The commands MSPACE and PSPACE toggle between the model and paper space mode. See Chapter 11 for additional information.

DRAWING AIDS

AutoCAD provides six different tools to make your drafting and design easier. The tools include grid, snap, ortho, coordinates display, object snap, and XYZ filters. The following paragraphs are brief explanations of these tools; a more detailed explanation is provided in Chapters 2, 3, and 4.

The GRID command displays a reference grid of dots on the screen bounded by the limits with any spacing you wish to specify. The grid helps you to get a sense of the sizes of drawing objects and their relationships. You can turn the grid display on and off at will, and change the dot spacing easily. The grid is not considered part of the drawing; it is for visual reference only and never plotted. The function key F7 or Ctrl + G toggles the display of the grid on and off.

If the coordinates you wish to specify coincide with points on a uniformly spaced grid, then the snap mechanism helps you enter points by locking into the rectangular grid. By turning on snap mode, you enter points work quickly, letting AutoCAD ensure that they line up precisely. You can set the snap spacing the same as grid spacing or to some increment in between grid points. A change in the snap value only affects the coordinates of points you subsequently enter. Objects already in the drawing retain their coordinates, even if they do not line up with the new snap value. You can even set up a snap and grid which parallels the three axes of an isometric grid. The function key F9 or Ctrl + B toggles the snap lock on and off.

The ortho (short for orthogonal) setting, when turned on, limits the selectable point to be right angles from the last point. This means you can use the ortho mode if you want the new point to be displaced from the base point along an orthogonal line (horizontal or vertical); Ortho mode restricts the rubberband line and the new point accordingly. It also forces lines to be parallel to one of the three isometric axes (depending on the current Isoplane) when the snap style has been set to Isometric. The function key F8 or Ctrl + O toggles the ortho mode on and off.

The Coordinates Display is a report in the status bar at the bottom of the screen. It has three settings. On most systems the function key ⌨F6 or ⌨Ctrl + ⌨D toggles between the three settings. You can also toggle the coordinate display in the status bar. The three settings are as follow:

1. The first (default) setting causes the display to report the location of the cursor. The display is constantly updated as you move the cross-hair cursor about the drawing area.

2. The second setting is similar to the previous one, except that the display for the second location changes to a relative polar mode when you are prompted for a second point that could be specified relative to the first point. In this case the report is in the form of the direction/ distance. The direction is given in terms of the current angular units setting and the distance in terms of the current linear units setting.

3. The third setting saves either the location in the display at the time you toggle to this setting or the last point entered. It does not change dynamically with the movement of the cursor and does not change until you select a new point.

The osnap (short for object snap) feature permits you to specify a geometric point on an existing object. You place the cursor near the object for the location of the specified point and be assured that the object is the one chosen. The key word above is near. For example, draw a line starting at point 0,0 for a distance of 3 units and at an angle of 30 degrees. If you wish to draw a circle using the endpoint of the line as the center point, AutoCAD allows automatic placement by just picking the endpoint of that line by using the ENDpoint object snap. If you wish to use the endpoint of the line without using osnap, you would have to stop and calculate its coordinates. You could do so and arrive at the point where the X coordinate is 2.598076211 and Y coordinate is 1.500000000. Then you would have to read your calculator, key-in the numbers, and hope that you did not make a mistake in the reading, typing in, or method of calculation. Also, you are limiting yourself to the accuracy of the number of significant figures on your calculator. In most cases, eight places are accurate enough. By using the osnap mode called ENDpoint while AutoCAD is asking for a point, you can put the cursor near the end of the line, press the pick button, and have that endpoint used as the response to the prompt. Also, the accuracy is to 14 significant figures.

Other osnap modes include CENter, INSertion point, INTersection, App Intersection, MIDpoint, NEAr, NODe, PERpendicular, QUAdrant, FROM and TANgent. You may not need to make your drawing as accurate as AutoCAD permits, but if the precision is there, why not use it? In most cases it is quicker and easier to use osnap mode with all of its accuracy than to not use it. For example, if you wish to start a line at the center of a circle, trying to place the cursor at the center of the circle on the screen is not as easy as picking somewhere on the circle itself after invoking the osnap mode called CENTER. The Osnap menu is selected from the Object Snap toolbar, typing the appropriate object mode at the prompt, or selecting from the cursor menu.

The XYZ filters feature allows you to specify a point by specifying separate coordinates (2D and 3D) or combinations of coordinates (3D) in separate steps. Coordinates input can combine keyboard and pointing methods. It is especially useful in combination with the osnap mode, by which you can specify a point on an existing object and then have the XYZ Filter feature extract the desired coordinates (X, Y, and/or Z) for use in the point for which you are being prompted. A detailed explanation of all the drawing aids are provided in Chapters 2 through 5.

DRAW COMMANDS

AutoCAD gives you an ample variety of drawing elements called objects. It also provides you with many ways to generate each object in your drawing. You will learn about the properties of these objects as you progress in this text. It is important to keep in mind that the examples in this text of how to generate the various lines, circles, arcs, and other objects are not always the only methods available. You are invited, even challenged, to find other more expedient methods to perform tasks demonstrated in the lessons. You progress at a better rate if you make an effort to learn as much as possible as soon as possible about the descriptive properties of the individual objects. When you become familiar with how the CAD program creates, manipulates, and stores the data that describes the objects, you are then able to create drawings more effectively.

You can add text to a drawing by means of the TEXT, DTEXT, and MTEXT commands. TEXT objects can be drawn with a variety of character patterns or fonts, and can be stretched, compressed, obliqued, mirrored, or drawn in a vertical column by applying a style to the font. Each text string can be rotated and justified to fit your requirements. Text can be of any size (height and width). The DTEXT command allows you to see the text on the screen as you enter it and also allows you to enter multiple lines of text in one command. The MTEXT command allows you to place text of multiple lines in a paragraph format. AutoCAD even provides a spell checker to check the spelling in the drawing. AutoCAD comes with various types of fonts. For the list of fonts available see Appendix J; many other fonts are available from third-party vendors. You can also create your own text fonts.

You can create filled areas with the SOLID command, filled lines (having width) with the TRACE command, or filled and/or tapered line-arc combinations with the PLINE (for polyline) command. TRACE command is easier to learn before advancing to polyline.

Repeating graphic patterns for filling areas can be drawn with the BHATCH (short for boundary hatch) command. The patterns are made from combinations of continuous and/or broken and dotted lines. Lines within one family of the pattern are similar and parallel to each other, and may be combined with families of lines going in another direction. You should note that the area selected to be filled must be a closed area; that is, the lines and/or arcs that define it must meet at intersections and/or endpoints; otherwise, the results will be unpredictable. AutoCAD also comes with various types of hatch patterns. For the list of available patterns see Appendix I. Many other hatch patterns are available from third-party vendors. You can also create your own hatch patterns.

Draw commands are invoked from the Draw toolbar (see Figure 1–26). See Table 1–1 for a brief description of the draw commands available in AutoCAD. A detailed explanation of all the object draw commands are provided in Chapters 2 through 6.

Figure 1–26 Draw commands are invoked from the Draw toolbar

MODIFY COMMANDS

To modify an object is to make a change to one of its existing characteristics. There are several options open to a user among the modify and construct commands offered by AutoCAD.

When a modify command is activated, the first step is to select the object that you wish to modify. Another option permits selecting objects first and then modifying them with modify and construct

Table 1-1 Objects created by the Draw commands

OBJECT TYPE	DESCRIPTION
LINES	Draws lines with 2D or 3D coordinates with different linetypes.
XLINE	Draws construction lines
MLINE	Draws multiple, parallel lines
SPLINE	Creates a quadratic or cubic spline (NURBS) curve
ARCs & CIRCLE	Draws using several methods with different linetypes.
POINT	Draws with 2D or 3D coordinates, appear as a dot, square, circle, X, or any combination of these.
SKETCH	Creates a series of freehand line segments
TEXT	Appears in a variety of fonts, sizes, and orientations.
TRACE	2D, solid-filled lines of any user-specified width.
SOLID	2D, solid-filled triangular or quadrilateral objects.
BLOCK	Compound objects formed from groups of other objects.
INSERT	Places a named block or drawing into the current drawing
DIMENSION	Compound object containing all the lines, arcs, arrows, and text comprising a dimension annotation.
POLYLINE	2D connected line and arc segments, with optional linetypes, widths, and tapers.
ELLIPSE	Creates an ellipse or an elliptical arc
POLYGON	Creates an equilateral closed polyline
3D POLYLINE	3D objects composed of connected straight-line segments.
3DFACE	3D triangular or quadrilateral plane sections.

commands. To identify an object, the user moves the cross-hair to touch the object and presses the pick button. When this is done, the object is highlighted to indicate that this is the one chosen.

The editing facilities of AutoCAD make it easy to correct or revise a drawing. Often, the experienced CAD operator creates an object in anticipation of using a particular modify and construct command. For instance, if you wish to draw two parallel lines of equal length, you can draw one line and then use the OFFSET command to create the second line. And, if you wish to create an array of radial lines similar to spokes on a wheel, you only need to draw one line, then you can generate the other spokes with the construct command called ARRAY. Some modify and construct functions are specific to certain objects. Modify commands are invoked from the Modify toolbar (Figure 1–27). See Table 1–2 for a brief description of the modify commands available in AutoCAD. A detailed explanation of all the modify commands is provided in Chapters 2 through 6.

Figure 1–27 Modify commands are invoked from the Modify toolbar

Table 1-2 The Modify Commands

COMMAND	DESCRIPTION
ALIGN	Moves and rotates objects to align with other objects.
ARRAY	Makes multiple copies of selected objects in a rectangular or circular (polar) pattern; each resulting object can be manipulated independently.
ATTDEF	Constant or variable text information to each instance of a block.
BHATCH	Block patterns, either system-generated or user-created, that fill in a specified drawing area. One or more sets of parallel lines (continuous or broken lines) with spaces, arrangements, and angles designed to fill a space with a specific pattern.
BREAK	Removes a part of a line, trace, circle, arc, or 2D polyline.
CHAMFER	Trims two intersecting lines a specified distance from the intersection and connects the trimmed ends with a new line segment.
CHANGE	Changes the properties (layer, color, thickness, etc.) of existing objects or modifies objects by trimming or extending their ends or cutting sections.
COPY	Copies one or more objects at the specified displacement without changing their orientation or size, leaving the originals intact.
ERASE and OOPS	ERASE removes unwanted objects; OOPS retrieve objects accidently removed.
EXPLODE	Breaks down a block reference and associative dimension into their constituent, simple objects, forms lines and arcs from 2D and 3D polylines.
EXTEND	Lengthens existing objects so they end precisely at boundary edges defined by other objects.
FILLET	Connects lines, arcs, and circles by a smoothly fitted arc of specified radius.
LENGTHEN	Lenthens an objects.
MIRROR	Makes a mirror image of existing objects, either deleting or retaining the original objects.
MOVE	Move one or more objects from their current location to a new location without changing their orientation or size.
OFFSET	Constructs an object parallel to another object at a specified distance or through a specified point.
PEDIT	Editing 2D and 3D polylines and polyfaces.
REGION	Creates a region object from a selection set of existing objects.
ROTATE	Changes the orientation of existing objects by rotating them about a specified base point.
SCALE	Changes the size of existing objects, larger or smaller.
STRETCH	Moves a selected portion of a drawing, preserving connectives to parts of the drawing left in place.
TRIM	Used on some objects so they end precisely at a cutting edge or edges defined by one or more other obejcts.

DISPLAYING AND VIEWING THE DRAWING

AutoCAD offers many ways for you to display or view your drawing. You can magnify or shrink the visual image of the drawing on the screen. This is accomplished with the ZOOM command, which allows you to adjust the size of your viewing area. You can tell AutoCAD how large or small an area of the world you wish to have displayed on your screen. This operates similar to a zoom lens on a camera (without the perspective effect).

The PAN command allows you to move across the drawing in any direction. Panning also allows you to view a different portion of the drawing without changing its magnification.

AutoCAD lets you divide your display into several smaller displays (or windows) called viewports. Each viewport may be different, perhaps with a closer view, or a view from a different angle, or of a different area of the drawing. Panning and zooming are performed independently in each viewport. A drawing can have as many as 32,000 viewports but only 16 viewports at any time display the drawing (the others are blank); but only one can be active at any time. You can draw objects from one viewport to another by activating the viewport as you go along.

For a detailed explanation of the DISPLAY commands, refer to Chapters 2, 4, and 11.

LAYER STRUCTURE

AutoCAD offers a means of grouping objects in a drawing in a manner similar to the manual drafter drawing groups of objects on separate transparent sheets superimposed in a single stack. You can assign various portions or groups of objects of your drawing to different layers, and define as many layers as you like. Layering allows you to view and plot related aspects of a drawing separately or in any combination. There is only one current layer. The current layer could be compared to the manual drafter's top sheet on the stack of transparencies. A color and a linetype is associated with each layer, and you can elect to use these instead of specifying individually each object's color and linetype. You can turn off a specific layer if you do not want to see it on the screen or be plotted and freeze selected layers which will be excluded when the drawing is regenerated and plotted. Whenever you like, you can thaw a frozen layer. For a detailed explanation of layers, see Chapter 3.

BLOCKS AND ATTRIBUTES

The term "block" seems to have its origin in word processing software. By marking the beginning and end of one or more characters or words, they become a block that is edited as a single grouping. For example, if you had a paragraph you wanted to move to another place in the text, the word processor's Move command is applied to the whole group. Other commands can be used to copy and delete the entire group.

AutoCAD provides a similar but more powerful feature by means of the BLOCK command. It permits you to group objects under a user-determined name and gives you the ability to perform certain modifying commands on the group as though it is a single object.

With the WBLOCK command you save a block or an entire drawing to a file as a mini-drawing for insertion later or insertion into another drawing. WBLOCK causes blocks to take with them the layer, linetype, system variable settings, and other environmental characteristics of the parent drawing.

When you insert a block, you specify a scale factor or separate X and Y scale factors (making ellipses out of circles and rectangles out of squares). You can also specify a rotation angle.

Blocks can contain other blocks, called nested blocks. They (or parts of them) are usually created on the default layer (0) and then when inserted those parts shift to the current layer, while parts created on layers other than zero stay on their respective layers.

Using the BLOCK command can conserve computer memory and reduce the size of the drawing data file. Blocks can improve drafting and design speed and reduce burden on the designer to create symbols each time they are needed.

You can attach constant or variable text information to any instance of a block. This text information is referred to as attributes. In addition to creating blocks in AutoCAD Release 13, you can also create a group to name selection set of objects. The block-related commands are invoked from the Draw toolbar. Attribute-related commands are invoked from the Attributes toolbar (see Figure 1–28).

For a detailed explanation of blocks and attributes, see Chapter 9.

Figure 1–28 Attribute toolbar

EXTERNAL REFERENCE DRAWING

AutoCAD supports a feature that lets you display or view the contents of as many as 32,000 drawing files while working in your current drawing file. This function can be accomplished using an external reference file. When a drawing is externally referenced, the user can view and snap to the referenced drawing from the current drawing. If necessary, you can move, copy, rotate, or scale a reference file by using the regular AutoCAD modify and construct commands. You can also control the visibility, color, and linetype of the layers belonging to an external drawing file. All the manipulations performed on an external reference file does not affect the original drawing file because the reference file is only an image.

When you attach a drawing file as an external reference file, it is permanently attached until it is detached or bound to the current drawing. When you load your drawing into AutoCAD, AutoCAD automatically reloads each external reference drawing file; thus, each external drawing file reflects the latest state of the referenced drawing file. If necessary, you can make an external reference file a permanent part of your current drawing. This is similar to inserting a drawing with the INSERT command. You can also make layers, linetypes, text style, and/or dimension style as part of the current drawing file. The external reference-related commands are invoked from External reference toolbar (see Figure 1–29). For a detailed explanation of the external reference file, see Chapter 10.

Figure 1–29 External Reference toolbar

INQUIRY COMMANDS

AutoCAD provides commands that print, in the prompt area or on the text screen, information about objects in the drawing. The commands are found in the Inquiry Menu and are briefly described below.

The LIST command prints object data such as endpoint coordinates, length of a line or an arc, center and radius of a circle or an arc, significant angles associated with certain objects, and angles of rotation. Data concerning objects selected includes the properties that are stored about those objects in the drawing data file.

The DBLIST command prints lists of data about all of the objects in the drawing. It can take a long time to scroll through all the data in a large drawing. DBLIST can, like other commands, be terminated by 🔲.

The ID command prints out the coordinates of a point selected on the screen either by picking with the pointing device or osnapping to it using a selected osnap mode on an object.

The DIST command prints out the distance, in the current units, between two points either selected on the screen or keyed in from the keyboard.

The AREA command prints out the area and perimeter of an enclosed shape selected on the screen by either entering a series of points defining the shape or selecting a closed entity such as a polygon, circle, or closed polyline.

For a detailed explanation of the Inquiry commands, see Chapter 5.

DIMENSIONING

AutoCAD provides a comprehensive set of commands and system variable settings for placing dimensions on your drawing. A great variety of discipline-related conventions are accommodated. Once the variables are set, you can simply pick two points on an object and one point to establish the location of the dimension line and AutoCAD does the rest. AutoCAD automatically provides the gap between the object and the extension line draws the extension lines, the dimension line, the arrowheads, and determines the distance or angle text. Variables set how far the extension lines extend past the dimension line, the size of arrows, and height of text. You can change or override some of the variable settings while placing a dimension. Dimensioning-related commands are invoked from the Dimensioning toolbar (see Figure 1–30). For a detailed explanation of AutoCAD dimensioning, see Chapter 6.

Figure 1–30 Dimensioning toolbar

PLOTTING

Hardcopy refers usually to something you can hold in your hand and read or view such as a letter printed out by a printer or a drawing plotted on a sheet of vellum, mylar, or other medium.

The three primary objectives of the computer-designer/drafter when producing a CAD drawing are:

1. To view objects on the screen,

2. To plot the drawing, and

3. To use the data generated for analysis and design.

Of these three, plotting (producing a hard copy) is the most common end product of a computer-generated drawing. If this is your objective, you should keep the desired sheet in mind when you create a drawing. And, in light of this, you must be aware of the relationship between the plot and the display. When the PLOT command is invoked, you are prompted to specify the view you wish to plot. So, when you create a drawing in anticipation of making a plot from it, be sure that the desired view is one that can be displayed on the screen also.

Other options allow rotating the whole drawing (but not any object by itself within the drawing) from the plot command. Changing an individual object on your plot requires one of the modifying commands such as ROTATE.

Plotting can be done on a pen plotter, electrostatic plotter, or a printer with graphics capability at any scale factor. You can instruct AutoCAD to write the plot output in a disk file (for later transmission to a plotter). See Chapter 7 for a detailed explanation of the PLOT command.

SPECIAL FEATURES

Following are some of the special features of AutoCAD:

Slides

The current display can be saved as a slide that can be recalled quickly to be displayed again. AutoCAD slides are recognized by many desktop publishing programs, so you can use slides to incorporate your drawings in other applications. You can also group slides into a slide library, and write a script file to display them in a slide show.

Drawing Interchange Capability

AutoCAD can write drawing information in a format easily processed by user-written programs. Translations between AutoCAD and other CAD systems data base formats, and special-purpose analysis and modification of AutoCAD drawings is accomplished by means of Data Interchange Format (DXF) and Initial Graphics Exchange Standard (IGES) formats.

Object Handles

You can choose to have AutoCAD assign each object a handle. An object handle is a unique, permanent identifier that is saved with the object in a drawing file. Handles can be used to link the AutoCAD drawing file to external data bases.

AutoLISP

AutoCAD provides an embedded programming language with which you can use expressions and variables, define your own functions and commands, and perform calculations. These can be done from the keyboard or saved for later use by writing them in American Standard Code for Information Interchange (ASCII) format in a file with the extension of .LSP. You can also customize the .MNU file which controls how the many menu devices (screen, mouse buttons, etc.) respond to input. With AutoLISP it is possible to develop third-party software for enhancing the off-the-shelf AutoCAD program.

ADS

The AutoCAD Development System (ADS) provides a variation of the open architecture available with AutoLISP described above, except it is in a C-language environment. Whether you choose AutoLISP or ADS depends upon your particular needs relative to the strengths of the two approaches.

Rendering

AutoCAD allows you to create rendering from AutoCAD 3D models. Render lets you use AutoCAD's standard dialog-box driven user interface to create high-quality renderings. The first time you use Render, you will fully appreciate the magnitude of this benefit.

For an additional explanation of special features, see Chapters 13, 14, 15, and 18.

WARNINGS

Following are the warnings that are to be kept in mind while working in AutoCAD. These things can get you into trouble if you are not careful.

UNDO Command

When AutoCAD introduced the UNDO command it unleashed a potential "drawing eater" if indiscriminately turned loose. The UNDO command undoes the previous operation that AutoCAD has performed. You can undo the UNDO with the REDO command one time only! If you UNDO two things in a row, then the REDO command can only be used to restore the undoing of the last UNDO, not the prior one. Imagine this, you have made an error by copying a selected group of objects to the wrong location, perhaps on top of another group of separate objects. It would take quite a long time to select and erase each entity from the copied group. UNDO does it with a single command entry. You invoke the UNDO command and before using another command you glance away from the screen and inadvertantly lay a book (or your elbow) on the spacebar long enough to hear the "beeeeeeeeeeep" from the keyboard telling you that the last command (UNDO) has been going wild in your drawing, that is, if there is any drawing left. There are occasions when you might wish to invoke multiple UNDOs. Just remember, you can only REDO the last UNDO.

COLOR and LINETYPE Commands

There are two reasons for using color in a CAD drawing: one is for visually distinguishing objects on the screen; the other is for communicating to the plotter which pen to use (permitting different plotted colors and line widths). The original (and still the most common) means to achieve different colors is to assign colors to layers and draw objects that need to be a particular color on a layer having that color. Recent versions of AutoCAD permit you to also use the COLOR command to assign individual objects different colors on the same layer. Unless you have a very specific reason to do so, this usage along with different layer colors can cause confusion as the drawing becomes more complex. Therefore, you are advised to **not** use the COLOR command indiscriminately. While the COLOR command is easy to use, it is not the best way to achieve the two primary purposes of using colors in all but the most advanced applications.

Linetypes (center, hidden, dotted, etc.) are likewise achieved through both the layer assignments and using the LINETYPE command. Like the COLOR command, you are advised **not** to attempt to achieve different linetypes by using the LAYER command's LTYPE and LINETYPE command.

If the individual objects that make up a block have been assigned various colors/linetypes by the two methods mentioned above, and then the block has been placed on a particular layer with its assigned color/linetype, you can (or maybe you can not) imagine the resulting misinterpretations that might occur.

MENU Command

Normally, beginning AutoCAD users do not need the MENU command. It calls up files that allow AutoCAD commands to be accessed by various devices, such as the screen menu, the pull-down screen menus, the tablet menu, and the mouse/puck buttons menu. The ACAD.MNX is compiled (what AutoCAD does to make it load and execute more quickly) from a file called ACAD.MNU. The compiled file is automatically called into operation whenever you call up a new drawing or an existing drawing that was previously saved while the ACAD menu was in effect. For beginning students, the ACAD.MNU offers as complete an access to the AutoCAD drafting features as you could need. Custom (third-party) programs designed for use with AutoCAD often come with a menu (filename.MNX) that can be called into use when necessary. Therefore, unless you know what a particular menu file is for, know its filename, and have a need for it, you should forego using the MENU command.

LOAD Command

The term load shows up in several places. For one, LOAD is the name of a command that loads shape files to become available for use. It is normally for advanced usage with symbols that you (or third parties) can create using the SHAPE command. Emphasis will be placed using blocks rather than shapes in this textbook because of their more universal usage. Another use of load is explained in the LINETYPE command. The use of (load "filename") in AutoLISP is covered in *Practical AutoLISP*, a text/reference book for custom AutoLISP programmers.

Running Object Snap

There are two ways to work with the powerful object snap feature that causes AutoCAD to snap to a specified endpoint, midpoint, center, etc. on existing objects. One way is to enter an osnap mode when prompted to select a point; for example, starting point of a line, location of text, etc. This method does not require using the word OSNAP in the process.

The second method is to invoke the OSNAP command and then specify the particular mode(s) that you wish to have used automatically for all subsequent point selections. This is referred to as the "running osnap." You should learn early the difference between a one-time osnap mode usage and the running osnap usage. Once invoked, the running osnap mode is there whether you want it or not. You must take action to disable it, either for one particular point selection or for all following selections. The concepts of this feature and its importance to accurate drafting dictate that you study and practice deliberately until you are confident and comfortable using it.

ZOOM All—Object Too Small

The All option to the ZOOM command causes the screen to display the drawing limits, the area that you have set up as your electronic drawing sheet. It also displays any objects drawn outside the limits. Normally, this is not a problem as long as you can see the area defined by the limits on the screen and at the same time see any object(s) located outside the limits. If you inadvertantly cause an object to be drawn an extreme distance outside the limits and then use the ZOOM command's All option, that distance might reduce the limits and the objects to such a small size that they will be difficult to spot. It might even appear that there is nothing is on the screen. This can happen if you mistakenly key in a coordinate or distance; e.g., 1.23456 as 123456, leaving out the decimal point. As you can see, the omission of a decimal point can cause an error factor in the magnitude of 100000 to 1. So do not panic if everything seems to disappear from view during the ZOOM All. Use the F2 key to flip to the text screen if necessary and review the previous sequences and values to find a clue. Other tactics can be employed. You can use ZOOM 0.8x to increase the area you are viewing so that the errant object will shows up inside the viewing area instead of on one edge. Or you can use the UNDO command to get back to a point before the mistake was made.

ZOOM All may display an expanded area caused by an object drawn outside the limits and placed on a layer that is currently turned off. Solutions to these problems become clearer as you progress through the chapters.

RELEASE 13 ENHANCEMENTS

Following are the important enhancements that were added to AutoCAD Release 13:

Improved Ease of Use

Geometry
Construction line and Rays have been added.
True geometrical ellipse is now available in lieu of connected polylines.
The new SPLINE command offers true splines defined as Non-Uniform Rational B-Splines.
Splines and Ellipses can both be used with grips.

Construction and Editing
Object Snap modes now include extended and apparent intersections and relative points.
The LENGTHEN command adds to the editing power.
The GROUP command permits naming a selection set of objects.
The EXPLODE command now works on blocks with different X and Y scale factors.

Text
Multiline text editing with applications of the MLINE feature offers paragraph-oriented text with a variety of justification and word processor-type features.
Spell checker.

Hatching
   Associative hatching that changes to suit changes in objects to which it is associated.

Linetypes
   A library of ISO standard linetypes is now available.
   Custom linetypes can now be created to include repeating objects and text.

Dimensioning
   Geometric tolerancing accessible through a new dialog box.
   New library of blocks for arrow and tick marks.
   Direct command level accessible to dimensioning commands in addition to dialog box.

Solid Modeling
   Solid modeling is now a standard feature.

Rendering
   Enhancements include spotlights, colored lights, light attenuation, phong and gourand rendering, wide variety of file formats for images saved, and 3D Studio file importing and exporting.

On-line documentation
   The Command reference is easily accessible "on-line."

This chapter is designed to give you a quick overview of the AutoCAD program. For a detailed explanation of all the AutoCAD commands, refer to the corresponding chapters.

Fundamentals I

INTRODUCTION

This chapter introduces some of the basic commands and concepts in AutoCAD that can be used to complete a simple drawing. The project drawing used in this chapter is relatively uncomplicated, but for the newcomer to AutoCAD it presents ample challenge. It has fundamental problems that are "grist for the mill" for lessons in drawing setup, creating and editing objects, and placing text. Also introduced are several different drawing aids to make your drafting and design layout quicker, easier, and more accurate. These can be created by using certain commands from the toolbars and pull-down menus. When you learn how to access and use the commands, how to find your way around the screen, and how AutoCAD makes use of coordinate geometry, you can apply these skills to the chapters containing more advanced drawings and projects.

After completing this chapter, you will be able to:

■ Create a new drawing and open an existing drawing
■ Perform drawing set up
■ Construct geometric figures — Line, Rectangle, Trace
■ Use viewing commands (e.g., Zoom, Pan, Redraw, and Regen)
■ Create text using appropriate style and size to annotate drawings
■ Use and control accuracy enhancement tools (e.g., Grid, Snap, Ortho, and Object Snap)
■ Use coordinate systems
■ Use object selection
■ Use the Erase command
■ Save drawings to storage devices

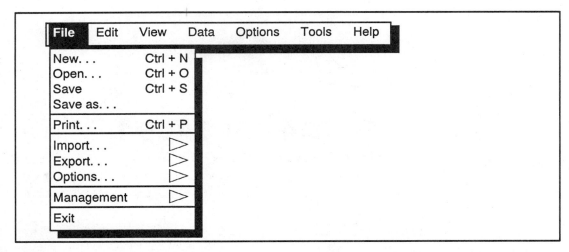

Figure 2-1 Invoke the NEW Command from the pull-down menu File

BEGINNING A NEW DRAWING

When you enter AutoCAD for the first time, you begin with an unnamed drawing. You can begin to work immediately and save the drawing to a filename later, using SAVE or SAVEAS commands. Or, you can specify a filename for your drawing first and then begin work, using the NEW command.

The NEW command allows you to specify a filename for a new drawing before beginning work; it also works in the middle of an editing session for an unnamed drawing. The NEW command is invoked from the pull-down menu File (see Figure 2-1), Standard toolbar (see Figure 2-2), or at the "Command:" prompt, type **NEW** and press ⏎ or spacebar.

Figure 2-2 Invoke the NEW Command from the Standard toolbar

Command: **new**

AutoCAD displays the **Create New Drawing** dialog box, similar to the one shown in Figure 2-3.

Enter a name for your drawing in the **New Drawing Name...** edit box and click **OK.** AutoCAD displays the name of the drawing just above the menu bar.

> **NOTE:** Only one drawing can be OPEN at a time. Therefore, using the NEW command (or the OPEN command that is explained next) means that the current drawing (whether it is the "noname" startup drawing or a named drawing being edited) will have to be either saved in its present state or abandoned. If abandoned, it will revert to its state when it was last saved. So, using the NEW or OPEN command requires that you leave the current drawing.

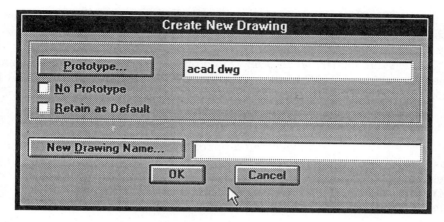

Figure 2-3 The Create New Drawing dialog box

Filenames

The name you enter will be the name of a file in which information about the drawing is stored. It must satisfy the requirements for filenames as specified by the particular operating system your computer uses. DOS and UNIX are the two most common operating systems.

Filenames in DOS In PC-DOS (TM) and MS-DOS (TM) each drawing is a file with a "file specification." The file specification, or filespec as it is called, is the full name of the file. A filespec has two parts. The first part is called the filename; the second part is called the extension or the file type. For example, in the filespec PLAN.DWG, PLAN is the filename and .DWG is the extension. The filename is the group of characters (with a limit of eight) that precede the extension. The filename and extension are separated by a period with the extension limited to three characters. Filenames may contain a combination of uppercase and lowercase letters, numbers, the underscore (_), the hyphen (-), and the dollar sign ($). DOS converts all of the characters to uppercase. No blank spaces are allowed in the filename; it must be one word.

Valid examples are as follow:
    Pipeplan
    lab1
    abc-xyz
    $floor12
    PART_NO3

Examples of improper filenames are as follows:

*special	asterisk not a valid character
nametoolong	name too long; more than eight characters

When AutoCAD prompts for a drawing name, just type the filename and AutoCAD automatically assumes the extension .DWG. In some other programs, you have the freedom to select any valid characters as an extension (three or less), but in AutoCAD drawings must have the extension of .DWG. For example, if you type to the new drawing name as PLOTPLAN, then AutoCAD opens a drawing file with the filespec PLOTPLAN.DWG. Again, just type in the filename and AutoCAD automatically assumes the extension .DWG.

As you progress through the lessons, take note of how various functions ask for names of files. If AutoCAD performs the file processing, it usually adds the proper extension. If you use DOS, you should include the extension.

The Path   If you wish to create a new drawing or edit a drawing that is on a drive and/or directory other than the current drive/directory, then you must furnish what is called the path to the drawing file as part of the file specification. Specifying a path requires only that you use the correct pathfinder symbols: the slash (/ or \) and/or the colon (:). The backslash separates the names of the directories where the drawing is (or will be) located. The drive with a letter name (usually A through Z) is identified as such by a colon, which immediately follows it.

Examples of path and filename combinations are as follows:

a:plan	in working directory on drive A
b:/jones/elev	elev is in the /jones subdirectory on drive B
\houses\smith	in /houses subdirectory on the current drive
ACME\doors	in working subdirectory's ACME subdirectory
./PENNCAD/valves	in parent directory's PENNCAD subdirectory

You can also select the appropriate directory or drive from the directory's list box.

> **NOTE:** When naming a drawing file, you may use either forward or backward slashes to specify the path to a directory. AutoCAD accepts either, unlike specifying directory paths while at the operating systems prompt.

Instead of providing the drawing name in the **New Drawing Name...** edit box, you can click on the **New Drawing Name...** button. AutoCAD displays a dialog box listing any existing drawings as shown in Figure 2-4. If you specify the same name as one of the drawing names from the list, AutoCAD alerts you that the drawing already exists and allows you to replace it. If you replace it, then AutoCAD uses that filename for your new drawing.

> **NOTE:** If you pick **OK** while leaving the drawing name blank, the dialog box clears and the new drawing remains unnamed for now.

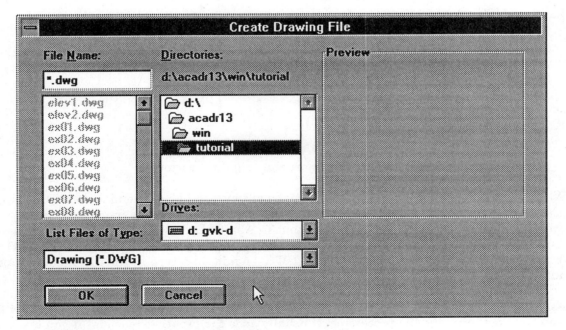

Figure 2-4 Dialog Box listing existing drawings

Prototype Drawing

Just as the board drafter starts a drawing in an environment, the blank screen (electronic drawing) of the AutoCAD Drawing Screen has an environment. Placing a blank sheet on the drafting board limits the area in which you can draw. Likewise, there are limits set in your electronic drawing, but less restrictive because you can change the electronic sheet size any time during the drawing process. The drawing instrument in your hand, combined with your dexterity, determine the type of line you can place on the paper. Likewise, linetypes in an AutoCAD drawing determine whether lines are continuous or dashed. The Color feature in AutoCAD can be used in conjunction with plotting parameters to determine line widths through pen assignments. The board drafters scale corresponds to a system variable called LUNITS in the AutoCAD drawing (the setting of the linear units corresponds to the value assigned to the system variable UNITS). Just as the board drafter picks up the architectural scale, you can set the UNITS to architectural. UNITS is another property of the drawing environment.

System Variables The electronic drawing sheet that you start with when you begin a new drawing has many properties associated with it. The above mentioned LIMITS, LINETYPE, and UNITS are just a few of the AutoCAD commands that affect one of the 200 or so environmental properties that can be either used as they come off the shelf or, if not acceptable, changed to suit your drawing needs. To create a drawing, it is not necessary to learn the names of the system variables that store environmental settings. Their settings are automatically changed during an editing session as you use the AutoCAD commands that affect individual system variables. The important thing to note is that they do exist and are set to some value that affects the drawing environment. In addition to the system variables being affected automatically as you draw by the various AutoCAD commands, you can change their settings directly by using the SETVAR command or typing the system variable name at the "Command:" prompt.

ACAD.DWG The ACAD.DWG (drawing) file will be occasionally referred to throughout the text. The ACAD.DWG file is a drawing data file with preset system variables settings which determine the environment of a drawing even before you add objects to it. It is like the blank sheet of vellum, drawing instruments, scale, and drafting machine that the board drafter starts out with. The blank sheet has properties such as size, thickness, and type of material. You are considered to have started a board drawing by just positioning it on the drafting board. In a similar manner, when you launch AutoCAD, your beginning drawing environment copies all of the settings of the ACAD.DWG file. The ACAD.DWG file in this situation is known as the prototype drawing.

In the Create New Drawing dialog box, the ACAD Filename appears in the **Prototype. . .** edit box. This is the default prototype drawing. To specify a different prototype drawing, enter the name of the desired prototype drawing in the edit box or click the **Prototype. . .** button. AutoCAD displays a standard file dialog box, "Prototype Drawing File," listing the names of all drawings in the current subdirectory. Select one of the filenames from the list, and its complete pathname appears in the **Prototype. . .** edit box. This becomes your current prototype drawing.

The original ACAD.DWG environment settings were set up according to certain defaults. The settings of the linear and angular units and the area that displays on the screen when you ZOOM All are a couple of the environmental settings. When you change the ACAD.DWG settings and do not configure another prototype drawing, your start-up settings will conform to the latest ACAD.DWG environmental settings. However, you may revert to the original defaults by clicking the No Prototype check box in the dialog box. The **Prototype. . .** button and edit box gray out and replace any entry in the **Prototype. . .** edit box with the word: *None*.

Click the Retain as Default check box, to retain a drawing as the default prototype or to retain no prototype as the default.

OPENING AN EXISTING DRAWING

When you want to open an existing drawing to view, edit and/or add objects, invoke the OPEN command from the pull-down menu File, Standard toolbar (see Figure 2–5), or at "Command:" prompt type **OPEN** and press ⌷Enter⌷ or spacebar.

Figure 2-5 Invoke the OPEN Command from the Standard toolbar

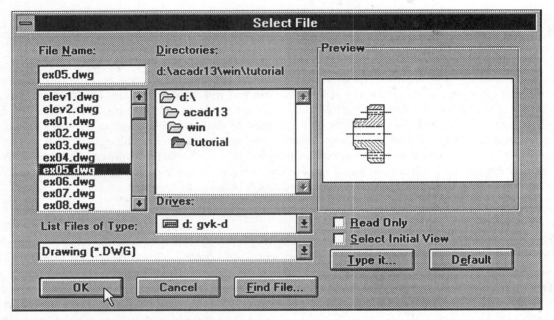

Figure 2-6 The Open Drawing dialog box

Command: **open**

AutoCAD displays a file dialog box entitled "Open Drawing" similar to the one shown in Figure 2–6. The dialog box is almost identical to the standard file dialog box, except that it includes check boxes for selecting an initial view and for setting read-only mode. In addition, when you click on the filename, AutoCAD displays a bitmap image in the dialog box.

The Select Initial View list box permits you to specify a view name in the named drawing to be the startup view. If there are named views in the drawing, an M or P beside their name will tell if the view is Model or Paper space, respectively.

You may open a drawing in the read-only mode, which permits you to view the drawing but not save it with its current name. However, you can edit and save it under a different name.

Find File causes the Browse/Search dialog box to be displayed. Various drives and directories are searched using search criteria.

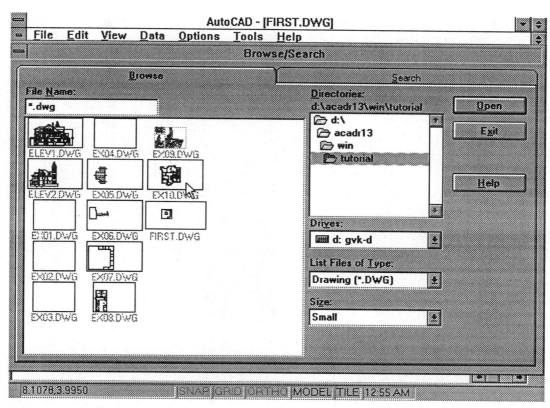

Figure 2-7 Browse dialog box

The Browse/Search dialog box combines the usual Windows file/path search of files by name (and normally with the .dwg extension) with small pictures of the drawings on the specified path to enable you to visually distinguish and select the drawing you wish to open.

Browse The Browse tabbed section, as shown in Figure 2-7, displays bitmap images of the drawings on the specified path.

File Name permits you to read the names of the available drawings and change the currently selected drawing.

Directories permits you to read the names of the available directories and change the currently selected directory.

Drives permits you to read the names of the available drives and change the currently selected drive.

List Files permits you to read the available file types and change the current file type.

Size permits you to change the size of the bit map images.

Select the appropriate drawing file to open from the Browse section.

Search The Search tabbed section, as shown in Figure 2-8, permits you to search a specific path or paths and then displays bitmap images of the drawings that meet the search criteria and are on the specified path(s). It also displays each drawing's name and path.

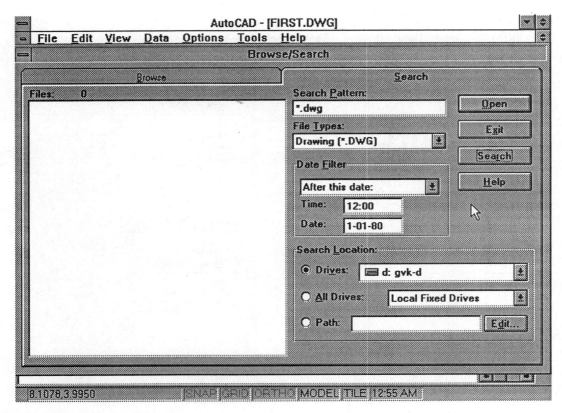

Figure 2-8 Search dialog box

Files permits you to read a list of files that meet the search criteria.

Search Pattern permits you to specify a criteria by which to search for files with the specified file type.

File Types permits you to specify the file type.

Date Filter permits you to tell AutoCAD whether to search forward or back from a specified date and time.

The **Time** edit field permits you to specify the time from which to search forward or back.

The **Date** edit field permits you to specify the date from which to search forward or back.

Search Location permits you to specify the drive/path on which AutoCAD will search.

All Drives causes AutoCAD to search all available drives.

Path permits you to specify drive/directory paths for searching.

Edit permits you to edit the path.

Select the appropriate drawing file to open from the Search section.

> **NOTE:** You can open and edit an AutoCAD Release 11 or Release 12 drawing in Release 13. If necessary, you can save the drawing in AutoCAD Release 12 format by using the SAVEASR12 command.

DRAWING SETTINGS

In conventional drafting, the drawing is done to a certain scale such as 1/4" = 1'-0" or 1" = 1'-0". But in AutoCAD, you draw full scale with the 1 = 1 scale factor. All lines, circles, and other objects are drawn and measured in full size. For example, if a part is 150 feet long, it is drawn 150 feet in actual size. When you are ready to plot, the drawing is scaled to fit a given sheet size.

DDUNITS and UNITS Command

DDUNITS and UNITS are the two commands you can use to set linear and angular units in AutoCAD. The DDUNITS command allows you to set units through the AutoCAD **Units Control** dialog box. With this format, you use the cursor to select the choices listed in the dialog box. The UNITS command allows you to set units at the command prompt level.

Whenever you start a new drawing in AutoCAD, you should invoke the DDUNITS or UNITS command first. The DDUNITS and UNITS commands are used to set the display format measurement and precision of your drawing units. When you begin a new drawing, the default display format measurement and precision are governed by the prototype drawing. You can change them as often as you wish while drawing. DDUNITS and UNITS commands allow you to change any one or all of the following:

Unit display format	Angle display precision
Unit display precision	Angle base
Angle display format	Angle direction

The DDUNITS command is invoked from the pull-down menu Data (see Figure 2–9), or at the "Command:" prompt, type DDUNITS and press [Enter]. AutoCAD displays the **Units Control** dialog box (see Figure 2–10).

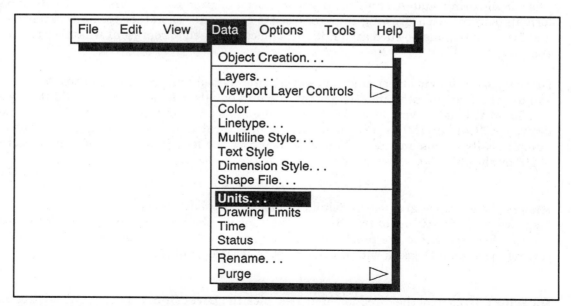

Figure 2-9 Invoke the DDUNITS Command from the pull-down menu Data

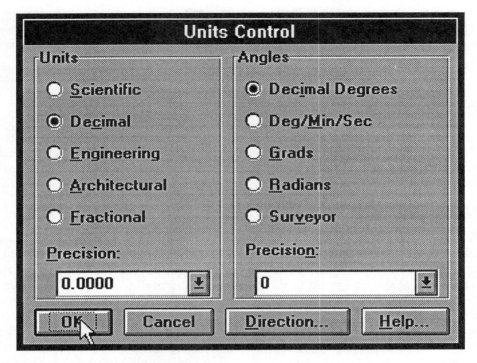

Figure 2-10   The Units Control dialog box

Units   The UNITS area of the **Units Control** dialog box allows you to change the units of linear measurement. Select one of the five radio buttons for the report format you prefer to use. For the selected report format, choose the precision from the popup list. The default setting of the prototype ACAD drawing is Decimal and precision is set to four decimal places.

The Engineering and Architectural report formats produce feet and inches displays. These formats assume each drawing unit represents one inch. The other formats (scientific, decimal, and fractional) make no such assumptions, and can be used to represent whatever real-world units you like.

Drawing a 150-ft long object might, however, differ depending on the units chosen. For example, if you use the Decimal unit and decide that one unit equals one foot, then the 150-ft long object will be 150 units long. If you decide that one unit equals one inch, then the 150-ft long object will be drawn 1800 units (150 × 12) long. In Architectural and Engineering unit modes, the unit automatically equals one inch. You may then give the length of the 150-ft long object as 150' or 1800" or simply 1800.

Angles   The Angles area on the Units Control dialog box allows you to set the drawing's angle measurement. Select one of the five radio buttons for the angle format you prefer to use. For the selected format, choose the precision from the popup list. The prototype ACAD drawing's default setting is Decimal Degrees with precision set to zero decimal places.

Direction   To control the direction of angles, pick the **Direction. . .** button and a Direction Control subdialog box appears, similar to the one shown in Figure 2-11.

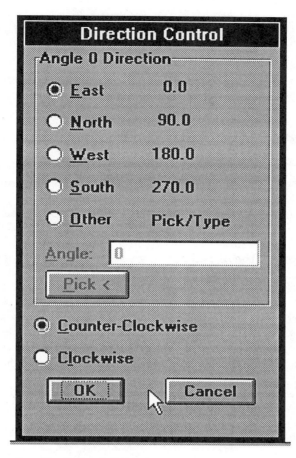

Figure 2-11 The Direction Control subdialog box

AutoCAD, by its default setting, assumes that 0 degrees is to the right, East, or 3 o'clock (see Figure 2-12), and that angles increase in the counterclockwise direction.

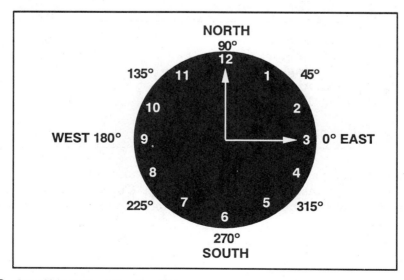

Figure 2-12 Specifying an angle direction

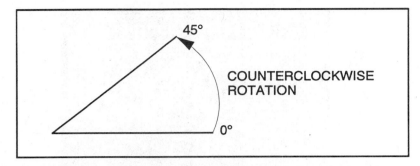

Figure 2-13 The default, counterclockwise angle direction of angle measurement

You can change measuring angles to start with any direction by selecting one of the five radio buttons.

You can also show AutoCAD the direction you want for angle 0 by specifying two points. This can be done by selecting the radio button for **Other** and click on the **pick<** button. AutoCAD prompts for two points and sets the direction for angle 0.

Finally, select the direction in which the angles are measured, clockwise or counterclockwise. This can be done by selecting one of the two radio buttons for the direction in which angles are measured.

If you accept the default, the angles are measured in a counterclockwise direction (see Figure 2-13).

Once you are satisfied with all of the settings in the **Units Control** dialog box, click the **OK** button to set the appropriate settings to the current working drawing and close the dialog box.

The UNITS command is invoked by typing **UNITS** at the "Command:" prompt and pressing [Enter].

    Command: **units**

When you invoke the UNITS command, your screen flips to text mode (unless you are operating at a dual-monitor station). Remember, you flip (toggle) back and forth between the text screen and graphics screen by pressing the [F2] key. The text screen displays the following:

Report formats:	**(Examples)**
1. Scientific	1.55E+01
2. Decimal	15.50
3. Engineering	1'-3.50"
4. Architectural	1'-3 1/2"
5. Fractional	15 1/2
Enter choice, 1 to 5 <default>:	

Choose the report format you prefer. To illustrate the various report formats, the menu shows a distance of 15.5 drawing units displayed in each format. The current format has its corresponding number displayed where <default> is shown. The prototype default is 2 (Decimal).

Once you have selected the report format, AutoCAD asks for the precision. If you select 1, 2, or 3, the following prompt appears:

    Number of digits to right of decimal point (0 to 8) <default>:

and for 4 or 5, the following prompt is displayed:

Denominator of smallest fraction to display
(1, 2, 4, 8, 16, 32, or 64) <default>:

After you have selected the report format and precision, AutoCAD prompts for an angle format:

Systems of angle measure:	(Examples)
1. Decimal degrees	45.0000
2. Degrees/minutes/seconds	45d0'0"
3. Grads	50.0000g
4. Radians	0.7854r
5. Surveyor's units	N 45d0'0" E
Enter choice, 1 to 5 <default>:	

The menu illustrates the various formats by showing how an angle of 45 degrees would be displayed in each format.

Angle Display Precision After specifying the angle format, AutoCAD prompts for the precision with which angles should be displayed. The prompt is:

Number of fractional places for display of angles (0 to 8) <default>:

You can specify a precision of up to eight places. If you are working with degrees/minutes/seconds, the number you enter determines the accuracy of the minutes and seconds. If you specify 0, for example, only degrees are displayed; if you specify 1 or 2, minutes also are displayed; 3 or 4 display degrees, minutes, and seconds; and 5 to 8 will display additional fractional seconds (one to four decimal places).

Next, AutoCAD prompts for the direction for angle 0. The following prompt appears:

Direction for angle 0:			
East	3 o'clock	=	0
North	12 o'clock	=	90
West	9 o'clock	=	180
South	6 o'clock	=	270
Enter direction for angle 0 <current>:			

You can change measuring angles starting in any direction by supplying the starting direction to this prompt. Note that you always respond to this prompt with an angle specified in the default mode. For example, if you want to make North (12 o'clock) as 0 degrees, then at the prompt type **90** and press Enter. You can also show AutoCAD the direction you want for angle 0 by specifying two points.

The final prompt controls the direction in which the angles are measured, clockwise or counter-clockwise. The prompt follows:

Do you want angles measured clockwise? <n>:

If you answer with **y** or **yes**, AutoCAD measures, angles in the clockwise direction and for n or no, measures angles in the counterclockwise direction.

NOTE: When AutoCAD prompts for a distance, displacement, spacing, or coordinates you can always reply with numbers in integer, decimal, scientific, or fractional format. If Engineering or Architectural report format is in effect, you can also input feet, inches, or a combination of feet and inches. However, feet-and-inches input format differs slightly from the report format because it cannot contain a blank. For example, a distance of 75.5 inches can be entered in the feet/inches/fractions format as 6'3-1/2". Note the absence of spaces and the hyphen in the unconventional location between the inches and the fraction. Normally, it will be displayed in the status area as 6'-3 1/2.

If you wish, you can use the SETVAR command to set the UNITMODE system variable to 1 (default UNITMODE system variable is 0) to display feet-and-inches output in the accepted format. For example, if you set UNITMODE to 1, AutoCAD displays the fractional value of 45 1/4 as you enter it: 45-1/4. The feet input should be followed by an apostrophe (') and inches with a trailing double quote (").

When Engineering or Architectural report format is in effect, the drawing unit equals one inch, so you can omit the trailing double quote (") if you like. When you enter feet-and-inches values combined, the inches values should immediately follow the apostrophe, without an intervening space. Distance input does not permit spaces because the spacebar is the same as Enter key.

LIMITS Command

The LIMITS command allows you to place an imaginary rectangular drawing sheet in the CAD drawing space. But, unlike the limitations of the drawing sheet of the board drafter, you can move or enlarge the CAD electronic sheet (the limits) after you have started your drawing. The LIMITS command does not affect the current display on the screen. The defined area determined by the limits governs the portion of the drawing indicated by the visible Grid (see GRID command on p. 2-45). Limits are also factors that determine how much of the drawing is displayed by the ZOOM All command (see ZOOM All on p. 2-57).

As mentioned earlier, when you start a new drawing, the area that is displayed on your screen is determined by the default setting of the limits. The default limits form a rectangle whose lower left corner is at coordinate 0,0 and upper right corner is 12,9. It should be re-emphasized that the default linear units are decimals and can be inches, meters, miles, millimeters, or whatever you decide. These conditions are contingent upon the ACAD.DWG file (the drawing whose properties the new drawings assume) not being altered. Novices are advised to **not** alter ACAD.DWG.

The limits are expressed as a pair of 2D points in the World Coordinate System, a lower left and an upper right limit. For example, to set limits for an A-size sheet, set lower left as 0,0 and upper right

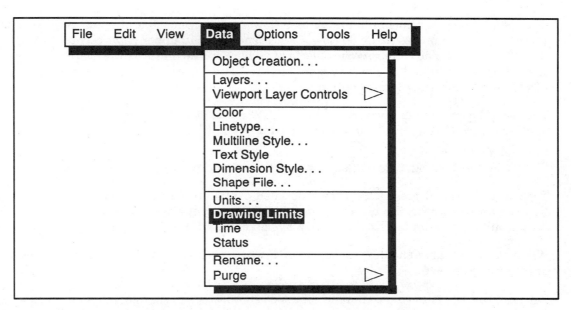

Figure 2–14   Invoke the LIMITS Command from the pull-down menu Data

as 11,8.5 or 12,9; for a B-size sheet set lower left as 0,0 and upper right as 17,11 or 18,12. Most architectural floor plans are drawn at a scale of 1/4" = 1'-0". To set limits to plot on a C-size (22" x 17") paper at 1/4" = 1'-0", the limits are set lower left as 0,0 and upper right as 88',68' (4 x 22, 4 x 17).

The LIMITS command is invoked from the pull-down menu Data (see Figure 2–14) or, at the "Command:" prompt, type **LIMITS** and press ⏎ or spacebar.

> Command: **limits**
> ON/OFF/<lower left corner> <default>:

You accept the default by pressing ⏎ or you can enter a new value for the lower left corner and press ⏎. The response you give for the lower left corner gives the location of the lower left corner of the imaginary rectangular drawing sheet. Then AutoCAD prompts:

> Upper right corner <default>:

You accept the default by pressing ⏎ or you can enter a new value. The response you give for the upper right corner gives the location of the upper right corner of the imaginary rectangular drawing sheet.

There are two additional options available for the LIMITS command. When AutoCAD prompts for the lower left corner, you may respond to the ON or OFF options. The ON/OFF options determine whether or not you can specify a point outside the limits when prompted to do so. When you select the ON option, then limits checking is on and you cannot start or end an object outside the limits, nor can you specify displacement points required by the MOVE or COPY commands outside the limits. You can, however, specify two points (center and point on circle) that draw a circle, part of which might be outside the limits. The limits check is simply an aid to help you avoid drawing off the imaginary rectangular drawing sheet. Leaving the limits checking ON is a sort of safety net to keep you from inadvertently specifying a point outside the limits.   On the other hand, limits checking is a hinderance if you need to specify such a point.

When you select the OFF option (default), AutoCAD disables limits checking, allowing you to draw the objects and specify points outside the limits.

Whenever you change the limits, you will not see any change on the screen unless you use the All option of the ZOOM command. ZOOM All lets you see entire newly set limits on the screen. For example, if your current limits are 12 by 9 (lower left corner 0,0 and upper right corner 12,9) and you change the limits to 42 by 36 (lower left corner 0,0 and upper right corner 42,36), you still see the 12 by 9 area. You can draw the objects anywhere on the limits 42 by 36 area, but you will see on the screen the objects that are drawn only in the 12 by 9 area. To see the entire limits, execute the ZOOM command using the All option.

The ZOOM command is invoked from the VIEW menu or at the "Command:" prompt, type **ZOOM** and press [Enter]. AutoCAD displays the following prompt line:

Command: **zoom**
All/Center/Dynamic/Extents/Left/Previous/Vmax/Window/<Scale(X/XP)>:

Type **A** or **ALL** and press [Enter]. (For a detailed explanation of the ZOOM command (see p. 2-54). You see on the screen the entire limits or current extents (whichever is greater). If objects are drawn outside the limits, ZOOM All displays all objects.

Whenever you change the limits, you should always invoke ZOOM All to see on the screen the entire limits or current extents.

For example, the following command sequence shows steps to change limits for an existing drawing (see Figures 2-15a and 2-15b).

Command: **limits**
ON/OFF/<lower left corner><-10'-0",-10'-0">: [Enter]
Upper right corner <50'-0",35'-0">: **100',70'**
Command: **zoom**
All/Center/Dynamic/Extents/Left/Previous/Vmax/Window/<Scale(X/XP)>:**all**

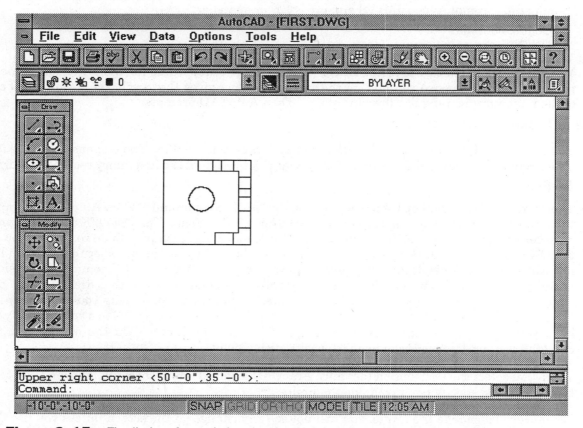

Figure 2-15a The limits of an existing drawing before being changed by the LIMITS Command

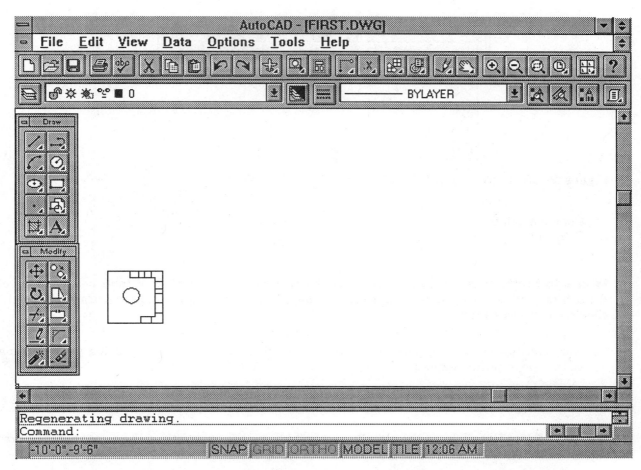

Figure 2-15b The new limits of the drawing, after being changed by the LIMITS Command

DRAW COMMANDS

The primary drawing object is the line. A series of connected straight line segments can be drawn by invoking the LINE command and then selecting the proper sequence of endpoints. AutoCAD connects the points with a series of lines. The LINE command is one of the few AutoCAD commands that automatically repeats in this fashion. It uses the ending point of one line as the starting point of the next, continuing to prompt you for each subsequent ending point. To terminate this continuing feature you must give a null response (press Enter). Even though a series of lines is drawn using a single LINE command, each line is a separate object as though it had been drawn with a separate LINE command.

You can specify the endpoints using either 2D (x,y) or 3D (x,y,z) coordinates, or a combination of the two. If you enter 2D coordinates, AutoCAD uses the current elevation as the Z element of the point (zero is the default). This chapter is concerned only with 2D points whose elevation is zero. (3D concepts and nonzero elevations are covered in later chapters.)

LINE Command

Invoke the LINE command from the Line flyout located in the Draw toolbar (see Figure 2-16), or at the "Command:" prompt, type **LINE** and press Enter or spacebar.

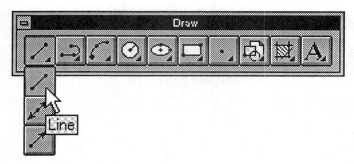

Figure 2-16 Invoke the LINE Command from the Draw toolbar

Command: **line**
From point:

Where to Start? The first point of the first object in a drawing normally establishes where all of the points of other objects must be placed. It is like the cornerstone of a building. Careful thought should go into locating the first point.

You can specify the starting point of the line by absolute coordinates or by using your pointing device (mouse or puck). After specifying the first point, AutoCAD prompts:

To point:

Where to From Here? In addition to the first point being the cornerstone, the direction of the first object is also critical to where all other points of other objects are located with respect to each other.

You can specify the end of the line by absolute coordinates, relative coordinates, or by using your pointing device to specify the end of the line on the screen. Again, AutoCAD repeats the prompt:

To point:

You can enter a series of connected lines. To save time, the LINE command remains active and prompts for a new "To point:" after each point you specify. When you have finished entering a connected series of lines, give a null reply (press Enter) to terminate the LINE command.

If you are placing points with a cursor instead of providing coordinates, a rubberband line is displayed between the starting point and the cross-hairs. This helps you see where the resulting line will go. In Figure 2-17 the dotted lines represent previous cursor positions.

Most of the AutoCAD commands have a variety of options. For the LINE command there are three options available: Continue, Close and Undo.

Continue Option When you invoke the LINE command and respond to the "From point:" prompt with a null response, AutoCAD automatically sets the start of the line to the end of the most recently drawn line or arc. This provides a simple method for constructing a tangentially connected line in an arc-line continuation.

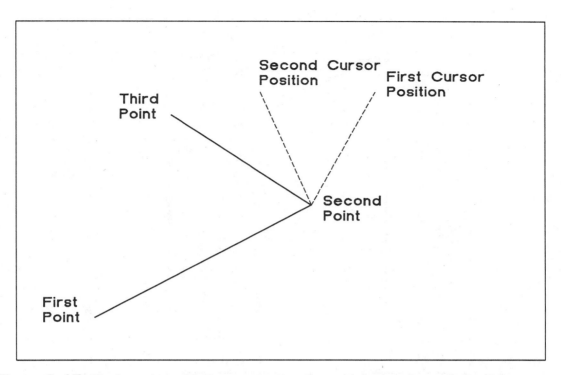

Figure 2-17 Placing points with the cursor rather than with keyboard coordinates input

The subsequent prompt sequence depends on whether a line or arc was more recently drawn. If the line is more recent, the starting point of the new line will be set as the ending point of that most recent line, and the "To point:" prompt appears as usual. If an arc is more recent, its end defines the starting point and the direction of the new line. AutoCAD prompts for:

Length of the line:

Specify the length of the line to be drawn, and then AutoCAD continues with the normal "To point:" prompt.

The following command sequence shows an example using the Continue option (see Figure 2-18).

Command: **line**
From point: *(pick point 1)*
To point: *(pick point 2)*
To point: *(pick point 3)*
To point: Enter
Command: *(to continue line from the point 3, press* Enter *or spacebar)*
From point: *(AutoCAD automatically picks the last point of the previous line)*
To point: *(pick point 4)*
To point: *(pick point 5)*
To point: Enter
Command:

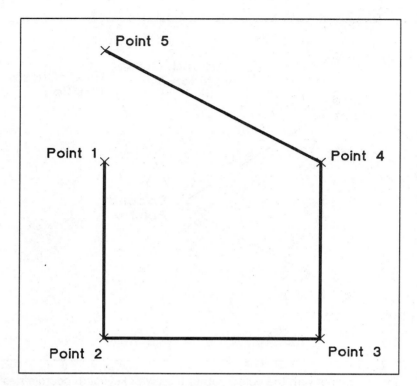

Figure 2-18 Using the LINE Command's Continue option

Close Option If the sequence of lines you are drawing forms a closed polygon, then you can use the Close option to join the last and first point automatically. AutoCAD draws the closing line segment if you respond to the "To point:" prompt with a **C** or **close** and press ⌷Enter⌷. AutoCAD performs two steps when you select the Close option. The first step closes the polygon and the second step terminates the LINE command (equivalent to a null response) and brings you back to the "Command:" prompt.

The following command sequence shows an example of using the Close option (see Figure 2-19).

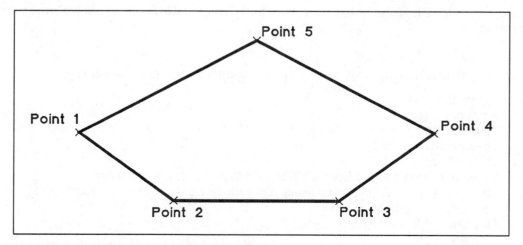

Figure 2-19 Using the LINE Command's Close option

Command: **line**
From point: *(pick point 1)*
To point: *(pick point 2)*
To point: *(pick point 3)*
To point: *(pick point 4)*
To point: *(pick point 5)*
To point: **C**
Command:

Undo Option When drawing a series of connected lines, you may wish to erase the most recent line segment and continue from the end of the previous object. You can do so by staying in the LINE command without exiting by using the Undo option. Whenever you wish to erase the most recent line segment, at the "To point:" prompt, enter **U** or **undo** and press Enter. If necessary, you can enter multiple U's or repeat the Undo option from the menu, and it will erase the most recent object one at a time. Once you are out of the LINE command, it is too late to use the Undo option of the LINE command to erase the most recent line segment.

The following command sequence shows an example using the Undo option (see Figure 2–20).

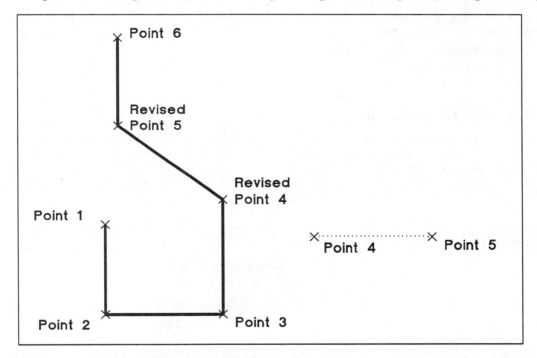

Figure 2-20 Using the LINE Command's Undo option

Command: **line**
From point: *(pick point 1)*
To point: *(pick point 2)*
To point: *(pick point 3)*
To point: *(pick point 4)*
To point: *(pick point 5)*
To point: **U**
To point: **U**
To point: *(pick revised point 4)*
To point: *(pick revised point 5)*
To point: *(pick point 6)*
To point: Enter
Command:

RECTANGLE Command

When it is necessary to create a rectangle box, you can use the RECTANGLE command. Invoke the RECTANGLE command from the Polygon flyout in the Draw toolbar (see Figure 2–21), or at the "Command:" prompt, type **RECTANG** and press [Enter] or the spacebar.

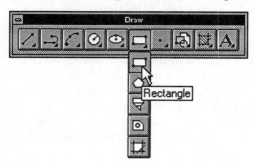

Figure 2-21 Invoke the RECTANGLE Command from the screen menu DRAW1

The following command sequence shows placement of points to draw a 3 by 5 rectangle using the RECTANGLE command.

 Command: **rectang**
 First corner: **2,2**
 Other corner: **5,7**

TRACE Command

When it is necessary to draw thick lines, the TRACE command may be used instead of the LINE command. Traces are entered just like lines except that the line width is set first. To specify the width, you can type a distance or select two points and let AutoCAD use the measured distance between them. When you draw using the TRACE command, the previous TRACE segment is not drawn until the next endpoint is specified.

Invoke the TRACE command from the Miscellaneous toolbar (see Figure 2–22) or, at the "Command:" prompt, type **TRACE** and press [Enter] or spacebar.

Figure 2-22 Invoke the TRACE Command from the Miscellaneous toolbar

 Command: **trace**
 Trace width <default>:

Specify the trace width and press [Enter]. The remaining prompts are similar to the LINE command.

For example, the following command sequence shows placement of connected lines using the TRACE command (see Figure 2-23).

 Command: **trace**
 Trace width <default>: **.05**
 From point: *(pick point 1)*
 To point: *(pick point 2)*
 To point: *(pick point 3)*
 To point: *(pick point 4)*
 To point: [Enter]
 Command:

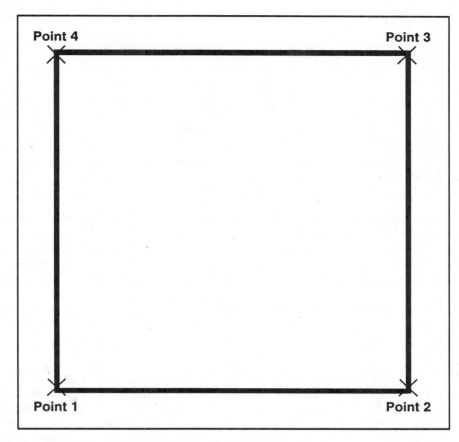

Figure 2–23   Placing wide connected lines using the TRACE Command

COORDINATE SYSTEMS

In accordance with the convention of the Cartesian coordinate system, horizontal distances increase in the positive X direction toward the right and vertical distances increase in the positive Y direction upward. Distances perpendicular to the XY plane that you are viewing increase toward you in the positive Z direction. This set of axes defines the World Coordinate System, abbreviated as the WCS.

The significance of the WCS is that it is always in your drawing; it cannot be altered. An infinite number of other coordinate systems can be established relative to it. These others are called user coordinate systems (UCS) and can be created with the UCS command. Even though the WCS is fixed, you can view it from any angle, side, or rotation without changing to another coordinate system.

AutoCAD provides what is called a coordinate system icon to help keep your bearings among different coordinate systems in a drawing. The icon will show you the orientation of your current UCS by indicating the positive directions of the X and Y axes. Figure 2-24 shows some examples of coordinate system icons.

Computer-aided drafting permits you to always draw an object at its true size and then make the border, title block, and other nonobject associated features fit the object. The completed combination is reduced (or increased) to fit the plotted sheet size you require when you plot.

A more complicated condition is when you wish to draw objects at different scales on the same drawing. This can be handled easily by one of several methods with the more advanced commands provided in AutoCAD.

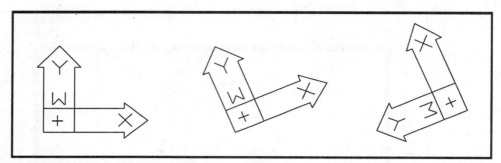

Figure 2–24 Examples of the UCS icons

Drawing a schematic that is not to scale is one situation where the graphics and computing power is hardly used to its potential. But even though the symbols and distances between them have no relationship to any real-life dimensions, the sheet size, text size, line widths and other visible characteristics of the drawing must be considered in order to give your schematic the readability you desire. Some planning, including sizing, needs to be applied to all drawings.

When AutoCAD prompts for a location of a point, you can use one of several point entry techniques available, which include absolute rectangular coordinates, relative rectangular coordinates, relative polar coordinates, spherical coordinates and cylindrical coordinates.

Absolute Rectangular Coordinates

The rectangular coordinates method is based on specifying a point location by giving its distances from two intersecting perpendicular axes in two-dimensional (2D) or from three intersecting perpendicular planes for three-dimensional (3D) points. Each point distance is measured along the X axis (horizontal), Y axis (vertical), and Z axis, (toward or away from the viewer). The intersection of the axes, called the origin (X,Y,Z=0,0,0) divides the coordinates into four quadrants for 2D or eight sections for 3D (see Figure 2–25).

Points are located by absolute rectangular coordinates in relation to the origin. You specify the reference to the WCS origin or UCS origin. In AutoCAD, by default the origin (0,0) is located at the lower left corner of the drawing as shown in Figure 2–26.

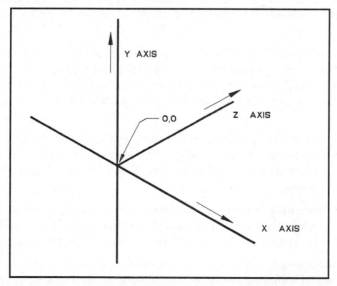

Figure 2–25 Specifying rectangular coordinates using the intersections of the X, Y, and Z axes

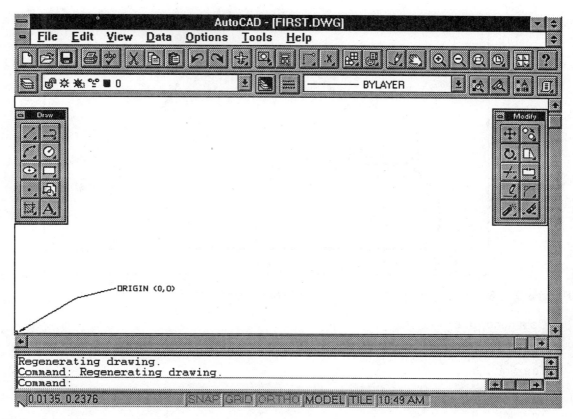

Figure 2–26 The default location of AutoCAD's origin

As mentioned earlier, the horizontal distance increases in the positive X direction from origin, and the vertical distance increases in the positive Y direction from origin. You specify a point by typing its X,Y,Z coordinates in decimal, fractional, or scientific notation separated by commas.

For example, the following command sequence shows placement of connected lines as shown in Figure 2–27 by absolute coordinates (see Figure 2–28):

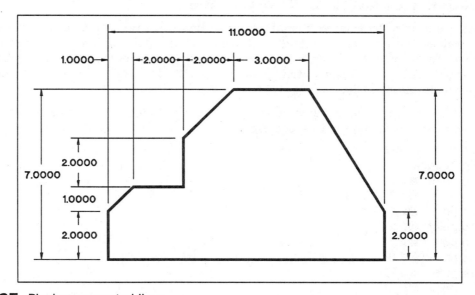

Figure 2–27 Placing connected lines

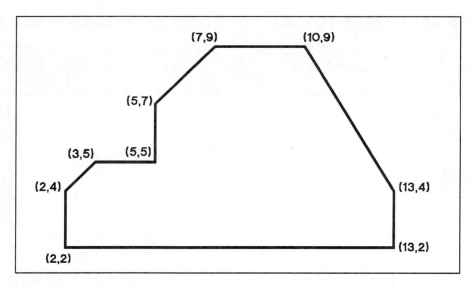

Figure 2-28 Placing connected lines using absolute coordinates

Command: **line**
From point: **2,2**
To point: **2,4**
To point: **3,5**
To point: **5,5**
To point: **5,7**
To point: **7,9**
To point: **10,9**
To point: **13,4**
To point: **13,2**
To point: **2,2**
To point: Enter
Command:

Relative Rectangular Coordinates

Points are located by relative rectangular coordinates in relation to the last specified position or point, rather than the origin. This is like specifying a point as an offset from the last point you entered. In AutoCAD, whenever you specify relative coordinates, the @ (at symbol) must precede your entry. This symbol is selected by holding the Shift key and pressing the **2** key at the top of the keyboard simultaneously.

The following command sequence shows placement of connected lines as shown in Figure 2-27 by relative rectangular coordinates (see Figure 2-29):

Command: **line**
From point: **2,2**
To point: **@0,2**
To point: **@1,1**
To point: **@2,0**
To point: **@0,2**
To point: **@2,2**
To point: **@3,0**
To point: **@3,-5**
To point: **@0,-2**
To point: **@2,2**

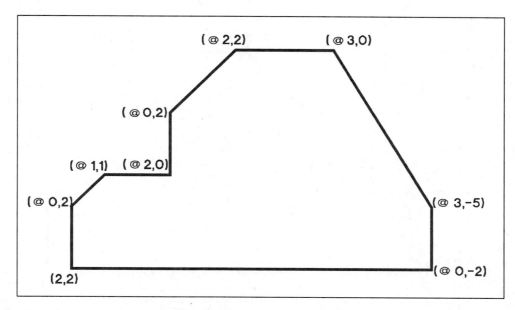

Figure 2–29 Placing connected lines using relative rectangular coordinates

To point: [Enter]
Command:

Relative Polar Coordinates

Polar coordinates are based on a distance from a fixed point at a given angle. In AutoCAD, a polar coordinate point is determined by distance and angle measured from the previous point. In AutoCAD, by default the angle is measured in the counterclockwise direction. It is important to remember that points located using polar coordinates are always positioned relative to the previous point and not the origin (0,0). You can specify a point by entering its distance from the previous point and its angle in the XY plane, separated by < (not a comma). This symbol is selected by holding the [Shift] key and pressing the "," key at the bottom of the keyboard simultaneously.

The following command sequence shows placement of connected lines as shown in Figure 2–27 by using a combination of polar and rectangular coordinates (see Figure 2–30).

    Command: **line**
    From point: **2,2**
    To point: **@2<90**
    To point: **@1,1**
    To point: **@2<0**
    To point: **@2<90**
    To point: **@2,2**
    To point: **@3,0**
    To point: **@3,-5**
    To point: **@2<270**
    To point: **@2,2**
    To point: [Enter]
    Command:

If you are working in a UCS and would like to enter points in reference to the WCS, enter coordinates preceded by an * (asterisk). For example, to specify the point with an X coordinate of 3.5, and Y coordinate of 2.57 in reference to the WCS, regardless of the current UCS, enter:

    *3.5,2.57

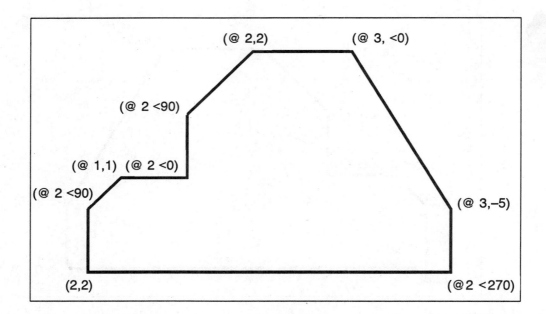

Figure 2–30 Placing connected lines using a combination of polar and rectangular coordinates

In the case of relative coordinates, the * (asterisk) will be preceded by @ symbol. For example:

> **@*4,5**

It represents as offset 4,5 from the previous point in relation to the WCS.

Coordinate Display

The Coordinates Display is a report in the status toolbar at the bottom of the screen. It has three settings. On most systems the function key F6 toggles between the three settings. The three settings are as follows:

1. This setting causes the display to report the location of the cursor when the prompt is in the "Command:" status or when you are being prompted for the first point selection of a command. It then changes to a relative polar mode when you are prompted for a second point that could be specified relative to the first point. In this case the report is in the form of the direction/distance. The direction is given in terms of the current angular units setting and the distance in terms of the current linear units setting.

2. This setting is similar to the previous one, except that the display for the second location is given in terms of its coordinates, rather than relative to the first point.

3. This setting is used to save either the location in the display at the time you toggle to this setting or the last point entered. It does not change dynamically with the movement of the cursor and will not change until you select a new point.

EXERCISES

In exercises 2–1 through 2–4, write down the coordinates necessary to draw the figures. See Figure 2–31 for an example of how this is done.

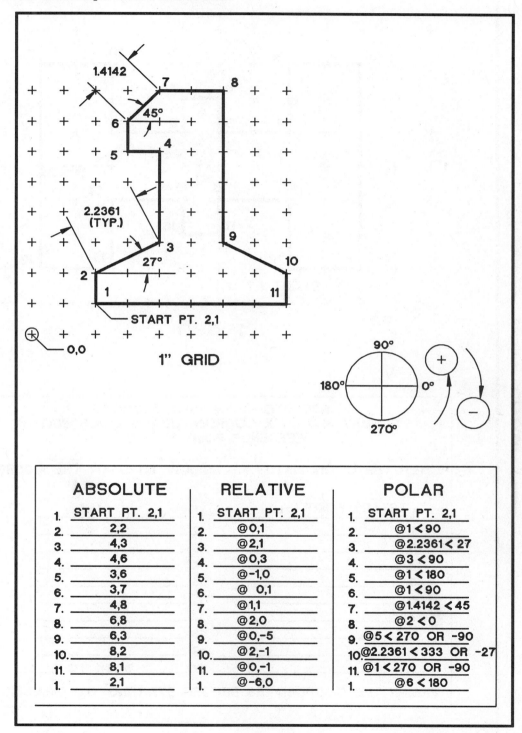

Figure 2–31 Review of absolute, relative, and polar coordinates

Exercise 2-1

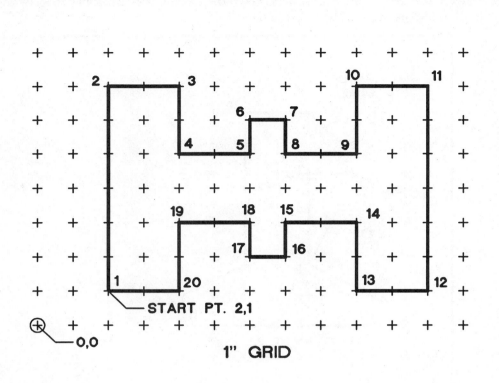

START PT. 2,1

0,0

1" GRID

ABSOLUTE COORDINATE EXERCISE
FORMAT IS X,Y (X COORDINATE),(Y COORDINATE)
REFERENCE POINT IS   0,0

ENTER THE COORDINATES NECESSARY TO DRAW THE FIGURE

1. START POINT IS 2,1
2. _____
3. _____
4. _____
5. _____
6. _____
7. _____
8. _____
9. _____
10. _____

11. _____
12. _____
13. _____
14. _____
15. _____
16. _____
17. _____
18. _____
19. _____
20. _____ BACK TO 1._____

FILL IN THE COORDINATES BEFORE STARTING THE DRAWING

Exercise 2-2

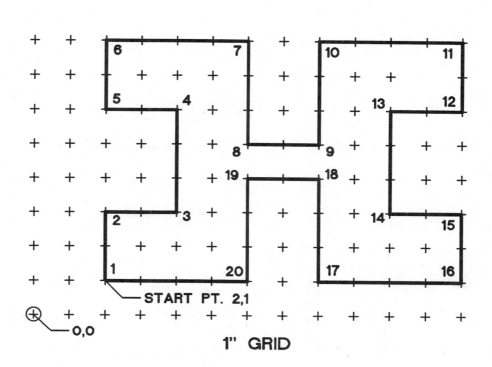

1" GRID

RELATIVE COORDINATE EXERCISE
FORMAT IS @X,Y
X= (DIST. + OR - ALONG THE X AXIS)
Y= (DIST. + OR - ALONG THE Y AXIS)
REFERENCE POINT IS THE LAST POINT ENTERED

ENTER THE COORDINATES NECESSARY TO DRAW THE FIGURE

1. START POINT IS 2,1
2. _____
3. _____
4. _____
5. _____
6. _____
7. _____
8. _____
9. _____
10. _____

11. _____
12. _____
13. _____
14. _____
15. _____
16. _____
17. _____
18. _____
19. _____
20. _____ BACK TO 1. _____

FILL IN THE COORDINATES BEFORE STARTING THE DRAWING

Exercise 2-3

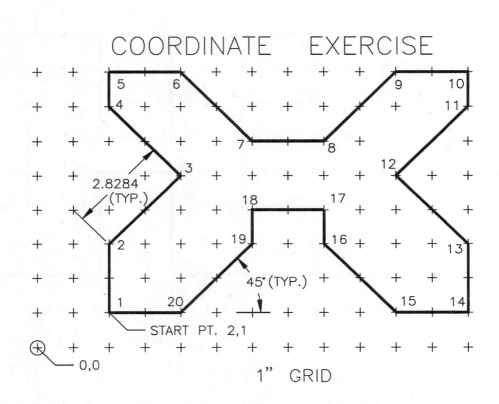

COORDINATE EXERCISE

2.8284 (TYP.)

45° (TYP.)

START PT. 2,1

0,0

1" GRID

POLAR COORDINATE EXERCISE
FORMAT IS @ DISTANCE < ANGLE
REFERENCE POINT IS THE LAST POINT ENTERED

ENTER THE COORDINATES NECESSARY TO DRAW THE FIGURE

1. STARTING POINT IS 2,1   11._____
2. _____   12._____
3. _____   13._____
4. _____   14._____
5. _____   15._____
6. _____   16._____
7. _____   17._____
8. _____   18._____
9. _____   19._____
10._____   20._____ BACK TO 1._____

FILL IN THE COORDINATES BEFORE DOING THE DRAWING

Exercise 2–4

NAME: _____   DATE: _____

COORDINATE TEST

4.   5.

6.

3.

45°
TYP.2   2.83 TYP.2

2.   7.

8.

9.

1.   11.

10.

START PT. 2,1

0,0   INSTRUCTIONS: FILL IN THE COORDINATE ENTRY FOR
ABSOLUTE, RELATIVE, AND POLAR COORDINATES. GRID
SPACING IS 1".

ABSOLUTE   RELATIVE   POLAR

ABSOLUTE	RELATIVE	POLAR
1. _____	1. _____	1. _____
2. _____	2. _____	2. _____
3. _____	3. _____	3. _____
4. _____	4. _____	4. _____
5. _____	5. _____	5. _____
6. _____	6. _____	6. _____
7. _____	7. _____	7. _____
8. _____	8. _____	8. _____
9. _____	9. _____	9. _____
10. _____	10. _____	10. _____
11. _____	11. _____	11. _____

Fundamentals I

SAVING AND QUITTING A DRAWING

While working in AutoCAD, you should save your drawing once every 10 to 15 minutes without exiting AutoCAD. By saving your work periodically, you are protecting your work from possible power failures, editing errors, and other disasters. This can be done automatically by setting the system variable SAVETIME to a specific interval (in minutes). In addition, you can also manually save by using the SAVE and SAVEAS commands.

Briefly, here's what each command does:

SAVE – Requests a filename if the drawing has not been named initially and saves the drawing on the given name. If the drawing is named, then AutoCAD saves the current named drawing without requesting a filename.

SAVEAS – Prompts for a filename and saves and sets the current drawing to the new filename. If the drawing is named, then AutoCAD saves the drawing to current drawing name, prompts for a new filename and sets the current drawing to the new filename you specify.

In addition you can save the current drawing in AutoCAD Release 12 format. Type SAVEASR12 at the "Command:" prompt and press [Enter]. AutoCAD prompts for a filename and it saves the drawing on the given filename in AutoCAD Release 12 format. In addition, AutoCAD saves the original Release 13 drawing to a backup file with file extension .BAK.

If the current drawing is unnamed, both commands SAVE and SAVEAS act like SAVEAS. AutoCAD displays a standard file dialog box entitled "Save Drawing As." Enter the drawing name in the **File:** edit box (.dwg is assumed) or select a filename from the **Files:** list box. The current drawing is set to the filename you specify.

If the current drawing is already named and you accept the current default filename, SAVE and SAVEAS commands update the current drawing. At this time, a .bak (backup file) is created and any previous backup file is updated. After saving your work, you remain in AutoCAD to continue to work on the updated drawing. If for some reason you enter a different filename that already exists as a drawing file, AutoCAD displays a message to warn that you are about to overwrite another drawing file. If you do not want to overwrite it, simply choose another filename.

When saving a drawing, if you enter a filename different from the current drawing name, AutoCAD does not create a .bak file, instead a new .dwg file under the new name is created.

The SAVE command is invoked from the pull-down menu File (see Figure 2-32), or at the "Command:" prompt, type **SAVE** and press [Enter] or spacebar.

    Command: **save**

A standard file dialog box appears if the drawing has not been named initially and prompts you for a filename. If the drawing already has a designated filename, then the SAVE command saves the current named drawing without requesting a filename.

The SAVEAS command is invoked from the pull-down menu File, or at the "Command:" prompt, type **SAVEAS** and press [Enter].

    Command: **saveas**

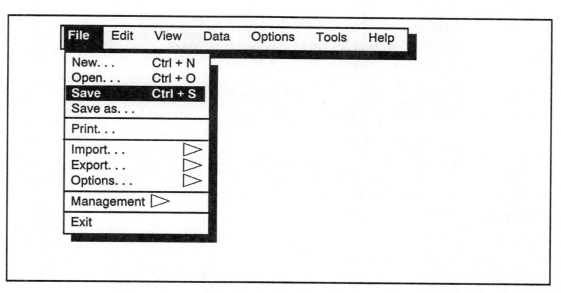

Figure 2-32 Invoke the SAVE Command from the pull-down menu File

AutoCAD displays a standard file dialog box, requests a filename, and sets the current drawing to that new filename.

The END command saves your drawing, and at the same time exits AutoCAD to return to the operating system.

The END command is invoked by typing END at the "Command:" prompt and pressing Enter.

    Command: **end**

When you issue the END command, AutoCAD automatically saves the drawing to the given drawing filename and appends the file extension .DWG. The old version, if present, is saved as a backup, with the file extension .BAK.

> **NOTE:** If you haven't named the current drawing, AutoCAD displays a standard file dialog box entitled "Create Drawing File." It allows you to name the drawing before exiting AutoCAD.

The QUIT command allows you to exit the AutoCAD without saving the change to the drawing since the last time you saved the drawing.

The QUIT command is invoked by typing QUIT at the "Command:" prompt and pressing Enter or spacebar.

    Command: **quit**

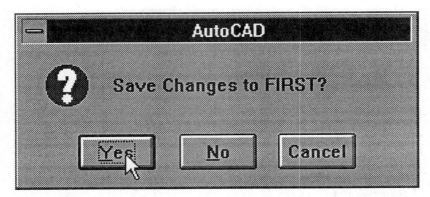

Figure 2-33 The Drawing Modification box when quitting the drawing named FIRST

If you have not saved any of your changes, AutoCAD allows you to save them, discard them, or cancel the command. This is accomplished by selecting one of the three buttons—**Yes, No,** or **Cancel**—from the AutoCAD dialog box (see Figure 2-33).

If you pick the **Yes** button, AutoCAD displays the standard file dialog "Save Drawing As." Specify the name of the drawing to which you want to save the drawing. Instead, if you pick the **No** button, AutoCAD quits the program without saving the current drawing, and take you back to the operating system prompt. If you pick the **Cancel** button, AutoCAD cancels the QUIT Command and takes you back to the "Command:" prompt.

OBJECT SELECTION

Many AutoCAD modify and construct commands prompt you to select one or more objects for manipulation. When you select one or more objects, AutoCAD highlights them by displaying them with broken lines. The group of objects selected for the manipulation is called the "selection set." There are several different ways of selecting the objects for manipulation. The selection options include: Window, Window Polygon (WP), Crossing, Crossing Polygon (CP), Fence, All, Last, Previous, Group Add, Remove, and Undo.

All modify and construct commands require a selection set, for which AutoCAD prompts:

Select objects:

AutoCAD replaces the screen cross-hairs with a small box called the "object selection target." With the target cursor, select individual objects for manipulation. Using your pointing device (or the keyboard's cursor keys), position the target box so it touches only the desired object or a visible portion of it. The object selection target helps you point to the object without having to be very precise. Every time you select an object, the "Select objects:" prompt reappears. To indicate your acceptance of the selection set, give a NULL reply at the "Select objects:" prompt.

Window Option The Window option in the selection of the objects allows you to designate all the objects contained completely in a rectangular area, or dynamically manipulated window. The Window option is invoked from the Select Objects toolbar, as shown in Figure 2-34. The window can be placed by providing two points diagonally opposite from left to right on the screen to the "Select Objects:" prompt. AutoCAD prompts for two diagonally opposite corner points describing the rectangle.

Figure 2-34 Invoke the Window option from the Select Objects toolbar

First corner:
Other corner:

If there is an object that is partially inside the rectangular area, then that object is not included in the selection set. You can select only objects currently visible on the screen. To select a partially visible object, you must include all its visible parts within the window. See Figure 2-35, in which only the lines will be included, not the circles, as a portion of the circles are outside the rectangular area.

Crossing Option The Crossing option is similar to the Window option, but selects all objects within or crossing the rectangle. If an object is partially inside the rectangular area, then the whole object is included in the selection set. The Crossing option is invoked from the Select Objects toolbar, as

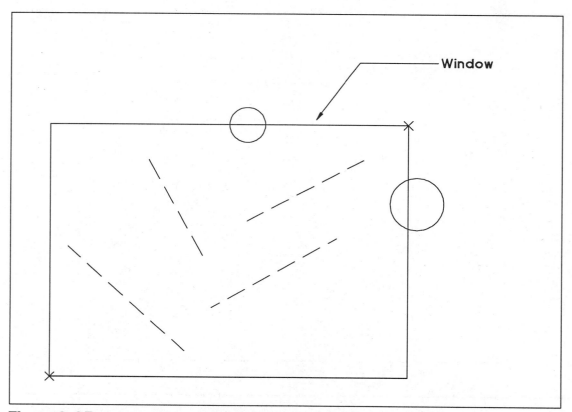

Figure 2-35 Selecting a partially visible object with the Window option

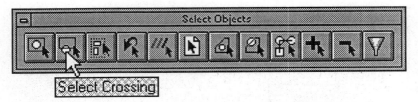

Figure 2-36 Invoke the Crossing option from the Select Objects toolbar

shown in Figure 2–36. The crossing can be placed by providing two points diagonally opposite from right to left on the screen to the "Select Objects:" prompt. Crossing displays a dashed box to differentiate it from a window selection box. See Figure 2–37 in which all the lines and circles are included though parts of the circles are outside the rectangle.

Previous Option The previous option enables you to perform several operations on the same object or group of objects. AutoCAD remembers the most recent selection set and allows you to reselect it with the Previous option. For example, if you moved several objects and now wish to copy them elsewhere, you can issue the COPY command and respond to the "Select objects:" prompt with **p** to select the same objects again or invoke the Select option from the Select Objects toolbar, as shown in Figure 2–38. (There is a command called SELECT that does nothing but create a selection set; you can then use the Previous option to refer to this set in subsequent commands.)

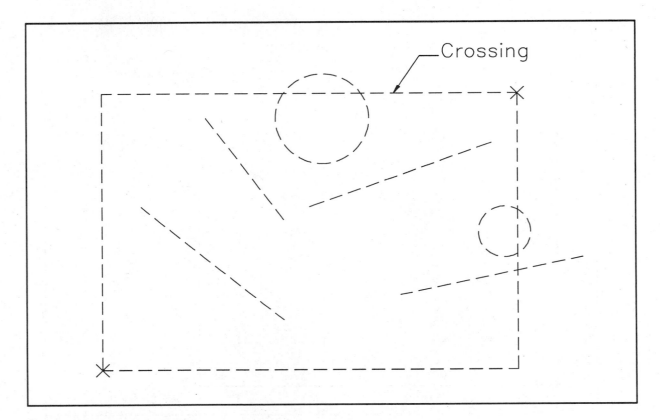

Figure 2-37 Selecting objects with the Crossing option

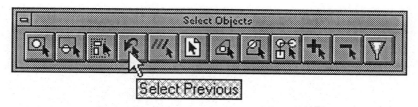

Figure 2-38 Invoke the Select option from the Select Objects toolbar

Last Option The Last option is an easy way to select the most recently created object currently visible. Only one object is designated, no matter how often you use the Last option when constructing a particular selection set. The last option is invoked from the Select Objects toolbar, as shown in Figure 2–39.

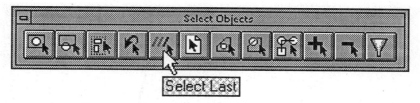

Figure 2-39 Invoke the Last option from the Select Objects toolbar

WPolygon, CPolygon, Fence, All, Group, Add and Remove options are explained in Chapter 4.

MODIFY COMMANDS

AutoCAD not only allows you to draw objects easily, but also allows you to modify the objects you have drawn. Of the many modifying commands available, the ERASE command probably will be the one you use most often. Everyone makes mistakes, but in AutoCAD it is easier to erase them. Or, if you are through with an object that you have created for construction of other objects, you may wish to erase it. The ERASE command lets you select objects that you want removed from the drawing.

ERASE Command

Invoke the ERASE command from the Modify toolbar (see Figure 2–40), or at the "Command:" prompt, type **ERASE** and press the spacebar or [Enter].

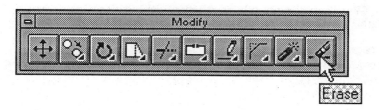

Figure 2-40 Invoke the ERASE Command from the Modify toolbar

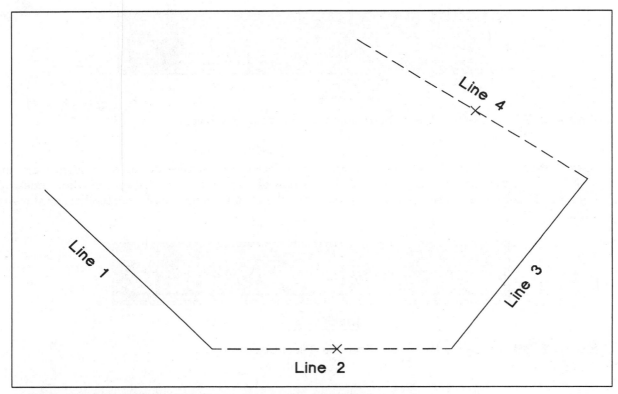

Figure 2-41 Use the ERASE Command to erase individual objects

Command: **erase**
Select objects: *(select objects to be erased and then press the spacebar or* Enter *)*

You can use one or more object selection methods available from the Modify toolbar. After selecting the object(s), press Enter (null response) in response to the next "Select objects:" prompt to complete the ERASE command. All the objects that were selected will disappear.

The following command sequence shows an example of erasing individual objects as shown Figure 2-41.

Command: **erase**
Select objects: *(pick line 2, the line is highlighted)* 1 selected, 1 found
Select objects: *(pick line 4, the line is highlighted)* 1 selected, 1 found
Select objects: Enter
Command:

The following command sequence shows an example of erasing a group of objects as shown in Figure 2-42 by the Window option:

Command: **erase**
Select objects: *(select window option from the screen menu or type w and press* Enter *)*
First corner: *(pick point 1)*
Other corner: *(pick point 2)* 4 found
Select objects: Enter
Command:

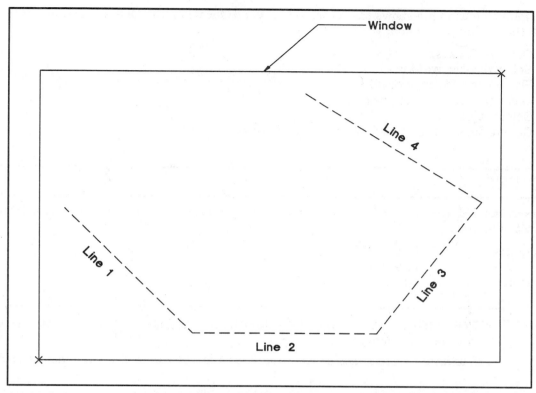

Figure 2-42 Use the Window option of the ERASE Command to erase a group of objects

OOPS Command

The OOPS command restores objects that have been unintentionally erased. Whenever the ERASE command is used, the last group of objects erased is remembered. The OOPS command will help you to restore the objects and can be used at any time. It only restores the objects erased by the most recent ERASE command. See Chapter 5 on the UNDO command, if you need to step back further than one ERASE command.

Invoke the OOPS command from the Miscellaneous toolbar (see Figure 2–43), or at the "Command:" prompt, type **OOPS** and press the spacebar or [Enter]. There are no options available for the OOPS command.

Figure 2-43 Invoke the OOPS Command from the Miscellaneous toolbar

```
Command: oops
Command:
```

The following example shows the command sequence for using the OOPS command in conjunction with the ERASE command:

Command: **erase**
Select objects: **window**
First corner: *(select a point)*
Other corner: *(select a point)*
Select objects: [Enter]
Command: **oops** *(will restore the erased objects)*

EXERCISES

In exercises 2–5 through 2–8, use absolute, relative, and polar coordinates in any combination to draw the figures.

Set limits   lower left: 0,0
                          upper right: 17,11
Set Units   Decimal (precision-2)

> **NOTE:** When you change the limits do not forget to ZOOM All. Do not add the dimensions.

Exercise 2-5

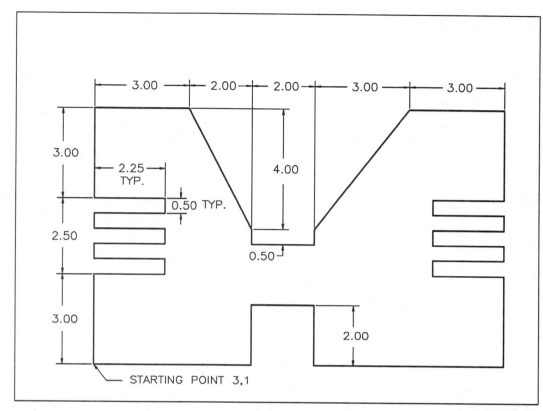

STARTING POINT 3,1

Exercise 2-6

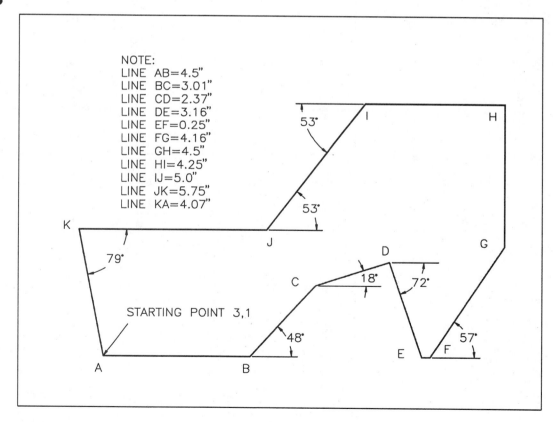

NOTE:
LINE AB=4.5"
LINE BC=3.01"
LINE CD=2.37"
LINE DE=3.16"
LINE EF=0.25"
LINE FG=4.16"
LINE GH=4.5"
LINE HI=4.25"
LINE IJ=5.0"
LINE JK=5.75"
LINE KA=4.07"

STARTING POINT 3,1

Fundamentals I

Exercise 2-7

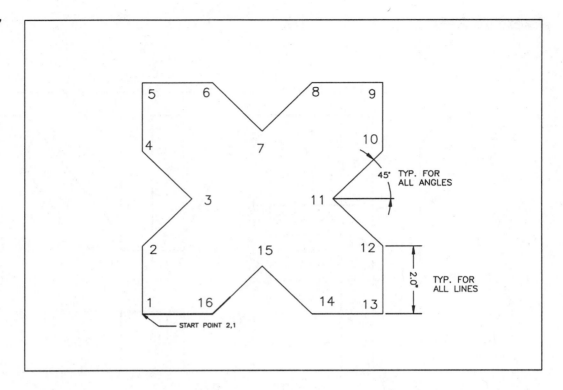

Exercise 2-8

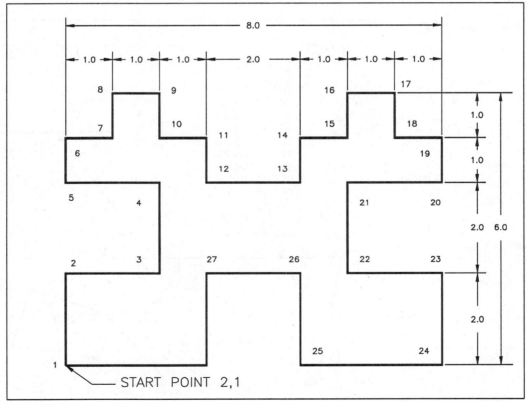

DRAWING TOOLS

The following drawing tools assist you in rapid drawing while ensuring the highest degree of precision.

GRID Command

The GRID command displays a visible array of dots with row and column spacings that you specify. AutoCAD creates a Grid that is similar to a sheet of graph paper. You can turn the Grid display on and off at will, and can change the dot spacing. The Grid is a drawing tool, and not part of the drawing; it is for visual reference and is never plotted. In the WCS, the Grid fills the area defined by the limits.

The Grid has several uses within AutoCAD. First, it shows the extent of the drawing limits. For example, if you set the limits to 42 x 36 units and grid spacing to 0.5 units, then you will have 84 x 72 dots in the X and Y directions respectively. This will give you a better sense of the drawing's size relative to the limits than if it were on a blank background.

Second, using the Grid with the SNAP command (discussed in the next section) is helpful when you create a design in terms of evenly spaced units. For example, if your design is in multiples of 0.5 units, then you can set grid spacing as 0.5 to facilitate point entry. You could check your drawing visually by comparing the locations of the Grid dots and the cross-hairs. Figure 2-44 shows a drawing with a grid spacing of 0.5 units with limits set to 0,0 and 17,11.

The GRID command is invoked by typing GRID at the "Command:" prompt and pressing the spacebar or [Enter].

Command: **grid**
Grid Spacing (X) or ON/OFF/Snap/Aspect <default>:

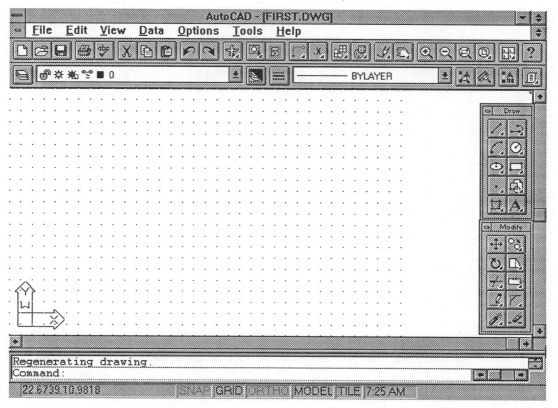

Figure 2-44 A grid spacing of 0.5 units, with limits set to (0,0) and 17,11)

You can accept the default by pressing the spacebar or [Enter] or you may enter a new value representing a new grid spacing and press the spacebar or [Enter]. The grid is turned on automatically when you either accept the default grid spacing or enter a new grid spacing value. It is often useful to set the grid spacing equal to the snap resolution or a multiple of it. To specify the grid spacing as a multiple of the snap value, enter **X** after the value. For example, to set up the grid value three times the current snap value (snap=0.5 units), enter **3X** for the prompt, which is the same as setting to 1.5 units.

ON Option The ON option turns on the grid and has the same effect as accepting the default Grid-space value.

OFF Option The OFF option turns off the grid. Also, you can toggle the grid on and off with the function key [F7], double-click GRID on the status bar, or with the [Ctrl] + [G] key combination.

Snap Option The Snap option provides a simple means of locking the grid spacing to the current snap resolution.

Aspect Option The Aspect option will allow you to set different X and Y values for the grid. When you select the Aspect option, AutoCAD prompts for the X and Y values. This is handy if you are dealing with modules of unequal dimensions. For example, suppose you want a horizontal grid spacing of 0.5 and vertical spacing of 0.25. Enter the following:

    Command: **grid**
    Grid spacing (X) or ON/OFF/Snap/Aspect <0>: **A**
    Horizontal spacing (X)<0>: **0.5**
    Vertical spacing (Y)<0>: **0.25**

The Aspect option provides the Grid dot spacing as shown in Figure 2-45.

If the spacing of the visible Grid is set too small, AutoCAD displays the following message and does not show the dots on the screen:

    Grid too dense to display

To display the Grid, issue another GRID command and specify a larger spacing.

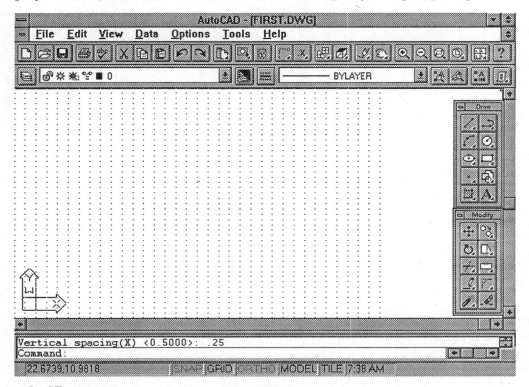

Figure 2-45 Using the Aspect option of the GRID Command

SNAP Command

The SNAP command provides an invisible reference grid. When turned on, the snap feature forces the cursor to lock in to the nearest point on the specified grid. Using the SNAP command, you can enter points quickly, letting AutoCAD ensure that they are placed precisely. You can always override the snap spacing by entering absolute or relative coordinate points from the keyboard, or by simply turning off the snap mode. When the snap mode is turned off, it has no effect on the cursor. When turned on, you cannot pick a point with the pointing device that is not on one of the specified snap locations. Snap and grid can be used together.

The SNAP command is invoked by typing SNAP at the "Command:" prompt and pressing [Enter] or spacebar.

> Command: **snap**
> Snap spacing or ON/OFF/Aspect/Rotate/Style <default>:

You can accept the default by pressing [Enter] or you can enter a new value representing a new snap spacing and press [Enter]. The grid is turned on automatically when you either accept the default snap spacing or enter a new snap spacing value. It is often useful to set the grid spacing equal to the snap resolution or a multiple of it. When the snap mode is on, the word **SNAP** appears in the status bar at the bottom of your screen (see Figure 2-46).

ON Option The ON option turns on the snap and has the same effect as accepting the default snap spacing value.

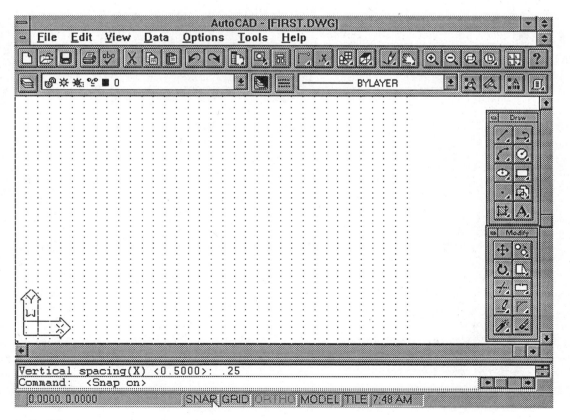

Figure 2-46 The status of Snap mode displayed on the status bar

OFF Option The OFF option turns off the snap mode. Also you can toggle snap on and off with function key [F9], double-click SNAP on the status bar, or with the [Ctrl] + [B] key combination.

Aspect Option The Aspect option is the same as in GRID Command, allows you to set X and Y spacings to different values.

Rotate Option The Rotate option allows you to rotate both the visible grid and the invisible snap grid at any angle. First, AutoCAD prompts for a base point (the point around which the grid will be rotated) and then prompts for the angle of rotation. The sequence of prompts is as follows:

Command: **snap**
Snap spacing or ON/OFF/Aspect/Rotate/Style <current>: **r**
Base point <0,0>: *(select or specify new origin)*
Rotation angle <0>: *(specify new angle of rotation)*

Style Option The Style option permits you to select one of the two available formats, Standard and Isometric. Standard refers to the normal rectangular type of grid (default) and Isometric refers to a grid and snap designed for Isometric drafting purposes (see Figure 2–47).

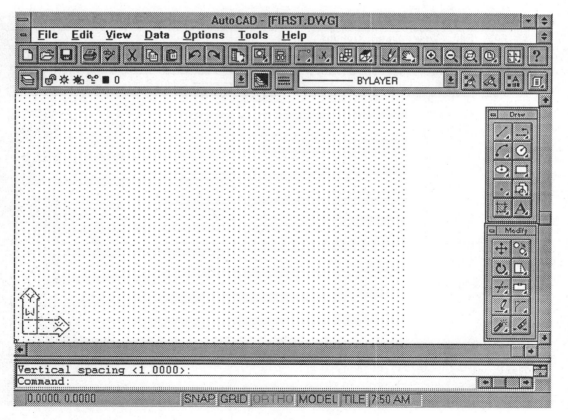

Figure 2–47 Setting the Snap for isometric drafting

ORTHO Command

The ORTHO command lets you draw lines parallel to the X and Y axes and are therefore perpendicular to each other. This mode is helpful when you need to draw lines that are exactly horizontal or vertical. It also forces lines to be parallel to one of the three isometric axes when the snap style has been set to Isometric.

At the "Command:" prompt, type **ORTHO** and press [Enter] or spacebar.

> Command: **ortho**
> Ortho On/Off:

The ORTHO command has only two options, ON and OFF. The ON option turns the ortho mode on, while the OFF option turns the ortho mode off. When on, the word **ORTHO** appears in the status bar at the bottom of the screen (see Figure 2–48). Also, you can toggle Ortho on and off with function key [F8], double-click ORTHO on the status bar, or with the [Ctrl] + [O] key combination (Ctrl + letter O, not Ctrl + number 0).

When Ortho mode is active, you can draw linear and specify displacements only in the horizontal or vertical directions, regardless of the cursor's on-screen position. The direction in which you draw is determined by the change in the X value of the cursor movement compared to the change in the cursor's distance to the Y Axis. AutoCAD allows you to draw horizontally, if the distance in X is greater than the distance in Y; conversely, if the change in Y is greater than X, then it forces you to draw vertically.

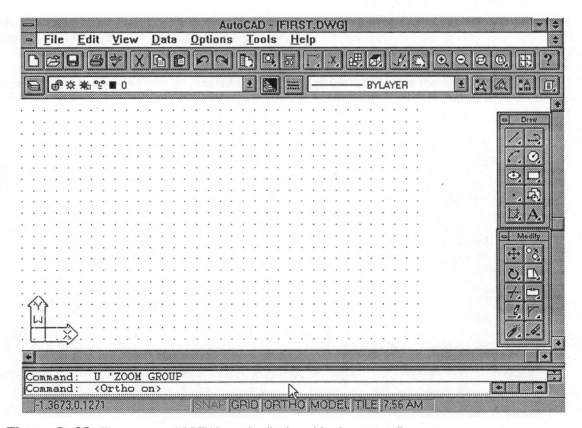

Figure 2–48 The status of ORTHO mode displayed in the status line

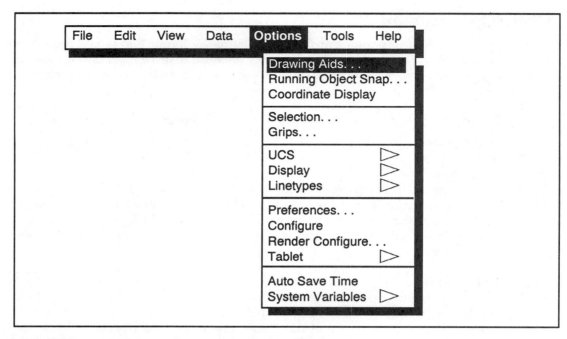

Figure 2–49 Setting the drawing tools using the pull-down menu Options

DDRMODES Dialog Box

The AutoCAD drawing tools can be set or changed using a dialog box. Select **Drawing Aids...** from the pull-down menu Options (see Figure 2–49), or, at the "Command:" prompt, type **DDRMODES** and press the spacebar or [Enter]; the **Drawing Aids** dialog box is displayed.

Use the dialog box to set grid and snap spacing. In addition, you can also turn on grid, snap, ortho, isometric style, and other utility commands such as Solid Fill, Quick Text, Blips, and Highlight. Figure 2–50 shows grid spacing set to 0.25, snap to 0.25, with grid, snap, and ortho turned ON.

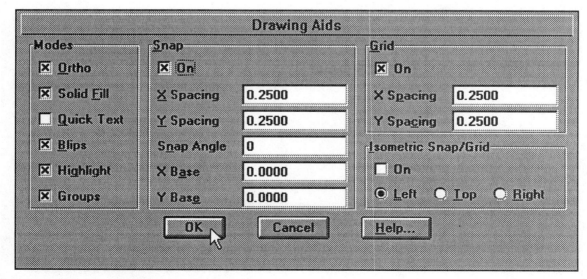

Figure 2–50 The Drawing Aids dialog box

Object Snap—Linear Applications

The Object Snap (or OSNAP, for short) feature lets you specify points on existing objects in the drawing. For example, if you need to draw a line from an endpoint of an existing line then you use the Osnap mode called ENDpoint. This feature is similar to the basic SNAP command, which locks to invisible reference grid points.

Osnap modes can be invoked while executing an AutoCAD command which requests a point, such as LINE, CIRCLE, MOVE, and COPY. The Osnap modes may be typed at the prompt line, selected from the Object Snap toolbar, from the cursor menu, or from the Object Snap flyout located in the Standard toolbar. Each Osnap mode has a specific application. When typed at the prompt line, only the first three letters are required. Whenever you are in an Osnap mode, a target is added to the crosshairs to indicate the area within which AutoCAD searches for Osnap candidates (see Figure 2-51). Following are the Osnap modes available in AutoCAD:

CENter	Snaps to the center of an arc or circle
ENDpoint	Snaps to the closest endpoint of a line, trace, polyline, or arc
INSert	Snaps to the insertion point on a block, shape, or text object
INTersection	Snaps to the intersection of two objects
App Int	Snaps to the apparent intersection of two objects that may or may not actually intersect in space.
MIDpoint	Snaps to the midpoint of an arc or line
NEArest	Snaps to a point on an object nearest to the cross-hairs
NODe	Snaps to a point object; drawn with the POINT command

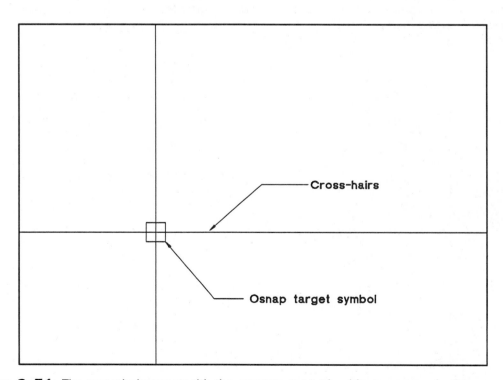

Figure 2-51 The cross-hair cursor with the aperture target in object snap mode

PERpend	Snaps to a perpendicular on an object
QUAdrant	Snaps to the closest quadrant point of an arc or circle
QUIck	Allows Osnap to find the quickest selection for the specified osnap mode that is selected immediately after QUIck
TANgent	Forms a line tangent to a picked arc or circle
NONe	Turns running Osnap off

In this section, Osnap modes ENDpoint and MIDpoint are explained. The remaining modes are explained in later chapters.

OSNAP ENDpoint Option To specify a point on the endpoint of an existing line or arc, use the ENDpoint option. Make sure you are in the appropriate AutoCAD command, and select the ENDpoint option from the Object Snap toolbar (see Figure 2-52).

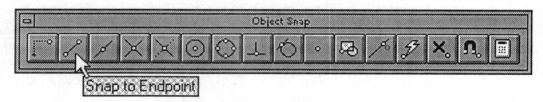

Figure 2-52 Invoke the Osnap ENDpoint option from the Object Snap toolbar

For example, to connect a line to the endpoint of an existing line as shown in Figure 2-53, the following command sequence is used:

Command: **line**
From point: **endpoint of** *(move the aperture cursor near the end of Line A and pick)*
To point: *(pick a point)*
To point: Enter

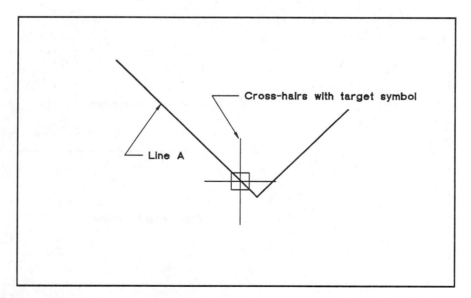

Figure 2-53 Connecting a line to another line's endpoint using the ENDpoint object snap

OSNAP MIDpoint Option To connect a line or arc, or to place a center point of a circle, arc, or ellipse on the midpoint of an existing line or arc, use the MIDpoint object snap. Make sure you are in the appropriate AutoCAD command, and select the MIDpoint option from the Object Snap toolbar (see Figure 2-54).

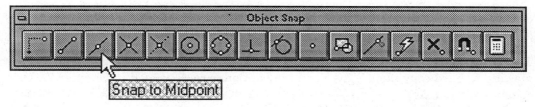

Figure 2-54 Invoke the Osnap MIDpoint option from the Object Snap toolbar

For example, to connect a line to the midpoint of an existing line as shown in Figure 2-55, the following command sequence is used:

Command: **line**
From point: **Midpoint of** *(move the aperture cursor to anywhere on the Line A and pick)*
To point: *(pick a point)*
To point: Enter

Normally, you should not allow the aperture box to cover more than one object (or intersection in the case of the intersection mode). Otherwise, there is a chance the wrong point may be used.

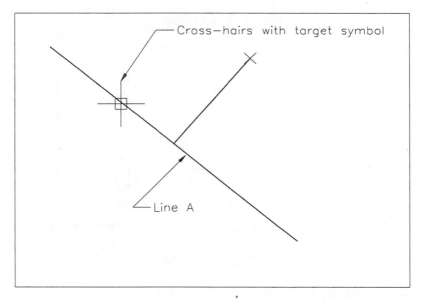

Figure 2-55 Connecting a line to another line's midpoint using the MIDpoint Object Snap

APERTURE Command

The APERTURE command permits you to set the size of the selection target box used during object snap. At the "Command:" prompt type **APERTURE** and press [Enter] or spacebar. AutoCAD prompts:

Object snap target height (1–50 pixels)<current>: (Enter an integer from 1 to 50 or press [Enter])

The size of the target box will be increased as the value entered increases. For an object to be eligible for an object snap mode, it must touch or be within the target box.

VIEW COMMANDS

There are many ways to view a drawing in AutoCAD. These viewing options vary from on-screen viewing to hard copy plots. The hard copy options are discussed in Chapter 7. Using the display commands, you can select the portion of the drawing to be displayed, establish 3D perspective views and much more. By letting you see your drawing in different ways, AutoCAD gives you the means to draw faster, more easily, and more accurately.

The commands that are explained in this section are like utility commands. They make your job easier and help you to draw more accurately.

ZOOM Command

The ZOOM command is like a zoom lens on a camera. You can increase or decrease the viewing area, although the actual size of objects remains constant. As you increase the visible size of objects, you view a smaller area of the drawing in greater detail. As you decrease the visible size of objects, you view a larger area. This ability provides the means for accuracy and detail.

The ZOOM command is invoked from the pull-down menu View (see Figure 2–56), the Standard toolbar, or at the "Command:" prompt, type **ZOOM** and press [Enter] or spacebar.

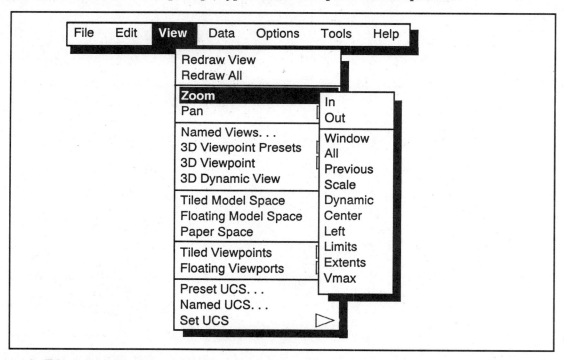

Figure 2–56 Invoke the ZOOM Command from the pull-down menu View

Command: **zoom**
All/Center/Dynamic/Extents/Left/Previous/Vmax/Window/<Scale(X/XP)>:

Default Option The default option of the ZOOM command is a windowed zoom. After the ZOOM command presents its long list of options, simply pick two points on the screen that represent a rectangle. AutoCAD enlarges the view to fit the rectangle. See the related Window option.

Scale Option The Scale option lets you enter a display scale (or magnification) factor. The scale factor when entered as a number (must be a numerical value and not expressed in units of measure) is applied to the area covered by the drawing limits. For example, if you enter a scale of 3, each object appears three times as large as it does in the full view. A scale factor of 1, displays the entire drawing (the full view), which is defined by the established limits. If you enter a value less than 1, AutoCAD decreases the magnification about the full view. For example, if you enter a scale of 0.5, each object appears half the size as it does in the full view while the viewing area is twice the size in horizontal and vertical dimensions. When you use this option, the object in the center of the screen remains centered. You can also invoke the Zoom Scale option from the Zoom flyout located in the Standard toolbar, as shown in Figure 2–57.

See Figures 2–58a and 2–58b for the difference between the full view and after 0.5 zoom.

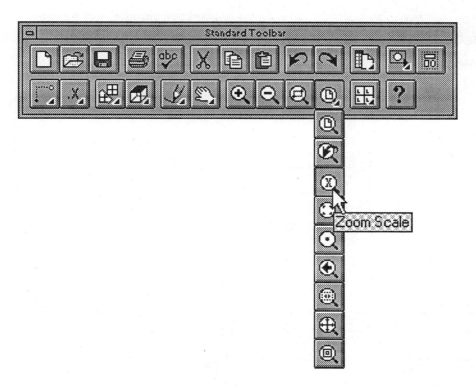

Figure 2–57 Invoke the Zoom Scale option from the Standard toolbar

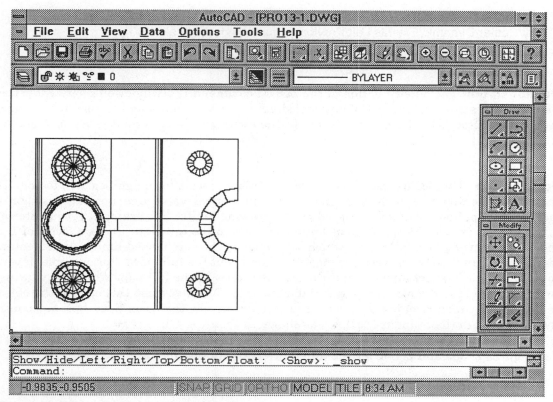

Figure 2-58a The drawing at ZOOM All

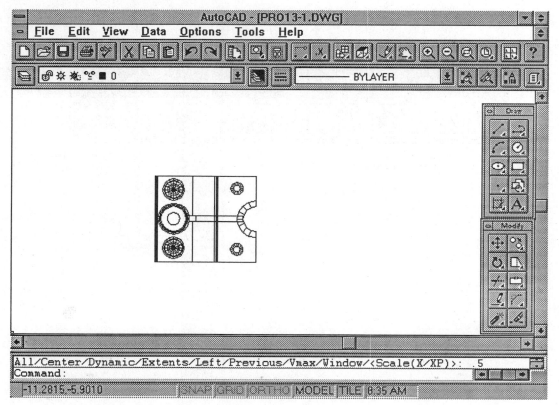

Figure 2-58b The drawing after a ZOOM 0.5

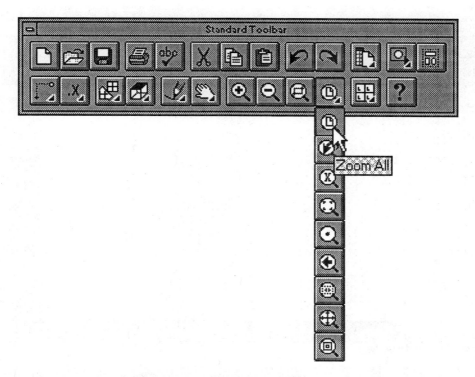

Figure 2-59 Invoke the Zoom All option from the Standard toolbar

If you enter a number followed by X, the scale is determined relative to the current view. For instance, entering 2X causes each object to be displayed 2 times its current size on the screen.

The scale factor XP option is explained in Chapter 11 as it is related to paper and model space units.

All Option The All option lets you see the entire drawing. In a plan view, it zooms to the drawing's limits or current extents, whichever is larger. If the drawing extends outside the drawing limits, the display shows all objects in the drawing. You can also invoke the Zoom All option from the Zoom flyout located in the Standard toolbar, as shown in Figure 2–59.

Extents Option The Extents option lets you see the entire drawing on-screen. Unlike the All Option, the Extents Option uses only the drawing extents and not the drawing limits. See Figures 2-60a and 2-60b, which illustrate the difference between the options All and Extents.

Previous Option The Previous option displays the last displayed view. While editing or creating a drawing, you may want to zoom into a small area, back out to view the larger area, and then zoom into another small area. To do this, AutoCAD saves the coordinates of the current view whenever it is being changed by any of the zoom options, or other view commands. So, you can return to the previous view by entering the Previous option, which can restore the previous 10 views.

Window Option The Window option lets you specify an area of the drawing you wish to see by placing two opposite corner points of a rectangular window. The center of the area selected becomes

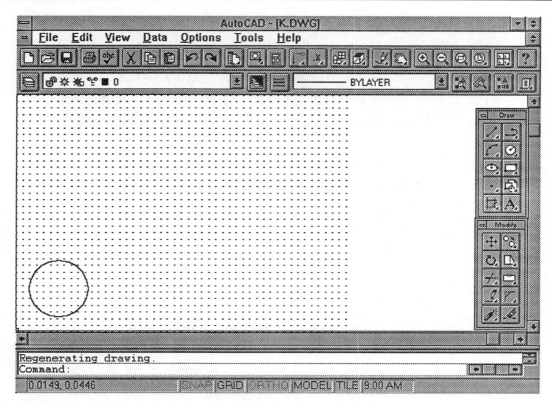

Figure 2-60a The drawing after a ZOOM All

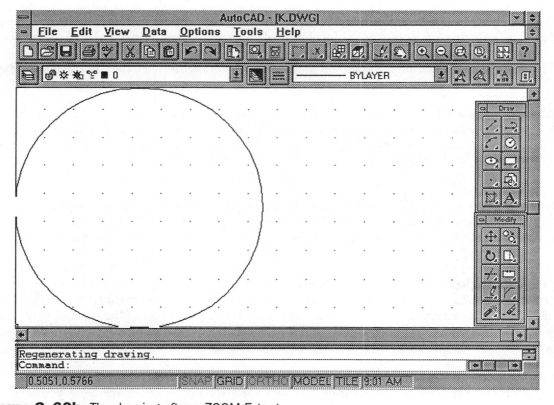

Figure 2-60b The drawing after a ZOOM Extents

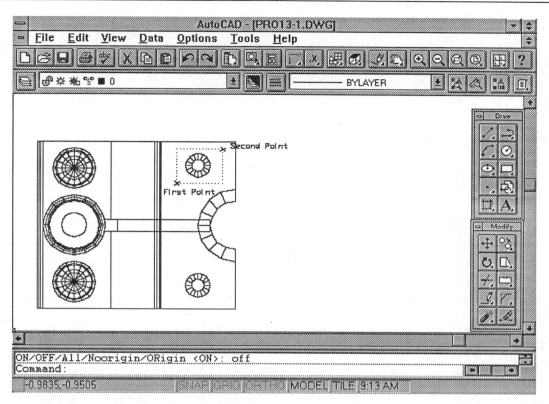

Figure 2-61a Specifying a ZOOM Window area

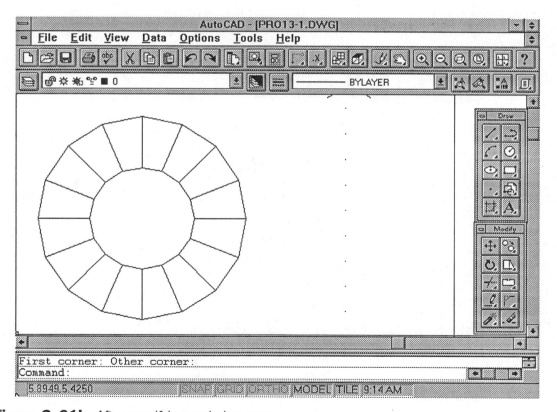

Figure 2-61b After specifying a window area

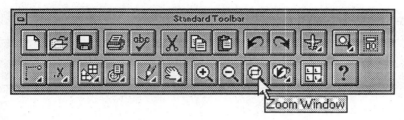

Figure 2-62 Invoke the Zoom Window option from the Standard toolbar

the new display center, and the area inside the window is enlarged to fill the display as completely as possible.

Command: **zoom**
All/Center/Dynamic/Extents/Left/Previous/Vmax/Window/<Scale(X/XP)>: W
First corner: *(pick a point)*
Other corner: *(pick a point)*

You can enter two opposite corner points to specify an area by coordinates or with the pointing device (see Figures 2-61a and 2-61b). You can also invoke the Zoom Window option from the Standard toolbar, as shown in Figure 2-62.

PAN Command

The PAN command lets you view a different portion of the drawing in the current view, without changing the magnification. You can move your viewing area to see details that are currently off-screen. Imagine that you are looking at your drawing through the display window and that you can slide the drawing left, right, up, and down without moving the window.

The PAN command is invoked from the pull-down menu View (see Figure 2-63), from the Standard toolbar (see Figure 2-64) or, at the "Command:" prompt, type **PAN** and press the spacebar or Enter.

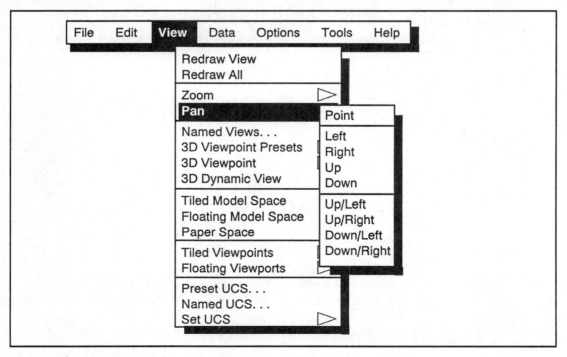

Figure 2-63 Invoke the PAN command from the pull-down menu View

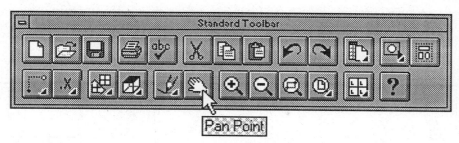

Figure 2-64 Invoke the PAN Command from the Standard toolbar

Command: **pan**
Displacement:

You must specify the direction to move the view of the drawing, and how far to move it. You can designate two points, in which case AutoCAD computes the displacement from the first point to the second. For example, the following command sequence moves the drawing by placing two data points as shown in Figure 2-65.

Command: **pan**
Displacement: *(pick first displacement point)*
Second point: *(pick second displacement point)*

AutoCAD calculates the distance and direction between the two points and pans the drawing accordingly. Sometimes it is useful to pan in exactly the horizontal or vertical direction. In that case, turn Ortho mode on before starting the PAN command to constrain cursor movement of the X or Y axis. You can enter a single coordinate pair indicating the relative displacement of the drawing with respect to the screen. If you give a null response to the second point prompt, you are indicating the coordinates provided are the displacement of the drawing with respect to the origin. If you provide the coordinates for the second point instead of giving a null response, then AutoCAD

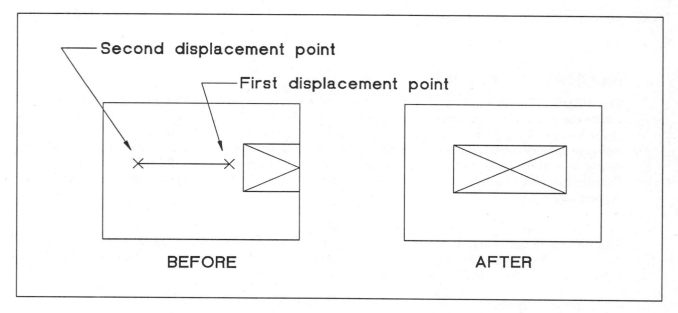

Figure 2-65 Moving the view with the PAN Command by specifying two pick points

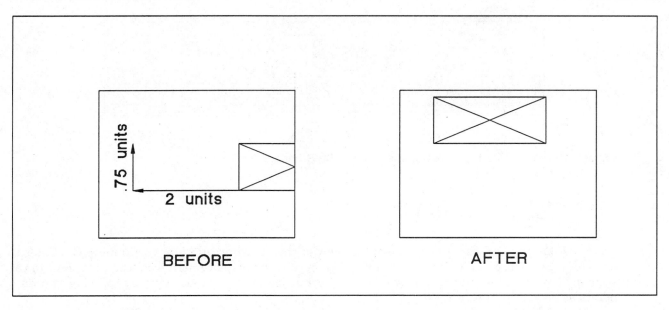

Figure 2-66 Moving the view with the PAN Command by specifying a pair of coordinates

computes the displacement from the first point to the second. For example, the following command sequence moves the drawing by 2 units to the left and 0.75 units up, as shown in Figure 2–66.

Command: **pan**
Displacement: **-2,.75**
Second point: [Enter]

REDRAW Command

The REDRAW command is used to refresh the on-screen image. You can use this command whenever you see an imcomplete image of your drawing. If you draw two lines in the same place and erase one of the lines, it appears as if both the lines are erased. By invoking the REDRAW command, the second line will reappear. The REDRAW command is also useful if the drawing seems to contain garbage that was not there before. Also, use the REDRAW command to remove the blip marks on the screen. A redraw is considered as a screen refresh as opposed to a data base regeneration.

The REDRAW command does not have any options. The REDRAW command is invoked from the pull-down menu View (see Figure 2–67), the Standard toolbar (see Figure 2–68), or at the "Command:" prompt, type **REDRAW** and press [Enter].

Command: **redraw**
Command:

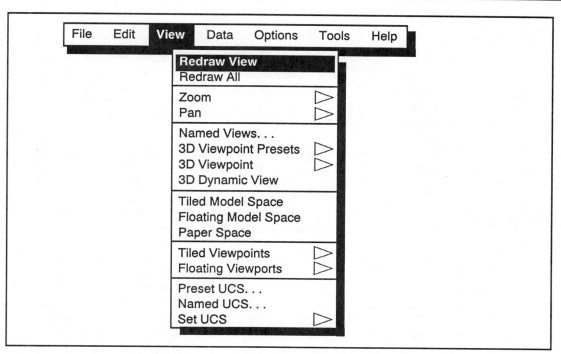

Figure 2-67 Invoking the REDRAW command from the pull-down menu View

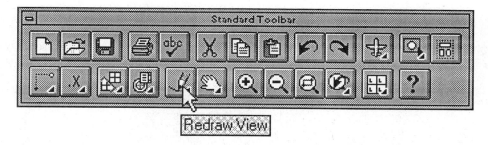

Figure 2-68 Invoking the REDRAW command from the Standard toolbar

REGEN Command

The REGEN command is used to regenerate the drawing's data on the screen. In general, you should use the REGEN command if the image presented by REDRAW does not correctly reflect your drawing. REGEN goes through the drawing's entire data base and projects the most up-to-date information on the screen; this command will give you the most accurate image possible. Because of the manner in which it functions, a REGEN takes significantly longer than a REDRAW.

There are certain AutoCAD commands where REGEN takes place automatically unless REGENAUTO is turned off.

The REGEN command does not have any options. The REGEN command is invoked at the "Command:" prompt by typing **REGEN** and pressing the spacebar or Enter .

    Command: **regen**
    Command:

PLACING TEXT

You have learned how to draw the geometric shapes with LINE command that make up your design. Now it is time to learn how to annotate your design. When you draw on paper, adding descriptions of the design components and the necessary shop and fabrication notes is a time-consuming, tedious process. AutoCAD provides several text commands and tools (including spell checker) that greatly reduce the time and tedium of text placement.

Text is used to label the various components of your drawing and used in placing the necessary shop or field notes needed for fabrication and construction of your design. AutoCAD includes a large number of text fonts. Text can be stretched, compressed, obliqued, mirrored, or drawn in a vertical column by applying a style from the font. Each text string can be sized, rotated, and justified to meet your drawing needs. You should be aware that AutoCAD considers a text string, (all the characters that comprise the line of text) as one object.

> **NOTE:** If you do not know how to type, you can place text quickly and easily after a period of learning the keyboard and developing typing skills. If you create drawings that require a lot of text entry, it may be worth your time to learn to type with all ten fingers. There are several computer programs that can help you teach yourself to type, and almost all colleges offer typing classes. If you do not have time to learn proper typing, there is no need to worry, many "two-finger" typists productively place text in their drawings.

TEXT Command

The TEXT command is invoked from the Text flyout located in the Draw toolbar (see Figure 2–69), or at the "Command:" prompt, type **TEXT** and press the spacebar or ⏎.

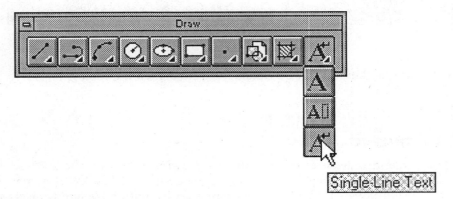

Figure 2-69 Invoke the TEXT Command from the Draw toolbar

```
Command: text
Justify/Style/<Start point>:
```

Start Point Option This is the default option. It allows you to select a point on the screen where you want the text to begin. This point indicates the lower left corner of the text. You can specify the starting point by absolute coordinates or by using your pointing device. After you specify the starting point, AutoCAD prompts:

```
Height <default>:
```

```
Sample Text Left Justified
└─ Start Point
```

Figure 2-70 Using the TEXT Command to place text by specifying a start point to create Left Justified

This allows you to select the text height. You can accept the default text height by giving a null response, or typing in appropriate text height. Next, AutoCAD prompts:

>   Rotation angle <default>:

This allows you to place the text at any angle in reference to 0 degrees (default is 3 o'clock or east, measured in counterclockwise direction). The default value of the rotation angle is 0 degrees and the text is placed horizontally at the specified start point. The last prompt is:

>   Text:

Type the desired text and press [Enter]. If you need to place another line of text, go back to the TEXT command and give a null response to the "Start point:" prompt; AutoCAD skips the prompts for height and rotation angle and immediately displays the text prompt. The text is placed directly beneath the previous line of text.

For example, the following command sequence shows placement of text by providing the starting point (left justified) of the text, as shown in Figure 2-70.

>   Command: **text**
>   Justify/Style/<Start point>: *(pick point)*
>   Height <.20>: **.25**
>   Rotation angle <0>: [Enter]
>   Text: **Sample Text Left Justified**

Justify Option This option allows you to place text in one of the 14 available alignment options. When you select this option, AutoCAD prompts:

>   Align/Fit/Center/Middle/Right/TL/TC/TR/ML/MC/MR/BL/BC/BR:

Type in the option you would like to place the text.

The **Center** option allows you to select the center point for the base line of the text. Base line refers to the line along which the bases of the capital letters lie. Letters with descenders, such as g, q, or y, dip below the base line. After providing the center point, enter the text height and rotation angle.

For example, the following command sequence shows placement of text, as shown in Figure 2-71, by providing the center point (center justified) of the text.

>   Command: **text**
>   Justify/Style/<Start point>: **j**
>   Align/Fit/Center/Middle/Right/TL/TC/TR/ML/MC/MR/BL/BC/BR: **center**
>   Height <.20> **.25**
>   Rotation angle <0>: [Enter]
>   Text: **Sample Text Center Justified**

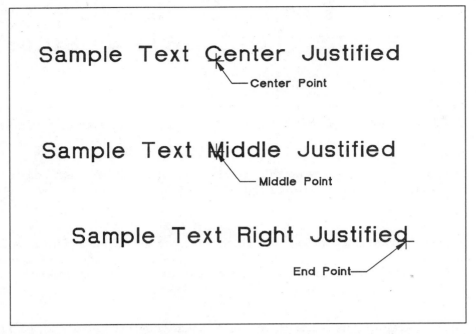

Figure 2-71 Using the TEXT Command to place text by specifying a center point (center justified), a middle point (middle justified), and an end point (right justified)

The **Middle** option allows you to center the text both horizontally and vertically at a given point. After providing the middle point, enter the text height and rotation angle. For example, the following command sequence shows placement of text by providing the middle point (middle justified) of the text as shown in Figure 2-71.

```
Command: text
Justify/Style/<Start point>: j
Align/Fit/Center/Middle/Right/TL/TC/TR/ML/MC/MR/BL/BC/BR:  middle
Height <.20> .25
Rotation angle <0>: Enter
Text: Sample Text Middle Justified
```

The **Right** option allows you to place the text in reference to its lower right corner (right justified). Here, the point you provide is where the text will end. After providing the right point, enter the text height and rotation angle. For example, the following command sequence shows placement of text, by right justified, as shown in Figure 2-71.

```
Command: text
Justify/Style/<Start point>: j
Align/Fit/Center/Middle/Right/TL/TC/TR/ML/MC/MR/BL/BC/BR:  right
Height <.20> .25
Rotation angle <0>: Enter
Text: Sample Text Right Justified
```

Other options are combinations of the above mentioned options and are listed as follows:

TL – top left
TC – top center
TR – top right
ML – middle left

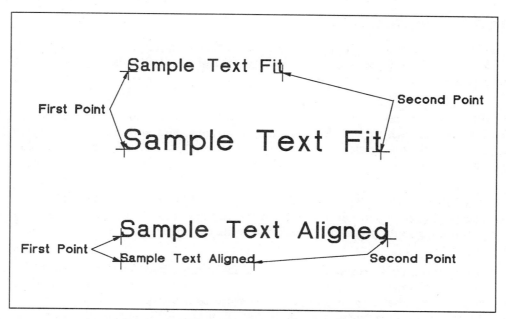

Figure 2-72 Using the Align and Fit option of the TEXT command to place text

MC – middle center
MR – middle right
BL – bottom left
BC – bottom center
BR – bottom right

The **Align** option allows you to place the text by designating the endpoints of the base line. AutoCAD computes the text height and orientation such that the text just fits proportionally between two points. The overall character size adjusts in proportion to the height. The height and width of the character will be same. For example, the following command sequence shows placement of text using the Align option as shown in Figure 2-72.

Command: **text**
Justify/Style/<Start point>: **j**
Align/Fit/Center/Middle/Right/TL/TC/TR/ML/MC/MR/BL/BC/BR: **align**
First text line point: *(specify the first point)*
Second text line point: *(specify the second point)*
Text: **Sample Text Aligned**

The **Fit** option is similar to the Align option, but in the case of Fit option, AutoCAD uses the current text height and adjusts only the text's width, expanding or contracting it to fit between the points you specify. For example, the following command sequence shows placement of text using the Fit option as shown in Figure 2-72.

Command: **text**
Justify/Style/<Start point>: **j**
Align/Fit/Center/Middle/Right/TL/TC/TR/ML/MC/MR/BL/BC/BR: **fit**
First text line point: *(specify the first point)*
Second text line point: *(specify the second point)*
Height <default>: **0.25**
Text: **Sample Text Fit**

The Style option is explained in Chapter 5.

DTEXT Command

The DTEXT command functions exactly as the TEXT command with one major difference: DTEXT lets you see the text on the screen as you type it in from the keyboard and also allows you to type multiple lines of text.

You will notice the same sequence of prompts that you used in the TEXT command. After you select your Start point with any of the justification options, you will then be prompted to enter a text height and a rotation angle. A box cursor appears on the screen at the starting point you have selected.

After you enter the line of text and press [Enter], you will notice the box cursor drops down to the next line anticipating that you wish to enter more text. If this is the case, type the next line of text; when you are through, press [Enter] to terminate the command.

If you are in the DTEXT command when you notice a mistake (or simply want to change a value or word) press backspace to the text you want to change. This, however, deletes all of the text you backspaced over to get back to the point you want to change. If this would involve erasing several lines of text it may be faster to use the CHANGE or DDEDIT command to make changes to the text string.

One feature of DTEXT that will speed up your text entry on your drawing is the ability to move the cross-hair cursor to a new point on the drawing while staying in the DTEXT command. As you move the cross-hair cursor to a new point on your drawing and pick point with your pointing device, you will notice the cursor box move to this new point allowing you to enter a new string of text and quickly move the cursor to the next point to enter more text. However, you must remember to give a null response to terminate the command.

The DTEXT command is invoked from the Text flyout located in the Draw toolbar (see Figure 2–73), or at the "Command:" prompt, type **DTEXT** and press [Enter] or spacebar.

Command: **dtext**
Justify/Style/<Start point>:

The options are similar to the TEXT command, explained earlier. All the options that are available to the TEXT command are available to the DTEXT command.

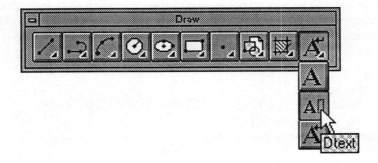

Figure 2-73 Invoke the DTEXT Command from the Draw toolbar

PROJECT EXERCISES

The concepts introduced in chapter 2 provide you with a foundation of AutoCAD knowledge and skills necessary to start creating simple designs. You can now apply these concepts to produce a complete drawing in step-by-step fashion, as shown in Figure P2-1.

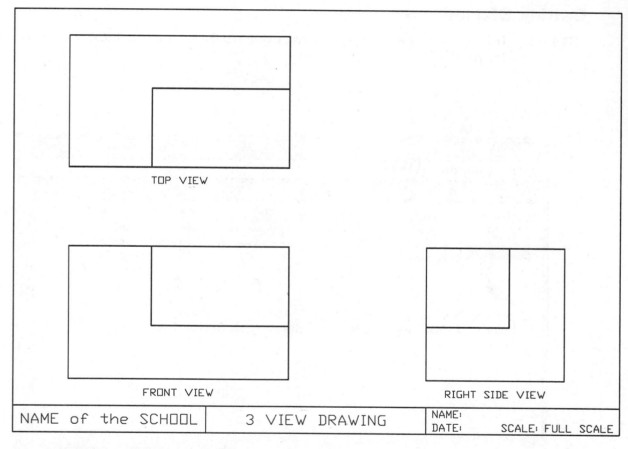

Figure P2-1 Completed project design

> **NOTE:** The step-by-step instructions for this project are designed to provide practice in the concepts presented in chapter 2. It is not necessarily the most efficient way to draw the design.

Fundamentals I

The concepts that are used in this project include:

- Creating a new drawing
- Drawing setup—units, limits
- Drawing tools—grid, snap, ortho
- Use of coordinate display
- Display commands—Zoom-All, Extents, Window, Previous
- Draw commands—Line, Rectangle, Text, Dtext
- Use of absolute, relative and polar coordinates

Getting Started

STEP 1   Invoke the AutoCAD program from the Windows Program Manager, as shown in Figure P2–2.

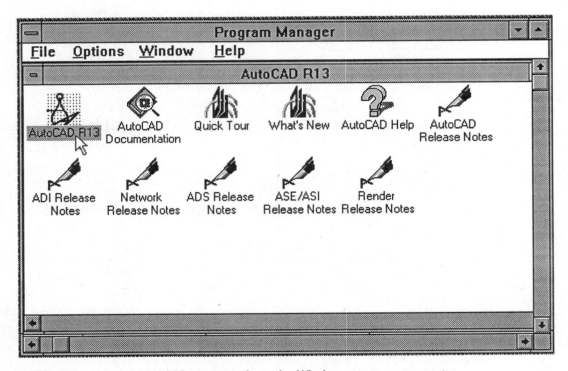

Figure P2–2 Invoke the AutoCAD program from the Windows program manager

STEP 2   Invoke the NEW command from the pull-down menu File or type New at the "Command:" prompt. Enter CH2-PROJ as the name of the drawing file. Make sure ACAD.DWG is selected as the prototype drawing.

STEP 3   Invoke the UNITS Command from the pull-down menu Data to open the **Units Control** dialog box. Set up units to decimal with two decimal places and degrees to decimal as shown in Figure P2–3.

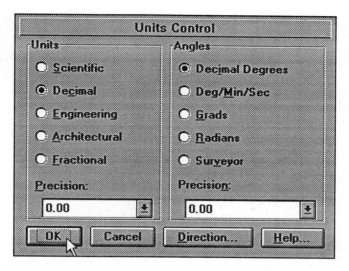

Figure P2-3 Units Control Dialog Box

STEP 4 Open the Drawing Aids dialog box by selecting Drawing Aids. . . from the pull-down menu Tools. Set the grid to 0.5 units and snap to 0.5 units. Turn on the Grid and Snap as shown in Figure P2–4.

STEP 5 Invoke the RECTANGLE command from the Draw toolbar (see Figure P2–5) to draw a border (11" by 8") as shown in Figure P2–6.

Command: **rectang**
From point: **.5,5** [Enter]
To point: **11.5, 8.5** [Enter]

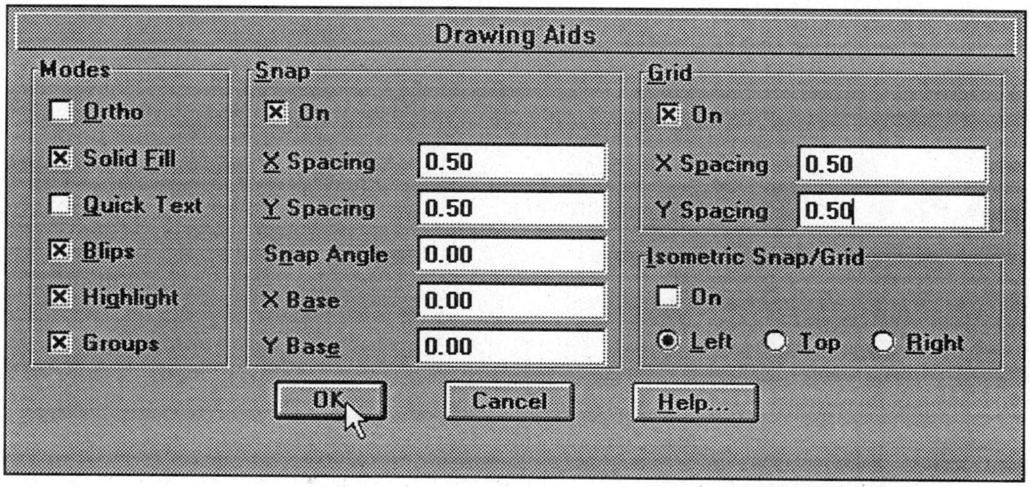

Figure P2-4 Drawing Aids dialog box

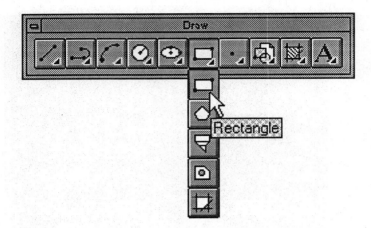

Figure P2-5 Invoke the RECTANGLE Command from the Draw toolbar

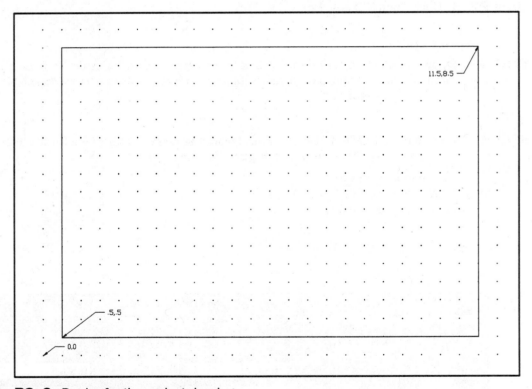

Figure P2-6 Border for the project drawing

STEP 6 Invoke the LINE command from the Draw toolbar (see Figure 2–7) to complete the title block as shown in Figure P2-8.

Command: **line**
From point: **.5,1** [Enter]
To point: **@11<0** [Enter]
To point: [Enter]

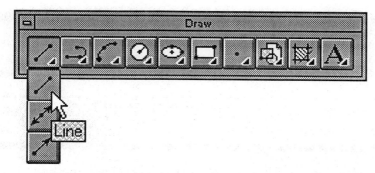

Figure P2-7   Invoke the LINE Command from the Draw toolbar

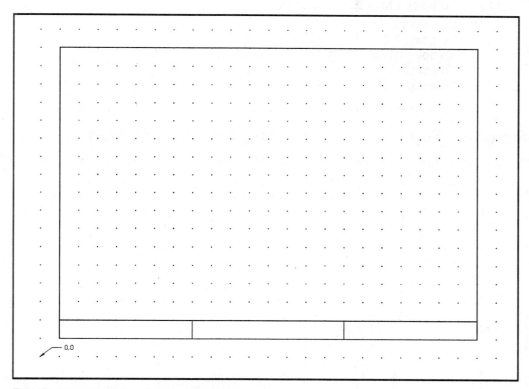

Figure P2-8   Title Block for the project drawing

Command: **line**
From point: **4,1** [Enter]
To point: **4,5** [Enter]
To point: [Enter]

Command: **line**
From point: **8,1** [Enter]
To point: **8,5** [Enter]
To point: [Enter]

Draw the Front View by Entering the Coordinates

Create the front view (the lower left one in the drawing) by typing the coordinates using the LINE command. Figure P2-9 shows an isometric view with letters added to aid in the drawing of the three views. Figure P2-10 shows the front view with letters to aid in the drawing of the front view.

> **NOTE:** Other input methods work just as well, but we are going to practice by typing the coordinates

STEP 7 Invoke the LINE command from the Draw toolbar.

Command: **line**
From point: **1.5, 1.5** [Enter] *(For point A)*
To point: **@2.5<90** [Enter] *(For point B)*
To point: **@4<0** [Enter] *(For point H)*
To point: **@2.5<270** [Enter] *(For point F)*
To point: **close** [Enter] *(For point A)*

Command: **line** (or [Enter])
To point: **5.5, 2.5** [Enter] *(For point E)*
To point: **@2.5<180** [Enter] *(For point D)*
To point: **@1.5<90** [Enter] *(For point C)*
To point: [Enter]

Draw the Top View by Entering the Coordinates

Create the top view, as shown in Figure P2–11, by typing the coordinates using the LINE command.

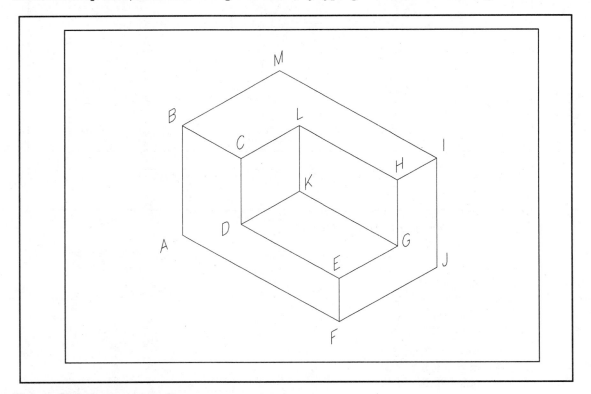

Figure P2-9 Isometric view

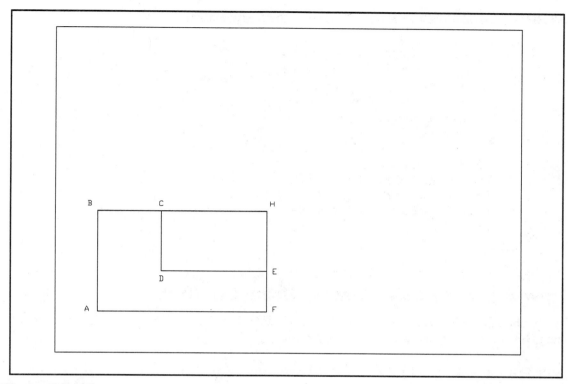

Figure P2-10 Front view

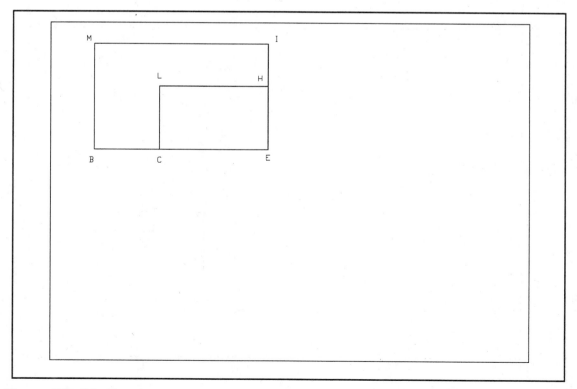

Figure P2-11 Top view

STEP 8   Invoke the LINE command from the Draw toolbar.

Command: **line**
From point: **1.5, 5.5** [Enter] *(For point B)*
To point: **@2.5<90** ([Enter]) *(For point M)*
To point **@4<0** [Enter] *(For point I)*
To point: **@2.5<270** [Enter] *(For point E)*
To point: **close** *(For point B)*
To point: [Enter]

Command: **line** or [Enter]
From point: **3, 5.5** [Enter] *(For point C)*
To point: **@1.5<90** [Enter] *(For point L)*
To point: **@2.5<0** [Enter] *(For point H)*
To point: [Enter]

Draw the Right Side View by Using the Grid

Create the right side view, as shown in Figure P2-12 by typing the coordinates for point F then using the cursor to select the remaining points.

STEP 9   Invoke the LINE command from the Draw toolbar.

Command: **line**
From point: **8, 1.5** [Enter] *(For point F)*

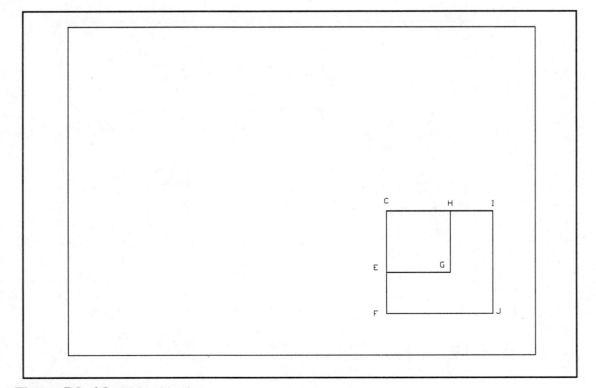

Figure P2-12 Right side view

To point: *(Place a point for point C, five grid units above point F)*
To point: *(Place a point for point I five grid units to the right of point C)*
To point: *(Place a point for point J, five grid units below point I).*
To point: *(Select the close option from the side menu for point F)*

Command line: **line** (or ⌷Enter⌷)
From point: **8, 2.5** *(For point E and press enter.)*
To point: *(Place a point for point G, three grid units to the right of point E)*
To point: *(Place a point for point H, three grid units above point G)*
To point: ⌷Enter⌷

Placing Text on the Drawing

Place the descriptive text below each of the three views, and in the title block as shown in Figure P2–13.

STEP 10 Set Grid and Snap to 0.25.

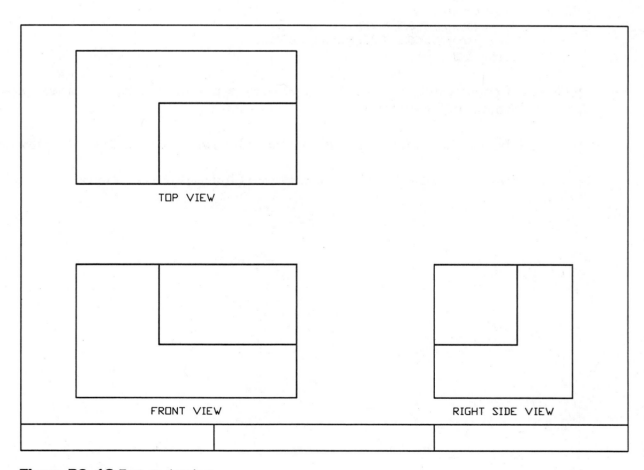

Figure P2-13 Text on drawing

STEP 11 Place appropriate text as indicated below by invoking the DTEXT command from the Draw toolbar (see Figure P2–14).

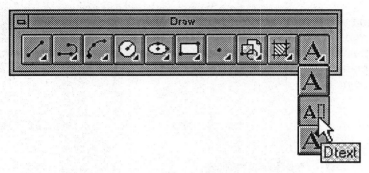

Figure P2–14 Invoke the DTEXT Command from the Draw toolbar

Command: **dtext**
Justify/Style/<Start point>: **m**
Middle point: **3.5,1.25**
Height<default>: **.125**
Rotation angle<0>: [Enter]
Text: **Front View**
Text: *(snap it at 3.5, 5.25)* **Top View**
Text: *(snap it at 9.5, 1.25)* **Right Side View**
Text: [Enter]

STEP 12 Complete the drawing with appropriate information for the title block, as shown in Figure P2–1.

STEP 13 Invoke the SAVE command from the pull-down menu File to save the drawing.

Congratulations. You just successfully applied several AutoCAD concepts in creating a simple drawing.

EXERCISES

Exercise 2-9

Create the drawing according to the Settings given in the following table.

Settings	Value
1. Units	Decimal
2. LIMITS	
lower left corner	0, 0
upper right corner	18,12
3. Grid Spacing	0.250
4. Snap Spacing	0.125
5. Text Size	0.125

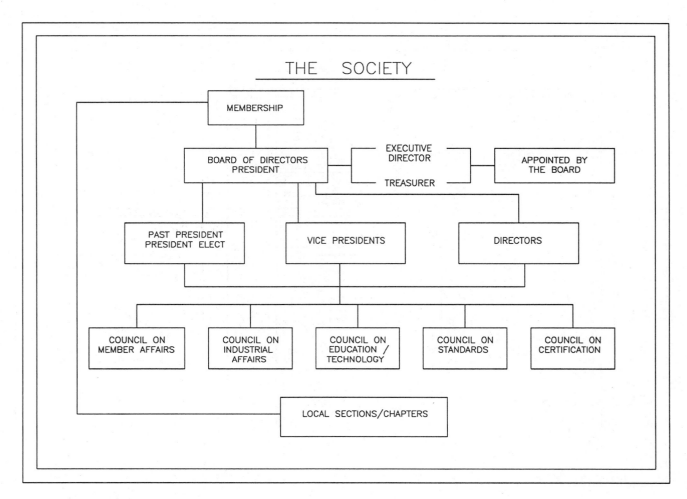

Fundamentals I

Exercise 2-10

Create the drawing according to the Settings given in the following table: (Do Not Dimension).

Settings	Value
1. Units	Architectural
2. LIMITS	
lower left corner	0, 0
upper right corner	40', 30'
3. Grid Spacing	2'-0"
4. Snap Spacing	0'-3"
5. Text Size	0'-4"

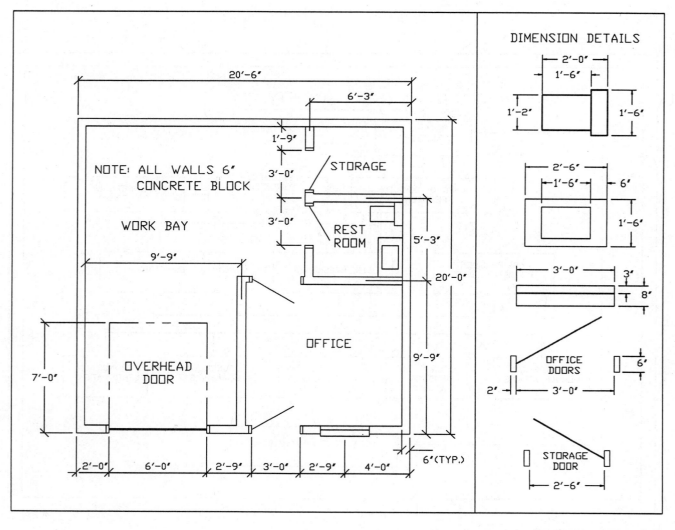

Exercises 2-11 to 2-18

Create the drawings (orthographic projections) according to the settings given in the following table:

Settings	Value
1. Units	Decimal
2. LIMITS	
lower left corner	0, 0
upper right corner	12, 9
3. Grid Spacing	0.25
4. Snap Spacing	0.25

NOTE: Grid lines in the drawings are spaced 0.25 units apart

Fundamentals I

**Exercise
2-11**

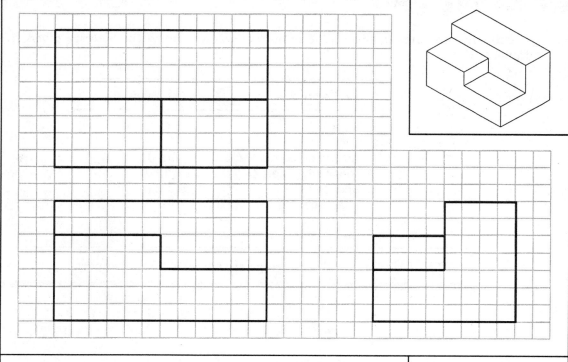

**Exercise
2-12**

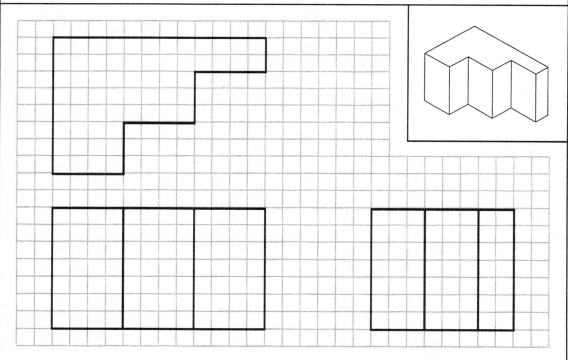

Exercise 2-13

2-83

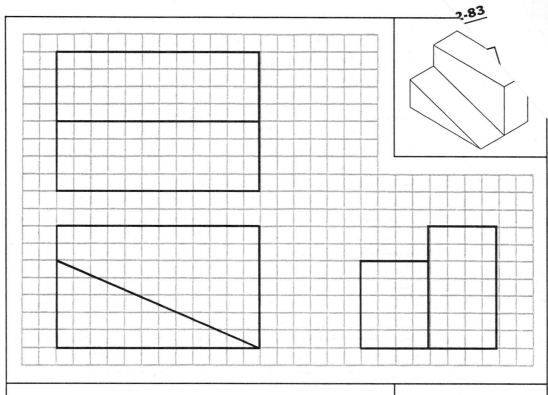

Exercise 2-14

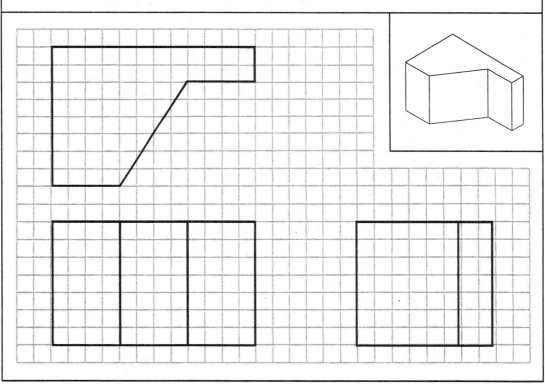

Fundamentals I

**cise
-15**

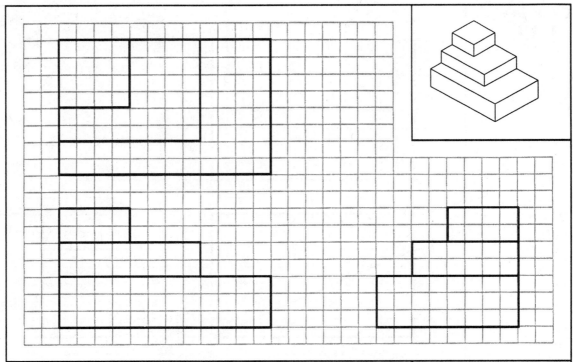

**Exercise
2-16**

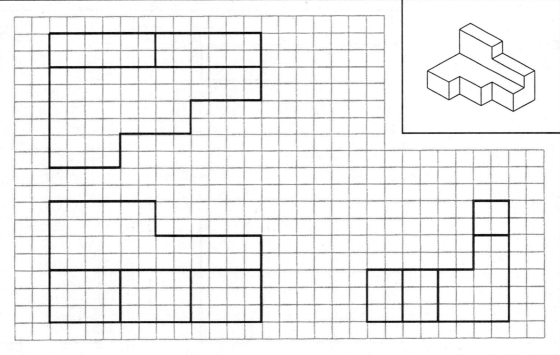

Exercise 2-17

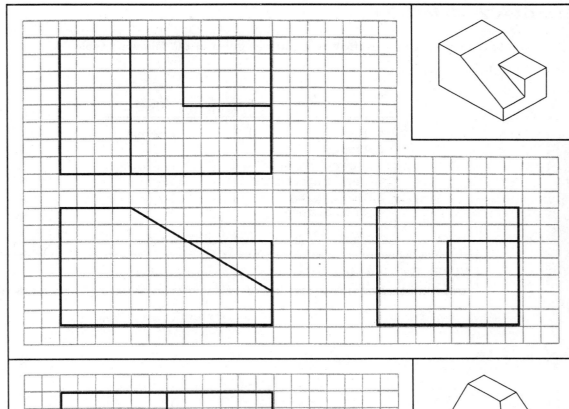

Exercise 2-18

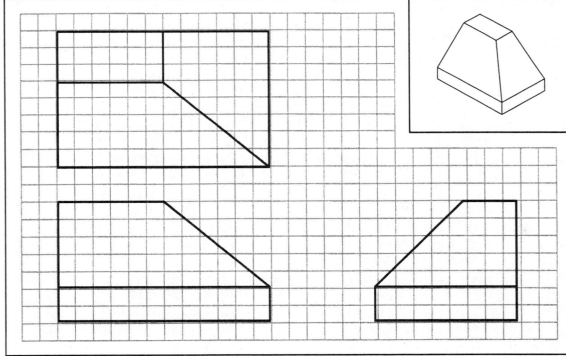

Fundamentals I

Exercises 2-19 to 2-20

Create the drawings according to the settings given in the following table:

Settings	Value
1. Units	Decimal
2. LIMITS	
lower left corner	0, 0
upper right corner	17, 11
3. Grid Spacing	1
4. Snap Spacing	1

NOTE: Grid lines in the drawings are spaced 1 unit apart

**Exercise
2–19**

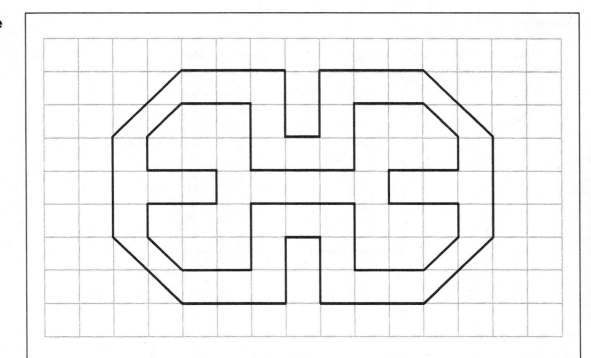

**Exercise
2–20**

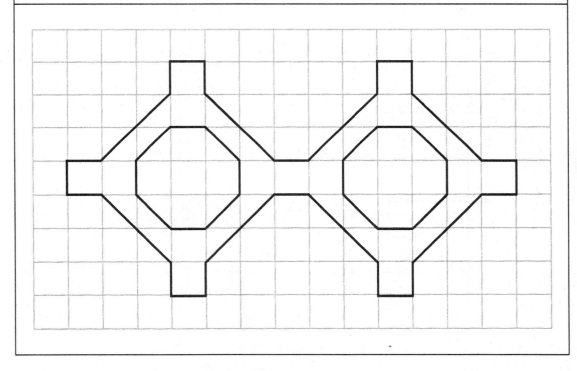

Fundamentals I

Exercise 2-21

Create the drawing according to the settings given in the following table: (Do Not Dimension)

Settings	Value
1. Units	Architectural
2. LIMITS	
lower left corner	0, 0
upper right corner	150', 100'
3. Grid Spacing	2'-0"
4. Snap Spacing	1'-0"
5. Text Size	6"

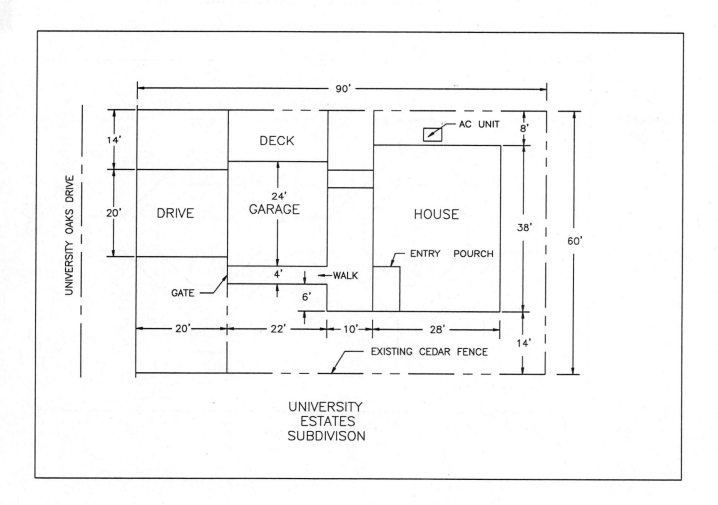

Exercises 2-22 to 2-23

Create the drawing exercises according to the settings given in the following table: (Do Not Dimension)

Settings	Value
1. Units	Decimal
2. LIMITS	
lower left corner	0, 0
upper right corner	17, 11
3. Grid Spacing	0.5
4. Snap Spacing	0.25

Exercise 2-22

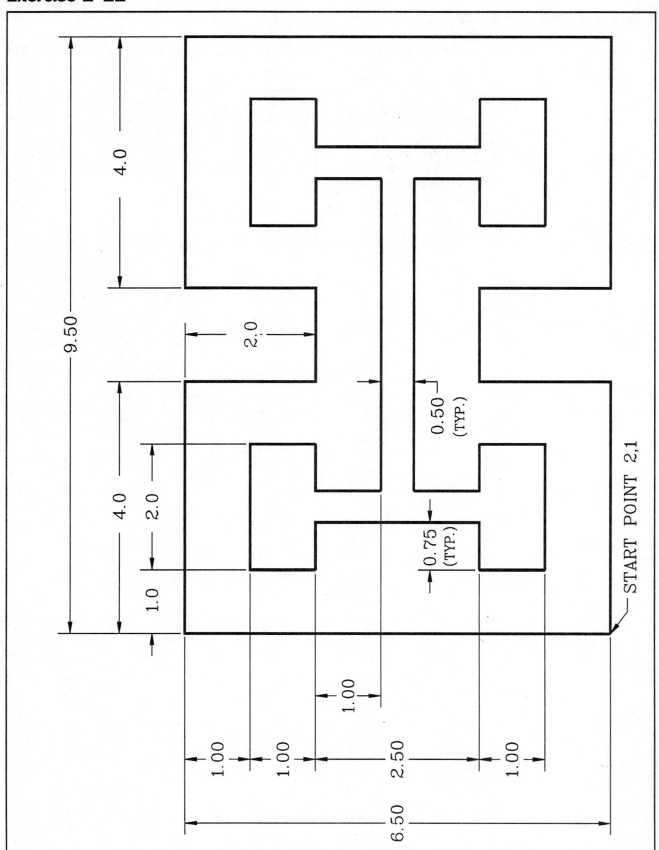

Exercise 2-23

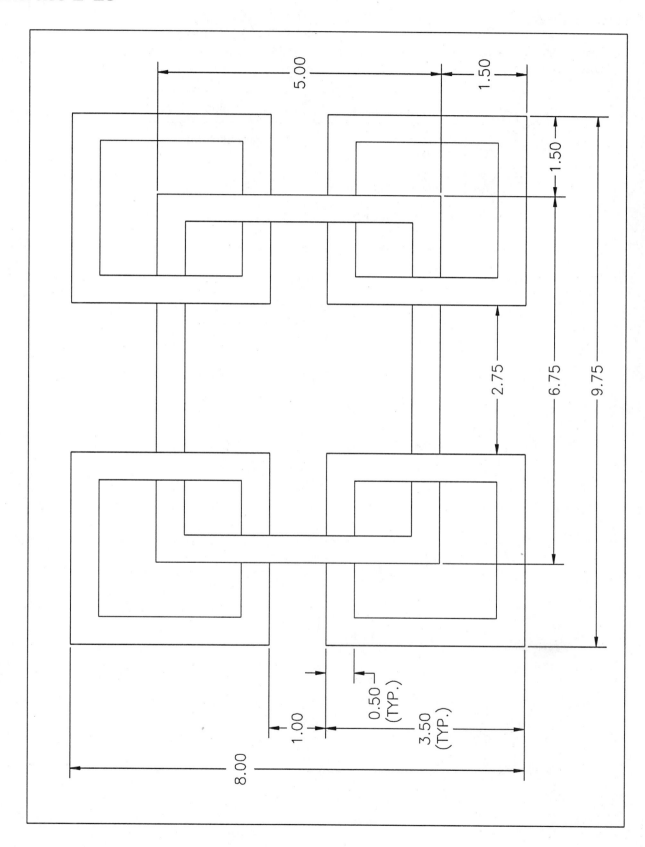

Fundamentals I

Exercise 2-24

Create the drawing exercise according to the settings given in the following table: (Do Not Dimension)

Settings	Value
1. Units	Architectural
2. LIMITS	
lower left corner	0, 0
upper right corner	80', 60'
3. Grid Spacing	2'-0"
4. Snap Spacing	1'-0"
5. Text Size	0'-6"

Exercise 2-24

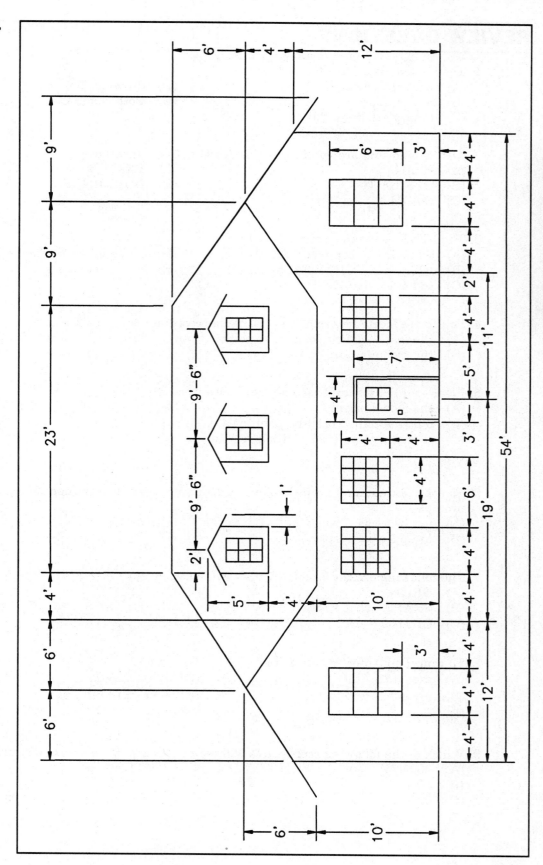

REVIEW QUESTIONS

1. The file extension .BAK stands for
   - (A) backup drawing file
   - (B) binary file
   - (C) binary attribute file
   - (D) drawing file
   - (E) Both B and C

2. All the following are valid AutoCAD drawing file names except
   - (A) PLAN
   - (B) OFFICE-1
   - (C) ROOM-1
   - (D) EXAM_3
   - (E) BUILDINGS

3. The HELP command cannot be used
   - (A) while in the command LINE
   - (B) while in the CIRCLE option TTR
   - (C) to list commands
   - (D) while in the command END
   - (E) for a text string

4. Points are located by relative rectangular coordinates in relation to
   - (A) the last specified position or point
   - (B) the global origin
   - (C) lower -left corner of the screen
   - (D) All of the above

5. Polar coordinates are based on a distance from
   - (A) the global origin
   - (B) a last specified position point at a given angle
   - (C) to the last specified position or point
   - (D) All of the above

6. To enter a command from the keyboard, simply enter the command name at the "Command:" prompt
   - (A) in lower-case letters
   - (B) in upper-case letters
   - (C) a and b
   - (D) None of the above

7. The following are the AutoCAD tools available, except
   - (A) GRID
   - (B) SNAP
   - (C) ORTHO
   - (D) TSNAP
   - (E) OSNAP

8. To cancel an AutoCAD command
   - (A) press Ctrl + A
   - (B) press Ctrl + B
   - (C) press Esc
   - (D) press Ctrl + D
   - (E) press Ctrl + E

9. Which of the following coordinates will define a point at the screen default origin point?
   - (A) 000
   - (B) 00
   - (C) 0,0
   - (D) 112
   - (E) @0,00

10. The SAVE command
    (A) saves your work
    (B) does not exit you out of AutoCAD
    (C) is a valuable feature for periodically storing information to disk .
    (D) All of the above

11. A flip screen can be accomplished by
    (A) pressing [Enter] twice
    (B) entering [Ctrl] and [Enter] at the same time
    (C) pressing the escape [Esc] key
    (D) pressing the [F2] function key
    (E) Both B and C

12. To draw a line at a distance of eight feet, four and five-eighths inches in the 12 o'clock direction from the last point, type
    (A) @8'4-5/8<90
    (B) 8'-4-5/8<90
    (C) @8'-45/8<90
    (D) 8'-45/8<90
    (E) None of the above

13. Which polar coordinates entry is expressed in a positive mode?
    (A) @1.25<43
    (B) @1.25<-43
    (C) @-1.25<-43
    (D) A and B
    (E) None of the above

14. The smallest number that is displayed in the denominator when setting units to architectural is
    (A) 1/8
    (B) 1/16
    (C) 1/64
    (D) 1/128
    (E) None of the above

15. If the spacing of the visible grid is set too small, AutoCAD responds as follows:
    (A) does not enter the command
    (B) produces a "Grid too dense to display" prompt
    (C) produces a display size that is distorted
    (D) asks you to reenter the command
    (E) AutoCAD draws the grid anyway

16. What is a correct response for a drawing name when performing a SAVE command?
    (A) OFFICE.A.DWG
    (B) OFFICE 1.DWG
    (C) OFFICE-1
    (D) OFFICE.1
    (E) OFFICE-1DWG

17. What direction does a positive number indicate when specifying angles in degrees?
    (A) Clockwise
    (B) Counterclockwise
    (C) Has no impact when specifying angles in degrees
    (D) None of the above

18. How can an AutoCAD command be repeated from the keyboard without reentering it?
    - (A) [Enter] key
    - (B) Space bar
    - (C) [Esc] key
    - (D) A and B

19. Which of the following statements about LIMITS are TRUE?
    - (A) Attempts to draw outside the preset boundaries will be rejected
    - (B) Limits determine the area in which the grid will be shown
    - (C) The limits determine the area ZOOM Extents will display
    - (D) A and B

20. The ERASE command:
    - (A) Erases part of an object
    - (B) Erases any object
    - (C) Erases any group of objects
    - (D) Both B and C

CHAPTER

3

FUNDAMENTALS II

After completing this chapter, you will be able to:

- Construct geometric figures (Circle, Arc, Polygon, Ellipse)
- Use layering techniques
- Use the Construct commands (Copy, Offset, Mirror, Fillet, and Chamfer)
- Use the Modify commands (Move, Trim, Break, and Extend)
- Use the Object Snap options (Center, Quadrant, Tangent and Perpendicular modes)

Fundamentals II

DRAW COMMANDS

In this chapter, four additional DRAW commands are explained—the CIRCLE, ARC, POLYGON, and ELLIPSE commands—in addition to the commands explained in Chapter 2.

CIRCLE Command

The CIRCLE command offers five methods for drawing circles. The default is the Center-Radius method. The other methods include Center-Diameter, 2 Point, 3 Point, and Tangent, Tangent, Radius (TTR) methods (for which you must override the default on the first prompt). The CIRCLE command is invoked from the Circle flyout located in the Draw toolbar, or at the "Command:" prompt, type **CIRCLE** and press Enter or the spacebar.

Command: **circle**
3P/2P/TTR/<Center point>:

Center-Radius Option The Center-Radius option is invoked from the Circle flyout located in the Draw toolbar (Figure 3–1). First, AutoCAD prompts for the center point of the circle, followed by radius for the circle. The following command sequence shows an example (see Figure 3–2).

Command: **circle**
3P/2P/TTR/<Center point>: **2,2**
Diameter/<Radius>: **1**

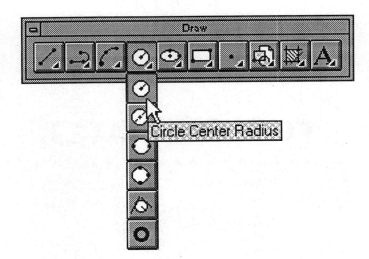

Figure 3–1 Invoke the Circle Center Radius option from the Draw toolbar

The same circle can be generated as follows (see Figure 3–3):

    Command: **circle**
    3P/2P/TTR/<Center point>: **2,2**
    Diameter/<Radius>: **3,2**

In the last example, AutoCAD used the distance between the center point and the second point given for the radius of the circle.

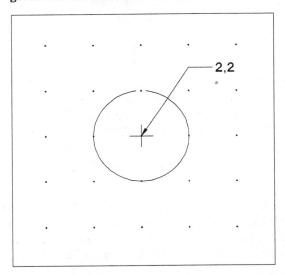

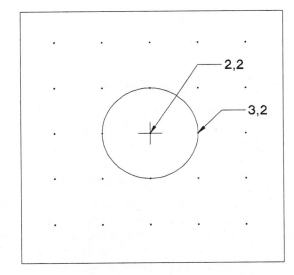

Figure 3–2 A circle drawn with the CIRCLE Command's default options: Center, Radius

Figure 3–3 A circle drawn with the Center-Radius option

Center-Diameter Option (Overriding the Second Prompt) The Center-Diameter method of drawing a circle begins in the same way as the Center-Radius method, by specifying the center of the circle and then prompts for the diameter of the Circle. The Circle Center-Diameter option is invoked from the Circle flyout located in the Draw toolbar (Figure 3–4). The sequence to draw the previous circle is as follows:

    Command: **circle**
    3P/2P/TTR/<Center point>: **2,2**
    Diameter/<Radius>: **d**
    Diameter: **2**

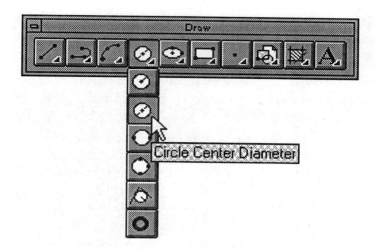

Figure 3-4 Invoke the Circle Center-Diameter option from the Draw toolbar

> **NOTE:** The **d** response allows you to override the Radius default, or you can select the option from the toolbar.

The same circle can be generated as follows (see Figure 3–5):

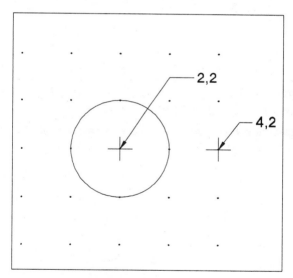

Figure 3-5 A circle drawn using the Center-Diameter option

```
Command: circle
3P/2P/TTR/<Center point>: 2,2
Diameter/<Radius>: d
Diameter: 4,2
```

> **NOTE:** Specifying a point causes AutoCAD to use the distance to the point specified from the previously selected center as the value for the diameter of the circle to be drawn.

Three-Point Circle Option (Overriding the First Prompt) If you wish to draw a circle by specifying three known points on the circle, invoke the Circle 3 Point Option from the Circle flyout located in the Draw toolbar (Figure 3–6).

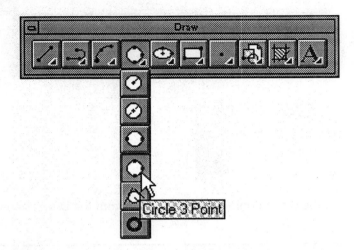

Figure 3-6 Invoke the Circle 3 Point Option from the Draw toolbar

The following command sequence shows an example (see Figure 3–7).

```
Command: circle
3P/2P/TTR/<Center point>: 3P
First point: 2,1
Second point: 3,2
Third point: 2,3
```

NOTE: The **3P** response allows you to override the Center Point default, or you can select the 3 Point option from the toolbar.

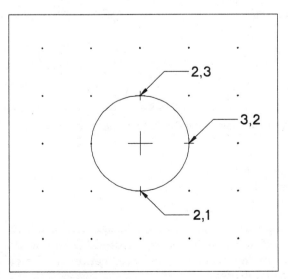

Figure 3-7 A circle drawn with the Three-Point option

Two-Point Circle Option If you wish to draw a circle by specifying the two endpoints of one of its diameters, invoke the Circle 2 Point Option from the Circle flyout located in the Draw toolbar (Figure 3–8).

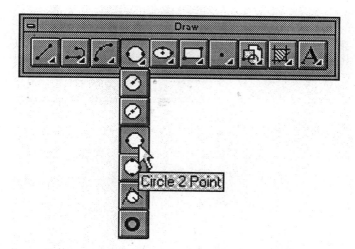

Figure 3-8 Invoke the Circle 2 Point Option from the Draw toolbar

The following command sequence shows an example (see Figure 3–9).

Command: **circle**
3P/2P/TTR/<Center point>: **2P**
First point on diameter: **1,2**
Second point on diameter: **3,2**

> *NOTE:* The **2P** response allows you to override the Center Point default, or you can select the 2 Point option from the toolbar.

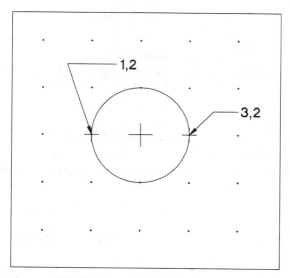

Figure 3-9 A circle drawn with the Two-Point option

Tangent, Tangent, Radius (TTR) Option The TTR option allows you to draw a circle by selecting two objects (either lines, arcs, or other circles) to which the circle will be tangent and by specifying the radius. The Circle Tan Tan Radius option is invoked from the Circle flyout located in the Draw toolbar (Figure 3–10).

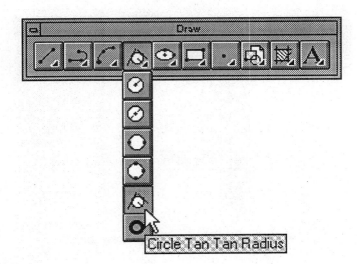

Figure 3-10 Invoke the Circle Tan Tan Radius option from the Draw toolbar

The following sequence of prompts appear:

> Command: **circle**
> 3P/2P/TTR/<Center point>: **TTR**
> Enter Tangent spec: *(select first line, arc, or circle)*
> Enter second Tangent spec: *(select other line, arc, or circle)*
> Radius: *(enter a value)*

For specifying the "tangent-to" objects, it normally does not matter where on the objects you make your selection. However, if more than one circle can be drawn to the specifications given, AutoCAD will draw the one whose tangent point is nearest to the selection made.

The Uppercase Rule Note the "P" in the 2P option is uppercase. When options are shown by the prompt, you must enter all initial letters shown in uppercase. The P is uppercase and has no lowercase letters preceding it. Therefore, the P must be included.

> **NOTE:** The radius/diameter you specify in any one of the options becomes the default setting for subsequent circles to be drawn until it is changed.

ARC Command

The ARC command offers eleven combinations to draw an arc. The combinations are as follows:

1. Three point (3-points)
2. Start, center, end (S,C,E)

3. Start, center, included angle (S,C,A)
4. Start, center, length of chord (S,C,L)
5. Start, end, included angle (S,E,A)
6. Start, end, direction (S,E,D)
7. Start, end, radius (S,E,R)
8. Center, start, end (C,S,E)
9. Center, start, included angle (C,S,A)
10. Center, start, length of the chord (C,S,L)
11. Continuation from line or arc (ArcCont or LinCont)

Methods 8, 9, and 10 are just rearrangements of methods 2, 3, and 4 respectively.

The ARC command is invoked from the Arc flyout located in the Draw toolbar, or at the "Command:" prompt, type **ARC** and press [Enter] or the spacebar.

> Command: **arc**
> Center/<Start point>:

Once the command is invoked, you can use the default Three-Point method or you may override an option being prompted for by entering the initial letter of the override option: A for included Angle, C for Center, D for starting Direction, E for Endpoint, L for Length of chord, and R for Radius. Or, you can select any of the options from the Arc flyout located in the Draw toolbar.

Three-Point Arc Option (3-point) AutoCAD begins the ARC command by prompting for the Start point, followed by second point and then end point. The 3 Points option is invoked from the Arc flyout located in the Draw toolbar (Figure 3–11).

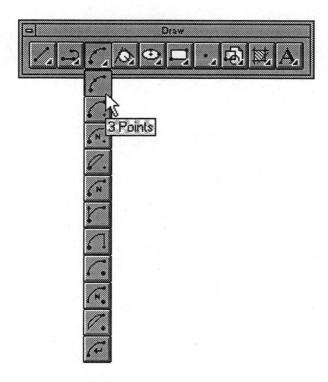

Figure 3–11 Invoke the Arc 3 Points option from the Draw toolbar

The following command sequence shows an example (see Figure 3–12).

> Command: **arc**
> Center/<Start point>: **1,2**
> Center/End/<Second point>: **2,1**
> Endpoint: **3,2**

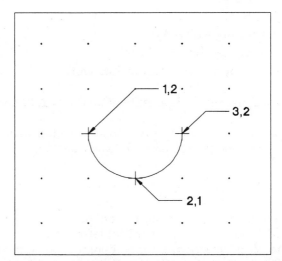

Figure 3-12 An arc drawn with the ARC Command's default option: S,S,E

Start, Center, End Option (or S,C,E for short) In this option, AutoCAD prompts for "center" point of the arc instead of "Second point." The Arc Start Center End option is invoked from the Arc flyout located in the Draw toolbar (Figure 3–13).

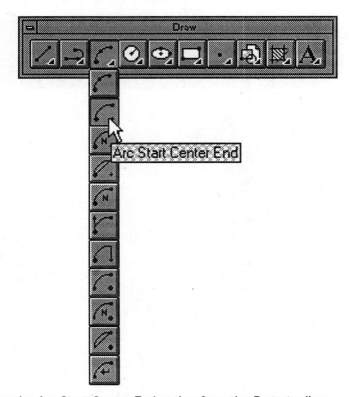

Figure 3-13 Invoke the Arc Start Center End option from the Draw toolbar

The following command sequence shows an example (see Figure 3–14).

```
Command: arc
Center/<Start point>: 1,2
Center/End/<Second point>: c
Center: 2,2
Angle/Length of chord/<Endpoint>: 2,3
```

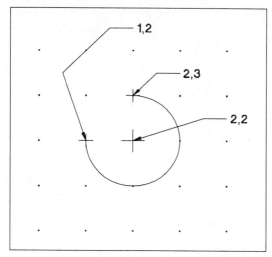

Figure 3–14 An arc drawn with the Start, Center, End (S,C,E) option

Arcs drawn by this method are always drawn counterclockwise from the starting point. The radius is determined by the distance between the center and the starting point. Therefore, the point specified in response to "Endpoint" only needs to be on the same radial line of the desired endpoint. For example, specifying the point 2,2.5 or 2,4 draws the same arc.

An alternative to the same method is to specify the center point first, as follows (see Figure 3-15):

```
Command: arc
Center/<Start point>: c
Center: 2,2
Start point: 1,2
Angle/Length of chord/<Endpoint>: 2,3
```

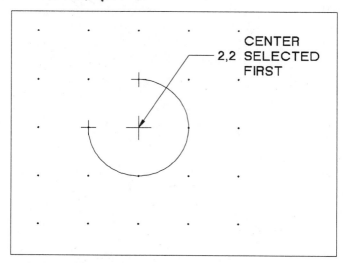

Figure 3–15 An arc drawn by specifying the center point first

Start, Center, Included Angle Option (or S,C,A for short) This method draws an arc similar to the start, center, end method, but places the endpoint on a radial line the specified angle from the line between the center and the start point. The angle will be counterclockwise if positive and clockwise if negative. The Arc Start Center Angle option is invoked from the Arc flyout located in the Draw toolbar (Figure 3–16).

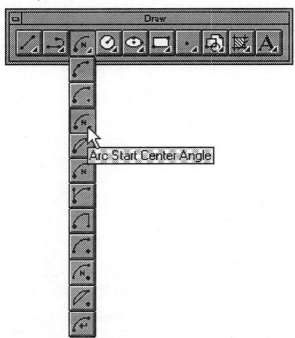

Figure 3-16 Invoke the Arc Start Center Angle option from the Draw toolbar

The following command sequence shows an example (see Figure 3–17).

```
Command: arc
Center/<Start point>: 1,2
Center/<Endpoint>: c
Center: 2,2
Angle/Length of chord/<Endpoint>: a
Included angle: 270
```

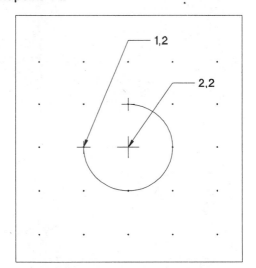

Figure 3-17 An arc drawn with the Start, Center, Included Angle (S,C,A) option

NOTE: If a point directly below the specified center were selected (in the previous example) in response to the "Included angle:" prompt, AutoCAD would read the angle (270 degrees) of the line (from zero) as the included angle for the arc. In Figure 3–17, the point selected in response to the "Included angle:" prompt causes AutoCAD to read the angle between the line it establishes from the center and the zero direction (east in the default coordinate system). It does not measure the angle between the line the point establishes from the center and the line established from the center to the start point.

Start, Center, Length of Chord Option (or S,C,L for short) This method uses the specified chord length as the straight line distance from the start point to the endpoint. With any chord length (equal to or less than the diameter length) there are four possible arcs that can be drawn: a major arc in either direction and a minor arc in either direction. Therefore, all arcs drawn by this method are counterclockwise from the start point. A positive value for the length of chord will cause AutoCAD to draw the minor arc; a negative value will result in the major arc. The Arc Start Center Length option is invoked from the Arc flyout located in the Draw toolbar (Figure 3–18).

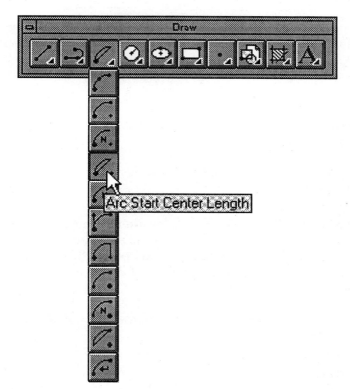

Figure 3-18 Invoke the Arc Start Center Length option from the Draw toolbar

The following command sequence shows an example of drawing a minor arc, as shown in Figure 3–19.

    Command: **arc**
    Center/<Start point>: **1,2**
    Center/<Endpoint>: **c**
    Center: **2,2**
    Angle/Length of chord/<Endpoint>: **L** *(letter l, not number 1)*
    Length of chord: **1.414**

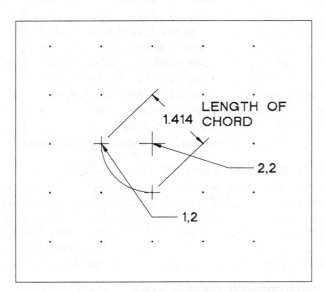

Figure 3-19 A minor arc drawn with the Start-Center-Length of Chord (S,C,L) option.

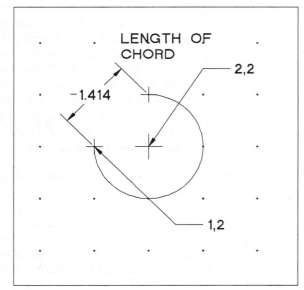

Figure 3-20 A major arc drawn with the Start-Center-Length of Chord (S,C,L) option

The following command sequence shows an example of drawing a major arc, as shown in Figure 3–20.

Command: **arc**
Center/<Start point>: **1,2**
Center/<Endpoint>: **c**
Center: **2,2**
Angle/Length of chord/<Endpoint>: **L** *(letter L, not number 1)*
Length of chord: **-1.414**

Start, End, Included Angle Option (or S,E,A for short) This method draws an arc similar to the start, center, included angle method. It also places the endpoint on a radial line that is the specified angle from the line between the center and the start point. The angle will be counterclockwise if positive and clockwise if negative. The Arc Start End Angle option is invoked from the Arc flyout located in the Draw toolbar (Figure 3–21).

The arc shown in Figure 3–22 is drawn using the following sequence:

Command: **arc**
Center/<Start point>: **3,2**
Center/End/<Second point>: **e**
End point: **2,3**
Angle/Length of chord/<Endpoint>: **a**
Included angle: **90**

The arc shown in Figure 3–23 is drawn with a negative angle using the following sequence:

Command: **arc**
Center/<Start point>: **3,2**
Center/End/<Second point>: **e**
End point: **2,3**
Angle/Length of chord/<Endpoint>: **a**
Included angle: **-270**

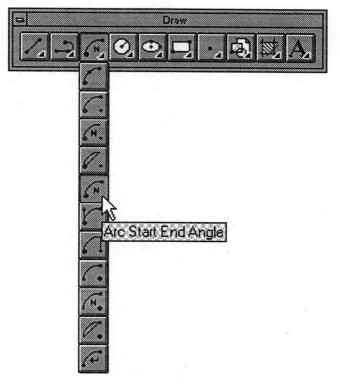

Figure 3-21 Invoke the Arc Start End Angle option from the Draw toolbar

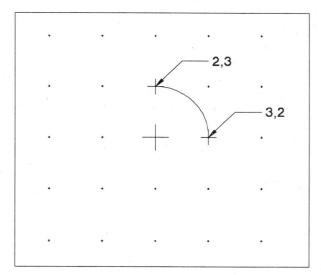

Figure 3-22 An arc drawn counterclockwise with the Start, End, Included Angle (S,E,A) option

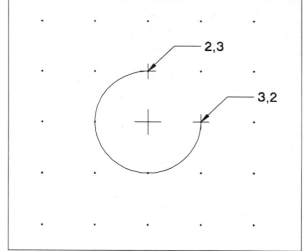

Figure 3-23 An arc drawn clockwise with the Start, End, Included Angle (S,E,A) option

Start, End, Starting Direction Option (or S,E,D for short) This method allows you to draw an arc between selected points by specifying a direction in which the arc will start from the selected start point. The direction can either be keyed in or you may select a point on the screen with your pointing device. If you select a point on the screen, AutoCAD uses the angle from the start point to

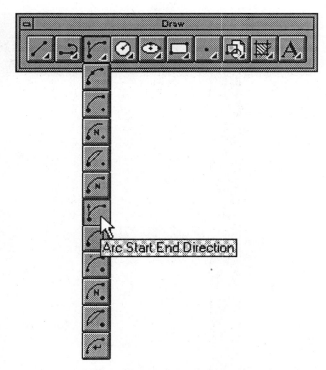

Figure 3-24 Invoke the Arc Start End Direction option from the Draw toolbar

the selected point as the starting direction. The Arc Start End Direction option is invoked from the Arc flyout located in the Draw toolbar.

The arc shown in Figure 3–25 is drawn using the following sequence:

Command: **arc**
Center/<Start point>: **3,2**
Center/End/<Second point>: **e**
Endpoint: **2,3**
Angle/Direction/Radius/<Center point>: **d**
Direction from start point: **90**

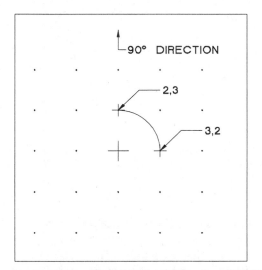

Figure 3-25 An arc drawn with the Start, End, Starting Direction (S,E,D) option

Start, End, Radius Option (or S,E,R for short) This method allows you to specify a radius after selecting the two endpoints of the arc. As with the Chord Length method, there are four possible arcs that can be drawn: a major arc in either direction and a minor arc in either direction. Therefore, all arcs drawn by this method are counterclockwise from the start point. A positive value for the radius causes AutoCAD to draw the minor arc; a negative value results in the major arc. The Start End Radius option is invoked from the Arc flyout located in the Draw toolbar (Figure 3–26).

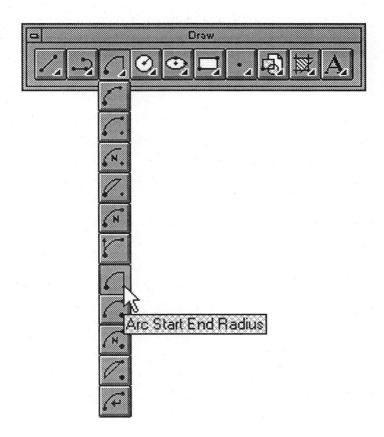

Figure 3-26 Invoke the Arc Start End Radius option from the Draw toolbar

The following command sequence shows an example of drawing a minor arc, as shown in Figure 3–27.

Command: **arc**
Center/<Start point>: **1,2**
Center/End/<Second point>: **e**
Endpoint: **2,3**
Angle/Direction/Radius/<Center point>: **r**
Radius: **-1**

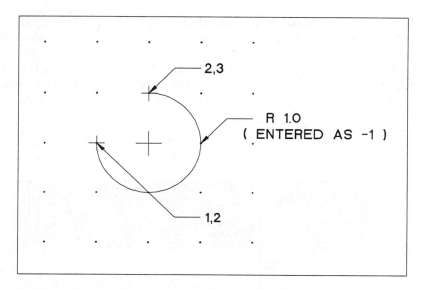

Figure 3-27 A minor arc drawn with the Start, End, Radius (S,E,R) option

The following command sequence shows an example of drawing a major arc, as shown in Figure 3–28.

    Command: **arc**
    Center/<Start point>: **2,3**
    Center/End/<Second point>: **e**
    Endpoint: **1,2**
    Angle/Direction/Radius/<Center point>: **r**
    Radius: **1**

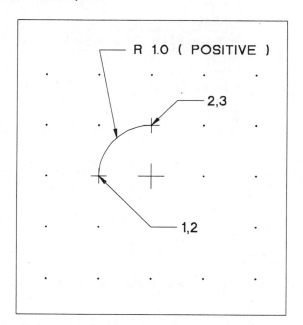

Figure 3-28 A major arc drawn with the Start, End, Radius (S,E,R) option

Center, Start, End Option (or C,S,E for short) This method is similar to the Start, Center, End (S,C,E) method, except in this option the beginning point is the center point of the arc, rather than the start point.

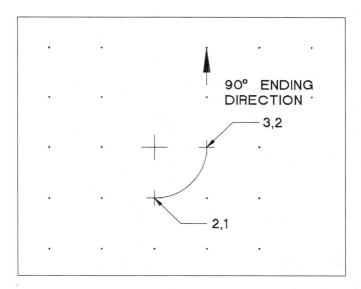

Figure 3–29 An arc drawn with a start point (2,1), and endpoint (3,2), and a radius of 1.0

Center, Start, Included Angle Option (or C,S,A for short) This method is similar to the Start, Center, Included Angle (S,C,A) method, except in this option the beginning point will be the center point of the arc rather than the start point.

Center, Start, Length of Chord Option (or C,S,L for short) This method is similar to the Start, Center, Length of the chord (S,C,L) method, except that the beginning point is the center point of the arc, rather than the start point.

Line-Arc and Arc-Arc Continuation Option You can use an automatic Start point, Endpoint, Starting direction method to draw an arc by pressing [Enter] as a response to the first prompt of the ARC command. After pressing [Enter], the only other input is to select or specify the endpoint of the arc you wish to draw. AutoCAD uses the endpoint of the previous line or arc (whichever was drawn last) as the start point of the new arc. AutoCAD then uses the ending direction of that last drawn object as the starting direction of the arc. Examples are shown in the following sequences and figures.

The start point of the existing arc is 2,1 and the endpoint is 3,2 with a radius of 1. This makes the ending direction of the existing arc 90 degrees, as shown in Figure 3–29.

The following command sequence continues drawing an arc, from the last-drawn arc, as shown in Figure 3–30 (arc-arc continuation).

    Command: **arc**
    Center/<Start point>: [Enter]
    Endpoint: **2,3**

The arc, as shown in Figure 3–29, is drawn clockwise instead, with its start point at 3,2 to an endpoint of 2,1 (see Figure 3–31).

The following command sequence will draw the automatic Start point, Endpoint, Starting direction arc, as shown in Figure 3–32.

    Command: **arc**
    Center/<Start point>: [Enter]
    Endpoint: **2,3**

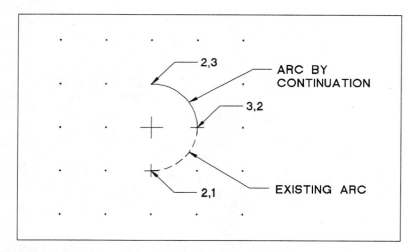

Figure 3-30 An arc drawn with the Arc-Arc Continuation method

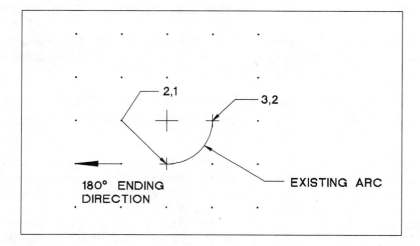

Figure 3-31 An arc drawn clockwise with start point (3,2) and endpoint (2,1)

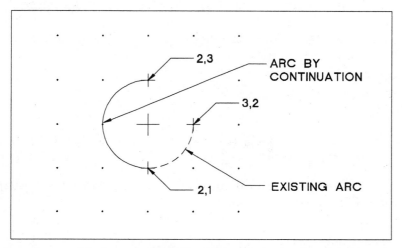

Figure 3-32 An arc drawn with the automatic Startpoint-Endpoint-Starting Direction

In the last case, the direction used is 180 degrees. The same arc would have been drawn if the last "line-or-arc" drawn was a line starting at 4,1 and ending at 2,1.

> ***NOTE:*** This method uses the last drawn of either an arc or a line. If you draw an arc, then a line, then draw a circle, and then use this continuation method, AutoCAD will use the line as the basis for the start point and direction. That is because the line was the last of the "line-or-arc" objects drawn.

POLYGON Command

The regular (all edges are equal length) 2D polygons are drawn with the POLYGON command. The minimum number of sides is three (forms an equilateral triangle); maximum number of sides is 1024. There are three ways to use the POLYGON command. The POLYGON command is invoked from the Polygon flyout located in the Draw toolbar (Figure 3–33), or at the "Command:" prompt, type **POLYGON** and press Enter or the spacebar.

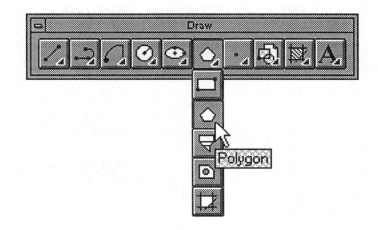

Figure 3-33 Invoke the POLYGON Command from the Draw toolbar

> Command: **polygon**
> Number of sides:

Polygon Inscribed in Circle Option   After specifying the number of sides and center of the polygon, this option allows you to specify the distance from the center to a vertex between edges. This defines the radius of a circle in which the polygon is inscribed (see Figure 3–34).

For example, the following command sequence shows steps in drawing a six-sided polygon (see Figure 3–35).

> Command: **polygon**
> Number of sides: **6**
> Edge/<Center of polygon>: **3,3**
> Inscribed in circle/Circumscribed about circle (I/C): **i**
> Radius of circle: **2**

This example draws a polygon with six sides, centered at 3,3, whose edge vertices are 2.0 units from the center of the polygon. Specifying the radius with a keyed-in value causes the direction of the bottom edge to be aligned with the zero rotation angle of the current coordinate system.

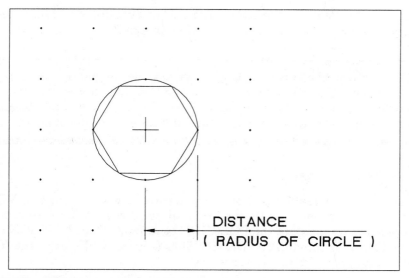

Figure 3-34 A Polygon drawn with the Inscribed Circle option

Another option for specifying the radius is to specify the coordinates, use relative coordinates, or to select a point on the screen, as follows:

Command: **polygon**
Number of sides: **8**
Edge/<Center of polygon>: **3,3**
Inscribed in circle/Circumscribed about circle (I/C): **i**
Radius of circle: **@2<90** *(or @0,2 or 3,5)*

This method of selecting the point of one of the vertices causes the angle of rotation of the polygon to conform to the angle necessary to have a vertex at the selected point.

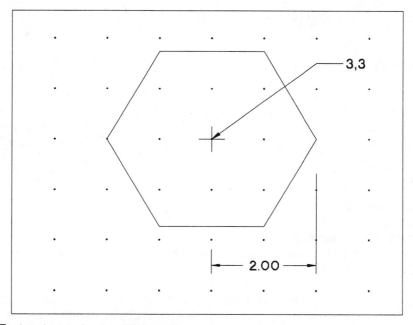

Figure 3-35 A polygon drawn with six sides

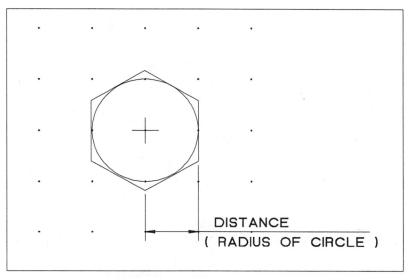

Figure 3-36 A Polygon drawn with the Circumscribed about a Circle option

Polygon Circumscribed About a Circle Option This option allows you to specify the distance from the center to the midpoint (shortest or perpendicular distance) of one of the edges, as shown in Figure 3–36. This defines the radius of a circle about which the polygon is circumscribed.

An example of the circumscribed method, as shown in Figure 3–37, is as follows:

    Command: **polygon**
    Number of sides: **8**
    Edge/<Center of polygon>: **3,3**
    Inscribed in circle/Circumscribed about circle (I/C): **c**
    Radius of circle: **2**

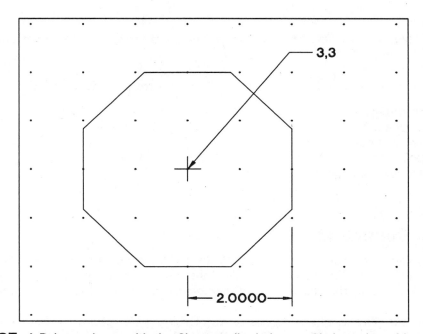

Figure 3-37 A Polygon drawn with the Circumscribed about a Circle option with a radius of 2.0

Fundamentals II

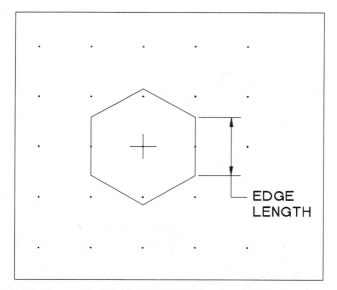

Figure 3-38 A Polygon drawn with the Length of Polygon Edge option

Another option to specifying the radius is to specify the coordinates, use relative coordinates, or select a point on the screen as follows:

    Command: **polygon**
    Number of sides: **6**
    Edge/<Center of polygon>: **3,3**
    Inscribed in circle/Circumscribed about circle (I/C): **c**
    Radius of circle: **5,3** *(or @2<0 or @2,0)*

This method (of selecting one of the edge midpoints) causes the angle of rotation of the polygon to conform to the angle necessary to have an edge midpoint at the selected point.

Length of Polygon Edge Option This option allows you to specify the length of one of the edges, as shown in Figure 3–38.

An example of the edge-length method, as shown in Figure 3–39, is as follows:

    Command: **polygon**
    Number of sides: **7**
    Edge/<Center of polygon>: **e**
    First endpoint of edge: **1,1**
    Second endpoint of edge: **3,1**

ELLIPSE Command

AutoCAD provides several convenient methods of drawing ellipses. The ELLIPSE command should be used with certain precautions. The more you know about the geometry of an ellipse and how AutoCAD draws it, the better you will be able to apply the ELLIPSE command.

Ellipses, the Old Way Earlier releases of AutoCAD used a special method of creating an ellipse by inserting a circle with different X and Y scale factors. You can still apply this method once

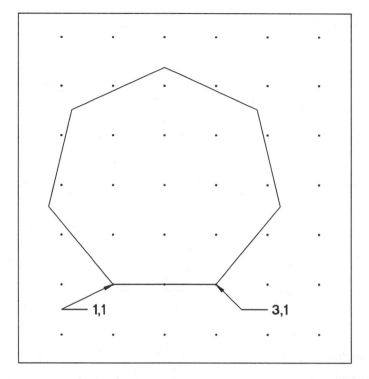

Figure 3-39 A Polygon drawn with the Edge-Length method

you become familiar with the concept of unit blocks (described in Chapter 9). For example, you can draw a circle one unit in diameter, store it by using the BLOCK command, and later use the INSERT command to generate an ellipse (from the circle) by using the appropriate X and Y scale factors.

The ELLIPSE command is invoked from the Ellipse flyout located in the Draw toolbar, or at the "Command:" prompt type **ELLIPSE** and press Enter or the spacebar.

    Command: **ellipse**
    Arc/Center/<Axis endpoint 1>:

Axis and Eccentricity Option   The Axis and Eccentricity option method (if you are not in the isometric Snap mode) is to select the endpoints of one axis, and then select one endpoint of the other axis. The Ellipse Axis End option is invoked from the Ellipse flyout located in the Draw toolbar (Figure 3–40).

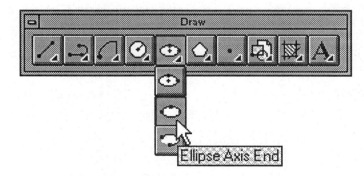

Figure 3-40 Invoke the Ellipse Axis End option from the Draw toolbar

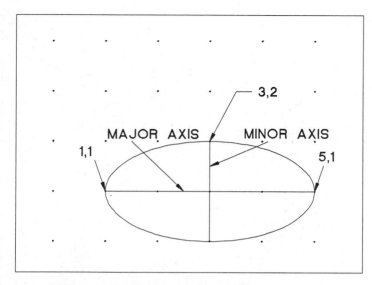

Figure 3-41 An Ellipse drawn by specifying the major and minor axis

The prompts are as follows:

    Command: **ellipse**
    Arc/Center/<Axis endpoint 1>: **1,1**
    Axis endpoint 2: **5,1**
    <Other Axis distance>/Rotation: **3,2**

The above responses generate an ellipse whose major axis is 4.0 units long in a horizontal direction and whose minor axis is 2.0 units long in a vertical direction, as shown in Figure 3–41.

An ellipse of similar proportions whose long axis is vertical is generated using the following sequences:

    Command: **ellipse**
    Arc/Center/<Axis endpoint 1>: **2,1**
    Axis endpoint 2: **4,1**
    <Other Axis distance>/Rotation: **3,3**

    or

    Command: **ellipse**
    Arc/Center/<Axis endpoint 1>: **3,-1**
    Axis endpoint 2: **3,3**
    <Other Axis distance>/Rotation: **2**

Note that the last response was a distance. This will be interpreted by AutoCAD as the distance from the center of the ellipse to the second axis endpoint (or half the length of the second axis).

Center Option This method allows you to specify the center point of the ellipse and one endpoint of the major and minor axis. The Ellipse Center option is invoked from the Ellipse flyout located in the Draw toolbar (Figure 3–42).

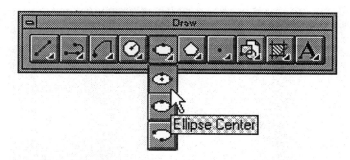

Figure 3-42 Invoke the Ellipse Center Option from the Draw toolbar

The prompts are as follows:

> Command: **ellipse**
> Arc/Center/Axis endpoint 1>: **c**
> Center of ellipse: **3,1**
> Axis endpoint 2: **1,1**
> <Other Axis distance>/Rotation: **3,2**

The previous responses generate an ellipse similar to previous example with the major axis 4.0 units long in a horizontal direction and minor axis 2.0 units long in a vertical direction.

Rotation Angle Option   You can specify eccentricity by giving the rotation angle (or the angle about which a circle would be rotated to project an ellipse). Another way to describe this method is that the angle of rotation specified is the angle that your line of sight makes with the plane in which the circle lies that you are viewing. This method is shown in the following sequence:

> Command: **ellipse**
> Arc/Center/<Axis endpoint 1>: **3,-1**
> Axis endpoint 2: **3,3**
> <Other Axis distance>/Rotation: **r**
> Rotation around major Axis: *(specify rotation angle)*

See Figure 3-43 for examples of ellipses with various rotation angles.

Isometric Circles (or Isocircles) Option   The isometric planes by definition (iso meaning same and metric meaning measure) are all being viewed at the same angle of rotation (see Figure 3-44). That angle is approximately 54.73561031 degrees. Therefore, AutoCAD uses this angle of rotation automatically for ellipses drawn in the Isocircle mode. It can also be shown that a circle of

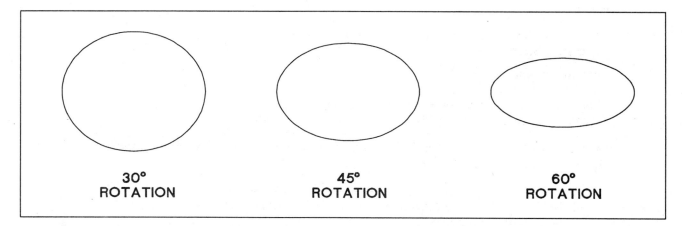

30° ROTATION   **45° ROTATION**   **60° ROTATION**

Figure 3-43 Ellipses drawn with different rotation angles

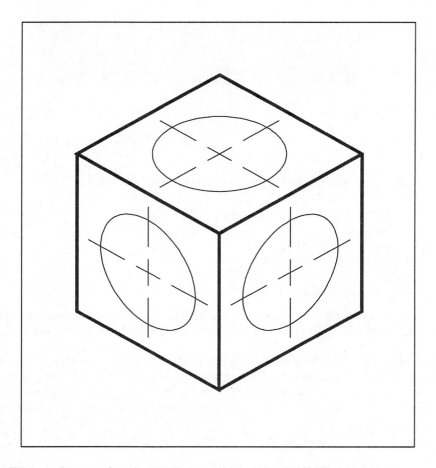

Figure 3-44 Ellipses drawn using the Isocircle option of the ELLIPSE Command

one unit in diameter that is being viewed in an isometric plane will project a short axis dimension of 0.8164965809 units. However, lines in isometric that are one unit in length and parallel to one of the three main axes also project to 0.8164965809 units long. Therefore, you automatically increase the entire projection by a fudge factor of 1.224744871 (the reciprocal of 0.8164965809) in order to use true dimensioning along the isometric axes. This means that circles of one unit long will be measured along one of their isometric diameters rather than their long axis. This facilitates using true lengths as the lengths of distances projected from lines parallel to one of the isometric axes.

The Isometric Circle method becomes one of the options of the ELLIPSE command when you are in the isometric Snap mode.

> Command: **ellipse**
> Arc/Center/Isocircle/<Axis endpoint 1>: **i**
> Center of circle: *(select the center of the isometric circle)*
> <Circle radius>/Diameter: *(enter the radius or override with d)*

If you override the last prompt default by typing **d**, the following prompt will appear:

> Circle diameter: *(enter the desired diameter)*

> **NOTE:** The Iso and Diameter options will work only when you are in the isometric Snap mode.

EXERCISES

Exercise 3-1

Create the drawing according to the settings given in the following table:

SETTINGS	VALUE
1. UNITS	DECIMAL
2. LIMITS	
LOWER LEFT	0, 0
UPPER RIGHT	17, 11
3. GRID	0.50
4. SNAP	0.25
5. TEXT SIZE	0.25

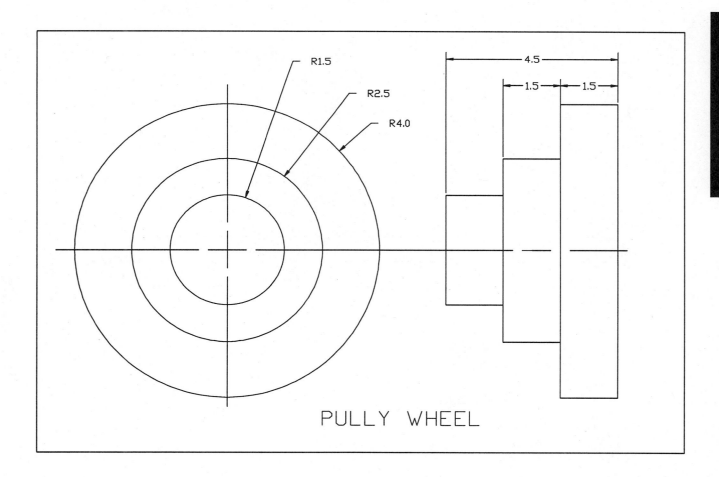

Exercise 3-2 to 3-3

Create the drawings according to the settings given in the following table:

SETTINGS	VALUE
1. UNITS	DECIMAL
2. LIMITS	
LOWER LEFT	0, 0
UPPER RIGHT	22, 17
3. GRID	0.50
4. SNAP	0.25
5. TEXT SIZE	0.25

Exercise 3-2

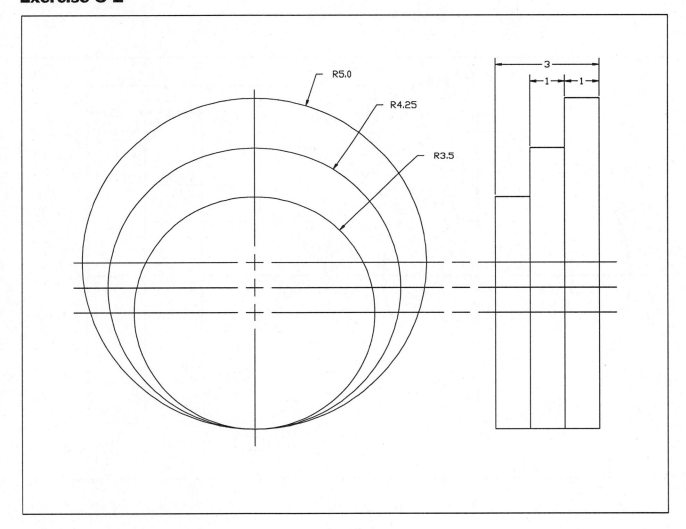

Exercise 3-3

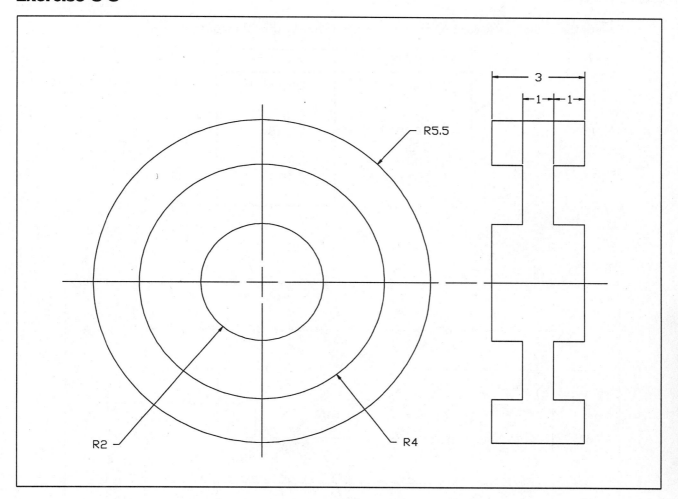

Exercise 3-4

Create the drawings according to the settings given in the following table:

SETTINGS	VALUE
1. UNITS	DECIMAL
2. LIMITS	
LOWER LEFT	0, 0
UPPER RIGHT	24, 18
3. GRID	1"
4. SNAP	0.5"
5. TEXT SIZE	0.18"

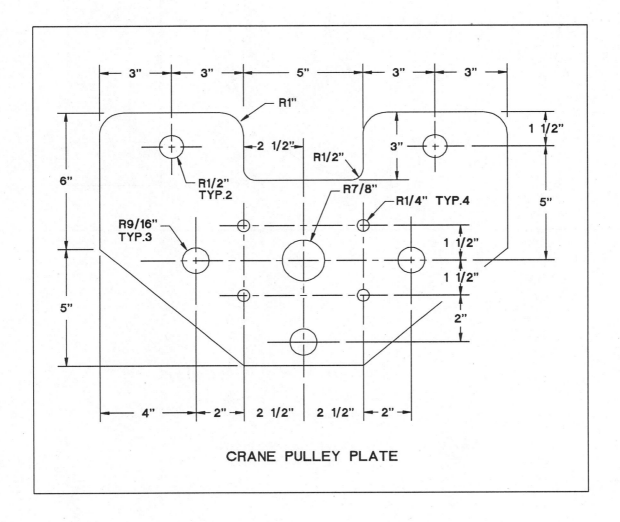

CRANE PULLEY PLATE

LAYER COMMANDS

AutoCAD offers a means of grouping objects on layers in a manner similar to the manual drafter separating complex drawings on individual transparent sheets superimposed in a single stack. Under these conditions, the manual drafter would be able to draw on the top sheet only. Likewise, in AutoCAD you can only draw on the current layer. However, AutoCAD permits you to transfer selected objects from one layer to another (neither of which needs to be the current layer) with commands called CHANGE and CHPROP. Let's see the manual drafter try that.

A common application of the layer feature is in using one layer for construction (or layout) lines. You can create geometric constructions with objects, such as lines, circles, and arcs. These generate intersections, endpoints, centers, points of tangency, midpoints, and other useful data that might take the manual drafter considerable time to calculate on a calculator or hand-measure on the board. From these you can create other objects using intersections or other data generated from the layout. Then the layout layer can be turned off (making it no longer visible). The layer is not lost, but can be recalled (turned on) for viewing later as required.

The same drawing limits, coordinate system, and zoom factors apply to all layers in a drawing. There is a limit of 32,000 layers in a drawing, more than enough for any drawing need. There is no limits to the number of objects per layer.

To draw an object on a particular layer, first make sure that layer is set as the "current layer." There is one and only one current layer. Whatever you draw will be placed on the current layer. The current layer can be compared to the manual drafter's top sheet on the stack of transparencies. To draw an object on a particular layer, first that layer must have been created, and if it is not the current layer you must make it the current layer.

You can always move, copy, or rotate any object whether it is on the current layer or not. When you copy an object that is not on the current layer, the copy will be placed on the layer that the original object is on. This is also true with the mirror or an array of an object or group of objects.

A layer can be visible (on) or invisible (off). Only visible layers are displayed or plotted. Invisible layers are still part of the drawing, they just are not displayed or plotted. You can turn layers on and off at will, in any combination. It is possible to turn off the current layer. If this happens and you draw an object, it will not appear on the screen; it will be placed on the current layer and will appear on the screen when that layer is turned on (provided you are viewing the area in which the object was drawn). This is not a common occurrence, but it can cause concern to both the novice and even the more experienced operator who has not faced the problem before. Do not turn off the current layer; the results can be very confusing. When the system variable TILEMODE is off, you can make specified layers visible only in certain viewports. For additional information see Chapter 11.

Each layer in a drawing has an associated name, color, and linetype. The name of a layer may be up to 31 characters long. It may contain letters, digits, and the special characters dollar ($), hyphen (-), and underscore (_), but no blank spaces. The layer name has to be one word. All layer names are converted to uppercase. Always give descriptive names appropriate to your application, such as floor-plan, plumbing, etc. The first several characters of the current layer's name are displayed in the layer list box located in the Object Properties toolbar (see Figure 3–45). You can change the name of a layer any time you wish, and you can delete unused layers. These functions are handled by the RENAME and PURGE commands. They are described in Chapter 12.

One color can be assigned to any number of layers in a drawing. You can assign to a layer any one of the 256 available colors. If your graphics monitor is monochrome, all color numbers will produce the same visual effect. Even in this case, color numbers are useful because they can be assigned to

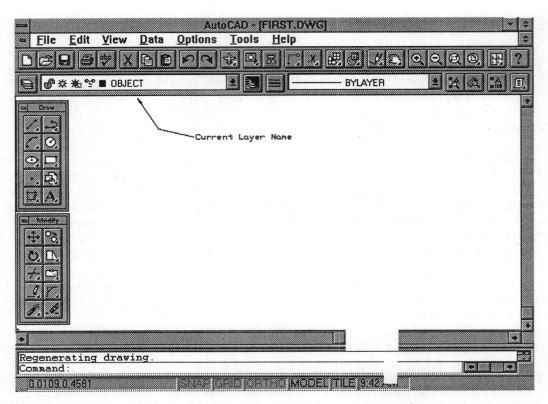

Figure 3-45 The current layer name as displayed in the layer list box located in the Object Properties toolbar

a different pen on a pen plotter to plot in different line weights and colors. This works even for single-pen plotters; you can ask AutoCAD to pause for pen changes.

A linetype is a repeating pattern of dashes, dots, and blank spaces. AutoCAD Release 13 adds the capability of including the repeated objects in the custom linetypes. The assigned linetype is used to draw all objects on the layer. The following are some of the linetypes that are provided in the AutoCAD in a library file called ACAD.LIN:

Border	Dashdot	Dot
Center	Dashed	Hidden
Continuous	Divide	Phantom

See Appendix K for examples of each of these linetypes. Linetypes are another means of conveying visual information. You can assign the same linetype to any number of layers. In some drafting disciplines, conventions have been established giving specific meanings to particular dash-dot patterns. If a line is too short to hold even one dash-dot sequence, AutoCAD draws a continuous line between the endpoints. When you are working on large drawings, you may not see the gap between dash-dot patterns in a linetype, unless the scaling for the linetype is set for a large value. This can be done by the LTSCALE command. This command is discussed in more detail later in this chapter.

Every drawing will have a layer called layer 0 (zero). By default, layer 0 is assigned color white and linetype continuous and is turned on. Layer 0 cannot be renamed nor can it be deleted.

If you need additional layers, you must create them and assign specific names. By default, each new layer is assigned color white and linetype continuous. If necessary, you can always reassign the color and linetype of the new layer.

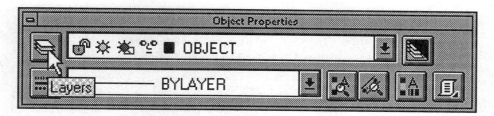

Figure 3-46 Invoke the DDLMODES Command from the Object Properties toolbar

The DDLMODES command or LAYER command can be used to set up and control layers. The DDLMODES command allows you to set up and control layers through the Layer Control Dialog box. The LAYER command allows you to set up and control layers at the "Command:" prompt level.

DDLMODES Command

The DDLMODES command is invoked from the Object Properties toolbar (see Figure 3–46), pull-down menu Data (see Figure 3–47), or at the "Command:" prompt, type **DDLMODES** and press Enter or spacebar.

    Command: **DDLMODES**

AutoCAD displays the Layer Control dialog box similar to the one shown in Figure 3–48. The dialog box has four columns titled Layer Name, State, Color, and Linetype and a large number of buttons.

To create a new layer, enter its name in the edit box located just below the **New** button. After entering the name, pick the **New** button. The new layer is added to the Layer Name list box. By default, new layers are turned on and assigned color number 7 (white) and linetype CONTINUOUS. If you want to create more than one layer, enter each name separated with a comma (but no spaces). After you pick **NEW**, the new layers are added to the Layer Name list box.

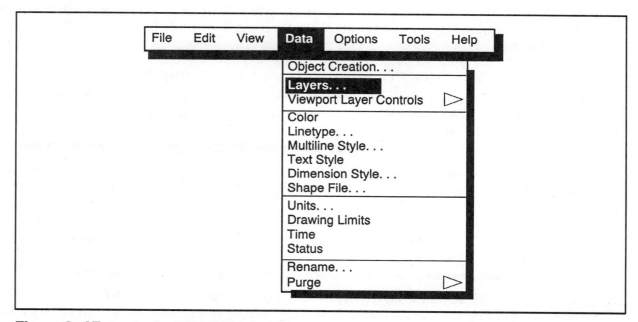

Figure 3-47 Invoke the DDLMODES Command from the pull-down menu Data

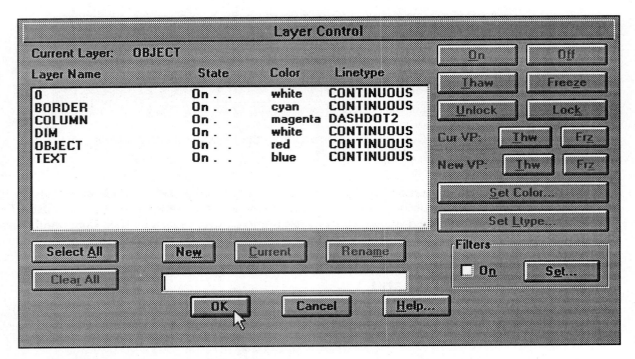

Figure 3-48 The Layer Control dialog box

> **NOTE:** The names you enter may not contain wild-card characters (* and !), spaces, or existing layer names.

To make an existing layer current, select its name in the Layer Name list box and pick the **Current** button. The current layer name appears in the **Current Layer:** label located just above the Layer Name List box.

When you set a layer that is OFF as Current Layer, AutoCAD turns it ON.

> **NOTE:** The **Current** button becomes active only after you select one of the layers in the Layer List box.

To rename a layer, select the layer in the Layer Name list box. The layer is highlighted and its name appears in the edit box. Edit the name and pick the **Rename** button. The new name is shown in the Layer Name list box.

> **NOTE:** The **Rename** button becomes active only after you select one of the layers in the Layer List box.

To turn layers off, select the layer(s) you want to turn off, and pick the **OFF** button in the upper right corner of the Layer Control dialog box. AutoCAD indicates whether a layer is off by displaying "." next to the layer's name in the State Column.

When you turn off a layer, the objects will not be displayed on the graphics monitor and they are not plotted. The objects still exist in the drawing; they are made invisible. They are still calculated during the regeneration of the drawing, even though they are invisible.

To turn layers on, select the desired layers and pick the **ON** button in the upper right-hand corner of the Layer Control dialog box. AutoCAD indicates whether a layer is on by displaying ON next to the layer's name in the State column.

Each designated layer is turned on using the color and linetype previously associated with it. Turning a layer on does not cause it to be the current layer.

> **NOTE:** The **ON** and **OFF** buttons become active only after you select one or more layers in the Layer List box.

To freeze or thaw layers, select the layer(s) you want and pick either the **Freeze** or **Thaw** button in the Layer Control dialog box. AutoCAD indicates whether a layer is frozen or thawed by displaying an F (or "." if it is thawed) next to the layer's name in the State column.

The layers that are frozen will not be visible on the display nor will they be plotted on the finished drawing. In this respect, **Freeze** is similar to **OFF.** However, layers that are simply turned off still go through a screen regeneration each time the system regenerates your drawing. The layers that are Frozen are not considered during a screen regeneration. Later, if you want to see the frozen layer, you simply Thaw it and automatic regeneration of the screen takes place.

> **NOTE:** The **Freeze** and **Thaw** buttons become active only after you select one or more of the layers in the Layer List box.

To lock or unlock layers, select one or more layers in the Layer List box, and pick the **Lock** or **UnLock** button in the Layer Control dialog box. AutoCAD indicates whether a layer is locked or unlocked by displaying an L (or "." for unlocked) next to the layer's name in the State column.

Objects on locked layers are visible on the display but cannot be modified with the modifying commands. It is, however, still possible to draw on a locked layer by making it the current layer, changing the linetypes and colors, freezing them, and using any of the inquiry commands and object snap modes on them.

> **NOTE:** The **Lock** and **UnLock** buttons become active only after you select one or more of the layers in the Layer List box.

The Set Color. . . option allows you to change the color of a selected layer or layers. The **Set Color...** button is activated after you select the layers you want to change. When you pick the **Select Color. . .** button, AutoCAD displays a standard color dialog box that allows you to change the color of the selected layers. Use the cursor to pick the color you want, or enter its name or number in the Color edit box. The color you select appears in the Color edit box. When you pick **OK,** it is added as the color for the selected layer(s). It is listed under the Color column in the Layer Control dialog box.

> **NOTE:** The **Color. . .** button becomes active only after you select one or more of the layers in the Layer List box.

The Set Ltype. . . option allows you to change the linetype of a selected layer or layers. The **Set Ltype. . .** button is activated after you select the layer(s) you want to change. When you pick the **Set Ltype. . .** button, AutoCAD displays the Select Linetype dialog box. Use the cursor to select the linetype you want to select, or enter its name in the Linetype edit box for a particular layer(s). The linetype you select appears in the Linetype edit box. When you pick **OK,** it is added as the linetype for that layer. It is listed under the Linetype column in the Layer Control dialog box.

> ***NOTE:*** The Set Ltype sub-dialog box displays only the linetypes already loaded into the Current drawing. If you haven't loaded the linetypes, only the Continuous linetype appears in the dialog box. To load the linetypes, pick the Load. . . button. AutoCAD lists the available linetypes from default linetype file ACAD.LIN. Select all the line types needed to be loaded and pick the OK button to load the line types into the current drawing.

The Filters area allows you to select layer names in the Layer Name list box based on their properties. You can filter layers with respect to their name, color, linetype, whether they are ON or OFF, Frozen or Thawed, and Locked or UnLocked. In addition, you can select all the layers listed in the Layer Name list box by clicking the **Select All** button. To clear the selection, click on the **Clear All** button.

You can also toggle On/Off, Freeze/Thaw, LOck/Unlock, or Freeze/Thaw for paper space viewports, in addition to making a layer current from the Layer list box provided in the Object Properties toolbar. Click on the icon provided next to the layer name to toggle, as shown in Figure 3–49.

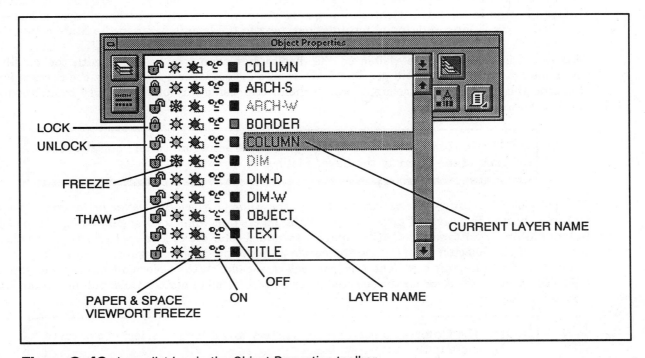

Figure 3-49 Layer list box in the Object Properties toolbar

LAYER Command

The LAYER command is invoked by typing LAYER at the "Command:" prompt and pressing the spacebar or ⌨Enter⌨.

> Command: **layer**
> ?/Make/Set/New/ON/OFF/Color/LType/Freeze/Thaw/LOck/UnLock:

? Option The ? option lists the names of layers defined in the current drawing, showing their on/off/frozen/thaw/lock/unlock state, color, and linetypes. When you select this option, AutoCAD prompts:

> Layer name(s) to list <*>:

You can enter a list of layer names, using wild cards if you wish, or press the spacebar or ⌨Enter⌨ to accept the default to list all layer names.

Make Option The Make option effectively does three things. When this option is invoked, AutoCAD prompts you for a layer name. Once you enter a name, Make does the following:

1. Searches for the layer to determine whether it exists.
2. Creates it if the layer does not exist, assigns the color white and linetype continuous.
3. Sets the newly made layer to be the current layer.

When you select this option, AutoCAD prompts:

> New current Layer <default>:

If the layer you selected exists and is presently turned off, AutoCAD turns it on automatically, using the color and linetype previously assigned to that layer and makes it the current layer.

Set Option The Set option tells AutoCAD on which layer you want to draw (make current). When you select this option, AutoCAD prompts:

> Current Layer <default>:

Enter the layer's name (it must be an existing layer) and press the spacebar or ⌨Enter⌨. This layer becomes the current layer. The first several characters of the layer name are placed on the status line.

New Option The New option allows you to create new layers. When you select this option, AutoCAD prompts:

> New Layer name(s):

You can enter more than one name at a time by separating the names with a comma. It you need to separate characters in the name, use the underscore (_) instead of pressing the spacebar (in AutoCAD pressing the spacebar is the same as pressing ⌨Enter⌨). Each layer thus created is automatically turned on, and is assigned color white and linetype continuous.

OFF Option The OFF option allows you to turn off selected layers. When you select this option, AutoCAD prompts:

> Layer name(s) to turn off:

The list should contain only existing layer names. The names may include wild card characters. When you turn off a layer, it's associated objects will not be displayed on the graphics monitor and they are not plotted. The objects still exist in the drawing; they are just invisible. They are still calculated during the regeneration of the drawing, even though they are not visible.

ON Option The ON option allows you to turn on layers that have been turned off. When you select this option, AutoCAD prompts:

> Layer name(s) to turn on:

This list should contain only existing layer names. The name may include wild-card characters. Each designated layer is turned on using the color and linetype previously associated with it. Turning a layer on does not cause it to be the current layer.

Color Option The Color option allows you to change the color associated with that specific layer. When you select this option, first AutoCAD prompts:

> Color:

Reply with one of the standard color names or with a legal color number between 0 and 255. After you specify the color, AutoCAD prompts:

> Layer name(s) to color n <default>:

This prompt will actually have the code number of the color selected in place of the "n" shown above.

Reply with the names of existing layers separated by commas. The names may include wild-card characters. The specified layers are given the color you designated and are then automatically turned on if they are off. If you would prefer to assign the color but turn the layers off, precede the color with a minus sign (–).

Linetype Option The Linetype option allows you to change the linetype associated with a specific layer. When you select this option, AutoCAD prompts:

> Linetype (or ?) <continuous>:

Reply with the name of an existing defined linetype. AutoCAD then asks for a list of layer names to which the linetype should be applied. For example, if you had replied to the first prompt with the linetype named HIDDEN, the next prompt would be:

> Layer names(s) for linetype hidden <default>:

Reply with the names of existing layers separated by commas. The names may include wild-card characters.

Freeze and Thaw Options The layers that are frozen will not be visible on the display nor will they be plotted out on the finished drawing. In this respect, Freeze is similar to OFF. However, layers that are simply turned off still go through a screen regeneration each time the system regenerates your drawing. Later, if you want to see the frozen layer, you simply Thaw it and automatic regeneration of the screen takes place. The layers that are frozen will not be regenerated.

When you select the Freeze option, AutoCAD prompts:
> Layer name(s) to Freeze:

You can enter more than one name at a time by separating the names with a comma.

When you select the Thaw option, AutoCAD prompts:
> Layer name(s) to Thaw:

You can enter more than one name at a time by separating the names with a comma.

LOck and UnLock Options Objects on locked layers are visible on the display but cannot be modified with the modify commands. When you select the Lock option, AutoCAD prompts:
> Layer name(s) to Lock:

You can enter more than one name at a time by separating the names with a comma.

When you select the UnLock option, AutoCAD prompts:
> Layer name(s) to UnLock:

You can enter more than one name at a time by separating the names with a comma.

> **NOTE:** Turning layers on and off is extremely useful. However, like many other advanced features, you must consider the effects when editing. If objects on layers that are turned on are associated with objects on layers that are turned off, and you wish to move them, those that are on the *OFF* layer will not be affected by the modifying command unless they are all part of the same block.

Whenever you give a null response to the LAYER command, it returns you to the "Command:" prompt.

DDLTYPE Command

The DDLTYPE command causes the Select Linetype dialog box to be displayed. It permits you to load linetype definitions from a library file (filename.lin) or add new definitions to a library file. The DDLTYPE command is invoked from the Objects Properties toolbar or at the "Command:" prompt type **DDLTYPE** and press [Enter] or spacebar. AutoCAD displays the Select Linetype dialog box, as shown in Figure 3–50.

The **Loaded Linetypes** section displays names of linetypes that have been loaded and are available for use. To make a linetype current you may select it from this list and press OK.

> **NOTE:** It is recommended to assign a linetype to appropriate layer before it is used.

The **ISO Pen Width** option permits you to specify the pen width in millimeters for ISO linetypes.

The **Linetype Scale:** edit field permits you to specify the linetype scale for new or existing objects.

The **Linetype:** edit box displays the name of the current linetype. You may enter a different name here.

The **Load. . .** button causes the Load or Reload Linetypes dialog box to be displayed. Select the linetype(s) from the available linetypes to load into the current drawing. The Select All button allows you to select all the available linetypes from the selected linetype file. This function can also be performed in the Layer Control dialog box.

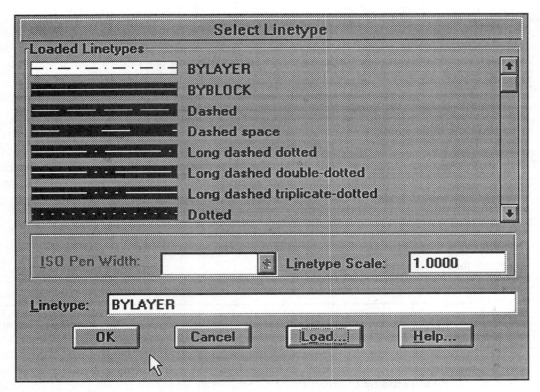

Figure 3-50 Select Linetype dialog box

LTSCALE COMMAND

Before using linetypes, the effect of the linetype scale (set by the LTSCALE command) should be understood. The definition of a linetype tells AutoCAD how many units long to make dashes and spaces between dashes and dots. As long as the LTSCALE is set to 1.0, the displayed lengths of dashes and spaces coincides with the definition in the ACAD.LIN file.

However, the linetype looks continuous at large scales or short distances. The LTSCALE Command lets you make the linetype visible again. The sequence of prompts is as follows:

Command: **ltscale**
New scale factor <default>: *(a positive integer)*

Changing the linetype scale affects all linetypes in the drawing. If you want dashes which have been defined as 0.5 units long in the DASHED linetype to be displayed as 10 units long, you set the LTSCALE to 20. This also makes the dashes that were defined as 1.25 units long in the CENTER linetype display as 25 units long and the short dashes (defined as 0.25 units long) display as 5 units long. Note that the 1.25-unit long dash in the CENTER linetype is 2.5 times longer than the 0.5-unit long dash in the DASHED linetype. This ratio will always remain the same, no matter what the setting of the LTSCALE. So if you wish to have some other ratio of dash and space lengths between different linetypes, you will have to change the definition of one of the linetypes in the ACAD.LIN file.

Remember that linetypes are for visual effect. The actual length of dashes and spaces are bound more to how they should look on the final plotted sheet than to distances or sizes of any objects on the drawing. An object plotted full size can probably use an LTSCALE setting of 1.0. A 50'-long object plotted on an 18" x 24" sheet might be plotted at a 1/4" = 1'-0" scale factor. This would equate to 1=48. An LTSCALE setting of 48 would make dashes and spaces plot to the same lengths as the full-size plot with a setting of 1.0.

EXERCISES

Exercise 3-5

Create the drawing according to the settings given in the following table. Draw the objects in the appropriate layers.

SETTINGS	VALUE	
1. UNITS	ARCHITECTURAL	
2. LIMITS		
LOWER LEFT	0, 0	
UPPER RIGHT	100', 80'	
3. GRID	6'	
4. SNAP	3'	
5. TEXT SIZE	8"	
6. LAYERS		

LAYER NAME	COLOR	LINETYPE
GAS	CYAN	GAS_LINE
CABLE	YELLOW	DASHDOT
ELECTRIC	BLUE	CONTINUOUS
SEWER	RED	HIDDEN
WATER	MAGENTA	CENTER
BORDER	WHITE	PHANTOM
HOUSE	WHITE	CONTINUOUS
TEXT	GREEN	CONTINUOUS

Fundamentals II

Exercise 3-5

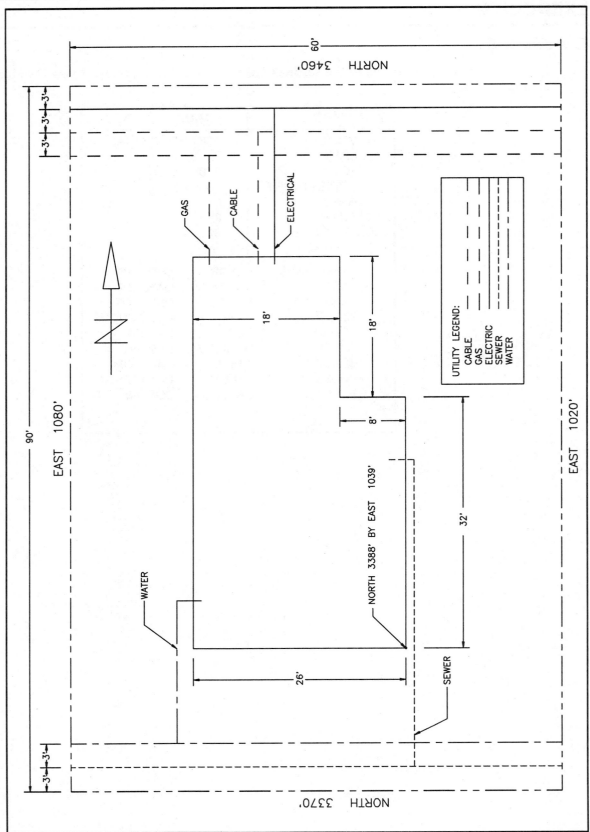

Exercise 3-6

Create the drawings according to the settings given in the following table. Draw the objects in the appropriate layers.

SETTINGS	VALUE
1. UNITS	DECIMAL
2. LIMITS	
LOWER LEFT	0, 0
UPPER RIGHT	12, 9
3. GRID	0.50
4. SNAP	0.25
5. TEXT SIZE	0.125
6. LAYERS	

LAYER NAME	COLOR	LINETYPE
OBJECT	WHITE	CONTINUOUS
CENTER	YELLOW	CENTER
HIDDEN	CYAN	HIDDEN
TEXT	GREEN	CONTINUOUS

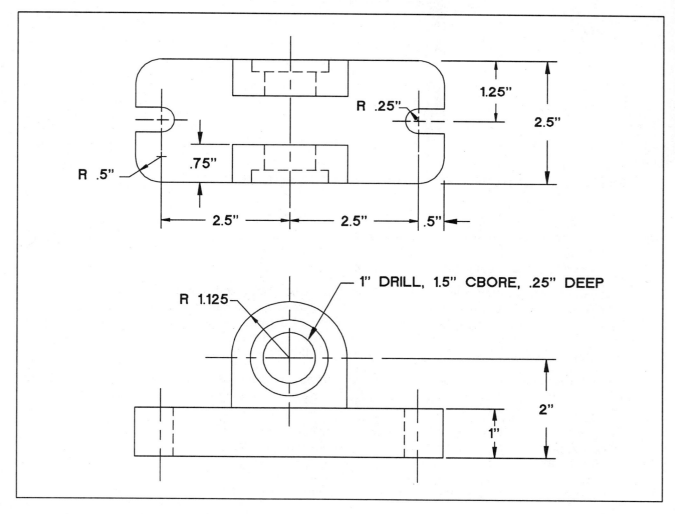

Fundamentals II

CONSTRUCT COMMANDS

AutoCAD not only allows you to draw objects easily, but also allows you to construct additional objects from existing objects. This section discusses six important commands that will make your job easier. The commands include the Copy, Array, Offset, Mirror, Fillet and Chamfer commands.

COPY Command

The COPY command places copies of the selected objects at the specified displacement, leaving the original objects intact. The copies are oriented and scaled the same as the original. If necessary, you can make multiple copies of selected objects. Each resulting copy is completely independent of the original and can be edited and manipulated like any other simple object.

The COPY command is invoked from the Copy flyout located in the Modify toolbar (see Figure 3-51), or at the "Command:" prompt, type **COPY** and press the spacebar or Enter.

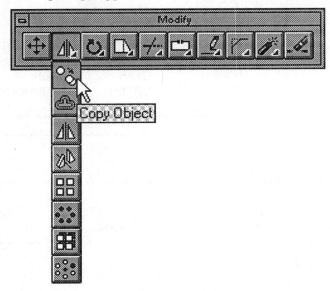

Figure 3-51 Invoke the COPY Command from the Modify toolbar

```
Command: copy
Select objects: (show what to copy and then give a null response)
<Base point or displacement>/Multiple: (first point or x,y,z point)
Second point of displacement: (second point or null response)
```

You can use one or more object selection methods available from the Select Objects toolbar. If you specify or pick two data points, AutoCAD computes the displacement and places a copy accordingly. If you provide a null response to the second point of displacement AutoCAD considers the point provided as the second point of displacement vector with the origin (0,0,0) as the first point, indicating how far to copy the objects and in what direction.

The following command sequence shows an example of copying a group of objects selected by the Window option, as shown in Figure 3-52, by placing two data points:

```
Command: copy
Select objects: (pick a point to place one corner of a window) Enter
Other corner: (pick a point to place opposite corner of the window)
Select objects: Enter
<Base point or displacement)/Multiple: (pick base point)
Second point of displacement: (pick second point)
```

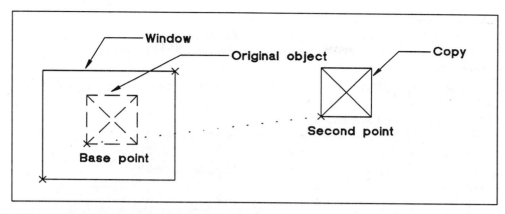

Figure 3-52 Using the Copy Window option to copy a group of objects by specifying two pick points

Multiple Copies To make multiple copies using one COPY command, respond to the base point prompt by entering **m** for multiple. The base point prompt then reappears followed by repeated second point prompts, and a copy of the selected objects is made at a location determined by each displacement you enter. Each displacement is relative to the original base point. When you have made all the copies you need, give a null response to the second point prompt.

The following command sequence shows an example of placing multiple copies of a group of objects selected by the Window option, as shown in Figure 3-53.

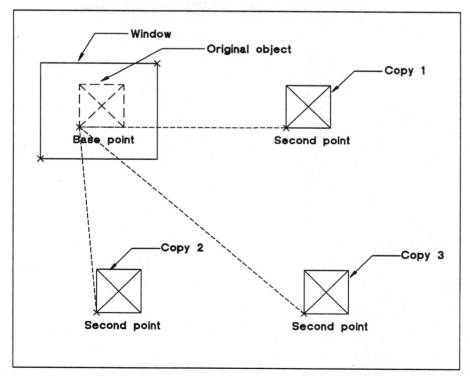

Figure 3-53 Using the Copy Window Command to make multiple copies of a group of objects

Command: **copy**
Select objects: *(pick a point to place one corner of the window)*
Other corner: *(pick a point to place the opposite corner of the window)*
Select objects: Enter
<Base point or displacement>/Multiple: *(pick Multiple option from the screen menu or type* **M** *and press* Enter*)*
Multiple base point: *(pick base point)*
Second point of displacement: *(pick second point for copy 1)*
Second point of displacement: *(pick second point for copy 2)*
Second point of displacement: *(pick second point for copy 3)*
Second point of displacement: Enter
Command:

ARRAY Command

The ARRAY command is used to make multiple copies of selected objects in either rectangular or polar arrays. In the rectangular array, you can specify the number of rows, the number of columns, and the spacing between rows and columns (row and column spacing may differ). The whole rectangular array can be rotated at a selected angle. In the polar array, you can determine the angular intervals, the number of copies, the angle that the group covers, and whether or not the objects are rotated about the center of the group.

Rectangular Array The Rectangular ARRAY command is invoked from the Copy flyout located in the Modify toolbar (Figure 3–54), or at the "Command:" prompt type **ARRAY** and press Enter or spacebar.

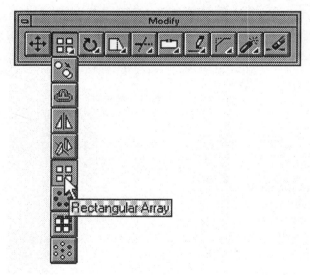

Figure 3-54 Invoke the Rectangular ARRAY Command from the Modify toolbar

Command: **array**
Select objects: *(select objects)*
Rectangular or Polar array (R/P): **r**

Number of rows (---) <1>: *(enter a number)*
Number of columns (|||) <1>: *(enter a number)*
Unit cell or distance between rows <--->: *(specify the distance)*
Distance between columns <|||>: *(specify the distance)*

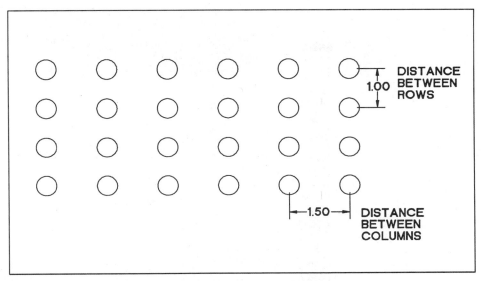

Figure 3–55   Using the ARRAY Command to place a rectangular array

Any combination of whole numbers of rows and columns may be entered (except both 1 row and 1 column which would not create any copies). AutoCAD includes the original object in the number you enter. The next prompt(s) requests the distances of the spacing between objects to be arrayed. Row and column spaces can be different from each other. They can be entered separately when prompted, or you may select two points which specify the opposite corners of a rectangle called a unit cell. AutoCAD uses the width of the unit cell as the horizontal distance(s) between columns and the height as the vertical distance(s) between rows. A positive number for the column and row spacing causes the elements to array toward the right and upward, respectively. Negative numbers for the column and row spacing cause the elements to array toward the left and downward, respectively.

The following command sequence shows an example of placing a rectangular array with 6 rows and 4 columns, as shown in Figure 3–55.

    Command: **array**
    Select objects: *(select objects)*
    Rectangular or Polar array (R/P): **r**
    Number of rows (---)<1>: **6**
    Number of columns (|||)<1>: **4**
    Unit cell or distance between rows <--->: **1**
    Distance between columns <|||>: **1.5**

Polar Array   The Polar ARRAY command is invoked from the Copy flyout located in the Modify toolbar (Figure 3–56), or at the "Command:" prompt type ARRAY and press [Enter] or spacebar. AutoCAD prompts after selecting the objects:

    Center point of array:

Enter the point around which you want the array to form. To create the polar array AutoCAD needs information on two of the three parameters as described below:

1. Specify the number of items in the array (include the original item).
2. Specify the angle to fill and a positive value specifies counterclockwise rotation and a negative value for clockwise rotation.
3. Specify the angle between items.

If you specify two of the above mentioned parameters, then the array is completely specified. But, if you specify only one of the first two parameters, AutoCAD will prompt you for the third parameter.

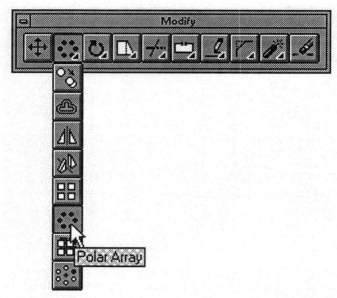

Figure 3-56 Invoke the Polar ARRAY Command from the Modify toolbar

The last prompt in the case of a polar array is:

Rotate objects as they are copied? <Y>:

A **Y** response will rotate the objects as they are copied.

The following command sequence shows an example of placing a rotated polar array.

Command: **array**
Select objects: *(select objects)*
Rectangular or Polar array (R/P): **p**
Center point of array: *(specify the center point)*

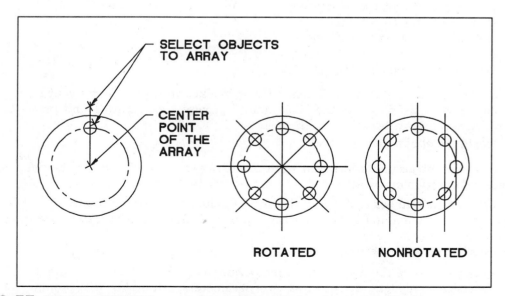

Figure 3-57 Using the ARRAY Command to place rotated and nonrotated polar arrays

Number of items: **8**
Angle to fill (+=CCW, –=CW) <360>: **270**
Rotate objects as they copied? <Y>: Enter

In Figure 3–57 both nonrotated and rotated polar arrays are shown.

OFFSET Command

The OFFSET command generates objects that are similar and parallel to existing objects. There are several rules that must be followed when using the OFFSET command. There are also some "rules of thumb" to prevent unpredictable results from occurring when using the OFFSET command on arbitrary curve/line combinations in polylines.

The OFFSET command is invoked from the Copy flyout located in the Modify toolbar (Figure 3–58), or at the "Command:" prompt type **OFFSET** and press Enter or spacebar.

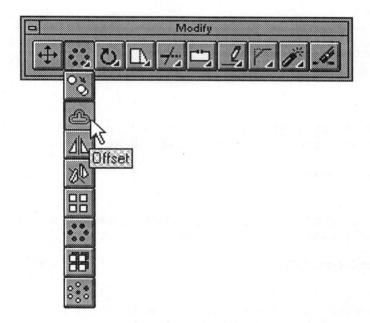

Figure 3-58 Invoke the OFFSET Command from the Modify toolbar

Command: **offset**
Offset distance or Through<last>: *(specify distance)*
Select object to offset: *(select object)*
Side to offset?: *(pick a point to one side of the object)*
Select object to offset: Enter

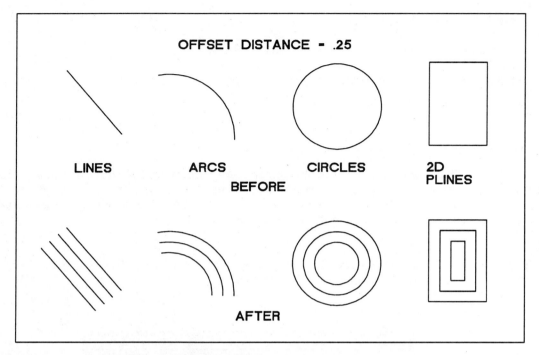

Figure 3-59 Examples using the OFFSET Command

Valid Objects to Offset Valid objects include the line, arc, circle, and 2D polyline. If you select another type of object, such as text, you will get the following error message:

   Cannot offset that object.

The object selected for offsetting must be in a plane parallel to the current coordinate system. Otherwise you will get the following error message:

   Object not parallel with UCS.

Repeating Command Once you specify the side, the object selected is offset. You are then prompted to select another object for offsetting. In order to return to the "Command:" prompt, you must press ⌨Enter or ⌨Esc.

Figure 3–59 shows examples of using the OFFSET command.

Offsetting Miters and Tangencies The OFFSET command affects single objects in a manner different from a polyline made up of the same objects. Polylines whose arcs join lines and other arcs in a tangent manner are affected differently than polylines with nontangent connecting points. For example, in Figure 3-60 the seven lines are separate objects. When OFFSET to the side shown, there are gaps and overlaps at the ends of the newly created lines.

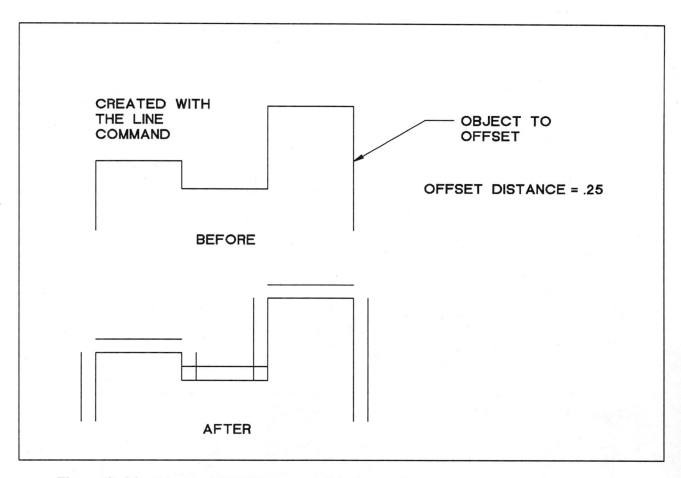

Figure 3-60 Using the OFFSET Command with single objects as opposd to polylines

Fundamentals II

In Figure 3-61, the lines have been joined together (see the section on PEDIT) as a single polyline. See how the OFFSET command affects the corners where the new polyline segments join.

> *NOTE:* The results of offsetting polylines with arc segments that connect other arc segments and/or line segments in dissimilar (nontangent) directions might be unpredictable. Examples of offsetting such polylines are shown in Figure 3–62.

If you are not satisfied with the resulting new polyline configuration, you can use the PEDIT command to edit it. Or, you can explode the polyline and edit the individual segments.

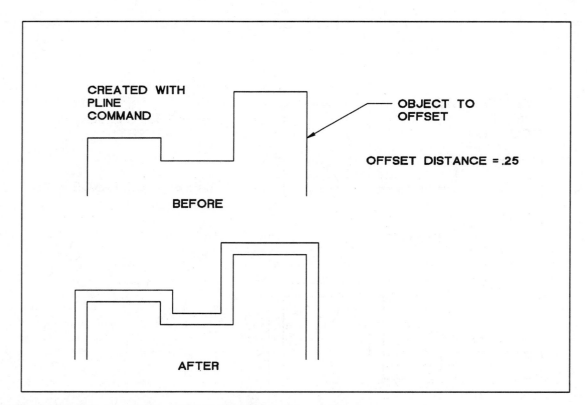

Figure 3-61 Using the OFFSET Command with polylines

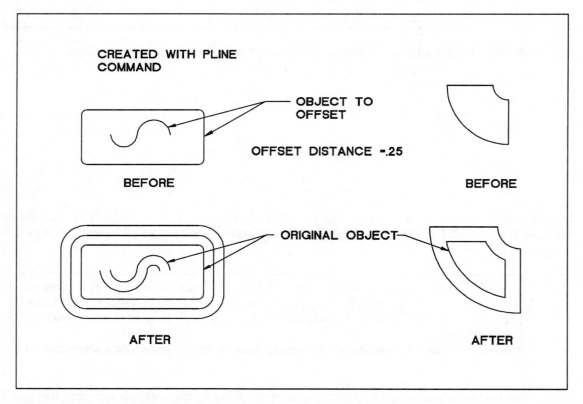

Figure 3-62 Using the OFFSET Command with nontangent arc and/or line segments

MIRROR Command

The MIRROR command creates copies of selected objects in reverse, or mirrored about a specified line. One option includes mirroring the selected objects and then deciding whether to have the original deleted from the drawing. Another option is to have the text move to mirrored locations, but not mirrored itself. In this case, text retains its original orientation for readability.

The MIRROR command is invoked from the Copy flyout located in the Modify toolbar (Figure 3–63), or at the "Command:" prompt, type **MIRROR** and press [Enter] or spacebar.

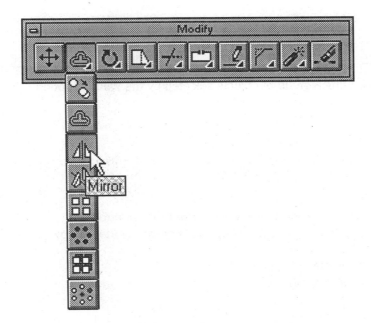

Figure 3-63 Invoke the MIRROR Command from the Modify toolbar

```
Command: mirror
Select objects: (select the objects)
First point of mirror line: (select point)
Second point: (select point)
Delete old objects? <N>: (select y or n)
```

You can use one or more object selection methods available from the Select Objects toolbar to select objects. The first and second points (which must not be the same) define an invisible line (called the "mirror line") about which the selected objects will be mirrored. You can place the mirror line at any angle.

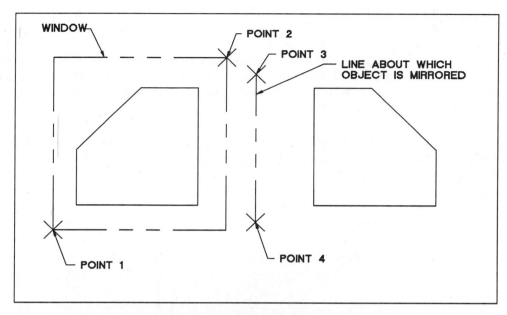

Figure 3-64 Mirroring a group of objects selected by the Window option

The following command sequence shows an example of mirroring a group of objects selected by the Window option, as shown in Figure 3–64:

Command: **mirror**
Select objects: *(pick a point to place one corner for a window)*
Second corner: *(pick a point to place opposite corner of the window)*
Select objects: Enter
First point of mirror line: *(pick point 3)*
Second point: *(pick point 4)*
Delete old objects?<N>: Enter

The location of mirrored text is mirrored relative to other objects within the selected group. But the text retains its original orientation depending upon the setting of the system variable called MIRRTEXT. If the value of the MIRRTEXT is 1, then text items in the selected group have their orientations and location mirrored. That is, if their characters were normal and they read left-to-right in the original group, in the mirrored copy they will read right-to-left and the characters will be backwards. If the value of the MIRRTEXT is set to 0 (zero), then the text strings in the group will have their locations mirrored but the individual text strings would retain their left-to-right, normal character appearance. The MIRRTEXT system variable, like other system variables, is changed by the SETVAR command or by typing **MIRRTEXT** at the "Command:" prompt as follows:

Command: **setvar**
Variable name or ?: **mirrtext**
New Value for MIRRTEXT <1>: **0**

The above setting causes mirrored text to retain its readability. Figures 3–65a and 3–65b show the result of the MIRROR command when the MIRRTEXT variable is set to 1 and 0, respectively.

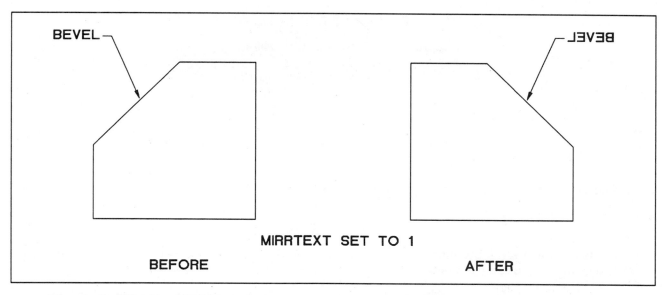

Figure 3-65a The MIRROR Command with the MIRRTEXT variable set to 1

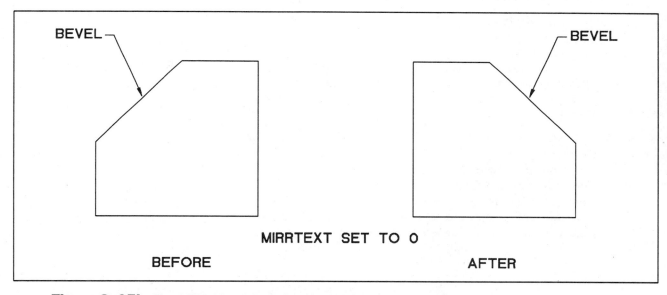

Figure 3-65b The MIRROR Command with the MIRRTEXT variable set to 0

FILLET Command

The FILLET command joins two lines, arcs, or circles with an arc of a specified radius. The setting of the TRIMMODE system variable controls the trimming of the intersecting lines to the endpoints of the fillet arc. If the value of the TRIMMODE is set to 1, then fillet trims the intersecting lines to the endpoints of the fillet arc. And if it is set to 0 (zero), then fillet leaves the intersecting lines to the endpoints of the fillet arc. The FILLET command is invoked from the Feature flyout located in the Modify toolbar (Figure 3–66), or at the "Command:" prompt type **FILLET** and press ⏎Enter or the spacebar.

> Command: **fillet**
> Polyline/Radius/Trim/<Select first object>: *(select the first object to fillet)*
> Select second object:

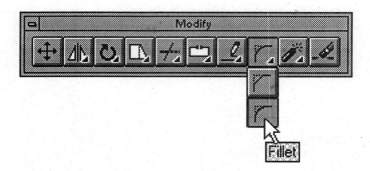

Figure 3-66 The FILLET Command is invoked from the Modify toolbar

By default, AutoCAD prompts to select two objects to draw a rounded corner to the default radius. If necessary, you can change the radius by selecting the Radius option as shown below:

    Command: **fillet**
    Polyline/Radius/Trim/<Select first object>: **r** *(or select radius from the menu)*
    Enter fillet radius <current>: *(enter value)*

The following sequence draws a fillet with a radius of .25, as shown in Figure 3-67.

    Command: **fillet**
    Polyline/Radius/Trim/<Select first object>: **r**
    Enter fillet radius <current>: **0.25**
    Command: Enter *(to repeat FILLET Command)*
    Polyline/Radius/Trim/<Select first object>: *(select first object)*
    Select second object: *(select second object)*

The following sequence draws a fillet with a 0 radius, as shown in Figure 3-68.

    Command: **fillet**
    Polyline/Radius/<Select first object>: **r**
    Enter fillet radius <current>: **0**
    Command: Enter *(to repeat FILLET command)*
    Polyline/Radius/Trim/<Select first object>: *(select first object)*
    Select second object: *(select second object)*

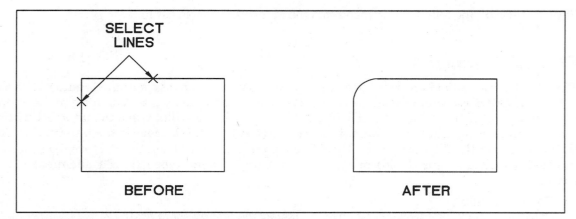

Figure 3-67 A fillet drawn with a radius of 0.25

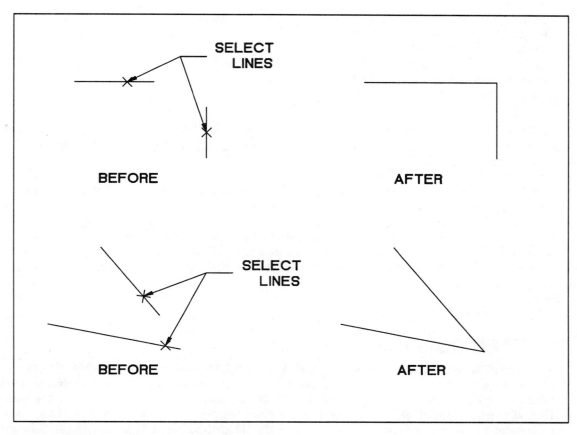

Figure 3-68 A fillet drawn with a radius of 0.0

Polyline Option By selecting the Polyline option, fillets are drawn at all vertices of a polyline at the corners in one step.

The following sequence draws a fillet with a radius of 0.50 on a polyline, as shown in Figure 3-69.

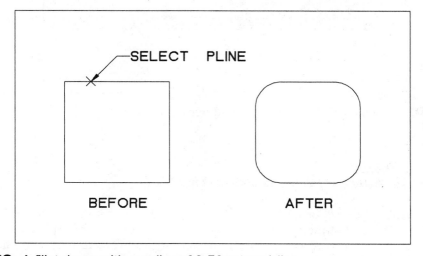

Figure 3-69 A fillet drawn with a radius of 0.50 to a polyline

Command: **fillet**
Polyline/Radius/Trim/<Select first object>: **r**
Enter fillet radius <current>: **0.50**
Command: [Enter] *(to repeat FILLET Command)*
Polyline/Radius/Trim/<Select first object>: **p**
Select 2D polyline: *(select polyline)*

Trim Option   The Trim option (Trim/No Trim) controls whether AutoCAD trims the selected edges to the fillet arc endpoints. This option is similar to setting the TRIMMODE system variable from 1 to 0 or vice versa.

If both objects to be filleted are on the same layer, AutoCAD creates the fillet arc on that layer. If not, AutoCAD creates the fillet line on the current layer.

AutoCAD allows you to draw a fillet to parallel lines, xlines, and rays. The first selected object must be a line or ray, but the second object can be a line, xline, or ray. The diameter of the fillet arc is always equal to the distance between the lines. The current fillet radius is ignored and remains unchanged.

CHAMFER Command

The CHAMFER command operates similar to the FILLET command. CHAMFER allows you to draw an angled corner on a pair of intersecting lines. The size of the chamfer is determined by its distance from the corner. If it is to be a 45-degree chamfer, the two distances are the same. The setting of the TRIMMODE system variable controls the trimming of the intersecting lines to the endpoints of the chamfer line. If the value of the TRIMMODE is 1, then CHAMFER trims the intersecting lines to the end points of the chamfer line. And if it is set to 0 (zero), then CHAMFER leaves the intersecting lines to the endpoints of the chamfer line. The CHAMFER command is invoked from the Feature flyout located in the Modify toolbar (Figure 3-70), or at the "Command:" prompt type **CHAMFER** and press [Enter] or the spacebar.

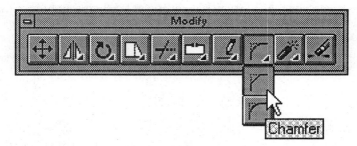

Figure 3-70   Invoke the CHAMFER Command from the Modify toolbar

Command: **chamfer**
Polyline/Distance/Angle/Trim/Method/<Select first lines>:

By default, AutoCAD prompts you to identify the two objects to be chamfered. The angled corner is drawn to the default distances from the corner. To override the default distances, select the Distance option or enter **d** at the prompt, and specify the first and second chamfer distances as follows:

Command: **chamfer**
Polyline/Distance/Angle/Trim/Method/<Select first lines>: **d**
Enter first chamfer distance <current>: *(specify a chamfer distance)*
Enter second chamfer distance <current>: *(press* Enter *to accept the default or type in a new distance)*

After you specify the new chamfer distances, they remain in effect for subsequent chamfers until changed.

The following sequence draws a chamfer with chamfer distances of 0.5 and 1.0 as shown in Figure 3–71.

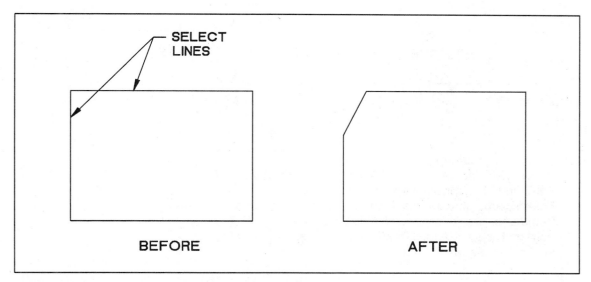

Figure 3-71   A chamfer drawn with distances of 0.5 and 1.0

Command: **chamfer**
Polyline/Distance/Angle/Trim/Method/<Select first line>: **d**
Enter first chamfer distance <current>: **0.5**
Enter second chamfer distance <current>: **1**
Command: Enter *(to repeat CHAMFER Command)*
Polyline/Distance/<Select first line>: *(pick the first line)*
Select second line: *(pick the second line)*

Angle Option   The Angle option is similar to the Distance option, instead of prompting for first and second chamfer distances, AutoCAD prompts for first chamfer distance and an angle from the first line. This is another method by which to create the chamfer line.

Method Option   The Method option controls whether AutoCAD uses two distances or a distance and an angle to create the chamfer line.

Polyline Option   By selecting the Polyline option, chamfers are drawn at all vertices of a polyline.

The following sequence draws chamfers around a polyline with both distances 0.5 from the corners, as shown in Figure 3–72.

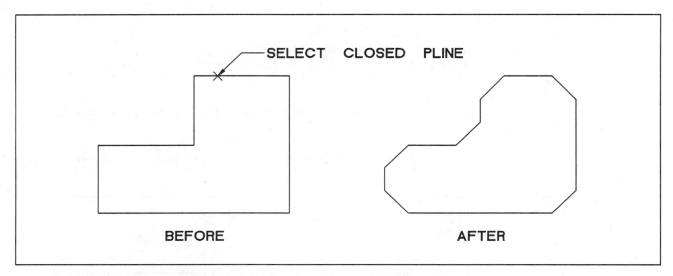

Figure 3-72 A chamfer drawn with distances of 0.5 along a polyline

```
Command: chamfer
Polyline/Distance/Angle/Trim/Method/<Select first line>: d
Enter first chamfer distance <current>: 0.5
Enter second chamfer distance <.5>: [Enter] (to accept default value)
Command: [Enter] (to repeat CHAMFER Command)
Polyline/Distance/Angle/Trim/Method/<Select first line>: p
Select polyline: (pick the polyline)
```

Trim Option The Trim option (Trim/No Trim) controls whether AutoCAD trims the selected edges to the chamfer line endpoints. This option is similar to setting the TRIMMODE system variable from 1 to 0 or vice versa.

If both objects to be chamfered are on the same layer, AutoCAD creates the chamfer line on that layer. If not, AutoCAD creates the chamfer line on the current layer.

> **NOTE:** Chamfer set to a zero distance operates the same way the FILLET command operates set to zero radius.

MODIFY COMMANDS

In this section, four additional Modify commands are explained: the Move, Trim, Break, and Extend commands, in addition to the Erase command explained in Chapter 2.

MOVE Command

The MOVE command lets you move one or more objects from their present location to a new one without changing orientation or size. After you define the selection-set of objects to be moved, AutoCAD prompts for "Base point or displacement:". Here, you should provide the move-from point or displacement vector to indicate how far the objects are to be moved, and in which direction. Then AutoCAD prompts for "Second point of displacement:". Here, you provide the move-to point or give a null response if the first point provided is a displacement vector.

The MOVE command is invoked from the Modify toolbar (see Figure 3–73), or at the "Command:" prompt, type **MOVE** and press the spacebar or [Enter].

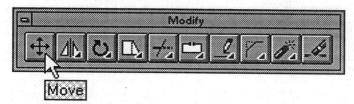

Figure 3-73 Invoke the MOVE Command from the Modify toolbar

> Command: **move**
> Select objects: *(show what to move and then give a null response)*
> Base point or displacement: *(first point or x,y,z point)*
> Second point of displacement: *(second point or null response)*

For example, to specify a displacement using the keyboard, enter **0,0,0** in response to the first point. When AutoCAD prompts for a second point, enter **X,Y,** and **Z** displacement amount as if they were absolute X,Y,Z coordinates. Alternatively, you can enter the displacement amount in response to the first prompt and give a null response to the second prompt. Or, you can use your pointing device to specify a displacement by picking a "from point" and a "to point." AutoCAD assists you in visualizing the displacement by drawing a rubberband line from the first point as you move the cross-hairs to the second point.

The following command sequence shows an example of moving a group of objects selected by the Window option by vector displacement, as shown in Figure 3–74.

> Command: **move**
> Select objects: *(pick a point to place one corner for a window)*
> Other corner: *(pick a point to place the opposite corner of the window)*
> Select objects: [Enter]
> Base point or displacement: **2,3**
> Second point of displacement: [Enter]

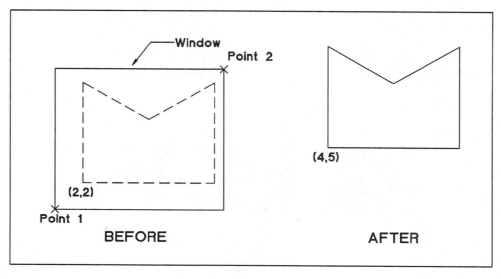

Figure 3-74 Using the MOVE Window Command to move a group of objects by vector displacement

The following command sequence shows an example of moving a group of objects selected by the Window option by specifying or picking two data points, as shown in Figure 3–75.

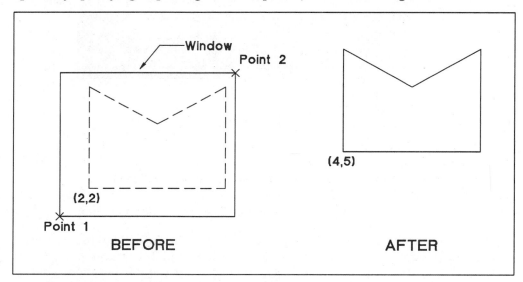

Figure 3-75 Using the MOVE Window Command to move a group of objects by specifying two data points

Command: **move**
Select objects: *(pick a point to place one corner for a window)*
Other corner: *(pick a point to place the opposite corner of the window)*
Select objects: Enter
Base point or displacement: *(pick base point)*
Second point of displacement: *(pick second point)*

TRIM Command

The TRIM command changes the endpoint(s) of lines, circles, and arcs. TRIM, however, is used for segments that extend past a selected cutting edge or an implied intersection and removes the portion of the object(s) that is drawn past the cutting edge or from an implied intersection.

The TRIM command is invoked from the Trim flyout located in the Modify toolbar (Figure 3–76), or at the "Command:" prompt type **TRIM** and press Enter or spacebar.

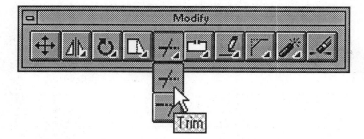

Figure 3-76 Invoke the TRIM Command from the Modify toolbar

```
Command: trim
Select cutting edge(s):
Select objects: (select the cutting edge)
Select objects: (press Enter if selection is completed)
<Select object to trim>/Project/Edge/Undo: (select the object to trim)
<Select object to trim>/Project/Edge/Undo: (press Enter if selection is completed)
```

The TRIM command initially prompts you to "Select cutting edge(s):" After selecting one or more cutting edges to trim, then press Enter. After pressing Enter you are prompted to "Select object to trim." Select one or more objects to trim and then press Enter to terminate the command.

> **NOTE:** Don't forget to press Enter after selecting the cutting edge(s). Otherwise, the program will not respond as expected. In fact, trim continues expecting more cutting edges until you terminate the edge selecting mode.

Edge Option The Edge option determines whether objects that extend past a selected cutting edge or to an implied intersection are trimmed. AutoCAD prompts as follows when Edge option is selected:

Extend/No extend <current>: (enter an option or press Enter)

The Extend selection extends the cutting edge along its natural path to intersect an object in 3D (implied intersection).

The No Extend selection specifies that the object is to be trimmed only at a cutting edge that intersects it in 3D space.

Undo Option The Undo option reverses the most recent change made by Trim.

Figure 3-77 shows examples of using the TRIM command.

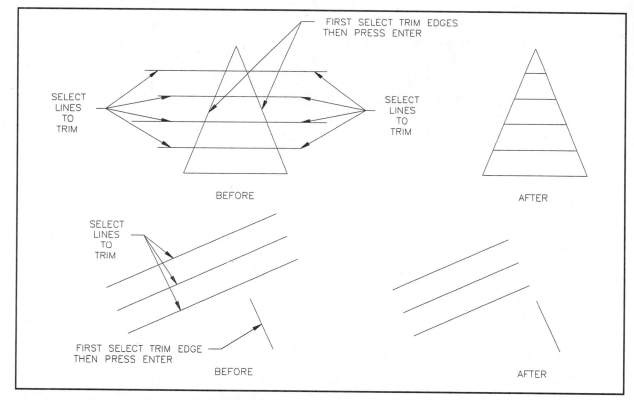

Figure 3-77 Examples using the TRIM Command

BREAK Command

The BREAK command is used to remove parts of objects from the drawing. The BREAK command can be used on lines, arcs, circles, traces, and 2D polylines.

The BREAK command removes the part of an object between two selected points or from a selected point to an end beyond which a second point is selected.

The BREAK command can be used on only one object at a time. There are four different procedures for using the 2 point feature of the BREAK command and two different procedures for using the single point feature of the BREAK command. One 2 point procedure is to select an object by pointing to it and have AutoCAD use that point (by which the object was selected) as the first point for breaking. The other procedure is to select an object by the window, crossing, last, or pointing option and then select the first break point. Or, if you wish to use the pointing method of selecting the object but have for the first break point one other than that used to select the object, then you may respond to the second prompt with **f**. Then AutoCAD will prompt you for first and second point, respectively.

One single point procedure is to select an object and have AutoCAD break (separate) the object at that point without removing any portion of the object. The second single point procedure is to select the object and then select a point on the object for separating the object into two parts at that point.

Object selection can be done by any normal method. If the method used includes more than one object in the selection set, AutoCAD uses the last object. If the object to be used is not eligible for use with the BREAK command, you are prompted to select another object.

The BREAK command is invoked from the Break flyout located in the Modify toolbar (Figure 3–78), or at the "Command:" prompt, type **BREAK** and press [Enter] or the spacebar.

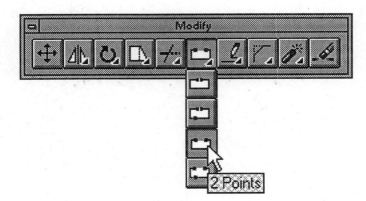

Figure 3–78 Invoke the BREAK Command from the Modify toolbar

The sequence of prompts is as follows:

Command: **break**
Select object: *(select first point of deletion)*
Enter second point: *(select second point of deletion or past end to be removed)*

If the selection is by pointing and you wish to have a different point as the first break point. Then select the 2 Points Select option from the Break flyout located in the Modify toolbar (Figure 3–79).

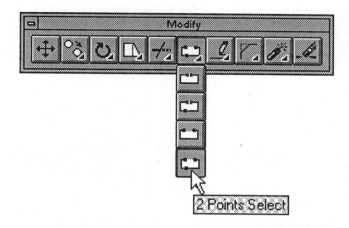

Figure 3-79 Invoke the BREAK Command's 2 Points Select Option from the Modify toolbar

Command: **break**
Select object: *(point to object)*
Enter second point (or F for first point): **f**
Enter first point: *(select first point)*
Enter second point: *(select second point)*

If the second point is not on the object, AutoCAD will use a point nearest the one selected.
An object can be broken into two without removing any of the object by selecting the same point for first and second points, then select 1 Point option from the Break flyout located in the Modify toolbar (Figure 3–80).

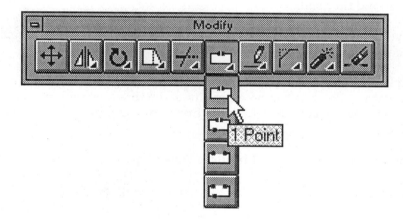

Figure 3-80 Invoke the BREAK Command's 1 Point Select Option from the Modify toolbar

The sequence is as follows:

Command: **break**
Select object: *(select first point)*
Select second point (or F for first point): **@**

As mentioned earlier, the @ symbol means last point.

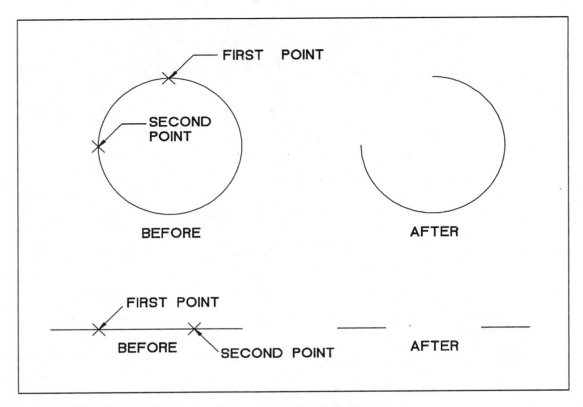

Figure 3-81 Examples of application of the BREAK command

A line, trace, or arc will have the part between the two selected points removed or will be divided into two parts where the two points coincide or has one end removed in the direction where the second point is beyond that end.

A circle will have that part removed between the two selected points that is counterclockwise from the first to the second point.

A closed 2D polyline will have that part removed between two selected points in the direction of the first to the last vertex. If one of the break points is the first vertex, one open polyline will result. Otherwise, there will be two polylines, from the first vertex and from the closing vertex to the break points, respectively.

2D polylines and traces with width will result in square ends at the break points.

The BREAK command cannot be applied to viewport object borders.

See Figure 3-81 for examples of the BREAK command.

EXTEND Command

The EXTEND command is used to change one or both endpoints of selected lines to extend to a selected line or arc. Arcs, if possible, can also be extended to reach a specified line or other arc.

The EXTEND command is invoked from the Trim flyout located in the Modify toolbar (Figure 3-82), or at the "Command:" prompt, type **EXTEND** and press Enter or spacebar.

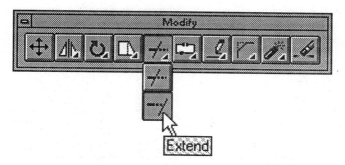

Figure 3-82   Invoke the EXTEND Command from the Modify toolbar

Command: **extend**
Select boundary edge(s):
Select objects: *(select an object to extend to)*
Select objects: *(press* Enter *if selection is completed)*
<Select object to extend>/Project/Edge/Undo: *(select an object to extend)*
<Select object to extend>/Project/Edge/Undo: *(press* Enter *if selection is completed)*

The EXTEND command first prompts to "Select boundary edge(s):" These are edges to which a line or arc will be extended to meet. After selecting the boundary edges, press Enter and then AutoCAD prompts to select the objects to extend. You can select one or more objects to extend and then press Enter to terminate the command.

The EXTEND and TRIM commands are very similar in this method of selecting. With EXTEND you are prompted to select the boundry edge to extend to and with TRIM you are prompted to select a cutting edge.

Edge Option   The Edge option determines whether objects are extended past selected boundary or to an implied edge. AutoCAD prompts as follows when Edge option is selected.

Extend/No extend <current>: *(enter an option or press* Enter*)*

The Extend selection extends the boundary object along its natural path to intersect another object in 3D space (implied edge).

The No Extend selection specifies that the object is to extend only to a boundary object that actually intersects it in 3D space.

Undo Option   The Undo option reverses the most recent change made by Extend.

Figure 3-83 shows examples of the use of the EXTEND command.

OBJECT SNAP — CIRCULAR APPLICATIONS

In this chapter, four additional OSNAP modes are explained, the CENter, QUAdrant, and TANgent modes (which are exclusive to circles and arcs) and the PERpendicualr mode as it pertains to circular applications.

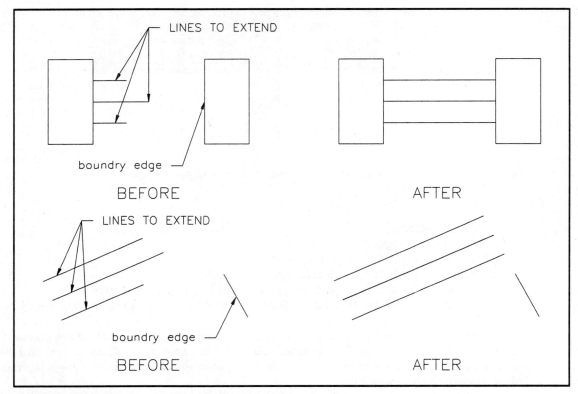

Figure 3-83 Examples of applications of the EXTEND Command

CENter Mode

The CENter osnap mode uses the coordinates of the center of the selected circle or arc when prompted for a point. It is important to note that, part of the circle or arc must be in the aperture pick box in order to work, as shown in Figure 3-84.

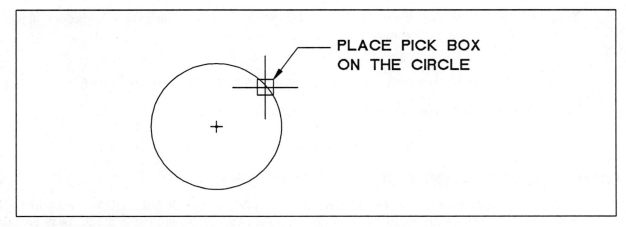

Figure 3-84 Picking a circle (or arc) with the CENter object snap mode

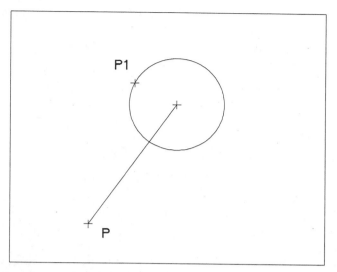

Figure 3-85 Selecting a point with the CENter object snap mode

In Figure 3-85 a line is drawn to the center of the circle as follows:

    Command: **line**
    From point: *(select point p)*
    To point: **cent**
        of *(select point P1 on circle)*

QUAdrant Mode

The QUAdrant osnap mode selects a point located at one of the quadrant points of a circle or arc. The quadrant points are located 0 degrees, 90 degrees, 180 degrees, and 270 degrees from the center of the circle or arc, as shown in Figure 3-86. The quadrant points are determined by the 0 degree direction of the current coordinate system.

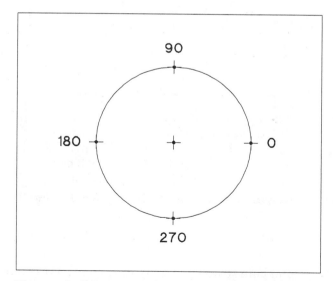

Figure 3-86 The quadrant points recognized by the QUAdrant object snap mode

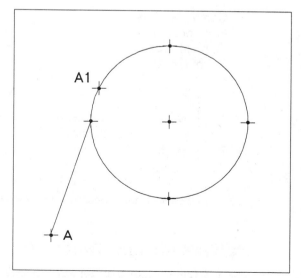

Figure 3-87 Drawing a line to a circle's quadrant point (Method 1)

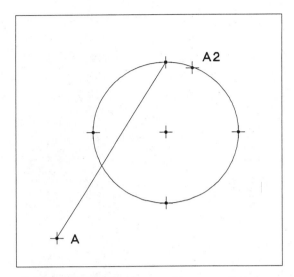

Figure 3-88 Drawing a line to a circle's quadrant (Method 2)

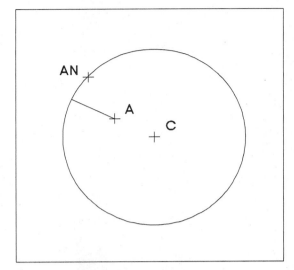

Figure 3-89 Specifying a line's endpoint perpendicular to a circle (from inside the near side of a circle) with the PERpendicular object snap mode

In Figure 3-87 a line is drawn to a quadrant as follows:

Command: **line**
From point: *(select point A)*
To point: **qua**
    of *(select point A1)*

A line can also be drawn to a quadrant as follows (see Figure 3-88):

Command: **line**
From point: *(select point A)*
To point: **qua**
    of *(select point A2)*

> *NOTE:* Special precautions should be taken when attempting to select circles or arcs in blocks or ellipses that are rotated at an angle that is not a multiple of 90 degrees. When a circle or an arc in a block is rotated, the point that QUAdrant osnap mode is also rotated. But when a circle/arc not in a block is rotated, the QUAdrant osnap points stay at the 0, 90, 180, 270 degree points.

PERpendicular Mode

The PERpendicular osnap mode specifies a second point (relative to the first point), perpendicular to another line, circle or an arc, as shown in Figure 3-89. The following sequences show examples of how you can draw lines using the PERpendicular osnap mode.

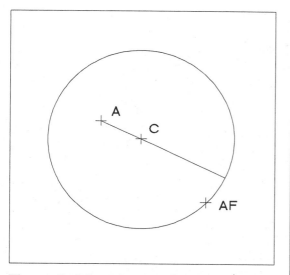

Figure 3-90 Specifying a line's endpoint perpendicular to a circle (from inside the far side of a circle) with the PERpendicular object snap mode

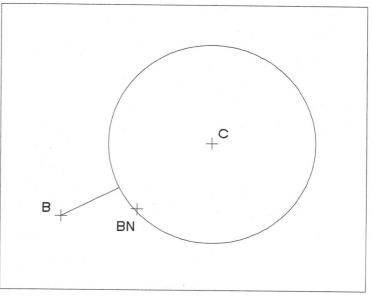

Figure 3-91 Specifying a line's endpoint perpendicular to a circle (from outside the near side of a circle) with the PERpendicular object snap mode

From inside the circle:

    Command: **line**
    From point: *(select point A)*
    To point: **per**
        to *(select near side point AN, as shown in Figure 3–89)*

    Command: **line**
    From point: *(select point A)*
    To point: **per**
        to *(select far side point AF, as shown in Figure 3–90)*

From outside the circle:

    Command: **line**
    From point: *(select point B)*
    To point: **per**
        to *(select near side point BN, as shown in Figure 3–91)*

    Command: **line**
    From point: *(select point B)*
    To point: **per**
        to *(select far side point BF, as shown in Figure 3–92)*

When drawing a line perpendicular to another line, the point that AutoCAD establishes can be off the line selected (in response to the "perpendicular to" prompt) and the new line will still be drawn to that point. In Figure 3-93 lines from both A and B can be drawn perpendicular to line L.

Applying the PERpendicular osnap mode to an arc works in a manner similar to a circle. Unlike drawing a perpendicular to a line, the point established must be on the arc.

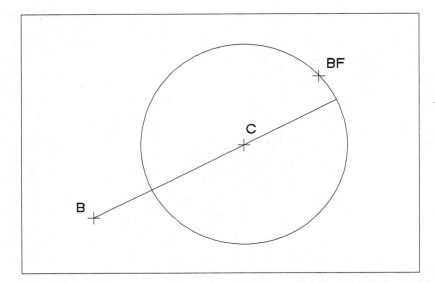

Figure 3-92 Specifying a line's endpoint perpendicular to a circle (from outside the far side of a circle) with the PERpendicular object snap mode

In Figure 3-94 a line can be drawn perpendicular to arc from A, but not from B.

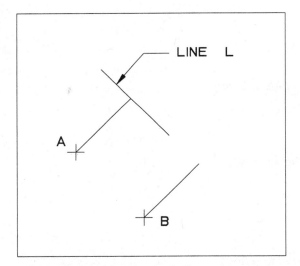

Figure 3-93 Using the PERpendicular osnap mode to draw a line perpendicular to another line

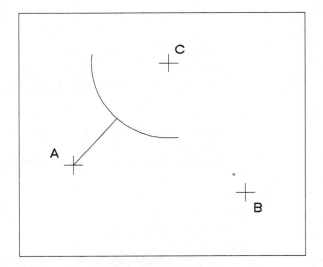

Figure 3-94 Using the PERpendicular osnap mode to draw a line perpendicular to an arc

TANgent Mode

The TANgent osnap mode was illustrated in the TTR option of the CIRCLE command. In this section, examples are provided to draw lines tangent to circles and arcs.

From a point A, outside of a circle, you can draw lines to two points of tangency on the circle, as shown in Figure 3-95.

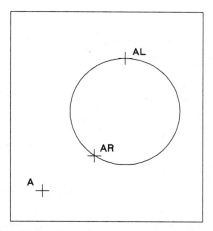

Figure 3-95 Using the TANgent osnap
mode to draw lines to two points of tangency
on a circle from outside a circle

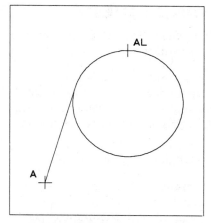

Figure 3-96 Using the TANgent osnap
mode to draw a line from a point outside a
circle tangent to a left point on a circle

The following command sequence draws a line from point A tangent to a point on the circle, as
shown in Figure 3-96.

    Command: **line**
    From point: *(select point A)*
    To point: **tan**
        to *(select point AL toward left semicircle)*

A line can also be drawn from point A tangent to a point on the circle, as shown in Figure 3-97.

    Command: **line**
    From point: *(select point A)*
    To point: **tan**
        to *(select point AR toward right semicircle)*

With the TANgent osnap mode you can select an arc also. Like the PERpendicular osnap mode, the
tangent point must be on the arc selected (see Figure 3-98).

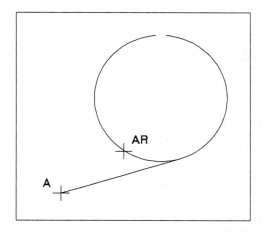

Figure 3-97 Using the TANgent osnap
mode to draw a line from a point outside a
circle tangent to a right point on a circle

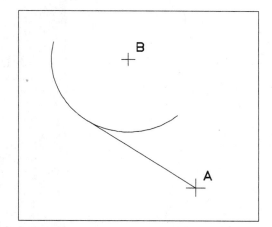

Figure 3-98 Using the TANgent osnap
mode to draw lines of tangency to a
point on an arc

Fundamentals II

INVOKING OBJECT SNAP MODES

The Object Snap (OSNAP) modes are invoked in two ways. One method is to respond to a prompt for a point with the name of the particular Object Snap mode desired. This is a one-time-only usage.

The second method is to use the OSNAP command and respond with the name of one or more object snap modes. This causes AutoCAD to always use the mode(s) specified (running OSNAP) when you are requested to specify a point. This will be very helpful in dimensioning. You can specify more than one mode by separating the names with a comma as follows:

Command: **osnap**
Object snap modes: **mid,endp,cen**

Normally, you would specify only one Object Snap mode for a running OSNAP. If you wish to override the running OSNAP mode with another mode or none at all, simply respond to the prompt for a point with the name of the other mode or with "NON" for no OSNAP mode. You can also select the running object snap modes in the Running Object Snap dialog box (see Figure 3–99) invoked from the Options pull-down menu. To clear the object snap modes, click the Clear All button.

One important difference between a one-time Object Snap and running OSNAP is that if during a one-time Object Snap, you select a point on the screen where no valid point exists, AutoCAD will display an error message to select again. However, if the running OSNAP mode is on, you may select other points and have AutoCAD use them. For example, if CENTER mode is on and you select a point on, off, or near an object that does not have a center, AutoCAD will still use the point selected.

> **NOTE:** If you have a running OSNAP mode in force, say endpoint, and you respond to a prompt for a point with the coordinates of a point that, if selected with the cursor, would include an object in the aperture box that has an endpoint, then AutoCAD will Snap to that endpoint. In this case it is wise to override the running OSNAP mode with "NON" before typing in the point coordinates.

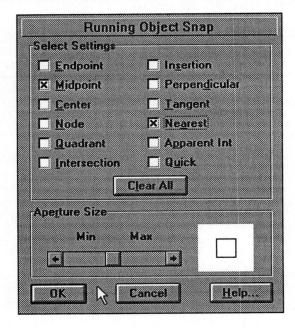

Figure 3-99 Running Object Snap dialog box

PROJECT EXERCISE

In this project, you apply AutoCAD concepts and skills discussed in chapters 1 through 3 to create the machine part in a step-by-step fashion, as shown in Figure P3–1.

NOTE: Do not dimension, dimensions are for reference only.

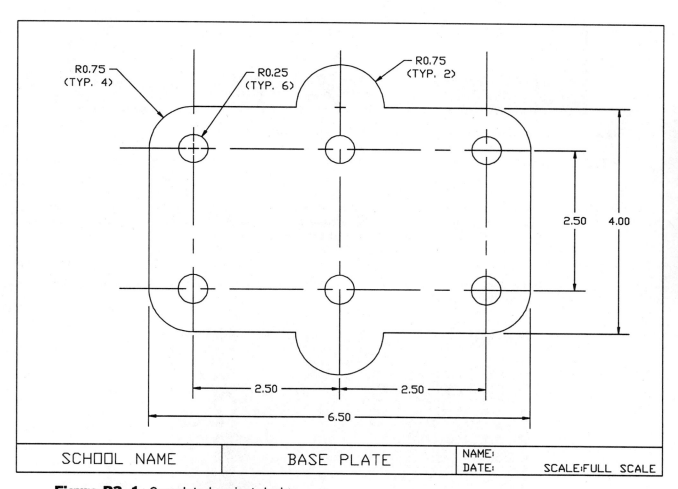

Figure P3–1 Completed project design

NOTE: The step-by-step instructions for this project are designed to provide pratice in the concepts presented in chapters 1 through 3. It is not necessarily the most efficient way to draw the design.

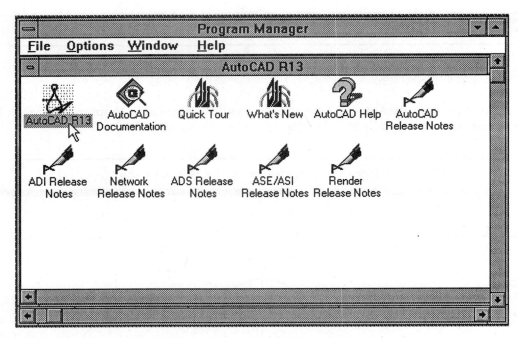

Figure P3–2 Invoke the AutoCAD program from the Windows Program Manager

STEP 1 Invoke the AutoCAD program from the Windows Program Manager, as shown in Figure P3–2.

STEP 2 Invoke the NEW command from the pull-down menu File or type New at the command prompt. Enter CH3-PROJ as the name of the drawing file. Make sure ACAD.DWG is selected as the prototype drawing.

STEP 3 Invoke the UNITS Command from the pull-down menu Data to open the DDUNITS dialog box. Set up units to decimal with four decimal places and degrees to decimal as shown in Figure P3–3.

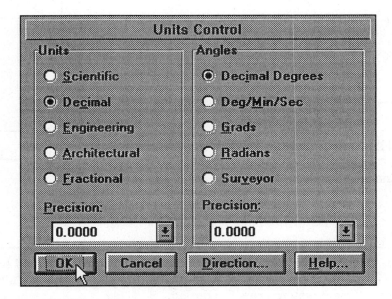

Figure P3–3 DDUNITS Dialog Box

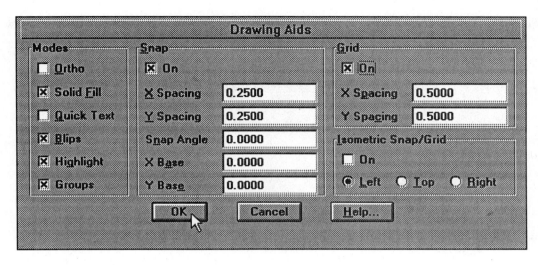

Figure P3-4 Drawing Aids Dialog Box

STEP 4   Open the Drawing Aids dialog box from the pull-down menu Options and set grid to 0.50 units and snap to 0.25 units and turn ON the grid and snap tools as shown in Figure P3-4.

STEP 5   Invoke the LAYER command from the pull-down menu Data, create layers named border, object, center, and text with appropriate colors and linetype as shown in the dialog box Figure P3-5. Set Layer "Border" as the current layer.

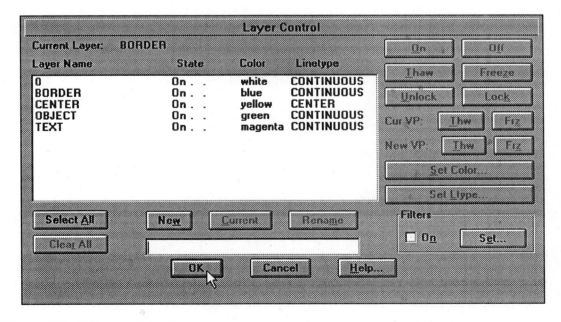

Figure P3-5 Layer dialog box

STEP 6 Invoke the LINE command from the Draw toolbar (see Figure P3–6) to draw a border (11" by 8") as shown in Figure P3-7.

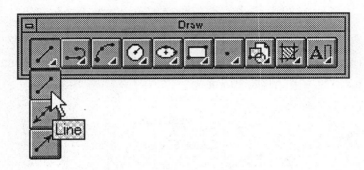

Figure P3-6 Invoke the LINE Command from the Draw toolbar

Command: **line**
From point: **0.5,0.5**
To point: **@11<0**
To point: **@8<90**
To point: **@11<180**
To point: **close**

Figure P3-7 Border for the project drawing

Figure P3-8 Title block for the project drawing

STEP 7   Invoke the LINE command from the Draw toolbar to complete the title block as shown in Figure P3-8.

Command: **line**
From point: **0.5,1**
To point: **@11<0**
To point: Enter

Command: **line**
From point: **4,1**
To point: **4,0.5**
To point: Enter

Command: **line**
From point: **8,1**
To point: **8,0.5**
To point: Enter

STEP 8   Set the current layer to center from the Object Properties toolbar (see Figure P3-9).

STEP 9   Draw the top horizontal line 7.5" to the right starting at x=2.25 and y=6.25.

Command: **line**
From point: **2.25,6.25**
To point: **@7.5<0**
To point: Enter

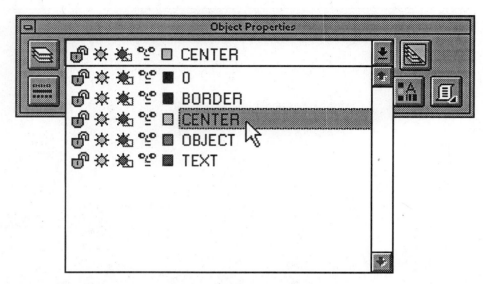

Figure P3-9 Layer list box in the Object Properties toolbar

STEP 10 Draw the left vertical line 6.25" up from x=3.5 and y=1.75.

Command: **line**
From point: **3.5,1.75**
To point: **@6.25<90**
To point: [Enter]

STEP 11 Invoke the Offset command from the Modify toolbar (see Figure P3–10) to construct the parallel lines.

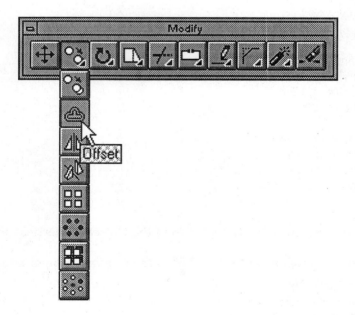

Figure P3-10 Invoke the OFFSET Command from the Modify toolbar

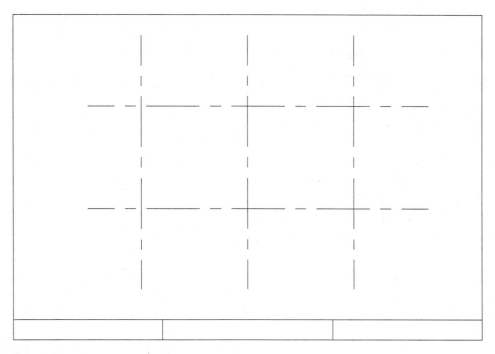

Figure P3-11 Drawing with all the center lines drawn

> Command: **offset**
> Offset distance or Through<Through>: **2.5**
> Select object to offset: *(Select the vertical center line)*
> Side to offset? *(Select any point to the right of the line previously selected)*
> Select object to offset: *(Select the new center line)*
> Side to offset? *(Select a point to the right of the line)*
> Select object to offset: *(Select the horizontal center line)*
> Side to offset: *(Select any point below the line previously selected line)*
> Select object to offset: Enter

Figure P3-11 shows the drawing with all the center lines drawn.

STEP 12 Set object as the current layer from the Object Properties toolbar (see Figure P3-12).

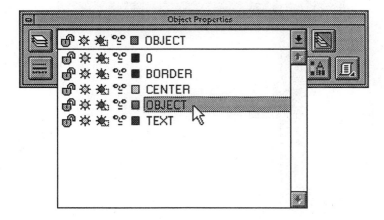

Figure P3-12 Layer list box in the Object Properties toolbar

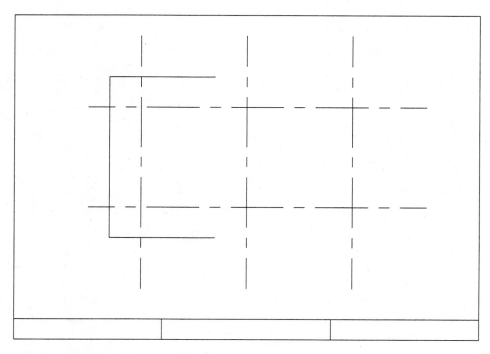

Figure P3-13 Layout of the object lines

STEP 13 Draw the object lines as shown in Figure P3-13.

Command: **line**
From point: **5.25,3**
To point: **@-2.5,0**
To point: **@0,4**
To point: **@2.5,0**
To point: Enter

STEP 14 Invoke the Mirror command from the Modify toolbar (see Figure P3-14) to mirror the object lines about the vertical center line as shown in Figure P3-15.

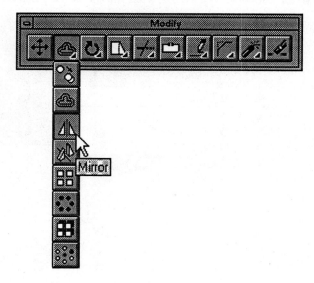

Figure P3-14 Invoke the MIRROR Command from the Modify toolbox

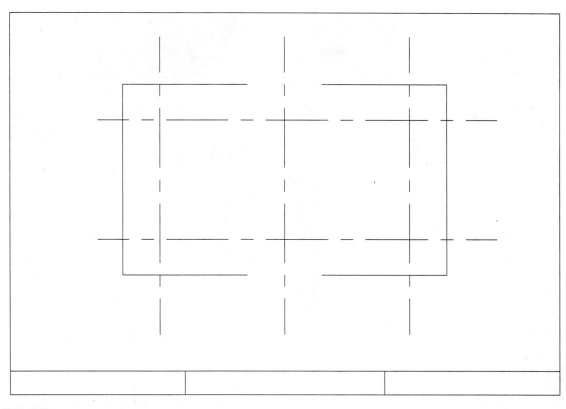

Figure P3-15 Mirrored object lines

Command: **mirror**
Select objects: *(Select the three object lines)*
Select objects: [Enter]
First point of mirror lines: **6,3**
Second point: **6,7**
Delete old objects?<N>: [Enter]

STEP 15   Invoke the ARC command from the Draw toolbar (see Figure P3–16) by selecting the Start,Center,End option to draw the arcs shown in Figure P3-17.

Command: **arc**
Center/<Start point>: **5.25,3**
Center/End/<Second point>: _Center **6,3**
Angle/Length of chord/<End point>: **6.75,3**

Command: **arc**
Center/<Start point>: **6.75,7**
Center/End/<Second point>: _Center **6,7**
Angle/Length of chord/<End point>: **5.25,7**

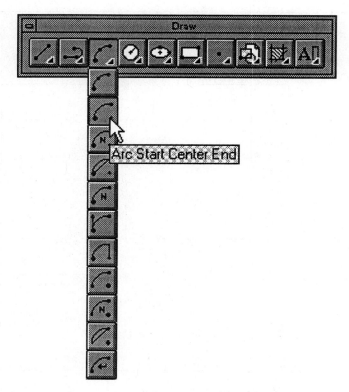

Figure P3-16 Invoke the Arc Start Center End option from the Draw toolbar

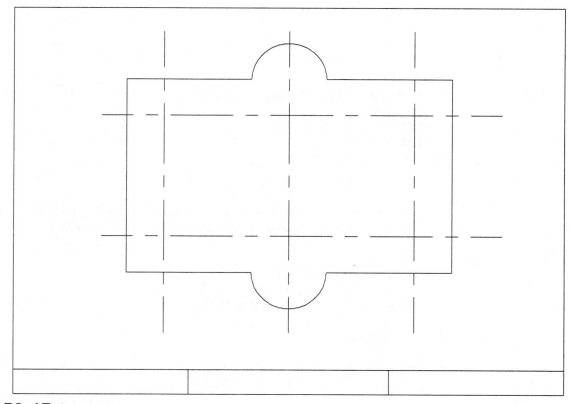

Figure P3-17 Drawing arcs

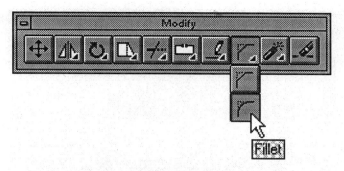

Figure P3-18 Invoke the FILLET Command from the Modify toolbar

STEP 16   Invoke the FILLET command from the Modify toolbar (see Figure P3–18) to round off the four corners of the base plate as shown in Figure P3–19.

Command: **fillet**
Polyline/Radius/<Select first object>: **r**
Enter fillet radius<0.0000>: **0.75**
Command: ⌨Enter⌨ *(to repeat the Fillet Command)*
Fillet Polyline/Radius/<Select first object>: *(Identify the top horizontal line close to the left corner)*
Select second object: *(Identify the left most vertical line)*

Similarly place the fillets to remaining three corners with a fillet radius to 0.75. After the fillets are placed, the drawing should be similar to Figure P3–19.

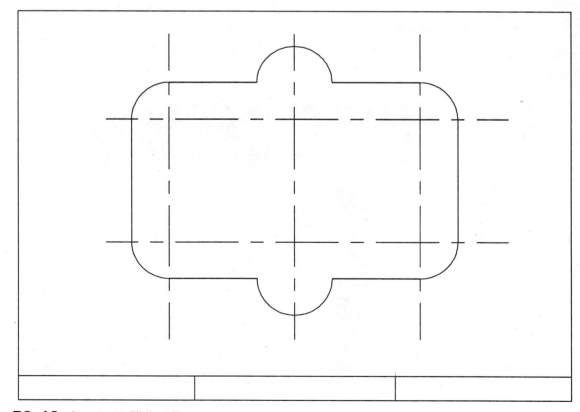

Figure P3-19 Construct fillet radius

STEP 17   Invoke the CIRCLE command from the Draw toolbar (see Figure P3–20) to draw the
0.25 radius circle.

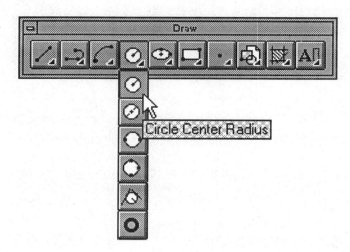

Figure P3-20 Invoke the CIRCLE Command from the Draw toolbar

Command: **circle**
3P/2P/TTR/<Center point>: **3.5,3.75**
Diameter/<Radius>: **0.25**

STEP 18   Invoke the COPY command from the Modify toolbar (see Figure P3–21) to construct
the circles as shown in Figure P3-22.

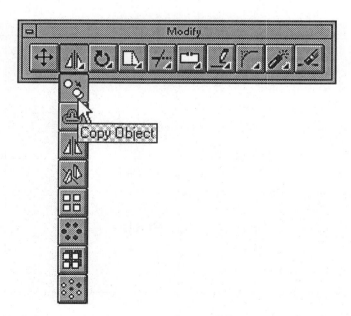

Figure P3-21 Invoke the COPY Command from the Modify toolbar

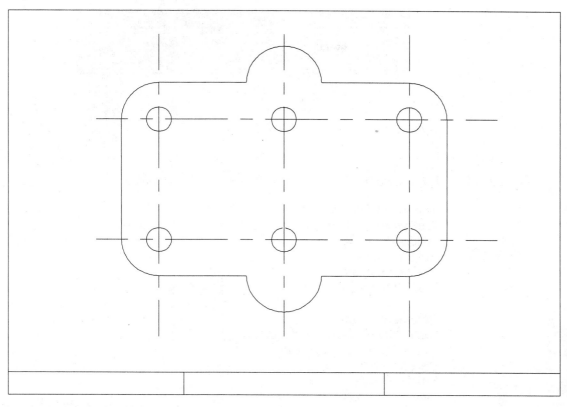

Figure P3-22   Construct circles

Command: **copy**
Select objects: *(Select the circle)*
Select objects: [Enter]
<Base point or displacement>/Multiple: **m**
Base point: **3.5,3.75**
Second point of displacement: **@2.5<0**
Second point of displacement: **@5<0**
Second point of displacement: **@2.5<90**
Second point of displacement: **@2.5,2.5**
Second point of displacement: **@5,2.5**
Second point of displacement: [Enter]

STEP 19   Invoke the DTEXT Command from the Draw toolbar (see Figure P3–23) to place
appropriate text, as shown in P3–24.

Command: **dtext**
Justify/Style/<Start point>: **m**
Middle Point: **2.25, 0.75**
Height<.125>: [Enter]
Rotation angle<0>: [Enter]
Text: *(Enter the name of your school)*

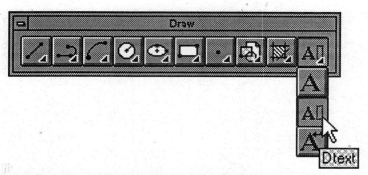

Figure P3-23 Invoke the DTEXT Command from the Draw toolbar

Command: **dtext**
Justify/Style/<Start point>: **m**
Middle Point: **6, 0.75**
Height<.125>: [Enter]
Rotation angle<0>: [Enter]
Text: **3 View Drawing**

Command: **dtext**
Justify/Style/<Start point>: [Enter]
Middle Point: **8.125, 0.8125**
Height<.125>: [Enter]
Rotation angle<0>: [Enter]
Text: *(Enter your name)*

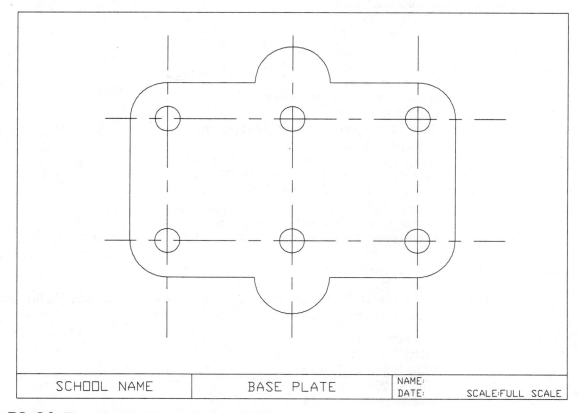

| SCHOOL NAME | BASE PLATE | NAME:
DATE: | SCALE:FULL SCALE |

Figure P3-24 The completed drawing with the title block

Command: **dtext**
Justify/Style/<Start point>: `Enter`
Right Point: **8.125, 0.5625**
Height<.125>: `Enter`
Rotation angle<0>: `Enter`
Text: *(Enter the date)*

Command: **dtext**
Justify/Style/<Start point>: **r**
Middle Point: **11.375, 0.5625**
Height<.125>: `Enter`
Rotation angle<0>: `Enter`
Text: Scale: **Full Scale**

STEP 20   Invoke the SAVE command from the pull-down menu File to save the drawing.

Congratulations. You just successfully applied several AutoCAD concepts in creating a simple drawing.

EXERCISES

Exercise 3-7 to 3-8

Create the drawings according to the settings given in the following table. Draw the objects in the appropriate layers.

SETTINGS	VALUE	
1. UNITS	DECIMAL	
2. LIMITS		
LOWER LEFT	0, 0	
UPPER RIGHT	17, 11	
3. GRID	0.50	
4. SNAP	0.25	
5. TEXT SIZE	0.125	
6. LAYERS		
LAYER NAME	**COLOR**	**LINETYPE**
OBJECT	WHITE	CONTINUOUS
CENTER	YELLOW	CENTER
HIDDEN	CYAN	HIDDEN
TEXT	GREEN	CONTINUOUS

Exercise 3-7

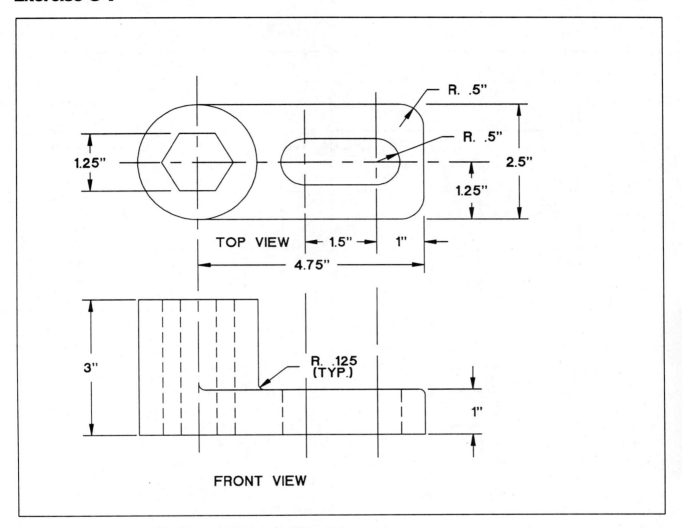

Exercise 3-8

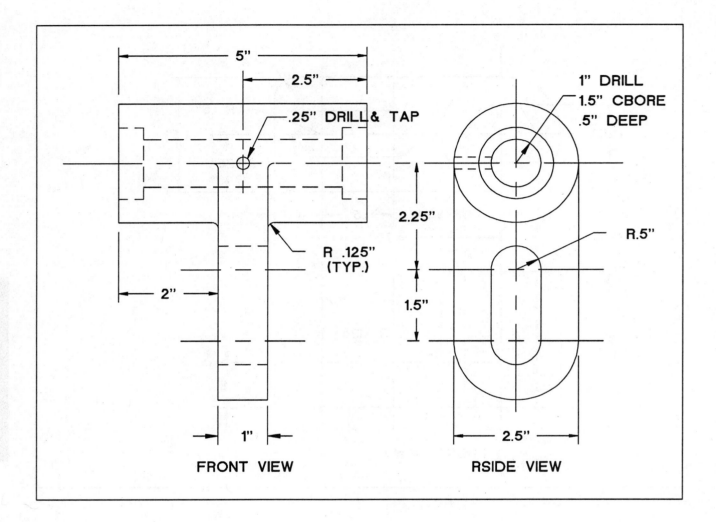

5"

2.5"

.25" DRILL & TAP

1" DRILL
1.5" CBORE
.5" DEEP

2.25"

R .125"
(TYP.)

2"

1.5"

R.5"

1"

2.5"

FRONT VIEW

RSIDE VIEW

Exercise 3-9 to 3-10

Create the drawings according to the settings given in the following table. Draws the objects in the appropriate layers.

SETTINGS	VALUE	
1. UNITS	DECIMAL	
2. LIMITS		
LOWER LEFT	0, 0	
UPPER RIGHT	24, 18	
3. GRID	1"	
4. SNAP	0.5"	
5. TEXT SIZE	0.18	
6. LAYERS		

LAYER NAME	COLOR	LINETYPE
OBJECT	WHITE	CONTINUOUS
BORDER	BLUE	CONTINUOUS
HIDDEN	CYAN	HIDDEN
CENTER	YELLOW	CENTER
TEXT	GREEN	CONTINUOUS

Exercise 3-9

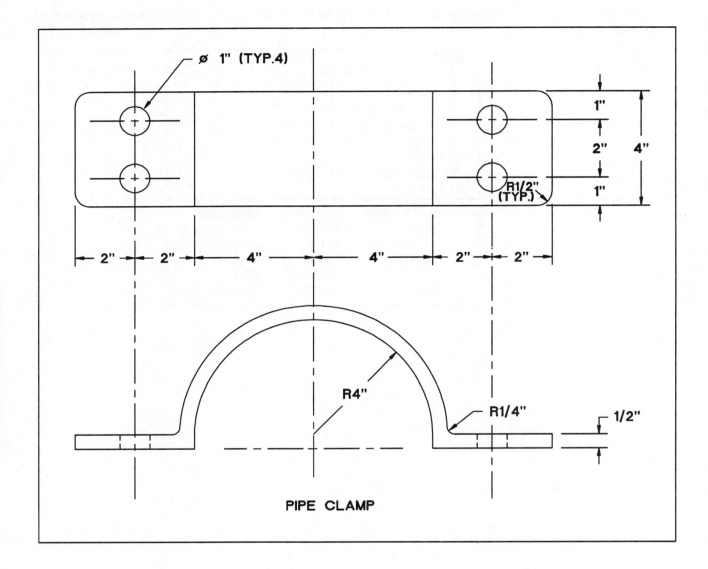

PIPE CLAMP

Exercise 3-10

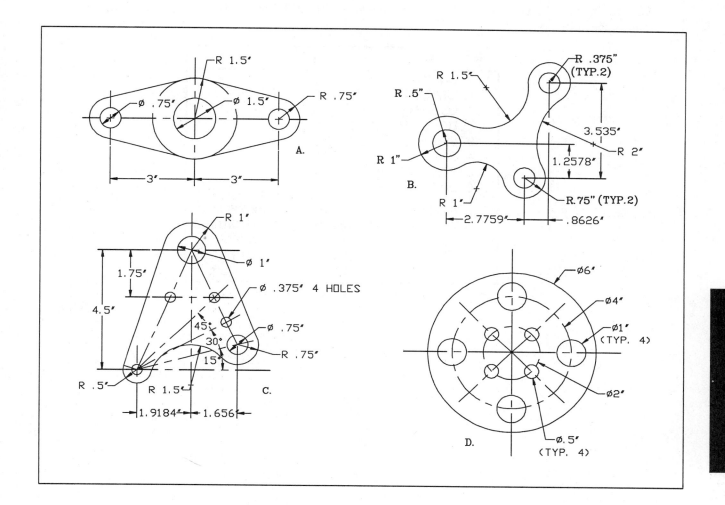

Exercise 3-11 to 3-13

Create the drawings according to the settings given in the following table. Draw the objects in the appropriate layers.

SETTINGS	VALUE		
1. UNITS	DECIMAL		
2. LIMITS			
LOWER LEFT	0, 0		
UPPER RIGHT	17, 11		
3. GRID	0.50		
4. SNAP	0.25		
5. TEXT SIZE	0.125		
6. LAYERS			
LAYER NAME	**COLOR**	**LINETYPE**	
OBJECT	WHITE	CONTINUOUS	
CENTER	YELLOW	CENTER	
TEXT	GREEN	CONTINUOUS	

Exercise 3-11

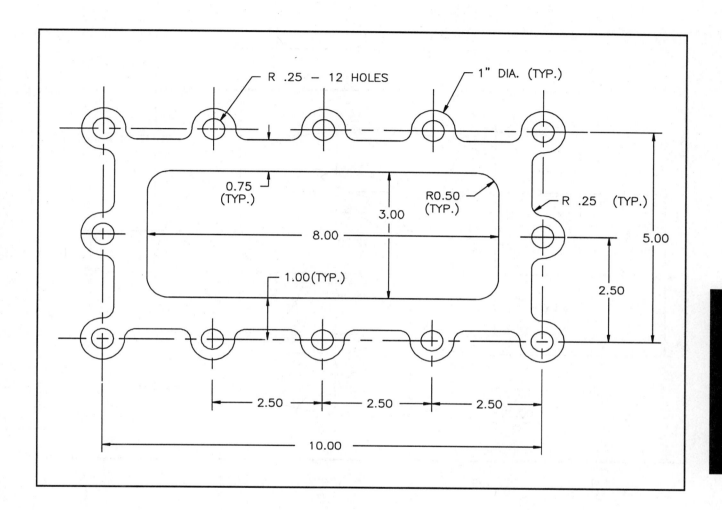

Fundamentals II

Exercise 3-12

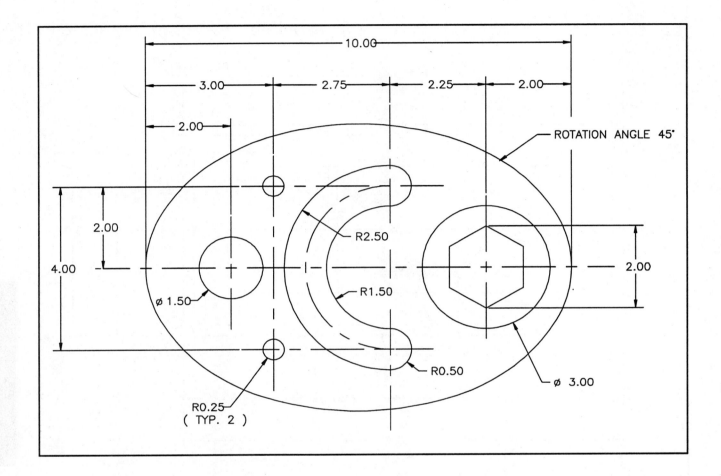

Exercise 3-13

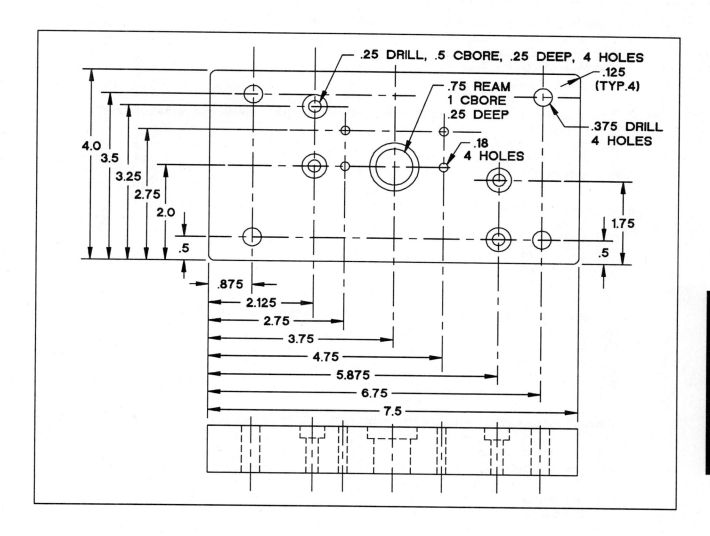

REVIEW QUESTIONS

1. Regarding ARC options, what does "S.C.E." mean?
   (A) Start, Center, End
   (B) Second, Continue, Extents
   (C) Second, Center, End
   (D) Start, Continue, End

2. Which command allows you to change the location of the objects and remain intact?
   (A) CHANGE
   (B) MOVE
   (C) COPY
   (D) MIRROR

3. The maximum number of sides accepted by the POLYGON command is:
   (A) 8 sides
   (B) 100 sides
   (C) 1024 sides
   (D) 1050 sides
   (E) 16 sides

4. The number of different methods by which a circle can be drawn is
   (A) 3
   (B) 2
   (C) 5
   (D) 1
   (E) None of the above

5. When drawing a circle with the two-point option, the distance between the two points is equal to
   (A) the circumference
   (B) the perimeter
   (C) the shortest chord
   (D) the radius
   (E) the diameter

6. A circle may be created through any of the following options except
   (A) 2P
   (B) 3P
   (C) 4P
   (D) Cen,Rad
   (E) TTR

7. Portions of objects can be erased or removed by using the
   (A) ERASE command
   (B) REMOVE command
   (C) BREAK command
   (D) EDIT command
   (E) PARERASE command

8. What happens when you use the Arc Continue option?
   (A) Continues an Arc immediately after drawing a Line
   (B) Continues an Arc Tangent to the previous arc
   (C) Increases the Radius of an Arc
   (D) A and B

9. All of the following are considered valid options of the LAYER command except
   - (A) On
   - (B) Use
   - (C) Make
   - (D) Lock
   - (E) Set

10. Which of the following is not a valid option of the Layer Control dialog box (DDLMODES)?
    - (A) Close
    - (B) Lock
    - (C) On
    - (D) Freeze
    - (E) Color

11. The assignment of a specific color to a specific layer is permitted by the LAYER command option
    - (A) Set
    - (B) New
    - (C) Color
    - (D) Make
    - (E) On

12. Two lines are drawn. Then the first line is erased and the second line is moved. Executing the OOPS command at the "Command:" prompt will
    - (A) restore only the erased line
    - (B) return control to the beginning of the LINE command
    - (C) restore both lines to their original positions
    - (D) result in an "Invalid Command" response
    - (E) None of the above

13. When a layer is on and thawed
    - (A) the objects on that layer are visible on the monitor
    - (B) the objects on that layer are not visible on themonitor
    - (C) the objects on that layer are ignored during REGEN
    - (D) the drawing REGEN time is decreased
    - (E) the objects on that layer are ignored during a COPY

14. A layer where objects may not be edited or deleted but are still visible on the screen and may be osnapped and dimensioned is considered
    - (A) Frozen
    - (B) Locked
    - (C) On
    - (D) Set
    - (E) Unlocked

15. To efficiently MOVE multiple objects, which option should be chosen?
    - (A) Objects
    - (B) Last
    - (C) Window
    - (D) Add
    - (E) Undo

16. The MOVE command allows you to
    - (A) move objects to new locations on the screen
    - (B) dynamically drag objects on the screen
    - (C) move only the objects that are on the current layer
    - (D) Both A and B

17. The LAYER command will allow you to
    - (A) assign colors
    - (B) assign linetypes
    - (C) list the previously created layers
    - (D) selectively turn ON and OFF the Layers
    - (E) All of the above

Fundamentals II

4

FUNDAMENTALS III

After completing this chapter, you will be able to:

- Use the Pline, Point, Solid and Doughnut commands
- Use additional Object Selection options and Object Selection Modes
- Use the Modify commands — Lengthen, Stretch, Change, Chprop, Modify, Rotate, Scale, and Pedit commands
- Edit with Grips
- Use Filter Selection Sets and Grouping of objects
- Use View Command Zoom — Dynamic, Center, Left, and Vmax
- Use the Object Snap options — Intersection, Apparent Intersection, Node, Nearest, and Insert modes

DRAW COMMANDS

In this section, additional DRAW commands are explained, including PLINE, POINT, SOLID, and DOUGHNUT.

PLINE (Polyline) Command

The "poly" in polyline means a single object with multiple connected straight line and/or arc segments. The polyline is drawn by invoking the PLINE command and then selecting series of points. In this respect, PLINE functions much like the LINE command. However, when completed, the segments act like a single object when operated on by modify commands. You specify the endpoints using only 2D (x,y) coordinates.

The versatile PLINE command also draws lines and arcs of different widths, linetypes, tapered lines, and a filled circle. The area and perimeter of a 2D Polyline can be calculated.

Where to Start Invoke the PLINE command from the Polyline flyout located in the Draw toolbar, (Figure 4-1), or at the "Command:" prompt, type **PLINE** and press ⏎ or spacebar.

    Command: **pline**
    From point:

You can specify the start point of the polyline by coordinates or by using your pointing device. As soon as you select the start point of the polyline, the current line-width is displayed:

    Current line-width is 0.0000.

This width remains the same for all the following polyline segments until you specify a different width. AutoCAD continues with the prompt:

    Arc/Close/Halfwidth/Length/Undo/Width/<Endpoint of line>:

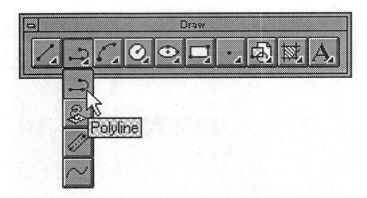

Figure 4-1 Invoke the PLINE Command from the Draw toolbar

Where to from Here? The default option, "<Endpoint of line>", assumes you are going to enter straight-line segments. Therefore, it expects another point to be given to complete the line segment. You can specify the end of the line by absolute coordinates, relative coordinates, or by using your pointing device to pick the end of the line on the screen. After you do, AutoCAD repeats the prompt:

Arc/Close/Halfwidth/Length/Undo/Width<Endpoint of line>:

Having drawn a connected series of lines, you can give a null reply (press [Enter]) to terminate the PLINE command. The resulting figure is recognized by AutoCAD modify and construct commands as a single object.

To access other features of the PLINE command, enter just a capitalized initial letter indicated in the prompt. For example, the following command sequence shows placement of connected lines, as shown in Figure 4-2.

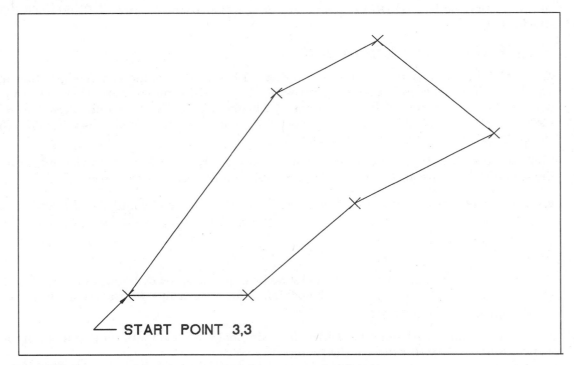

START POINT 3,3

Figure 4-2 Using the PLINE Command to place connected lines

Command: **pline**
From point: **3,3**
Current line-width 0.0
Arc/Close/Halfwidth/Length/Undo/Width/<Endpoint of line>: **@3,0**
Arc/Close/Halfwidth/Length/Undo/Width/<Endpoint of line>: **@4,3**
Arc/Close/Halfwidth/Length/Undo/Width/<Endpoint of line>: **@3,2**
Arc/Close/Halfwidth/Length/Undo/Width/<Endpoint of line>: **@5,2**
Arc/Close/Halfwidth/Length/Undo/Width/<Endpoint of line>: **@-3,3**
Arc/Close/Halfwidth/Length/Undo/Width/<Endpoint of line>: **@-3,-2**
Arc/Close/Halfwidth/Length/Undo/Width/<Endpoint of line>: Enter

Close and Undo Options Close and Undo options work similar to the LINE command.

Width Option After selecting a starting point you may enter a **W** to specify a starting and ending width for a wide segment. When you select this option, AutoCAD prompts:

Starting width <default>:
Ending width <default>:

You can specify a width by entering a value at the prompt or by selecting points on the screen. When entering points on the screen, AutoCAD uses the distance from the starting point of the polyline to the point selected as the starting width. You can accept the default value for the starting width by providing a null response, or type in a new value. The starting width you enter becomes the default for the ending width. If necessary, you can change the ending width to another width, which results in a tapered segment or an arrow. The ending width, in turn, becomes the uniform width for all subsequent segments until you change the width again.

For example, the following command sequence shows placement of connected lines with tapered width, as shown in Figure 4-3.

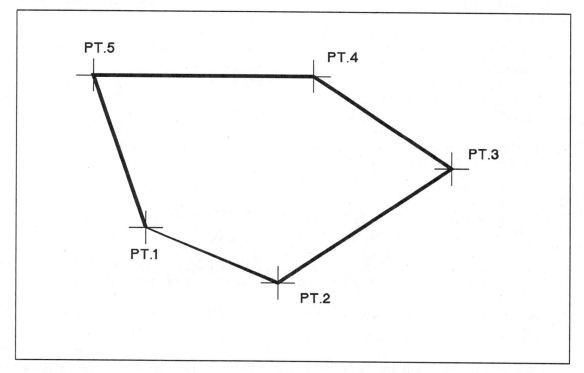

Figure 4-3 Using the PLINE Command to place connected lines with tapered width

```
Command: pline
From point: (pick point 1)
Current line-width 0.0
Arc/Close/Halfwidth/Length/Undo/Width/<Endpoint of line>: w
Starting width <0.000>: 0.1
Ending width <0.125>: 0.25
Arc/Close/Halfwidth/Length/Undo/Width/<Endpoint of line>: (pick point 2)
Arc/Close/Halfwidth/Length/Undo/Width/<Endpoint of line>: (pick point 3)
Arc/Close/Halfwidth/Length/Undo/Width/<Endpoint of line>: (pick point 4)
Arc/Close/Halfwidth/Length/Undo/Width/<Endpoint of line>: c
```

Halfwidth Option This option is similar to the width option, including the prompts, except this lets you specify the width from the center of a wide polyline to one of its edges. In other words, you specify half of the total width. For example, it is easier to input 1.021756 as the halfwidth rather than to figure out the total width by doubling. You can specify a halfwidth by selecting a point on the screen in the same manner used to specify the full width.

Arc Option The Arc option allows you to draw a polyline arc. When you select the Arc option AutoCAD displays another submenu:

   Angle/CEnter/CLose/Direction/Halfwidth/Line/Radius/Second pt/Undo/Width/<Endpoint of arc>:

If you respond with a point, it is interpreted as the endpoint of the arc. The endpoint of the previous segment is the starting point of the arc and the starting direction of the new arc will be the ending direction of the previous segment (whether the previous segment is a line or an arc). This resembles the ARC command's Start, End, Direction (S,E,D) option, but requires only the endpoint to be specified or selected on the screen.

The CLose, Width, Halfwidth, and Undo options are similar to the straight-line segments described above.

The Angle option lets you specify the included angle by prompting:

   Included angle:

The arc is drawn counterclockwise if the value is positive, clockwise if it is negative. After the angle is specified, AutoCAD prompts for the endpoint of the arc.

The CEnter option lets you override with the location of the center of the arc and AutoCAD prompts:

   Center point:

When you provide the center point of the arc, AutoCAD prompts for additional information:

   Angle/Length/<Endpoint>:

If you respond with a point, it is interpreted as the endpoint of the arc. Selecting A (Angle) or L (Length) allows you to specify the arc's included angle or chord length.

The Direction option lets you override the direction of the last segment and AutoCAD prompts:

   Direction from starting point:

If you respond with a point, it is interpreted as the starting point of the direction and AutoCAD prompts for the endpoint for the direction.

The Line option reverts to drawing straight line segments.

The Radius option allows you to specify the radius by prompting:

Radius:

After the radius is specified, you are prompted for the endpoint of the arc.

The Second point option causes AutoCAD to use the three-point method of drawing an arc by prompting:

Second point:

If you respond with a point, it is interpreted as the second point and then you are prompted for the endpoint of the arc. This resembles the ARC command's Three-Point option.

Length Option The Length option continues the polyline in the same direction as the last segment for a specified distance.

POINT Command

The POINT command draws points on the drawing and these points are drawn on the plotted drawing sheet with a single "pen down." Drafter/designers usually enter such points to be used as reference points for object snapping when necessary. When the drawing is finished, simply erase them from the drawing or freeze their layer. Points are entered by specifying coordinates or with the pointing device. You can object snap to a point by using the NODE option of the object snap (OSNAP) feature.

The POINT command is invoked from the Point flyout located in the Draw toolbar (Figure 4–4), or at the "Command:" prompt type **POINT** and press ⏎.

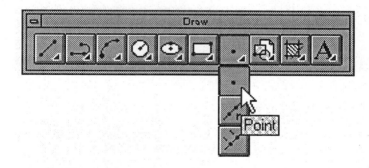

Figure 4–4 Invoke the POINT Command from the Draw toolbar

Command: **point**
Point: *(enter coordinates or specify a point with the pointing device)*

Point Modes When you draw the point, it appears on the display as a blip (+) if system variable BLIPMODE is on (default is on). After a REDRAW command, it appears as a dot (.). You can make the point appear as a +, x, 0 or | by changing the system variable PDMODE. This can be done by entering PDMODE at the "Command:" prompt and entering the appropriate value. You can also change the PDMODE value by using the icon menu as shown in Figure 4–5, invoked by typing DDPTYPE at the "Command:" prompt and pressing ⏎. The default value of PDMODE is zero, which means the point appears as a dot. If the PDMODE is changed, all previous points remain the

Fundamentals III

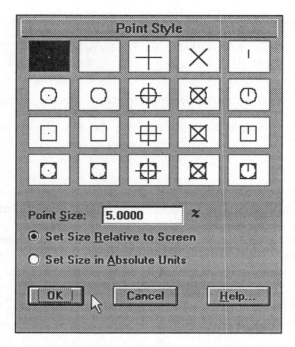

Figure 4–5 The Point Style icon menu lets you select the shape and size of the point object

same until you regenerate the drawing. After a screen regeneration, all points appear as the last PDMODE value entered.

Point Size The size that the point appears on the screen depends on the value to which the system variable PDSIZE is set. You can set this size by the PDSIZE command. Like PDMODE, the default for PDSIZE is zero (one pixel in size). Any positive value larger than this will increase the size of the point accordingly.

SOLID Command

The SOLID command creates a solid filled, straight sided area whose outline is determined by points you specify on the screen. Two important factors should be kept in mind when using the SOLID command: one, the points must be selected in a specified order or else the four corners generate a bowtie instead of a rectangle; two, the polygon generated has straight sides. (Further study reveals that even filled doughnuts and PLINE-generated curved areas are actually straight sided, just as arcs and circles generate as straight line segments of small enough length to appear smooth.)

NOTE: Be sure the Fill mode is ON. Check at the "Command:" prompt by typing **FILL** and pressing [Enter]. AutoCAD responds that Fill is ON or OFF. If Fill is OFF the PLINE, TRACE, SOLID, and DOUGHNUT commands display the outline of the shapes. With Fill ON, the shapes you create with these commands appear solid. If Fill is reset to ON after it has been OFF you must use the REGEN command for the screen to display as filled any unfilled shapes created by these commands. Remember, Fill is only a toggle switch. Switching between ON and OFF affects only the appearance of shapes created with TRACE, PLINE, SOLID, and the DOUGHNUT commands. Solids can only be selected or identified by picking the outlines. The solid area is not recognized as an object.

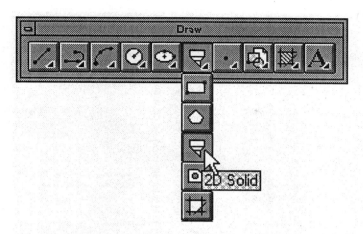

Figure 4–6 Invoke the SOLID Command from the Draw toolbar

The SOLID command is invoked from the Polygon flyout located in the Draw toolbar (Figure 4–6), or, at the "Command:" prompt type **SOLID** and press Enter or spacebar.

    Command: **solid**
    First point: Enter

Figure 4–7 shows an example of how to create a solid rectangular shape.

    Command: **solid**
    First point: *(pick point 1)*
    Second point: *(pick point 2)*
    Third point: *(pick point 3)*
    Fourth point: *(pick point 4)*

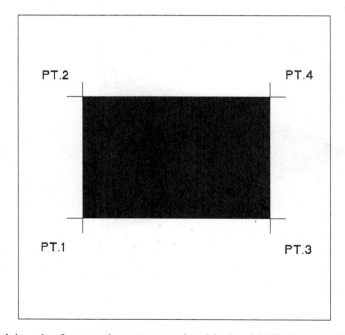

Figure 4–7 The pick order for creating a rectangle with the SOLID Command.

Fundamentals III

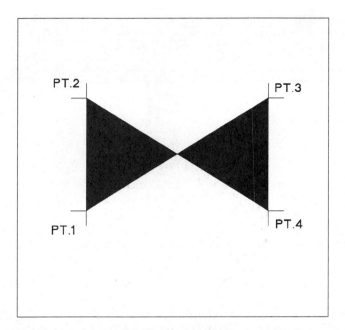

Figure 4–8   Results of using the SOLID Command when odd/even points are not specified correctly

To create the solid shape, odd-numbered picks must be on one side and the even-numbered picks on the other side. If not, you get one of the following effects, as shown in Figure 4–8.

You can use the SOLID command to create an arrowhead or triangle shape, as shown in Figure 4–9. Polygon shapes can be created with the SOLID command by keeping the odd picks along one side and the even picks along the other side of the object, as shown in Figure 4–10.

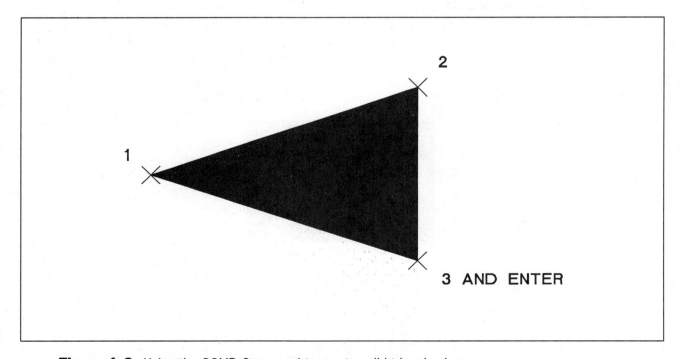

Figure 4–9   Using the SOLID Command to create solid triangle shape

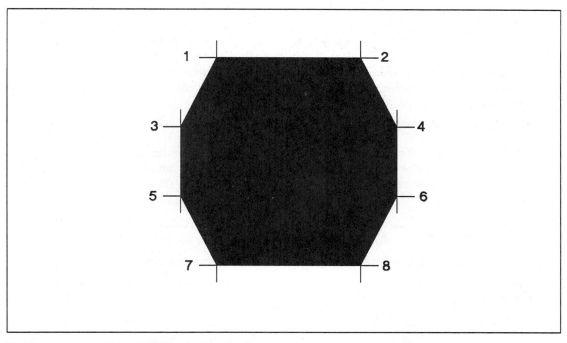

Figure 4–10 Using the SOLID Command to create polygon shape

DOUGHNUT (or DONUT) Command

The DOUGHNUT (or DONUT) command lets you draw a solid filled circle or ring by specifying outer and inner diameters of the filled area. A filled circle is generated by specifying zero as the value of the inner circle.

The DOUGHNUT command is invoked from the Circle flyout located in the Draw toolbar (Figure 4–11), or at the "Command:" prompt type **DOUGHNUT** or **DONUT** and press Enter or spacebar.

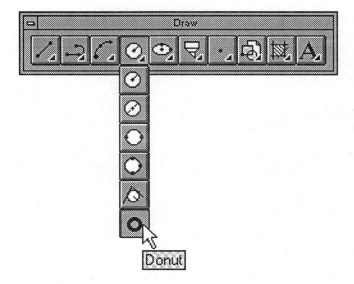

Figure 4–11 Invoke the DOUGHNUT Command from the Draw toolbar

Command: **doughnut**
Inside diameter <current>: *(enter a value 0 or greater)*
Outside diameter <current>: *(enter a value greater than inside diameter)*

The diameters of your last selection appear as the current default. To give a new diameter, enter a numeric value or select two points on the display to show AutoCAD the diameter. After entering the diameters AutoCAD prompts:

Center of doughnut:

You may select the center point specifying its coordinates or by picking it with your pointing device. After selecting the center point, AutoCAD prompts for the center of the next doughnut and continues prompting subsequent center points. To terminate the command enter a null response.

NOTE: Be sure Fill is set to ON or the circles will not appear solid.

For example, the following command sequence shows placement of a solid filled circle, as shown in Figure 4-12, by using the DOUGHNUT command.

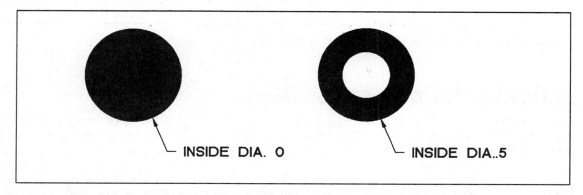

Figure 4-12 Using the DOUGHNUT Command to place a solid filled circle and a filled circular shape

Command: **doughnut**
Inside diameter <.5>: **0**
Outside diameter <1>: **1**
Center of doughnut: **3,2**
Center of doughnut: [Enter]

The following command sequence show placement of a filled circular shape, as shown in Figure 4-12, by using the DOUGHNUT command.

Command: **doughnut**
Inside diameter <0.0>: **0.5**
Outside diameter <0.0>: **1**
Center of doughnut: **6,4**
Center of doughnut: [Enter]

OBJECT SELECTION

All modifying commands include the "Select Objects:" prompt. In most modifying commands, the prompt allows you to easily select any number of objects for editing. The BREAK, PEDIT, DIVIDE, and MEASURE commands are restricted to only one object, as is the Linear Dimensioning option that permits dimensioning an object by just selecting that object. The FILLET and CHAMFER commands require exactly two objects. The DIST and ID Inquiry commands actually require point selection, while the AREA command permits either point or object selection. The options covered in this section give you more flexibility and ease of use when you are prompted to select objects for use by the above commands.

This section covers the WPolygon (WP), CPolygon (CP), Fence, All, Multiple, Box, Auto, Undo, Add, Remove, and Single options, in addition to the options that are explained in Chapter 2.

WPolygon (WP) Option

The WPolygon option is similar to the Window option but allows you to define a polygon shape window rather than a rectangular area. You define the selection area as you pick the points about the objects you want to select. The polygon is formed as you select the points. The polygon can be of any shape but may not intersect itself. The polygon is formed as you pick points and includes rubber-band lines to the graphics cursor. When you have selected points, press [Enter]. Only those objects that are totally inside the polygon shape are selected. To select the WPolygon option, type **WP** and press [Enter] at the "Select Objects:" prompt or invoke the option from the Select Objects toolbar, as shown in Figure 4–13. Undo option lets you undo the most recent polygon pick point.

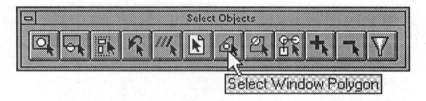

Figure 4–13 Invoke the WPolygon option from the Select Objects toolbar

CPolygon (CP) Option

The CPolygon option is similar to the WPolygon option, but selects all objects within or crossing the polygon boundary. If there is an object that is partially inside the polygon area, then the whole object is included in the selection set. To select the CPolygon option type CP and press [Enter] at the "Select Objects" prompt or invoke the option from the Select Objects toolbar, as shown in Figure 4–14.

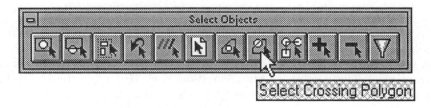

Figure 4–14 Invoke the CPolygon option from the Select Objects toolbar

Fundamentals III

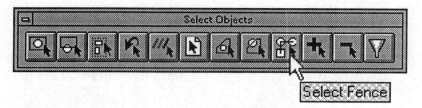

Figure 4–15 Invoke the Fence option from the Select Objects toolbar

Fence (F) Option

This option is similar to the CPolygon option, except that you do not close the last vector of the polygon shape. The selection fence only selects those objects it crosses or intersects. Unlike the WPolygons and CPolygons, the fence can crossover and intersect itself. To select the Fence option type F and press [Enter] at the "Select Objects" prompt or invoke the option from the Select Objects toolbar, as shown in Figure 4–15.

All Option

This option selects all the objects in the drawing, including objects on frozen or locked layers. After selecting all the objects, you may use the Remove (R) option to remove some of the objects from the selection set. The All options must be spelled out in full (ALL) and not applied as an abbreviation like you may do with the other options, or you can invoke the All option from the Select Objects toolbar, as shown in Figure 4–16.

Figure 4–16 Invoke the All option from the Select Objects toolbar

Multiple Option

The Multiple option helps you overcome the limitations of the Point, Window, and Crossing options. The Point option is time-consuming for use in selecting many objects. AutoCAD does a complete scan of the screen each time a point is picked. By using the Multiple modifier option, you can pick many points without delay and when you press [Enter], AutoCAD applies all of the points during one scan.

Selecting one or more objects from a crowded group of objects is sometimes difficult with the Point option. It is often impossible with the Window option. For example, if two objects are very close together and you wish to point to select them both, AutoCAD normally selects only one no matter how many times you select a point that touches them both. By using the Multiple option, AutoCAD excludes an object from being selected once it has been included in the selection set. As an alternative, use the Crossing option to cover both objects. If this is not feasible, then the Multiple modifier may be the best choice.

Box Option

The Box option is usually employed in a menu macro to give the user a double option of Window and Crossing depending on how and where the picks are made on the screen. It must be spelled out in full (BOX) and not applied as an abbreviation like you may do with the others; i.e., W for Window. Because of this, you normally would not go to the trouble to use the Box option from the keyboard when a single key (W or C) provides a decidedly faster option.

When the Box modifier is invoked as a response to a prompt to select an object, the options are applied as follows:

> If the picks are made left to right (the first point is to the left of the second), then the two points become diagonally opposite corners of a rectangle that is used as a Window option. That is, all visible objects totally within the rectangle are part of that selection.

> If the picks are right to left, then the selection rectangle becomes the Crossing option. That is, all visible objects that are within or partially within the rectangle are part of that selection.

> **NOTE:** The Box option is the default option when you are prompted for "Select Objects:".

Auto Option

The Auto option offers a triple option. It includes the Point option with the two Box options. If the target box touches an object, then that object is selected as you would in using the Point option. If the target box does not touch an object, then the selection becomes either a Window or Crossing option, depending upon where the second point is picked in relation to the first.

Undo Option

The Undo option allows you to remove the last item(s) selected from the selection set without aborting the "Select Objects:" prompt and then continue adding to the selection set. It is a short way to use the combined Remove/Last/.../Add sequence of options. It should be noted that if the last option to the selection process included more than one object, the Undo option will remove all the objects from the selection set that were selected by that last option.

Add Option

The Add option lets you switch back from the Remove mode in order to continue adding objects to the selection set by whatever and however many options you wish to use. The Add option is invoked from the Select Objects toolbar, as shown in Figure 4–17.

Figure 4–17 Invoke the Add option from the Select Objects toolbar

Figure 4–18 Invoke the Remove option from the Select Objects toolbar

Remove Option

The Remove option lets you remove objects from the selection set. The "Select Objects:" prompt always starts in the Add mode. The Remove mode is a switch from the Add mode, not a standard option. Once invoked, the objects selected by whatever and however many options you use will be removed from the selection set. It will be in effect until reversed by using the Add option. The Remove option is invoked from the Select Objects toolbar, as shown in Figure 4–18.

Single Option

The Single option causes the Object Selection to terminate and the command in progress to proceed after you use only one Object Selection option. It does not matter if one object is selected or a group is selected with that option. If no object is selected and the point selected cannot be the first point of a Window or Crossing rectangle, AutoCAD will not abort the command in progress; however, once there is a successful selection, the command proceeds.

OBJECT SELECTION MODES

AutoCAD provides four selection modes that will enhance an object selection. You can toggle on/off one or more object selection modes from the Object Selection Settings dialog box. The dialog box is invoked by selecting **Selection. . .** from the pull-down menu Options, as shown in Figure 4–19, or at the "Command:" prompt, type DDSELECT and press Enter or spacebar.

Command: **ddselect**

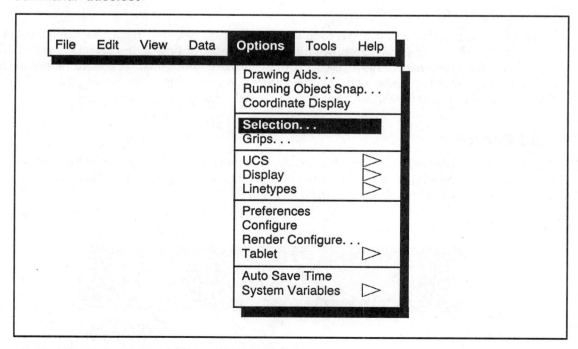

Figure 4–19 Invoke the Selection. . . Command from the pull-down menu Options

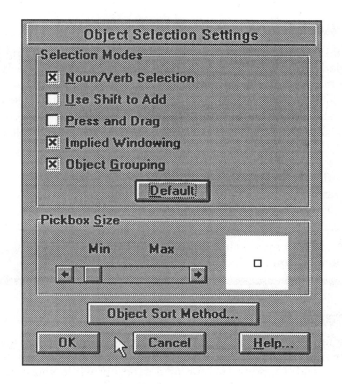

Figure 4–20 The Object Selection Settings dialog box

AutoCAD displays the Object Selection Settings dialog box, similar to the one shown in Figure 4–20.

You can toggle any one or more combinations of the settings provided under the selection modes or reset the settings to the original defaults by clicking the **Default** button. Noun/Verb Selection, Implied Windowing and Object Grouping are the defaults.

Noun/Verb Selection

The Noun/Verb Selection feature allows the traditional verb-noun command syntax to be reversed for most modifying commands. When the Noun/Verb Selection is toggled on, you can select the objects first at the modifying prompt, and then invoke the appropriate modifying command you want to use on the selection set. For example, instead of entering the COPY command followed by selecting the objects to be copied, with Noun/Verb Selection turned on, you can select the objects first and then enter the COPY command.

When Noun/Verb Selection is turned on, the cursor at the "Command:" prompt changes to resemble a running-osnap cursor. Whenever you want to use the Noun/Verb feature, first create a selection set at the "Command:" prompt. Subsequent modifying commands you invoke execute using the objects in the current selection set without prompting for object selection. To clear the current selection set, press ⌨ at the "Command:" prompt. This clears the selection set so any subsequent editing command will once again prompt for object selection.

> **NOTE:** Another way to set Noun/Verb Selection is to use the PICKFIRST system variable. TRIM, EXTEND, BREAK, CHAMFER, and FILLET are the commands not supported by the Noun/Verb feature.

Use Shift to Add

The Use Shift to Add feature controls how you add objects to an existing selection set. When Use Shift to Add is toggled on, it activates an additive selection mode, in which the ⌈Shift⌋ key must be held down while adding more objects to the selection set. For example, if you first pick an object, it is highlighted. If you pick another object, it is highlighted and the first object is no longer highlighted. The only way you can add objects to the selection set is to select objects by holding the ⌈Shift⌋ key. Similarly, you can also remove the objects from the selection set is to select objects by holding down the ⌈Shift⌋ key.

When Use Shift to Add is toggled off (default), objects are added to the selection set by just picking them individually or by using one of the selection options; AutoCAD adds the objects to the selection set.

> **NOTE:** Another way to select objects with this method is to set the PICKADD system variable appropriately.

Press and Drag

The Press and Drag feature controls the manner by which you draw the selection window with your pointing device. When Press and Drag is toggled on, you can create a selection window by holding down the pick button and dragging the cursor diagonally while you create the window. In other words, create the window using one pick of the pointing device button.

When Press and Drag is toggled off (default), you need to use two separate picks of the pointing device to create the selection window. In other words, pick once to define one corner of the selection window, and pick a second time to define its diagonal corner.

> **NOTE:** Another way to control how selection windows are drawn is to set the PICKDRAG system variable appropriately.

Implied Windowing

The Implied Windowing feature allows you to automatically create a selection window when the "Select objects:" prompt appears. When Implied Windowing is toggled on (default), it works like the Box option explained earlier. If Implied Windowing is turned off, you can create a selection window by using the Window or Crossing selection set methods.

> **NOTE:** Another way to control Implied Windowing option is to set the PICKAUTO system variable appropriately.

MODIFY COMMANDS

In this section, eight additional Modify commands are explained: the Lengthen, Stretch, Change, Chprop, Modify, Rotate, Scale, and Pedit commands, in addition to the Modify commands explained in Chapter 2 and 3.

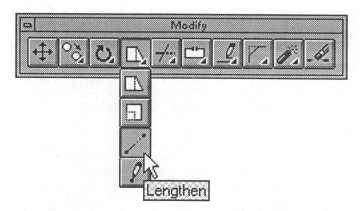

Figure 4–21 Invoke the LENGTHEN Command from the Modify toolbar

LENGTHEN Command

The LENGTHEN command is used to increase or decrease the length of line objects or the included angle of an arc.

The LENGTHEN command is invoked from the Resize flyout located in the Modify toolbar (Figure 4–21), or at the "Command:" prompt, type **lengthen** and press Enter or spacebar.

> Command: **lengthen**
> Delta/Percent/Total/DYnamic/<Select object>:

Select an object and AutoCAD displays the length, and where applicable, the included angle of the selected object.

Delta Option   The Delta option changes the length or, where applicable, the included angle from the end point of the selected object closest to the pick point. A positive value results in an increase in extension and a negative value results in a trim. When you select the Delta option, AutoCAD prompts:

> Angle/<Enter delta length (current)>: *(specify positive or negative value)*
> <Select object to change>/Undo: *(select an object and its length is changed on the end nearest the selection point)*
> <Select object to change>/Undo: *(select additional objects; when done, press Enter to exit the command sequence)*

The Undo option reverses the most recent change made by the LENGTHEN command. Instead of specifying the delta length, if you select the Angle option, AutoCAD prompts:

> Enter delta angle <current>: *(specify positive or negative angle)*
> <Select object to change>/Undo: *(select an object and its included angle is changed on the end nearest the selection point)*
> <Select object to change>/Undo: *(select additional objects; when done, press Enter to exit the command sequence)*

The Undo option reverses the most recent change made by the LENGTHEN command.

Percent Option   The Percent option sets the length of an object by a specified percentage of its total length. It will increase the length/angle for values greater than 100 and decrease them for values less than 100. For example, a 12-unit-long line will be changed to 15 units by using a value of 125. A 12-unit-long line will be changed to 9 units by using a value of 75. When you select the Percent option, AutoCAD prompts:

Enter percent length (current)>: *(specify positive nonzero value and press* Enter*)*
<Select object to change>/Undo: *(select an object and its length is changed on the end nearest the selection point)*
<Select object to change>/Undo: *(select additional objects; when done, press* Enter *to exit the command sequence)*

Total Option The Total Option changes the length/angle of an object to become the value specified. When you select the Total option, AutoCAD prompts:

Angle/<Enter total length (current)>: *(specify distance or enter A for angle and then specify an angle for change)*

The options and prompts are similar to the Delta option.

Dynamic Option The Dynamic option changes the length/angle of an object in response to the cursor's final location relative to the end point nearest to where the object is selected. When you select the Dynamic option, AutoCAD prompts:

<Select object to change>/Undo: *(select an object to change the end point)*
<Select object to change>/Undo: *(reposition the object if necessary, or press* Enter *to exit the command sequence).*

The options and prompts are similar to the Delta option.

STRETCH Command

The STRETCH command allows you to stretch the shape of an object without affecting other crucial parts that remain unchanged. A common example is to stretch a square into a rectangle. The length is changed while the width remains the same.

The STRETCH command is invoked from the Resize flyout located in the Modify toolbar (Figure 4–22), or at the "Command:" prompt type **STRETCH** and press Enter or spacebar.

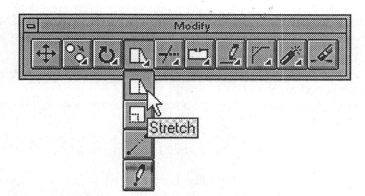

Figure 4–22 Invoke the STRETCH Command from the screen menu MODIFY

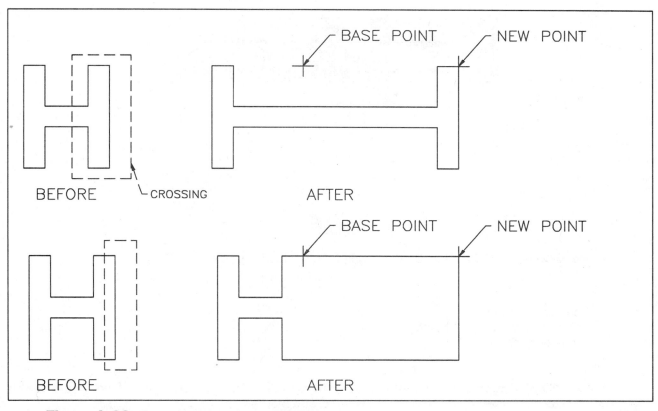

Figure 4–23 Examples of using the STRETCH command

Command: **stretch**
Select objects to stretch by crossing — window or polygon. . .
Select objects: **c**
First corner: *(select the first corner of the crossing box)*
Other corner: *(select the second corner)*
Select objects: Enter
Base point: *(select the base point for the stretch to begin)*
New point: *(select the new point to stretch)*

Figure 4–23 shows examples of using the STRETCH command.

CHANGE Command

The CHANGE command lets you modify some of the characteristics of lines, circles, text, and blocks. It also allows you to change certain properties of the objects you have selected, including the color, linetype, ltscale, thickness and layer.

The CHANGE command is invoked from the Resize flyout located in the Modify toolbar (Figure 4-24), or at the "Command:" prompt type **CHANGE** and press Enter or spacebar.

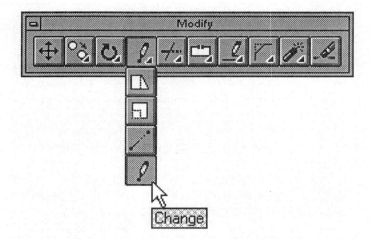

Figure 4–24 Invoke the CHANGE Command from the Modify toolbar

Command: **change**
Select objects: *(select the objects)*
Properties/<Change point>:

Change Point Option The default option is the Change Point option which allows you to modify some of the characteristics of lines, circles, text, and blocks.

Line – If you select one or more lines, the closest endpoint(s) are moved to the new change point, as shown in Figure 4–25.

Circle – If you select a circle, the new circle passes through the new change point, as shown in Figure 4–25. The distance from the center to the point selected determines the new radius.

Text – If you select a text string, AutoCAD allows you to change one or more parameters as shown in the following prompt sequence:

Enter text insertion point: *(select a new point or press* [Enter]*)*
Name of the style or RETURN for no change:
New height <default>:
New rotation angle <default>:
New text <text>:

If you do not wish to change any of the above parameters, press [Enter] (null response) to accept the default.

Block – If you select a block, the change point you select becomes the new origin of the block. As with text, you may press [Enter] when prompted for a new change point. Doing this will leave the block in the same location and you are prompted for a new scale factor and rotation angle. If you do not wish to change any of the above parameters, press [Enter] (null response) to accept the default.

Properties Option The Properties option allows you to change one or more properties of the selected objects. The properties include Color, Layer, Linetype, Ltscale, Elevation, and Thickness.

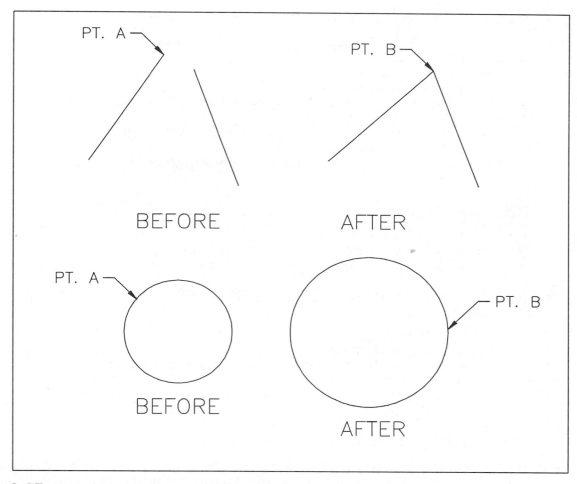

Figure 4–25 Using the Change Point option of the CHANGE Command

Color – The Color option under the Properties allows you to change an object's color. Enter a color number or name to change. To make the object inherit the color of the layer, enter "BYLAYER" or, to inherit the color of the block upon insertion, enter "BYBLOCK".

LAyer – The LAyer option under the Properties allows you to move an object from one layer to another. The layer you enter must already exist.

LType – The Linetype option under the Properties allows you to change an object's linetype. Enter the desired linetype name. To make the object inherit the linetype of the layer, enter "BYLAYER" or, to inherit the linetype of the block upon insertion, enter "BYBLOCK".

ltScale – The linetype scale factor under the Properties allows you to change the linetype scale factor of the selected objects.

Elevation – The Elevation option under the Properties allows you to change an object's current elevation. Enter a numeric value.

Thickness – The Thickness option under the Properties allows you to change an object's extrusion thickness. Enter a numeric value. This option does not have any effect on objects that are drawn with 3DFACE, 3DPLINE, MESH, DIMENSIONS, or VIEWPORT commands.

Fundamentals III

The following command sequence shows changing the color and layer of an object to BYLAYER and to layer text, respectively.

> Command: **change**
> Select objects: *(select the objects)*
> Properties/<Change point>: **p**
> Change what property (Color/Elev/LAyer/LType/ltScale/Thickness)? **c**
> New color <default>: **bylayer**
> Change what property (Color/Elev/LAyer/LType/ltScale/Thickness)? **la**
> New layer <default>: **text**
> Change what property (Color/Elev/LAyer/LType/ltScale/Thickness)? [Enter]

CHPROP Command

The DDCHPROP and CHPROP commands are quicker alternatives to the CHANGE command. The choices are the same as the CHANGE command's Properties option. DDCHPROP lets you change object properties by using a dialog box; CHPROP lets you change at the command prompt.

The CHPROP command is invoked by typing DDCHPROP at the "Command:" prompt and pressing [Enter] or spacebar.

> Command: **chprop**
> Select objects: *(select the objects)*
> Change what property (Color/LAyer/LType/LtScale/Thickness)?

Enter the desired option to change the properties of the selected object(s).

DDMODIFY Command

The DDMODIFY command functions similar to the CHANGE and CHPROP commands. It lets you select a single object, its properties are displayed by the Modify dialog box. From the dialog box, you can change many of the object's properties. You can modify the color, linetype, layer, thickness, start and end point of lines and polylines; center point and radius of circles and arcs; position of 3D faces; block insertion point, and the X, Y, and Z scale; attribute's tag, prompt and default value; external reference location; dimension properties; and text position, size, orientation, justification, and text string.

The DDMODIFY command is invoked from the Object Properties toolbar (Figure 4–26), or at the "Command:" prompt type **DDMODIFY** and press [Enter] or spacebar.

> Command: **ddmodify**
> Select object to modify:

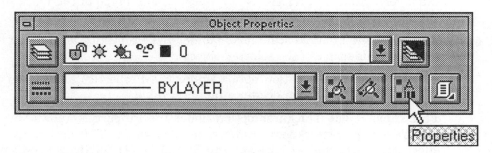

Figure 4–26 Invoke the DDMODIFY Command from the Object Properties toolbar

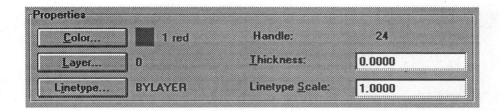

Figure 4–27 Dialog box displayed when an arc object is selected

Select a single object, and AutoCAD displays the appropriate dialog box. Make the necessary changes and click OK to make the modifications.

The options provided in the Modify dialog box differ by type of object selected.

If the PICKFIRST system variable is set for noun/verb mode (1), selecting an object and then entering DDMODIFY will cause the dialog box to be displayed for that object previously selected in the selection mode.

Every DDMODIFY dialog box will have a Properties section, as shown in Figure 4–27. It permits you to control the selected object's color, layer, linetype, linetype scale and thickness.

The **Color...** button displays the Select Color dialog box from which you can change the color of the selected object.

The **Layer...** button causes the Select Layer dialog box to be displayed. The desired layer may be selected from the list box or by entering its name in the Set Layer Name: edit box for the selected object.

The **Linetype...** button displays the Select Linetype dialog box, from which you may select the linetype for the selected object.

The **Handle:** field displays the selected object's handle. However, it cannot be changed from this dialog box.

The **Thickness:** edit field displays the current thickness of the selected object. If necessary, you can change the value by typing the new value in the Thickness: edit field.

The **Linetype Scale:** edit field displays the current linetype scale factor of the selected object. If necessary, you can change the value by typing the new value in the Linetype Scale: edit field.

Following are the salient features of the various dialog boxes that are displayed by AutoCAD for the type of objects selected.

Modify Line When you select a line, AutoCAD displays the Modify Line dialog box, as shown in Figure 4–28.

The **From Point** and **To Point** sections of the dialog box allow you to change the starting and ending point of the selected line object respectively.

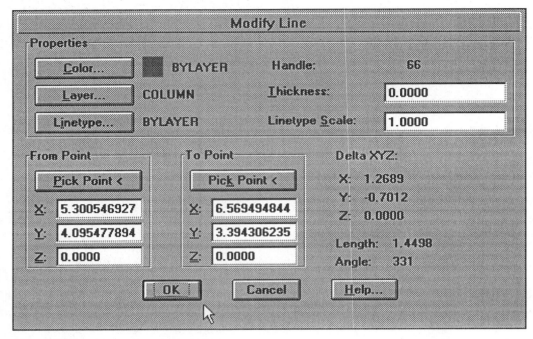

Figure 4–28 Modify Line dialog box

The **Delta X Y Z:** section displays the change in X, Y, and Z coordinate distances between the starting point and the ending point of the selected line. The **Length:** and **Angle:** sections display the length of the line and angle of the line, respectively, of the selected line object.

Modify Polyline When you select a 2D polyline, 3D polyline, or 3D polygon mesh, AutoCAD displays the Modify Polyline dialog box, as shown in Figure 4–29.

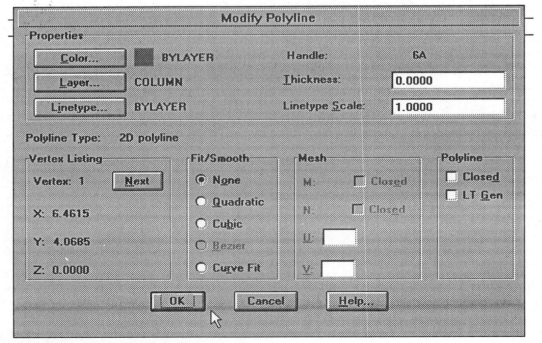

Figure 4–29 Modify Polyline dialog box

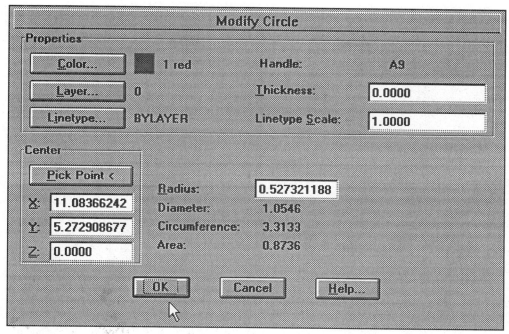

Figure 4-30   Modify Circle dialog box

The **Polyline Type:** field displays the type of polyline selected. AutoCAD displays the coordinates of the first vertex in the **Vertex Listing** section of the dialog box. The **Next** button allows you to cycle through the vertices. The **Fit/Smooth** section permits you to select the type of line or surface curve fitting.

The **Mesh** section of the dialog box is enabled when a 3D polygon mesh is selected. Selection of M Closed/N Closed opens or closes the mesh in the M/N direction, respectively. The U/V edit field permits you to control the accuracy of the surface approximation.

The **Polyline** section is enabled when a 2D or 3D polyline is selected. Closed selection permits you to open or close the polyline. LT Gen selection permits you to control the manner in which linetype patterns are assigned to the 2D polyline selected.

Modify Circle   When you select a circle, AutoCAD displays the Modify Circle dialog box, as shown in Figure 4–30.

The **Center** section of the dialog box allows you to change the location of the center of the selected circle object. The **Radius:** edit field permits you to specify the radius of the selected circle. The **Diameter:, Circumference:,** and **Area:** fields display the selected circle object's diameter, radius, and area, respectively.

Modify Arc   When you select an arc, AutoCAD displays the Modify Arc dialog box, as shown in Figure 4–31.

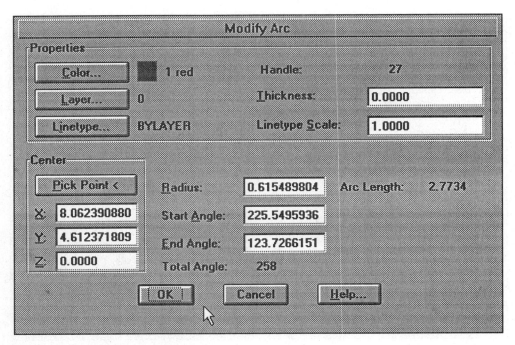

Figure 4-31 Modify Arc dialog box

The **Center** section of the dialog box allows you to change the location of the center of the selected arc object. The **Radius:** edit field permits you to specify the radius of the selected arc. The **Start Angle:** and **End Angle:** edit fields permit you to specify the start angle and end angle of the selected arc, respectively. The **Total Angle:** and **Arc Length:** fields display the selected arc object's total angle and arc length, respectively.

Modify Ellipse When you select an ellipse, AutoCAD displays the Modify Ellipse dialog box, as shown in Figure 4-32.

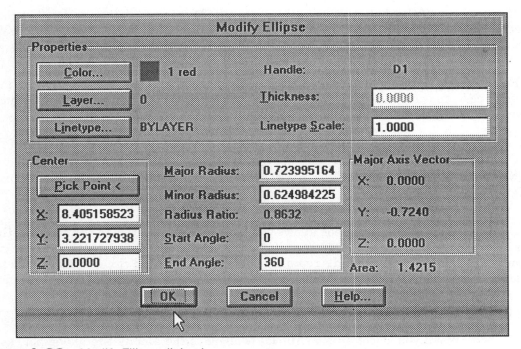

Figure 4-32 Modify Ellipse dialog box

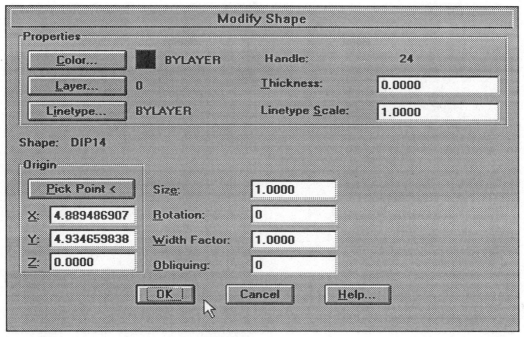

Figure 4-33 Modify Shape dialog box

The **Center** section of the dialog box allows you to change the location of the center of the selected ellipse object. The **Major Radius:** and **Minor Radius:** edit fields permit you to specify the major and minor radii of the selected ellipse, respectively. The **Start Angle:** and **End Angle:** edit fields permit you to specify the start angle and end angle of the selected ellipse. The **Radius Ratio:** and **Area:** fields display the radius ratio and area of the selected ellipse object. The **Major Axis Vector** displays the major axis direction of the selected ellipse object.

Modify Shape When you select a shape, AutoCAD displays the Modify Shape dialog box, as shown in Figure 4–33.

The **Shape:** field displays the name of the selected shape. The **Origin** section of the dialog box allows you to change the shape's insertion point. The **Size:**, **Rotation:**, **Width Factor:**, and **Obliquing:** edit fields permit you to specify the size, rotation, width factor, and obliquing angle of the selected shape, respectively.

Modify Point When you select a point, AutoCAD displays the Modify Point dialog box, as shown in Figure 4–34.

The **Location** section of the dialog box allows you to change the location of the selected point object.

Modify Multiline When you select a multiline, AutoCAD displays the Modify Multiline dialog box, as shown in Figure 4–35.

Fundamentals III

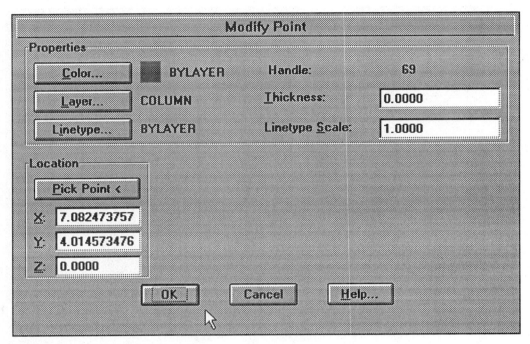

Figure 4-34 Modify Point dialog box

The **MLine Style:** field displays the current multiline's style. The **MLine Edit...** button causes the Multiline Edit Tools dialog box to be displayed. For detailed explanation of the Multiline Edit Tools dialog box, see the section on MLSTYLE command.

Modify Spline When you select a spline, AutoCAD displays the Modify Spline dialog box, as shown in Figure 4-36.

The **Control Points** section of the dialog box displays the information about the control points of the selected spline object. The **Next** button allows you to cycle through the vertices. The **Degree:**

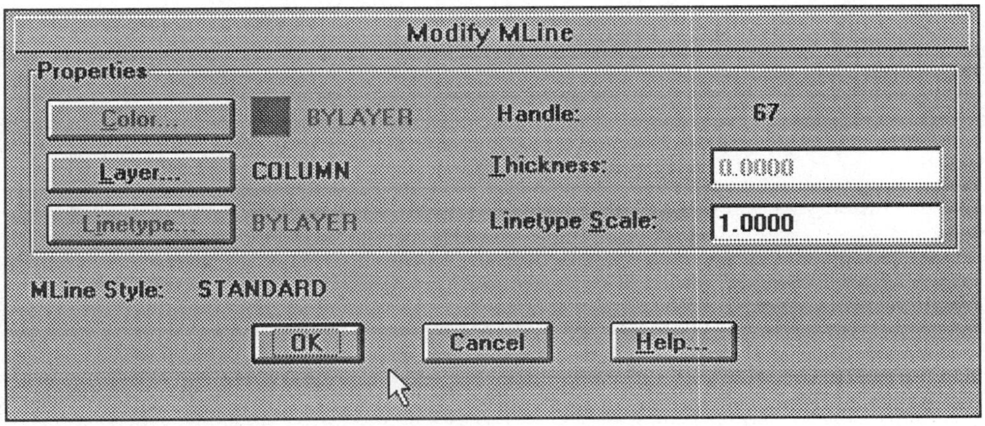

Figure 4-35 Modify Multiline dialog box

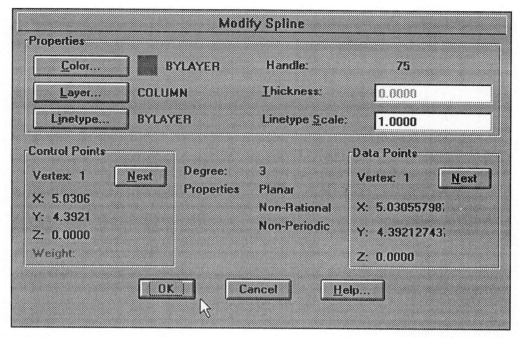

Figure 4-36   Modify Spline dialog box

and **Properties:** fields display the degree and data point information of the spline. The **Data Points** section of the dialog box displays the information about the data points of the selected spline object. The **Next** button allows you to cycle through the vertices.

Modify Trace   When you select a trace, AutoCAD displays the Modify Trace dialog box, as shown in Figure 4-37.

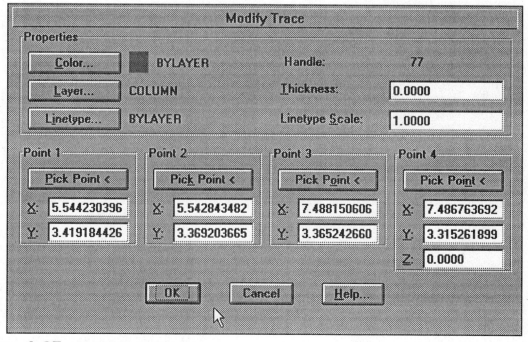

Figure 4-37   Modify Trace dialog box

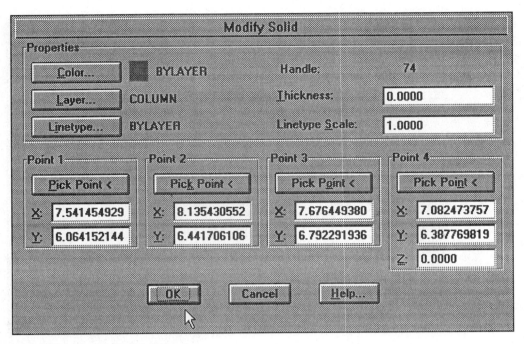

Figure 4-38 Modify Solid dialog box

The **Point 1, Point 2, Point 3,** and **Point 4** sections of the dialog box permit you to change the location of any of the four corner points by selecting a point on the screen or entering its coordinates.

Modify Solid When you select a solid, AutoCAD displays the Modify Solid dialog box, as shown in Figure 4–38.

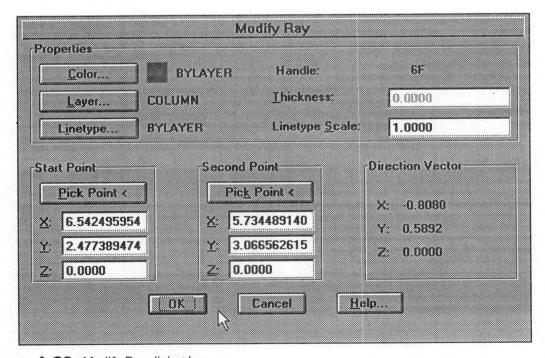

Figure 4-39 Modify Ray dialog box

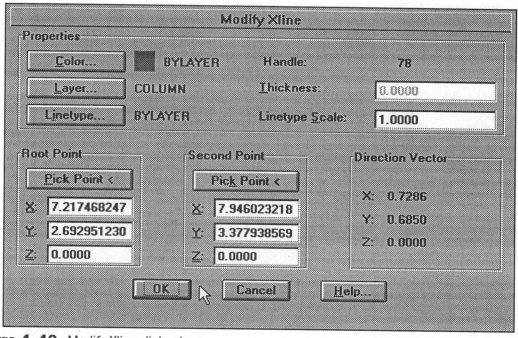

Figure 4–40 Modify Xline dialog box

The **Point 1, Point 2, Point 3,** and **Point 4** sections of the dialog box permits you to change the location of any of the four corner points by selecting a point on the screen or entering its coordinates.

Modify Ray When you select a ray, AutoCAD displays the Modify Ray dialog box, as shown in Figure 4–39.

The **Start Point** and **Second Point** sections of the dialog box allow you to change the starting and second point of the selected ray object, respectively.

The **Direction Vector** section displays the change in X, Y, and Z coordinate values between the starting point and the ending point of the selected ray.

Modify Xline When you select an xline, AutoCAD displays the Modify Xline dialog box, as shown in Figure 4–40.

The **Root Point** and **Second Point** sections of the dialog box allow you to change the root point and second point of the selected xline object, respectively.

The **Direction Vector** section displays the change in X, Y, and Z coordinate values between the starting point and the ending point of the selected ray.

Modify Text When you select text, AutoCAD displays the Modify Text dialog box, as shown in Figure 4–41.

The **Text:** edit field displays the selected text; if necessary you can edit the characters in the edit box. The **Origin** section of the dialog box allows you to change the insertion point of the selected text. The **Height:, Rotation:, Width Factor:,** and **Obliquing:** edit fields permit you to change the height, rotation, width factor and obliquing angle of the selected text, respectively. The **Justify:**

Fundamentals III

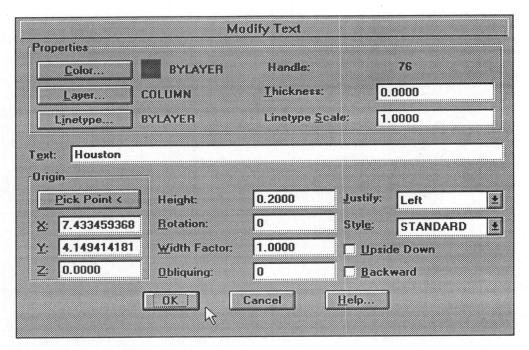

Figure 4-41 Modify Text dialog box

list box allows you to change the existing justification of the selected text. The **Style:** list box allows you to change the existing style of the selected text. The **Upside Down** and **Backward** check boxes allow you to specify whether text is typed upside down and/or backwards, respectively.

Modify MText When you select paragraph or leader text, AutoCAD displays the Modify MText dialog box, as shown in Figure 4–42.

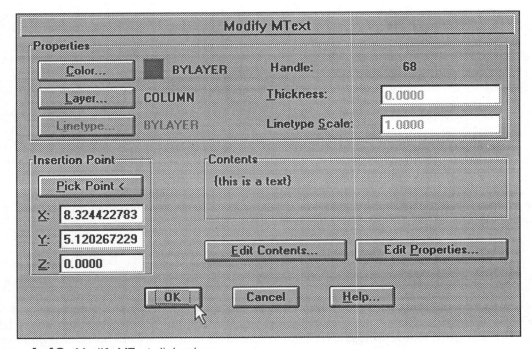

Figure 4-42 Modify MText dialog box

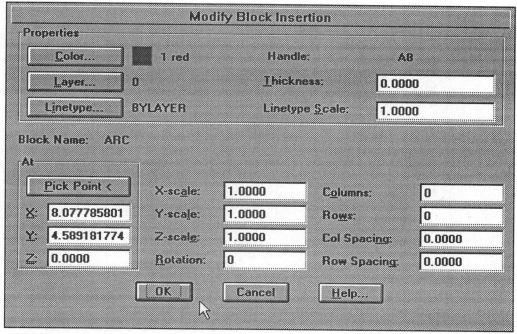

Figure 4–43 Modify Block Insertion dialog box

The **Contents** section of the dialog box displays the selected paragraph text. The **Insertion Point** section of the dialog box allows you to change the insertion point of the selected paragraph text. The **Edit Contents...** button causes the Edit MText dialog box to be displayed. For a detailed explanation of the Edit MText dialog box, see the section on MTEXT. The **Edit Properties...** button causes the MText Properties dialog box to be displayed. For a detailed explanation of the MText Properties dialog box, see the section on MTPROP.

Modify Block Insertion When you select a block, AutoCAD displays the Modify Block Insertion dialog box, as shown in Figure 4–43.

The **Block Name:** field displays the name of the selected block. The **At** section of the dialog box allows you to change the insertion of the selected block. The **X-scale:, Y-scale:, Z-scale:,** and **Rotation:** edit fields allow you to change the x-scale, y-scale, z-scale, and rotation angle of the selected block. The **Columns:, Rows:, Column Spacing:,** and **Row Spacing:** edit fields allows you to change the number of columns, rows, column spacing, and row spacing, respectively, when using a rectangular array-inserted set of blocks.

Modify Attribute Definitions When you select an attribute, AutoCAD displays the Modify Attribute Definition dialog box, as shown in Figure 4–44.

The **Tag:** edit field permits you to change the attribute tag. The **Prompt:** and **Default:** edit fields permit you to change the prompt and default value, respectively, for the selected attribute. The **Origin** section allows you to change the insertion point for the selected attribute. The **Height:, Rotation:, Width Factor:,** and **Obliquing:** edit fields permit you to change the height rotation, width factor and obliquing angle of the selected text, respectively. The **Justify:** list box allows you to change the existing justification of the attribute text. The **Style:** list box allows you to change the existing style of the selected attribute text. In addition, the Modify Attribute Definition dialog box

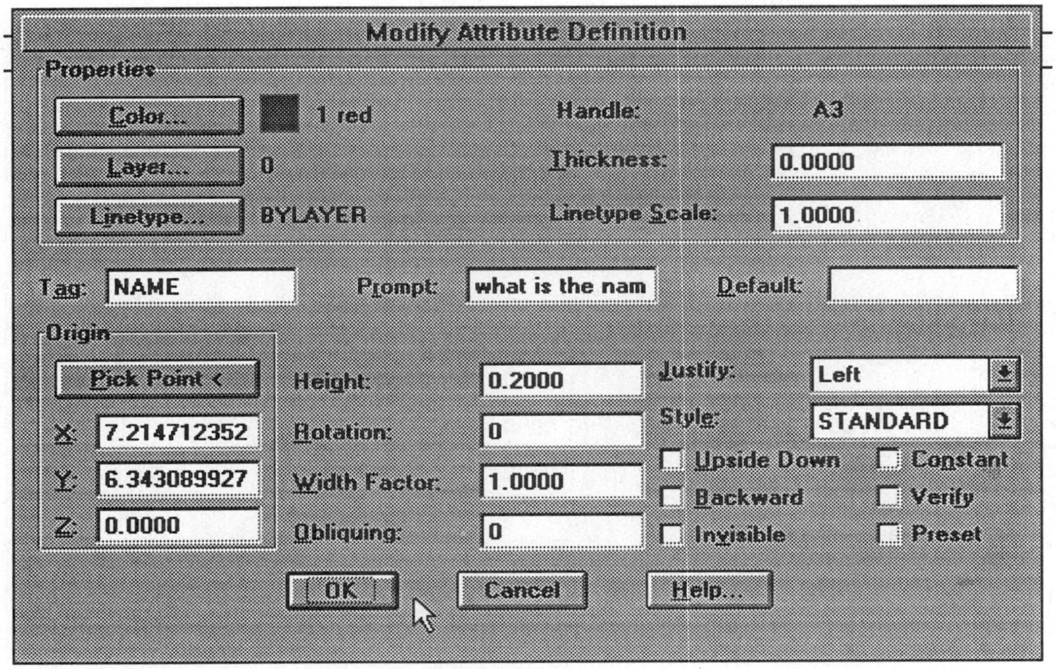

Figure 4-44 Modify Attribute Definition dialog box

allows you to change the settings of the attribute modes. See Chapter 9 for a detailed explanation of Blocks and Attributes.

Modify Associative Hatch When you select an associative hatch, AutoCAD displays the Modify Associative Hatch dialog box, as shown in Figure 4–45.

The **Block Name:** field displays the anonymous (named for unique identity for current drawing session only) name of the selected block. The **Hatch Edit...** button causes the Hatch edit dialog box to be displayed. For a detailed explanation of the Hatch edit dialog box, refer to Chapter 8.

Modify Dimension When you select a dimension or geometric tolerance, AutoCAD displays the Modify Dimension dialog box, as shown in Figure 4–46.

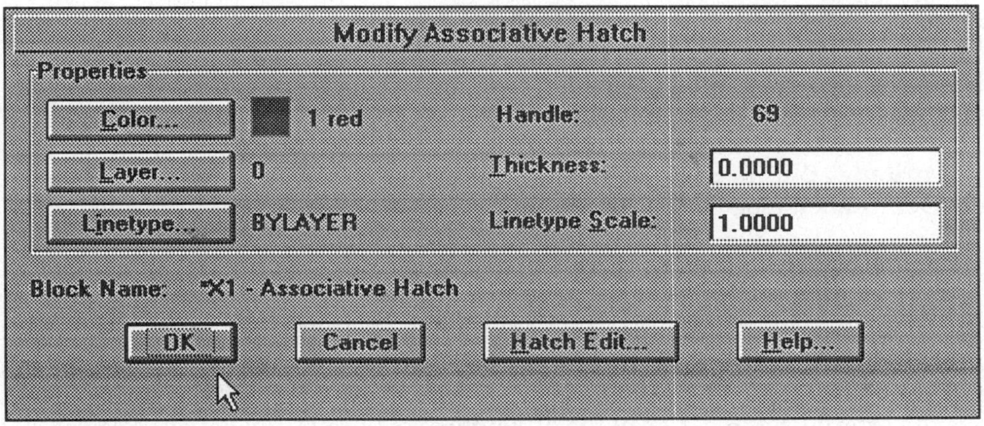

Figure 4-45 Modify Associative Hatch dialog box

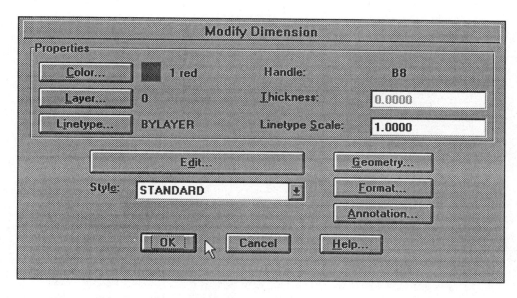

Figure 4-46 Modify Dimension dialog box

The **Edit...** button causes the Edit MText dialog box to be displayed, permitting you to edit the dimension text. The **Style:** list box permits you to specify the dimension text style for the selected dimension. The **Geometry...** button displays the Geometry sub-dialog box. For a detailed explanation of the Geometry subdialog box, refer to Chapter 6. The **Format...** button displays the Format and dialog box. For a detailed explanation of the Format sub-dialog box, refer to Chapter 6. The **Annotation...** button displays the Annotation sub-dialog box. For a detailed explanation of the Annotation sub-dialog box, refer to Chapter 6.

Modify Leader When you select a leader, AutoCAD displays the Modify Leader dialog box, as shown in Figure 4-47.

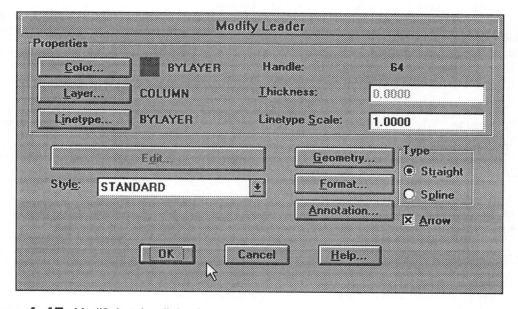

Figure 4-47 Modify Leader dialog box

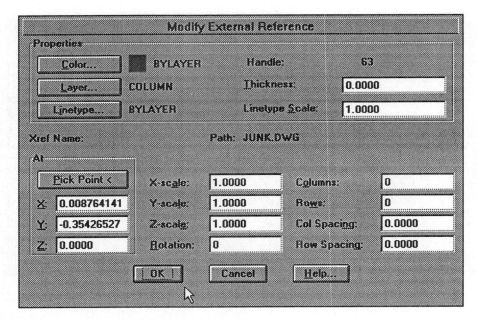

Figure 4-48 Modify External Reference dialog box

The **Edit...** button causes the Edit MText dialog box to be displayed, permitting you to edit the leader text. The **Style:** list box permits you to specify the dimension text style for the selected leader. The **Geometry...**, **Format...**, and **Annotation...** buttons operate as described in the previous section. The **Type** section permits you to specify the leader type. The **Arrow** check box permits you to control whether or not an arrow is placed at the beginning of the leader.

Modify External Reference When you select an external reference (xref), AutoCAD displays the Modify External Reference dialog box, as shown in Figure 4–48.

The **Xref Name:** and **Path:** fields display the xref name and path, respectively. The **At** section of the dialog box allows you to change the insertion of the selected external reference. The **X-scale:**, **Y-scale:**, **Z-scale:**, and **Rotation:** edit fields allow you to change the x-scale, y-scale, z-scale, and rotation angle of the selected external reference. The **Columns:**, **Rows:**, **Column Spacing:**, and **Row Spacing:** edit fields allow you to change the number of columns, number of rows, column spacing, and row spacing, respectively, when using rectangular array of the selected xref.

Modify Region When you select a region, AutoCAD displays the Modify Region dialog box, as shown in Figure 4–49.

AutoCAD allows you to modify only the Properties of the selected region.

Modify 3D Solid When you select a 3D solid, AutoCAD displays the Modify 3DSolid dialog box, as shown in Figure 4–50.

AutoCAD allows you to modify only the Properties of the selected 3DSolid.

Modify 3D Face When you select a 3D face, AutoCAD displays the Modify 3D Face dialog box, as shown in Figure 4–51.

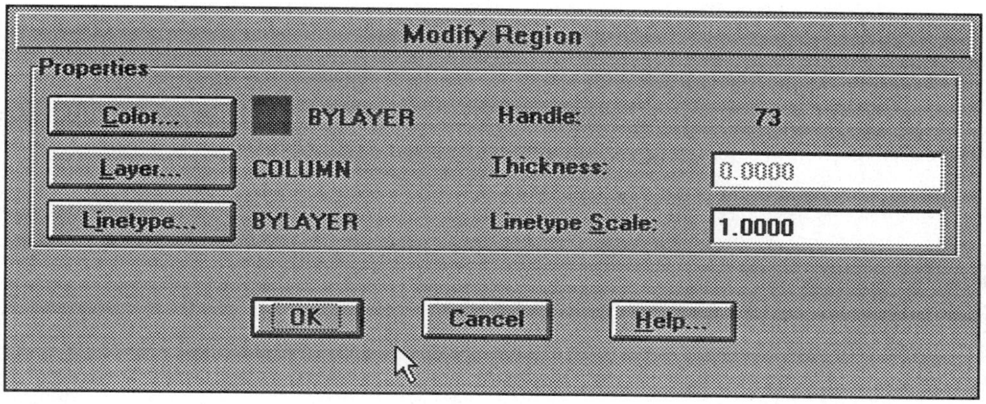

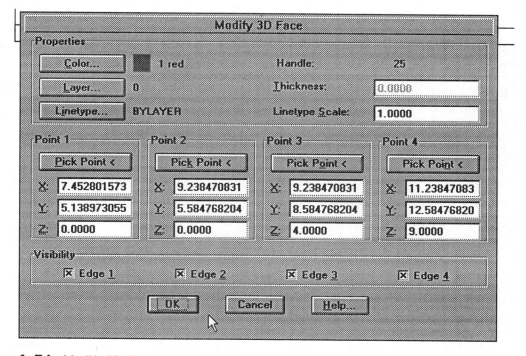

Figure 4-49 Modify Region dialog box

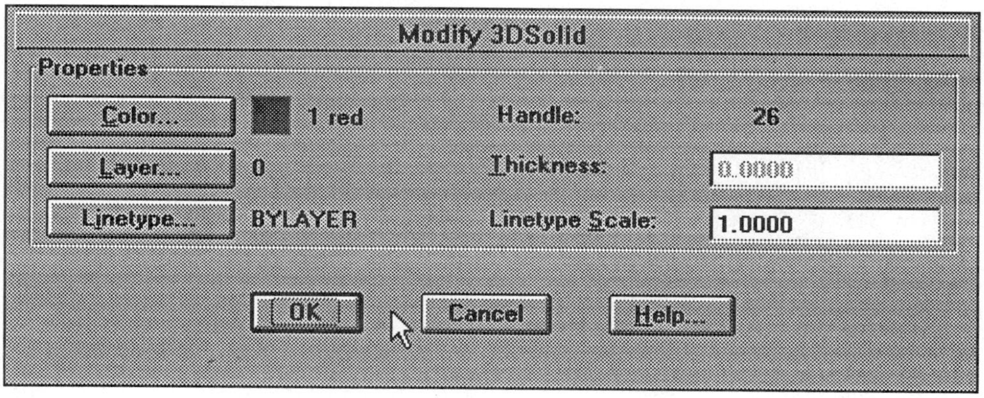

Figure 4-50 Modify 3DSolid dialog box

Figure 4-51 Modify 3D Face dialog box

The **Point 1, Point 2, Point 3,** and **Point 4** sections of the dialog box permit you to change the location of any of the four vertices by selecting a point on the screen or entering its coordinates. The **Edge 1, Edge 2, Edge 3,** and **Edge 4** check boxes allow you to control the visibility of the four edges. If the SPLFRAME system variable is set to 1 (On), all edges are visible, regardless of the visibility setting.

ROTATE Command

The ROTATE command changes the orientation of existing objects by rotating them about a specified point, labeled as the base point. Design changes often require that an object, feature, or view be rotated. By default, a positive angle rotates the object in counterclockwise direction, and a negative angle rotates in clockwise direction.

The ROTATE command is invoked from the Rotate flyout located in the Modify toolbar (see Figure 4-52), or at the "Command:" prompt, type **ROTATE** and press Enter or spacebar.

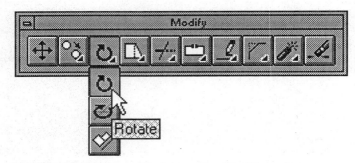

Figure 4-52 Invoke the ROTATE Command from the Modify toolbar

> Command: **rotate**
> Select objects: *(show what to rotate and then give a null response)*
> Base point: *(pick a point about which object(s) are to be rotated)*
> <Rotation angle>/Reference: *(type a positive or negative rotation angle or pick a point on screen)*

The base point can be anywhere in the drawing. If a portion of a selected object lies on the base point, that portion remains on the base point as the object's orientation changes.

The following command sequence shows an example of rotating a group of objects selected by the Window option, as shown in Figure 4-53.

> Command: **rotate**
> Select objects: *(pick a point to place one corner for a window)*
> Other corner: *(pick a point to place opposite corner of the window)*
> Select objects: Enter
> Base point: *(pick base point)*
> <Rotation angle>/Reference: **45**
> Command:

Reference Angle Option If an object has to be rotated in reference to current orientation, you can use the Reference option to do the same. Specify the current orientation as reference angle or show

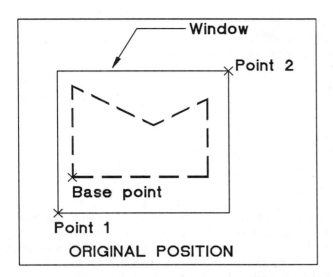

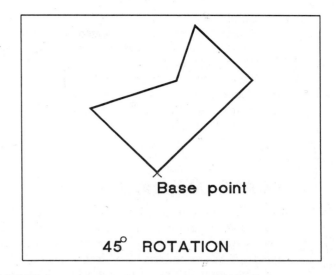

Figure 4–53 Using the Window option of the ROTATE Command to rotate a group of objects

AutoCAD the angle by pointing to the two endpoints of a line to be rotated and specify the desired new rotation. AutoCAD automatically calculates the rotation angle and rotates the object appropriately. This method of rotation is very useful when you want to straighten an object or align it with other features in a drawing.

The following command sequence shows an example of rotating a group of objects selected by the Window option in reference to current orientation, as shown in Figure 4-54.

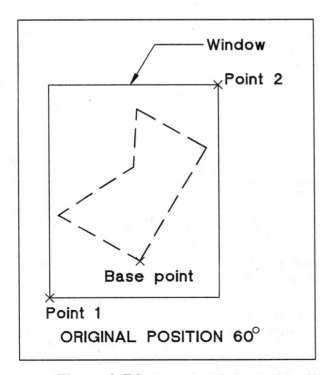

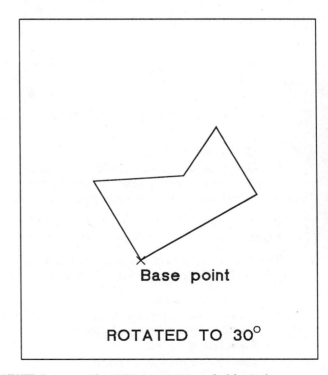

Figure 4–54 Using the Window option of the ROTATE Command to rotate a group of objects in reference to current orientation

Command: **rotate**
Select objects: *(pick a point to place one corner for a window)*
Other corner: *(pick a point to place the opposite corner of the window)*
Select objects: [Enter]
Base point: *(pick base point)*
<Rotation angle>/Reference: **R**
Reference angle: **60**
New angle: **30**
Command:

SCALE Command

The SCALE command lets you change the size of existing objects or the complete drawing. Objects are made larger or smaller; the same scale factor is applied to X and Y dimensions. To enlarge an object, enter a scale factor greater than 1. For example, a scale factor of 3 makes the selected objects 3 times larger. To shrink an object, use a scale factor between 0 and 1. Do not give a negative scale factor. For example, a scale factor of 0.75 would shrink the selected objects to three-quarter their current size.

The SCALE command is invoked from the Resize flyout located in the Modify toolbar (see Figure 4-55), or at the "Command:" prompt, type **SCALE** and press [Enter] or spacebar.

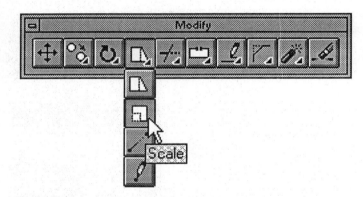

Figure 4-55 Invoke the SCALE Command from the Modify toolbar

Command: **scale**
Select objects: *(select objects to scale and then give a null response)*
Base point: *(pick a point on or near the object or enter coordinates)*
<Scale factor>/Reference: *(type a scale factor)*

The base point can be anywhere in the drawing. If a portion of the selected object lies on the base point, that portion remains on the base point as the object's size changes.

The following command sequence shows an example of using the SCALE command to enlarge a group of objects selected by the Window option, as shown in Figure 4-56.

Command: **scale**
Select objects: *(pick a point to place one corner for a window)*
Other corner: *(pick a point to place opposite corner of the window)*
Select objects: [Enter]
Base point: *(pick base point)*
<Scale Factor>/Reference: **3**
Command:

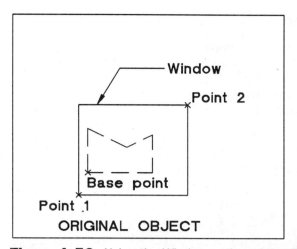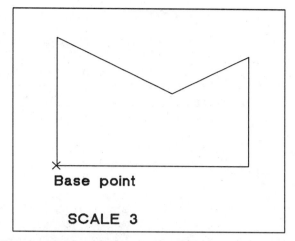

Figure 4–56 Using the Window option of the SCALE Command to enlarge a group of objects

Reference Scale Option   You can use the Reference option to scale objects relative to a current dimension rather than to unify. Specify the current dimension as a reference length or select two endpoints of a line to be scaled and specify the desired new length. AutoCAD will automatically calculate the scale factor and enlarge or shrink the object appropriately.

The following command sequence shows an example of using the SCALE command to enlarge a group of objects selected by the Window option in reference to a current dimension, as shown in Figure 4–57.

Command: **scale**
Select objects: *(pick a point to place one corner for a window)*
Other corner: *(pick a point to place the opposite corner of the window)*
Select objects: Enter
Base point: *(pick base point)*
<Scale Factor>/Reference: **R**
Reference length: **3.8**
New length: **4.8**
Command:

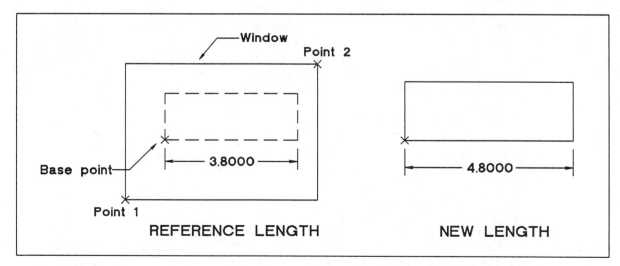

Figure 4–57 Using the Window option of the SCALE Command to enlarge a group of objects in reference to a current dimension

PEDIT (Polyline Edit) Command

The PEDIT command allows you to modify polylines. Other construct and modify commands (such as MOVE, COPY, BREAK, TRIM, and EXTEND) also work with polylines. But, because polylines are complex combinations of joined lines and/or arcs that may or may not have varying widths, AutoCAD has made available special editing features in one command for dealing with the unique properties of polylines. The PEDIT command is perhaps AutoCAD's most complex, with a multioption menu and several multioption submenus totalling some 70 command options.

The PEDIT command is invoked from the Special Edit flyout located in the Modify toolbar (Figure 4-58), or at the "Command:" prompt type **PEDIT** and press Enter or spacebar.

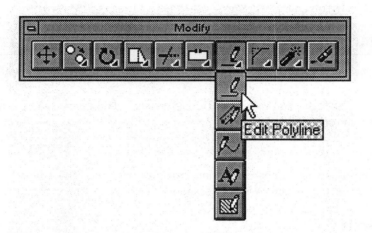

Figure 4-58 Invoke the PEDIT Command from the Modify toolbar

> Command: **pedit**
> Select polyline: *(select line or arc or polyline)*

If you select a line or arc instead of a polyline, you are prompted as follows:

> Object selected is not a polyline.
> Do you want it to turn into one? <Y>

Responding **Y** or pressing Enter turns the selected line or arc into a single segment polyline which can then be edited. Normally this is done in order to use the Join option to add other connected segments which, if not polylines, will also be transformed into polylines. It should be emphasized at this time that in order to join segments together into a polyline, their endpoints must coincide. This occurs during line-line, line-arc, arc-line, and arc-arc continuation operations or by using endpoint object snap mode. Joining segments to create one polyline can be done by using the following sequence:

> Command: **pedit**
> Select polyline: *(select line or arc)*
> Entity selected is not a polyline.
> Do you want it to turn into one? <Y>
> Close/Join/Width/Edit vertex/Fit curve/Spline/Decurve/Ltype gen/Undo/eXit <X>: **j**
> Select objects: *(proceed with object selection)*

The second prompt does not appear if the first segment selected is already a polyline. It may even be a multisegment polyline. After the object selection process, you will be returned to the multi-option prompt. Another reason for turning a line or an arc into a polyline or polyarc is to be able to give it width.

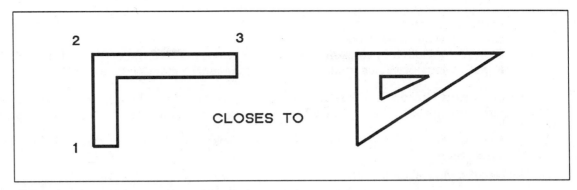

Figure 4–59 Using the PEDIT Command's Close option with polylines

This section covers features of the PEDIT command that affect 2D polylines.

Close Option The Close option performs in a manner similar to the Close option of the LINE command. If, however, the last segment was a polyarc (or polyline arc), then the next segment will be similar to the arc-arc continuation, using the direction of the last polyarc as the starting direction and draws another polyarc with the first point of the first segment as the ending point of the closing polyarc.

Figure 4–59 and Figure 4–60 show examples of the application of the Close option.

Open Option The Open option deletes the segment that was drawn with the Close option. If the polyline had been closed by drawing the last segment to the first point of the first segment without using the Close option then the Open option will not have a visible effect.

Join Option The Join option takes selected lines, arcs, and/or polylines and combines them with a previously selected polyline into a single polyline if all segments are connected at sequential and coincidental endpoints.

Width Option The Width option permits uniform or varying widths to be specified for polyline segments.

Edit Vertex Option A vertex is the point where two segments join. When you select the Edit Vertex option, the visible vertices are marked with an X to indicate which one is to be modified. You can modify vertices of polylines in several ways. When you select the Edit vertex option, AutoCAD prompts you with additional suboptions:

Fundamentals III

Figure 4–60 Using the PEDIT Command's Close option with polyarcs

Command: **pedit**
Select polyline: *(select a polyline)*
Close/Join/Width/Edit vertex/Fit curve/Spline curve/Decurve/Undo/eXit<X>: **e**
Next/Previous/Break/Insert/Move/Regen/Straighten/Tangent/Width/eXit <N>:

Next and Previous – Whether or not you have modified the marked vertex, when you wish to move the mark to the next or previous vertex, you can use the N (Next) or P (Previous) option.

Break – The Break option establishes the marked vertex as one vertex for the Break option and then prompts:

Next/Previous/Go/eXit <N>:

The choices of the Break option permit you to step to another vertex for the second break point, or to initialize the break, or to exit the option. If two vertices are selected, you may use the Go option to have the segment(s) between the vertices removed. If you select the endpoints of a polyline, this option will not work. If you select the Go option immediately after the Break option, the polyline will be divided into two separate polylines. Or, if it is a closed polyline, it will be opened at that point.

Insert – The Insert option allows you to specify a point and have the segment between the marked vertex and the next vertex become two segments meeting at the specified point. The selected point does not have to be on the polyline segment.

For example, the following command sequence shows the application of the Insert option, as shown in Figure 4–61.

Command: **pedit**
Select polyline: *(select a polyline)*
Close/Join/Width/Edit vertex/Fit curve/Spline curve/Decurve/Undo/eXit<X>: **e**
Next/Previous/Break/Insert/Move/Regen/Straighten/Tangent/Width/eXit <N>: **i**
Enter location of new vertex: *(select a new vertex)*

Move – The Move option allows you to specify a point and have the marked vertex be relocated to the selected point.

For example, the following command sequence shows the application of the Move option, as shown in Figure 4–62.

Command: **pedit**
Select polyline: *(select a polyline)*
Close/Join/Width/Edit vertex/Fit curve/Spline curve/Decurve/Undo/eXit<X>: **e**
Next/Previous/Break/Insert/Move/Regen/Straighten/Tangent/Width/eXit<N>: **m**
Enter new location: *(specify the new location)*

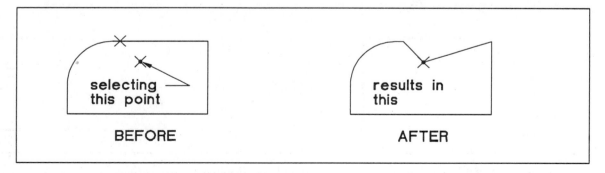

Figure 4–61 Using the PEDIT Command's Insert option

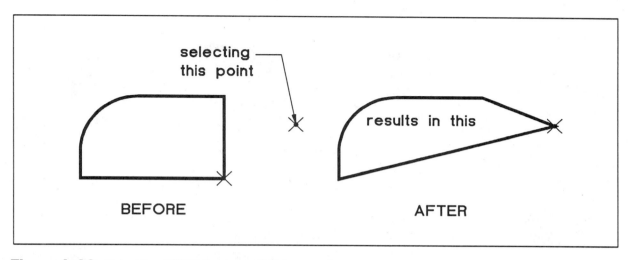

Figure 4–62 Using the PEDIT Command's Move option

Regen – The Regen option regenerates the polyline without needing to cancel the PEDIT command to invoke the REGEN command at the "Command:" prompt.

Straighten – The Straighten option establishes the marked vertex as one vertex for the Straighten option and then prompts:

    Next/Previous/Go/eXit <N>:

These choices of the Straighten option permit you to first step to another vertex for the second point, or to exit the option. When the two vertices are selected, you may use the Go option to have the segment(s) between the vertices replaced with a single straight line segment.

For example, the following command sequence shows the application of the Straighten option, as shown in Figure 4–63.

    Command: **pedit**
    Select polyline: *(select a polyline)*
    Close/Join/Width/Edit vertex/Fit curve/Spline curve/Decurve/Undo/eXit <X>: **e**
    Next/Previous/Break/Insert/Move/Regen/Straighten/Tangent/Width/eXit <N>: **s**
    Next/Previous/Go/eXit <N>: **n**
    Next/Previous/Go/eXit <N>: **n**
    Next/Previous/Go/eXit <N>: **x**

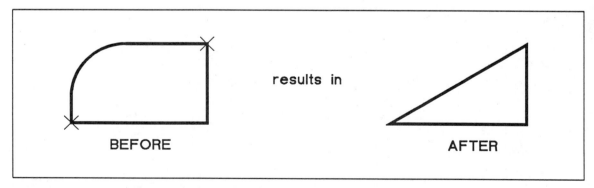

Figure 4–63 Using the PEDIT Command's Straighten option

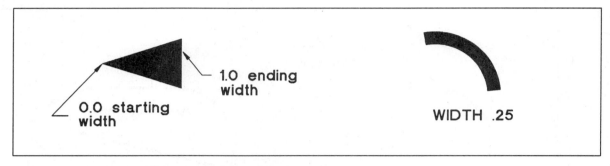

Figure 4–64 Using the PEDIT Command's Width option

Tangent – The Tangent option permits you to assign to the marked vertex a tangent direction that can be used for the curve fitting option. The prompt is as follows:

Direction of tangent:

You can specify the direction with a point or type the coordinates from the keyboard.

Width – The Width option permits you to specify the starting and ending width of the segment between the marked vertex and the next vertex. The prompt is as follows:

Enter new width for all segments <current>:

For example, the following command sequence shows the application of the Width option, as shown in Figure 4–64.

Command: **pedit**
Select polyline: *(select a polyline)*
Close/Join/Width/Edit vertex/Fit curve/Spline curve/Decurve/Undo/eXit <X>: **e**
Next/Previous/Break/Insert/Move/Regen/Straighten/Tangent/Width/eXit <N>: **w**
Enter new width for segments<default>: **0.25**

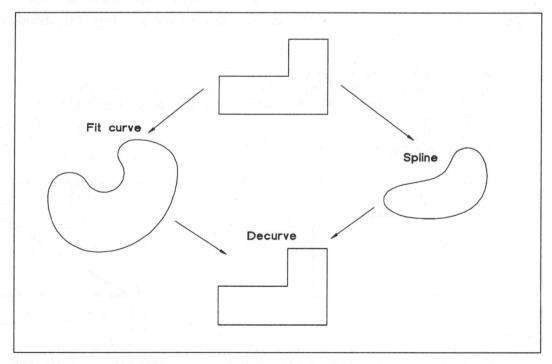

Figure 4–65 Comparing PEDIT Command's Fit Curve, Spline Curve, and Decurve Options

eXit – The eXit option exits from the Vertex editing option and returns to the PEDIT'S multioption prompt.

Fit Curve Option   The Fit Curve option draws a smooth curve through the vertices, using any specified tangents.

Spline Curve Option The Spline Curve option provides several ways to draw a curve based on the polyline being edited. These include Quadratic B-spline and Cubic B-spline curves.

Decurve Option The Decurve option returns the polyline to the way it was originally drawn.

See Figure 4–65 for differences between fit curve, spline, and decurve.

Undo Option The Undo option reverses the latest PEDIT operation.

eXit Option The eXit option exits the PEDIT command.

GRIPS

The Grips feature allows you to construct and modify AutoCAD drawings in an entirely different way to using the traditional AutoCAD construct and modify commands. Using grips you can move, stretch, rotate, copy, scale, and mirror selected objects without entering an AutoCAD command. A grip is a small square that appears at specific points on objects. To enable grips, the system variable GRIPS should be set to 1. At the "Command:" prompt, type **GRIPS**, and press ⏎. Enter 1 to turn on and 0 to turn it off. Another way is to call up the GRIPS dialog box and toggle the Enable Grips check box. This can be done by selecting **Grips. . .**from the pull-down menu Options, as shown in Figure 4–66, or at the "Command:" prompt type **DDGRIPS** and press ⏎ or spacebar.

    Command: **ddgrips**

AutoCAD then displays the Grips Setting dialog box similar to the one shown in Figure 4–67.

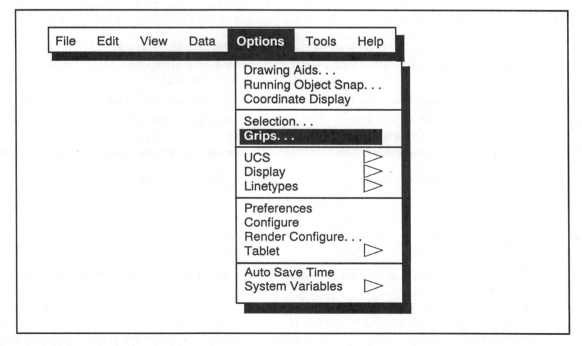

Figure 4–66 Invoke the GRIP Command from the pull-down menu Options

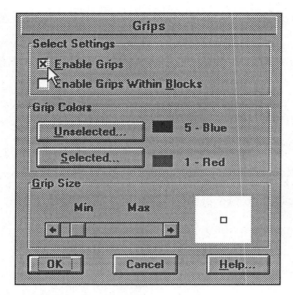

Figure 4-67 The Grips dialog box

The Select Settings area of the Grips dialog box allows you to enable grips for selected objects. Pick the Enable Grips check box to turn it on; this activates grips for all objects you select. As mentioned earlier, this can also be done by changing the System Variable Grips from 0 to 1. The Enable Grips Within Blocks check box assigns grips to the objects within a block. If you turn off this check box, the block is assigned one grip at its insertion point.

The Grip Colors area of the Grips dialog box allows you to assign colors to the selected and unselected grips. To change the default colors, select the **Unselected. . .** and/or **Selected. . .** buttons. Each displays a standard color dialog box, allowing you to choose the color you want to use.

The Grip Size area of the Grips dialog box allows you to change the size of grips. To adjust the size of grips, move the slider box left or right. As you move the slider, the size is illustrated to the right of the slider.

AutoCAD gives you a visual cue when grips are enabled by displaying a pick box at the intersection of the cross-hairs, even when you are at the "Command:" prompt as shown in Figure 4-68.

> **NOTE:** The pick box is also displayed on the crosshairs when the PICKFIRST (Noun/Verb selection) system variable is on.

To place grips, select one or more objects directly from the "Command:" prompt you wish to manipulate.

> **NOTE:** To place grips, you can select objects individually, or place two points diagonally opposite corners of a rectangle to select multiple objects.

Grips appear on the endpoints and midpoint of lines and arcs, the vertices and endpoints of polylines, quadrants and center of circles, dimension, text, solid, 3dface, 3dmesh, viewport, and the insertion point on a block. Figure 4-69 shows location of the grips on some of the commonly used objects.

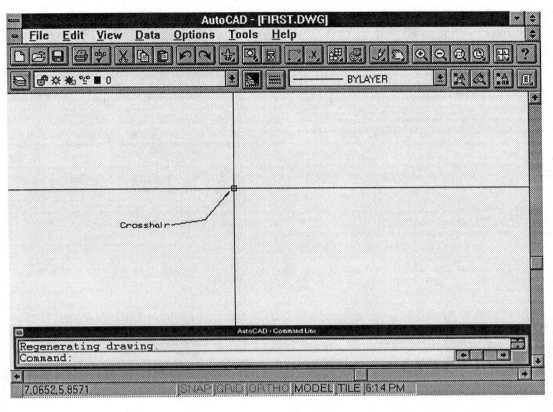

Figure 4–68 The pick box displayed at the intersection of the cross-hairs at the "Command:" prompt

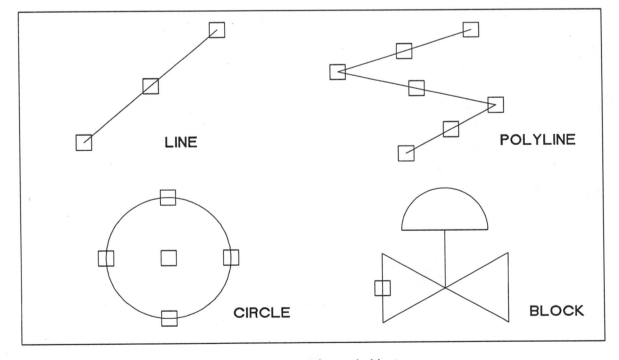

Figure 4–69 Location of Grips on most commonly used objects

Using Grips

This section explains how to utilize grips in modifying your drawing. Learning to use grips speeds up the editing of your drawing while at the same time maintaining the accuracy of your work.

Snapping to Grips When you move your cursor over a grip, it automatically snaps to the grip point. This allows you to specify exact locations in the drawing without having to use grid, snap, ortho, object snap, or coordinate entry.

Condition of Grips Grips are categorized as being hot, warm, or cold depending upon their use.

A grip is considered to be hot if you select it with your cursor. It has a solid filled color, and is the grip that will be operated on. You can make more than one grip be hot. Hold down the [Ctrl] key while selecting the grips.

A grip is considered to be warm that you haven't picked with the cursor that is on an object in the current selection set. The object(s) are highlighted to indicate that they are in the selection set.

A grip is considered to be cold on an object that is not in the current selection set. The objects with cold grips will look identical to warm grips, except the objects with cold grips are not highlighted but you can still use it to snap to. Figure 4-70 shows examples of hot, warm, and cold grips.

Clearing Out Grips To clear grips from a selection set, press [Esc] twice. The first time all the warm grips will turn to cold grips. The second time all the grips will clear.

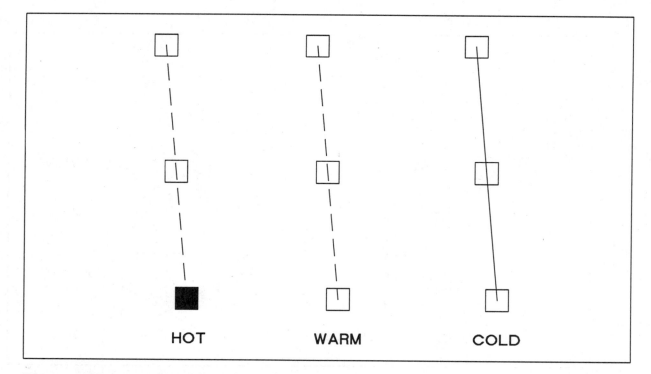

Figure 4-70 Examples of hot, warm, and cold grips

Editing with Grips

To use grips to edit the selected objects, pick a grip at the "Command:" prompt to act as the base point for the editing operation. Picking a grip starts the Grip modes, which includes STRETCH, MOVE, ROTATE, SCALE, and MIRROR. You can cycle through the grip modes by pressing the spacebar or entering a keyboard shortcut. To cancel Grip mode, enter **x** (for the mode's eXit option); AutoCAD returns to the "Command:" prompt. You can also use a combination of the current Grip mode and a multiple copy operation on the selection set.

Stretch Mode The Stretch mode works similarly to the STRETCH command. It allows you to stretch the shape of an object without affecting other crucial parts that remain unchanged. When you are in the Stretch Mode, the following prompt appears:

    STRETCH
    <Stretch to point>/Base point/Copy/Undo/eXit:

The default <Stretch to point> refers to the stretch displacement point. As you move the cursor, you see the shape of the object is stretched dynamically from the base point. You can specify the new point with the cursor or by entering coordinates. The displacement is applied to all selected hot grips.

If necessary, you can change the base point to be other than the base grip, by entering **base** or **b** to the prompt. Then pick the point with the cursor or enter the coordinates.

To make multiple copies while stretching objects, enter **copy** or **c** to the prompt. Then specify destination copy points by picking the point(s) with the cursor or enter the coordinates.

Move Mode The Move mode works similarly to the MOVE command. It allows you to move one or more objects from their present location to a new one without changing orientation or size. In addition, you can also make copies of the selected objects at the specified displacement, leaving the original objects intact. To reach Move mode, cycle through the other modes by entering a null response, or by entering **Move** or **m** from the keyboard. When you are in the Move Mode, the following prompt appears:

    MOVE
    <Move to point>/Base point/Copy/Undo/eXit:

The default <Move to point> refers to the move displacement point. As you move the cursor, AutoCAD moves all the objects in the current selection set to a new point relative to the base point. You can specify the new point with the cursor or by entering coordinates.

If necessary, you can change the base point to be other than the base grip, by entering **base** or **b** to the prompt. Then pick the point with the cursor or enter the coordinates.

To make multiple copies while moving objects, enter **copy** or **c** to the prompt and then specify destination copy points by picking the point(s) with the cursor or enter the coordinates.

Rotate Mode The Rotate mode works similarly to the ROTATE command. It allows you to change the orientation of objects by rotating them about a specified base point. In addition, you can also make copies of the selected objects and at the same time rotate them about a specified base point.

Fundamentals III

To reach Rotate mode, cycle through the other modes by entering a null response, or by entering **Rotate** or **R** from the keyboard. When you are in the Rotate Mode, the following prompt appears:

> ****ROTATE****
> <Rotation angle>/Base point/Copy/Undo/Reference/eXit:

The default <Rotation angle> refers to the rotation angle to which objects are rotated. As you move the cursor, AutoCAD allows you to drag the rotation angle to position all the objects in the current selection set at the desired orientation. You can specify the new orientation with the cursor or by specifying an angle. If you specify an angle by entering a value from the keyboard, this is taken as the amount that the objects should be rotated from their current orientation, around the base point. A positive angle rotates in counterclockwise rotation, and a negative angle rotates in clockwise rotation. Similar to the ROTATE command, you can use the Reference option to specify the current rotation and the desired new rotation.

If necessary, you can change the base point to be other than the base grip, by entering **base** or **b** to the prompt. Then pick the point with the cursor or enter the coordinates.

To make multiple copies while rotating objects, enter **copy** or **c** to the prompt. Then specify destination copy points by picking the point(s) with the cursor or enter the coordinates.

Scale Mode The Scale mode works similarly to the SCALE command. It allows you to change the size of objects about a specified base point. In addition, you can also make copies of the selected objects and at the same time change the size about a specified base point. To reach Scale mode, cycle through the other modes by entering a null response, or by entering **Scale** or **S** from the keyboard. When you are in the Scale mode, the following prompt appears:

> ****SCALE*****
> <Scale factor>/Base point/Copy/Undo/Reference/eXit:

The default <Scale factor> refers to the scale factor to which objects are made larger or smaller. As you move the cursor, AutoCAD allows you to drag the scale factor to change all the objects in the current selection set at the desired size. You can specify the new scale factor with the cursor or by specifying a scale factor. If you specify scale factor by entering a value from the keyboard, this is taken as a relative scale factor by which all dimensions of the objects in the current selection set are to be multiplied. To enlarge an object, enter a scale factor greater than 1. To shrink an object, use a scale factor between 0 and 1. Similar to the SCALE command, you can use the Reference option to specify the current length and the desired new length.

If necessary, you can change the base point to be other than the base grip, by entering **base** or **b** to the prompt. Then pick the point with the cursor or enter the coordinates.

To make multiple copies while scaling objects, enter **copy** or **c** to the prompt and then specify destination copy points by picking the point(s) with the cursor or enter the coordinates.

Mirror Mode The Mirror mode works similarly to the MIRROR command. It allows you to make mirror images of existing objects. To reach Mirror mode, cycle through other modes by entering a null response, or by entering **Mirror** or **M** from the keyboard. When you are in the Mirror Mode, the following prompt appears:

> ****MIRROR****
> <Second point>/Base point/Copy/Undo/eXit:

Two points are required in AutoCAD to define a line about which the selected objects are mirrored. AutoCAD considers the base grip point as the first point and the second point is the point you pick or enter in response to the default <Second point>.

If necessary, you can change the base point to be other than the base grip, by entering **base** or **b** to the prompt. Then pick the point with the cursor or enter the coordinates.

To make multiple copies while retaining original objects, enter **copy** or **c** to the prompt. Then specify mirror points by picking the point(s) with the cursor or enter the coordinates.

GROUP COMMAND

The GROUP command, introduced in AutoCAD Release 13, adds flexibility in modifying a group of objects. It allows you to name a selection set. Naming a selection set combines two powerful AutoCAD drawing features. One is being able to modify a group of unrelated objects as a group. It is similar to using "Previous" to select the last selection set when prompted to "Select object:" for a modify command. The advantage of using GROUP instead of "Previous" is that you are not restricted to only the last selection set. The other feature combined in the GROUP command is that of giving a name to a selected group of objects for later recalling by the name of the group. This is similar to the BLOCK command. The advantage of using GROUP instead of BLOCK is that the GROUP's "selectable" switch can be turned off for modifying an individual member without losing its "membership" in the group. Also, named groups, like blocks, are saved with the drawing.

A named group can be selected for modifying as a group only when its "selectable" switch is on. Figure 4–71 shows the result of trimming an object with selectable switch set to on/off. Modifying

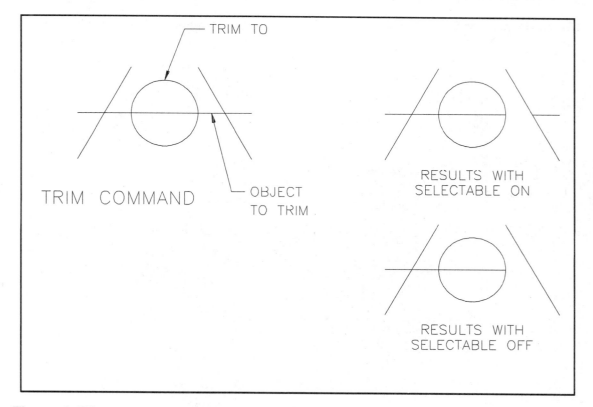

Figure 4–71 Trimming an object with selectable switch set to on/off

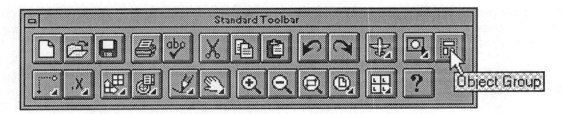

Figure 4–72 Invoke the GROUP command from Standard toolbar

(such as MOVE or COPY) objects that belong to a group can be selected by two methods. One is to select one of its members. The other method is by selecting the Group option from the Select Objects toolbar or type **g** at the "Select Objects:" prompt. AutoCAD prompts for the group's name. Enter the group name and press Enter or spacebar. AutoCAD highlights the objects that belong to the selected group.

To create a new group or edit an existing group, invoke the GROUP Command. The GROUP command is invoked from the Standard toolbar (see Figure 4–72), or at the "Command:" prompt, type GROUP and press Enter or spacebar. The Object Grouping dialog box appears as shown in Figure 4–73.

The dialog box is divided into four areas. The areas include:

Group Name list box
Group Identification
Create Group
Change Group

Group Name list box The Group Name list box lists the names of the existing groups defined in the current drawing. The Selectable column indicates whether a group is selectable. If it is listed

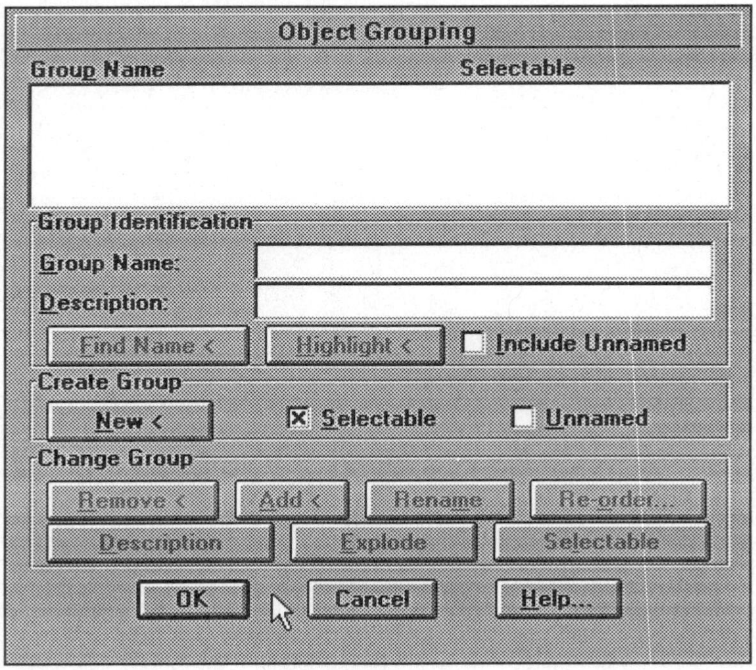

Figure 4–73 Object Grouping dialog box

as selectable, then selecting a single group member selects all the members except those on locked layers. If it is listed as unselectable, then selecting a single group member selects only that object.

Group Identification AutoCAD displays the Group Name and Description in the Group Identification area when a group is selected in the Group Name list.

Click the **Find Name** button to list the groups to which an object belongs. AutoCAD prompts for the selection of an object and displays the Group Member List dialog box, which lists the group or groups to which the selected object belongs.

Click the **Highlight** button to see the members of the selected group from the Group Name list box.

The **Include Unnamed** toggle controls the listing of the unnamed groups in the Group Name list box.

Create Group The Create Group area is used for creating a new group with or without a group name. In addition, you can set whether or not it is initially selectable.

To create a new group, type the group name and description in the Group Name and Description edit field. Group names can be up to 31 characters long and can include letters, numbers, and the special charcters $, _, and _. To create a unnamed group, turn on the **Unnamed** toggle button. AutoCAD assigns a default name, *An, to unnamed groups. The n represents a number that increases with each new group.

Set the **Selectable** button to on or off and then click the **New <** button. AutoCAD prompts for the selection of objects. Select all the objects to be included in the new group and press Enter or spacebar to complete the selection.

Change Group The Change Group area is for making changes to individual members of a group or to the group itself. The buttons are disabled until a group name is selected in the Group Name list box.

The **Remove** button allows you to remove the selected objects from the selected group. To remove objects from the selected group click the **Remove** button, AutoCAD prompts:

> Remove objects: *(select objects that are to be removed from the selected group and press* Enter *or spacebar)*

AutoCAD redisplays the Object Grouping dialog box.

The **Add** button allows you to add the selected objects to the selected group. To add objects from the selected group, click the Add button; AutoCAD prompts:

> Select objects: *(select objects that are to be added to the selected group and press* Enter *or spacebar)*

AutoCAD redisplays the Object Grouping dialog box.

Fundamentals III

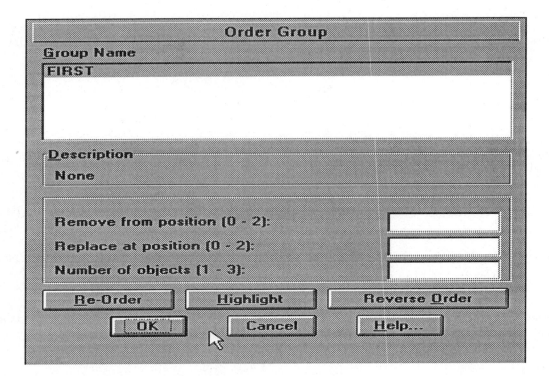

Figure 4–74 Order Group sub-dialog box

The **Rename** button allows you to change the name of the selected group to the name entered in the Group Name edit box in the Group Identification area.

The **Re-Order** option allows you to change the numerical order of objects within the selected group. Initially, the objects are numbered in the order in which they were selected to form a group. Reordering is useful when creating tool paths. Click the **Re-Order. . .** button; AutoCAD displays Order Group sub-dialog box as shown in Figure 4–74.

The Group Name lists the names of the groups defined in the current drawing. Members of a group are numbered sequentially starting with number 0 (zero).

  Remove from position (0 – n) identifies the position number of an object.

  Replace at position (0 – n) identifies the new position number of the object.

  Number of objects (0 – n) identifies the number/range of objects to reorder.

  The **Re-Order** and **Reverse Order** buttons allow you to change the numerical order of objects as specified and reverses the order of all members respectively.

  The **Highlight** button allows AutoCAD to display the members of the selected group in the graphics area.

  The **Description** button assigns an optional description up to 64 characters long.

The **Explode** button deletes the selected group from the current drawing. Thus, the group no longer exists as a group. The members remain in the drawing and in any other group(s) of which they are members.

The **Selectable** button switches the selectability of the group. If it is on, it is switched off and vice versa.

FILTER — SELECTION SET

The FILTER command displays a dialog box that lets you create filter lists that you can apply to the selection set. Using the FILTER command, you can select objects based on object properties, such as location, object type, color, linetype, layer, block name, text style, and thickness. For example, you could use FILTER command to select all the blue lines and arcs with a radius of 2.0 units. You can even name filter lists and save them to a file.

The new selection set that is created by the FILTER command can be used as Previous Option at the next "Select object:" prompt. If you use the FILTER command transparently, then AutoCAD passes the new selection set directly to the command in operation. This will save you a considerable amount of time.

The FILTER command is invoked from the Select Objects toolbar (Figure 4–75), or at the "Command:" prompt type **FILTER** and press ⏎.

Figure 4–75   Invoke the FILTER Command from the Select Objects toolbar

Command: **filter**

AutoCAD displays the Object Selection Filters dialog box similar to the one shown in Figure 4–76. The list box displays the filters being used currently as a selection set. If this is the first time you are using the FILTER command in the current drawing, then the list box is empty.

The **Select Filter** area lets you add filters to the list box based on object properties. Select the object or logical operator from the popup list. You can use the grouping operators AND, OR, XOR,

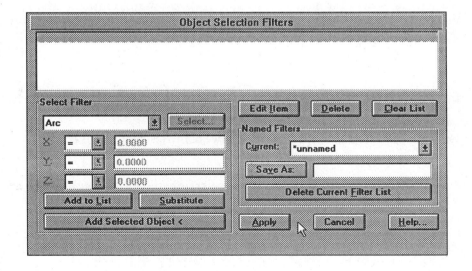

Figure 4–76   Object Selection Filters dialog box

and NOT from the popup list. The grouping operators must be paired and balanced correctly in the filter list. For example, each Begin OR operator must have a matching End OR operator. If you select more than one filter, AutoCAD by default uses an AND as a grouping operator between each filter.

The **Select. . .** button displays a dialog box that lists all items of the specified type within the drawing. From the list, you can select as many items as you want to filter. This process saves you from typing the specific filter parameters. Click on the **Add to List** button to add the current Select Filter to the filter list.

The **Add Selected Object<** button allows you to select an object from the drawing and adds it to the filter list. The **Delete** and **Clear List** buttons delete the highlighted filter in the list box and delete the current Filter list, respectively. The **Edit Item** button lets you edit the highlighted filter in the object list box. The filter and its values appear in the edit boxes. Edit the filter and values and click the **Substitute** button. The edited filter replaces the highlighted filter.

The **Save As:** button lets you save a filter list. Enter the name of the filter list in the edit box and click the **Save As:** button. AutoCAD saves the filter list in the filter.nfl file. You can select a named filter list from the current popup list. Click the **Apply** button to exit and perform the filter operation. If AutoCAD finds an error in your filter list, it displays an error message at the bottom of the dialog box.

ZOOM—ADDITIONAL OPTIONS

In this section, four additional options of the ZOOM command are explained, including Dynamic, Center, Left, and Vmax, in addition to the options explained in Chapter 2.

Dynamic Option   AutoCAD's ZOOM Dynamic command provides a quick and easy method to move to another view of the drawing. With the ZOOM Dynamic, you can see the entire drawing and then select the location and size of the next view by simple cursor manipulations. Using ZOOM Dynamic is the only means by which you can visually select a new display area that is not entirely within the current display. The only other method of visually selecting the entire new display is ZOOM Window, which is restricted to an area inside the current display. Other methods of visually selecting part of the new display within the current area are ZOOM Left Corner and ZOOM Center. But these methods (Window, Center, and Left Corner) do not permit visual selections that are entirely outside the current display. The command sequence for ZOOM Dynamic is as follows:

Command: **zoom**
All/Center/Dynamic/Extents/Left/Previous/Vmax/Window/<Scale(X/XP): **d**

The current viewport is then transformed into a selecting view that displays the drawing extents, as shown in Figure 4–77.

When the selecting view is displayed, you see the drawing extents marked by a white or black box, the current display marked by a green or magenta dotted box, and the generated area marked at the corners in red. A new view box, the same size as the current display, appears. Its location is

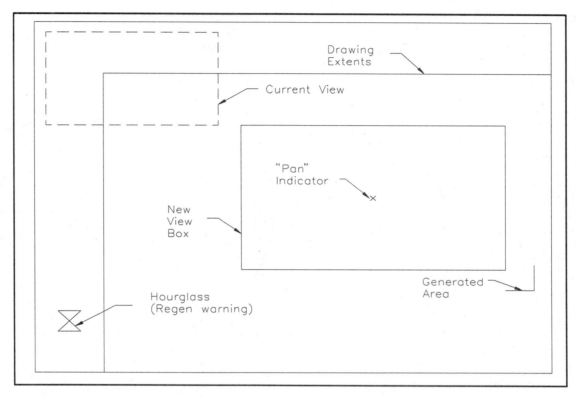

Figure 4-77 Using the ZOOM Dynamic to display the drawing extents

controlled by movement of the pointing device. Its size is controlled by a combination of the pick button and cursor movement. When the new view box has an X in the center, the box pans around the drawing in response to cursor movement. After pressing the pick button on the pointing device, the X disappears and an arrow appears at the right edge of the box. The new view box is now in zoom mode. While the arrow is in the box, moving the cursor left decreases the box size; moving the cursor right increases the size.

When the desired size has been chosen, press the pick button again to pan or press ⌨Enter to accept the view defined by the location/size of the new view box. Pressing ⌨Esc cancels the ZOOM Dynamic and returns you to the current view.

The hourglass symbol appears when the new view being selected is not entirely within the area defined by the four corners of the generated area. This means that a REGEN is necessary, thus requiring more time than REDRAW. If used transparently, AutoCAD will not permit this and will display a message:

> ***Requires regen, cannot be transparent***

Center Option The Center option of the ZOOM command lets you select a new view by specifying its center point and the height of the view in current units. The following command sequence shows an example of the Center option, as shown in Figure 4-78.

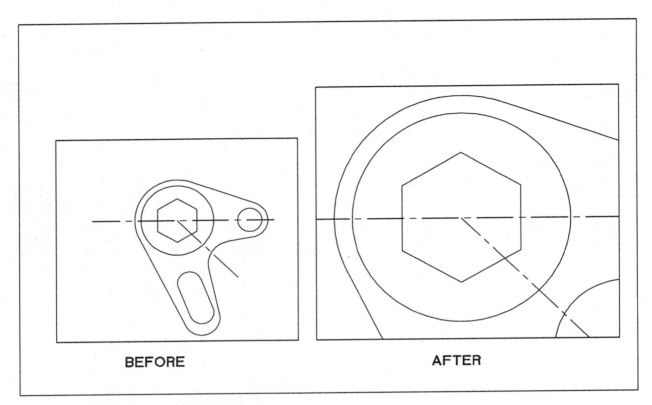

BEFORE   AFTER

Figure 4–78 Using the ZOOM Command's Center option

```
Command: zoom
All/Center/Dynamic/Extents/Left/Previous/Vmax/Window/<Scale(X/XP): c
Center point: 8,6
Magnification or Height <current height>: 4
```

The center point may be picked on the screen. The height can also be specified in terms of the current view height by specifying the magnification value followed by an X. A response of 3X will make the new view height three times as large as the current height. The model space view height may be specified in terms of paper space by entering a value followed by XP.

Left Corner Option The Left Corner option of the ZOOM command operates exactly like ZOOM Center, except the point specified becomes the lower left corner of the new view instead of the center. X and XP magnification are used in the same manner as in the Center option.

Vmax Option The Vmax option of the ZOOM command causes the new view to be the same as the current viewport's Virtual Screen. This provides the largest display without causing a regeneration.

Aerial View

The DSVIEWER command is used to activate the Aerial View, which provides a quick method of visually panning and zooming. The DSVIEWER command is invoked from the Standard Toolbar (Figure 4–79) or at the "Command:" prompt type DDVIEWER and press Enter or spacebar. AutoCAD displays the Aerial View window with the entire drawing displayed in the window, as shown in Figure 4–80.

Figure 4–79 Invoke the DSVIEWER Command from Standard toolbar

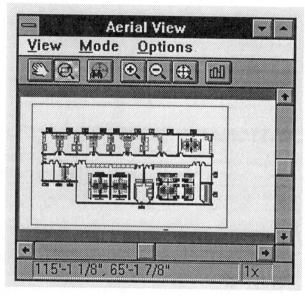

Figure 4–80 Aerial View window

View Menu The View menu in the Aerial View window has three options available. Option **Zoom In** causes the view to appear closer, enlarging the details of objects, but covering a smaller area. Option **Zoom Out** causes the view to appear farther away, decreasing the size of details of objects, but covering a larger area. Option **Global** causes the entire drawing to be viewable in the Aerial View window. You can also select the three options from the toolbar provided in the Aerial View window.

Mode Menu The Mode menu in the Aerial View window has two options available. The selection of the **Pan** mode option causes the view to move in response to slide bar movements. Selection of the **Zoom** mode option changes the view by increasing and decreasing the magnification of the area in the Aerial View window. You can also change the mode selection from the toolbar provided in the Aerial View window.

Options Menu The Options Menu in the Aerial View window has four options available. **Auto Viewport** causes the active viewport to be displayed in model space. **Dynamic Update** toggles whether the view is updated in response to editing. **Locator Magnification** causes the Magnification dialog box to be displayed, as shown in Figure 4–81.

You can enter a magnification value or use the + or – to change the magnification. You can increase magnification up to 32 times the area under the cursor. The **Display Statistics** option causes the Display Driver Info dialog box to be displayed.

Figure 4–81   Magnification dialog box

Locator Tool   The Locator Tool available in the toolbar in the Aerial View window allows you to specify an area on the drawing to be displayed in the Aerial View window. When you select the Locator Tool from the toolbar, the cursor becomes a circle with a cross through it, like a target. You can then drag the cursor onto the area of the drawing to be displayed in the Aerial View window.

OBJECT SNAP—ADDITIONAL OPTIONS

In this section, the remaining seven object snap modes are explained, including INTersection, Apparent Intersection, NODe, NEArest, INSert, and QUICK, in addition to OSNAP modes explained in Chapters 2 and 3.

INTersection Mode   The INTersection object snap mode lets you specify an intersection of two objects in response to a prompt requiring a point. Intersections can be of a line, arc, spline, elliptical arc, ellipse, ray, xline, mline or circle (see Figure 4–82).

Apparent Intersection Mode   The Apparent Intersection object snap mode snaps to the apparent intersection of two objects (line, arc, spline, elliptical arc, ellipse, ray, xline, mline, or circle) which may or may not actually intersect in 3D space.

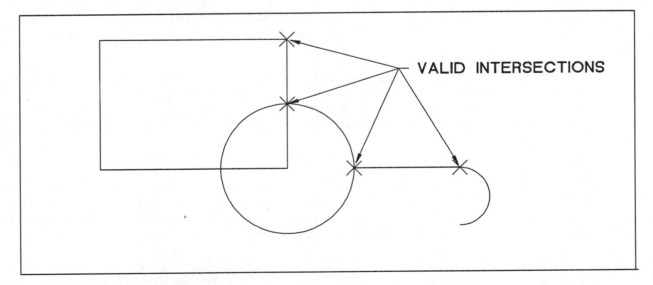

Figure 4–82   Valid Intersections that can be selected using the OSNAP INT Mode

NOde Mode The NOde object snap mode snaps to a point object.

NEArest Mode The NEArest object snap mode lets you specify any object (except text and shape items) in response to a prompt for a point and AutoCAD uses the point on that object nearest the cursor. Some part of the object must be in the aperture box for a point on that object to be used.

INSert Mode The INSert object snap mode lets you specify the insertion point of a block, text string, attribute, or shape in response to a prompt for a point.

Quick Mode The Quick object snap mode snaps to the first snap point found. Quick must be used in conjunction with other object snap modes.

Fundamentals III

PROJECT EXERCISE

In this project, you apply AutoCAD concepts and skills discussed in chapters 1 through 4 to create the structural steel plan as shown in Figure P4–1.

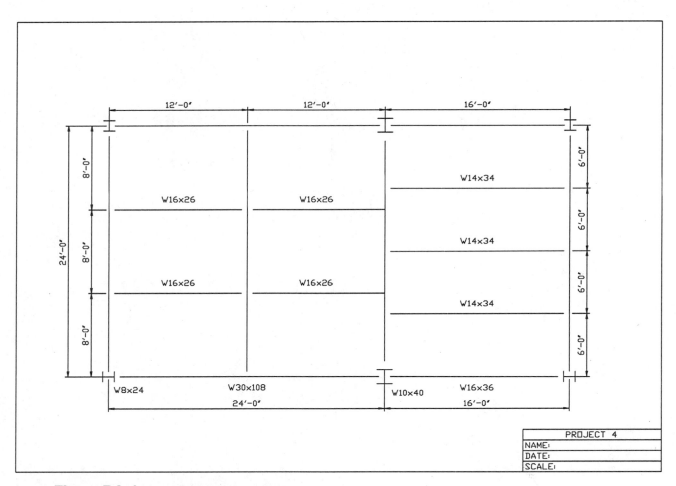

Figure P4–1 Completed project design

NOTE: The step-by-step instructions for this project are designed to provide practice in the concepts presented in chapters 1 through 4. It is not necessarily the most efficient way to draw the design. Do not dimension, provided only for reference.

STEP 1 Invoke the AutoCAD program from the Windows Program Manager.

STEP 2 Invoke the NEW command from the pull-down menu File or type New at the "Command:" prompt. Enter CH4-PROJ as the name of the drawing file. Make sure ACAD.DWG is selected as the prototype drawing.

STEP 3 Select the UNITS command from the pull-down menu Data to open the DDUNITS dialog box. Set up units to architectural and degrees to decimal as shown in Figure P4–2.

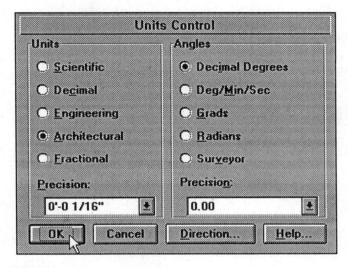

Figure P4–2 DDUNITS Dialog Box

STEP 4 Invoke the LIMITS command and set the limits as shown.

Command: **limits**
on/off/<Lower left corner><default>: **–10', –10'**
Upper right corner<default>: **50', 35'**

Command: zoom
All/Center/Dynamic/Extents/Left/Previous/Vmax/Window/Scale(X/XP)>: **a**

STEP 5 Open the Drawing Aids dialog box from the pull-down menu Options and set grid to 1', snap to 6" and turn ON the grid and snap tools as shown in Figure P4–3.

STEP 6 Invoke the LAYER command from the pull-down menu Data, create layers named border, plan, column, text, and dim with appropriate colors and linetype as shown in the dialog box in Figure P4–4. Set Layer "Plan" as the current layer.

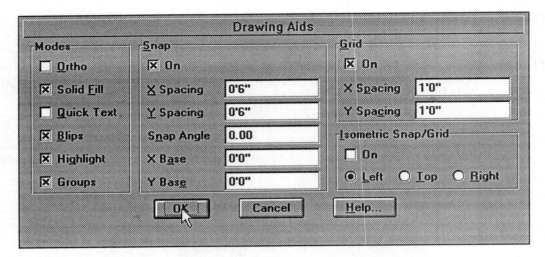

Figure P4–3 DDRMODES Dialog Box

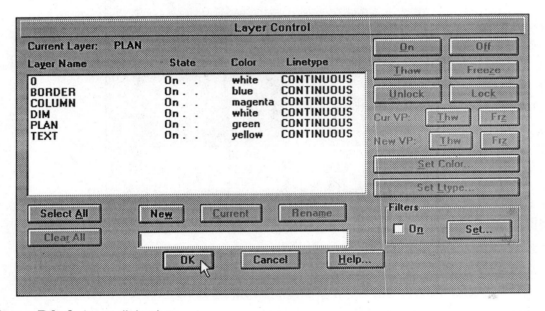

Figure P4–4 Layer dialog box

STEP 7   Create a layout of the lines where the beams will be drawn.

Command: **line**
From point: **0,0**
To point: **@40',0**
To point: **@0,24'**
To point: **@–40',0**
To point: **close**

Command: **line**
From point: **0,8'**
To point: **@24,0**
To point: Enter

Your drawing should look like Figure P4-5.

Command: **copy**
Select objects: *(select line 1 as shown in Figure P4-6)*
Select objects: Enter
<Base point or displacement>/Multiple: **0,0**
Second point of displacement: **@0,8'**

Command: **line**
From point: **24',6'**
To point: **@16',0**
To point: Enter

Command: **copy**
Select objects: *(select line 2 as shown in Figure P4–7)*
Select objects: Enter
<Base point or displacement>/Multiple: **m**
Base point: **0,0**
Second point of displacement: **@0,6'**
Second point of displacement: **@0, 12'**
Second point of displacement: Enter

Command: **line**
From point: **12',0**
To point: **@0,24'**
To point: Enter

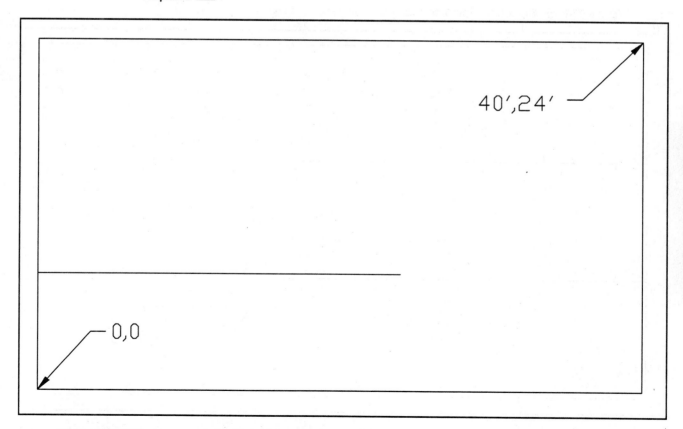

Figure P4–5 Layout of the lines for placing beams

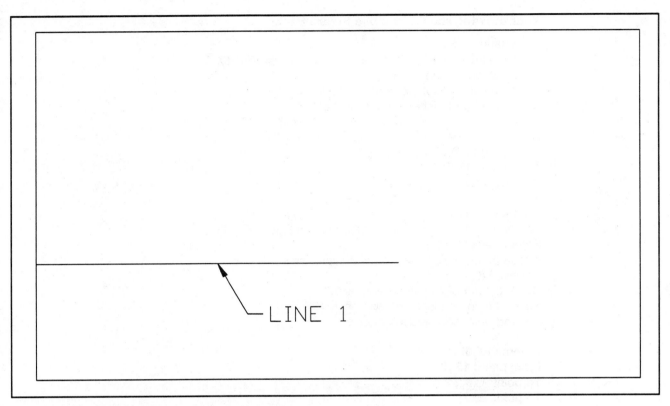

Figure P4–6 Selecting Line 1 to make a copy

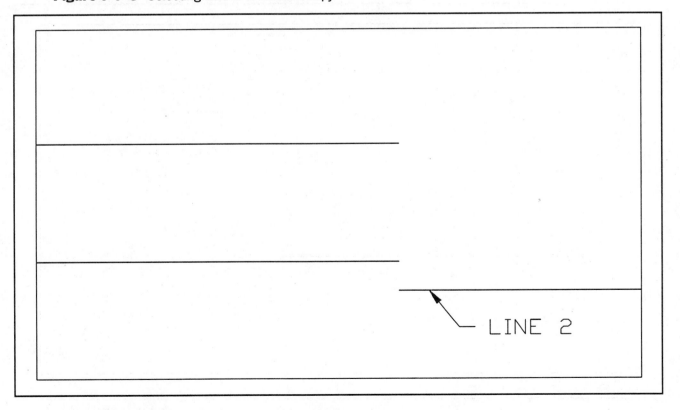

Figure P4–7 Selecting Line 2 to make multiple copies

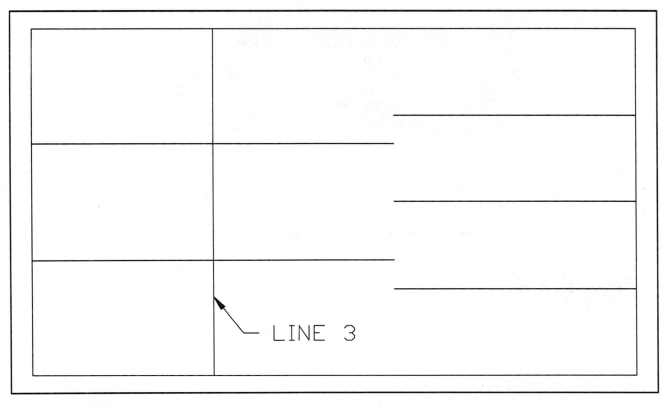

Figure P4–8 Selecting Line 3 to make a copy

Command: **copy**
Select objects: *(select line 3 as shown in Figure P4–8)*
Select objects: Enter
<Base point or displacement>/Multiple: **0,0**
Second point of displacement: **@12',0**

STEP 8 Set "Column" as the current layer from the Object Properties toolbar, as shown in Figure P4-9.

STEP 9 Create a 12" × 12" column using the PLINE command by snapping to the invisible dots:

Command: **zoom**
All/Center/Dynamic/Extents/Left/Previous/Vmax/Window/Scale(X/XP)>: **w**
First corner: *(select point 1 as shown in Figure P4-10)*
Other corner: *(select point 2 as shown in Figure P4-10)*

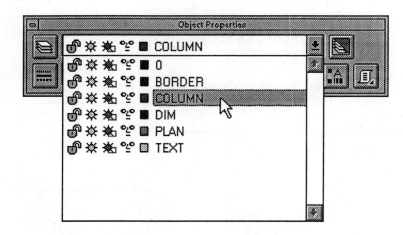

Figure P4–9 Setting "Column" as the current layer

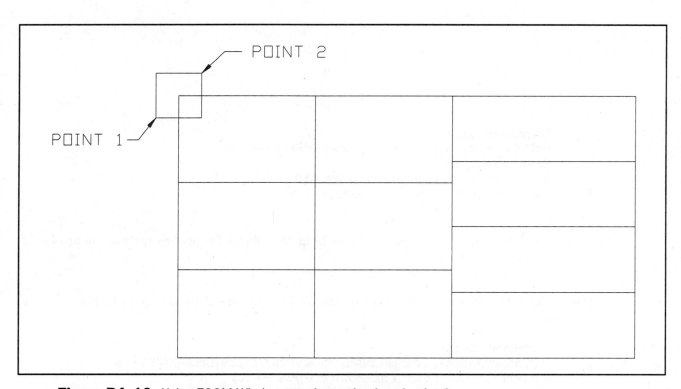

Figure P4–10 Using ZOOM Window to select point 1 and point 2

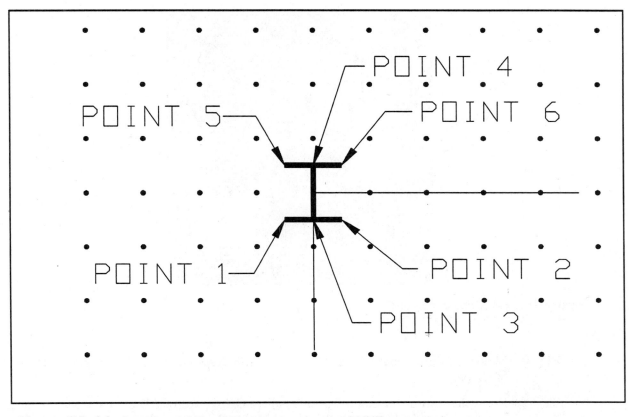

Figure P4–11   Creating a 12" × 12" column using the PLINE command

Command **pline**
From point: *(select point 1 as shownn in Figure P4-11)*
Current line-width is 0'-0"
Arc/Close/Halfwidth/Length/Undo/Width/<Endpoint of line>: **w**
Starting width<0'-0"> **1**
Ending width<0'-1"> Enter
Arc/Close/Halfwidth/Length/Undo/Width/<Endpoint of line>: *(select point 2 as shown in Figure P4-11)*
Arc/Close/Halfwidth/Length/Undo/Width/<Endpoint of line>: Enter

Command: **pline**
From point: *(select point 3 as shown in Figure P4–11)*
Current line-width is 0'-1"
Arc/Close/Halfwidth/Length/Undo/Width/<Endpoint of line>: *(select point 4 as shown in Figure P4-11)*
Arc/Close/Halfwidth/Length/Undo/Width/<Endpoint of line>: Enter

Command: **pline**
From point: *(select point 5 as shown in Figure P4-11)*
Current line-width is 0'-1"
Arc/Close/Halfwidth/Length/Undo/Width/<Endpoint of line>: *(select point 6 as shown in Figure P4-11)*
Arc/Close/Halfwidth/Length/Undo/Width/<Endpoint of line>: Enter

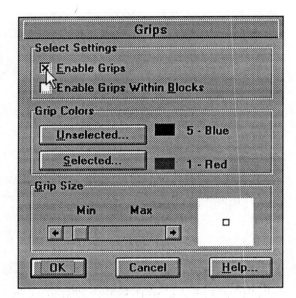

Figure P4–12 Grips dialog box

STEP 10 Make multiple copies of the 12" x 12" column drawn in the previous step with the help of Grips.

From the pull-down menu Options, select Grips. AutoCAD displays the Grips dialog box as shown in Figure P4-12. Enable the Grips and click OK button to close the dialog box.

Place grips on the column drawn in the previous step and then select the top left grip to make it hot grip as shown in Figure P4-13.

AutoCAD prompts:

Command:
STRETCH
<Stretch to point>/Base point/Copy/Undo/eXit: ⌷Enter⌷
MOVE
<Move to point>/Base point/Copy/Undo/eXit: **c**
** MOVE (multiple) **
<Move to point>/Base point/Copy/Undo/eXit: **b**
Base point: *(Use object snap to snap to the mid point of the column as shown in Figure P4-14)*
** MOVE (multiple) **
<Move to point>/Base point/Copy/Undo/eXit: **@24',0**
** MOVE (multiple) **
<Move to point>/Base point/Copy/Undo/eXit: **@40',0**
** MOVE (multiple) **
<Move to point>/Base point/Copy/Undo/eXit: **@0, –24'**
** MOVE (multiple) **
<Move to point>/Base point/Copy/Undo/eXit: **x**

Press ⌷Esc⌷ twice to remove the grips from the column.

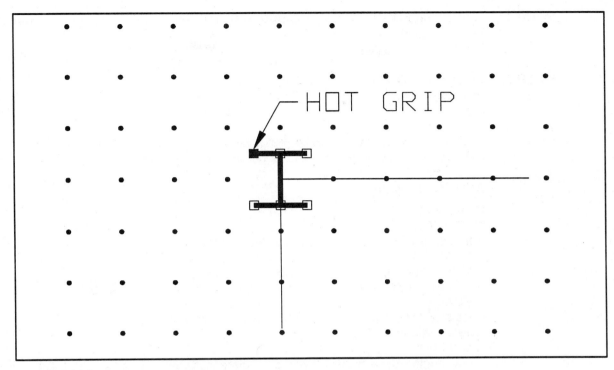

Figure P4–13 Column with grips

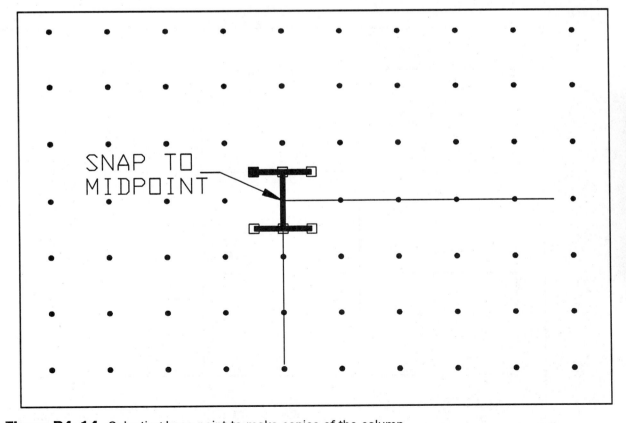

Figure P4–14 Selecting base point to make copies of the column

STEP 11   Invoke the ZOOM ALL command to return to the full drawing view. Your drawing should look like Figure P4-15.

STEP 12   Invoke the ZOOM WINDOW command to display the top middle column in the drawing view.

STEP 13   Place grips on the column to increase the size of the column from 12" × 12" to 16" × 16". Select the top left grip to make it a hot grip as shown in Figure P4-16.

AutoCAD prompts:

Command:
** STRETCH **
<Stretch to point>/Base point/Copy/Undo/eXit:**sc**
** SCALE **
<Scale factor>/Base point/Copy/Undo/Reference/eXit: **b**
Base point: *(Use object snap to snap to the mid point of the column)*
** SCALE **
<Scale factor>/Base point/Copy/Undo/Reference/eXit:**r**
Reference length <0'-1">: **12**
** SCALE **
<New length>/Base point/Copy/Undo?Reference?eXit: **16**

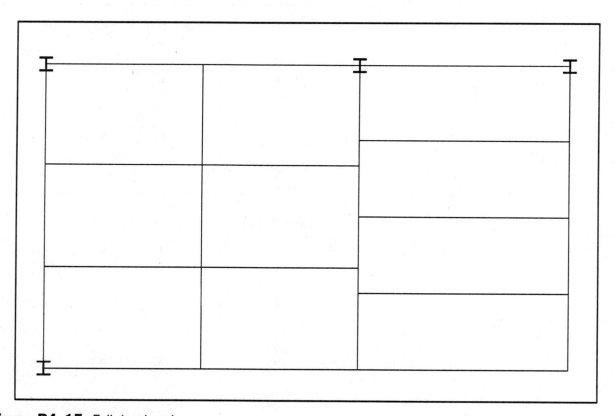

Figure P4–15 Full drawing view

STEP 14   Make a copy of the 16" × 16" column by selecting the top left grip to make it a hot grip.

Command:
** STRETCH **
<Stretch to point>/Base point/Copy/Undo/eXit: [Enter]
** MOVE **
<Move to point>/Base point/Copy/Undo/Reference/eXit: **c**
** MOVE (multiple) **
<Move to point>/Base point/Copy/Undo/Reference/eXit: **b**
Base point: *(Use object snap to snap to the mid point of the column)*
** MOVE (multiple) **
<Move to point>/Base point/Copy/Undo/Reference/eXit: **@0, –24'**
** MOVE (multiple) **
<Move to point>/Base point/Copy/Undo/Reference/eXit: **x**

Press [Esc] twice to remove the grips from the column.

STEP 15   Invoke the ZOOM ALL command to return to the full drawing view. Your drawing should look like Figure P4–17.

STEP 16   Invoke the ZOOM WINDOW command to display the bottom left column in the drawing view.

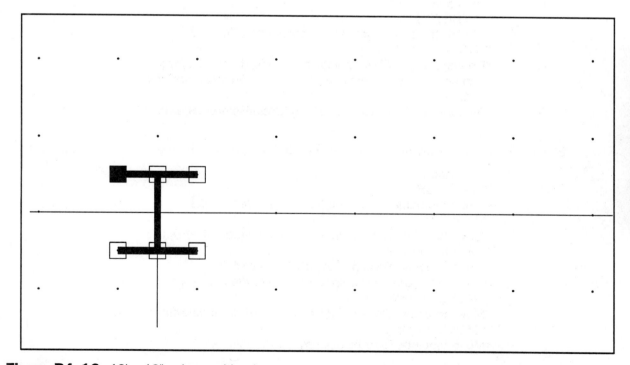

Figure P4–16   12' × 12" column with grips

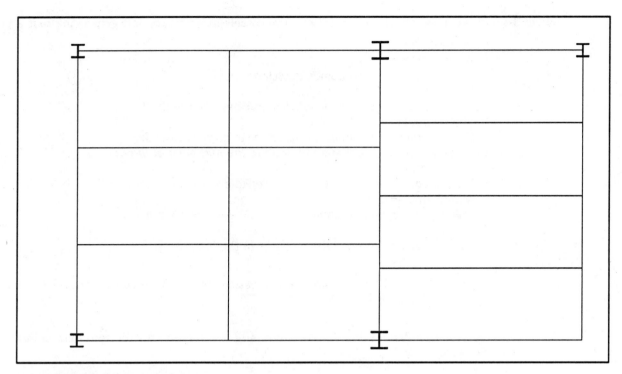

Figure P4–17 Full drawing view

STEP 17 Place grips on the column to rotate 90 degrees. Select the top left grip to make it hot. AutoCAD prompts:

Command:
** STRETCH **
<Stretch to point>/Base point/Copy/Undo/eXit: **RO**
** ROTATE **
<Rotation angle>/Base point/Copy/Undo/Referentce/eXit: **b**
Base point: *(Use object snap to snap to the mid point of the column)*
** ROTATE **
<Rotation angle>/Base point/Copy/Undo/Reference/eXit: **90**

STEP 18 Make a copy of the rotated column by selecting the top left grip to make it hot.

Command:
** STRETCH **
<Stretch to point>/Base point/Copy/Undo/eXit: [Enter]
** MOVE **
<Move to point>/Base point/Copy/Undo/Referentce/eXit: **c**
** MOVE (multiple) **
<Move to point>/Base point/Copy/Undo/eXit: **b**
Base point: *(Use object snap to snap to the mid point of the column)*
** MOVE (multiple) **
<Move to point>/Base point/Copy/Undo/Reference/eXit: **@40'<0**
** MOVE (multiple) **
<Move topoint>/Base point/Copy?Undo/eXit: **x**

Press [Esc] twice to remove the grips from the column.

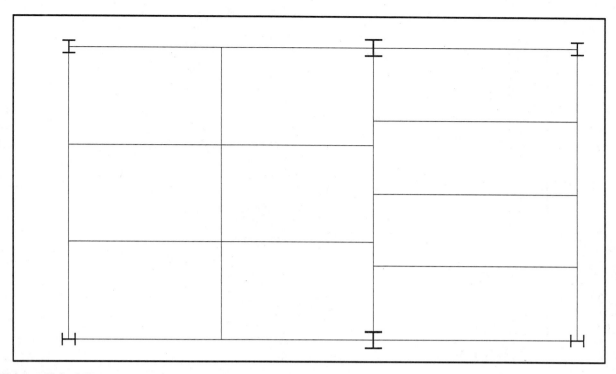

Figure P4–18 Full drawing view

STEP 19   Invoke the ZOOM ALL command to return to the full drawing view. Your dawing should look like Figure P4–18.

STEP 20   Use the LENGTHEN command to leave a 6" gap between the beam intersection. Invoke the LENGTHEN command from the Modify toolbar, or type LENGTHEN at the "Command:" prompt and press ⌨Enter or spacebar.

Command: **lengthen**
DElta/Percent/Total/DYnamic/<Select objects>: **de**
Angle/<Enter delta length (0'–0")>: **–6**
<Select object to change>/Undo: *(select point 1 on Line 1 as shown in Figure P4–19)*
<Select object to change>/Undo: *(select point 2 on Line 1 as shown in Figure P4–19)*
<Select object to change>/Undo: *(continue selecting points on lines 2 to 6 and press ⌨Enter)*

STEP 21   Use the BREAK command to leave 6" gap between the column and beam. Invoke the BREAK command from the Modify toolbar or type BREAK at the "Command:" prompt and press ⌨Enter or spacebar.

Command: **break**
Select object: *(select point 1 on line 1 as shown in Figure P4–20).*
Enter second point (or F for first point): *(select point 2 on line 1 as shown in Figure P4–20)*

Continue with the BREAK command to leave 6" gap between the column and beam for the lines shown in Figure 4–20.

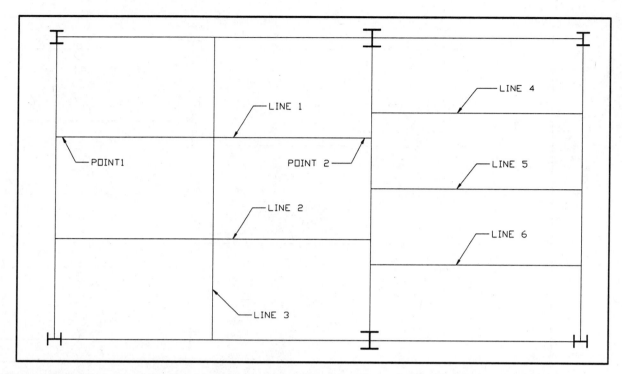

Figure P4–19 Layout showing the lines that has to be operated by LENGTHEN Command

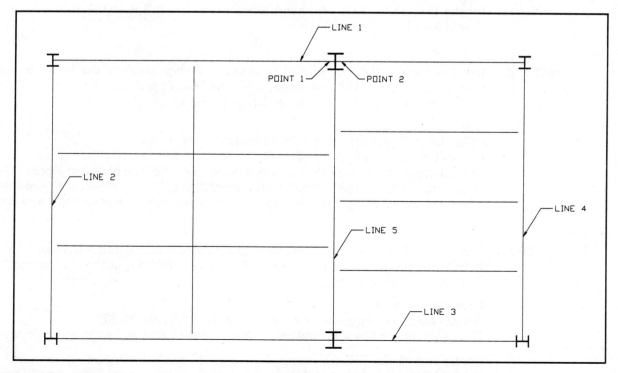

Figure P4–20 Layout showing the lines that has to be operated by BREAK Command

STEP 22   Set 'Text' as the current layer

STEP 23   Place appropriate text by invoking the TEXT command as follows:

Command: **text**
Justify/Style/<Start point>: **m**
Middle point: **6', 17'**
Height<default>: **6**
Rotation angle<0>: [Enter]
Text: **W16x26**

Command: [Enter]
Justify/Style/<Start point>: **m**
Middle point: **32', 19'**
Height<default>: **6**
Rotation angle<0>: [Enter]
Text: **W14x34**

Command: [Enter]
Justify/Style/<Start point>: **m**
Middle point: **12', –1'**
Height<default>: **6**
Rotation angle<0>: [Enter]
Text: **W30x108**

Command: [Enter]
Justify/Style/<Start point>: **m**
Middle point: **32', –1'**
Height<default>: **6**
Rotation angle<0>: [Enter]
Text: **W16x36**

Command: **copy**
Select objects: *(Select the text W16x26)*
Select objects: [Enter]
<Base point or displacement>/Multiple: **m**
Base point: **0,0**
Second point of displacement: **@12',0**
Second point of displacement: **@0.–8'**
Second point of displacement: **@12',–8'**
Second point of displacement: [Enter]

Command: **copy**
Select objects: *(Select the text W14x34)*
Select objects: [Enter]
<Base point or displacement>/Multiple: **m**
Base point: **0.0**
Second point of displacement: **@0,–6'**
Second point of displacement: **@0,–12'**
Second point of displacement: [Enter]

The drawing should look like Figure P4–21.

Fundamentals III

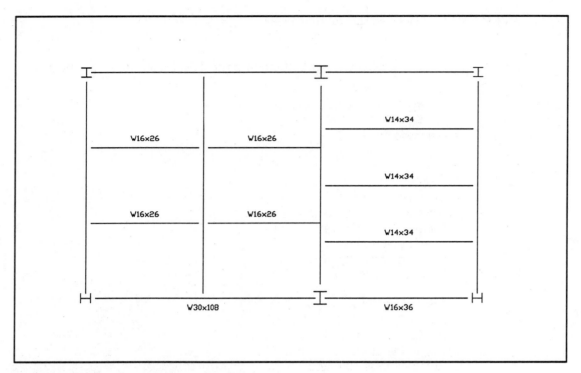

Figure P4–21 Placing text as the appropriate beams

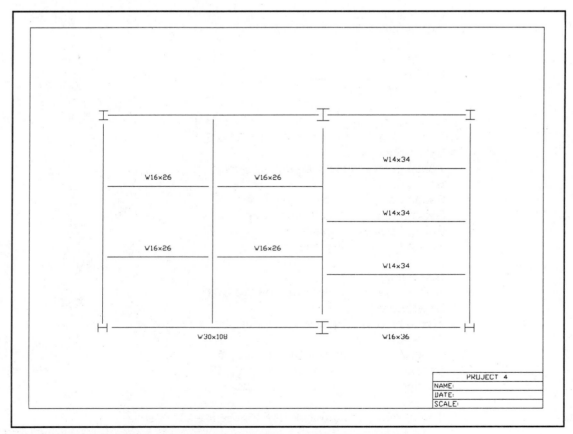

Figure P4–22 The title block and border surround the completed drawing

STEP 24   Set "Border" as the current layer.

STEP 25   Draw a border and create a title block, as shown in Figure P4–22.

STEP 26   End the drawing:
Command: **end**

Congratulations. You just successfully applied several AutoCAD concepts in creating a simple drawing.

EXERCISES

Exercise 4–1

Create the drawing according to the settings given in the following table.

Settings	Value
1. UNITS	Architectural
2. LIMITS	
lower left	0, 0
upper right	12',9'
3. GRID	1"
4. SNAP	0.5"
5. TEXT SIZE	0.75"
6. LAYERS	

LAYER NAME	COLOR	LINETYPE
OBJECT	WHITE	CONTINUOUS
HIDDEN	CYAN	HIDDEN
CENTER	YELLOW	CENTER
SOLID	BLUE	CONTINUOUS
TEXT	GREEN	CONTINUOUS

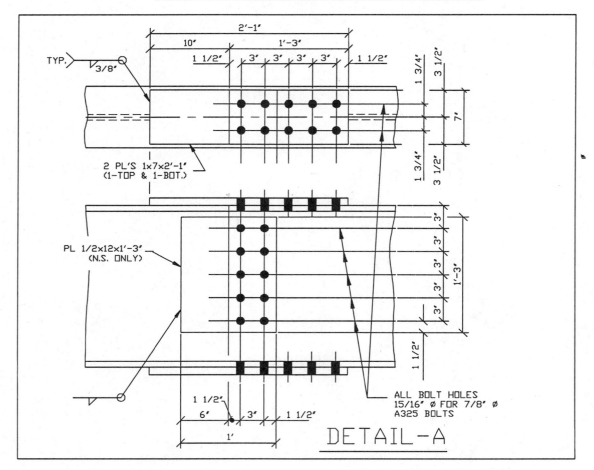

Exercise 4-2

Create the drawing according to the settings given in the following table.

Settings	Value	
1. UNITS	Decimal	
2. LIMITS		
lower left corner	0, 0	
upper right corner	12,9	
3. GRID	.25	
4. SNAP	.25	
5. TEXT SIZE	.18	
6. LAYERS		
LAYER NAME	COLOR	LINETYPE
OBJECT	WHITE	CONTINUOUS
HIDDEN	CYAN	HIDDEN
CENTER	YELLOW	CENTER
SOLID	BLUE	CONTINUOUS
TEXT	GREEN	CONTINUOUS

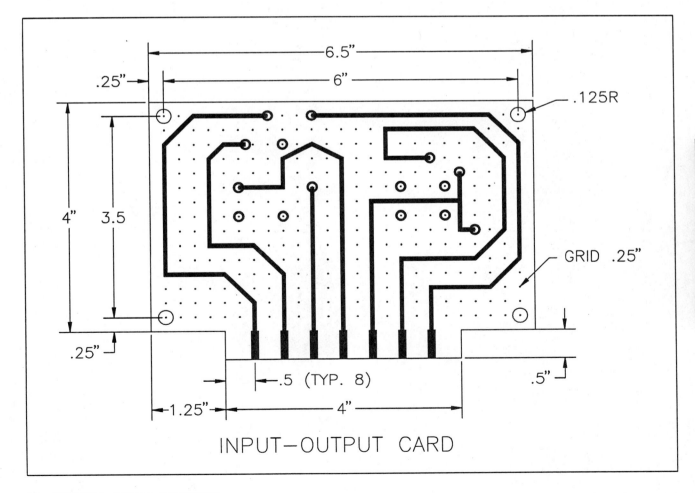

INPUT—OUTPUT CARD

Fundamentals III

Exercises 4-3 to 4-4

Create the drawings according to the settings given in the following table.

Settings	Value	
1. UNITS	Architectural	
2. LIMITS		
lower left	0, 0	
upper right	12',9'	
3. GRID	4"	
4. SNAP	0.5"	
5. TEXT SIZE	0.375	
6. LAYERS		
LAYER NAME	COLOR	LINETYPE
OBJECT	WHITE	CONTINUOUS
HIDDEN	CYAN	HIDDEN
CENTER	YELLOW	CENTER
TEXT	GREEN	CONTINUOUS

Exercises 4-3

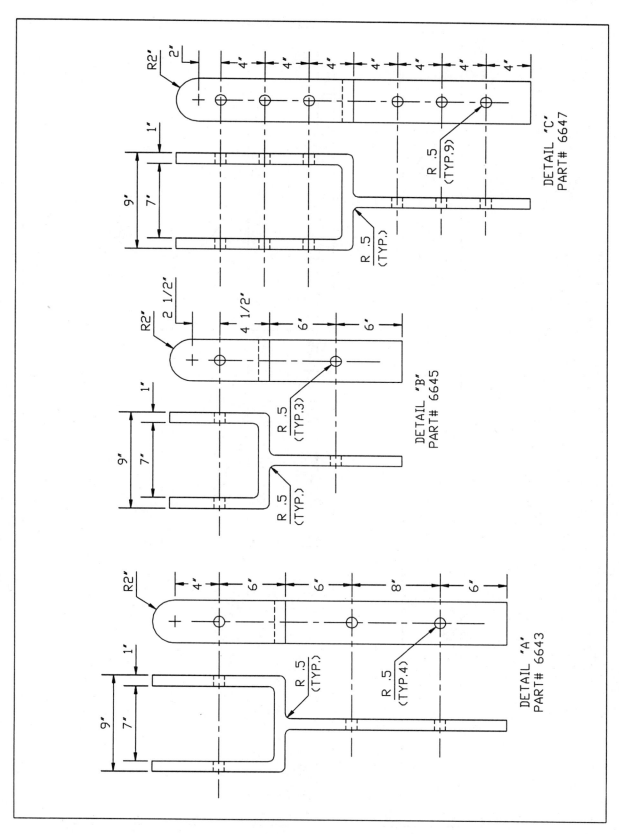

DETAIL "C"
PART# 6647

DETAIL "B"
PART# 6645

DETAIL "A"
PART# 6643

Exercises 4–4

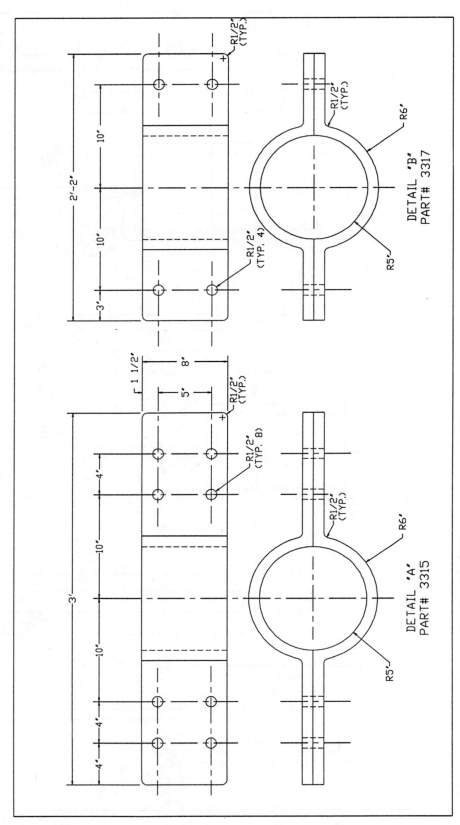

REVIEW QUESTIONS

1. A polyline
   - (A) can have width
   - (B) can be exploded
   - (C) is one object
   - (D) All of the above

2. The CHPROP command does not let you modify
   - (A) an object's linetype
   - (B) an object's line width
   - (C) an object's color
   - (D) an object's layer

3. In regard to using the solid command, which of the following statements is true?
   - (A) The points must be selected in a particular order
   - (B) The order of point selection is unimportant
   - (C) FILL must be turned off in order to use SOLID
   - (D) The points must be selected on the line segments that are already drawn

4. Polylines are
   - (A) made up of line and arc segments, each of which is treated as an individual object
   - (B) are connected sequences of line and arc
   - (C) Both A and B
   - (D) None of the above

5. What command is used to make a filled rectangle?
   - (A) FILL-ON
   - (B) PLINE
   - (C) RECTANGLE
   - (D) LINE
   - (E) SOLID

6. To turn a series of line segments into a polyline, one uses the PEDIT option _____.
   - (A) Join
   - (B) Fit curve
   - (C) Spline
   - (D) Edit vertex

7. The following are all options of the PLINE command except
   - (A) Undo
   - (B) Halfwidth
   - (C) Arc
   - (D) Ltype and color
   - (E) Width

8. Which command allows you to change the scale of an object where X and Y scales are changed equally?
   - (A) ROTATE
   - (B) SCALE
   - (C) TRIM
   - (D) EXTEND

9. Using the SCALE command, what number would you enter to enlarge an object by 50%?
   (A) 0.5
   (B) 50
   (C) 3
   (D) 1.5

10. To avoid changing the location of an object when rescaling it with the SCALE command,
   (A) the reference length should be less than the limits
   (B) the scale factor should be less than one
   (C) the scale factor should be between zero and one
   (D) the base point should be on the object
   (E) the base point should be at the origin

11. The ROTATE command is used to rotate around
   (A) any specified point
   (B) point –1, –1 only
   (C) point 0,0 only
   (D) point 1,1 only
   (E) None of the above

12. The Grips dialog box allows you to change except
   (A) grip size
   (B) grip colors
   (C) toggle grips system variable on/off
   (D) specifying the coordinates for placing the grips

13. Grips do not allow you to _____ an object.
   (A) copy
   (B) mirror
   (C) erase
   (D) move
   (E) stretch

14. The following command is not supported by the Noun/Verb feature.
   (A) copy
   (B) move
   (C) trim
   (D) rotate
   (E) erase

15. When Noun/Verb Selection is turned on, you may add objects to the selection set by
   (A) picking the objects
   (B) windowing the objects
   (C) using Shift to add
   (D) using Ctrl to add

CHAPTER

5

FUNDAMENTALS IV

After completing this chapter, you will be able to:

- Use the Construction line (XLINE), Ray, Multiline, Spline and Sketch commands
- Create or edit an existing multiline style
- Modify the intersection of two or more multilines
- Use the MTEXT command to draw text by processing the words in paragraph form
- Draw text using special text character and symbol options, edit text, spell check the drawing, create or edit an existing text style
- Use inquiry commands
- Use wildcards and named objects
- Change the system variables
- Use the Undo and Redo commands

DRAWING CONSTRUCTION LINES AND RAYS

AutoCAD provides a tool to draw lines that extend to infinity in one or both directions. They have no effect, however, on the ZOOM Extents command. They can be moved, copied, and rotated like other objects. These infinite lines can be used as a reference (construction lines) for creating other objects. To keep them from being plotted, you can place construction lines on a layer that is turned off during plotting.

AutoCAD provides two powerful commands, XLINE and RAY, to draw lines that extend to infinity in one or both directions. The XLINE command allows you to draw lines that extend infinitely in both directions from the point selected when being created. The RAY command creates a line that extends from a point infinitely in a specified direction.

XLINE Command

The XLINE command is invoked from the Line flyout located in the Draw toolbar (see Figure 5–1), or at the "Command:" prompt type XLINE and press Enter or spacebar.

```
Command: xline
Hor/Ver/Ang/Bisect/Offset/<From point>:
```

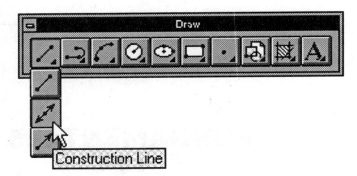

Figure 5–1   Invoke the XLINE Command from the Draw toolbar

From Point Option   Specify a point to define the root of the construction line. This point becomes the conceptual midpoint of the construction line. AutoCAD prompts:

Through point: *(specify a point through which the construction line should pass)*

AutoCAD draws a line that passes through two points extending infinitely. AutoCAD continues to prompt for additional points to draw construction lines. To terminate the command sequence, press [Enter] or spacebar.

Horizontal Option   The Horizontal option allows you to draw a construction line through a point you specify and parallel to the X axis of the current UCS.

Vertical Option   The Vertical option allows you to draw a construction line through a point you specify and parallel to the Y axis of the current UCS.

Angle Option   The Angle option allows you to draw a construction line at a specified angle. AutoCAD prompts:

Reference/<Enter angle(current)>: *(specify an angle at which to place the construction line)*
Through point: *(specify a point through which the construction line should pass)*

AutoCAD draws the construction line through the specified point, using the specified angle.

The **Reference** option allows you to draw a construction line at a specific angle for a selected reference line. The angle is measured counterclockwise from the reference line.

Bisect Option   The Bisect option allows you to draw a construction line through the first point bisecting the angle determined by the second and third points with the first point being the vertex. AutoCAD prompts:

Angle vertex point: *(select a point for the vertex of an angle to be bisected and through which the construction line will be drawn)*
Angle start point: *(select a point to determine one boundary line of an angle)*
Angle endpoint: *(select a point to determine second boundary line of angle)*

The construction line lies in the plane determined by the three points.

Offset Option   The Offset option allows you to draw a construction line parallel to and at the specified distance from the line object specified and on the side selected. AutoCAD prompts:

Offset distance or Through <current>: *(specify an offset distance, enter t for through, or press*
    Enter *to accept the default value)*
Select a line object: *(select a line, pline, ray or xline)*
Side to offset? *(specify a point to draw a construction line parallel to the selected object)*

The **Through** option allows you to specify a point, through which a construction line is drawn to the line object selected.

RAY Command

The RAY command is invoked from the Line flyout located in the Draw toolbar (see Figure 5–2), or at the "Command:" prompt type RAY and press Enter or spacebar.

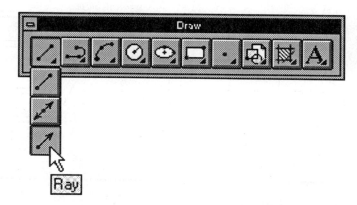

Figure 5–2   Invoke the RAY Command from the Draw toolbar

Command: **ray**
From point: *(specify a point)*
Through point: *(specify a point through which you want the ray to pass)*

A ray is drawn starting at the first point and extending infinitely through the second point. AutoCAD continues to prompt for through points until you provide a null response to terminate the command sequence.

MULTILINES

The MLINE command is used to draw multiple parallel line segments similar to polyline segments that have been offset one or more times. Examples of applying the MLINE command are shown in Figure 5–3.

The properties of each element of a multiline are determined by the style that is current when the multiline is drawn. Element properties include their offset, color and linetype. Properties of the multiline that can be determined by the style include whether to display a line at the joints (miters) and ends and whether to close the ends with a variety of half circles, connecting inner and/or outer elements. Refer to the section on the MLSTYLE Command for a detailed explanation on creating a new or editing an existing multiline style.

Fundamentals IV

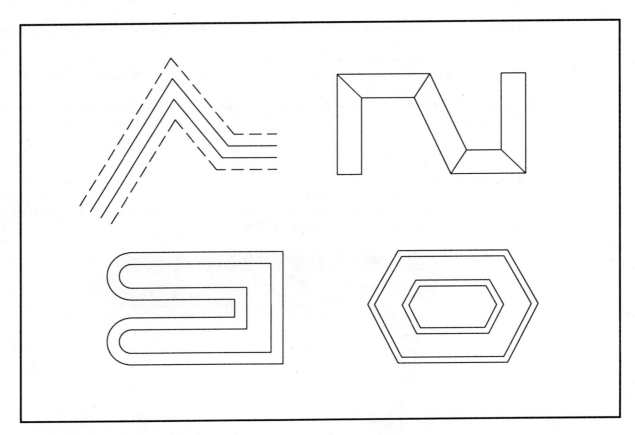

Figure 5–3 Examples of multilines

MLINE Command

The MLINE command is invoked from the Polyline flyout located in the Draw toolbar (see Figure 5–4), or at the "Command:" prompt type MLINE and press Enter or spacebar.

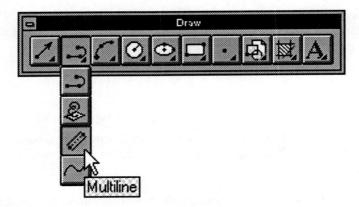

Figure 5–4 Invoke the MLINE Command from the Draw toolbar

```
Command: mline
Justification = Top, Scale = 1.00, Style = STANDARD
Justification/Scale/STyle/<From point>:
```

From point Option This option (default) lets you specify the starting point of the multiline known as its origin. Once you specify the starting point for a multiline, AutoCAD prompts:

<To point>:

When you respond by selecting a point, the first multiline segment is drawn according to the current style. You are then prompted:

Undo/<To point>:

If you specify a point, the next segment is drawn along with segments of all other elements specified by the current style. After two segments have been drawn the prompt will include the Close option:

Close/Undo/<To point>:

Choosing the Close option causes the next segment to join the starting point of the multiline, fillets all elements and exits the command.

Selecting Undo (u) after any segment is drawn (and the MLINE command has not been terminated) causes the last segment to be erased and you are prompted again for a point.

Justification Option The Justification option determines the relationship between the elements of the multiline and the line you specify by the placement of the points. The justification is set by selecting one of the three available sub-options.

Top/Zero/Bottom <current>:

Top Option The top option causes the element with the greatest offset value to be drawn on the line of selected points. All other elements will be to the right of the line of points as viewed from the starting point to the ending point of each segment. In other words, if the line is drawn left to right, the line of points (and element with the greatest offset value) will be on top of (above) all other elements.

Zero Option The zero option causes the base line to coincide with the line of selected points. Elements with positive offsets will be to the right and those with negative offsets will be to the left of the line of selected points as viewed from the starting point to the ending point of the each segment.

Bottom Option The bottom option causes the element with the least offset value to be drawn on the line of selected points. All other elements will be to the left of the line of points as viewed from the starting point to the ending point of each segment. In other words, if the line is drawn left to right, the line of points (and element with the least offset value) will be on the bottom of (below) all other elements. Figure 5–5 shows the location for various justifications.

Scale Option The Scale option determines the value used for offsetting elements when drawing them relative to the values assigned to them in the style. If the scale is changed to 3.0, elements that are assigned 0.5 and -1.5 will be drawn with offsets of 1.5 and - 4.5 respectively. If a negative value is given for the scale, then the signs of the values assigned to them in the style will be changed (positive to negative and negative to positive). The value can be entered in decimal form or as a fraction. A 0 (zero) scale value produces a single line.

Fundamentals IV

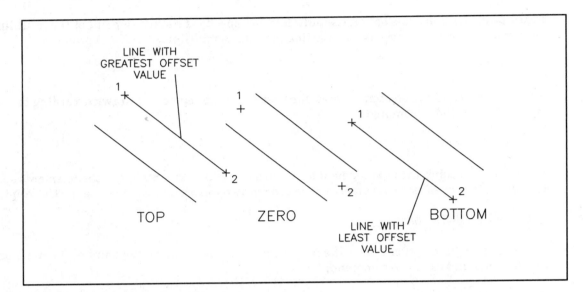

Figure 5–5   Location of various justifications

STyle Option The Style option sets the current multiline style from the available styles. AutoCAD prompts:

    Justification/Scale/STyle/<From point>: **ST**
    Multiline style name (or ?): *(specify the name of an existing style)*

MLEDIT Command

The MLEDIT command helps you modify the intersections of two or more multilines or cut holes in the lines of one multiline. The tools are available for the type of intersection operated on (cross, tee or vertex) and if one or more elements needs to be cut or welded.

The MLEDIT command is invoked from the Special Edit flyout located in the Modify toolbar (see Figure 5–6), or at the "Command:" prompt type MLEDIT and press Enter or spacebar. The Multiline Edit Tools dialog box appears as shown in Figure 5–7.

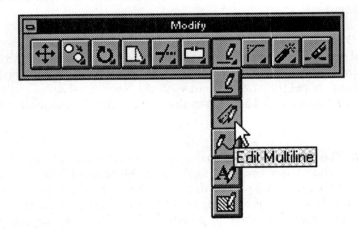

Figure 5–6   Invoke the MLEDIT Command from the Modify toolbar

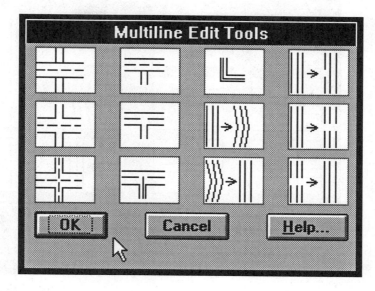

Figure 5–7   Multiline Edit Tools dialog box

Closed Cross   The Closed Cross option cuts all lines that make up the second multiline you select at the point where it crosses the first multiline, as shown in Figure 5–8. Click the Closed Cross image tile, as shown in Figure 5–9, to invoke the Closed Cross option, AutoCAD prompts:

> Select first mline: *(select the first multiline)*
> Select second mline: *(select the second multiline)*

After the closed cross intersection is created, AutoCAD prompts:

> Select first mline (or Undo): *(select another multiline, enter u, or press* Enter *)*

Selecting another multiline repeats the prompt for the second mline. Entering u undoes the closed cross just created.

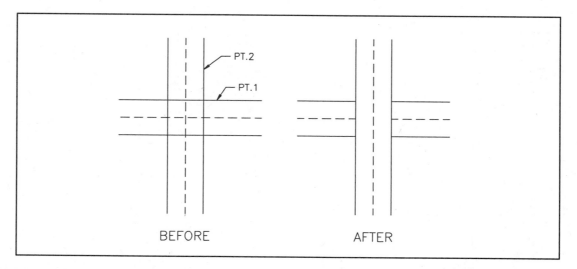

Figure 5–8   An example of closed cross

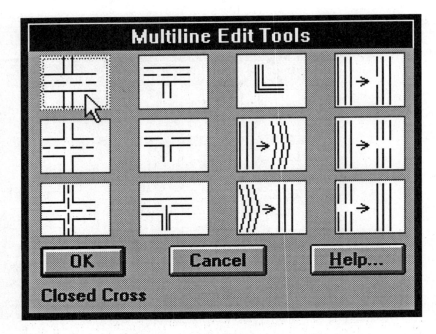

Figure 5–9   Invoke the Closed Cross option from the Multiline Edit dialog box

Open Cross   The Open Cross option cuts all lines that make up the first multiline you select and cuts only the outside line of the second multiline, as shown in Figure 5–10. Click the Open Cross image tile, as shown in Figure 5–11, to invoke the Open Cross option; AutoCAD prompts:

Select first mline: *(select a multiline)*
Select second mline: *(select a multiline that intersects the first multiline)*

After the open cross intersection is created, AutoCAD prompts:

Select first mline (or Undo): *(select another multiline, enter u, or press* [Enter] *)*

Selecting another multiline repeats the prompt for the second mline. Entering u undoes the open cross just created.

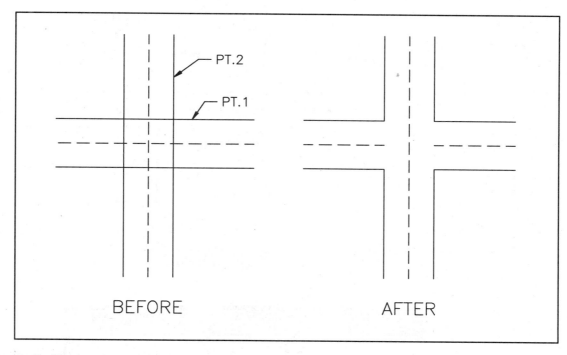

Figure 5–10   An example of open cross

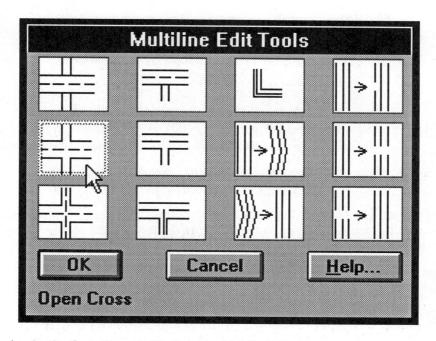

Figure 5–11   Invoke the Open Cross option from the Multiline Edit dialog box

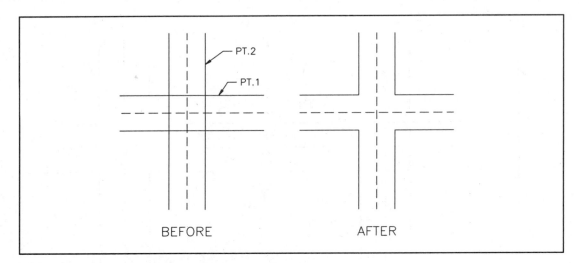

BEFORE   AFTER

Figure 5–12 An example of merged cross

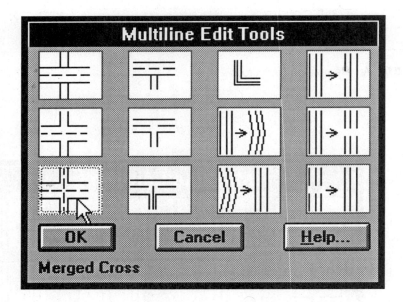

Figure 5–13 Invoke the Merged Cross option from the Multiline Edit dialog box

Merged Cross The Merged Cross option cuts all lines that make up the intersecting multiline you select, except the center lines, as shown in Figure 5–12. Click the Merged Cross image tile, as shown in Figure 5–13, to invoke the Merged Cross option; AutoCAD prompts:

Select first mline: *(select a multiline)*
Select second mline: *(select a multiline that intersects the first multiline)*

After the merged cross intersection is created, AutoCAD prompts:

Select first mline (or Undo): *(select another multiline, enter u, or press* Enter *)*

Selecting another multiline repeats the prompt for the second mline. Entering u undoes the merged cross just created.

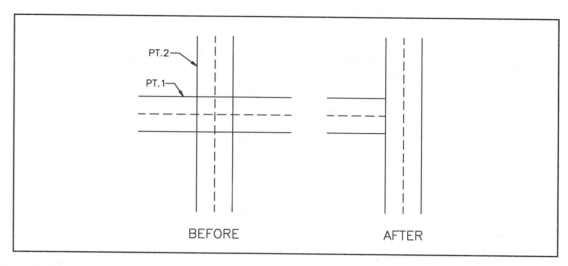

Figure 5–14 An example of closed tee

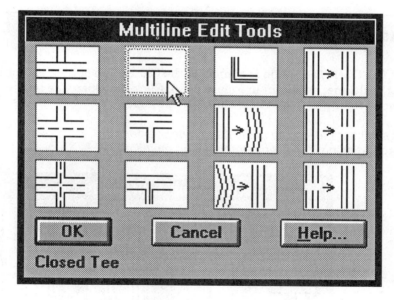

Figure 5–15 Invoke the Closed Tee option from the Multiline Edit dialog box

Closed Tee The Closed Tee option extends or shortens the first multiline you identify to its intersection with the second multiline, as shown in Figure 5–14. Click the Closed Tee image tile, as shown in Figure 5–15, to invoke the Closed Tee option; AutoCAD prompts:

Select first mline: *(select the multiline to trim or extend)*
Select second mline: *(select the intersecting multiline)*

After the closed tee intersection is created, AutoCAD prompts:

Select first mline (or Undo): *(select another multiline, enter u, or press ⌷Enter⌷)*

Selecting another multiline repeats the prompt for the second mline. Entering u undoes the closed tee just created.

Fundamentals IV

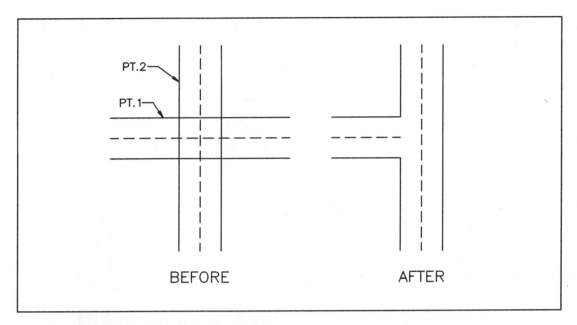

Figure 5–16 An example of open tee

Open Tee The Open Tee option is similar to the Closed Tee option, except it leaves an open end at intersecting multiline, as shown in Figure 5–16. Click the Open Tee image tile, as shown in Figure 5–17, to invoke the Open Tee option; AutoCAD prompts:

Select first mline: *(select the multiline to trim or extend)*
Select second mline: *(select the intersecting multiline)*

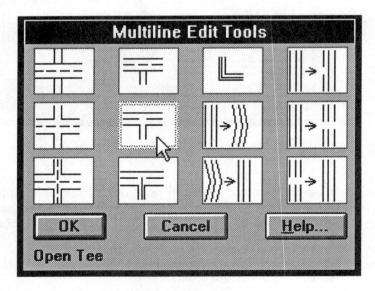

Figure 5–17 Invoke the Open Tee option from the Multiline Edit dialog box

After the open tee intersection is created, AutoCAD prompts:

Select first mline (or Undo): *(select another multiline, enter u, or press* ⌷Enter *)*

Selecting another multiline repeats the prompt for the second mline. Entering u undoes the open tee just created.

Merged Tee The Merged Tee option is similar to the Open Tee option, except the center line of the first multiline is extended to the center of the intersecting multiline, as shown in Figure 5–18. Click the Merged Tee image tile, as shown in Figure 5–19, to invoke the Merged Tee option; AutoCAD prompts:

Select first mline: *(select the multiline to trim or extend)*
Select second mline: *(select the intersecting multiline)*

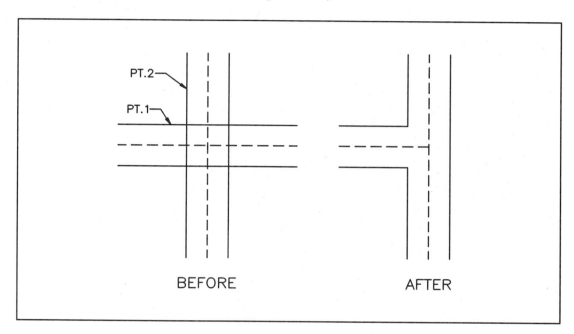

Figure 5–18   An example of merged tee

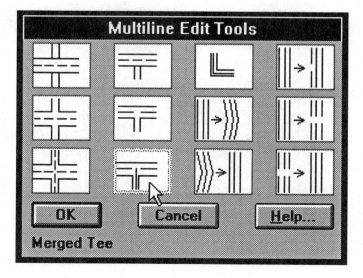

Figure 5–19   Invoke the Merged Tee option from the Multiline Edit dialog box

After the merged tee intersection is created, AutoCAD prompts:

Select first mline (or Undo): *(select another multiline, enter u, or press* Enter *)*

Selecting another multiline repeats the prompt for the second mline. Entering u undoes the merged tee just created.

Corner Joint The Corner Joint option lengthens or shortens each of the two multilines you select as necessary to create a clean intersection, as shown in Figure 5–20. Click the Corner Joint image tile, as shown in Figure 5–21, to invoke the Corner Joint option; AutoCAD prompts:

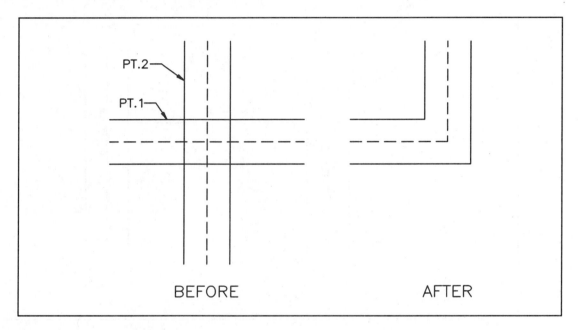

Figure 5–20 An example of corner joint

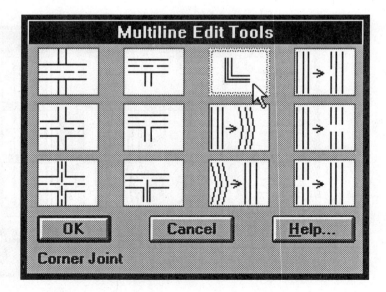

Figure 5–21 Invoke the Corner Joint option from the Multiline Edit dialog box

Select first mline: *(select the multiline to trim or extend)*
Select second mline: *(select the intersecting multiline)*

After the corner joint intersection is created, AutoCAD prompts:

Select first mline (or Undo): *(select another multiline, enter u, or press* [Enter] *)*

Selecting another multiline repeats the prompt for the second mline. Entering u undoes the corner joint just created.

Add Vertex The Add Vertex option adds a vertex to a multiline, as shown in Figure 5–22. Click the Add Vertex image tile, as shown in Figure 5–23 to invoke the Add Vertex option; AutoCAD prompts:

Select mline: *(select a multiline to add a vertex)*

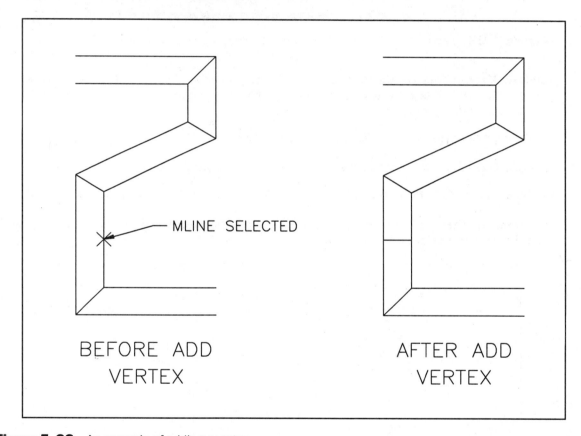

Figure 5–22   An example of adding a vertex

AutoCAD adds the vertex at the selected point and prompts:

Select mline (or Undo): *(select another multiline, enter u, or press* [Enter] *)*

Selecting another multiline allows you to add another vertex. Entering u undoes the vertex just created.

Fundamentals IV

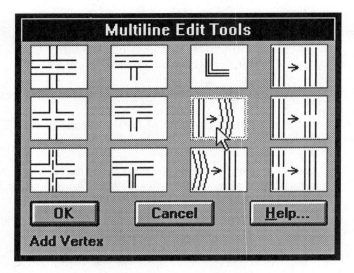

Figure 5–23 Invoke the Add Vertex option from the Multiline Edit dialog box

Delete Vertex The Delete Vertex option deletes a vertex from a multiline, as shown in Figure 5–24. Click the Delete Vertex image tile, as shown in Figure 5–25, to invoke the Delete Vertex option, AutoCAD prompts:

   Select mline: *(select a multiline to delete a vertex)*

AutoCAD deletes the vertex at the selected point and prompts:

   Select mline (or Undo): *(select another multiline, enter u, or press* Enter *)*

Selecting another multiline allows you to delete another vertex. Entering u undoes the operation and displays the Select mline prompt.

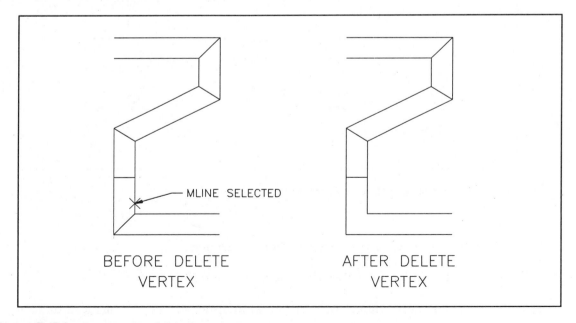

Figure 5–24 An example of deleting a vertex

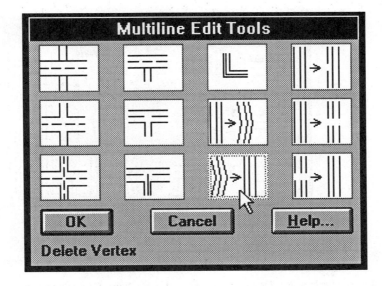

Figure 5–25 Invoke the Delete Vertex option from the Multiline Edit dialog box

Cut Single The Cut Single option cuts a selected element of a multiline between two cut points, as shown in Figure 5–26. Click the Cut Single image tile, as shown in Figure 5–27, to invoke the Cut Single option; AutoCAD prompts:

Select mline: *(select a multiline and the selected point becomes first cut point)*
Select second point: *(select the second cut point on the multiline)*

AutoCAD cuts the multiline and prompts:

Select mline (or Undo): *(select another multiline, enter u, or press* Enter *)*

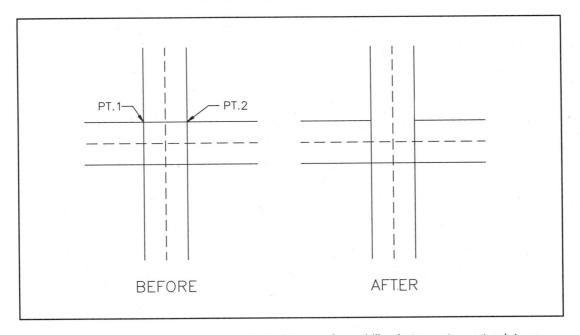

Figure 5–26 An example of removing a selected element of a multiline between two cut points

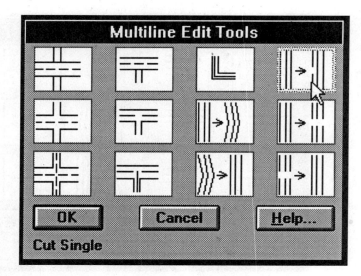

Figure 5–27 Invoke the Cut Single option from the Multiline Edit dialog box

Select another multiline to continue or entering u undoes the operation and displays the Select mline prompt.

Cut All The Cut All option removes a portion of the multiline you select between two cut points, as shown in Figure 5–28. Click the Cut All image tile, as shown in Figure 5–29, to invoke the Cut All option; AutoCAD prompts:

Select mline: *(select a multiline and the selected point becomes first cut point)*
Select second point: *(select the second cut point on the multiline)*

AutoCAD cuts all the elements of the multiline and prompts:

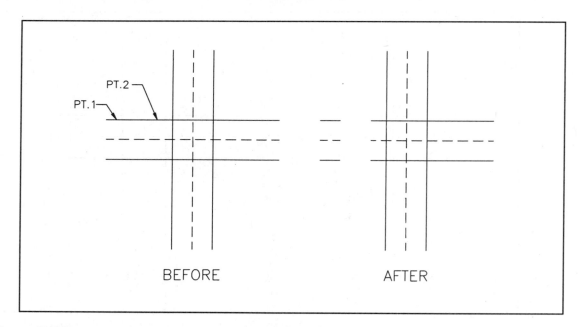

Figure 5–28 An example of removing a portion of the multiline between two cut points

Select mline (or Undo): *(select another multiline, enter u, or press* Enter *)*

Select another multiline to continue or enter u to undo the operation and display the Select mline prompt.

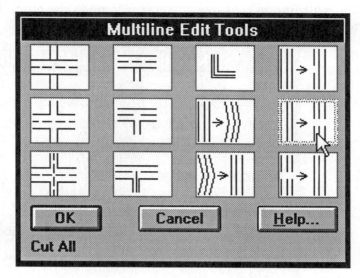

Figure 5-29 Invoke the Cut All option from the Multiline Edit dialog box

Weld All The Weld All option rejoins multiline segments that been cut, as shown in Figure 5-30. Click the Weld All image tile, as shown in Figure 5-31, to invoke the Weld All option; AutoCAD prompts:

Select mline: *(select a multiline)*
Select second point: *(select the end point on the multiline to be joined)*

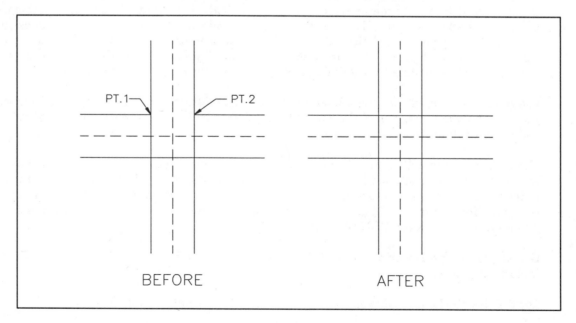

Figure 5-30 An example of rejoining multiline segments that have been cut

AutoCAD joins the multiline and prompts:

Select mline (or Undo): *(select another multiline, enter u, or press* Enter *)*

Select another multiline to continue or enter u to undo the operation and display the Select mline prompt.

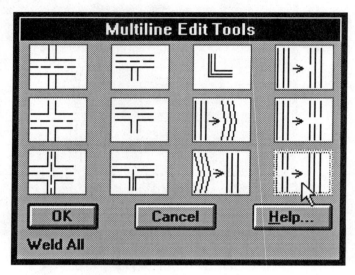

Figure 5–31   Invoke the Weld All option from the Multiline Edit dialog box

MLSTYLE Command

The MLSTYLE command is used to create a new or edit an existing multiline style. You can define a multiline style comprised of up to 16 lines called elements. The style controls the number of elements and the properties of each element. In addition you can specify the background color and the end caps of each multiline. The MLSTYLE command is invoked from the Object Properties toolbar (see Figure 5–32), or at the "Command:" prompt type MLSTYLE and press Enter or spacebar. The Multiline Styles dialog box appears as shown in Figure 5–33.

Current The Current list box allows you to select a multiline style from the available styles to set the current multiline. Select the multiline style from the list and click the OK button to set the current multiline style.

Name The Name: edit field allows you to specify a name for a new multiline style or rename an existing one. To create a new multiline style, define the element and multiline properties, then enter a name in the Name: edit field and click the Save. . . button. AutoCAD saves the definition in the multiline library file (ACAD.MLN) by default. To rename an existing multiline style, enter a name and then click the RENAME button.

Description The Description: edit field allows you to add a description up to 255 characters including spaces.

Load Click the Load. . . button to load a multiline style from the multiline library file.

Add Click the Add. . . button to add the multiline style in the Name edit box to the Current list.

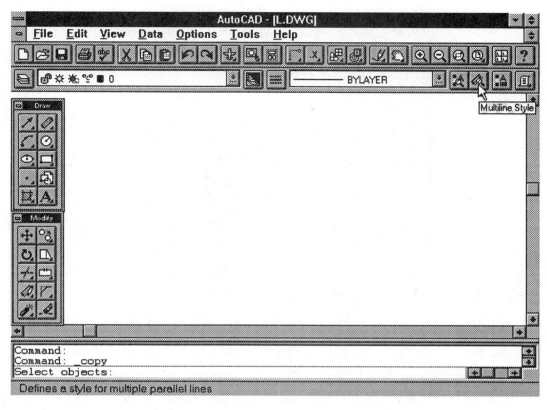

Figure 5–32 Invoke the MLSTYLE Command from the Object Properties toolbar

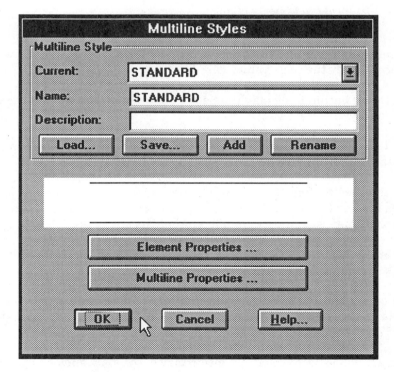

Figure 5–33 Multiline Styles dialog box

Fundamentals IV

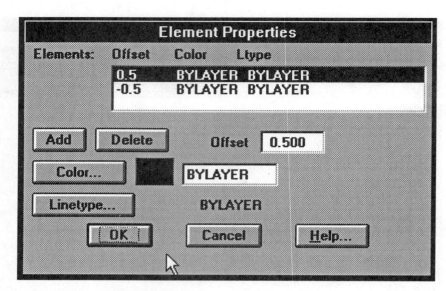

Figure 5–34 Element Properties dialog box

Element Properties Selecting the Element Properties. . . button displays an Element Properties dialog box, similar to the one shown in Figure 5–34, with options to set or change the offset, number, line type or color of the multiline elements.

The elements list box displays existing elements along with the color and linetype of each.

Click the **Add** or **Delete** button to add a line element to the multiline style or delete a line element from the multiline style, respectively.

The **Offset** edit box sets the element's distance from the base line. It will use this distance to offset the element when the multiline is drawn and the scale is set to 1.0. Otherwise, the offset will be a ratio determined by the scale value.

Click the **Color** button to display the Select Color dialog box and set the color for line elements in the multiline style.

Click the **Linetype** button to display the Select Linetype dialog box and set the linetype for line elements in the multiline style.

Multiline Properties Selecting the Multiline Properties. . . button displays a Multiline Properties dialog box, similar to the one shown in Figure 5–35, with options to change the type of joints, end caps (and their angles) and background color for the multiline.

The **Display Joints** toggle button controls the display of the joints (miter) at the vertices of each multiline segment, as shown in Figure 5–36.

The **Caps** option has four sub-options to specify the appearance of multiline start and end caps. The Line toggle button controls the display of the start and end caps by a straight line, as shown in Figure 5–37.

The Outer arc toggle button controls the display of the start and end caps by connecting the ends of the outermost elements with a semi-circular arc, as shown in Figure 5–38.

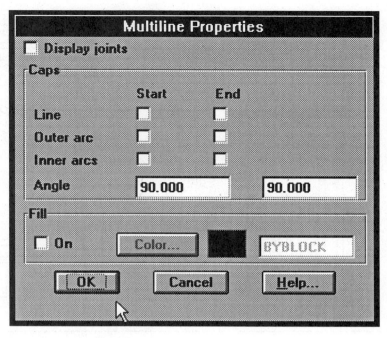

Figure 5–35 Multiline Properties dialog box

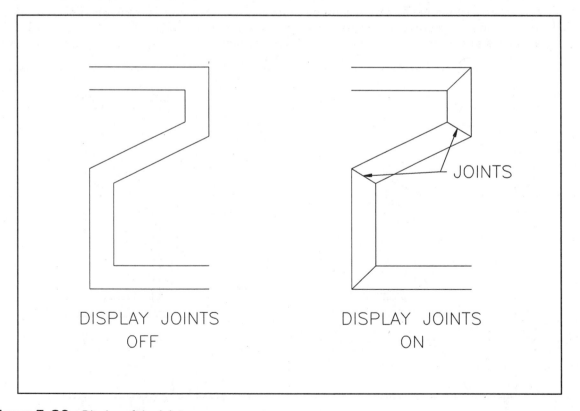

Figure 5–36 Display of the joints

Fundamentals IV

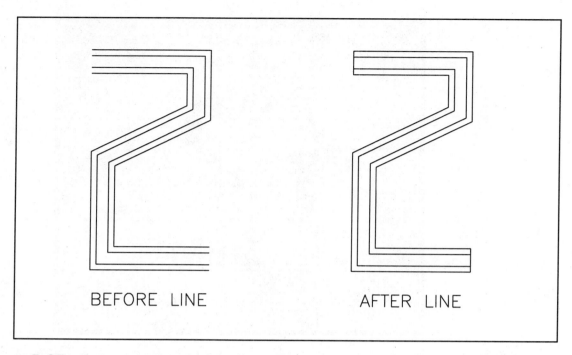

Figure 5–37 Display of the line for start and end caps

The Inner arcs toggle button controls the display of the start and end caps by connecting the ends of the innermost elements with a semi-circular arc, as shown in Figure 5–39. For a multiline with an odd number of elements, the center element is not connected. For an even number, connected elements are paired with elements that are the same number from each edge. For example, the

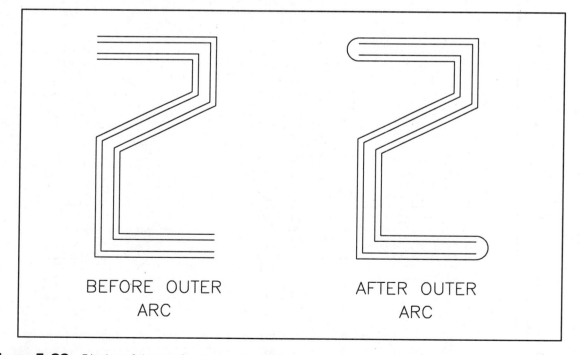

Figure 5–38 Display of the arc for start and end caps

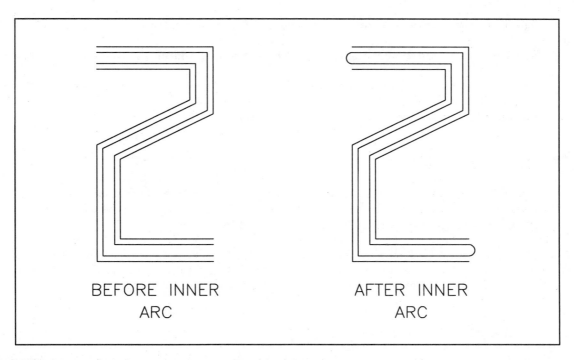

Figure 5–39   Display of the inner arc for start and end caps

second element from the left outer will be connected to the second from the right outer, the third to the third and so forth.

The Angle edit field sets the angle of endcaps, as shown in Figure 5–40.

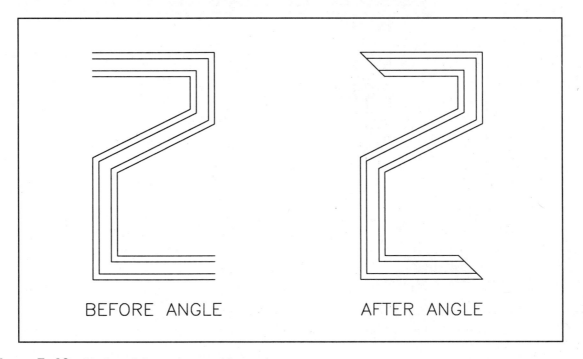

Figure 5–40   Display of the end caps with angular cap

Fundamentals IV

The **Fill** toggle button controls the background fill of the multiline.

The **Color...** button displays the Select Color dialog box and set the color of the background fill.

Once you set the appropriate element properties and multiline properties for a new multiline style, type the name and description in the Name and Description edit field respectively. Click the Save... button to save the newly created multiline style.

SPLINE CURVES

The SPLINE command is used to draw a curve through or near a series of points. The type of curve used is a non-uniform rational B-spline (NURBS). This type is used for drawing a curve with irregularly varying radii such as topographical contour lines.

The Spline curve is drawn through a series of two or more points with options to either specify end tangents or use Close to join the last segment to the first. Another option lets you specify a tolerance, which determines how close to the selected points the curve is drawn.

SPLINE Command

The SPLINE command is invoked from the Polyline flyout located in the Draw toolbar (see Figure 5–41), or at the "Command:" prompt type SPLINE and press [Enter] or spacebar.

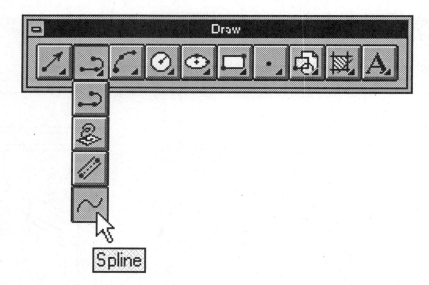

Figure 5–41   Invoke the SPLINE Command from the Draw toolbar

    Command: **spline**
    Object/<Enter first point>:

The default option lets you specify the point from which the spline starts and to which it can be closed. After entering the first point, a rubber band line appears. You will then be prompted:

    Enter point:

When you respond by selecting a point, the spline segments are displayed as a rubber band spline, curving from the first point, through the second point and ending at the cursor. You are then prompted:

Close/Fit Tolerance/<Enter point>:

If you specify a point, the next segment is added to the spline. This will occur with each additional point selected until you use the Close option or enter a null response by pressing Enter.

Choosing a null response terminates the selection of segment determining points. You are then prompted for end tangent determining points as follows:

Enter start tangent:

If you select a point (for tangency), its direction from the start point determines the start tangent. If you press Enter, the direction from the first point to the second point determines tangency. After the start tangency is established, you are prompted:

Enter end tangent:

If you select a point (for tangency), its direction from the end point determines the end tangent. If you press Enter, the direction from the first point to the second point determines tangency.

If you choose the Close option instead of pressing Enter at the "Close/Fit Tolerance/<Enter point>" prompt, AutoCAD uses the original starting point of the first spline segment as the end point of the last segment and terminates segment placing. You are then prompted:

Enter tangent:

You can select a point to determine the tangency at the connection of the first and last segments. If you press Enter, AutoCAD calculates the tangency and draws the spline accordingly. You can also use the Perp or Tan options to cause the tangency of the spline to be perpendicular or tangent to a specified object.

Instead, if you choose the Fit Tolerance option, you can vary how the spline is drawn relative to the selected points. You are then prompted:

Enter Fit Tolerance <current>:

Entering 0 (zero) causes the spline to pass through the selected points. A positive value causes the spline to pass within the specified value of the points.

Object Option The Object option is used to change spline fit polylines into splines. This can be used for 2D or 3D polylines which will be deleted if the DELOBJ system variable is set appropriately.

Editing Spline Curves

Splines created by using the SPLINE command have numerous characteristics that can be changed with the SPLINEDIT command. These include quantity and location of fit points, end characteristics such as open/close and tangencies, and tolerance of the spline (how near the spline is drawn to fit points).

Splinedit operations on control points (which are different than fit points) of the selected spline include adding control points (with the add or the order option) and changing the weight of individual control points, which determines how close the spline is drawn to individual control points.

The SPLINEDIT command is invoked from the Special Edit flyout located in the Modify toolbar (see Figure 5–42), or at the "Command:" prompt type SPLINEDIT and press Enter or spacebar.

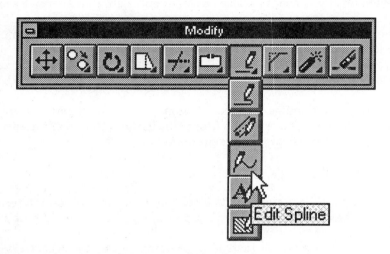

Figure 5–42   Invoke the SPLINEDIT Command from the Modify toolbar

```
Command: splinedit
Select Spline: (select a spline curve)
Fit Data/Close/Move Vertex/Refine/rEverse/Undo/eXit(X): (select an option)
```

Control points appear in grip color and if the spline has fit data, fit points also appear in grip color. If you select a spline whose fit data is deleted, then Fit Data option is not available. A spline can lose its fit data if you use the purge option while editing fit data, refine the spline, move its control vertices, fit the spline to a tolerance, or open or close the spline.

The Open option will replace Close if you select a Closed Spline and vice versa.

Fit Data Option The fit data option allows you to edit the spline by providing the following sub-options:

```
Add/Close/Delete/Move/Purge/Tangents/toLerance/eXit <X>:
```

The **Add** sub-option allows you to add fit points to the selected spline. AutoCAD prompts:

```
Select point: (select a fit point)
```

After selecting one of the fit points, AutoCAD highlights it and the next point you are prompted:

```
Enter new point: (specify a point)
Enter new point: (specify another point or press Enter)
```

Selecting a point places a new fit point between the highlighted ones.

The **Close** sub-option closes an open spline smoothly with a segment or smoothes a spline with coincidental start and end points.

The **Open** sub-option opens a closed spline, disconnecting it and changing the start and end points.

The **Delete** sub-option deletes a selected fit point.

The **Move** sub-option moves fit options to a new location by prompting:

Next/Previous/Select Point/eXit/<Enter new location> <N>:

The **Next** option steps forward through fit points.

The **Previous** option steps backwards through fit points.

The **Select** option permits you to select a fit point.

The **eXit** option exits this set of sub-options.

The **Enter New Location** option moves the highlighted point to the point selected.

The **Purge** sub-option deletes fit data for selected spline.

The **Tangents** sub-option edits the start and end tangents of a spline by prompting:

System Default/<Enter start tangent>: *(specify a point, enter an option, or press* Enter *)*
System Default/<Enter end tangent>: *(specify a point, enter an option, or press* Enter *)*

For a closed spline the prompt is <Enter tangent>:.

If you choose System Default, AutoCAD calculates the tangents. You can choose Tan or Perp and select an object for the tangent to be tangent to or perpendicular to the object selected.

The **Tolerance** sub-option refits the spline to the existing points with new tolerance values by prompting:

Enter Fit Tolerance <current>: *(enter a value or press* Enter *)*

The value you enter determines how close the spline will be fit to the points.

The **Exit** sub-option exits the Fit Data options and returns to the main prompt.

Close Option The Close option causes the spline to be joined smoothly at its start point.

Open Option The Open option opens a closed spline. Previously open splines with coincidental start and end points will lose their tangency. Others will be restored to a previous state.

Move Vertex Option The Move Vertex option relocates a spline's control vertices by providing the following sub-options:

Next/Previous/Select Point/eXit/<Enter new location> <N>:

The **Enter new location** sub-option moves the highlighted point to the point selected.

The **Next** sub-option steps forward through fit points.

The **Previous** sub-option steps backwards through fit points.

The **Select Point** sub-option permits you to select a fit point.

The **eXit** sub-option exits this set of sub-options.

Refine Option The Refine option allows you to fine tune a spline definition by providing the following sub-options:

Add control point/Elevate Order/Weight/eXit <X>:

The **Add control point** sub-option increases the number of control points that control a portion of a spline.

The **Elevate Order** sub-option increases the order of the spline. You can increase the current order of a spline up to 26 (the default is 4), causing an increase in the number of control points.

The **Weight** sub-option changes the weight at various spline control points by providing the following sub-options:

Next/Previous/Select Point/eXit/<Enter new weight> <current> <N>:

The **Next** sub-option steps forward through fit points.

The **Previous** sub-option steps backwards through fit points.

The **Select** point sub-option permits you to select a fit point.

The **eXit** sub-option exits this set of sub-options and returns to the Refine prompt.

The default weight value for a control point is 1.0. Increasing it causes the spline to be drawn near the selected point. A negative or zero value is not valid.

The **eXit** sub-option returns to the main prompt.

rEverse Option The rEverse option reverses the direction of the spline. Reversing the spline does not delete the Fit Data.

Undo Option The Undo option undoes the effects of the last sub-command.

eXit Option The eXit option terminates the SPLINEDIT command.

SKETCHING

The SKETCH command causes AutoCAD to draw connected lines of predetermined lengths immediately on the screen in response to mouse or puck movement. This feature makes a drawing that duplicates your tracing over a paper drawing fixed to a tablet or makes a sketch pad out of your computer screen with the cursor as your drawing implement, controlled by a mouse or puck.

Sketching may be used to generate irregular shapes not easily created through the more conventional means of placing objects. Maps and signatures are two examples of applications for sketching.

The connecting line segments that AutoCAD draws to create the sketch is the length that you specify. The shorter the length you specify, the smoother the shapes will appear. But a large sketch with many long sketch lines of short segment lengths can result in a memory-hungry drawing. Therefore, it is recommended that you specify increment lengths no shorter than necessary to achieve a reasonably smooth plot appearance.

Although AutoCAD places no limit on the kilo- (or mega-) bytes that a drawing requires, disk storage limits might be a factor. For example, you may simulate a circle with a polygon of six straight-line segments or with 1024 segments. If smoothness is your goal, you must be prepared to deal with a larger drawing. This means longer REGENS and more memory required for storage. Also, the smoothness of the visible object on the screen may not reflect the smoothness of the plotted object. Therefore, it may be necessary to make a test plot to determine the optimum length of increments that you should specify.

SKETCH Command

Before using the SKETCH command you should turn ORTHO and SNAP modes OFF. The SKETCH command is invoked from the Miscellaneous toolbar (see Figure 5–43), or at the "Command:" prompt type **SKETCH** and press Enter or spacebar.

Figure 5–43   Invoke the SKETCH Command from the Miscellaneous toolbar

Command: **sketch**
Record increment <default>: Enter

You may respond with a value in drawing units or you may accept the default value by pressing Enter. The prototype drawing default setting is 0.10 units. The current value is saved in the system variable called SKETCHING. You may also respond to the "Record increment <current>:" prompt by specifying two points, either keyed in or picked on the screen, causing AutoCAD to use the distance between the points as the "record (rec' ord) increment" (Note the accent). Once a record increment is specified, AutoCAD displays the following list of options:

Sketch   Pen   eXit   Quit   Record   Erase   Connect

Once you are in SKETCH mode, several optional subcommands can be used, created especially for the SKETCH mode. These are accessible as either single key entries, or as mouse/puck button, provided your mouse/puck has the number of buttons corresponding to the option. The following table shows the optional subcommands, their key, button number, and function. Normal button functions are not usable while in the SKETCH mode.

Command Character	Pointer Button	Function
P	Pick	Raise/lower pen
.(period)	1	Line to point
R	2	Record lines
X, Spacebar or Enter	3	Record lines and exit
Q, or Ctrl + C	4	Discard lines and exit
E	5	Erase
C	6	Connect

P (Pen up and down) An imaginary pen follows the cross-hairs as you move the cursor with the mouse or tablet puck. When the pen is down, AutoCAD sketches a connected segment whenever the cursor moves the specified increment distance from the previously sketched segment. When the pen is up, the pen follows the cursor movement without drawing.

The pen is raised (up) and lowered (down) by either pressing the pick button on the mouse/puck or by pressing **P** on the keyboard. An exercise to demonstrate this is to press the pick button or press **P** on the keyboard several times while slowly moving the cursor across the screen. When you invoke a "PEN UP" the current location of the pen will be the endpoint of the last segment drawn, which will be shorter than a standard increment length.

A "PEN UP" does not take you out of the SKETCH mode. Nor does a "PEN UP" permanently record the lines drawn during the current SKETCH mode.

. (Period; Line-to-Point) While the pen is up, you cause AutoCAD to draw a straight line from the last segment to the current cursor location and return to the "PEN UP" status by typing . (period) from the keyboard. This is convenient for long straight lines that might occur in the middle of irregular shapes.

R (Record) Lines being displayed while the cursor is moved (with pen down) are temporary. They will appear green (or red if the current color for that layer or object is green) on color monitors until they are permanently recorded. These temporary segments are subject to being modified with special Sketch options until you press **R** to record the latest lines. These may include several groups of connected lines drawn during "PEN DOWN" sequences separated by "PEN UPs." When the Record option is invoked by pressing **R**, Enter, or the third mouse/puck button, the total number of recorded segments is reported as follows:

nnn lines recorded

E (Erase) Prior to any group(s) of connected lines being recorded with the Record option, you may use the E (Erase) option to remove any or all of the lines from the last segment back to the first. The sequence of prompts is as follows:

Erase:
Select end of delete

The pen is automatically set to up and you may then use the cross-hairs to remove segments, starting from the last segment. When you are satisfied with the lines remaining, press **P** or the pick button to accept the erasure. To abort the erasure and return to the SKETCH mode, press **E** again (or any other option) and the following will be displayed:

Erase aborted

C (Connect) Whenever a disconnect occurs (pen up or erase), you can reconnect and continue sketching from the point of the last disconnect as long as you have not exited the SKETCH command. The sequence is as follows:

Connect:
Move to endpoint of line.

At this prompt you can move the cross-hairs near the end of the last segment. When you are within a specified increment length, sketching begins, connected to that last endpoint. This option is meaningless if invoked during "PEN DOWN." A message also tells you:

No last point known

if no last point exists. The Connect option can be canceled by pressing **C** a second time.

X (Record and Exit) The X option exits the SKETCH mode after recording all temporary lines. This can also be accomplished by pressing either ⟨Enter⟩ or spacebar.

Q (Quit) The Q option exits the SKETCH mode without recording any temporary lines. It is the same as pressing ⟨Esc⟩.

PLACING TEXT

In addition to TEXT and DTEXT commands, AutoCAD's MTEXT command is used to draw text by "processing" the words in paragraph form in accordance with the width and the top or bottom of a predetermined rectangular area called a boundary. It is an easy way to have your text automatically formatted as a multiline group with left, right or center justification as a group. It allows use of any text editor that will create an ASCII text.

MTEXT Command

The MTEXT command is invoked from the Draw toolbar (see Figure 5–44), or at the "Command:" prompt type MTEXT and press ⟨Enter⟩ or spacebar.

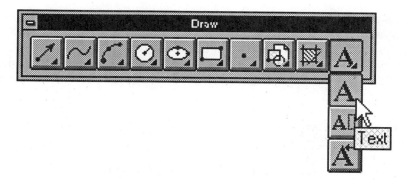

Figure 5–44   Invoke the MTEXT Command from the Draw toolbar

Command:**mtext**
Attach/Rotation/Style/Height/Direction/<Insertion point>:

Select a point and a grayed rectangle is displayed with one of the corners at the selected point. AutoCAD prompts:

Attach/Rotation/Style/Height/Direction/Width/2Points/<Other corner>:

Select a point for the diagonally opposite corner of the rectangle and it establishes the rectangular text boundary. You are then switched to the text editor, as shown in Figure 5–45, for entering text. See the PREFERENCE command for specifying a different text editor.

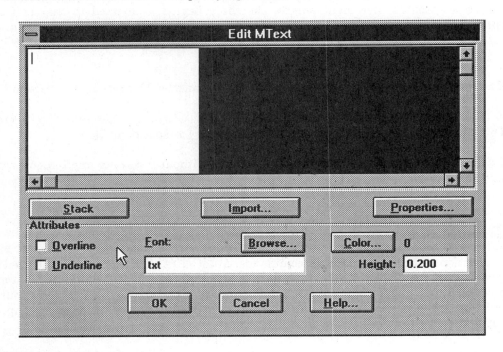

Figure 5–45 Edit MText dialog box

The large text box is where entered text is displayed. The scroll bars permit moving around to display different parts of the text when it exceeds the size of the text box.

The **Stack** button is used to place one part of a selected group of text over the remaining part. Before using the Stack button, the selected text must contain a forward slash (/) to separate the top part (on the left) from the bottom part (on the right of the /). The slash will cause the horizontal bar to be drawn between the upper and lower parts necessary for fractions. Instead of slash (/), you can use the caret (^) symbol. In this case, AutoCAD will not draw a horizontal bar between upper and lower parts, which is useful to place tolerance values.

The **Import. . .** button is used to import ASCII text file into an AutoCAD drawing. The imported text is displayed in the Edit MText dialog box. If necessary, you can make changes to the imported text.

The **Properties. . .** button causes the MText Properties dialog box to be displayed. It is described later in this chapter under the MTPROP command.

The **Overline** toggle button in the Attributes section causes AutoCAD to overline selected text or new text if none is selected. If you have specified a different text editor, you may begin overlining with \O control character and end it with \O.

The **Underline** toggle button in the Attributes section causes AutoCAD to underline selected text or new text if none is selected. If you have specified a different text editor, you may begin overlining with \U control character and end it with \U.

The **Font:** edit field allows you specify the font for selected text or new text if none is selected. The **Browse. . .** button displays the Change Font dialog box from which you can change the font of selected text or new text if none is selected.

The **Color. . .** button displays the Select Color dialog box from which you can change the color of selected text or new text if none is selected.

The **Height:** edit field specifies the height of selected text or new text if none is selected.

The Control Characters that can be used on displayed text are:

CTRL + C   Copies selected text from the Edit MText dialog box to clipboard

CTRL + X   Cuts selected text from the Edit MText dialog box to clipboard

CTRL + V   Pastes clipboard object at the location of the cursor in the Edit Mtext dialog box.

When your text entry is complete, save your changes and exit the text editor.

Attach The Attach option controls which part of the text boundary aligns at the insertion point. The option you select determines both text justification and text spill in relation to the text boundary. AutoCAD prompts:

TL/TC/TR/ML/MC/MR/BL/BC/BR:

The T, M, B, L, C and R are top, middle, bottom, left, center and right, respectively. Selecting one determines where the text will be attached to the boundary. For example, entering BL will make the bottom left corner of the rectangle the attaching point. This might be used to draw left justified text just above the title block in a drawing for general notes. In this manner, you will not have to wait and see how many lines of text are involved before you establish the insertion point for your text, as you normally would if you specified a top line insertion point. With this method text is bound by the width of the boundary and by its bottom. The height of the boundary has no effect in this case because the text will not be bounded by the top. Any excess will spill out the top.

Rotation The Rotation option causes the rectangle to be rotated at the specfied angle. AutoCAD prompts:

Rotation angle <0>:

Specify the angle of rotation and press Enter. AutoCAD returns to the previous prompt.

Style The Style option allows you to specify the text style to use for paragraph text. AutoCAD prompts:

Style name (or ?)<current>:

Specify a style name from the available styles, type ? to list the available style names in the current drawing, or press Enter to use the current style for the paragraph text. AutoCAD returns to the previous prompt.

Height The Height option sets the height of the text. AutoCAD prompts:

Height<current>:

Specify the height. AutoCAD returns to the previous prompt.

Direction The Direction option specifies the direction in which text is read. AutoCAD prompts:

Horizontal/Vertical:

Entering h or v causes the text to be horizontal or vertical, respectively, within the text boundary. AutoCAD returns to the previous prompt.

Width The Width option specifies the width of the text boundary. AutoCAD wraps the text within the text boundary. AutoCAD prompts:

Object width:

Specify the width. AutoCAD returns to the previous prompt.

2Points The 2Points option allows you to use a point other than the originally selected insertion point for the first point in determining the width of the text boundary. AutoCAD prompts:

First point: *(specify a point one end of the width)*
Second point: *(specify a point for other end of the width)*

Special Text Character and Symbol Options

To draw special symbols for text and dimensions, AutoCAD requires a sequence of control characters and it should precede the text string. The control characters for a symbol begin with a double percent sign (%%). The next character you enter represents the symbol. The following control sequences are defined by AutoCAD:

%%u	Toggle underscore mode on/off
%%o	Toggle overscore mode on/off
%%d	Draw degree symbol ($^{\circ}$)
%%p	Draw plus/minus tolerance symbol ($\pm$)
%%c	Draw circle diameter dimensioning symbol ($\emptyset$)
%%%	Force a single percent sign (%)
%%nnn	Draw special character number *nnn* (ASCII)

%%u The %%u control string allows you to underscore (underline) a text string. The control sequence has to be in the beginning of the string from where the underlining of the text string begins.

For example, to underscore the string of words "THIS IS A TEST FOR UNDERSCORE," type the text as follows:

%%uTHIS IS A TEST FOR UNDERSCORE

The resulting text string appears:

THIS IS A TEST FOR UNDERSCORE

%%o The *%%o* control string allows you to overscore (line above) a text string. The control sequence has to be in the beginning of the string from where the overscore of the text string begins.

For example, to overscore the string of words "THIS IS A TEST FOR OVERSCORE," type the text as follows:

%%oTHIS IS A TEST FOR OVERSCORE

The resulting text string appears:

THIS IS A TEST FOR OVERSCORE

You can underscore or overscore part of a line as follows:

THIS IS %%uA TEST%%u FOR UNDERSCORE

results in:

THIS IS A TEST FOR UNDERSCORE

%%d The *%%d* control string allows you to draw a degree symbol. For example, to draw the string "104.5°F," type the text as follows:

104.5%%dF

%%p The *%%p* control string allows you to draw a plus/minus tolerance symbol. For example, to draw the string "34.5±3," type the note as follows:

34.5%%p3

%%c The *%%c* control string allows you to draw a diameter symbol (∅). For example, to draw the string "56.06∅," type the text as follows:

56.06%%c

%%% The *%%%* control string allows you to draw a single percent sign. This is necessary only when you must precede another control sequence. For example, to draw the string "34.67%±1.5," type the text as follows:

34.67%%%%p1.5

%%nnn The *%%nnn* control string allows you to draw special symbols by entering *%%* followed by a three-number code. For example, to draw the @ symbol, type the control string as follows:

%%064

DDEDIT Command

The DDEDIT command allows you to edit text and attributes using a dialog box.

The DDEDIT command is invoked from the Special Edit flyout located in the Modify toolbar (Figure 5–46), or at the "Command:" prompt type **DDEDIT** and press Enter or spacebar.

Fundamentals IV

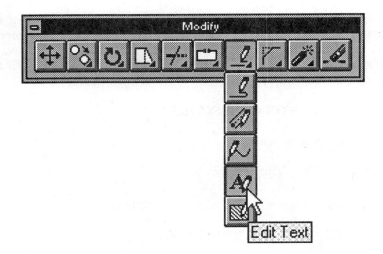

Figure 5–46 Invoke the DDEDIT Command from the Modify toolbar

Command: **ddedit**
<Select a TEXT or ATTDEF object>/Undo:

When you select a line of text, the Ddedit Text dialog box appears, as shown in Figure 5–47, highlighting the text string to be changed. Place the arrow cursor on the line of text and pick it with your pointing device. You now can edit the text string as you desire using the backspace, insert, and delete keys on the keyboard to make the necessary changes. When you are finished click the OK button. You are again prompted for a new text string to edit or you can enter a **U** to undo the last change made to the text. To terminate the command, give a null response.

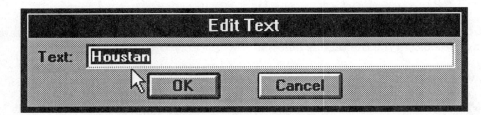

Figure 5–47 The Ddedit dialog box

SPELL CHECKING

The SPELL command is used to check the spelling of words in text objects created with the MTEXT, DTEXT or TEXT commands.

SPELL Command

The SPELL command is invoked from the Standard toolbar (see Figure 5–48), pull-down menu Tools, or at the "Command:" prompt type SPELL and press [Enter] or spacebar.

Command:**spell**
Select objects:

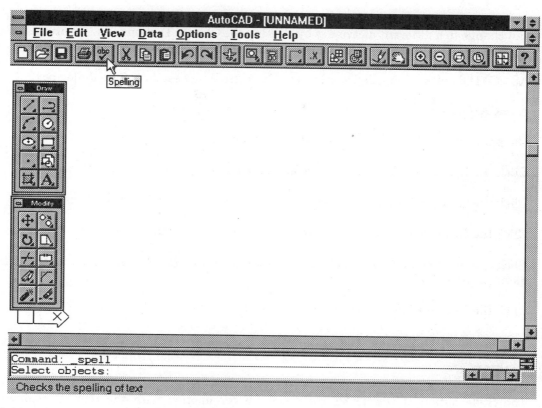

Figure 5–48   Invoke the SPELL Command from the Standard toolbar

Select the text by an object selection method. AutoCAD displays the Check Spelling dialog box, similar to Figure 5–49, only if it finds a dubious word in the specified text.

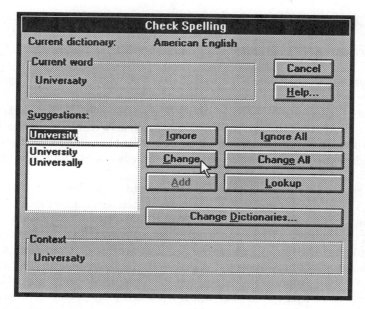

Figure 5–49   Check Spelling dialog box

Fundamentals IV

AutoCAD displays the name of the current dictionary in the top of the dialog box. If necessary, you can change to a different dictionary by clicking the Change Dictionaries. . . button and selecting the appropriate dictionary from the Change Dictionaries dialog box.

AutoCAD displays mispelled word in the **Current Word** section of the dialog box.

AutoCAD lists suggested alternate spellings in the **Suggestions** list box.

Click the **Ignore** button to skip the current word.

Click the **Ignore All** button to ignore all subsequent entries of the current word.

Click the **Change** button to replace the current word with the suggested word.

Click the **Change All** button to replace all entries of the current word.

Click the **Add** button to include the current word (up to 63 characters) in the current custom dictionary.

Click the **Lookup** button to check the suggested word for spelling.

TEXT STYLES

The Style option of the TEXT command (in conjunction with the STYLE command) lets you determine how text characters and symbols appear other than adjusting the usual height, slant and angle of rotation. To specify a text style from the Style option of the TEXT command, it must first be defined by using the STYLE command. In other words, the STYLE command creates a new style or modifies an existing style. The Style option under the TEXT command allows you to choose a specific style from those available styles.

STYLE Command

There are three areas of consideration when using the STYLE command.

First, you must make up a name for a style that you wish to define. Style names may contain up to 31 characters, numbers, and special characters ($, -, and _). Names like "titleblock," "notes," or "billofmaterials" can remind you of the purpose for which the particular style was designed. Abbreviated names like "tb," "n," or "bom" for the above would be easier to enter if used very often, but might be harder to remember. Arriving at a suitable name for text styles like layers, blocks, and other named items often means deciding between ease of use and ease of recognition.

Second, you may apply a particular font to a style. The font that AutoCAD uses as a default is called TXT. It has blocky looking characters, which are economical to store in memory. But the TXT.SHX font, made up entirely of straight line (noncurved) segments, is not considered as attractive or readable. Other fonts offer many variations in characters, including those for foreign languages. All fonts are stored for use in files of their font name with an extension of .SHX. The most effective way to get a distinctive appearance in text strings is to use a specially designed font. See Appendix J for a list of fonts that come with the AutoCAD program. If necessary, you can buy additional fonts from third-party vendors. AutoCAD can also read hundreds of PostScript fonts available in the marketplace.

The third consideration of the STYLE command is in how AutoCAD treats general physical properties of the characters, regardless of the font that is selected. These properties are the height, width-to-height ratio, obliquing angle, backwards, upside-down, and orientation (horizontal/vertical) options.

The STYLE command is invoked by typing **STYLE** at the "Command:" prompt and pressing [Enter] or spacebar.

Command: **style**
Text Style name (or ?) <current>: *(specify the style name)*
(AutoCAD displays the Select Font File dialog box. Select the appropriate font to apply to the style)
Height<default>: *(specify the text height)*
Width factor <default>: *(specify the scale factor)*
Obliquing angle <default>: *(specify the angle)*
Backwards? <N> *(yes or no)*
Upside-down? <N> *(yes or no)*
Vertical? <N> *(yes or no)*

The options and effects are discussed in the following sections.

Text Height If you respond with 0 (zero), then when you use this style in the TEXT and DTEXT commands, you are given an opportunity to change the text height with each occurrence of the command. If you give any other value, then that value will be used for this style and you will not be prompted for a text height during the TEXT and DTEXT commands.

Width Factor Font characters are drawn using the width/height factor of their definitions if the width factor is 1 (one). If you enter a value such as 0.5, then the characters are drawn at half the defined width for the defined height. That is, they will be tall and thin. If the width factor is 3, the characters will be three times wider than normal for the given height.

Obliquing Angle This option is contrary to AutoCAD's normal angle measuring convention. To have the characters drawn slanted, enter the angle in degrees. Zero degrees is vertically upward (or AutoCAD's 90 degrees). A positive value slants the top of the characters toward the right, or in a clockwise direction. A negative value slants the characters in a counterclockwise direction. Remember, this positive/clockwise and negative/counterclockwise convention is opposite to AutoCAD's default convention for applying angles in drawing. See Figure 5–50 for the differences in oblique angles.

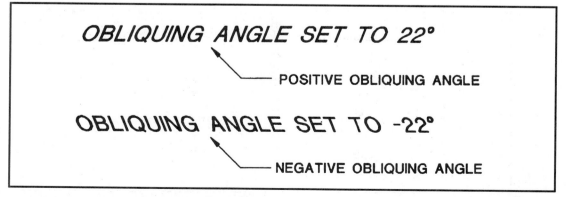

Figure 5–50   Positive and negative obliquing angles

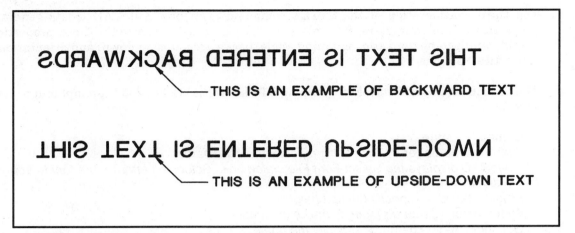

Figure 5–51   Examples of backward and upside-down text

Backward and Upside-down Options Responding **Y** to either of these options causes the text to be drawn right-to-left (with the characters backward) or upside-down (left-to-right), respectively. See Figure 5–51 for examples of backward and upside-down text.

Vertical Option Responding **Y** to this orientation option causes the text to be drawn vertically downward with each character centered below the previous one. See Figure 5–52 for examples of vertical orientation text.

When you have responded to each of the above options by entering a new value or by pressing ⌷Enter to keep the default value, the following appears in the prompt area:

    (Style name) is now the current text style.

The newly created style becomes the default style for the TEXT and DTEXT commands. If necessary, you can select a specific style from the available styles with the help of the Style option of the TEXT and DTEXT commands. The Style option is invoked as follows:

    Command: **text**
    Justify/Style/<Start point>: **s**

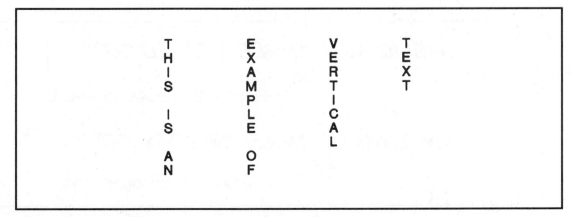

Figure 5–52   Examples of vertical orientation text

Style name(or ?)<STANDARD>: **style name**
Justify/Style/<Start point>:

After specifying a predefined style, you can continue with the TEXT command.

STANDARD is the default text style that is provided in the prototype drawing ACAD and is used for all text items including dimensioning and attributes unless specified otherwise.

MTPROP COMMAND

The MTPROP command is used to change some of the attributes of the text and boundary created by the MTEXT command.

The MTPROP command is invoked at the "Command:" prompt by typing MTPROP and pressing [Enter] or spacebar.

Command:**mtprop**
Select an MText object:

Select an MText object, AutoCAD displays MText Properties dialog box similar to the one shown in Figure 5–53.

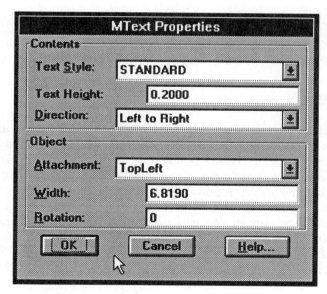

Figure 5–53 MText Properties dialog box

The **Text Style:** option lets you specify the style to be applied to the selected mtext.

The **Text Height:** edit box lets you specify the text height for the selected mtext.

The **Direction:** option lets you specify whether the text is drawn horizontally for languages like English and Spanish or vertically for languages like Chinese or Japanese.

The **Attachment:** option lets you specify the insertion point from which the text will be considered fixed and from which it will spill out of the top, bottom or both boundaries. Text spills out the bottom from a top insertion, the top from a bottom insertion, and both top and bottom from a middle insertion. Text is justified right, left or centered as specified.

The **Width:** edit box sets the horizontal size of the text boundary.

The **Rotation:** edit box sets the rotation angle of the text boundary.

QTEXT COMMAND

The QTEXT command is a support command for TEXT, DTEXT and MTEXT that is designed to reduce the redraw and regeneration time of a drawing. Regeneration times become a significant factor if the drawing contains a great deal of text and attribute information and/or if a fancy text font is used. Using QTEXT, the text is replaced with rectangular boxes of a height corresponding to the text height. These boxes are regenerated in a fraction of the time required for the actual text.

If a drawing contains many text and attribute items, it is advisable to switch QTEXT ON. However, before plotting the final drawing, or inspection of text details, the QTEXT command is turned OFF and is followed by the REGEN command.

The QTEXT command is invoked by typing **QTEXT** at the "Command:" prompt and pressing the [Enter] key or spacebar.

    Command: **qtext**
    ON/OFF:

Type **ON** and press [Enter] to turn on the qtext and OFF and press [Enter] to turn off the qtext.

INQUIRY COMMANDS

AutoCAD provides several commands that display useful information about the objects in the drawing. These commands do not create anything, nor do they modify or have any effect on the drawing or objects therein. The only effect on the AutoCAD editor is that on the single screen systems, the screen switches to the AutoCAD Text window (not to be confused with the TEXT command) and the information requested by the particular INQUIRY command is then displayed on the screen. If you are new to AutoCAD it is helpful to know the FLIP SCREEN feature that returns you to the graphics screen so you can continue with your drawing. On most systems this is accomplished with the F2 function key. You can also change back and forth between graphic and text screens with the GRAPHSCR and TEXTSCR commands typed in at the "Command:" prompt, respectively. INQUIRY commands include LIST, AREA, ID, DBLIST, and DIST.

LIST Command

The LIST command displays information about individual objects. It lets you find out information about the object stored by AutoCAD in the drawing database. The information includes the coordinates of endpoints of lines and arcs, center points of circles and arcs, lengths of lines and arcs, directions of lines and starting directions of arcs, and the angle that they turn. The LIST command is invoked from the Object Properties toolbar (see Figure 5–54), or at the "Command:" prompt, type **LIST** and press [Enter] or spacebar.

    Command: **list**
    Select objects: *(select objects)*

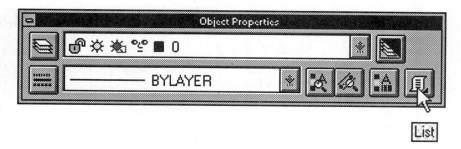

Figure 5–54   Invoke the LIST Command from the Object Properties toolbar

When you conclude the object selection process by pressing [Enter], the screen flips to the AutoCAD Text window and begins displaying the list of data about each object selected. Scrolling can be terminated by pressing [Esc], which terminates the LIST command.

In addition to the data mentioned above, the LIST command displays the following useful data:

The location, layer, object type, and space (Model or Paper) of any selected object as well as the color and linetype if not set to BYLAYER.

The distance in the main axes between endpoints of a line; i.e., the delta X, delta Y, and delta Z.

The area and circumference of a circle or the area of a closed polyline.

Insertion point, height, angle of rotation, style, font, obliquing angle, width factor, and actual string of a text object.

The object handle is reported in hexadecimal.

DBLIST Command

The DBLIST command prints lists of data about all of the objects in the drawing. It can take a long time to scroll through all the data in a large drawing. DBLIST can, like other commands, terminated by cancelling with [Esc].

AREA Command

The AREA command is used to report the area in square units of a selected closed geometric figure on the screen such as a circle, polygon, closed polyline, or a group of closed and end-connected objects. You may also specify a series of points which AutoCAD considers a closed polygon and compute the area and report. The AREA command is invoked from the Object Properties toolbar (see Figure 5–55), or at the "Command:" prompt, type **AREA** and press [Enter] or the spacebar.

Command: **area**
<First point>/Object/Add/Subtract:

The default option calculates the area when you select the vertices of the objects. If you want to know the area of a specific object like circle, polygon, or closed polyline, select the Object option.

The following command sequence shows an example of finding the area of a polygon using the Object option, as shown in Figure 5–56.

Fundamentals IV

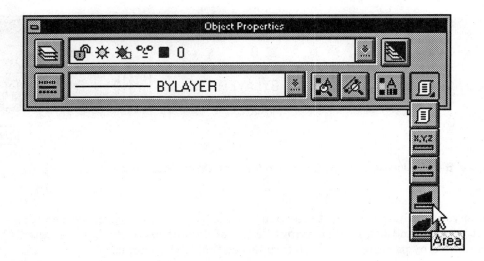

Figure 5–55 Invoke the AREA Command from the Object Properties toolbar

Command: **area**
<First point>/Object/Add/Subtract: **o**
Select circle or polyline: *(select an object)*
Area = 12.21   Perimeter = 13.79

The Add option allows you to add selected objects to form a total area; then you can use the Subtract option to remove selected objects from the running total.

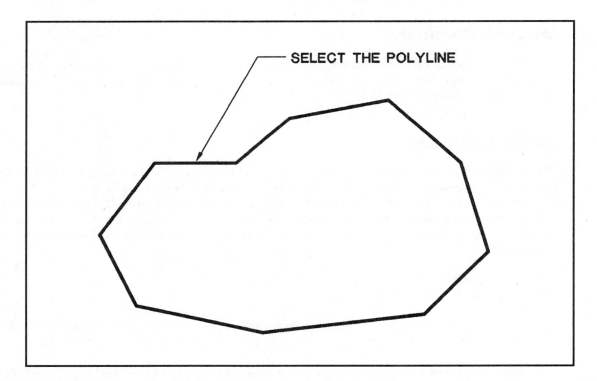

SELECT THE POLYLINE

Figure 5–56 Finding the area of a polygon using the AREA Command's Object option

The following example demonstrates the application of the Add and Subtract options. In the given example, the area is determined for the closed shape after subtracting the area of the four circles, as shown in Figure 5–57.

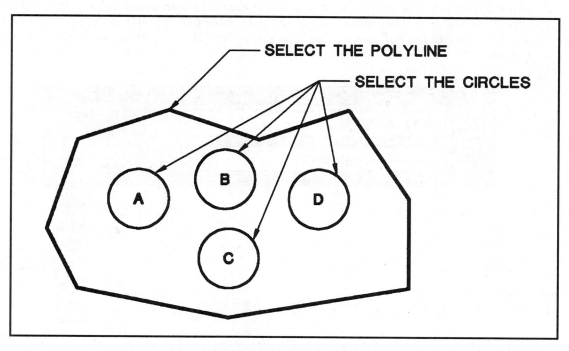

Figure 5–57   Using the Add and Subtract options of the AREA Command

Command: **Area**
<First point>/Object/Add/Subtract: **a**
<First point>/Object/Subtract: **o**
(ADD mode) Select circle or polyline: *(select polyline)*
Area = 12.9096, Perimeter = 15.1486
Total area = 12.9096
(ADD mode) Select circle or polyline: ⌷Enter⌷
<First point>/Object/Subtract: **s**
<First point>/Object/Add: **o**
(SUBTRACT mode) Select circle or polyline: *(select a circle)*
Area = 0.7125, Circumference = 2.9992
Total area = 12.1971
(SUBTRACT mode) Select circle or polyline: *(select second circle)*
Area = 0.5452, Circumference = 2.6175
Total area = 11.6179
(SUBTRACT mode) Select circle or polyline: *(select third circle)*
Area = 0.7125, Circumference = 2.9922
Total area = 10.9394
(SUBTRACT mode) Select circle or polyline: *(select fourth circle)*
Area = 0.5452, Circumference = 2.6175
Total area = 10.3942
(SUBTRACT mode) Select circle or polyline: ⌷Enter⌷
<First point>/Object/Add: ⌷Enter⌷
Command:

Fundamentals IV

ID Command

The ID command is used to obtain the coordinates of a selected point. If you do not use an object snap mode to select a point that is not in the current construction plane, AutoCAD assigns the current elevation as the Z coordinate of the point selected. The ID command is invoked from the Object Properties toolbar (see Figure 5–58), or at the "Command:" prompt, type **ID** and press [Enter] or spacebar.

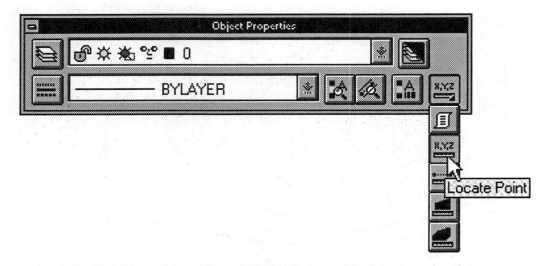

Figure 5–58   Invoke the ID Command from the Object Properties toolbar

```
Command: id
Point: (select a point)

X = <X coordinate>      Y = <Y coordinate>      Z = <Z coordinate>
```

If the BLIPMODE is ON, (the default), a blip appears on the screen at the pick point, provided it is in the viewing area.

DIST Command

The DIST command prints out the distance, in the current units, between two points, either selected on the screen or keyed in from the keyboard. Included in the report are the horizontal and vertical distances (delta-X and delta-Y, respectively) between the points and the angles in and from the XY plane. The DIST command is invoked from the Object Properties toolbar (see Figure 5–59), or at the "Command:" prompt, type **DIST** and press [Enter] or spacebar.

```
Command: dist
First point: (select point)
Second point: (select point)
```

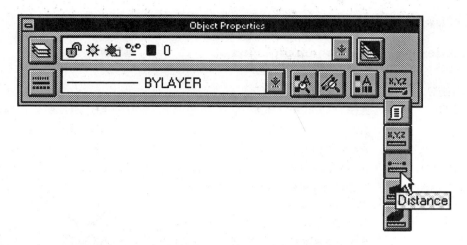

Figure 5–59   Invoke the DIST Command from the Object Properties toolbar

The following information is reported by AutoCAD:

Distance = *<straight line distance is reported>*
Angle in X-Y plane = *<angle is reported>*
Angle from X-Y plane = *<angle is reported>*
Delta X = *<horizontal distance is reported>*
Delta Y = *<vertical distance is reported>*
Delta Z = *<elevation distance is reported>*

WILD CARDS AND NAMED OBJECTS

AutoCAD lets you use a variety of wild cards for use in specifying selected groups of named objects when responding to prompts during commands. By placing one or more of these wild cards in the string (your response) you can specify a group that includes (or excludes) all of the objects with certain combinations or patterns of characters.

The type of objects associated with a drawing that are referred to by name includes blocks, layers, linetypes, text styles, dimension styles, named User Coordinate Systems, named views, shapes and named viewport configurations.

The wild card characters include the two commonly used in DOS (* and ?) as well as eight more that come from UNIX operating system. The list of wild cards and their use is shown below:

# (pound)	Matches any numeric digit
@ (at)	Matches any alpha character
. (period)	Matches any character except alphanumeric
* (asterisk)	Matches any string. It can be used anywhere in the search pattern; beginning, middle, or end of the string.
? (question mark)	Matches any single character
~ (tilde)	Matches anything but the pattern
[...]	Matches any one of characters enclosed
[~...]	Matches any character not enclosed
- (hyphen)	Specifies single character range
' (reverse quote)	Reads characters literally

The following table shows some examples of wild card patterns.

Pattern	Will match or include...	But not...
ABC	Only ABC	
~ABC	Anything but ABC	
?BC	ABC through ZBC	AB, BC, ABCD, XXBC
A?C	AAC through AZC	AC, ABCD, AXXC, ABCX
AB?	ABA through ABZ	AB, ABCE, XAB
A*	Anything starting with A	XAAA
A*C	Anything starting with A and ending with C	XA, ABCDE
*AB	Anything ending with AB	ABCX, ABX
AB	AB anywhere in string	AXXXB
~*AB*	All strings without AB	AB, ABX, XAB, XABX
[AB]C	AC or BC	ABC, XAC
[A-K]D	AD, BD, through KD	ABC, AKC, KD

SETVAR AND SYSTEM VARIABLES

The environmental state of the drawing is recorded in the drawing file and other files as "system variables." Such items as the LIMITS, CURRENT LAYER, UNITS settings, and the "Last Point" entered are just a few of the more than 200 system variables recorded by AutoCAD. The system variables are set to values that determine (or are determined by) conditions of the drawing environment. The SETVAR command reads and changes (if changeable) system variable settings as follows:

    Command: **setvar**
    Variable name or ?:

If you respond with ?, the following prompt appears:

    Variable(s) to list<*>:

More than one variable name can be specified, separated by commas, or you can use wild cards to have selected groups of system variables listed. A system variable can also be changed by typing the name of the variable at the "Command:" prompt.

Forms and Types of System Variables

Some system variables are "read only." This means that they cannot be changed directly by using the SETVAR command. For example, the system variable called CLAYER, which is "read only," when listed after the ? response, will display the name of the current layer. You can change it with the LAYER command only. But, you can change the status of the SNAP ON/OFF setting by properly applying the SETVAR command to the SNAPMODE system variable, which is not "read only."

Classification of System Variables

The system variables are classified by their type. The types are described below with the integers and points divided into two subtypes.

Integers (for switching) System variables that have limited nonnumerical settings can be switched by setting them to the appropriate integer value. For example, the snap can be either ON or OFF. The purpose of the SNAPMODE system variable is to turn the SNAP on or off by using the AutoCAD SETVAR command or the AutoLISP (setvar) function.

Turning snap ON or OFF is demonstrated in the following example by changing the value of its SNAPMODE system variable. First, its current value is set at "0", which is OFF.

    Command: **setvar**
    Variable name or ?: **snapmode**
    New value for SNAPMODE (0): **1**

The above sequence may seem rather unnecessary because the SNAP mode is so easily toggled with a press of a function key. Changing the SNAP with the SETVAR command is inconvenient, but performing the above does allow you to view the results immediately.

For any system variable whose status is associated with an integer, the method of changing the status is just like the above example. In the case of the SNAPMODE, "0" turns it OFF and "1" turns it ON. In a similar manner, the SNAPISOPAIR switches one isoplane to another by setting system variable to one of three integers: 0 is the left isoplane, 1 is the top, and 2 is the right isoplane.

It should be noted that the settings for the osnap system variable named OSMODE are members of the binomial sequence. The integers are 1, 2, 4,.....512, 1024, 2048. See Table 5–1 for the meaning of OSMODE values. While the settings are switches, they are more than just ON and OFF. There may

Table 5–1 The Values for System Variable

The OSMODE system variable values are as follows:	
NONe	0
ENDpoint	1
MIDpoint	2
CENter	4
NODe	8
QUAdrant	16
INTersection	32
INSert	64
PERpendicular	128
TANgent	256
NEArest	512
QUIck	1024
APP INT	2048

Fundamentals IV

be several object snap modes active at one time. It is important to note that the value of an integer (switching) has nothing to do with its numerical value.

Integers (for numerical value) System variables such as APERTURE and AUPREC are changed by using an integer whose value is applied numerically in some way to the setting, rather than just as a switch. For instance, the aperture (the target box that appears for selecting Osnap points) size is set in pixels (picture elements) according to the integer value entered in the SETVAR command. For example, setting the value of the APERTURE to 9 should render a target box that is three times larger than setting it to 3.

AUPREC is the variable that sets the precision of the ANGULAR units in decimal places. The value of the setting is the number of decimal places; therefore, is considered a numerical integer setting.

Point (x coordinate,y coordinate) LIMMIN, LIMMAX, and VIEWCTR are examples of system variables whose settings are points in the form of the X coordinate and Y coordinate.

Point (distance,distance) Some system variables whose type is point, are primarily for setting spaces rather than a particular point in the coordinate system. For instance, the SNAPUNIT system variable, though called a point type, uses its X and Y distances from (0,0) to establish the Snap X and Y resolution, respectively.

Real System variables that have a real number for a setting, such as the VIEWSIZE, are called REAL.

String These are names like the CLAYER, for the current layer name and the DWGNAME for the drawing name.

UNDO, U, AND REDO COMMANDS

The UNDO command undoes the effects of the previous command or group of commands, depending upon the option employed. The U command is a one-time UNDO, and the REDO command is a one-time reversal of the effects of the previous UNDO.

U Command

The U command undoes the effects of the previous command, displaying the name of that command. Pressing [Enter] after using the U command undoes the next previous command, and continues stepping back with each repetition until it reaches the state of the drawing at the beginning of the current editing session. The U command is invoked from the Standard toolbar (see Figure 5–60), or at the "Command:" prompt by typing **U** and pressing [Enter].

Command: **u**

For example, if the previous command sequences drew a circle and then copied it, two U commands will undo the two previous commands in sequence as follows:

Command: **u**
COPY
Command: [Enter]
CIRCLE

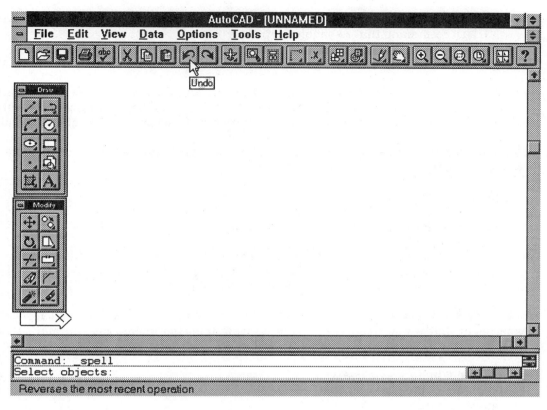

Figure 5–60   Invoke the U Command from the Standard toolbar

Using the U command after commands that involve transparent commands or subcommands causes the entire sequence to be undone. For example, when you set a dimension variable and then perform a dimension command, a subsequent U command nullifies the dimension drawn and the change in the setting of the dimension variable.

UNDO Command

The UNDO command permits you to select a specified number or marked group of prior commands for undoing. The UNDO command is invoked by typing **UNDO** at the "Command:" prompt and pressing Enter or spacebar.

> Command: **undo**
> Auto/Control/BEgin/End/Mark/Back/<Number>:

The number options can be shortened by using the UNDO Control option as follows:

> Command: **undo**
> Auto/Control/BEgin/End/Mark/Back/<Number>: **c**
> All/None/One <All>:

   All – This option enables all Undo options and is the default option of the UNDO command.

None – This option disables the U and UNDO commands except the Control option of the UNDO command that re-enables options.

One - This option prevents the U and UNDO commands from being used for multiple usage.

Limiting the U and UNDO commands frees the disk space that is otherwise being reserved to make multiple undoing possible. AutoCAD cautions that changes to the drawing cannot be undone except for the most recent one with the One option. With the None option, no reversal is available.

Number Option The Number option allows you to enter a number; (such as 3) at the full prompt (when Control is set to All) as follows:

Command: **undo**

Auto/Control/Begin/End/Mark/Back/<Number>: **3**

The above sequence causes the three previous operations to be undone. This is similar to using the U command three times in a row. The advantage of UNDO Number over multiple U's is that multiple screen regenerations will not occur, thus saving time.

Mark and Back Options If you are at a point in the editing session from which you would like to experiment, but would like the option of undoing the experiment, you can mark that point. An example of the Mark and Back option is demonstrated as follows:

Command: **line** *(draw a line)*
Command: **circle** *(draw a circle)*
Command: **undo**
Auto/Control/Begin/End/Mark/Back/<Number>: **m**
Command: **text** *(enter text)*
Command: **arc** *(draw an arc)*
Command: **undo**
Auto/Control/Begin/End/Mark/Back/<Number>: **b**

The Back option returns you to the state of the drawing that has the line and the circle. Following this UNDO Back with U removes the circle. Another U removes the line. Another U displays the prompt:

Everything has been undone

Using the Back option when no Mark has been established will prompt:

This will undo everything. OK? <Y>

Responding **Y** undoes everything since the current editing session was begun or since the last SAVE command.

> **NOTE:** The default is Y, think twice before pressing [Enter] in response to the "This will undo everything" prompt.

BEgin and End Options AutoCAD's U and UNDO commands treat the operations between an UNDO Begin and an UNDO End as one command. A Begin option entered after another Begin option (before an UNDO End) will automatically invoke an UNDO End option, thereby grouping the operations since that prior Begin option. If the UNDO Control has been set to None or One, the

Begin option will not work. Using the U command is permissible after Begin and before an UNDO End, to undo operations, but only back to the UNDO Begin .

The Begin and End options are normally intended for use in strings of menu commands where a menu pick involves several operations.

Auto Option The Auto option causes multiple operations invoked by a single menu pick to be treated as one command by the U or UNDO command. UNDO Begin should be placed at the beginning of a menu string with UNDO End at the end of the string. It has no effect if the UNDO Control has been set to None or One, however.

The effects of the following commands cannot be undone:

AREA, ATTEXT, DBLIST, DELAY, DIST, DXFOUT, END, FILES, FILMROLL, GRAPHSCR, HELP, HIDE, ID, IGESOUT, LIST, MSLIDE, PLOT, PRPLOT, QUIT, REDRAW, REDRAWALL, REGENALL, RESUME, SAVE, SHADE, SHELL, STATUS, and TEXTSCR.

REDO Command

The REDO command permits one reversal of a prior U or UNDO command. This will undo the undo. To undo the undo, the REDO command should be used immediately after using the U or UNDO command. The REDO command is invoked from the Standard toolbar (see Figure 5–61), or at the "Command:" prompt type **REDO** and press Enter or spacebar.

Command: **redo**

The REDO command does not have any options.

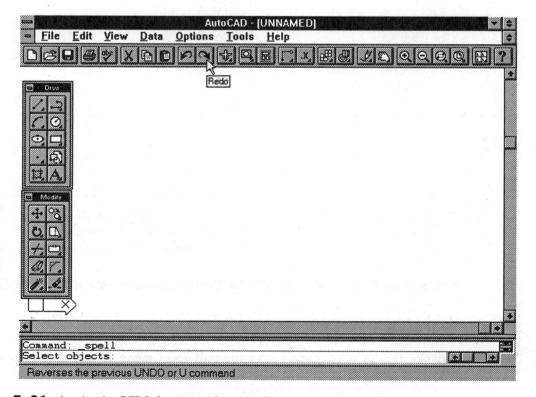

Figure 5–61   Invoke the REDO Command from the Standard toolbar

Fundamentals IV

PROJECT EXERCISE

In this project, you will apply AutoCAD concepts and skills discussed in chapters 2 through 5 to create the mechanical drawing as shown in Figure P5–1.

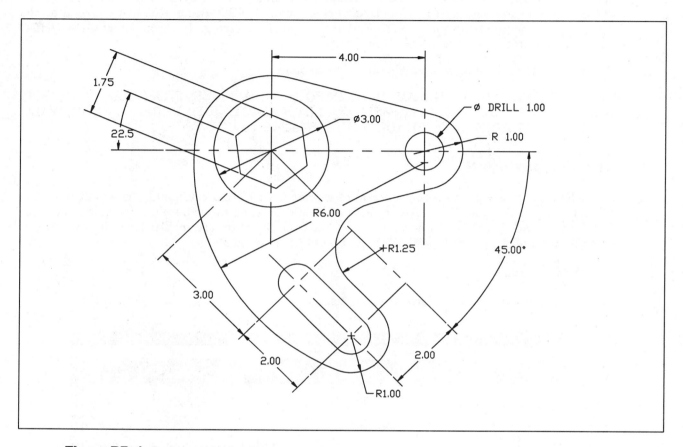

Figure P5–1 Completed project design

NOTE: The step-by-step instructions for this project are designed to provide practice in the concepts presented in chapters 2 through 5. After completing the steps, the student is challenged to discover more efficient ways to make this drawing.

STEP 1   Invoke the AutoCAD program from the Windows Program Manager.

STEP 2   Invoke the NEW command from the pull-down menu File or type New at the "Command:" prompt. Enter CH5-PROJ as the name of the drawing file. Make sure ACAD.DWG is selected as the prototype drawing.

STEP 3 Select the UNITS command from the pull-down menu Data to open the DDUNITS dialog box. Set units to decimal with 2 decimal places and degrees to decimal with 2 decimal places.

STEP 4 Invoke the LIMITS command and set the limits as shown.

> Command:**limits**
> on/off/<Lower left corner><0.0000,0.0000>: Enter
> Upper right corner<12.0000,9.0000>:**18,12**
> Command:**zoom**
> All/Center/Dynamic/Extents/Left/Previous/Vmax
> /Window/Scale(X/XP)>:**a**

STEP 5 Open the Drawing Aids dialog box from the pull-down menu Options and set grid to 0.5, snap to 0.5, and turn ON grid.

STEP 6 Invoke the LAYER command from the pull-down menu Data, create layers named border, centerline, object, and text with appropriate colors and linetypes as shown in the dialog box Figure P5–2. Set Layer "border" as the current layer.

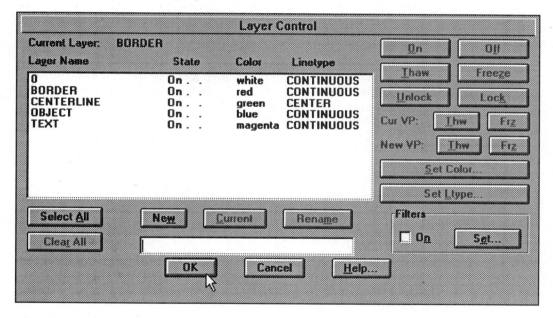

Figure P5–2 Layer dialog box

STEP 7 Invoke the RECTANGLE command to draw the border (17" by 11") as shown in Figure P5–3.

> Command:**rectang**
> First corner:**.5,.5**
> Other corner:**@17,11**

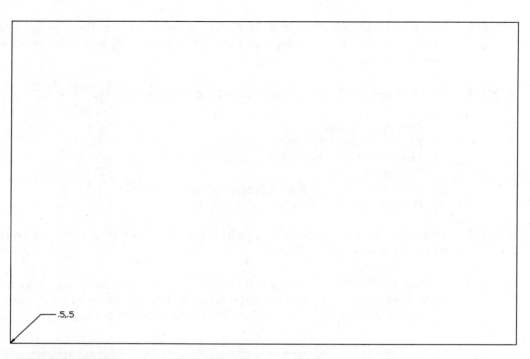

.5,.5

Figure P5-3 Border for Mechanical Drawing

STEP 8   Begin the layout of the drawing by drawing the center lines as shown in Figure P5–4. Set Layer "centerline" as the current layer. Invoke the LINE command from the Draw toolbar and draw lines 1, 2, 3, and 4.

Command:**line**
From point:**4,8**
To point:**@8.5<0**
To point: [Enter]
Command: [Enter]
LINE From point:**7,5.5**
To point:**@5<90**
To point: [Enter]
Command: [Enter]
LINE From point:**7,8**
To point:**@3.5<225**
To point: [Enter]
Command: [Enter]
LINE From point:**7,8**
To point:**@6.5<315**
To point: [Enter]
Command:

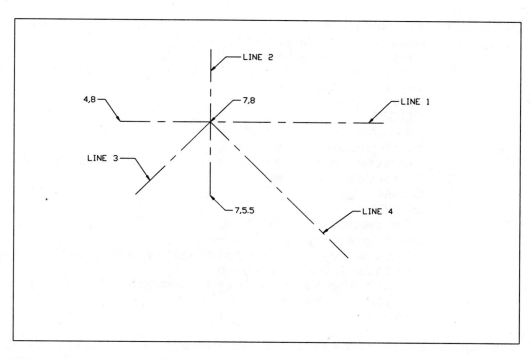

Figure P5–4 Placement of centerlines

STEP 9   Use the OFFSET command to construct additional center lines necessary for the completion of the project. Invoke the OFFSET command from the Modify toolbar and construct centerlines 2A, 3A, 3B and 4A as shown in Figure P5–5.

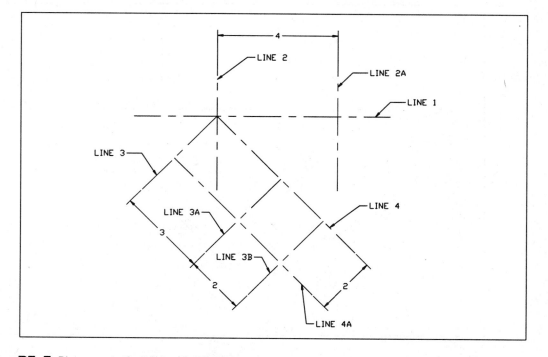

Figure P5–5 Placement of additional centerlines

Fundamentals IV

Command:**offset**
Offset distance or Through<Through>:**4**
Select object to offset:*(select line 2)*
Side to offset? *(pick to the right of line 2 to construct line 2A as shown in Figure P5–5)*
Select object to offset: Enter
Command: Enter
OFFSET
Offset distance or through<4.00>:**3**
Select object to offset:*(select line 3)*
Side to offset? *(pick a point to the right of line 3 to construct line 3A as shown in Figure P5–5)*
Select object to offset: Enter
Command: Enter
OFFSET
Offset distance or through<3.00>:**2**
Select object to offset:*(select line 3A)*
Side to offset? *(pick a point to the right of line 3A to construct line 3B as shown in Figure P5–5)*
Select object to offset:*(select line 4)*
Side to offset? *(pick a point below line 4 to construct line 4A as shown in Figure P5–5)*
Select object to offset: Enter
Command:

STEP 10   Erase lines 3 and 4 as shown in Figure P5–5 by invoking the ERASE command from the Modify toolbar.

Command:**erase**
Select objects:*(select lines 3 and 4)*

Your drawing will appear as shown in Figure P5–6.

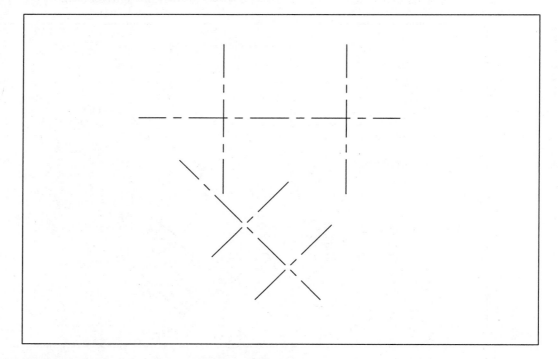

Figure P5–6 Drawing shown after lines 3 and 4 are erased

STEP 11   The intersection of the center lines you laid out in the previous steps will provide the center points for the circles to be drawn in step 11. Set Layer "object" as the current layer. Invoke the CIRCLE command from the Draw toolbar (Circle Center Radius) and draw the three circles as shown in Figure P5–7.

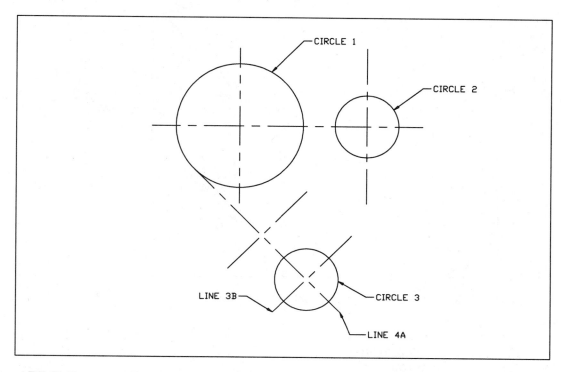

Figure P5–7 Placement of circles

Command:**circle**
3P/2P/TTR/<Center point>:**7,8**
Diameter/<Radius>:**2**
Command: [Enter]
Circle 3P/2P/TTR/<Center point>:**11,8**
Diameter/<Radius><2.00>:**1**
Command: [Enter]
Circle 3P/2P/TTR/<Center point>:**_int of**
(use the object snap tool "intersection" to snap to the intersection of line 3B and line 4A to identify the center of circle 3)
Diameter/<Radius><1.00>: [Enter]
Command:

STEP 12   Invoke the LINE command from the Draw toolbar and draw lines 5 and 6 tangent to the two circles as shown in Figure P5–8.

> ***NOTE:*** Use the object snap tool "tangent" to draw lines 5 and 6 tangent to the circle 1 and circle 2.

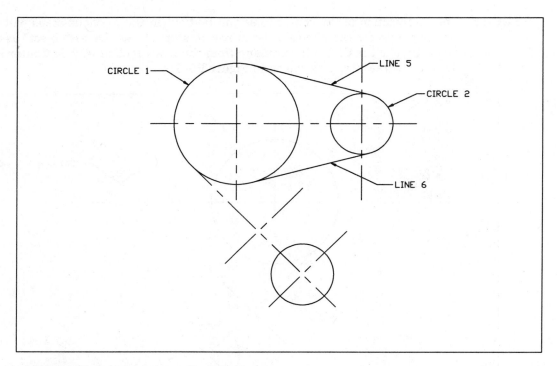

Figure P5–8 Lines 5 and 6 drawn tangent to two circles

Command:**line**
From point:**tan**
to *(select upper part of circle 1)*
To point:**tan** to *(select upper part of the circle 2)*
To point: [Enter]
Command: [Enter]

Repeat the same command sequence to draw line 6 tangent to the lower part of circle 1 and circle 2. Your drawing will appear as shown in Figure P5–8.

STEP 13   Use the OFFSET command to construct line 1A as shown in Figure P5–9. Invoke the OFFSET command from the Modify toolbar. AutoCAD prompts:

Command:**offset**
Offset distance or Through<2.00>:**1**
Select object to offset:*(select line 1 as shown in Figure P5–9)*
Side to offset?*(pick a point to the right of line 1 to construct line 1A as shown in Figure P5–9)*
Select object to offset: [Enter]
Command:

Step 14   Change the linetype of line 1A from centerline to continuous by changing the layer it is drawn on from centerline to object layer. Invoke the DDCHPROP command.

Command:**ddchprop**
Select object:*(select line 1A)*
Select objects: [Enter]

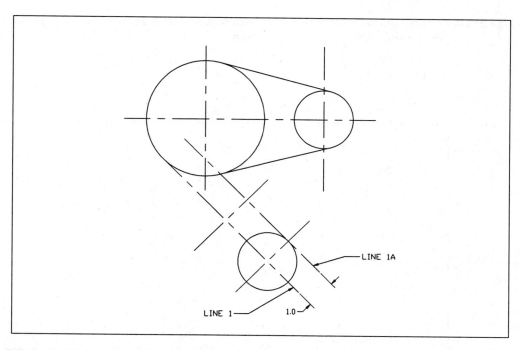

Figure P5–9 Drawing a parallel line by using the OFFSET command

AutoCAD displays the Modify Line dialog box, click on the "Layer..." button and select OBJECT layer, then click "OK" button to close the Select layer sub-dialog box. Click "OK" button again to close the Modify Line dialog box.

Your drawing will appear as shown in Figure P5–10.

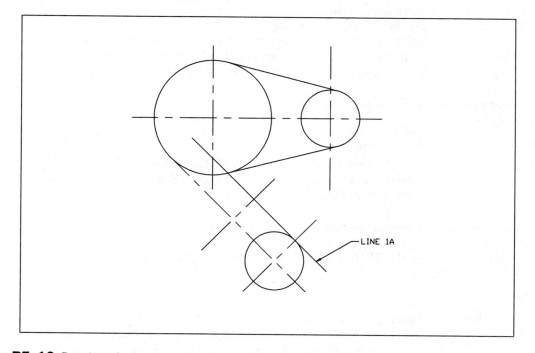

Figure P5–10 Drawing after changing the layer of the line 1A

Fundamentals IV

STEP 15 Draw two circles, circle 3 and circle 4 as shown in Figure P5–11 by invoking the CIRCLE command's Tan Tan Radius option.

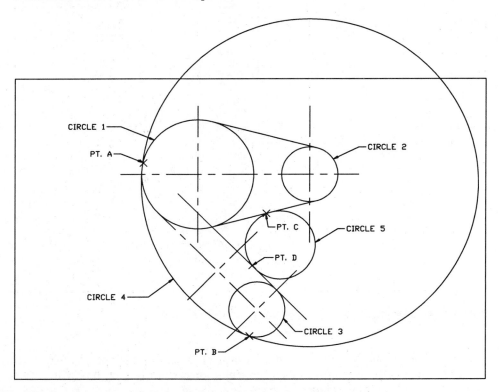

Figure P5–11 Placement of circle 3 and circle 4 tangent to two objects

> Command:**circle**
> 3P/2P/TTR/<Center point>:**ttr**
> Enter Tangent spec:*(select circle 1 at PT.A as shown in Figure P5–11)*
> Enter second Tangent spec:*(select circle 2 at PT.B as shown in Figure 5–11)*
> Enter second Tangent spec:Radius:<1.0000>:**6**

Invoke the CIRCLE command again:

> Command:**circle**
> 3P/2P/TTR/<Center point>:**ttr**
> Enter Tangent spec:*(select line at PT.C as shown in Figure P5–11)*
> Enter second Tangent spec:*(select line PT.D as shown in Figure 5–11)*
> Enter second Tangent spec:Radius:<6.0000>:**1.25**

Your drawing will appear as shown in Figure P5–11.

STEP 16 Invoke the TRIM command from the Modify toolbar to modify the two circles previously drawn in step 15.

> Command:**trim**
> Select cutting edge(s)...
> Select objects:*(select circle 1, circle 2, line 1 and line 2, see Figure P5–12, as the cutting edges and press* Enter*)*

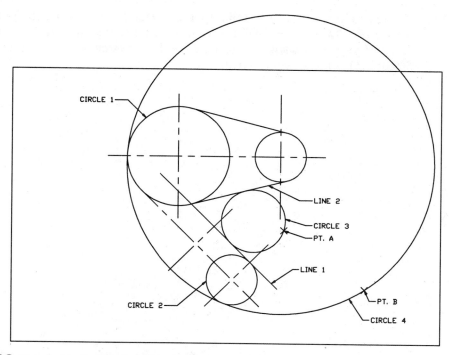

Figure P5–12 Drawing indicating the objects as the cutting edges

<Select object to trim>/Undo:*(select circle 3 at PT.A as shown in Figure P5–12)*
<Select object to trim>/Undo:*(select circle 4 at PT.B as shown in Figure P5–12)*

Your drawing will appear as shown in Figure P5–13.

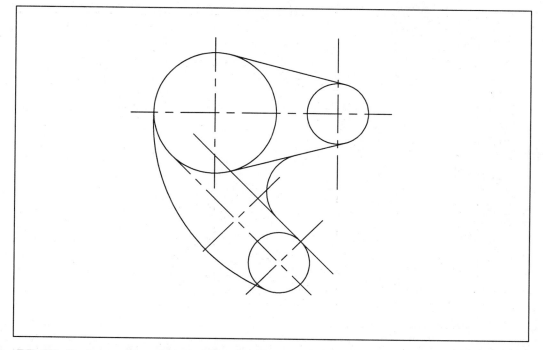

Figure P5–13 Circles modified with the TRIM Command

Fundamentals IV

STEP 17 Use the TRIM command to modify the circles and lines to achieve the layout shown in Figure P5–15. Invoke the TRIM command and select line 1, line 2, line 3, and line 4 as cutting edges as shown in Figure P5–14. Select circle 1, circle 2, and circle 3 as shown in Figure P5–14 as objects to trim.

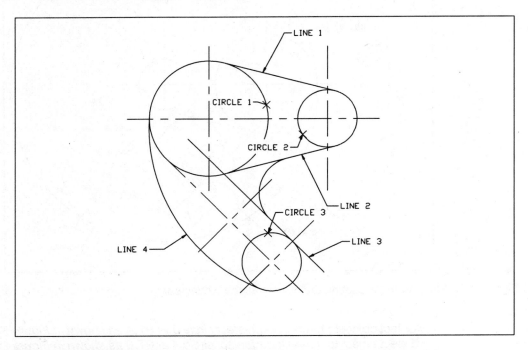

Figure P5–14 Drawing showing the selection of the objects as cutting and trim edges

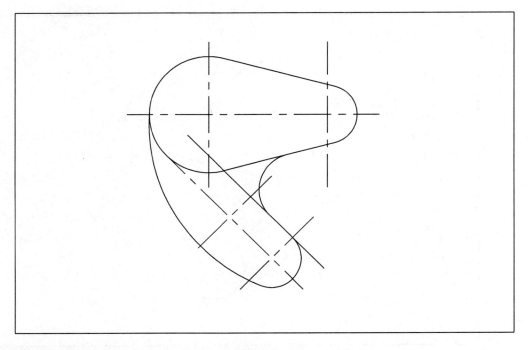

Figure P5–15 Result of the drawing after modifying the circles and lines

STEP 18   Continue to use the TRIM command to modify the figure to achieve the layout shown in Figure P5–17. Invoke the TRIM command and select arc 1, arc 2, and arc 3 as cutting edges, as shown in Figure P5–16. Select line 1, line 2, line 3, and line 4 to trim, as shown in Figure P5–16. Your drawing will appear as shown in Figure P5–17.

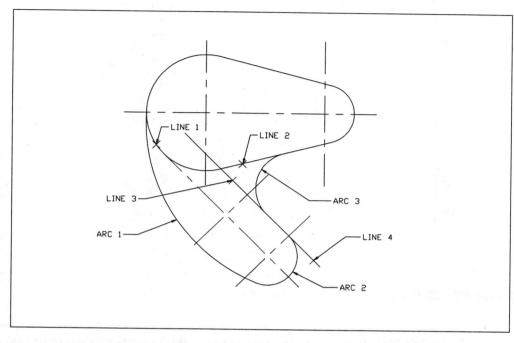

Figure P5–16 Drawing showing the selection of the objects as cutting and trim edges

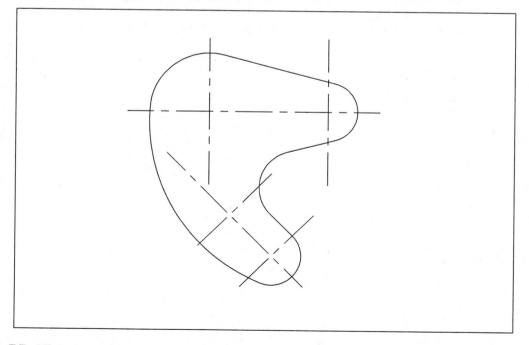

Figure P5–17 Result of the drawing after modifying the arcs and lines

STEP 19   Draw the circles necessary to complete the design. Invoke the CIRCLE command and draw circles point 1, point 2, point 3 as center point with a radius of 0.5. Draw another circle with center point at point 4 with a radius of 1.5, as shown in Figure P5–18.

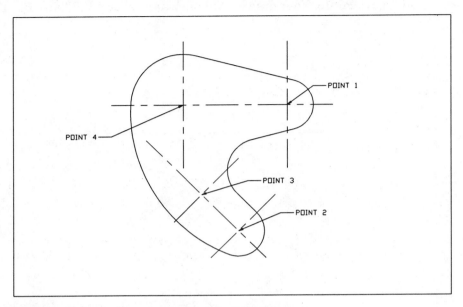

Figure P5–18 Drawing showing the center points to draw the circles

NOTE: Make sure to use the object snap tool intersection when selecting the center points.

After drawing the circles, your drawing will appear as shown in Figure P5–19.

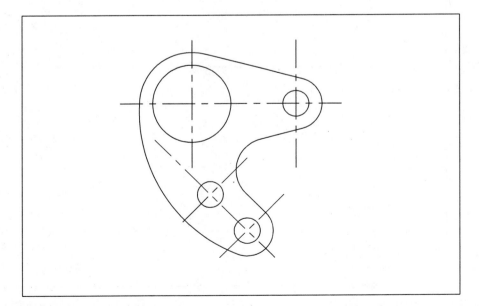

Figure P5–19 Design with the circles

STEP 20 Draw line A and line B needed to form the slot by invoking the LINE command, as shown in Figure P5–20.

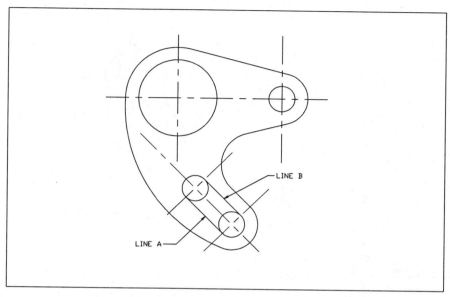

Figure P5–20 Lines drawn to form slot

Note: Use the object snap tool intersection to snap to the intersection of the center lines and circle, as shown in Figure P5–20.

STEP 21 Invoke the TRIM command and select lines A and B as cutting edges. Next, select the small circles as objects to trim at points 1 and 2, as shown in Figure P5–21.

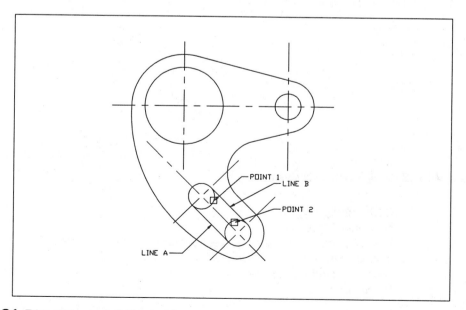

Figure P5–21 Trim edges and circles to trim

Fundamentals IV

Your drawing will appear as shown in Figure P5–22.

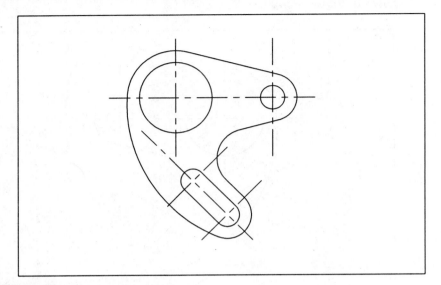

Figure P5–22 Drawing after trimming circles

STEP 22 Invoke the POLYGON command from the Draw toolbar to draw the polygon shown in Figure P5–23.

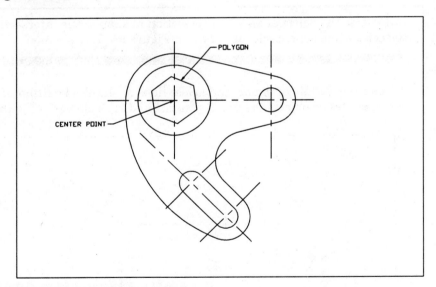

Figure P5–23 Design with a six sided polygon

Command:**polygon**
Number of sides<4>:**6**
Edge <Cener of polygon>:*(select center point as in Figure P5–23)*
Inscribed in circle/Circumscribed about circle(I/C):**c**
Radius of circle:**@0.875<67.5**
Command:

Your drawing will appear as shown in Figure P5–23.

STEP 23   Invoke the BREAK command from the Modify toolbar and select point 1 and point 2, as shown in Figure P5–24, to break the center line.

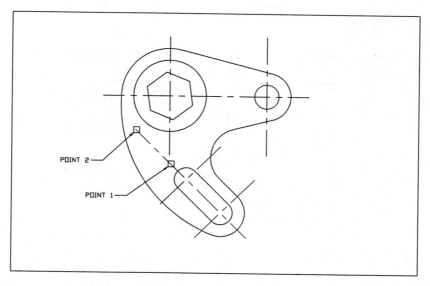

Figure P5–24 Showing the points where the BREAK Command will remove part of the center line

Your drawing will appear as shown in Figure P5–25 after removing the portion of the center line.

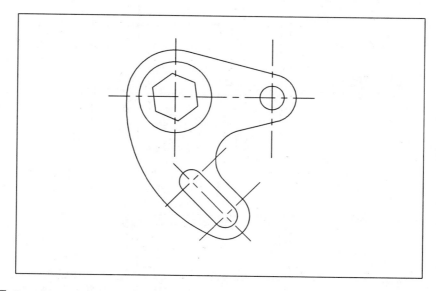

Figure P5–25 Drawing with the portion of the center line removed

STEP 24.   End the drawing by invoking the END command.

Command:**end**

Congratulations. You just successfully applied several AutoCAD concepts in creating a rather complex mechanical drawing.

EXERCISES

Exercise 5–1

Create the drawing according to the settings given in the following table:

Settings	Value
1. Units	Architectural
2. LIMITS	
lower left corner	0'-0", 0'-0"
upper right corner	65'-0", 54'-0"
3. Grid Spacing	1'-0"
4. Snap Spacing	6"
5. Text Size	6"

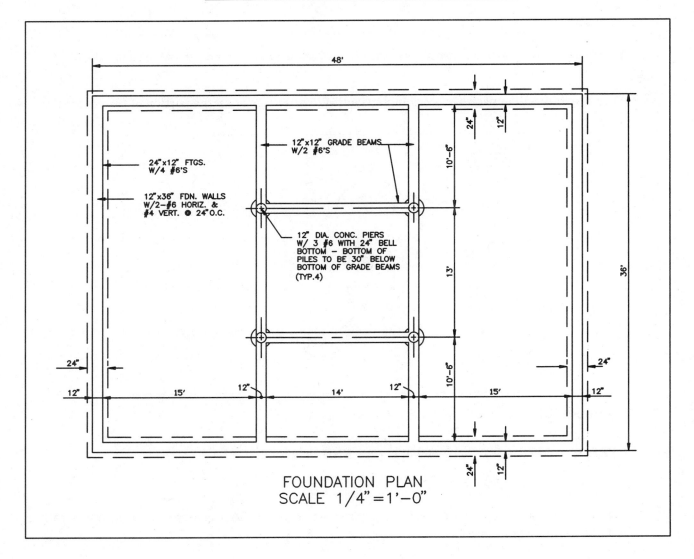

Exercise 5–2

Create the drawing according to the settings given in the following table:

Settings	Value
1. Units	Architectural
2. LIMITS	
lower left corner	0'-0", 0'-0"
upper right corner	50'-0", 40'-0"
3. Grid Spacing	1'-0"
4. Snap Spacing	6"
5. Text Size	6"

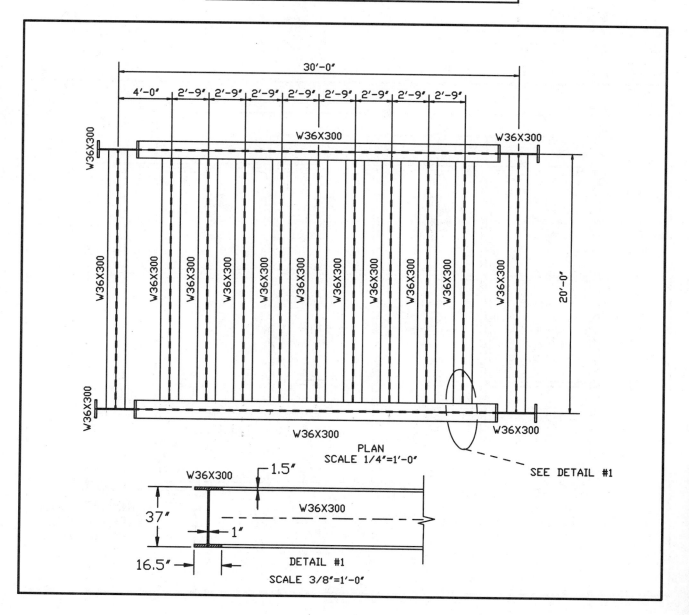

Exercise 5-3

Create the drawing according to the settings given in the following table:

Settings	Value
1. Units	Architectural
2. LIMITS	
lower left corner	0'-0", 0'-0"
upper right corner	70'-0", 50'-0"
3. Grid Spacing	1'-0"
4. Snap Spacing	6"
5. Text Size	6"

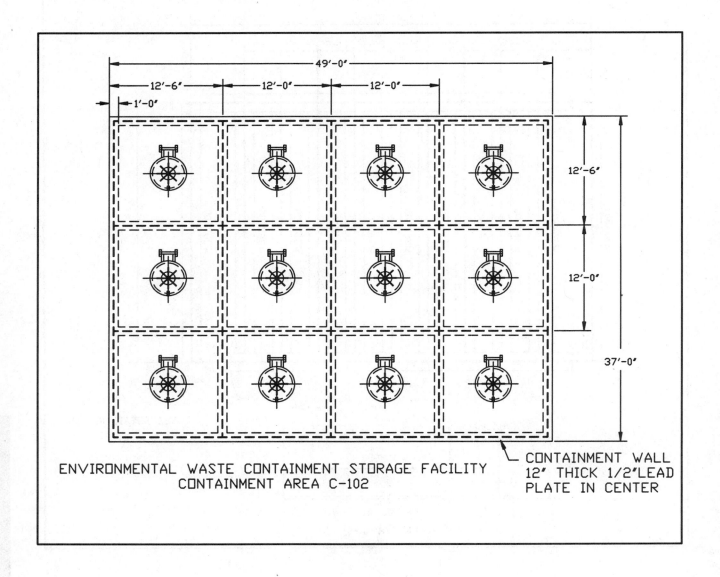

ENVIRONMENTAL WASTE CONTAINMENT STORAGE FACILITY
CONTAINMENT AREA C-102

CONTAINMENT WALL
12" THICK 1/2"LEAD
PLATE IN CENTER

Exercise 5–4

Create the drawing according to the settings given in the following table:

Settings	Value
1. Units	Architectural
2. LIMITS	
lower left corner	0'-0", 0'-0"
upper right corner	12'-0", 9'-0"
3. Grid Spacing	6"
4. Snap Spacing	3"
5. Text Size	3"

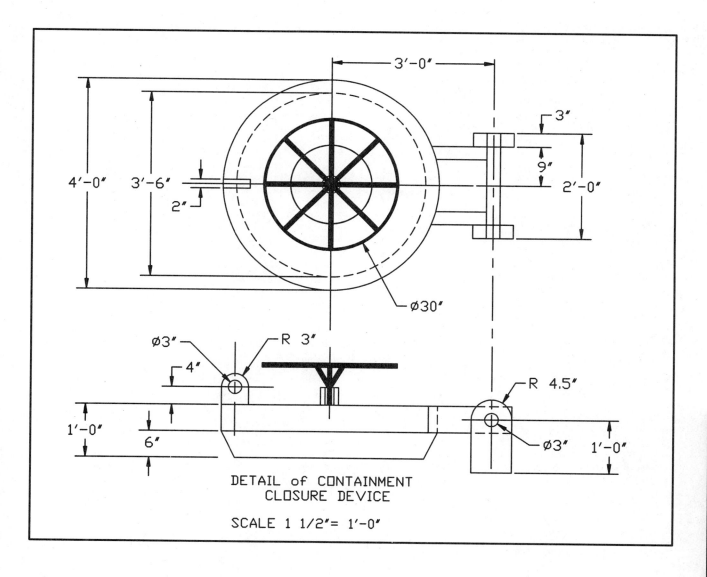

DETAIL of CONTAINMENT
CLOSURE DEVICE

SCALE 1 1/2"= 1'-0"

Exercise 5–5 to 5–6

Create the drawings according to the settings given in the following table:

Settings	Value
1. Units	Architectural
2. LIMITS	
lower left corner	0'-0", 0'-0"
upper right corner	60'-0", 45'-0"
3. Grid Spacing	1'-0"
4. Snap Spacing	6"
5. Text Size	6"

Exercise 5–5

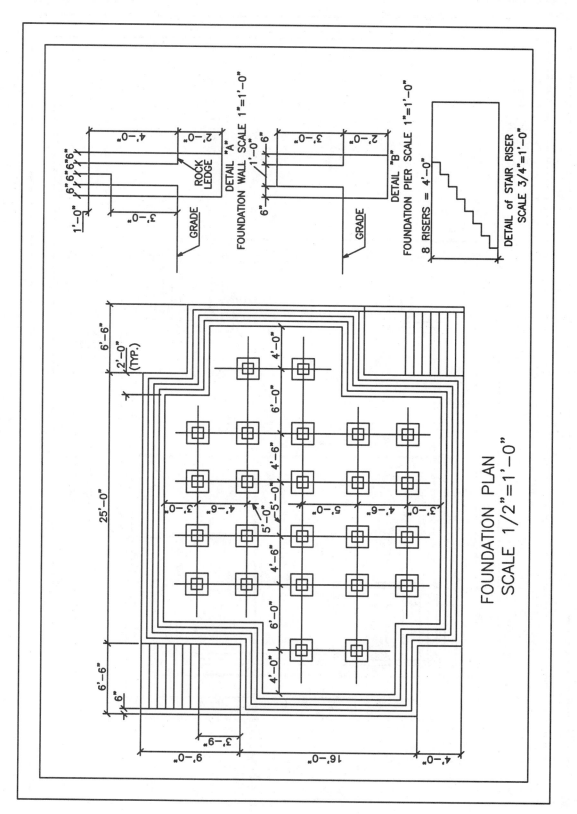

Exercise 5–6

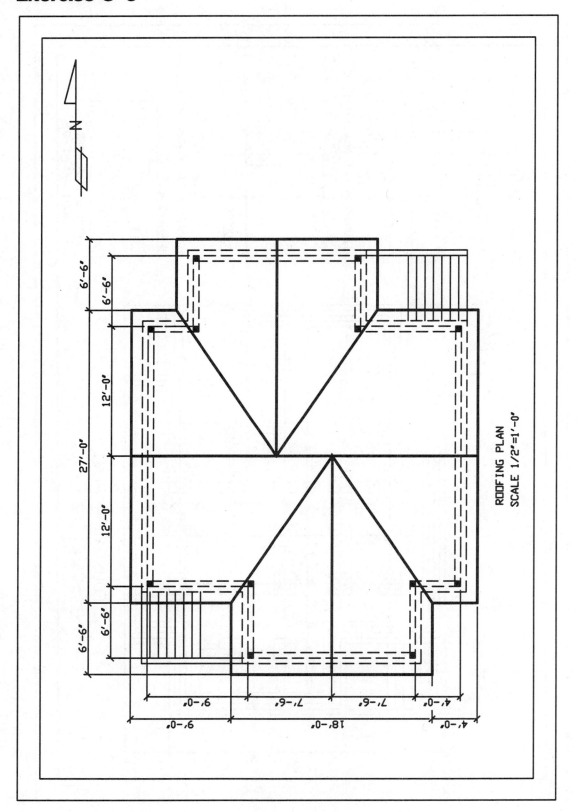

ROOFING PLAN
SCALE 1/2"=1'-0"

· · · · · · · · · · · · · · · ·

C H A P T E R

6

DIMENSIONING

· · · · · · · · · · · · · · ·

INTRODUCTION

AutoCAD provides a full range of dimensioning commands and utilities to enable the drafter to comply with the conventions of most disciplines, including architectural, civil, electrical, and mechanical.

After completing this chapter, you will be able to:

- Draw linear dimensioning
- Draw aligned dimensioning
- Draw angular dimensioning
- Draw diameter and radius dimensioning
- Draw leader with annotation and geometric tolerance
- Draw ordinate dimensioning
- Draw baseline and continue dimensioning
- Edit dimension text
- Create and modify dimensioning styles

DRAWING DIMENSIONS

AutoCAD makes drawing dimensions easy. For example, the width of the rectangle as shown in Figure 6–1 can be dimensioned by selecting the two endpoints of the top corners and then selecting a point to determine the location of the dimension line. AutoCAD drags a grayed image of the dimension to indicate how it will look while you move the cursor to specify the location of the dimension line. Another (even easier) method is to select the top line of the rectangle when prompted to select an object. AutoCAD acts as though you used an object snap feature to select the endpoints (or intersections) at the corners and again prompts for the location of the dimension line. This only takes two steps and does not require invoking object snap.

Once mastered, other types of dimensions such as diameter, radius, angular, baseline and ordinate dimensioning can be drawn quickly and accurately.

Dimension Types Dimension types available include linear, angular, diameter, radius and ordinate. There are primary and secondary commands available for each of the above types of dimensioning.

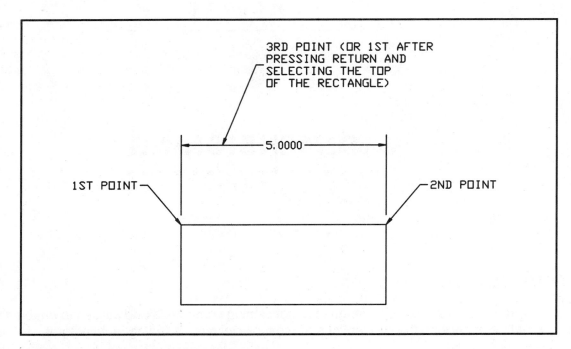

Figure 6–1 An example of a linear dimensioning

There are also other general utility, editing and style related commands and sub-commands that help you to draw the correct dimensions quickly and with accuracy.

Linear dimensioning commands include Horizontal, Vertical, Aligned and Rotated.

Angular dimensioning is covered by the Angular command.

Diameter, Radius and Ordinate dimensionings are covered by the Diameter, Radius and Ordinate commands respectively.

Dimension Variables Approximately 60 system variables are available specifically for dimensioning. Most of these begin with DIM... and are used for such things as determining the size of the gap between the extension line and the point selected on an object or whether one or both of the extension lines will be drawn or suppressed. It is combinations of these variable settings that can be named and saved as Dimension Styles and later recalled for applying when needed.

Dimension Utilities Dimension utilities include Override, Center, Leader, Baseline, Continue, and Feature Control Frames for adding tolerancing information.

Dimension Editing Dimension editing commands include Hometext, Newtext, Oblique, Tedit and Trotate.

DIMENSION TERMINOLOGY

The terms for the different parts that make up dimensions in AutoCAD are as follows:

Dimension Line The dimension line(s) is (are) parallel to and offset from the measured feature. The dimension line (sometimes broken into two lines if a single line with its related text will not fit between the extension lines) indicates the direction and length of the measured distance but is usually offset for clarity. If the dimension is measured between parallel lines of one or two objects, then it may not be offset, but can be drawn on the object or between two objects. Dimension lines are usually terminated with markers such as arrows or ticks (short slanted lines). Angular dimension lines become arcs.

Arrowheads The arrowheads are marks at the end of the dimension lines to indicate their termination. Shapes other than arrows are used in some styles.

Extension Line When the dimension line is offset from the measured feature, the extension lines (sometimes referred to as witness lines) indicate such offset. Unless you have invoked the oblique option, the extension lines are perpendicular to the direction of the measurement.

Dimension Text The dimension text is numbers, words, characters and symbols used to indicate the measured value and type of dimension. The number/symbol format usually conforms to the same linear and angular units as determined by the settings of the Units. The text style usually conforms to that of the current text style.

Leader The leader is a radial line used to point from the Dimension Text to the circle or arc whose diameter or radius is being dimensioned. A leader can also be used for general annotation.

Center Mark The center marks are lines or series of lines that cross in the center of a circle for the purpose of marking its center.

Figure 6–2 shows the different components of a typical dimensioning.

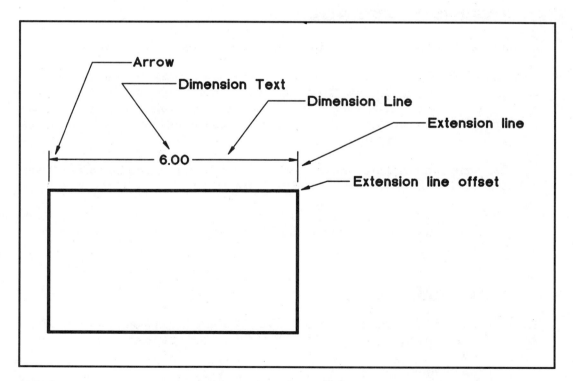

Figure 6–2 The different components of a typical dimensioning

ASSOCIATIVE/NORMAL DIMENSIONS

Dimensions in AutoCAD can be drawn either as associative or normal, determined by the setting of the DIMASO dimensioning variable.

Associative The associative dimension drawn with the DIMASO variable turned ON has all of its separate parts become members of a single associative dimension. Therefore, if any one of the members is selected for modifying, all members are highlighted and are subject to being modified. This is similar to the manner in which member objects of a block are treated. In addition to the customary visible parts, AutoCAD places point objects at the ends where the measurement actually occurs on the object. If you have dimensioned the width of a rectangle with an associative dimension and then selected one end of the rectangle to stretch, the dimension is stretched and the dimension text will be changed to correspond to the new measurement.

Normal The normal dimensions are placed while the DIMASO variable is turned OFF, the members are drawn as separate objects. If one is selected for modifying, it will be the only one modified.

> **NOTE:** An associative dimension can be converted to a normal dimension with the EXPLODE command. Once exploded, you cannot recombine the separate parts back into the associative dimension from which they were exploded (except by using the UNDO command if feasible). Note that when you explode an associative dimension, the measurement determining points remain in the drawing as point objects.

DIMENSIONING COMMANDS

In AutoCAD Release 13, there are two ways to enter dimensioning commands.

1. At the "Command:" prompt, enter DIM. You will be shifted to the Dimensioning Command Mode, at which the prompt becomes "DIM:". Only those commands valid during this special mode are acceptable. For example, you can enter "aligned" during this mode, but not at the "Command:" prompt. You cannot enter "line" while in the Dimensioning Command Mode because it is not one of the dimensioning commands.

   Other commands that are accessible while in the Dimensioning Command Mode include Exit, Redraw, Style, Undo (or U) and Update.

2. At the "Command: " prompt, enter DIMALIGNED (or other special dimensioning command), which is acceptable during the standard Command Mode, but not at the Dimensioning Command Mode.

Linear Dimensioning

The Linear Dimensioning command is invoked from the Dimensioning toolbar (Figure 6–3), or at the "Command:" prompt type **DIMLINEAR** and press [Enter] or spacebar.

Command:**dimlinear**
First extension line origin or RETURN to select:

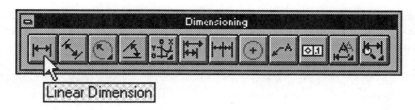

Figure 6–3 Invoke the Linear Dimensioning command from the Dimensioning toolbar

Specify a point and AutoCAD uses it as the start point (origin) for the first extension line. This point can be the endpoint of a line, or intersection of objects, the center point of a circle, and even the insertion point of a text object. You can select a point on the object itself. AutoCAD provides a gap between the object and extension line that is equal to the value of the dimensioning variable DIMEXE, which you can change at any time. After designating the start point (origin), then AutoCAD prompts:

Second extension line origin:

Designate a point at which the second extension line should start.

Dynamic horizontal/vertical dimensioning is an option after you have selected two points in response to the DIMLINEAR command. If you select two points on the same horizontal line, moving the cursor above or below the line causes the grayed image of the dimension to appear. AutoCAD assumes you wish to draw a horizontal dimension. Likewise, AutoCAD assumes a vertical dimension if the selected points are on the same vertical line.

Dynamic drag switching between horizontal and vertical is more applicable when the two points selected are not on the same horizontal or vertical line. That is, they can be considered diagonally opposite corners of an imaginary rectangle with both width and height. After the two points are selected, you are prompted to select the location of the dimension line. You will also be shown a grayed image of where the dimension will be by where the cursor is located relative to the imaginary rectangle formed by the two points. If the cursor is above the top line or below the bottom line of the rectangle, then the dimension will be horizontal. If the cursor is to the right or left of the right or left side of the rectangle, then the dimension will be vertical. If the cursor is dragged to one of the outside quadrants or inside of the rectangle it will maintain the type of dimension in effect before the cursor was moved.

After two points have been selected, AutoCAD prompts:

Dimension line location (Text/Angle/Horizontal/Vertical/Rotated):

If necessary, you can override the type of dimension to be drawn by typing **h** for horizontal, **v** for vertical or **r** for rotated.

The Rotated option allows you to place the dimension at a specified angle that is not horizontal, vertical, or at the angle determined by the two points specified in the case of aligned dimensioning (see the section on Aligned Dimensioning). When you select the Rotated option, AutoCAD prompts:

Dimension line angle <default>:

Specify the dimension line angle or pick two points on the drawing to rotate the dimension line. The points selected do not have to be parallel to the direction of the dimensioned distance.

The Text option allows you to change the measured dimension text. AutoCAD displays the measured distance as <> in the Edit MText dialog box, as shown in Figure 6–4. If necessary, add a prefix or suffix to <>. If you need to make any changes to the measured distance, delete the <>, then type the new measurement. Click the OK button to accept the change and close the Edit MText dialog box.

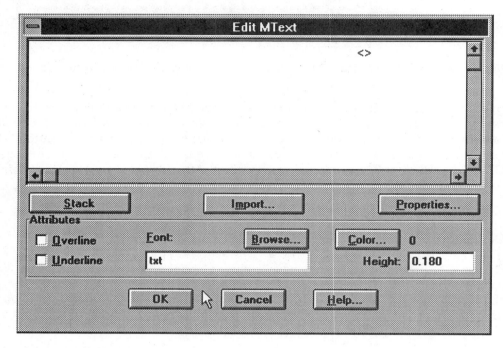

Figure 6–4 Edit MText dialog box

The Angle option allows you to change the rotation angle of the dimension text. After responding appropriately for Text or Angle, AutoCAD repeats the prompts for the dimension line location.

Specify a point where the dimension line is to be drawn. This places the line on which the dimension text is placed. If there is enough room between the extension lines, the dimension text is centered in or on this line. However, if the dimension line, arrows, and text do not fit between the extension lines, they are drawn outside. The text will be placed near the second extension line.

The following command sequence shows an example of placing linear dimensioning for a horizontal line by providing two data points for the first and second line origins, respectively, as shown in Figure 6–5.

> Command:**dimlinear**
> First extension line origin or RETURN: *(pick the origin for the first extension line)*
> Second extension line origin: *(pick the origin for the second extension line)*
> Dimension line location (Text/Angle/Horizontal/Vertical/Rotated): *(pick the location for the dimension line)*

The following command sequence shows an example of placing linear dimensioning for a vertical line by providing two data points for the first and second line origins, respectively, as shown in Figure 6–6.

> Command:**dimlinear**
> First extension line origin or RETURN: *(pick the origin for the first extension line)*
> Second extension line origin: *(pick the origin for the second extension line)*
> Dimension line location (Text/Angle/Horizontal/Vertical/Rotated): *(pick the location for the dimension line)*

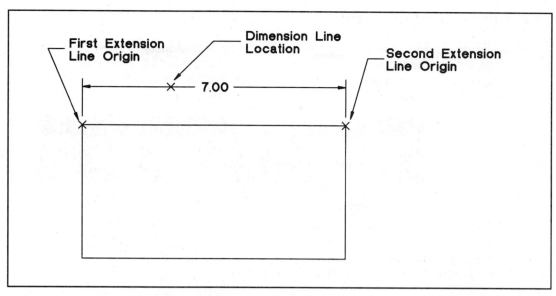

Figure 6–5   Placing linear dimensioning for a horizontal line

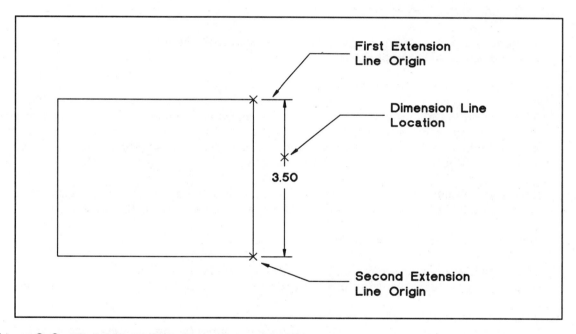

Figure 6–6   Placing linear dimensioning for a vertical line

Note: You can also invoke the Horizontal, Vertical, and Rotate mode in the Dimensioning Command Mode. At the "Command:" prompt, enter **DIM** and press [Enter]. You will be shifted to the Dimensioning Command Mode at which, the prompt becomes "DIM:". Type **hor**, **ver**, or **rot** and press [Enter] to invoke the horizontal, vertical, and rotated dimensioning commands respectively. AutoCAD prompts and options are identical to the one explained earlier.

Aligned Dimensioning

When dimensioning a line drawn at an angle, it may be necessary to align the dimension line with the object line. The dimension can be drawn by using the Aligned Dimensioning command. The Aligned Dimensioning command is invoked from the Dimensioning toolbar (Figure 6–7), or at the "Command:" prompt type **DIMALIGNED** and press [Enter] or spacebar.

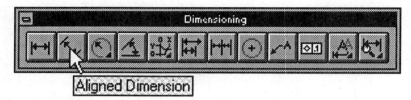

Figure 6–7   Invoke the Aligned Dimensioning command from the Dimensioning toolbar

Command:**dimaligned**
First extension line origin or RETURN to select:

Designate a point at which the first extension line should start. AutoCAD prompts:

Second extension line origin:

Designate a point at which the second extension line should start. After two points have been selected, AutoCAD prompts:

Dimension line location (Text/Angle):

The Text option allows you to change the measured dimension text. AutoCAD displays the measured distance as <> in the Edit MText dialog box. If necessary, add a prefix or suffix to <>. If you need to make any changes to the measured distance, delete the <>, then type the new measurement. Click the OK button to accept the change and close the Edit MText dialog box.

The Angle option allows you to change the rotation angle of the dimension text. After responding appropriately for Text or Angle, AutoCAD repeats the prompts for the dimension line location.

Specify a point where the dimension line is to be drawn.

The following command sequence shows an example of placing aligned dimensioning for an angular line by providing two data points for the first and second line origins, respectively, as shown in Figure 6–8.

Command:**dimaligned**
First extension line origin or RETURN: *(pick the origin for the first extension line)*
Second extension line origin: *(pick the origin for the second extension line)*
Dimension line location (Text/Angle): *(pick the location for the dimension line)*

> ***Note:*** You can also invoke the aligned dimensioning in the Dimensioning Command Mode. At the "Command:" prompt, enter **DIM** and press [Enter]. You will be shifted to the Dimensioning Command Mode at which the prompt becomes "DIM:". Type **ali** and press [Enter] to invoke the aligned dimensioning command. AutoCAD prompts and options are identical to the one explained earlier.

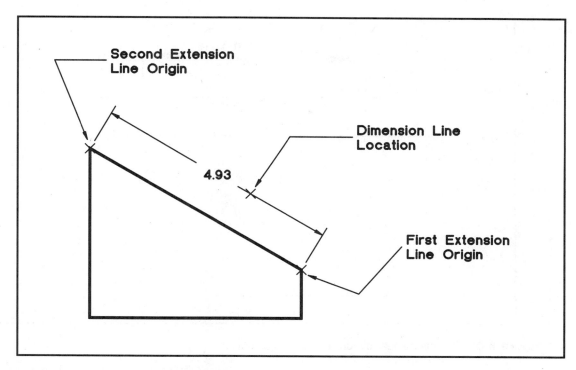

Figure 6–8 Placing angular dimensioning for a line drawn at an angle

Linear Dimensioning of Objects

If you press [Enter] in response to the prompt "First extension line origin or RETURN to select:", AutoCAD prompts:

    Select object to dimension:

If the selected object is a line object, AutoCAD automatically uses its endpoints as the first and second points to use for determining the distance to measure. You are prompted to select the location of the dimension line. If you are in the Horizontal mode, a horizontal dimension is drawn accordingly. Likewise, with the Vertical mode. If you have not yet determined the type of dimension to be drawn, then a horizontal dimension is drawn if the selection point for the dimension line is above or below the line object. A vertical dimension is drawn if the selection point for the dimension line is to the right or left of the line object. If you are in the aligned mode, AutoCAD uses the endpoints of the selected line object as the first and second points and its direction as the direction to measure. If you are in the rotated mode, AutoCAD uses the first two points selected to determine the direction of the dimension and measure the distance between the two endpoints of the line object in that direction. The dimension line passes through the last point selected.

The following command sequence shows an example of placing a linear dimension to a single object, as shown in Figure 6–9.

    Command:**dimlinear**
    First extension line origin or RETURN to select: [Enter]
    Select object to dimension: *(select the line)*
    Dimension line location (Text/Angle/Horizontal/Vertical/Rotated): *(pick the location for the
        dimension line)*

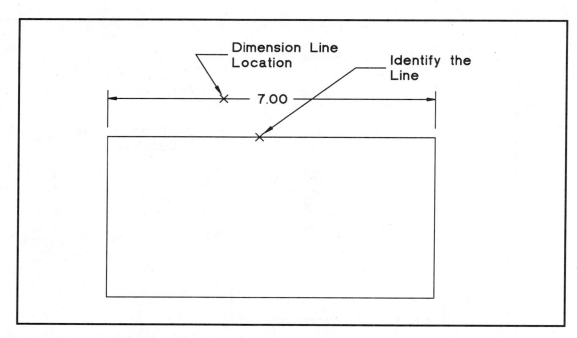

Figure 6–9   Placing a linear dimension to a single object

If the object is a circle, AutoCAD automatically uses the diameter of the circle as the distance to measure and the point at which you selected the circle as one diameter endpoint for one end of the measured direction. If you are in the Horizontal mode, a horizontal dimension is drawn using the endpoints of the horizontal diameter. Likewise with the Vertical mode, the endpoints of the vertical diameter are used. If you are in the rotated mode, AutoCAD uses the first two points selected to determine the direction of the dimension and measures the distance between the two endpoints of a diameter in that direction. The dimension line passes through the last point selected.

If the object is an arc, AutoCAD automatically uses its endpoints for the first and second points to use for determining the distance to measure. You are prompted to select the location of the dimension line. If you are in the Horizontal mode, a horizontal dimension is drawn accordingly. Likewise with the Vertical mode. If you have not yet determined the type of dimension to be drawn, then a horizontal dimension is drawn if the selection point for the dimension line is above or below the arc. A vertical dimension is drawn if the selection point for the dimension line is to the right or left of the arc. If you are in the aligned mode, AutoCAD uses the endpoints of the selected arc as the first and second points and its direction as the direction to measure. If you are in the rotated mode, AutoCAD uses the first two points selected to determine the direction of the dimension and measures the distance between the two endpoints of the arc in that direction. The dimension line passes through the last point selected.

Angular Dimensioning

The angular dimensioning command allows you to place angular dimension between two nonparallel lines, arc (between two endpoints of the arc and center as the vertex) and circle (between two points on the circle and center as the vertex). The Angular Dimensioning command is invoked from the Dimensioning toolbar (Figure 6–10), or at the "Command:" prompt type **DIMANGULAR** and press Enter or spacebar.

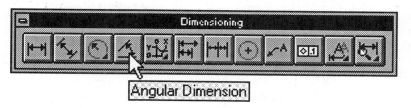

Figure 6–10 Invoke the Angular Dimensioning command from the Dimensioning toolbar

Command:**dimangular**
Select arc, circle, line or RETURN:

The default method of angular dimensioning is to select an object. If the object selected is an arc, as shown in Figure 6–11, AutoCAD automatically uses its center as the vertex and its endpoints for the first angle endpoint and second angle endpoint to determine the three points of a Vertex/Endpoint/ Endpoint angular dimension. AutoCAD prompts:

Dimension arc line location (Text/Angle):

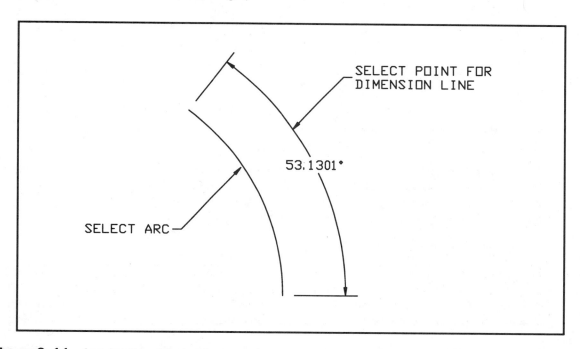

Figure 6–11 Angular dimensioning for an arc

The Text option allows you to change the measured dimension text. AutoCAD displays the measured distance as <> in the Edit MText dialog box. If necessary, add a prefix or suffix to <>. If you need to make any changes to the measured distance, delete the <>, then type the new measurement. Click the OK button to accept the change and close the Edit MText dialog box.

The Angle option allows you to change the rotation angle of the dimension text. After responding appropriately for Text or Angle, AutoCAD repeats the prompts for the dimension line location. Specify a point for the location of the dimension. AutoCAD automatically places radial extension lines.

If the object selected is a circle, as shown in Figure 6–12, AutoCAD automatically uses its center as the vertex and the point at which you selected the circle as the endpoint for the first angle endpoint. AutoCAD prompts:

Second angle endpoint:

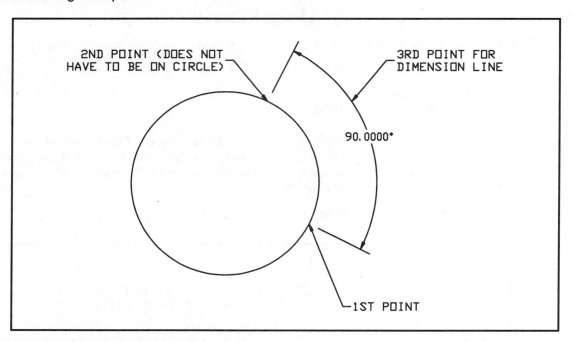

Figure 6–12   Angular dimensioning for a circle

Specify a point. AutoCAD uses this point as the second angle endpoint to use along with the previous two points as the three points of a Vertex/Endpoint/Endpoint angular dimension. Note that the last point does not have to be on the circle. However, it does determine the origin for the second extension line. Then, AutoCAD prompts:

Dimension arc line location (Text/Angle):

The Text option allows you to change the measured dimension text. AutoCAD displays the measured distance as <> in the Edit MText dialog box. If necessary, add a prefix or suffix to <>. If you need to make any changes to the measured distance, delete the <>, then type the new measurement. Click the OK button to accept the change and close the Edit MText dialog box.

The Angle option allows you to change the rotation angle of the dimension text. After responding appropriately for Text or Angle, AutoCAD repeats the prompts for the dimension line location. Specify a point for the location of the dimension. AutoCAD automatically places radial extension lines and draws either a minor or major angular dimension depending on whether the point used to select the location of the dimension arc is in the minor or major projected sector.

If the object selected is a line, as shown in Figure 6-13, then AutoCAD prompts:

Second line:

Select another line and AutoCAD uses the apparent intersection of the two lines as the vertex for drawing a Vertex/Vector/Vector angular dimension. You are then prompted to select the location of

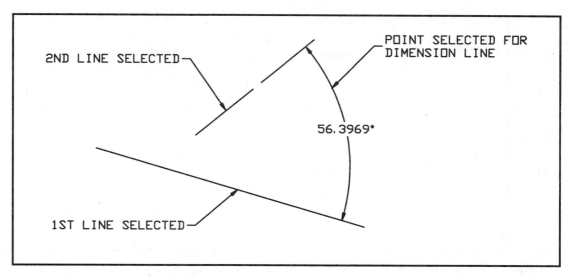

Figure 6–13 Angular dimensioning for a line

the dimension arc, which will always be less than 180 degrees. If the dimension arc is beyond the end of the either line AutoCAD adds the necessary radial extension line(s). Then, AutoCAD prompts:

   Dimension arc line location (Text/Angle):

The Text option allows you to change the measured dimension text. AutoCAD displays the measured distance as <> in the Edit MText dialog box. If necessary, add a prefix or suffix to <>. If you need to make any changes to the measured distance, delete the <>, then type the new measurement. Click the OK button to accept the change and close the Edit MText dialog box.

The Angle option allows you to change the rotation angle of the dimension text. After responding appropriately for Text or Angle, AutoCAD repeats the prompts for the dimension line location. Specify a point for the location of the dimension. AutoCAD automatically places extension lines and places the dimension text.

Instead of selecting an arc, circle, or line for an angular dimensioning, you can press [Enter] and AutoCAD allows you to do three point angular dimensioning. The following command sequence shows an example of placing angular dimensioning providing three data points, as shown in Figure 6–14.

   Command:**dimangular**
   Select arc, circle, line or RETURN: [Enter]
   Angle Vertex: *(select point)*
   First angle endpoint: *(select point)*
   Second angle endpoint: *(select point)*
   Dimension arc line location (Text/Angle): *(select dimension arc location)*

> ***Note:*** You can also invoke the angular dimensioning in the Dimensioning Command Mode. At the "Command:" prompt, type **DIM** and press [Enter]. You will be shifted to the Dimensioning Command Mode at which the prompt becomes "DIM:". Type **ang** and press [Enter] to invoke the angular dimensioning command. AutoCAD prompts and options are identical to the one explained earlier.

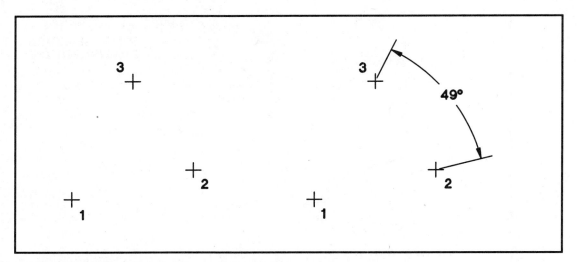

Figure 6–14   Using the three points for angular dimensioning

Diameter Dimensioning

The diameter dimensioning feature provides commands to create diameter dimensions for arcs and circles as shown in Figure 6–15. The type of dimensions that AutoCAD utilizes depends upon the dimension variable settings (see the section on Styles for changing the dimension variable settings to draw an appropriate diameter dimensioning).

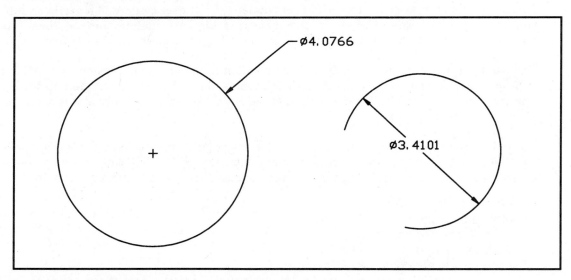

Figure 6–15   Diameter dimensioning for circles and arcs

The Diameter Dimensioning command is invoked from the Dimensioning toolbar (Figure 6–16), or at the "Command:" prompt, type **DIMDIAMETER** and press Enter or spacebar.

Command:**dimdiameter**
Select arc or circle: *(select a circle or an arc to dimension)*
Dimension line location (Text/Angle):

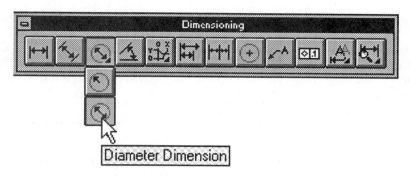

Figure 6-16   Invoke the Diameter Dimensioning command from the Dimensioning toolbar

The Text option allows you to change the measured dimension text. AutoCAD displays the measured distance as <> in the Edit MText dialog box. If necessary, add a prefix or suffix to <>. If you need to make any changes to the measured distance, delete the <>, then type the new measurement. Click the OK button to accept the change and close the Edit MText dialog box.

The Angle option allows you to change the rotation angle of the dimension text. After responding appropriately for Text or Angle, AutoCAD repeats the prompts for the dimension line location. Specify a point for the location of the dimension.

Selecting a point determines the location of the diameter dimension. It will be on the same radius as the point selected. Note that the dimension for an arc less than 180 degrees cannot be forced to where neither end of the dimension is on the arc.

The following command sequence shows an example of placing diameter dimensioning for a circle as shown in Figure 6-17.

Command:**dimdiameter**
Select arc, or circle: *(select the circle object)*
Dimension line location (Text/Angle): *(select a point to place the dimension)*

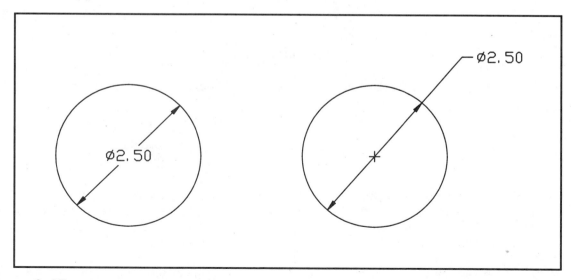

Figure 6-17   Diameter dimensioning for a circle

Radius Dimensioning

The radius dimensioning feature provides commands to create radius dimensions for arcs and circles as shown in Figure 6–18. The type of dimensions that AutoCAD uses depends upon the dimension variable settings (see the section on Styles for changing the dimension variable settings to draw an appropriate diameter dimensioning).

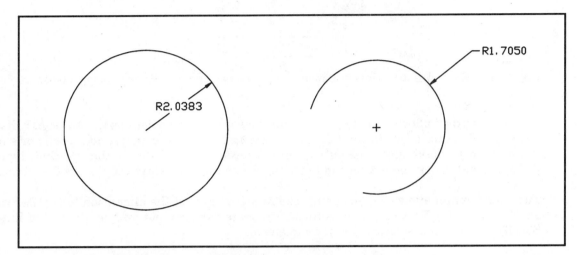

Figure 6–18   Radius dimensioning for circles and arcs

The Radius Dimensioning command is invoked from the Dimensioning toolbar (Figure 6–19), or at the "Command:" prompt, type **DIMRADIUS** and press [Enter] or spacebar.

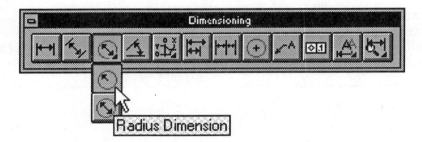

Figure 6–19   Invoke the Radius Dimensioning command from the Dimensioning toolbar

> Command:**dimradius**
> Select arc or circle: *(select a circle or an arc to dimension)*
> Dimension line location (Text/Angle):

The Text option allows you to change the measured dimension text. AutoCAD displays the measured distance as <> in the Edit MText dialog box. If necessary, add a prefix or suffix to <>. If you need to make any changes to the measured distance, delete the <>, then type the new measurement. Click the OK button to accept the change and close the Edit MText dialog box.

The Angle option allows you to change the rotation angle of the dimension text. After responding appropriately for Text or Angle, AutoCAD repeats the prompts for the dimension line location.

Specify a point for the location of the dimension. By default, dimension text for radius dimensioning is preceded by the letter R.

The following command sequence shows an example of placing radius dimensioning for a circle as shown in Figure 6–20.

> Command:**dimradius**
> Select arc, or circle: *(select the circle object)*
> Dimension line location (Text/Angle): *(select a point to place the dimension)*

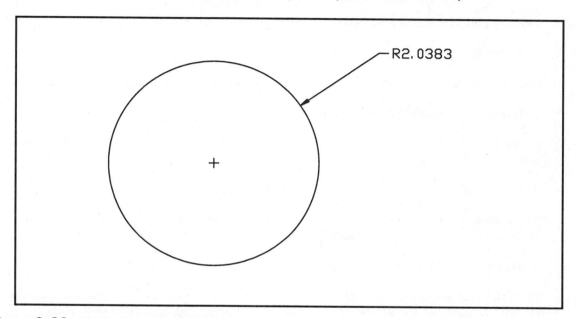

Figure 6–20   Radius dimensioning of a circle

> *Note:* You can also invoke the diameter and radius dimensioning in the Dimensioning Command Mode. At the "Command:" prompt, enter **DIM** and press [Enter]. You will be shifted to the Dimensioning Command Mode at which the prompt becomes "DIM:". Type **dia** or **rad** and press [Enter] for diameter and radius dimensioning respectively. AutoCAD prompts and options are identical to the one explained earlier.

Leader Dimensioning

The Leader command minimizes the steps required to draw the text with the line(s) and arrowhead pointing to an object or feature on an object for annotations and call-outs used to describe them.

The Leader Dimensioning command is invoked from the Dimensioning toolbar (Figure 6–21), or at the "Command:" prompt type **LEADER** and press [Enter] or spacebar.

> Command:**leader**
> From point:

Figure 6–21 Invoke the Leader command from the Dimensioning toolbar

Select a point for the arrowhead end of the leader, AutoCAD prompts:

To point:

Select another point for the end of the leader (opposite end from arrowhead), AutoCAD prompts:

To point (Format/Annotation/Undo)<Annotation>:

If you specify another point, AutoCAD connects another leader segment to the previous one and repeats the last prompt.

To point (Format/Annotation/Undo)<Annotation>:

Annotation The Annotation option allows you to place alphanumerics or symbols as text for the annotation at the end of the leader line opposite the arrowhead. AutoCAD prompts:

Annotation (or RETURN for options):

Type the alphanumerics or symbols that will be used as text for the annotation at the end of the leader line opposite the arrowhead. Instead, if you press Enter, AutoCAD prompts:

Tolerance/Copy/Block/None/<Mtext>:

The **Mtext** option displays the Edit MText dialog box and allows you to type multi-line text to place it at the end of the leader line

The **Tolerance** option allows you to draw a feature control frame for use in describing standard tolerances using the **Geometric Tolerance** dialog box, as shown in Figure 6–22.

The **Copy** option allows you to copy another text, feature control frame, mtext or block.

The **Block** option allows you to insert a named block. (Refer to Chapter 9 for explanation on Blocks).

The **None** option allows you to draw the leader without annotation.

Format The Format option is used to determine the appearance of the leader and arrowhead. AutoCAD prompts:

Spline/STraight/Arrow/None/<Exit>:

The **Spline** option allows you to draw a leader similar to using the SPLINE command.

The **STraight** option allows you to draw a leader with straight line segments.

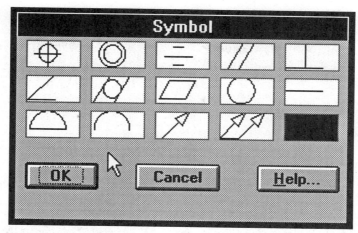

Figure 6–22   Geometric Tolerance dialog box

The **Arrow** option allows you to draw an arrowhead at the first selected point of the leader.

The **None** option allows you to draw a leader without an arrowhead.

The **Exit** option exits the Format option.

Undo The Undo option undoes the last segment of the leader line.

If the leader radial direction is more than 15 degrees from horizontal, AutoCAD adds a horizontal segment pointing towards the annotation that is equal to the length of an arrow as determined by the dimension variable DIMASZ.

> ***Note:*** You can also invoke the leader dimensioning in the Dimensioning Command Mode. At the "Command:" prompt, enter **DIM** and press Enter. You will be shifted to the Dimensioning Command Mode at which the prompt becomes "DIM:". Type **leader** for leader dimensioning and press Enter to invoke the command. AutoCAD prompts and options are identical to the one explained earlier.

Ordinate Dimensioning

AutoCAD uses the mutually perpendicular X and Y axes of the World Coordinate System or current User Coordinate System (see Chapter 14 for detailed explanation of creating User Coordinate System) as the reference lines from which to base the X or Y coordinate displayed in an Ordinate Dimension (sometimes referred to as a datum dimension).

The Ordinate Dimensioning command is invoked from the Dimensioning toolbar (Figure 6–23), or at the "Command:" prompt, type **DIMORDINATE** and press Enter or spacebar.

    Command:**dimordinate**
    Select feature:

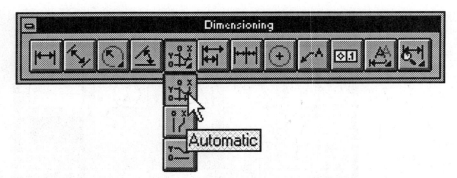

Figure 6–23 Invoke the Ordinate Dimensioning command from the Dimensioning toolbar

Although the default prompt is "Select feature:", AutoCAD is actually looking for a point that is significant in locating a feature point on an object such as the endpoint/intersection where planes meet or the center of a circle representing a hole or shaft. Therefore, an object snap mode such as endpoint, intersection, quadrant or center will normally have to be invoked when responding to the prompt to "Select feature:". Selecting a point determines the origin of a single orthogonal leader, which will point to the feature when the dimension is drawn. AutoCAD prompts:

Leader endpoint(Xdatum/Ydatum/Text):

If the Ortho Mode is on, the leader is a single horizontal line for a Ydatum ordinate dimension, as shown in Figure 6–24, or a single vertical line for an Xdatum ordinate dimension as shown in Figure 6–25.

If the Ortho Mode is off, the leader will be a three part line consisting of orthogonal lines on each end joined by a diagonal line in the middle. It may be necessary to use the non-ortho type of leader if the text has to be offset to keep from interfering with other objects in the drawing. The type of dimension (Ydatum or Xdatum) drawn depends on which is greater of the horizontal or vertical

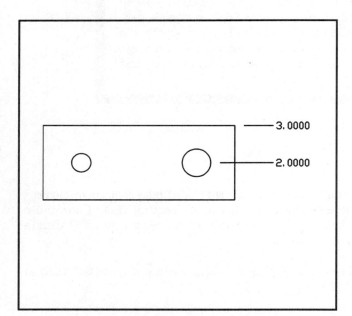

Figure 6–24 Y Datum dimension

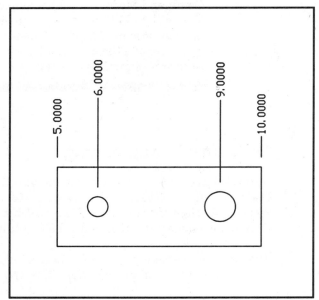

Figure 6–25 X Datum dimension

distance between the selected "feature" point and the "leader endpoint" point. A grayed image of the dimension is displayed during the "leader endpoint" selection.

Instead of providing a data point, type X or Y. AutoCAD then draws an Xdatum dimension or Ydatum dimension respectively, regardless of the location of the "leader endpoint" point relative to the "Select feature" point.

> **Note:** You can also invoke the ordinate dimensioning in the Dimensioning Command Mode. At the "Command:" prompt, enter **DIM** and press ⌨Enter. You will be shifted to the Dimensioning Command Mode at which the prompt becomes "DIM:". Type **ord** for ordinate dimensioning and press ⌨Enter to invoke the command. AutoCAD prompts and options are identical to the one explained earlier.

Baseline Dimensioning

Baseline dimensioning (sometimes referred to as parallel dimensioning) is used to draw dimensions to multiple points from a single datum baseline, as shown in Figure 6–26. The first extension line origin or the initial dimension (it can be a linear, angular or ordinate dimension) establishes the

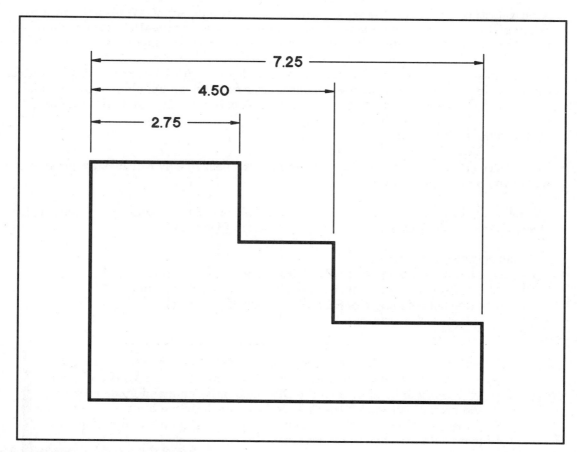

Figure 6–26 Baseline dimensioning

base from which the baseline dimensions are drawn. That is, all of the dimensions in the series of baseline dimensions share a common first extension line origin. AutoCAD automatically places a dimension line/arc beyond the initial (or previous baseline) dimension line/arc. The location of the new dimension line/arc is an offset distance established by the DIMDLI (for dimension line increment) dimensioning variable.

The Baseline Dimensioning command is invoked from the Dimensioning toolbar (Figure 6–27), or at the "Command:" prompt type **DIMBASELINE** and press Enter or spacebar.

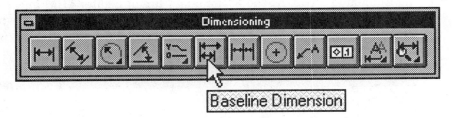

Figure 6–27   Invoke the Baseline Dimensioning command from the Dimensioning toolbar

Command:**dimbaseline**
Second extension line origin or RETURN to select:

After selecting a point for the second extension line origin, AutoCAD uses the first extension line origin of the previous linear, angular or ordinate dimension as the first extension line origin for the new dimension; the prompt is repeated. Press Esc to exit the command.

For the baseline dimension command to be valid, there must be an existing linear, angular or ordinate dimension. If the previous dimension was not a linear, angular or ordinate dimension, or if you press Enter without providing the second extension line origin, AutoCAD prompts:

Select base dimension:

You may select the base dimension, determining the base line by which extension line is nearest to where you pick the dimension.

The following command sequence shows an example of placing baseline dimensioning for a circular object to an existing angular dimension, as shown in Figure 6-28.

Command:**dimbaseline**
Second extension line origin or RETURN to select: (select a point)
Second extension line origin or RETURN to select: (select a point)
Second extension line origin or RETURN to select: (press Esc)

> ***Note:*** You can also invoke the baseline dimensioning in the Dimensioning Command Mode. At the "Command:" prompt, enter **DIM** and press Enter. You will be shifted to the Dimensioning Command Mode at which the prompt becomes "DIM:". Type **base** for baseline dimensioning and press Enter to invoke the command. AutoCAD prompts and options are identical to the one explained earlier.

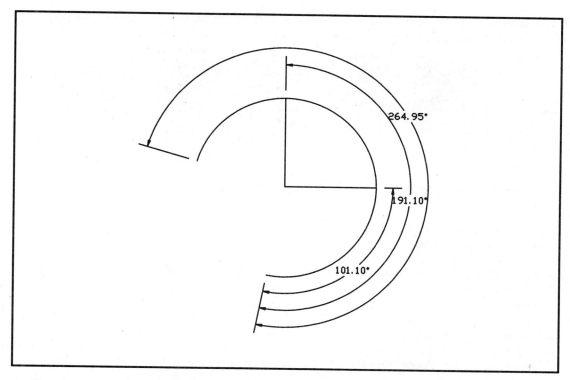

Figure 6–28   Baseline dimensioning for a circular object

Continue Dimensioning

Continue dimensioning, as shown in Figure 6–29, is used for drawing a string of dimensions each of whose second extension line origin coincides with the next dimension's first extension line origin.

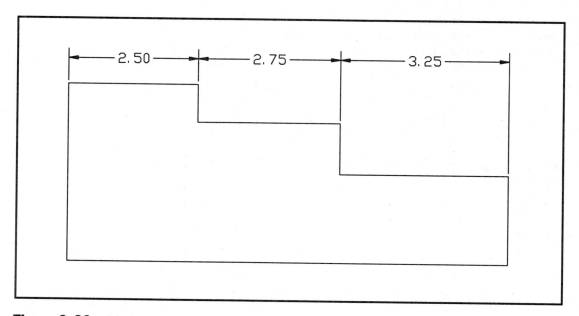

Figure 6–29   Continue dimensioning

The Continue Dimensioning command is invoked from the Dimensioning toolbar (Figure 6–30), or at the "Command:" prompt, type **DIMCONTINUE** and press ⌨Enter or spacebar.

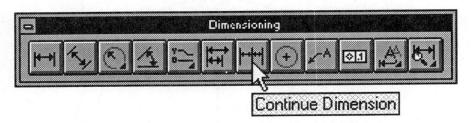

Figure 6–30   Invoke the Continue Dimensioning command from the Dimensioning toolbar

Command:**dimcontinue**
Second extension line origin or RETURN to select:

After selecting a point for the second extension line origin, AutoCAD uses the first extension line origin of the previous linear, angular or ordinate dimension as the first extension line origin for the new dimension; the prompt is repeated. Press ⌨Esc to exit the command.

For the continue dimension command to be valid, there must be an existing linear, angular or ordinate dimension. If the previous dimension was not a linear, angular or ordinate dimension or if you press ⌨Enter without providing the second extension line origin, AutoCAD prompts:

Select continued dimension:

You may select the continued dimension, determining the coincidental extension line origin to be the one nearest to where the existing dimension is picked.

The following command sequence shows an example of placing continue dimensioning for a linear object to an existing linear dimension, as shown in Figure 6–31.

Command:**dimcontinue**
Second extension line origin or RETURN to select: *(select a point)*
Second extension line origin or RETURN to select: *(select a point)*
Second extension line origin or RETURN to select: *(press ⌨Esc)*

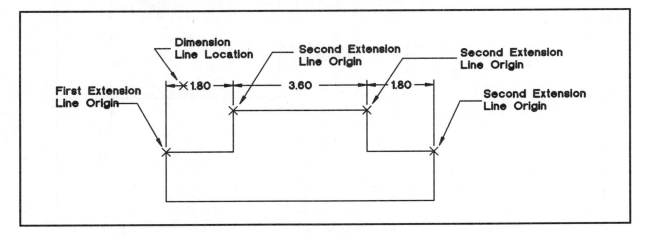

Figure 6–31   Continue dimensioning for a linear object

Note: You can also invoke the continue dimensioning in the Dimensioning Command Mode. At the "Command:" prompt, enter **DIM** and press [Enter]. You will be shifted to the Dimensioning Command Mode, at which the prompt becomes "DIM:". Type **cont** for continue dimensioning and press [Enter] to invoke the command. AutoCAD prompts and options are identical to the one explained earlier.

Dimcenter

The Dimcenter command is used to draw the cross marks, as shown in Figure 6–32, that indicate the center of an arc or circle.

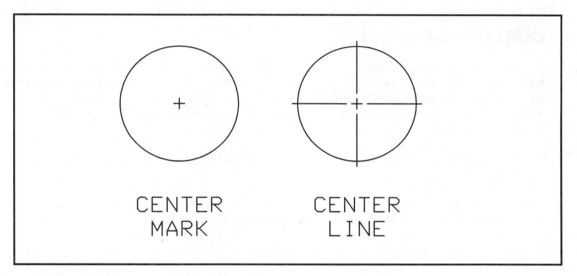

Figure 6–32 Circles with center cross marks

The Dimcenter Dimensioning command is invoked from the Dimensioning toolbar (Figure 6–33), or at the "Command:" prompt, type **DIMCENTER** and press [Enter] or spacebar.

    Command:**dimcenter**
    Select arc or circle:

Select an arc or circle, AutoCAD draws the crossing marks in accordance with the setting of the Dimensioning variable DIMCEN.

Note: You can also invoke the dimecenter dimensioning in the Dimensioning Command Mode. At the "Command:" prompt, enter **DIM** and press «. You will be shifted to the Dimensioning Command Mode, at which the prompt becomes "DIM:". Type **center** for center dimensioning and press « to invoke the command. AutoCAD prompts and options are identical to the one explained earlier.

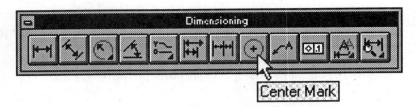

Figure 6–33 Invoke the Dimcenter Dimensioning command from the Dimensioning toolbar

EDITING DIMENSION TEXT

AutoCAD allows you to edit dimensions with Modify commands and grip editing modes. In addition, AutoCAD provides two additional editing commands, DIMEDIT and DIMTEDIT, specifically designed to work on dimension objects.

DIMEDIT Command

The options that are available in the DIMEDIT command allow you to replace the dimension text with new text, rotate the existing text, and if necessary, restore the text back to its home position, which is the position defined by the current style. In addition, it also allows you to change the angle of the extension lines (normally perpendicular) relative to the direction of the dimension line (with the oblique option).

The DIMEDIT command is invoked by typing **DIMEDIT** at the "Command:" prompt and pressing ⌷Enter⌷ or spacebar.

Command:**dimedit**
Dimension Edit (Home/New/Rotate/Oblique)<Home>:

Home The Home option returns the dimension text to its default position. AutoCAD prompts:

Select objects: *(select the dimension objects)*

New The New option allows you to change the original dimension text to the new text. AutoCAD displays the Edit MText dialog box. Make the necessary changes and click the OK button to close the dialog box. AutoCAD prompts:

Select objects: *(select the dimension objects for which the dimension text has to be replaced with new text)*

Rotate The Rotate option allows you to rotate the dimension text. AutoCAD prompts:

Enter text angle: *(specify the rotation angle for text)*
Select objects: *(select the dimension objects for which the dimension text has to be rotated)*

Oblique The Oblique option adjusts the obliquing angle of the extension lines for linear dimensions. This is useful for keeping the dimension parts from interfering with other objects in the drawing. Also, it is an easy method to generate the slanted dimensions used in isometric drawings. AutoCAD prompts:

Select objects: *(select the dimension objects)*
Enter obliquing angle: *(specify the angle)*

DIMTEDIT Command

The DIMTEDIT command is used to change the location of dimension text (with the Left/Right/Home options) along the dimension line and its angle (with the Rotate option).

The DIMTEDIT command is invoked by typing **DIMTEDIT** at the "Command:" prompt and pressing ⌷Enter⌷ or spacebar.

> Command:**dimtedit**
> Select dimension:

Select the dimension to modify and a grayed image of the dimension selected is displayed on the screen with the text located at the cursor. AutoCAD prompts:

> Enter text location (Left/Right/Home/Angle):

By default, AutoCAD allows you to position the dimension text by cursor and the dimension updates dynamically as it drags.

Left The Left option causes the text to be drawn toward the left extension line.

Right The Right option causes the text to be drawn toward the right extension line.

Home The Home option returns the dimension text to its default position.

Angle The Angle option changes the angle of the dimension text. AutoCAD prompts:

> Text angle:

The angle specified becomes the new angle for the dimension text.

DIMENSIONING STYLES

Each time a dimension is drawn, it conforms to the settings of the Dimension Variables in effect at the time. The entire set of Dimension Variable settings can be saved in their respective states as a Dimension Style with a name, by which it can be recalled for application to a dimension later in the drawing session or in a subsequent session. Some Dimension Variables effect every dimension. For example, every time a dimension is drawn, the DIMSCALE setting determines the relative size of the dimension. But DIMDLI, the variable that determines the offsets for baseline dimensions, comes into effect only when a baseline dimension is drawn. However, when a Dimension Style is created and named, all Dimension Variable settings (except DIMASO and DIMSHO) are recorded in that Dimension Style, whether they will have an effect or not. DIMASO and DIMSHO dimensioning variable settings are saved in the drawing separate from the Dimension Styles.

Parent Style and Style Families

A dimensioning style family lets different types of dimensions have variations to a parent style. That is, when you initially create a new style, you can make the settings of a particular dimensioning variable different for linear dimensions than they are for angular dimensions. While the settings may differ from one type to the other, they are still members of the same style family. When you create dimensions, AutoCAD uses the appropriate dimension style family for the kind of dimension you create. If the dimension style family member doesn't exist, AutoCAD uses the parent dimension style.

DIMENSION STYLES DIALOG BOX

AutoCAD provides a comprehensive set of dialog boxes for creating new and managing existing Dimension Styles, which in turn compile and store dimension variable settings. Creating Dimension Styles through use of the DDIM command's dialog boxes allows you to make the desired changes to the appearance of dimensions without having to memorize or search for the names of the dimension variables in order to change the settings directly.

The **DDIM** command is invoked from the Dimensioning toolbar (Figure 6–34), or at the "Command:" prompt, type **DDIM** and press Enter or spacebar.

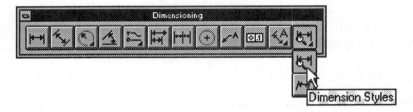

Figure 6–34 Invoke the DDIM Command from the Dimensioning toolbar

AutoCAD displays the **Dimension Styles** dialog box as shown in Figure 6–35.

The **Current** list box, located in the Dimension Style section of the Dimension Styles dialog box, lists the available dimension styles with the current one highlighted. Its name is recorded as the

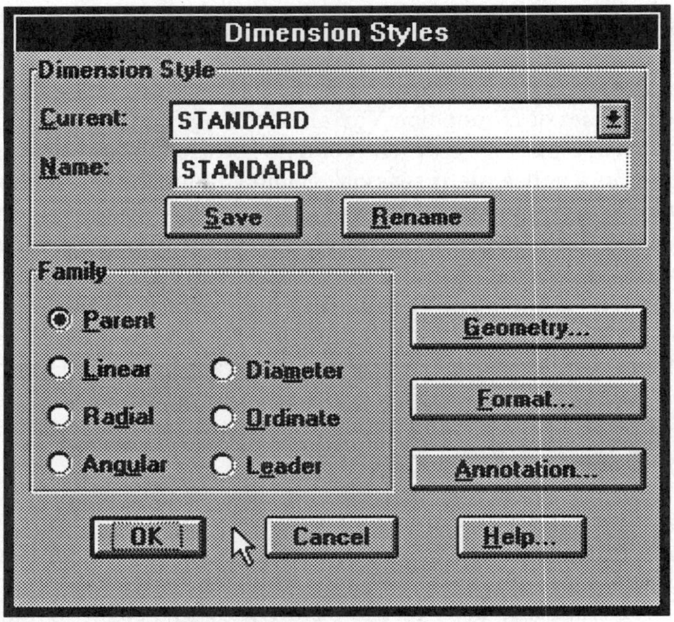

Figure 6–35 Dimension Styles dialog box

DIMSTYLE value. Styles from externally referenced drawings are listed, though not changeable in the current drawing. Making any change in the Dimension Styles dialog box creates a style from the current style and displaying the current style name prefixed with a + (plus sign). For example, making changes to a style named ARCH1 causes the name +ARCH1 to be displayed.

The **Name:** edit box located in the Dimension Style section lets you enter a name for a newly created style or rename the current style unless it is STANDARD which cannot be renamed.

The **Save** button, located in the Dimension Style section, allows you to save the settings in their current status as a style family by the name displayed in the **Name:** edit text box.

The **Rename** button, located in the Dimension Style section, renames the highlighted style family to the name displayed in the **Name:** edit text box.

Selecting one of the radio buttons in the Family section of the Dimension Styles dialog box assigns the current set of dimension variable values to that family member.

Clicking the **Geometry. . .** button displays the Geometry sub-dialog box. Clicking the **Format. . .** button displays the Format sub-dialog box. Clicking the **Annotation. . .** button displays the Annotation sub-dialog box.

Geometry Sub-dialog Box

The Geometry sub-dialog box, shown in Figure 6–36, lets you change the geometrical appearance of the dimensions including its scale. Sections include Dimension Line, Extension Line, Scale, Arrowheads and Center (marks).

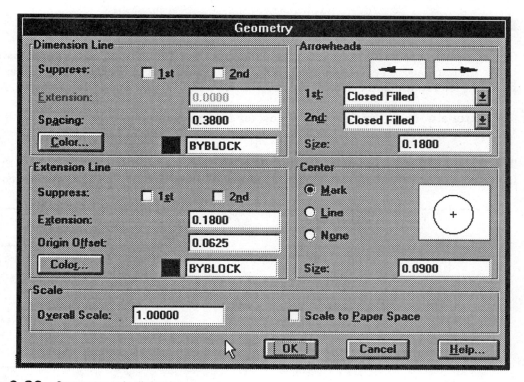

Figure 6–36 Geometry sub-dialog box

Dimension Line The Dimension Line section includes the following:

The **Suppress** option allows you to toggle the check box for 1st and 2nd for suppressing the display of the first and second dimension lines, respectively, as shown in Figure 6–37. Values (1 for ON or 0 for OFF) for 1st and 2nd are recorded in DIMSD1 and DIMSD2 dimension variable, respectively.

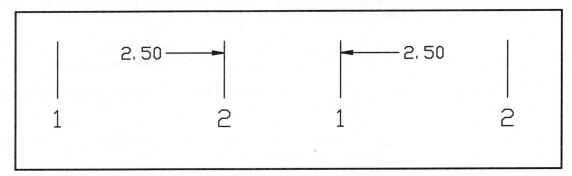

Figure 6–37 An example of suppressing the dimension line

The **Extension:** edit box determines how far the dimension line extends past the extension line when the termination marks are slashes. The value is recorded in DIMDLE dimension variable.

The **Spacing:** edit box determines how far a baseline dimension line is drawn beyond the previous dimension line. The value is recorded in DIMDLI dimension variable.

The **Color. . .** button displays the **Select Color** dialog box and allows you to set the color of the dimension line. The value is recorded in DIMCLRD dimension variable.

Extension Line The Extension Line section includes the following:

The **Suppress** option allows you to toggle the check box for 1st and 2nd for suppressing the display of the first and second extension lines, respectively, as shown in Figure 6–38. Values (1 for ON or 0 for OFF) for 1st and 2nd are recorded in DIMSE1 and DIMSE2 dimension variable, respectively.

The **Extension:** edit box determines how far the extension line extends past the dimension line. Values are recorded in DIMEXE dimension variable.

The **Origin Offset:** edit box determines how far the extension line is offset from the origin point (selected when drawing the dimension). The value is recorded in DIMEXO dimension variable.

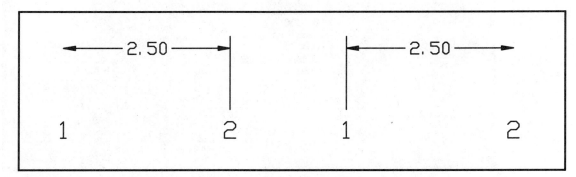

Figure 6–38 An example of suppressing the extension line

The **Color. . .** button displays the **Select Color** dialog box and allows you to set the color of the extension line. The value is recorded in DIMCLRE dimension variable.

Arrowheads The Arrowheads section lets you specify the type of arrowheads for the termination of the dimension lines. Unless you specify a different one for the second line end, AutoCAD defaults to the same as the first line end. The type of arrowhead(s) is recorded in DIMBLK dimension variable if both the first and second are the same, or in DIMBLK1 and DIMBLK2 dimension variables if they are different. The Arrowheads section includes the following:

The **1st:** list box lists available arrowheads for the first line end and allows you to set one current.

The **2nd:** list box lists available arrowheads for the second line end and allows you to set one current.

The standard library of arrowheads include None, Closed, Dot, Closed Filled, Oblique, Open, Origin, Right-Angle and User Arrow (see Figure 6–39).

The **User Arrow** option lets you use a previously-saved block by entering its name. The block should be created as though it were drawn for the right end of a horizontal dimension line with the insertion point inserted at the intersection of the extension line and the dimension line.

Note: You can also select the arrowheads by clicking the image tile of the arrowheads.

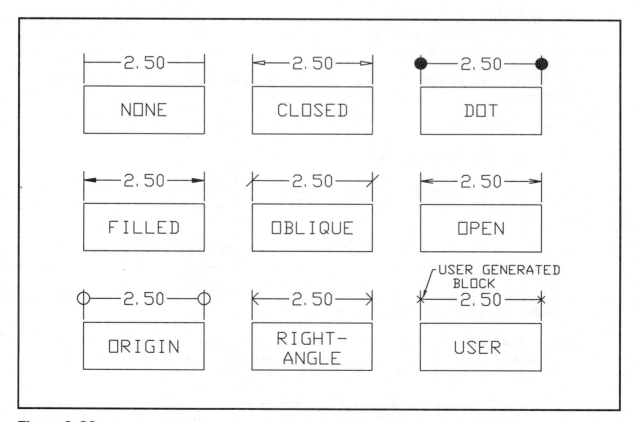

Figure 6–39 Arrowhead options

The **Size:** edit box lets you determine the arrowhead size relative to the other dimension components. The value is recorded in DIMASZ dimension variable.

Center The Center section lets you specify how and whether center marks will be placed for Radius and Diameter dimensions and the CENTER command. Center marks, when specified, will not be drawn if the dimensions are inside the circle or arc. The Center section includes four radio buttons.

Selecting the **Mark** radio button causes center cross marks to be drawn in accordance with the value in the Center Size. It is recorded as a positive value in DIMCEN dimension variable.

Selecting the **Line** radio button causes crossed center lines to be drawn in accordance with the value in the Center Size. It is recorded as a negative value in DIMCEN dimension variable.

Selecting the **None** radio button creates no cross marks or center lines drawn. It is recorded as a zero value in DIMCEN dimension variable.

The **Size:** edit box lets you specify the size of the cross marks or center lines. The value is recorded in DIMCEN dimension variable.

Scale The Scale section lets you increase or decrease the size of all of the dimensioning components uniformly by the factor entered. For example, you have set the sizes of the components to plot at a scale factor of 1/4" = 1'- 0" (1:48) and wish to draw a detail to true size (including the dimensions) and then scale it up to 3/4" = 1'- 0" (1:16). You can set the dimensioning scale to 1/3 so the components, when scaled up by a factor of three, will plot at the same size as those not scaled up. The Scale section includes the following:

The **Overall Scale:** edit box lets you set the scale factor to be applied to the components of the dimensions. This does not include distances, coordinates, angles or tolerances. The value is recorded in DIMSCALE dimension variable.

The **Scale to Paper Space** check box lets you set the scale factor based on a ratio of the model space to the paper space in the current viewport.

Format Sub-dialog box

The **Format** sub-dialog box, shown in Figure 6–40, lets you change where the dimension lines, extension lines, arrowheads and leader lines are drawn. The **Format** sub-dialog box includes the following:

User Defined The **User Defined** check box allows you to specify a location for the dimension text when you initially place a dimension. Selecting this option lets you determine where the text and/or arrow is to be drawn regardless of the justification in effect. If it is not selected, AutoCAD determines the location of the dimension text by the horizontal justification settings. The value is recorded in DIMUPT dimension variable.

Force Line Inside The **Force Line Inside** check box selection forces a line to be drawn inside the extension lines even if the dimension line and text are forced outside. The value is recorded in DIMTOFL dimension variable.

Fit The **Fit:** list box lets you specify how and where arrows and text are drawn. The value is recorded in DIMFIT dimension variable. The Fit option includes the following:

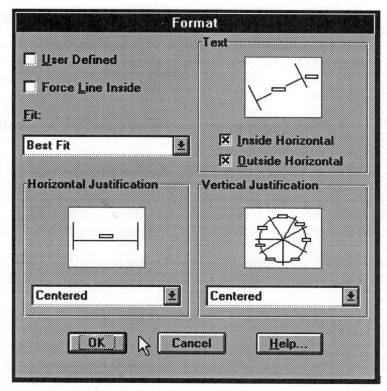

Figure 6–40 Format sub-dialog box

Selecting the **Text and Arrows** option causes both the text and arrows to be drawn outside if the dimension lines are forced outside and both to be drawn inside if space is available. If you have selected the User Defined check box and are placing diameter/radius text, you can force the leader to be drawn outside the circle/arc by selecting outside with the cursor.

Selecting the **Text Only** option causes the arrows to be drawn outside and the text inside the extension lines if there is room for the text only. When no space is available for both the text and the arrowheads, AutoCAD places them outside the extension lines.

With the **Best Fit** option, if space is available, AutoCAD places the text and arrowheads between the extension lines. If there is room for the text only, then AutoCAD places the text between the extension lines and arrows are drawn outside. If there is room for the arrowheads only, then AutoCAD places the arrowheads between the extension lines and text is drawn outside. When no space is available for both the text and the arrowheads, AutoCAD places them outside the extension lines.

Selecting the **Leader** option causes the text (if there is not enough room for it between the extension lines) to be placed above and to one side of the dimension line with a leader to the dimension line where the text would normally be placed.

Horizontal Justification The **Horizontal Justification** section of the Format dialog box lets you locate the text between the extension lines along the dimension line. The value is recorded in DIMJUST dimension variable. The section includes the following:

Selecting the **Centered** option causes the text to be centered between the extension lines.

Selecting the **1st Extension Line** option causes the text to be placed near the left extension line.

Selecting the **2nd Extension Line** option causes the text to be placed near the right extension line.

Selecting the **Over 1st Extension Line** option causes the text to be drawn in line with and above the first extension line.

Selecting the **Over 2nd Extension Line** option causes the text to be drawn in line with and above the second extension line.

Text The **Text** section lets you specify whether the text is drawn inside or outside the extension lines. Selecting **Inside** check box causes the text to be drawn horizontally between extension lines regardless of their angle. The value is recorded in DIMTIH dimension variable. Selecting **Outside** check box causes the text to be drawn outside the extension line with a leader to an extension of the dimension line. The value is recorded in DIMTOH dimension variable.

Vertical Justification The **Vertical Justification** section of the Format dialog box lets you specify the location of the text relative to the dimension line. The value is recorded in DIMTAD dimension variable. The section includes the following:

Selecting the **Centered** option causes the text to be drawn centered between the halves of a broken dimension line.

Selecting the **Above** option causes the text to be drawn above the dimension line.

Selecting the **Outside** option causes the text to be drawn on the side of the dimension beyond the dimensioned object.

Selecting the **JIS** option causes the text to be drawn in accordance with the Japanese Industrial Standards.

Annotation Sub-dialog Box

The **Annotation sub-dialog box**, shown in Figure 6–41, lets you change how the dimension text or leader text appears. It includes sections for Primary Units, Tolerance, Alternate Units and Text. The Annotation sub-dialog box includes the following:

Primary Units The Primary Units section controls the display of the primary measurement units and any prefixes and suffixes for the dimension text. The Primary Units section includes the following:

The **Prefix:** edit box allows you to include a prefix to the dimension text. The prefix text will override any default prefixes such as those used in radius (R) dimensioning. The value is recorded in DIMPOST dimension variable.

The **Suffix:** edit box allows you to include a suffix to the dimension text. If you specify tolerances, AutoCAD includes the suffix to the tolerances, as well as to the main dimension. The value is recorded in DIMPOST dimension variable.

AutoCAD displays how the prefixed and suffixed dimension text appears in the image tile.

The **Units. . .** button displays the **Primary Units** sub-dialog box, as shown in Figure 6–42, and allows you to set the primary measurement units.

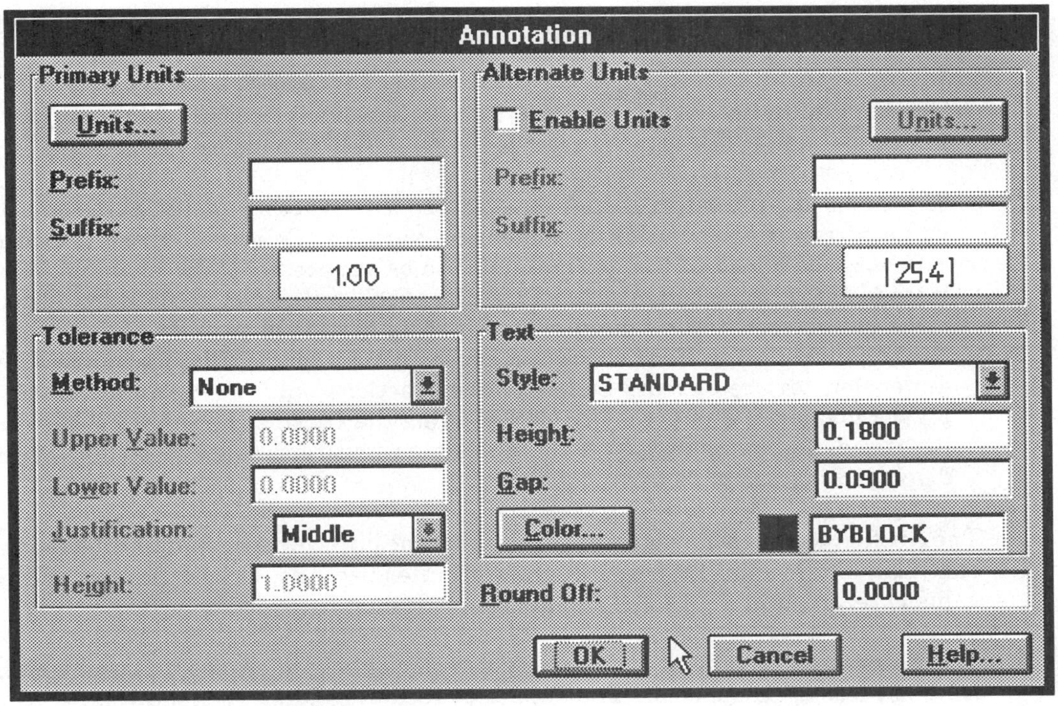

Annotation

Primary Units

[Units...]

Prefix: [   ]

Suffix: [   ]

[1.00   ]

Alternate Units

☐ Enable Units   [Units...]

Prefix: [   ]

Suffix: [   ]

[|25.4|]

Tolerance

Method: [None   ▼]

Upper Value: [0.0000]

Lower Value: [0.0000]

Justification: [Middle ▼]

Height: [1.0000]

Text

Style: [STANDARD   ▼]

Height: [0.1800]

Gap: [0.0900]

[Color...]   ▉ [BYBLOCK]

Round Off: [0.0000]

[OK]   ▷   [Cancel]   [Help...]

Figure 6–41   Annotation sub-dialog box

The **Units** section of the Primary Units sub-dialog box lets you set the format of the units for linear, radial, diameter, ordinate and leader dimension text. The list box include Architectural, Decimal, Engineering, Fractional and Scientific. The value is recorded in DIMUNIT dimension variable.

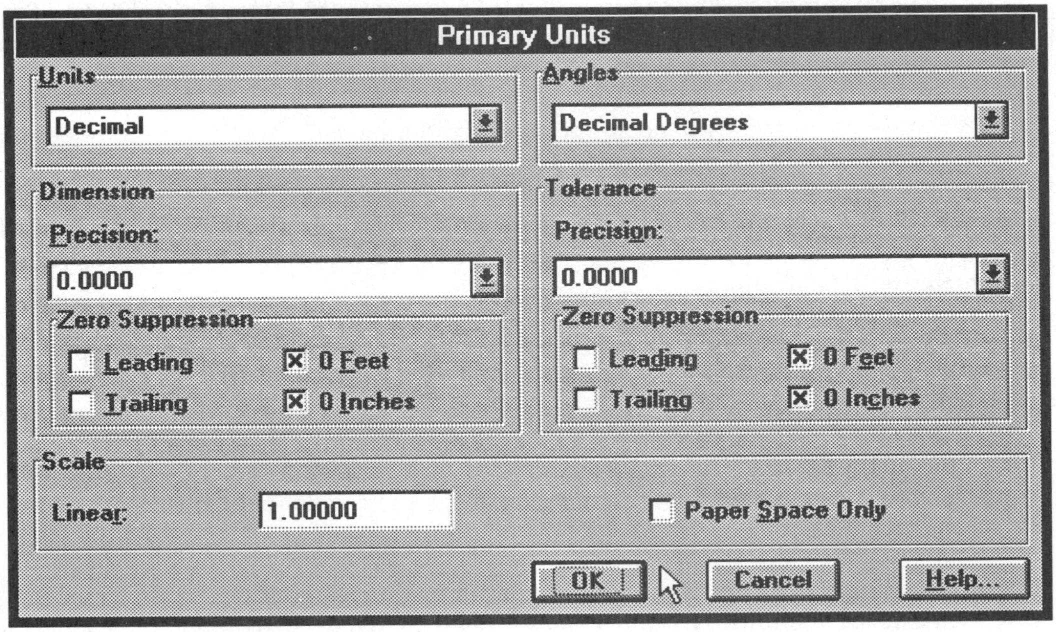

Primary Units

Units

[Decimal   ▼]

Angles

[Decimal Degrees   ▼]

Dimension

Precision:

[0.0000   ▼]

Zero Suppression

☐ Leading   ☒ 0 Feet

☐ Trailing   ☒ 0 Inches

Tolerance

Precision:

[0.0000   ▼]

Zero Suppression

☐ Leading   ☒ 0 Feet

☐ Trailing   ☒ 0 Inches

Scale

Linear: [1.00000]   ☐ Paper Space Only

[OK]   ▷   [Cancel]   [Help...]

Figure 6–42   Primary Units sub-dialog box

The **Dimension** section lets you specify the precision of a dimension and whether leading or trailing zeros are displayed. The Dimension section includes the following:

The **Precision** list box lets you determine to how many decimal places the text will be shown in decimal units. The value is recorded in DIMDEC dimension variable.

The **Zero suppression** section lets you specify whether or not zeros are displayed. The value is recorded in DIMZIN dimension variable. Selection of the **Leading** check box causes zeros ahead of the decimal point to be suppressed. For example, .700 is displayed instead of 0.700. Selection of the **Trailing** check box causes zeros behind the decimal point to be suppressed. For example, 7 or 7.25 is displayed instead of 7.000 or 7.250 respectively. Selecting the **Feet** check box causes zeros representing feet to be suppressed if the dimension text represents inches and/or fractions only. For example, 7" or 7 1/4" is displayed instead of 0'- 7" or 0'- 7 1/4". Selecting the **Inches** check box causes zeros representing inches to be suppressed if the dimension text represents feet only. For example, 7' is displayed instead of 7'- 0".

The **Angles** section is for setting the format of the units for the angular dimension text. The list box includes Decimal Degrees, Degrees/Minutes/Seconds, Grads, Radian and Surveyor. The value is recorded in DIMAUNIT dimension variable.

The **Tolerance** section lets you specify the precision of tolerance text and whether leading or trailing zeros are displayed. The Tolerance section includes the following:

The **Precision** list box lets you determine to how many decimal places the text will be shown in decimal units. The value is recorded in DIMTDEC dimension variable.

The **Zero suppression** section lets you specify whether or not zeros are displayed. The value is recorded in DIMTZIN dimension variable. Selection of the **Leading** check box causes zeros ahead of the decimal point to be suppressed. For example, .700 is displayed instead of 0.700. Selection of the **Trailing** check box causes zeros behind the decimal point to be suppressed. For example 7 or 7.25 is displayed instead of 7.000 or 7.250 respectively. Selection of the **Feet** check box causes zeros representing feet to be suppressed if the dimension text represents inches and/or fractions only. For example, 7" or 7 1/4" is displayed instead of 0'- 7" or 0'- 7 1/4". Selection of the **Inches** check box causes zeros representing inches to be suppressed if the dimension text represents feet only. For example, 7' is displayed instead of 7'- 0".

The **Scale** section lets you specify a scale factor for the linear measured distances of a dimension without affecting the components, angles or tolerance values. The Scale section includes the following:

The **Linear** edit box lets you specify the linear scale factor. For example, you are drawing with the intention of plotting at the quarter size scale or 3" = 1'- 0". You have scaled up a detail by a factor of 4 so that it will plot to full scale. If you wish to dimension it after it has been enlarged, you can set the Linear Scale factor in this section of the Primary Units dialog box to 0.25 so that dimensioned distances will represent the dimension of the object features before it was scaled up. This method keeps the components at the same size as dimensions created without a scale change. The value is recorded in DIMLFAC dimension variable.

Selecting the **Paper Space Only** check box causes the linear scale factor to apply to linear measured distances in dimensions drawn in paper space only. The value is recorded in DIMLFAC dimension variable.

Tolerance The Tolerance section in the Annotation sub-dialog box lets you specify whether or not a tolerance is drawn as part of the dimension text and what type of tolerance is drawn. The Tolerance section includes:

The **Method** list box lets you specify the type of tolerance. It includes the following:

The **None** selection suppresses tolerances. AutoCAD sets the DIMTOL dimension variable to 0.

The **Symmetrical** selection causes the tolerance to be displayed in equal positive and negative values. AutoCAD sets the DIMTOL dimension variable to 1 and DIMLIM dimension variable to 0.

The **Deviation** selection causes the tolerance to be displayed in unequal positive and negative values. AutoCAD sets the DIMTOL dimension variable to 1 and DIMLIM dimension variable to 0.

The **Limits** selection causes the tolerance text to be represented as maximum and minimum distances. AutoCAD sets the DIMTOL dimension variable to 0 and DIMLIM dimension variable to 1.

The **Basic** selection causes the dimension text to be drawn within a rectangular box.

The **Upper Value:** edit box lets you specify the upper value of the tolerance. The value is recorded in DIMTP dimension variable.

The **Lower Value:** edit box lets you specify the lower value of the tolerance. The value is recorded in DIMTM dimension variable.

The **Justification** list box lets you specify how tolerance text is placed relative to the dimension text. The Justification options includes the following:

The **Top** selection aligns the top of the tolerance text with the top of the dimension text. AutoCAD sets the DIMTOLJ dimension variable to 2.

The **Middle** selection aligns the middle of the tolerance text with the middle of the dimension text. AutoCAD sets the DIMTOLJ dimension variable to 1.

The **Bottom** selection aligns the bottom of the tolerance text with the bottom of the dimension text. AutoCAD sets the DIMTOLJ dimension variable to 0.

The **Height:** edit box lets you specify the height of the tolerance relative to the dimension text. For example, a value of 0.5 makes the tolerance text half the height of the dimension text.

Alternate Units The Alternate Units section in the Annotation sub-dialog box lets you control the display of alternate measurement units and prefixes and suffixes for dimension text. The Alternate Units section includes the following:

The **Enable Units** check box enables alternate units dimensioning. AutoCAD sets the DIMTALT dimension variable to 1 when the Enable Units check box is set to ON.

The remaining options available in the Alternate Units section are similar to the Primary Units section explained earlier in the chapter.

Text The Text section lets you change the style, text height, text gap, and color of the text. The Text section includes the following:

The **Style** list box lets you specify the text style for the dimension text. The value is recorded in DIMTXSTY dimension variable.

The **Height**: edit box lets you specify the height for the dimension text. The value is recorded in DIMTXT dimension variable.

The **Gap:** edit box lets you specify the gap distance between dimension text and dimension lines that are broken for placing the text. The value is recorded in DIMGAP dimension variable.

The **Color. . .** button displays the **Select Color** dialog box and allows you to set the color of the dimension text. Value is recorded in DIMCLRT dimension variable.

The **Round Off** edit text box lets you specify measured dimension distances that will be rounded off for display. For example, a value of 0.5 causes dimensions to be rounded to the nearest 0.5 units.

Once you have set all the dimension settings, make sure to save the settings by typing the appropriate style name in the **Name:** edit box in the Dimension Styles dialog box. Click the **OK** button to close the Dimension Styles dialog box.

DIMSTYLE COMMAND

The DIMSTYLE command creates and modifies dimension styles on the command line. The DIMSTYLE command is invoked by typing **DIMSTYLE** at the "Command:" prompt and pressing Enter or spacebar.

```
Command:dimstyle
Dimension Style Edit (Save/Restore/STatus/Variables/Apply/?)<Restore>:
```

Restore Option The Restore option allows you to restore to an existing dimension style. AutoCAD prompts:

```
?/Enter dimension style name or RETURN to select dimension:
```

Selecting **?** lists the styles that have been saved in the drawing.

If you enter a name of an existing dimensioning style at the prompt, AutoCAD restores it as the current style. Or you can press Enter to select a dimension. The dimensioning style of the selected dimension becomes the current style.

Instead, if you type a style name prefixed with the tilde (~style name), AutoCAD displays the difference between the style name and the current dimension style. For example, using the tilde as a prefix to the STANDARD style name, AutoCAD shows how the current style differs from the STANDARD style.

Save Option The Save option saves the current settings of the dimension system variables to a dimension style. The new dimension style becomes the current one. It remains current until you change any dimensioning system variables or until you save or restore another style.

STatus Option The STatus option lists all of the dimension variables and their current settings.

Variables Option The Variables option lists all of the dimension variables of a specified style and their settings without changing the current settings.

Apply Option The Apply option lets you select dimensions and have the current settings of the dimension variables applied to them.

DIMOVERRIDE

The DIMOVERRIDE command allows you to change the dimension variable settings of selected dimensions. The DIMOVERRIDE command is invoked by typing **DIMOVERRIDE** at the "Command:" prompt and pressing ⌨Enter or spacebar.

> Command:**dimoverride**
> Dimension variable to override (or Clear to remove overrides):

Specify the name of the dimension variable to override, AutoCAD prompts:

> Current value <current> New value:

Specify the new value for the dimension variable. AutoCAD repeats the prompt:

> Dimension variable to override:

If necessary, you can type another dimension variable to override, or press ⌨Enter. AutoCAD prompts:

> Select objects:

Select the dimension objects and AutoCAD applies the overrides.

Instead of typing the name of the dimension variable to override, you can enter **c** for Clear. AutoCAD prompts:

> Select objects:

The dimension objects selected will have the dimension variable setting overrides cleared.

PROJECT EXERCISES

PROJECT EXERCISE A

In this project, you will be adding dimensions to the drawing that was completed in the Chapter 2 project exercise (see Figure A-1).

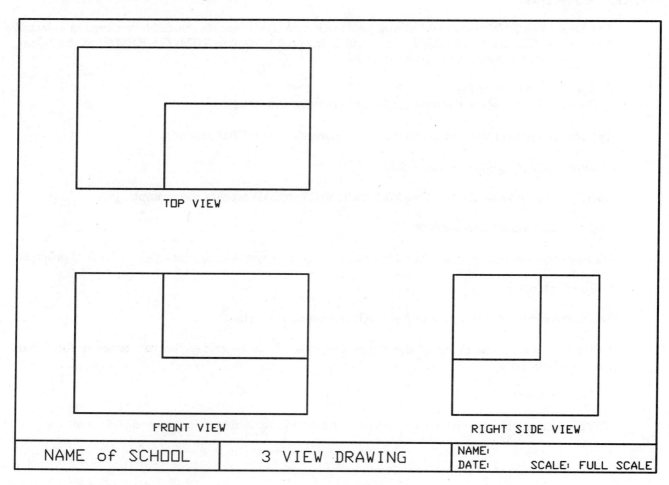

Figure A-1 Completed project design

> **NOTE:** The step-by-step instructions for this project are designed to provide practice in the concepts presented in chapter 6. It is not necessarily the most efficient way to draw the design.

STEP 1 Invoke the AutoCAD program from the Windows Program Manager.

Dimensioning

STEP 2   Invoke the OPEN command from the pull-down menu File or type **OPEN** at the "Command:" prompt. Select **CH2-PROJ** from the appropriate directory/drive from the **Open Drawing** dialog box. The drawing will appear as shown in Figure A–1.

STEP 3   Invoke the LAYER command from the pull-down menu Data, create a layer named "dimension", assign color: red and linetype: continuous. Set layer "dimension" as the current layer.

STEP 4   Invoke the DIMENSION STYLE. . . command from the pull-down menu Data. AutoCAD displays the **Dimension Styles** dialog box.

Click on the **Geometry. . .** button to open the **Geometry** sub-dialog box. Type 0.50 in the **Dimension Line Spacing:** edit box, 0.125 in the **Arrowheads Size:** edit box, and 0.125 in the **Extension Line Extension:** edit box. Click **OK** button to close the Geometry sub-dialog box

Click on the **Annotation. . .** button in the **Dimension Styles** dialog box to open the **Annotation** sub-dialog box. Click the **Units...** button in the Primary Units section of the **Annotation** sub-dialog box to open the **Primary Units** dialog box. Set **Precision:** to two decimal places and click **OK** button to close the **Primary Units** dialog box. Type 0.1250 in the **Text Height:** edit box in the Text section of the Annotation sub-dialog box. Click **OK** button to close the **Annotation** subdialog box.

Click **OK** button to close the **Dimension Styles** dialog box.

STEP 5   Set the running object snap to ENDpoint.

Command:**osnap**
Object snap modes:**endpoint**

STEP 6   Invoke the DIMLINEAR command from the Dimensioning toolbar, as shown in Figure A–2.

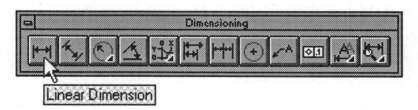

Figure A–2 Invoke the DIMLINEAR Command from the Dimensioning toolbar

Command:**dimlinear**
First extension line origin or RETURN to select:*(select PT.1 as shown in Figure A–3)*
Second extension line origin:*(select PT.2 as shown in Figure A–3)*
Dimension line location(Text/Angle/Horizontal/Vertical/Rotated):*(select PT.3 as shown in Figure A–3)*

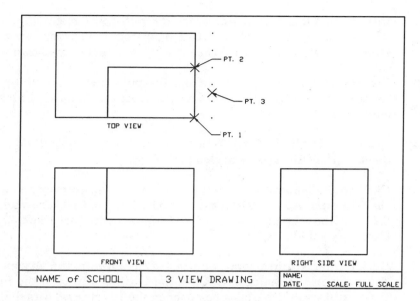

Figure A–3 Selection of dimension endpoints and location of dimension line

AutoCAD draws the linear dimension as shown in Figure A–4. Invoke the DIMBASELINE command from the Dimensioning toolbar, as shown in Figure A–5.

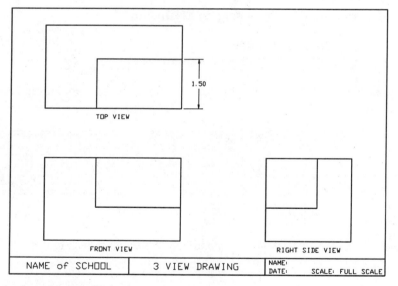

Figure A–4 Placement of linear dimension

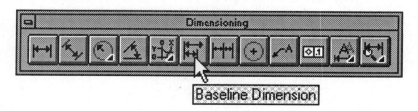

Figure A–5 Invoke the DIMBASELINE Command from the Dimensioning Toolbar

Command:**dimbaseline**
Second extension line origin:*(select PT.1 as shown in Figure A–6)*

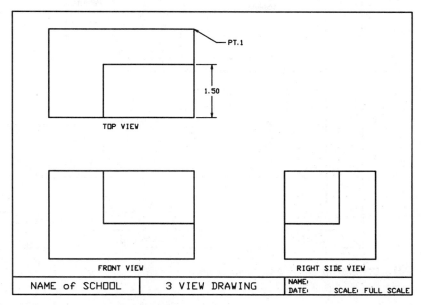

Figure A–6   Selection of second extension line origin

AutoCAD draws the baseline dimension as shown in Figure A–7.

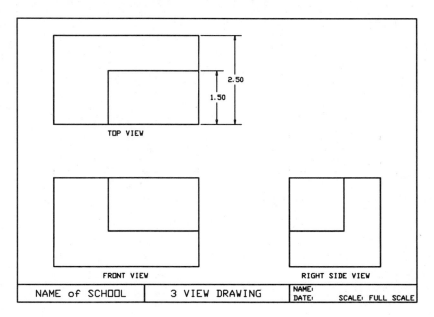

Figure A–7   Placement of baseline dimension

STEP 7   Continue placing dimensions by repeating STEP 6 to the front and right side views as shown in Figure A–8.

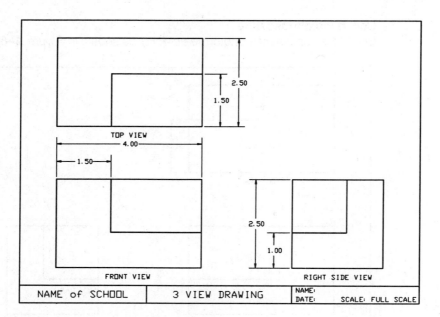

Figure A–8 Completed drawing with dimensions

STEP 8 End the drawing by invoking the **END** command.

Command:**end**

PROJECT EXERCISE B

In this project, you will be adding dimensions to the drawing that was completed in the Chapter 3 project exercise (see Figure B–1).

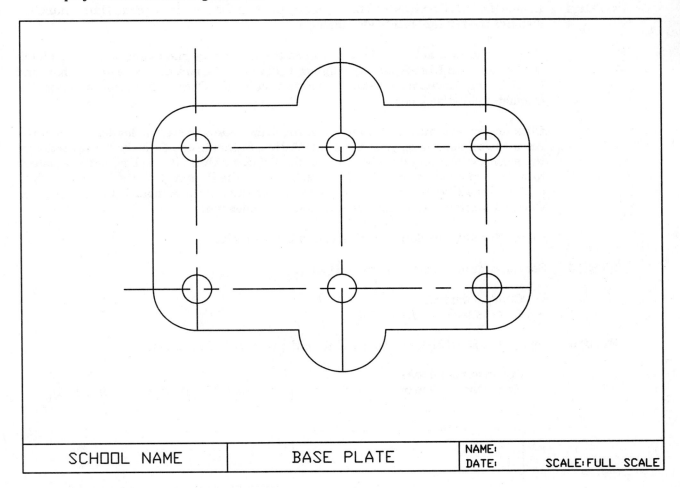

| SCHOOL NAME | BASE PLATE | NAME: DATE: | SCALE: FULL SCALE |

Figure B–1   Completed project design

> **NOTE:** The step-by-step instructions for this project are designed to provide practice in the concepts presented in chapter 6. It is not necessarily the most efficient way to draw the design.

STEP 1   Invoke the AutoCAD program from the Windows Program Manager.

STEP 2   Invoke the OPEN command from the pull-down menu File or type OPEN at the "Command:" prompt. Select **CH3-PROJ** from the appropriate directory/drive from the **Open Drawing** dialog box. The drawing will appear as shown in Figure B–1.

STEP 3 Invoke the LAYER command from the pull-down menu Data, create a layer named "dimension", assign color: red and linetype: continuous. Set layer "dimension" as the current layer.

STEP 4 Invoke the DIMENSION STYLE. . . command from the pull-down menu Data. AutoCAD displays the **Dimension Styles** dialog box.

Click on the **Geometry. . .** button to open the **Geometry** sub-dialog box. Type 0.50 in the **Dimension Line Spacing:** edit box, 0.125 in the **Arrowheads Size:** edit box, and 0.125 in the **Extension Line Extension:** edit box. Click **OK** button to close the Geometry sub-dialog box.

Click on the **Annotation. . .** button in the **Dimension Styles** dialog box to open the **Annotation** sub-dialog box. Click the **Units...** button in the Primary Units section of the **Annotation** sub-dialog box to open the **Primary Units** dialog box. Set **Precision:** to two decimal places and click **OK** button to close the **Primary Units** dialog box. Type 0.1250 in the **Text Height:** edit box in the Text section of the Annotation sub-dialog box. Click **OK** button to close the **Annotation** sub-dialog box.

Click **OK** button to close the **Dimension Styles** dialog box.

STEP 5 Set the running object snap to ENDpoint.

Command:**osnap**
Object snap mode:**endpoint**

STEP 6 Invoke the DIMLINEAR command from the Dimensioning toolbar.

Command:**dimlinear**
First extension line origin or Return to select:*(select PT.1 as shown in Figure B–2)*

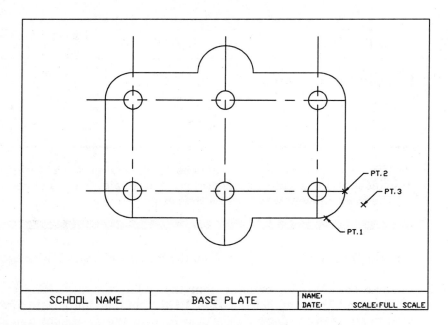

Figure B–2 Select dimension endpoints and locate dimension

Second extension line origin:*(select PT.2 as shown in Figure B–2)*
Dimension line location(Text/Angle/Horizontal/Vertical/Rotated):*(select PT.3 as shown in Figure B–2)*

AutoCAD draws the linear dimension as shown in Figure B–3. Invoke the DIMCONTINUE command from the Dimensioning toolbar, as shown in Figure B–4.

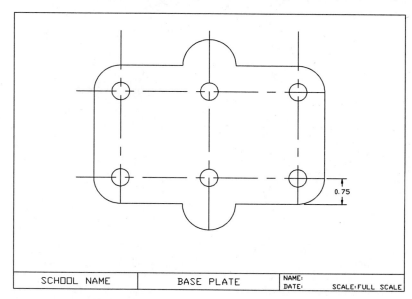

Figure B–3   Completed linear dimension

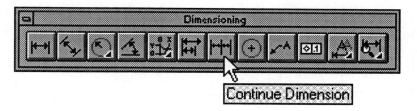

Figure B–4   Invoke the DIMCONTINUE Command from the Dimensioning toolbar

Command:**dimcontinue**
Second extension line origin:*(select PT.1 as shown in Figure B-5)*

AutoCAD draws the continue dimension as shown in Figure B–6.

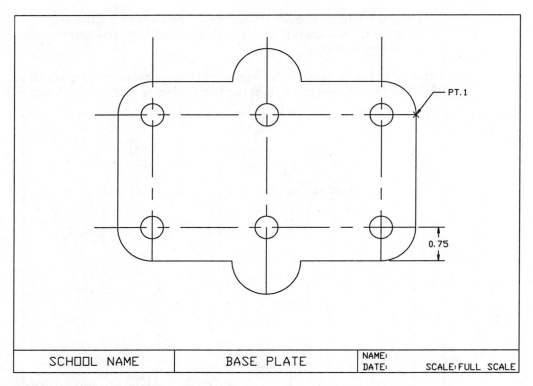

Figure B–5 Select second extension line origin

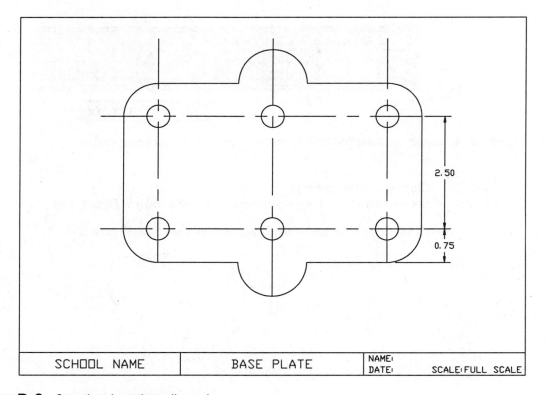

Figure B–6 Completed continue dimension

STEP 7   Continue placing linear dimensions by following STEP 6 to complete the linear dimensioning of the drawing as shown in Figure B–7.

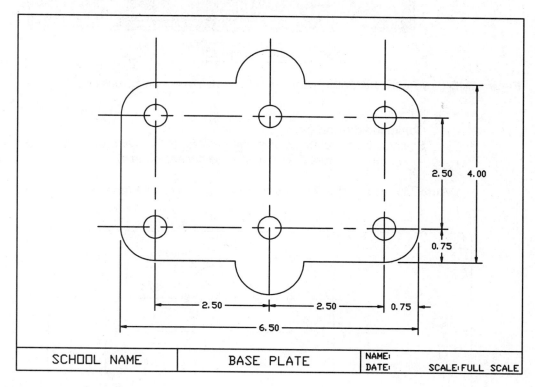

Figure B–7   Linear dimensions

STEP 8   Set the running object snap to NONE.

Command:**osnap**
Object snap mode:**none**

STEP 9   Invoke the DIMENSION STYLE. . . command from the pull-down menu Data. AutoCAD displays the **Dimension Styles** dialog box.

Click on the **Format. . .** button to open the **Format** sub-dialog box. Turn on the **User Defined** toggle button to allow you to place text outside the arc and circle. Click **OK** button to close the **Format** sub-dialog box.

Click **OK** button to close the **Dimension Styles** dialog box.

STEP 10   Invoke the DIMRADIUS command from the Dimensioning toolbar, as shown in Figure B–8.

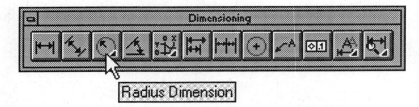

Figure B–8 Invoke the DIMRADIUS Command from the Dimensioning toolbar

> Command:**dimradius**
> Select arc or circle:*(select the larger arc at PT.1 and drag the leader line to PT.2 as shown in Figure B–9 to locate the dimension text)*

AutoCAD draws the radius dimension as shown in Figure B–9.

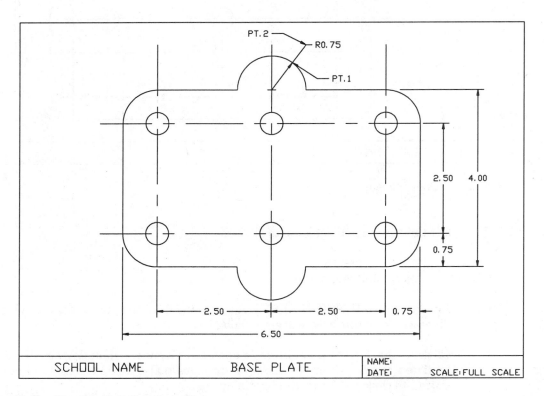

Figure B–9 Completed radius dimension

STEP 11 Continue to use the DIMRADIUS command to complete the dimensioning circles and arcs, as shown in Figure B–10.

STEP 12 Use the DTEXT command to add the (TYP.) callouts, as shown in Figure B–11.

STEP 13 End the drawing by invoking the END command.

> Command:**end**

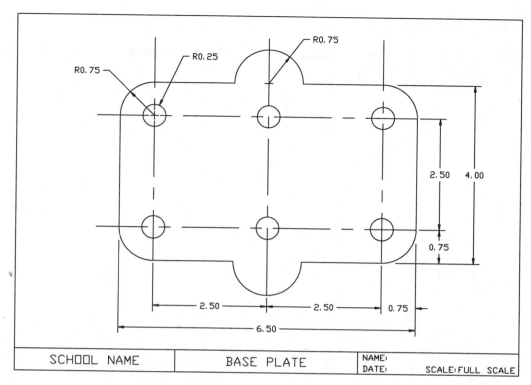

Figure B–10   Completed drawing with dimensioning

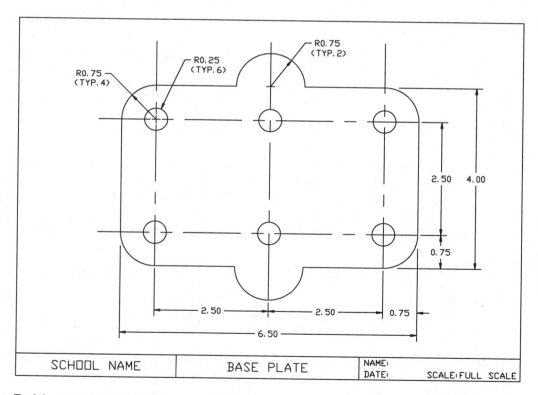

Figure B–11   Completed drawing with dimensions and callouts

PROJECT EXERCISE C

In this project, you will be adding dimensions to the drawing that was completed in the Chapter 4 project exercise (see Figure C–1).

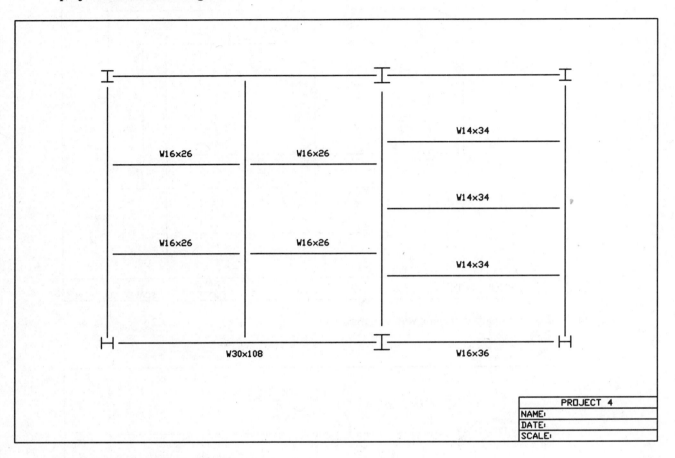

Figure C–1   Completed project design

> **NOTE:** The step-by-step instructions for this project are designed to provide practice in the concepts presented in chapter 6. It is not necessarily the most efficient way to draw the design.

STEP 1   Invoke the AutoCAD program from the Windows Program Manager.

STEP 2   Invoke the OPEN command from the pull-down menu File or type OPEN at the "Command:" prompt. Select CH4-PROJ from the appropriate directory/drive from the **Open Drawing** dialog box. The drawing will appear as shown in Figure C–1.

STEP 3   Invoke the LAYER command from the pull-down menu Data, create a layer named "dimension", assign color: red, and linetype: continuous. Set layer "dimension" as the current layer.

STEP 4   Invoke the DIMENSION STYLE. . . command from the pull-down menu Data. AutoCAD displays the **Dimension Styles** dialog box.

Click on the **Geometry. . .** button to open the **Geometry** sub-dialog box. Type 0.50 in the **Dimension Line Spacing:** edit box, 0.125 in the **Arrowheads Size:** edit box, 0.125 in the **Extension Line Extension:** edit box and 48 in the **Overall Scale:** edit box. Click **OK** button to close the Geometry sub-dialog box

Click on the **Annotation. . .** button in the **Dimension Styles** dialog box to open the **Annotation** sub-dialog box. Click the **Units. . .** button in the Primary Units section of the **Annotation** sub-dialog box to open the **Primary Units** dialog box. Set **Precision:** to two decimal places and click **OK** button to close the **Primary Units** dialog box. Type 0.1250 in the **Text Height:** edit box in the Text section of the Annotation sub-dialog box. Click **OK** button to close the **Annotation** sub-dialog box.

Click **OK** button to close the **Dimension Styles** dialog box.

> **NOTE:** It is necessary to increase the dimension scale factor to "48" so the dimensions will be drawn at the correct size in relation to the rest of the drawing.

STEP 5   Set the running object snap to ENDpoint.

> Command:**osnap**
> Object snap mode:**endpoint**

STEP 6   Invoke the DIMLINEAR command from the Dimensioning toolbar.

> Command:**dimlinear**
> First extension line origin or Return to select:*(select PT.1 as shown in Figure C–2)*

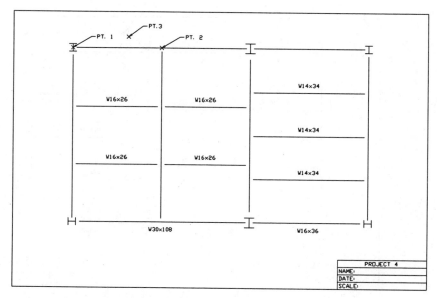

Figure C–2   Select dimension endpoints and locate dimension

Second extension line origin:*(select PT.2 as shown in Figure C–2)*
Dimension line location(Text/Angle/Horizontal/Vertical/Rotated):*(select PT.3 as shown in Figure C–2)*

AutoCAD draws the linear dimension as shown in Figure C–3. Invoke the DIMCONTINUE command from the Dimensioning toolbar.

Command:**dimcontinue**
Second extension line origin:*(select the point as shown in Figure C–4)*

AutoCAD draws the continue dimension as shown in Figure C–5.

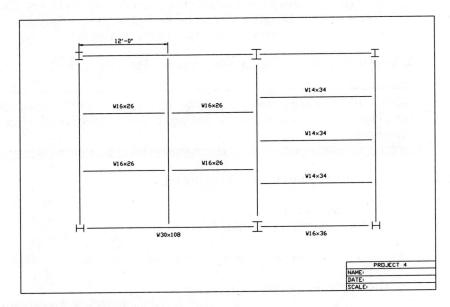

Figure C–3 Completed linear dimension

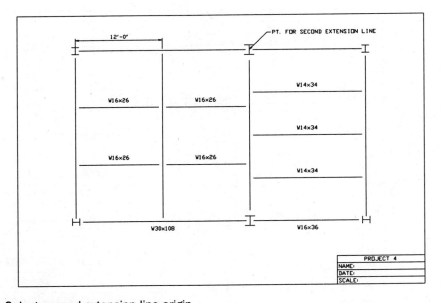

Figure C–4 Select second extension line origin

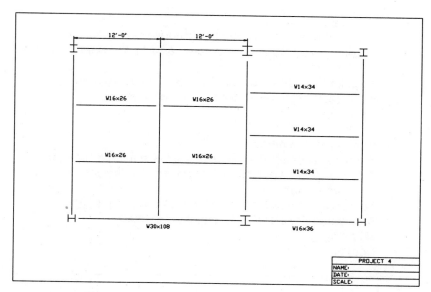

Figure C–5 Completed dimension

STEP 7   Continue to use the DIMLINEAR and DIMCONTINUE commands to complete the linear dimensions as shown in Figure C–6.

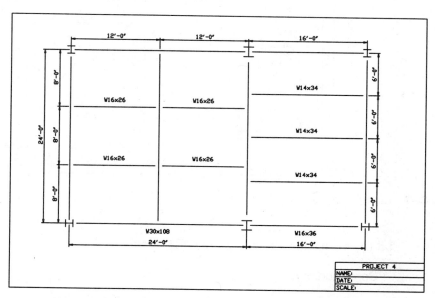

Figure C–6 Completed linear dimensions

STEP 8   Set the running object snap to NONE.

Command:**osnap**
Object snap mode:**none**

STEP 9   Invoke the DIMLEADER command from the Dimensioning toolbar to add two callouts as shown in Figure C–7.

Command:**dimleader**
From point:*(select the center of the lower left column)*
To point:*(drag your cursor down and to the right to locate the second point of the leader line)*
To point(Format/Annotation/Undo)<Annotation>: Enter
Annotation(or RETURN for options):**W8x24**
MText: Enter

Command:**dimleader**
From point:*(select the center of the lower middle column)*
To point:*(drag your cursor down and to the left to locate the second point of the leader line)*
To point(Format/Annotation/Undo)<Annotation>: Enter
Annotation(or RETURN for options):**W10x40**
MText: Enter
Command:

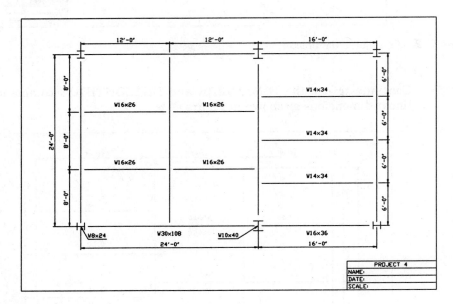

Figure C–7 Completed drawing

STEP 10 End the drawing by invoking the END command.

Command:**end**

PROJECT EXERCISE D

In this project, you will be adding dimensions to the drawing that was completed in the Chapter 5 project exercise (see Figure D–1).

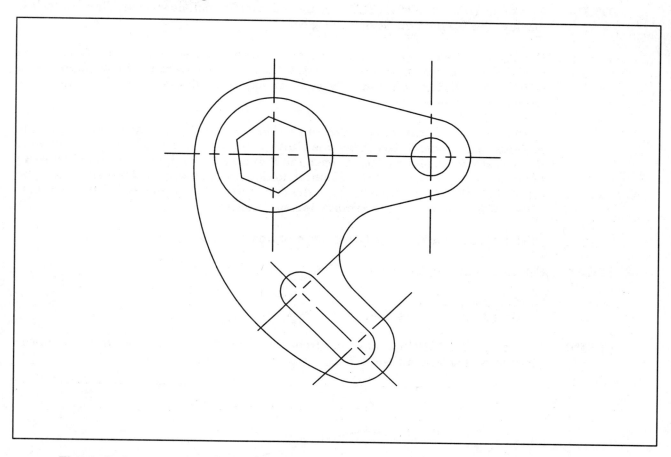

Figure D–1 Completed project design

NOTE: The step-by-step instructions for this project are designed to provide practice in the concepts presented in chapter 6. It is not necessarily the most efficient way to draw the design.

STEP 1 Invoke the AutoCAD program from the Windows Program Manager.

STEP 2 Invoke the OPEN command from the pull-down menu File or type OPEN at the "Command:" prompt. Select CH5-PROJ from the appropriate directory/drive from the **Open Drawing** dialog box. The drawing will appear as shown in Figure D–1.

STEP 3   Invoke the LAYER command from the pull-down menu Data, create a layer named "dimension", assign color: red, and linetype: continuous. Set layer "dimension" as the current layer.

STEP 4   Invoke the DIMENSION STYLE... command from the pull-down menu Data. AutoCAD displays the **Dimension Styles** dialog box.

Click on the **Geometry...** button to open the **Geometry** sub-dialog box. Type 0.50 in the **Dimension Line Spacing:** edit box, 0.125 in the **Arrowheads Size:** edit box, and 0.125 in the **Extension Line Extension:** edit box. Click **OK** button to close the Geometry sub-dialog box

Click on the **Annotation...** button in the **Dimension Styles** dialog box to open the **Annotation** sub-dialog box. Click the **Units...** button in the Primary Units section of the **Annotation** sub-dialog box to open the **Primary Units** dialog box. Set **Precision:** to two decimal places and click **OK** button to close the **Primary Units** dialog box. Type 0.1250 in the **Text Height:** edit box in the Text section of the Annotation sub-dialog box. Click **OK** button to close the **Annotation** sub-dialog box.

Click **OK** button to close the **Dimension Styles** dialog box.

STEP 5   Set the running object snap to CENter.

Command:**osnap**
Object snap mode:**center**

STEP 6   Invoke the DIMLINEAR command from the Dimensioning toolbar. Draw the linear dimension as shown in Figure D–2.

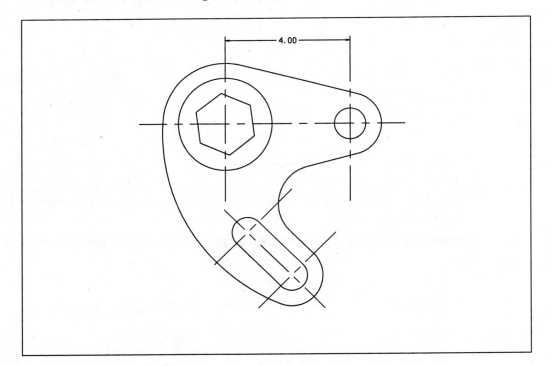

Figure D–2   Completed linear dimension

STEP 7 Invoke the DIMALIGINED command from the Dimensioning toolbar (see Figure D–3) to add the aligned dimensions to the drawing.

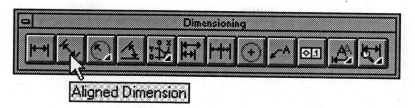

Figure D–3 Invoke the DIMALIGNED Command from the Dimensioning toolbar

Command:**dimaligned**
First extension line origin or RETURN to select:*(select the arc at PT. 1 as shown in Figure D–4)*
Second extension line origin:*(select the arc at PT.2 as shown in Figure D–4)*
Dimension line location (Text/Angle):*(select PT. 3 to locate the dimension as shown in Figure D–4)*

AutoCAD draws the dimension as shown in Figure D–5.

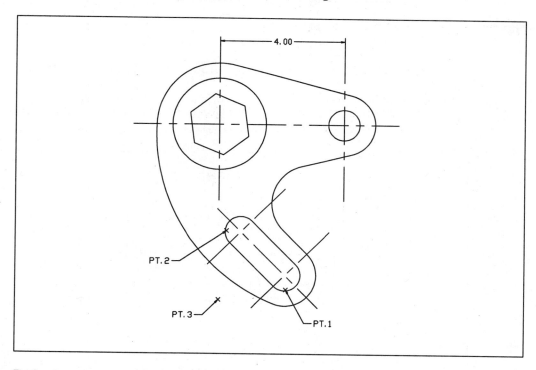

Figure D–4 Selecting points for the aligned dimension

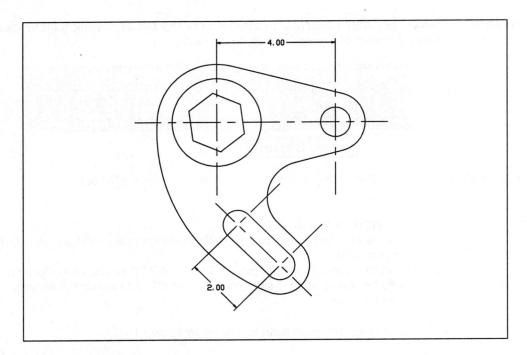

Figure D–5 Completed aligned dimension

Invoke the DIMCONTINUE command from the Dimensioning toolbar.

Command:**dimcontinue**
Second extension line origin or RETURN to select:*(select the large circle to continue the dimension as shown in Figure D–6)*

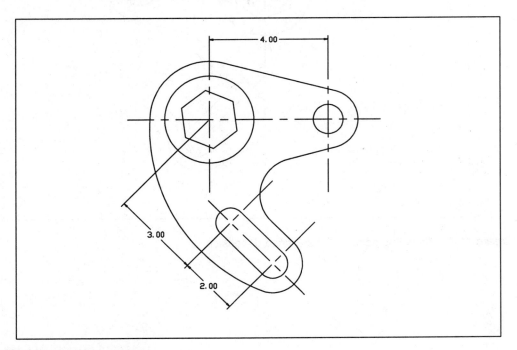

Figure D–6 Aligned dimension

STEP 8 Draw center lines to assist in completing the dimensioning exercise. Set "centerline" Layer as the current layer. Invoke the LINE command from the Draw toolbar and draw lines 1 and 2 as shown in Figure D–7.

> Command:**line**
> From point:7,8 *(start point for line 1)*
> To point:**@6.5<315**
> To point: Enter
>
> Command: Enter
> From point:7,8 *(start point for line 2)*
> To point:*(use the object snap tool "intersection" to draw the line to the intersection of the polygon as shown in Figure D–7)*

STEP 9 Set "dimension" Layer as the current layer. Invoke the DIMALIGINED command from the Dimensioning toolbar to draw the remaining aligned dimensions for the drawing.

> Command:**dimaligned**
> First extension line origin or RETURN to select:*(select the arc at PT.1 as shown in Figure D–8)*
> Second extension line origin:*(use the object snap tool "perpendicular" to select PT.2 as shown in Figure D–8)*
> Dimension line location (Text/Angle):*(select PT. 3 to locate the dimension as shown in Figure D–8)*

AutoCAD draws the dimension as shown in Figure D–9.

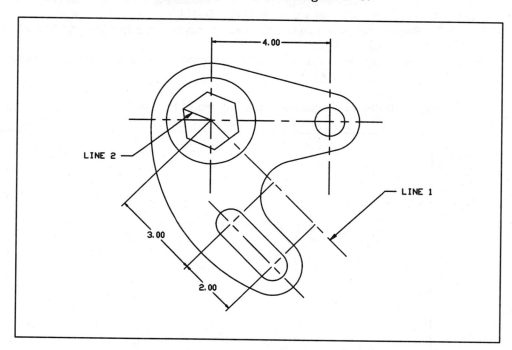

Figure D–7   Lines 1 and 2

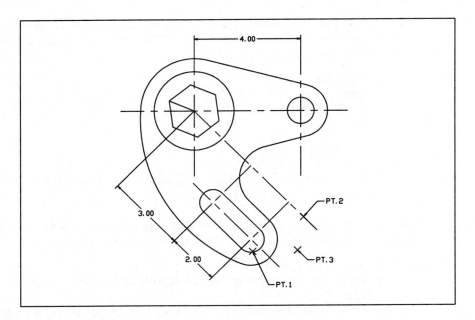

Figure D-8 Drawing the aligned dimension

Command:**dimaligned**
First extension line origin or RETURN to select:*(use the object snap tool "intersection" to locate PT.1 as shown in Figure D–10)*
Second extension line origin:*(use the object snap tool "perpendicular" to select PT.2 as shown in Figure D–10)*
Dimension line location (Text/Angle):*(select PT. 3 to locate the dimension as shown in Figure D–10)*

AutoCAD draws the dimension as shown in **Figure D–11.**

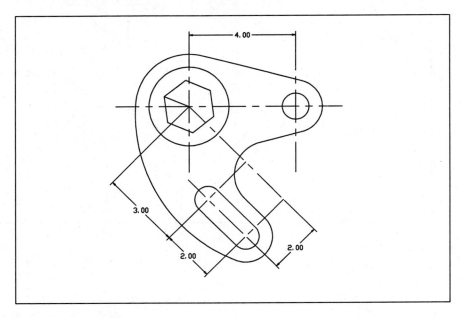

Figure D-9 Completed dimension

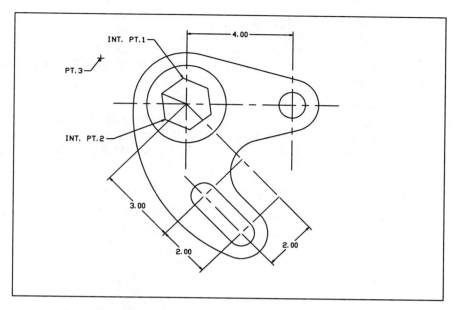

Figure D–10 Drawing the aligned dimension

STEP 10 Set the running object snap to NONE.

Command:**osnap**
Object snap mode:**none**

STEP 11 Invoke the DIMANGULAR command from the Dimensioning toolbar to draw the angular dimensions.

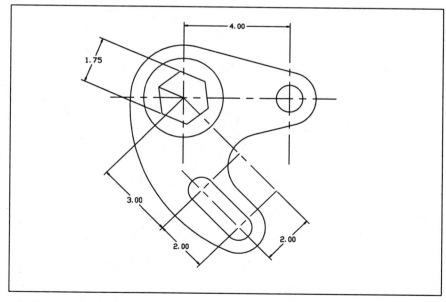

Figure D–11 Completed dimension

Command:**dimangular**
Select arc,circle,line,or RETURN:*(select line 1 as shown in Figure D–12)*
Second line:*(select line 2 as shown in Figure D–12)*
Dimension arc line location(Text,Angle):*(locate the dimension as at PT.1 as shown in Figure D–12)*

Command:**dimangular**
Select arc,circle,line,or RETURN:*(select line 4 as shown in Figure D–12)*
Second line:*(select line 5 as shown in Figure D–12)*
Dimension arc line location(Text,Angle):*(locate the dimension as at PT.2 as shown in Figure D–12)*

AutoCAD draws the dimensions as shown in Figure D–13.

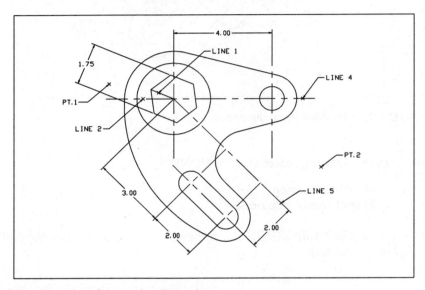

Figure D–12   Selecting points for angular dimensions

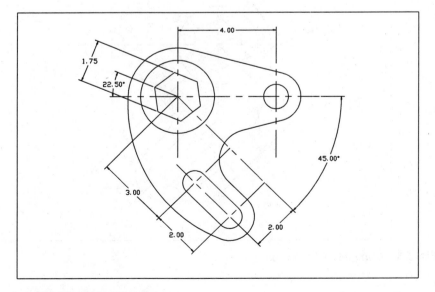

Figure D–13   Completed angular dimensions

STEP 12 Use DIMRADIUS and DIMDIAMETER to draw the radius and diameter dimensions as shown in Figure D–14.

> **NOTE:** Before using DIMRADIUS and DIMDIAMETER open the DIMENSION STYLE. . . dialog box from the pull-down menu Data. Click on the **Format. . .** button and turn on the "User Defined" option.

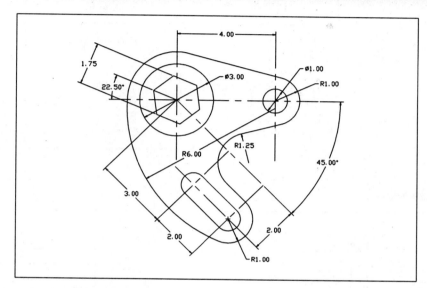

Figure D–14 Completed Dimensions

STEP 13 End the drawing by invoking the END command.

Command:**end**

EXERCISES

Exercises 6-1 through 6-3

Create the drawings with all the dimensions according to the settings given in the following table.

Settings	Value
1. Units	Architectural
2. LIMITS	
lower left corner	0', 0'
upper right corner	12'-, 9'
3. Grid Spacing	6"
4. Snap Spacing	3"
5. Text Size	2"

Exercise 6-1

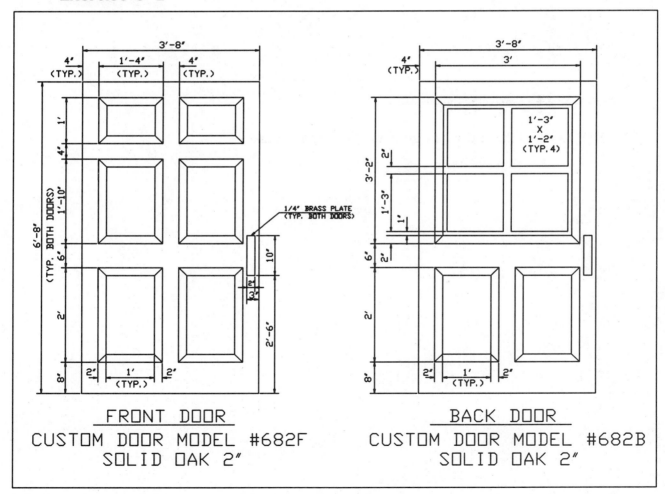

Exercise 6-2

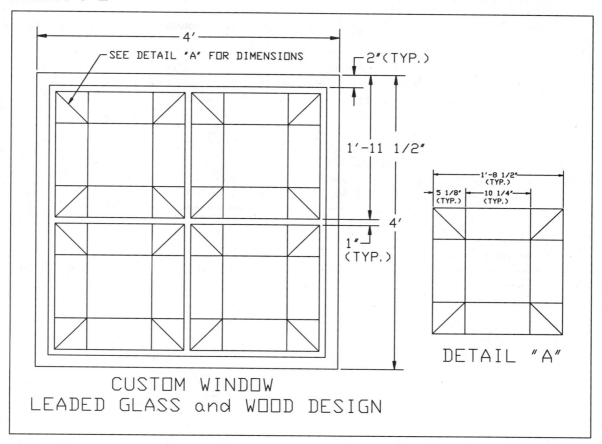

CUSTOM WINDOW
LEADED GLASS and WOOD DESIGN

DETAIL "A"

Exercise 6-3

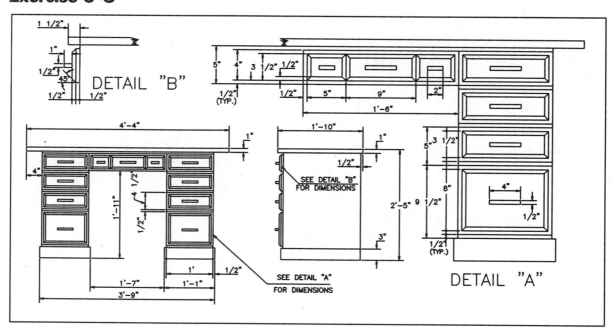

DETAIL "B"

DETAIL "A"

Exercises 6–4 through 6–6

Create the drawings according to the settings given in the following table. Show all dimensions.

Settings	Value
1. Units	Decimal
2. LIMITS	
lower left corner	0, 0
upper right corner	18, 12
3. Grid Spacing	0.5
4. Snap Spacing	0.25
5. Text Size	0.125

Exercise 6–4

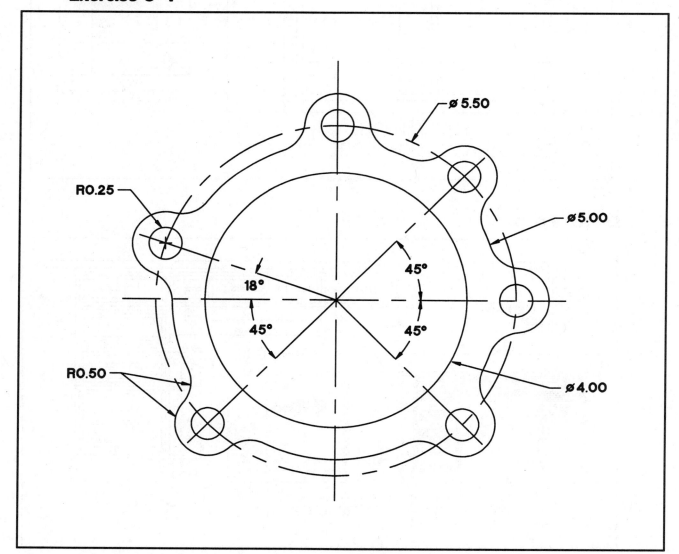

Exercise 6–5

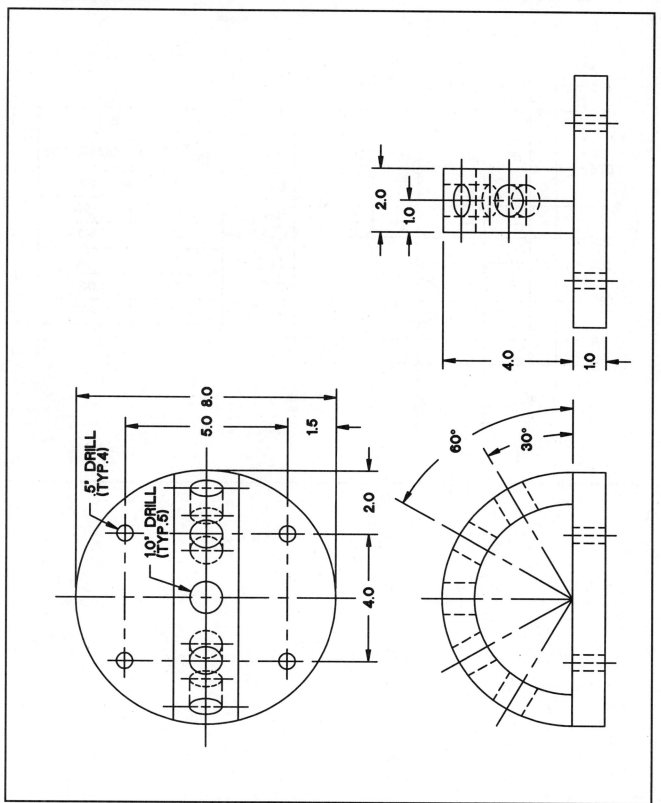

Exercise 6–6

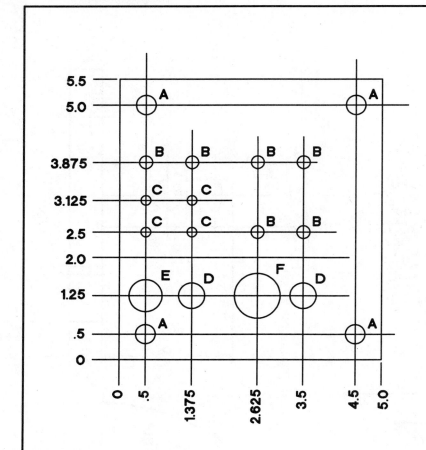

HOLE	
SIZE (SYMBOL)	DIAMETER
A	.375
B	.25
C	.1875
D	.5
E	.625
F	.875

Exercise 6–7

Create the drawing with all the dimensions according to the settings given in the following table.

Settings	Value
1. Units	Architectural
2. LIMITS	
lower left corner	0', 0'
upper right corner	8'-, 6'
3. Grid Spacing	4"
4. Snap Spacing	2"
5. Text Size	2"

Exercise 6–7

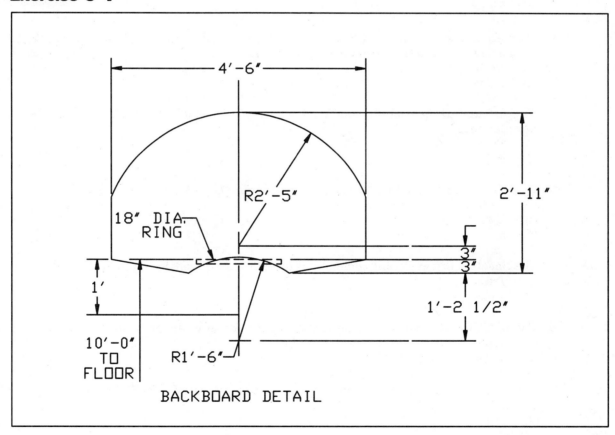

REVIEW QUESTIONS

1. Dimension types available in AutoCAD include:
   - (A) Linear
   - (B) Angular
   - (C) Diameter
   - (D) Radius
   - (E) All of the above

2. The Associative dimension drawn with the DIMASO variable turned ON has all of its separate parts drawn as separate objects.
   - (A) True
   - (B) False

3. The Linear Dimensioning command allows you to draw horizontal, vertical and aligned dimensions.
   - (A) True
   - (B) False

4. To place a linear dimension you must (1) select the first extension line origin, (2) locate the dimension line, and (3) select the second extension line.
   - (A) True
   - (B) False

5. The Angular Dimensioning command allows you to place angular dimensions between two parallel lines.
   - (A) True
   - (B) False

6. By default, dimension text for radius dimensioning is preceded by:
   - (A) Radius
   - (B) Rad
   - (C) R

7. The Baseline Dimensioning command is used to draw dimensions from a single datum baseline.
   - (A) True
   - (B) False

8. The DIMCENTER command allows you to place center cross marks or center lines in a circle.
   - (A) True
   - (B) False

9. You must explode a dimension before you can use the DIMTEDIT command to edit the dimension text.
   - (A) True
   - (B) False

10. The Suppress option in the Geometry sub-dialog box allows you to suppress only one extension line in a given dimension.
    - (A) True
    - (B) False

11. The Arrowhead section in the Geometry sub-dialog box allows you to change the size and style of your arrowheads.
    (A) True
    (B) False

12. You must use the UNITS command to determine how many decimal places will be shown in the dimension text.
    (A) True
    (B) False

CHAPTER

7

PLOTTING AND PRINTING

INTRODUCTION

One task has not changed much in the transition from board drafting to CAD; obtaining a hard copy. The term "hard copy" describes a tangible reproduction of a screen image. The hard copy is usually a reproducible medium from which prints are made and can take many forms, including slides, videotape, prints, or plots. This chapter describes the two most commonly used processes for getting a hard copy: plotting and printing.

In manual drafting, if you need your drawing to be done in two different scales, you physically draw the drawing for two different scales. In CAD, with minor modifications, you plot or print the same drawing in different scale factors on different sizes of paper. In AutoCAD, you can even compose your drawing in Paper Space with limits that equal the sheet size and plot it at 1:1 scale.

After completing this chapter, you will be able to:

- Plan the plotted sheet
- Compute the Plot Scale, Plot Size, and Limits
- Set LTSCALE and DIMSCALE
- Scale annotations and symbols
- Compose border and title block
- Set plotting parameters
- Import and export postscript files
- Plot the drawing

PLANNING THE PLOTTED SHEET

Planning ahead is still required in laying out the objects to be drawn on the final sheet. The objects drawn on the plotted sheet must be arranged. At least in CAD, with its true-size capability, an object can be started without first laying out a plotted sheet. But eventually, some limits or at least a displayed area must be determined. If this is done arbitrarily, the chances of the drawing being plotted to any standard scale are slight. For schematics, diagrams, and graphs, plotted scale is of little concern. But for architectural, civil, and mechanical drawings, plotting to a conventional scale is a professionally accepted practice that should not be abandoned just because it can be circumvented.

Setting up the drawing limits must take the plotted sheet into consideration to get the entire view of the object(s) on the sheet. So, even with all the power of the CAD system, some thought must still be given to the concept of scale, which is the ratio of true size to the size plotted. In other words, before you start drawing, you should have an idea at what scale the final drawing will be plotted or printed on a given size paper.

The limits should correspond to some factor of the plotted sheet. If the objects will fit on a 24" × 18" sheet at full size with room for a border, title block, bill of materials, dimensioning, and general notes, then set up your limits to (0,0) (lower left corner) and (24,18) (upper right corner). This can be plotted or printed at 1:1 scale, or one object unit equals one plotted unit.

Plot scales can be expressed in several formats. Each of the following five plot scales is exactly the same; only the display formats differ.

> 1/4" = 1'-0"
> 1" = 4'
> 1 = 48
> 1:48
> 1/48

A plot scale of 1:48 means that a line 48 units long in AutoCAD will plot with a length of 1 unit. The units can be any measurement system including inches, feet, millimeters, nautical miles, chains, angstroms, and light years, but, by default, plotting units in AutoCAD are inches.

Variables

There are four variables that control the relationship between the size of objects in the AutoCAD drawing and their sizes on a sheet of paper produced by an AutoCAD plot.

The four variables to consider are:

1. Size of the object in AutoCAD. For simplification it will be referred to as ACAD_size.

2. Size of the object on the plot. For simplification it will be referred to as ACAD_plot .

3. Maximum available plot area for a given sheet of paper. For simplification it will be referred to as ACAD_max_plot.

4. Plot scale. For simplification it will be referred as to ACAD_scale.

The relationship between the variables can be described the following three algebraic formulas:

$$ACAD\_scale = ACAD\_plot / ACAD\_size$$

$$ACAD\_plot = ACAD\_size \times ACAD\_scale$$

$$ACAD\_size = ACAD\_plot / ACAD\_scale$$

Example to Compute Plot Scale, Plot Size, and Limits

An architectural elevation of a building 48' wide and 24' high must be plotted on a 36" × 24" sheet. First, you determine the plotter's maximum available plot area for the given sheet size. This depends on the model of plotter you use to plot the drawings.

Some experimentation is required to determine the actual size of the plotter's maximum available plot area. An easy way to determine the limits is to plot a long line drawn from (0,0) along the X axis, using the plot to FIT option. The resulting width of the plot will be the maximum width the plotter can address at the chosen size. To determine the maximum height for a chosen size, plot to FIT a long line drawn from (0,0) along the Y axis.

In the case of a Summagraphics/Houston Instruments plotter, the available area for 36" × 24" is 33.5" × 21.5". Next, you determine the area needed for the title block, general notes, and other items such as an area for revision notes and a list of reference drawings. For the given example, let's say that an area of 27" × 16" is available for the drawing.

The objective is to arrive at one of the standard architectural scales in the form of x in. = 1 ft. The usual range is from 1/16" = 1'-0" for plans of large structures to 3" = 1'-0" for small details. To determine the plot scale, substitute these values for the appropriate variables in the formula:

ACAD_scale	= ACAD_plot / ACAD_size
ACAD_scale	= 27"/48' for X axis
	= 0.5625"/1'-0" or 0.5625"=1'-0"

The closest standard architectural scale that can be used in the given situation is 1/2" = 1'-0" (0.5" = 1'-0", 1/24 or 1:24).

To determine the size of the object on the plot, substitute these values for the appropriate variables in the formula:

ACAD_plot	= ACAD_size × ACAD_scale
ACAD_plot	= 48' × (0.5"/1') for X axis
	= 24" (less than the 27" maximum allowable space on the paper)
ACAD_plot	= 24' × (0.5"/1') for Y axis
	= 12" (less than the 16" maximum allowable space on the paper)

Instead of 1/2" = 1'-0" scale, if we go with a 3/4" = 1'-0" scale, then the size of the object on the plot will be 48' × (0.75"/1') = 36" for the X axis, which is more than the available space on the given paper. The drawing will not fit on the given size paper. You must select a larger paper size.

Once the plot scale is determined and verified that the drawing fits on the given paper size, the drafter can now determine the drawing limits for the plotted sheet size of 33.5" × 21.5".

To determine the limits for the X and Y axis, substitute the appropriate values in the formula:

$$\text{ACAD\_limits (X axis)} \quad = \quad \text{ACAD\_max\_plot} / \text{ACAD\_scale}$$
$$= \quad 33.5" / (0.5"/1'\text{-}0")$$
$$= \quad 67'$$
$$\text{ACAD\_limits (Y axis)} \quad = \quad 21.5" / (0.5"/1'\text{-}0")$$
$$= \quad 43'$$

Appropriate limits settings in AutoCAD for a 36" × 24" sheet with a maximum available plot area of 33.5" × 21.5" at a plot scale of 0.5" = 1'-0" would be:

    lower left corner: 0,0
    upper right corner: 67',43'

Another consideration in setting up a drawing for user convenience is to have the (0,0) coordinates at some point other than the lower left corner of the drawing sheet. Many objects have a reference point from which other parts of the object are dimensioned. Being able to set that reference point to (0,0) is very helpful. In many cases, the location of (0,0) is optional. In other cases, the coordinates should coincide with real coordinates, such as those on an industrial plant area block. In other cases, only one set of coordinates might be a governing factor.

In this example, the 48' wide × 24' high front elevation of the building is to be plotted on a 36" × 24" sheet at a scale of 1/2" = 1'-0". It has been determined that (0,0) should be at the lower left corner of the front elevation view as shown in Figure 7-1.

Centering the view on the sheet requires a few minutes of layout time. Several approaches allow the drafter to arrive at the location of (0,0) relative to the lower left corner of the plotted sheet or limits. Having computed the limits to be 67' wide × 43' high, the half-width and half-height (dimensions from the center) of the sheet are 33.5' and 21.5' to scale, respectively. Subtracting the

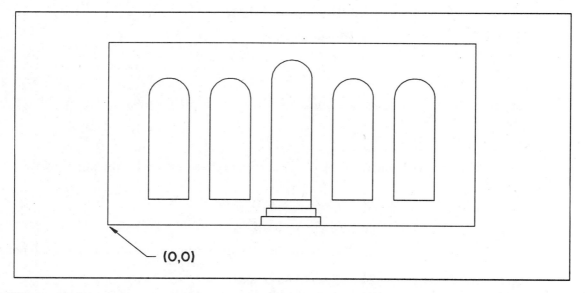

Figure 7-1 Setting the reference point to the origin (0,0) in a location other than the lower left corner

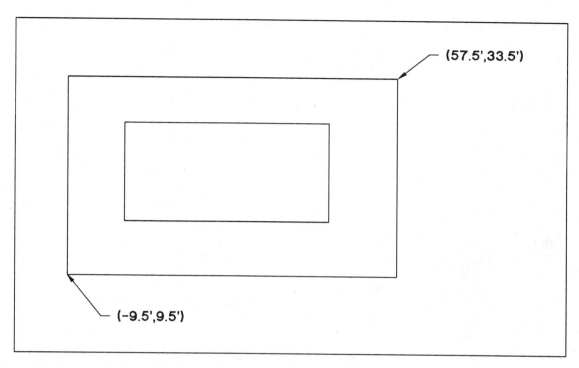

Figure 7-2 Setting the limits to the maximum available plot area by centering the view

half-width of the building from the half-width of the limits will set the X coordinate of the lower left corner at -9.5' (from the equation 24'-33.5'). The same is done for the Y coordinate -9.5' (12'-21.5'). Therefore, the lower left corner of the limits are at (-9.5',-9.5').

Appropriate limits settings in AutoCAD for a 36" × 24" sheet with a maximum available plot area of 33.5" × 21.5" by centering the view at a plot scale of 0.5" = 1'-0" (see Figure 7-2) is:

> lower left corner: -9.5',-9.5'
> upper right corner: 57.5',33.5'

Setting for LTSCALE

As explained earlier in Chapter 3, the LTSCALE provides a method of adjusting the linetypes to a meaningful scale for the drawing. This sets the length of dashes in linetypes. When the value of the LTSCALE is set to the reciprocal of the plot scale, the linetypes provided with AutoCAD plot out on paper at the sizes they are defined in ACAD.LIN.

> LTSCALE = 1 / ACAD_scale

Setting for DIMSCALE

As explained earlier in Chapter 6, AutoCAD provides a set of dimensioning variables that control the way dimensions are drawn. The dimension variable DIMSCALE is applied globally to all dimensions that govern sizes or distances, as an overall scaling factor. The default DIMSCALE is 1. When DIMSCALE is set to the reciprocal of the plot scale, it applies globally to all dimension variables for the plot scale factor.

> DIMSCALE = 1 / ACAD_scale

If necessary, you can set individual dimensioning variables to the size that you actually want the dimension to appear on the paper by substituting the appropriate values in the formula:

> size of the plotted dimvars_value = dimvars_value × ACAD_scale × DIMSCALE

As an example, to determine the arrow size DIMASZ for a plot scale of 1/2" = 1'-0", DIMSCALE of 1 and default DIMASZ is 0.18", then

$$\text{size of the plotted arrow} \quad = \quad 0.18" \times (1/24) \times 1$$
$$= \quad 0.0075"$$

Scaling Annotations and Symbols

How can you determine the size that text and symbols (blocks) will plot? As mentioned earlier, you almost always draw objects actual size, or real-world dimensions. Even in the case of text and placement of blocks, you place them to the real-world dimensions. In the previous example, the architectural elevation of a building 48' × 24' is drawn to actual size and plotted to a scale of 1/2" = 1'-0'. Let's say you wanted your text size to plot at 1/4" high. If you were to create your text and annotations at 1/4", they would be so small relative to the elevation drawing itself that you could not read the words.

Before you begin placing the text, you need to know the scale you will eventually plot the drawing. In the previous example of architectural elevation, the plot scale is 1/2" = 1'-0" and you want the text size to plot 1/4" high. You need to find a relationship between 1/4" on the paper and the size of the text for real-world dimensions in the drawing (model). If 1/2" on the paper equals 12" in the model, then 1/4"-high text on the paper equals 6", so text and annotations should be placed at 6" high in the drawing (model) to plot at 1/4" high to a scale of 1/2" = 1'-0". Similarly, you can calculate the various text sizes for a given plot scale.

Table 7–1 shows the model text size needed to achieve a specific plotted text size at some common scales.

Table 7–1　Text height conversion chart

DESIRED HEIGHT		1/16"	3/32"	1/8"	3/16"	1/4"	5/16"	3/8"	1/2"	5/8"
Scale	Factor									
1/16" = 1'-0"	192	12"	18"	24"	36"	48"	60"	66"	96"	120"
1/8" = 1'-0"	96	6"	9"	12"	18"	24"	30"	36"	48"	60"
3/16" = 1'-0"	64	4"	6"	8"	12"	16"	20"	24"	32"	40"
1/4" = 1'-0"	48	3"	4.5"	6"	9"	12"	15"	18"	24"	30"
3/8" = 1'-0"	32	2"	3"	4"	6"	8"	10"	12"	16"	20"
1/2" = 1'-0"	24	1.5"	2.25"	3"	4.5"	6"	7.5"	9"	12"	15"
3/4" = 1'-0"	16	1"	1.5"	2"	3"	4"	5"	6"	8"	10"
1" = 1'-0"	12	0.75"	1.13"	1.5"	2.25"	3"	3.75"	4.5"	6"	7.5"
1 1/2" = 1'-0"	8	0.5"	.75"	1"	1.5"	2"	2.5"	3"	4"	5"
3" = 1'-0"	4	0.25"	.375"	0.5"	0.75"	1"	1.25"	1.5"	2"	2.5"
1" = 10'	120	7.5"	11.25"	15"	22.5"	30"	37.5"	45"	60"	75"
1" = 20'	240	15"	22.5"	30"	45"	60"	75"	90"	120"	150"
1" = 30'	360	22.5"	33.75"	45"	67.5"	90"	112.5"	135"	180"	225"
1" = 40'	480	30"	45"	60"	90"	120"	150"	180"	240"	300"
1" = 50'	600	37.5"	56.25"	75"	112.5"	150"	187.5"	225"	300"	375"
1" = 60'	720	45"	67.5"	90"	135"	180"	225"	270"	360"	450"
1" = 70'	840	52.5"	78.75"	105"	157.5"	210"	262.5"	315"	420"	525"
1" = 80'	960	60"	90"	120"	180"	240"	300"	360"	480"	600"
1" = 90'	1080	67.5"	101.25"	135"	202.5"	270"	337.5"	405"	540"	675"
1" = 100'	1200	75"	112.5"	150"	225"	300"	375"	450"	600"	750"

Composing Border and Title Block

As mentioned earlier, you always draw objects actual size, or in real-world dimensions. After drawing the model, you add a border and title block, just like adding any other objects to the model. Instead of monotonously creating a border and title block for every new model you draw in AutoCAD, you can create a stand-alone title block of appropriate paper size limits (electronic sheet) and insert it as a block to a proper scale factor.

Create the border and title block full size (12" × 9", 18" × 12", 24" × 18", 36" × 24" or 48" × 36"). When creating the border, make sure to set the limits to the plotter's maximum available plot area for the given sheet size. This depends on the kind of plotter you are using to plot your drawings.

Once the plotter's maximum available plot area is determined for a given paper size, a border and title can be drawn that match these proportions. All text, attribute tags, logos, lines, and so forth should be drawn at the size they will plot. If necessary, you can also define attributes in the title block.

You insert the border and title to your model drawing as a block, at a scale factor inverse of the scale that you use to plot the drawing. Let's look at an example.

We'll take the same example we used before—architectural elevation of a building 48' wide and 24' high plotted on a 36" × 24" sheet to a plot scale of 1/2" = 1'-0" (1/24 or 1:24). Insert the border and title drawing into the model and scale it 24 times (inverse of the plot scale factor 1/24) larger to fit around the elevation drawing. It scales back to the original size when the drawing is plotted.

If 1/8" plotted on the paper is to represent 1" of the drawing geometry, the scale factor of the border and title block insertion will be 8. If 1/8" plotted on the paper is to represent 1' of the drawing geometry, the scale factor of the border and title block insertion is 96. This method is used even when the object is very small and needs to be enlarged on the final plot. For a plot scale factor of 2"= 1", then scale factor of the border and title block insertion is 0.5.

The second approach is to scale the model drawing down and insert it into the title block before you plot. This will allow you to plot at 1=1 scale, and "What You See is What You'll Plot (WYSWYP)."

You create a 1=1 border and title drawing as explained earlier, and insert the model drawing file into it at the appropriate scale. If you make changes to the model drawing file, reinsert it with an equal sign to redefine it.

You create the model drawing in real-size dimensions. Then, create a block of the entire drawing with the help of BLOCK command. Next, insert your title block at 1=1 scale on its own layer and zoom to the title block. Then, insert your entire drawing into the border and title drawing at the scale that you would have used to plot in the previously discussed method. If you need to make changes in the model, you can explode, then reblock to the same name.

Creating a Plot in Paper Space

One of the useful features of AutoCAD is the option to work on your drawing in two different environments, Model or Paper Space. In Paper Space you can compose the drawing at different scale factors and plot at a 1:1 scale. For a detailed explanation, refer to Chapter 11.

PLOTTING OPTIONS

The PLOT command is invoked by selecting the Print icon from the Standard toolbar (Figure 7–3), pull-down menu File, or at the "Command:" prompt type **PLOT** and press Enter or spacebar. The Plot Configuration dialog box appears as shown in Figure 7–4.

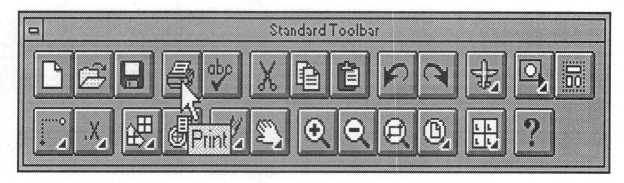

Figure 7-3 Invoke the PLOT Command from the Standard toolbar

The dialog box is divided into six areas. The three on the left include:

1. Device and Default Information
2. Pen Parameters
3. Additional Parameters

Three on the right include:

4. Paper Size and Orientation
5. Scale, Rotation, and Origin
6. Plot Preview

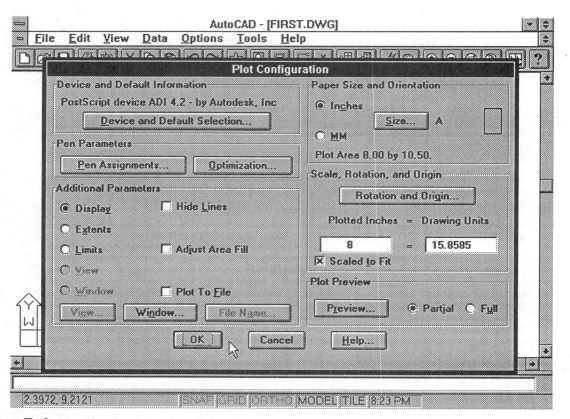

Figure 7-4 The Plot Configuration dialog box

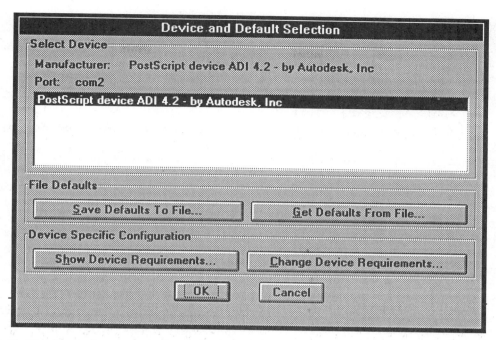

Figure 7-5 The Device and Default Selection dialog box

The first time you plot, this dialog box displays the default parameters and basic plot specifications as set when AutoCAD was configured. If you want to use these values, press Enter or pick OK. If necessary, you can change any of the parameters as explained below:

1. Device and Default Information

In this section of the dialog box, AutoCAD displays the description of the currently selected plotting device. By picking the **Device and Default Selection...** button, the Device and Default Selection dialog box appears as shown in Figure 7-5, from which you select another device if AutoCAD is configured for more than one plotter. In addition, you can save or get defaults from a .PCP file (plot configuration parameter file) and change device-specific configuration.

> **NOTE:** To add a plotter to the list of configured plotters or to update a driver, use the CONFIG command.

At the top of the Select Device area, as shown in Figure 7-5, AutoCAD displays the name of the current device and the port to which it is connected. In the list box, AutoCAD displays the names and/or descriptions of all of the configured plotters. The description is the text that was entered to describe the device when you did the configuration. If no description was provided during the configuration process, then AutoCAD uses the manufacturer's description of the device.

If you configured multiple plotters, you can select another one by picking the plotter description. AutoCAD automatically updates the manufacturer and port information. You can configure AutoCAD with up to 29 plotters, configure one plotter 29 different ways, or any combination.

> **NOTE:** Selecting another plotter may change the settings of other parameters in the plotting dialog boxes.

In addition, you can also save customized settings that you define in a plot configuration parameters file (.PCP) with a specific name. The .PCP files store ASCII text definitions of basic plot specifications and a variety of pen parameters relating to plotting. This can be done by picking the **Save Defaults To File. . .** button. AutoCAD displays a standard file dialog box in shich you can save the defaults to a new or existing file. By saving the parameters, the next person who plots will not overwrite your carefully constructed settings. To use the values from an existing .PCP file, pick the **Get Defaults From File. . .** button and AutoCAD displays a standard file dialog box from which you select an existing .PCP file.

Some plotting devices may have additional configuration requirements. The device reequirements can be viewed by picking the **Show Device Requirements. . .** button. If necessary, you can change the additional configuration requirements for the current plotting device by picking the **Change Device Requirements. . .** button.

> **NOTE:** If a plotter doesn't have additional configuration requirements, these buttons are grayed out.

2. Pen Parameters

In this section of the dialog box, you can assign a color, linetype, pen speed, and line weight to each pen. In addition, you control the level of optimization and improve plot quality.

By picking the **Pen Assignments. . .** button, the Pen Assignments dialog box appears as shown in Figure 7-6. This is where you map the colors on the screen to the pens on the plotter. You can use up to 255 linetypes, colors, pen speeds, and line widths.

The first column is a list of the numbers (from 1 to 255) AutoCAD uses to define colors. An object is automatically assigned the color of the layer on which it is drawn; you can assign a color to an object independent of the layer on which it is drawn. It is highly recommended to draw the objects by following colors assigned to the layers.

The second column shows the assignment of pen numbers to the colors. You can have the plotters plot the object in either the same color you used in the drawing file or in a different color. Generally, it is easier to keep track of your colors and pens if you have the same color. If necessary, you can assign the same pen number to all of the colors, and the plotting will be done in one color. If you have a single-pen plotter and you want to do a multiple-pen plot, AutoCAD stops the plotter and prompts you to change pens whenever a different pen is required.

The third column shows the assignment of plotter (not AutoCAD) linetypes to the colors. Some plotters are capable of generating their own linetypes. This feature is seldom used because it is simpler to assign linetypes to layers directly in the drawing.

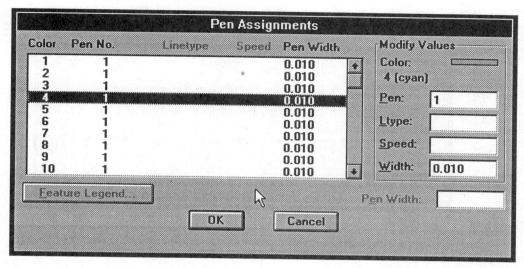

Figure 7-6 The dialog box that appears when the Pen Assignments. . . button is chosen

The fourth column controls the pen speed setting. This is important for pen-based plotters because different pens have different speed requirements. Refillable technical pens generally require slower speeds, while roller pens are capable of very high speeds.

The fifth column allows you to select the thickness of individual lines being plotted in solidly filled areas. AutoCAD allows you specify the width of the pen used in the plotter. This setting affects how solid-filled areas (trace, pline, solid, and doughnut) are plotted. If the value you give here is too high, the solid areas come out like a hatch pattern. If it is too low, the plotter wastes time drawing over areas the pen has already covered. The default pen width 0.010 is adequate in most conditions.

To modify parameters, pick the entry you want to modify from the list box. The edit boxes in the Modify values will display the entry you selected. You can make necessary changes for that entry.

> **NOTE:** Do not pick more than one entry. To deselect an entry, pick it again so that it is no longer highlighted.

If your plotter supports multiple linetypes, speeds, or pen widths, you view the available information by clicking the **Feature Legend. . .** button. If it is not available, the Feature Legend button will be grayed out.

> **NOTE:** If your current plotter doesn't support multiple pens, AutoCAD disables the list and edit boxes and displays the following message in the list box:
>
> Not available for this device.

By clicking the **Optimization. . .** button, the Optimizing Pen Motion dialog box appears as shown in Figure 7-7. By checking the appropriate buttons in the dialog box, you can minimize wasted pen motion and reduce plot time. Selecting each button will add that level of optimization and may improve plot quality. The default settings are dependent on the plotting device you've configured.

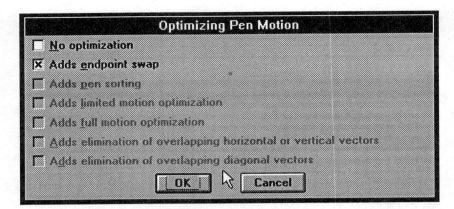

Figure 7-7 The Optimizing Pen Motion dialog box

3. Additional Parameters

In this section of the dialog box, you can specify a rectangular area of the drawing to be plotted by selecting the appropriate radio buttons. In addition, you control the removal of hidden lines from 3D drawings, adjust area fill, and create a plot file.

The plotting options (Figure 7–8) in the following section describe the radio buttons in this area of the dialog box:

Display Option This option plots what is currently displayed on the screen. An important point to remember is that the lower left corner of the current display is the origin point of the plot. This option is useful if you want to plot only part of the drawing. Before you select this option, make sure the view you want is displayed on the screen by using ZOOM and PAN commands.

Extents Option This option plots the entire drawing. It forces the lower left corner of the entire drawing, rather than the display, to become the origin of the plot. This option is similar to ZOOM Extents and ensures that the entire drawing is plotted, including any objects drawn outside the limits.

Limits Option This option plots the drawing to its limits. In general, this makes the origin of the drawing equal to the origin of the plot.

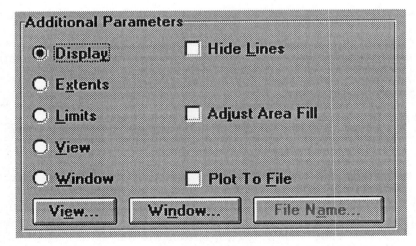

Figure 7-8 Additional Parameters section of the Plot Configuration dialog box

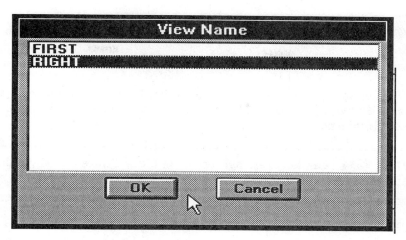

Figure 7-9 View Name dialog box

View Option This option plots a previously saved view. If you plot a previously created view, the plot is identical to the screen image after the VIEW Restore command is used to bring the view on-screen. View plotting makes it easy to plot predefined areas of a drawing. To select a view, pick the **View...** button. AutoCAD displays the View Name dialog box, as shown in Figure 7–9. Selecting a view name and pressing OK enables and selects the **View** radio button.

> *NOTE:* If no view has been saved, both the **View** radio button and the **View...** button are grayed out.

Window Option This option allows you to pick a window on the screen and plot the objects that are inside the window. The lower left corner of the window becomes the origin of the plot. This is similar to using the ZOOM Window command to zoom into a specific portion of the drawing, and then using the Display option of the PLOT command to plot. To specify the Window, pick the **Window...** button.   AutoCAD displays the **Window Selection** dialog box, as shown in Figure 7–10. You specify the coordinates of the two diagonal points or select **Pick** button from the dialog box and designate the window by using your pointing device.

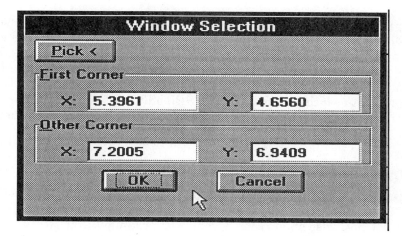

Figure 7-10 Window Selection dialog box

> *NOTE:* If no window has been specified, the **Window** radio button is grayed out.

Hide Lines   This option allows you to remove hidden lines from 3D drawings. Hidden lines are those that normally would be obscured by objects placed in front of them. This option is not applicable to 2D drawings.

> *NOTE:* For a complex drawing, removing hidden lines can add substantially to the time required for the plot.

Adjust Area Fill   This option allows you to compensate for pen width around the edges of a solid-filled area. When the plotter draws a solid-filled area, it finishes the area by drawing the boundary with the given pen width. If the plotter uses a wide-width pen, the solid area is too large. You can tell AutoCAD to compensate by selecting the radio button for adjusting the area fill. Generally, compensation for pen width is critical only when you are producing drawings, such as printed circuit artwork, photo etching, or similar artwork.

Plot to File   This option allows you to create a plot file rather than sending the drawing to the plotter directly. The creating of a plot file is useful if you need to use a plotter connected to another computer. You can copy the file to a floppy disk and then transfer the disk to the other computer. AutoCAD creates the plot file with .PLT as an extension to the given filename. Click on the radio button **Plot to File** to create a plot file. By default, the name of the plot file will be the same as the current drawing name. If you want to specify a different file name, pick the **File Name...** button. AutoCAD displays a standard file dialog box in which you can select or enter a new filename.

4. Paper Size and Orientation

In this section of the dialog box, you can specify the plot size specifications and set the paper size of the plot. In addition, AutoCAD displays the current plot area and an icon to the right of the **Size...** button indicating portrait or landscape orientation.

AutoCAD lets you plot your drawing in inches or millimeters. Select the appropriate radio button to plot your drawing in inches or millimeters.

To select the plotting sizes, pick the **Size...** button and AutoCAD displays the Paper Size and Orientation dialog box similar to the one shown in Figure 7–11. AutoCAD lists the sizes that your current plotter accommodates. A special MAX size is included in the list. This is the maximum area that the plotter can handle. If you set the size to any size other than the standard size of MAX, then it will be listed with a USER label as shown in Figure 7–11. To create a USER size, enter the appropriate width and height in a USER edit box. You can define up to five USER sizes. To select one of the sizes from the list, just pick the entry you want from the list.

5. Scale, Rotation, and Origin

In this section of the dialog box, you specify the plot rotation, origin, and plot scale.

To rotate the plot clockwise and to set a specific plot origin, pick the **Rotate and Origin...** button. AutoCAD displays the Plot Rotation and Origin dialog box similar to the one shown in Figure 7–12.

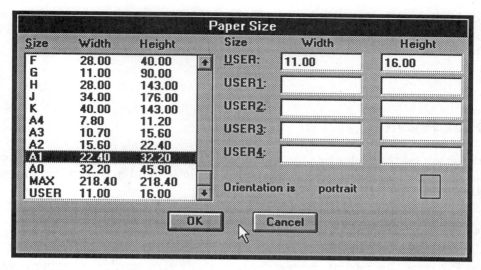

Figure 7-11 The Paper Size and Orientation dialog box

To rotate the plot, pick the radio buttons for 0, 90, 180, or 270 degrees. AutoCAD rotates the plot in a clockwise direction on the paper.

You specify the plot origin at another location by specifying X and Y coordinates in the edit boxes. The origin is the position on the plotter sheet where you tell AutoCAD to place the lower left corner of the drawing. By default, for most of the plotters the plot normally begins in the lower-left corner of the paper and for a printer the plot begins in the upper-left corner of the paper. To change the location of the origin, and thus change the location of the drawing on the sheet, you can give coordinates in inches or millimeters appropriately.

Next, you specify the plot scale in terms of plotted units = drawing units. Here, you decide the scale you want to plot your drawing. There are two optional responses to the prompt. First, you can respond with a plot inches or millimeters (as previously chosen) = drawing units. As explained earlier, you can express the plot scale in several different formats. For example, if you want to plot your drawing to a scale of 1/4" = 1'-0", you enter 1:48 or .25 = 12. Secondly, you can respond by

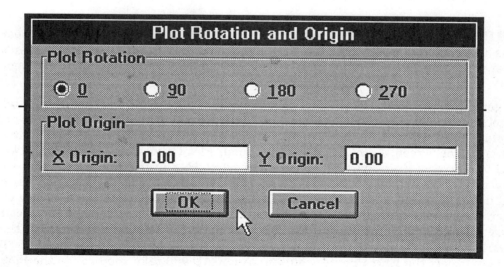

Figure 7-12 Plot Rotation and Origin dialog box

selecting the check box to scale for Fit. This allows you to plot the drawing to fit on the given sheet of paper, no matter how large the drawing. If Scaled for Fit is turned on, the edit boxes reflect the actual scale used to fit.

6. Plot Preview

In this section of the dialog box, AutoCAD allows you to preview your plot on your chosen paper size. This is helpful to see the plot before it is plotted and a convenient way to save time and supplies.

There are two methods of plot preview: Partial and Full.

Partial Preview The partial preview displays a pair of rectangles: one represents the media; the other rectangle represents the plotted drawing extents. The partial preview can be displayed by picking the radio button **Partial** and then the **Preview. . .** button. It is displayed based on the settings you have selected including:

> Drawing area to be plotted
> Paper size
> Plotting units to drawing units relationship
> Orientation and rotation

On color displays, paper size is displayed as a red line and effective area as a blue line. When the effective plotting area is the same as the paper size (in either X and/or Y directions), AutoCAD displays the coincident lines dashed in blue. In addition, you also see a small triangular rotation icon in the lower left corner when the default setting of zero rotation is in effect. If rotation is set to any of the other possible settings (90/180/270), the icon is moved to the other corners of the image area.

Using Partial Preview will also give you advanced notice of any AutoCAD warnings that may be encountered when you plot the drawing.

Full Preview A Full Preview displays the drawing on the screen as it would appear when plotted. This takes much longer than the partial preview, but it takes less time than a regular plot regeneration. Anyway, this is quicker than plotting wrong and starting all over again.

To get a full preview of your plot, pick the radio button **Full** and then the **Preview. . .** button. AutoCAD temporarily clears the plotting dialog boxes, draws an outline of the paper size, and displays the drawing as it would appear on the paper when it is plotted (see Figure 7–13). At the center of the screen, AutoCAD displays a small Plot Preview dialog box with two buttons, **Pan and Zoom** and **End Preview**. When you select **Pan and Zoom** option, you will see a screen very similar to the Zoom Dynamic window. By picking with the selection device you can pan and define the area to be previewed. This is helpful for checking the accuracy of small details. After AutoCAD performs the appropriate Pan and Zoom, it redisplays the Plot Preview dialog box with the Zoom Previous and End Preview options. To return to the view that was current when AutoCAD displayed the full screen, select the **Zoom Previous** button. To end the full preview, select the **End Preview** button. AutoCAD will take you back to the Plot Configuration dialog box.

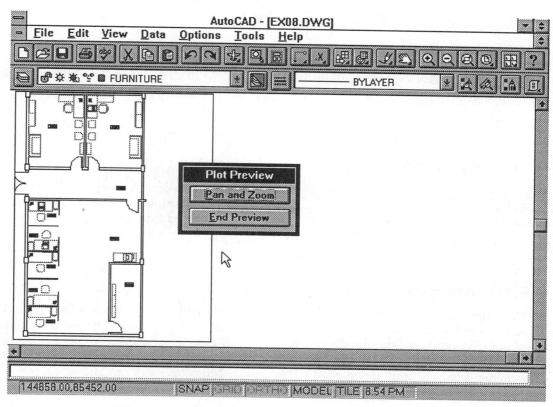

Figure 7-13 The Plot Preview dialog box

When all plot specifications are satisfactory, pick the **OK** button. The following prompt appears:

> Effecting plotting area: 13.5 wide by 9.5 high
> Position paper in plotter
> Press RETURN to continue or **S** to Stop for hardware setup.

This prompt tells you the size of your plotting area and reminds you to place paper into your plotter. If you have to change any of the options on the plotter hardware, type **S** and set up your options. If you try setting up your plotter without using the S option, AutoCAD overrides your settings when it starts to send its information to the plotter. Once you are through with setting up the paper, press `Enter`.

AutoCAD reports its progress as it converts the drawing into the plotter's graphics language by displaying the number of vectors processed.

If something goes wrong or if you want to stop abruptly, press `Esc` at any time. AutoCAD cancels the plotting.

Once the plot is done, the last prompt appears:

> Plot complete
> Press RETURN to continue

Press `Enter` to take you back to the "Command:" prompt.

PLOTTING FROM COMMAND PROMPT

If you invoke the Plot Command when the system variable CMDDIA is set to 0 (default is 1) the prompts will appear at the "Command:" prompt (text mode) similar to AutoCAD Release 11 instead of an interaction with a dialog box. The options are similar to the options available with a plot configuration dialog box.

POSTSCRIPT SUPPORT

PostScript is a graphical description language much like Hewlett Packard HPGL. It gives programmers the ability to write the programs that describe and manipulate graphic objects (lines, curves, boxes, etc.), as well as text through built-in and user-defined functions. These programs are then interpreted by an output device (either hardcopy or video) to render a graphic display.

PSIN Command — Importing PostScript Images

PSIN is the AutoCAD command for importing PostScript files into AutoCAD. These files usually have the .EPS extension (AutoCAD accepts EPS as the default extension) and may come from any program that produces standard encapsulated PostScript files or may be created manually by the not so faint of heart that wish to enter the world of PostScript programming. The PSIN command is invoked from the pull-down menu File under Import/Export option, or at the "Command:" prompt type **PSIN** and press [Enter] or spacebar.

Command: **psin**

AutoCAD displays a standard file dialog box where you can enter a filename. After selecting the EPS file, AutoCAD displays either a box containing the EPS filename or a graphical representation depending on the setting of the system variables PSDRAG and PSQUALITY. AutoCAD prompts for an insertion point followed by the scale factor. A copy of the specified PostScript file is inserted at the designated point in the current drawing to the specified scale.

> **NOTE:** AutoCAD imports these objects as anonymous blocks.

PSDRAG PSDRAG is the system variable that determines the look of the PostScript object during the initial placement or "dragging" process. If PSDRAG is set to 0 (zero) the object will appear as a box with the EPS filename inside. If PSDRAG is set to 1 the object appears graphically.

PSQUALITY The resolution at which PSIN operates is controlled by the system variable PSQUALITY. When PSQUALITY is set to 0 (zero) AutoCAD does not interpret the PostScript image but displays a box and filename scaled to represent the area of the image. When PSQUALITY is set to a value other than zero, that value is used to determine the resolution at which the PostScript image is rendered. Setting PSQUALITY to a positive value uses that value as the number of pixels per AutoCAD drawing unit and renders the image as filled polygons. The higher the positive value of PSQUALITY the finer the resolution. If PSQUALITY is set to a negative value the image is rendered in the same fashion as the positive value but images are rendered as unfilled objects, providing quicker drawing regeneration.

> **NOTE:** When PSQUALITY is set to zero, PSDRAG has no effect.

PSOUT Command — Exporting PostScript Images

The PSOUT command exports an AutoCAD drawing as an encapsulated PostScript (EPS) file. Once a drawing is placed in EPS format it can be used in many programs across numerous platforms. For example, a DOS version of a DWG file may be exported as an EPS and then imported into an Aldus PageMaket desktop publishing program and then printed on a PostScript device attached to the AMIGA. As you can probably see, PostScript offers a great deal of flexibility.

Using PSOUT command is very similar to plotting to a file. The PSOUT command is invoked from the pull-down menu File under Import/Export option, or at the "Command:" prompt type **PSOUT** and press [Enter] or spacebar.

> Command: psout

AutoCAD displays a standard file dialog box where you can enter a filename. Then AutoCAD prompts:

> What to export — Display, Extents, Limits, View or Window <default>:

The options available are similar to the ones that are provided under the PLOT command. The next prompt is regarding the inclusion of the screen preview.

> Include a screen preview image in the file (None/EPSI/TIFF) <None>:

The screen preview feature is used by some of the desktop publishing programs to which you export the file. If you do not save the screen preview image, many desktop publishing programs only display a bounding box surrounding a filename. You can instruct AutoCAD to write the image in either the EPSI format defined by Adobe or in the TIFF format commonly used on MS-DOS.

If you select EPSI or TIFF format, AutoCAD prompts for the pixel resolution to be used.

> Screen preview image size (128 x 128 is standard)? (128/256/512) <128>:

The higher the resolution, the greater degradation of performance.

> **NOTE:** If you include a TIFF screen preview, you can't print the EPS file directly to a PostScript printer and get the image output. In order to print, you need to import into a program that will read TIFF format and then print.

Next, AutoCAD prompts you for the size units (inches/millimeters):

> Size units (Inches or Millimeters) <current>:

AutoCAD lets you create the file in inches or millimeters. The next prompt allows you to select the scale factor for the EPS output. The following prompt appears:

> Specify scale by entering:
> Output units=Drawing units or Fit or ? <default>:

Here you decide at what scale you want to create the EPS file. The response is given similar to the PLOT command explained earlier in this chapter.

AutoCAD then displays a list of pre-defined output sizes and prompts you for the size of the image that you wish to generate:

Enter the Size or Width, Height (in Inches)<USER>:

You may enter the letter(s) in the standard size column that AutoCAD displays or you may enter your custom size.

AutoCAD exports an EPS file with the filename you specified and when finished, returns to the "Command:" prompt.

PSFILL

PSFILL command is used as a complement to PSOUT. It allows you to fill any 2D polyline with pre-defined as well as custom PostScript fill patterns. Patterns are defined in the ACAD.PSF (short for "Postscript Fill") file. To insert your own custom fill pattern simply place the required PostScript code in the ACAD.PSF file. AutoCAD does not display these patterns but uses them to provide fills for polylines when exporting images.

To invoke the PSFILL command, type **PSFILL** at the "Command:" prompt and press [Enter] or spacebar.

Command: **psfill**

AutoCAD prompts you to select the polyline and then specify the fill pattern that you want to use. See Appendix **I** for the list of fill patterns available in AutoCAD.

EXERCISES

Exercise 7-1

Open one of the drawings from Chapter 2 into AutoCAD. Use the PLOT command to plot it to fit on a B-size sheet.

Exercise 7-2

Plot the same drawing used in exercise 7-1 using the Limits option on a B-size sheet.

Exercise 7-3

Plot the project drawing from Chapter 4 on an A-size sheet to a scale of 3/16" = 1'-0".

Exercise 7-4

Open one of the drawings from Chapter 3 into AutoCAD. Display the drawing the way you want to plot, and use the PLOT command to plot using the Display option to fit on a C-size sheet.

Exercise 7-5

Plot the same drawing used in exercise 7-4 using the Extents option on a C-size sheet.

Exercise 7-6

Plot the project drawing from Chapter 3 on a B-size sheet to a scale of 1=1.

REVIEW QUESTIONS

1. If you want to plot a drawing requiring multiple pens and you are using a single pen plotter, AutoCAD will
   - (A) not plot the drawing with a single pen plotter
   - (B) pause when necessary to allow you to change pens
   - (C) invoke an error message
   - (D) None of the above

2. The drawing created at a 1:1 scale and plotted to "Fit" is plotted
   - (A) at 1:1 scale
   - (B) to fit the specified paper size
   - (C) unscaled
   - (D) at the prototype scale
   - (E) None of the above

3. To plot a full scale drawing at 1/4" = 1', use
   - (A) PLOT with a scale 0.25=12
   - (B) PLOT with scale 0.25=1
   - (C) PLOT with scale 48=1
   - (D) PLOT with scale 12=1/4
   - (E) PLOT with scale 24=1

4. What is the file extension assigned to all files created when plotting to a file?
   - (A) DWG
   - (B) DRW
   - (C) DRK
   - (D) PLO
   - (E) PLT

5. When plotting, pen numbers are assigned to
   - (A) colors
   - (B) layers
   - (C) thickness
   - (D) linetypes
   - (E) None of the above

6. Options within the Plot feature include
   - (A) assignment of pen numbers and pen speeds
   - (B) specification of plot origin, size, and scale
   - (C) rotation angle
   - (D) All of the above

. . . .

C H A P T E R

8

HATCHING AND BOUNDARIES

. . . .

After completing this chapter, you will be able to:

- Use the Bhatch and Hatch commands
- Fine tune the hatching boundaries by using the Bhatch Advanced Options dialog box
- Modify hatch patterns by using the Hatchedit command

WHAT IS HATCHING?

Drafter and designers use repeating patterns, called hatching, to fill regions in a drawing for various purposes. In a cut-away (cross-section) view, hatch patterns help the viewer differentiate between components of an assembly and indicate the material of each. In surface views, hatch patterns depict material and add to the readability of the view. In general, hatch patterns greatly improve the drafter/designer's purpose, that is, communicating information. Because drawing hatch patterns is a repetitive task, it is an ideal application of computer-aided drafting.

You can use patterns that are supplied in an AutoCAD support file called ACAD.PAT, patterns in files available from third-party custom developers, or you can create your own custom hatch patterns. See Appendix I for the list of patterns supplied with ACAD.PAT.

HATCH patterns are drawn as line segments. When properly defined, they appear as repeated shapes made up of straight line segments.

Hatching as a Block

AutoCAD normally combines the lines generated during one HATCH command into an anonymous block. This means you can use the ERASE, COPY, MOVE, CHANGE, or other commands that operate on a block to edit the hatch group as though it were a single object. Commands like BREAK and OFFSET will not work on a hatch pattern. A block, however, can be separated into its individual lines and segments by using the EXPLODE command. The segments from the exploded block are no longer part of a defined hatch pattern, but separate from each other. Another method to have hatching drawn as separate objects, instead of as a block, is to use the asterisk (*) to prefix the pattern name when responding to the prompt.

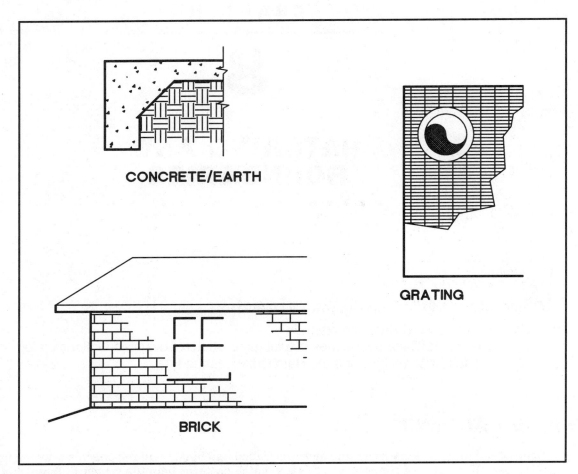

CONCRETE/EARTH

GRATING

BRICK

Figure 8-1   Examples of hatch patterns

Hatching is placed in the current user coordinate system, at the current ELEVATION, current THICKNESS, layer, color, line type and with respect to the current snap origin. The extrusion is the direction of the WCS positive Z direction.

THE BOUNDARY

A region of the drawing may be filled with a hatch pattern if it is enclosed by a boundary of connecting line, circle, or arc objects. Overlapping boundary objects can be considered as terminating at their intersections with other boundary objects. There may not be any gaps between boundary objects, however. Figure 8-2 illustrates variations of objects and the potential boundaries that might be established from them.

Note in Figure 8-2 how the enclosed regions are defined by their respective boundaries. A boundary might include all or part of one or more objects. In addition to lines, circles and arcs, boundary objects can also include 2D and 3D polylines, 3D faces, and viewports. Boundary objects should be parallel to the current UCS. In AutoCAD Release 13, you can also hatch blocks inserted into unequal X and Y scale factors.

When using the BHATCH command, the hatched region is determined by the selected objects being projected onto the XY plane of the current UCS. Remember that all regions are closed. There are no openings. The region selected for hatching (and, therefore, its boundary) should be entirely within the current viewport.

BHATCH versus HATCH

AutoCAD provides two commands for hatching: BHATCH and HATCH. The BHATCH command (introduced in AutoCAD Release 12) includes several features that greatly improve the ease of use over the HATCH command (introduced in Version 1.4). The BHATCH command automatically creates a boundary; conversely, you must define a boundary or it allows you to create it for the HATCH command. In Figure 8–3a, the HATCH command selects the four lines using the window option. These four lines comprise the hatching boundary. These four objects are valid boundary segments for use by the HATCH command. They connect at their endpoints and do not overlap. Instead of using the window option of the object selection process, you may select the four lines individually. This may be desirable if other unwanted objects were within a window used to select them.

In Figure 8–3b, the BHATCH command permits you to select a point in the region enclosed by the four lines. Then, AutoCAD creates a polyline with vertices that coincide with the intersections of the lines. There is also an option that allows you to retain or discard the boundary when the hatching is complete.

Hatching and Boundaries

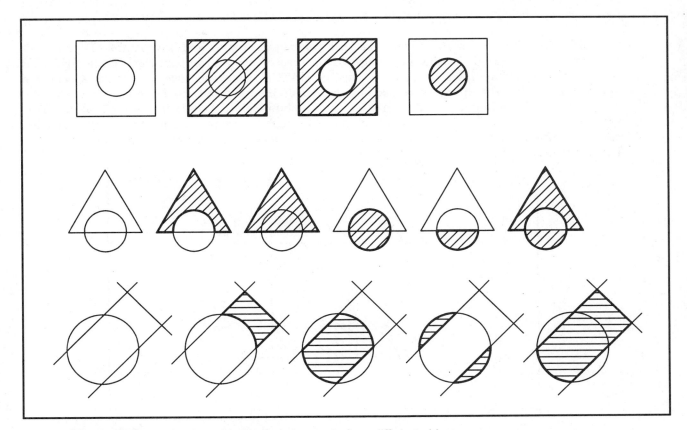

Figure 8–2   Allowed hatching boundaries made from different objects

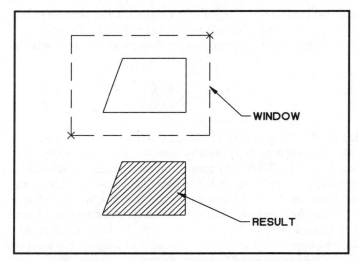

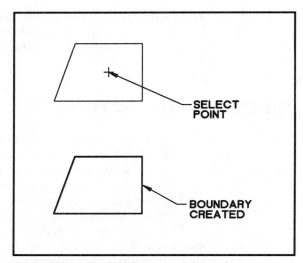

Figure 8–3a   The HATCH Command requires the user to select objects to define the boundary

Figure 8-3b   The BHATCH Command allows the user to pick a single point and automatically creates the boundary

For example, if the four lines shown in Figure 8–3a had been segments of a closed polyline, then you could have selected it by picking it with the cursor. Otherwise, all objects enclosing the region to be hatched must be selected when using the HATCH command, and those objects must be connected at their endpoints. For example, to use the HATCH command for the region in Figure 8–4, you would need to have drawn three lines (from 1 to 2, 2 to 3, and 3 to 4) and an arc from 4 to 1, selected these four objects or made them into a polyline and selected them (or it) to be the boundary.

The BHATCH command permits you to select a point in the region and have AutoCAD automatically create the needed polyline boundary. This ease of use and automation of the BHATCH command almost eliminates the need to use the HATCH command except for rare, specialized applications. Also, the dialog boxes used by the BHATCH command provide a variety of easy-to-select options, including a means to preview the hatching before completing the command. This saves time. Consider the variety of affects possible, such as areas to be hatched, angle, spacing between segments in a pattern, and even the pattern selected. The preview option lets you make necessary changes without having to start over.

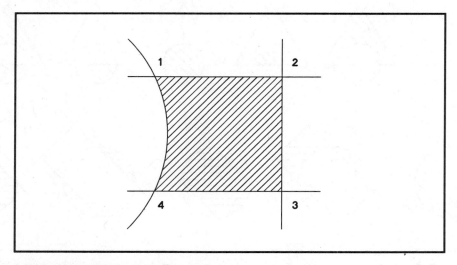

Figure 8–4   A Region bounded by three lines and an arc

BHATCH command

The BHATCH command is invoked from the Draw toolbar (see Figure 8–5), or at the "Command:" prompt type **BHATCH** and press Enter.

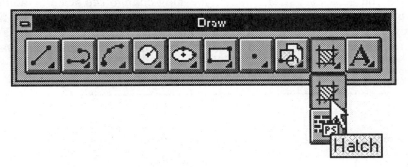

Figure 8–5 Invoke the BHATCH Command from the Draw toolbar

Command: **bhatch**

The Boundary Hatch dialog box appears, similar to the one shown in Figure 8–6. You may select one of the buttons that is not grayed out (disabled).

Pattern Type & Pattern Properties Select one of the three options, Predefined, User-defined, and Custom, from the Pattern Type list box.

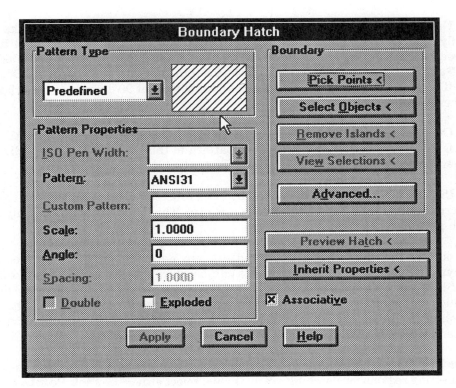

Figure 8–6 The Boundary Hatch dialog box

The Predefined pattern type allows you to select a pattern from those defined in the ACAD.PAT file. Select one of the available patterns by clicking the image tile located in the Pattern Type section of the dialog box. You can also select the pattern from the **Pattern:** list box located in the Pattern Properties section of the dialog box. The selected pattern becomes the value of the HPNAME system variable. Once you select a pattern name, you may change the scale or angle in the **Scale:** and **Angle:** edit box, respectively. Note that the angle 0 corresponds to the positive X of the current UCS. Scale and angle values (like the pattern name) are saved in system variables. For example the scale (default=1) and angle (default=0) values can be changed to suit the desired appearance, as shown in Figure 8–7.

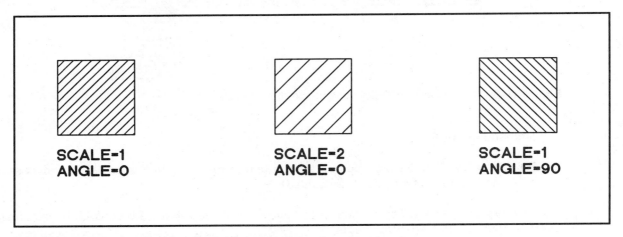

Figure 8–7   The same hatch pattern with different scale and angle values

The User-defined pattern type allows you to define a simple pattern using the current linetype on the fly. Specify a simple pattern of parallel lines or two groups of parallel lines (crossing at 90 degrees) at the spacing and angle desired. The angle and spacing can be specified by **Angle:** edit box, and **Spacing:** edit box, respectively, in the Pattern Properties section of the Boundary Hatch dialog box. If you want AutoCAD to draw a second set of lines at 90 degrees to the original lines, then turn on the **Double** check box.

The Custom pattern type allows you to specify a custom pattern in a .PAT file other than the ACAD.PAT file. Specify the name of the pattern in the **Custom Pattern:** edit field in the Pattern Properties section of the Boundary Hatch dialog box.

The **ISO Pen Width:** list box in the Pattern Properties section allows you to specify ISO-related pattern scaling based on the selected pen width. This option is available only if a predefined ISO hatch pattern is selected.

The objects that comprise a hatch pattern are normally grouped together and made into an anonymous block. The combined objects can be modified with commands like MOVE, COPY, and ERASE. If you wish to have the hatch pattern objects (actually line segments) drawn so they can be modified individually, then turn on the **Exploded** check box located in the Pattern Properties section of the Boundary Hatch dialog box or use the EXPLODE command on the resulting block created by the BHATCH command.

Boundary   Once a hatch pattern is selected, the regions to be hatched can be selected. Two methods for selecting regions for hatching are available: select either the **Pick Points <** button or the **Select Objects <** button located in the Boundary section of the Boundary Hatch dialog box.

The **Pick Points** < button permits you to specify the region(s) to be hatched by picking the point(s) inside and near the potential border(s). AutoCAD prompts:

Select internal point:*(specify a point within the hatched area)*
Select internal point:*(specify a point, enter u to undo the selection, or press « to end point specification)*

See Figure 8–8 for an example in hatching by picking a point inside a boundary.

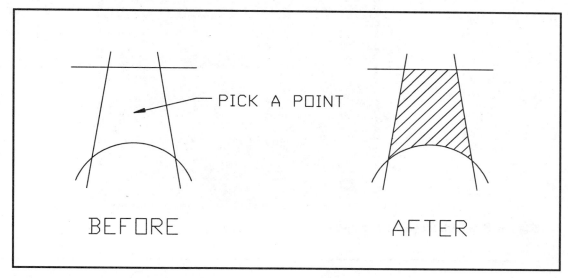

Figure 8–8   Hatching by picking a point

Before you click the **Pick Points** < button to pick a point, it is very important to make sure an appropriate hatching style is selected. The styles available are: Normal, Outer, and Ignore. You can select one of the three available hatching styles from the **Style** list box located in the Advanced Options dialog box as shown in Figure 8–9. The image tile to the right of the **Style** list box shows an example of the selected hatching style. The image shows a group of four nested objects: a circle, then inside the circle is a square, inside the square is a triangle, and inside the triangle is a text object.

The Normal style causes AutoCAD to hatch between alternate areas, starting with the outermost area. The Outer style hatches only the outermost area. The Ignore option causes AutoCAD to hatch the entire area enclosed by the outermost boundary. The Ignore style causes the hatching to fill the entire area, regardless of how you select object, as long as its outermost objects comprise a closed polygon and are joined at their endpoints.

For example, in Figure 8–10 picking point P1 in response to the **Pick Points** < option, results in hatching for Normal style as shown in the upper right, Outer style as shown in the lower left, and Ignore style as shown in the lower right.

Caution must be observed when hatching over dimensioning. Dimensions are not affected by hatching as long as the dimension variable DIMASO (short for associative dimensioning) is turned on when the hatching is created and the dimension has not been exploded. DIMASO toggles between associative and nonassociatvie dimensioning. If the dimensions are drawn with DIMASO off (or exploded into individual objects), then the lines (dimension and extension) have an unpredictable (and undesirable) effect on the hatching pattern. Therefore, selecting in this case should be done by picking the individual objects on the screen.

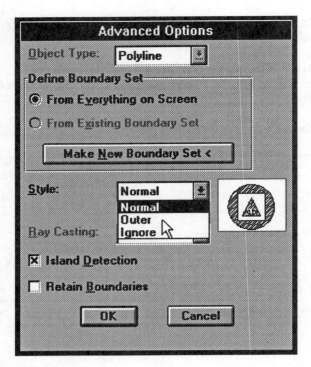

Figure 8–9 Advanced Options dialog box

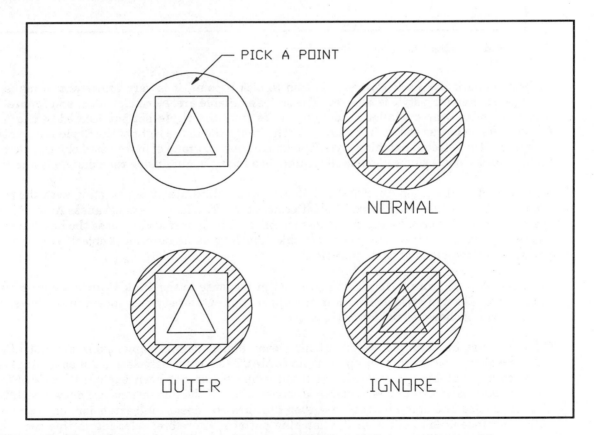

Figure 8–10 Examples of hatching by picking a point for Normal, Outer, and Ignore style

Blocks are hatched as though they are separate objects. Note, however, that when you select a block, all objects that make up the block are selected as part of the group to be considered for hatching.

If the selected items include text, shape, and/or attribute objects, AutoCAD does not hatch through these items if identified in the selection process. AutoCAD leaves an unhatched area around the textual objects so they can be clearly viewed, as shown in Figure 8–11. Using the Ignore style will negate this feature and the hatching is not interrupted when passing through the text, shape, and attribute objects.

When a filled solid or trace with width is selected in a group to be hatched, AutoCAD does not hatch inside that solid or trace. However, the hatching stops at the outline of the filled object, not leaving a clear space around the object as it does around text, shape, and attributes.

The **Select Objects** < button allows you to use one of the standard methods to select objects, which when selected determine the border(s) during a BHATCH command. The **Select Objects** < option can be used to select an object, such as text, to cause AutoCAD to NOT hatch over the selected object and also leave a clear unhatched area around the text to provide better readability.

> ***Note:*** When you select objects individually (after picking the **Select Objects** < button from the Boundary Hatch dialog box), AutoCAD no longer automatically creates a closed border. Therefore, any objects selected that will be part of the desired border must be either connected at their endpoints or a closed polyline.

The **Remove Islands** < removes the boundary set objects defined as a boundary by the **Pick Points** < option. You cannot remove the outermost boundary.

The **View Selection** < option causes AutoCAD to highlight the defined boundary set. This option is not available when no selection or boundary has been made.

Figure 8–11   Hatching in an area where there is text

Hatching and Boundaries

The **Preview Hatch** < option causes AutoCAD to display the hatching resulting from your selections. After viewing the hatch, press [Enter] or click the Continue button to redisplay the Boundary Hatch dialog box to either accept (Apply) or modify your selections. This option is not available if no selections have been made.

The **Inherit Properties** < option allows you to apply the properties of an existing associative hatch to the Current Type and Pattern Properties options. AutoCAD prompts:

Select hatch object: *(select an associative hatch pattern)*

AutoCAD sets the Current Type and Pattern Properties options to the selected hatch pattern.

> *Note:* AutoCAD does not allow the properties of a non-associative hatch pattern to be inherited.

The **Associative** check box controls associative hatching. Turn on the Associative check box and the new hatch pattern is associative. If you modify the objects, AutoCAD modifies the hatch pattern to reflect the change, as shown in Figure 8–12. If you set the Associative check box to off, any modification to the objects will not be reflected by the hatch pattern.

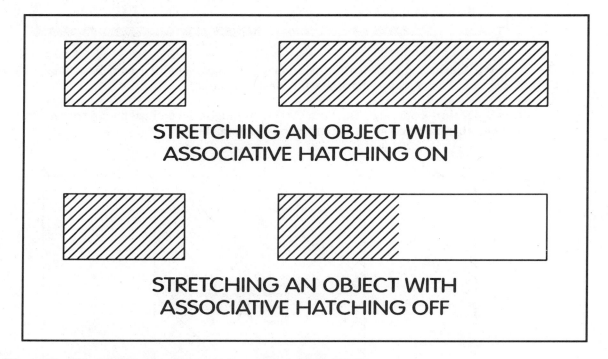

Figure 8–12   Modifying an object with hatch Association ON/OFF

Click the **Apply** Button to apply the hatch pattern. If necessary, before you click the Apply button, select the **Advanced. . .** button to fine tune the hatching parameters. When you click the **Advanced. . .** button on the Boundary Hatch dialog box, the Advanced Options dialog box will appear, similar to the one shown in Figure 8–13.

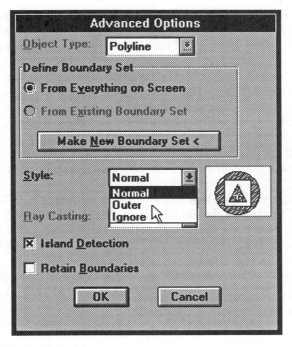

Figure 8–13   Advanced Options dialog box

Before describing how AutoCAD defines a boundary set, it is important to distinguish between a boundary and a boundary set. A boundary set is the group of objects from which AutoCAD creates a boundary. A boundary set is defined by a method of selecting objects in a manner similar to how you would select objects for some modifying commands. Or, the boundary set could be defined when you pick a point before the boundary is created and a particular set of objects is "assembled" in a group. The objects (or parts of them) in the group are used in the subsequent boundary. A boundary is created by AutoCAD after it has analyzed the objects (the boundary set) you have selected. It is the boundary that determines where the hatching begins and ends. The boundary consists of line/arc segments, which can be considered to be a closed polygon with segments that connect at their endpoints. If objects in the boundary set overlap, then AutoCAD only uses the parts of them between intersections with other objects in creating the boundary.

The **Object Type** list box in the Advanced Options dialog box controls the type of the new boundary object. From the list box you can select either region or polyline to be the boundary object.

Define Boundary Set The Define Boundary Set section provided in the **Advanced Options** dialog box permits you to single out objects to be considered by AutoCAD when creating boundaries. This is especially useful when a region to be hatched is enclosed by a boundary with edge determining objects that overlap (do not connect at endpoints) and the region has crossing objects that you do not wish to be considered during a **Pick Points <** option response.

Make New Boundary Set < Selecting the **Make New Boundary Set <** button clears the dialog box and displays the drawing for normal object selection. AutoCAD creates a boundary set from those objects selected that are hatchable. Existing boundary sets are abandoned. If hatchable objects are selected, they remain as a boundary set until you define a new one or exit the BHATCH command.

When you create a new boundary, AutoCAD enables the **From Existing Boundary Set** radio button. When you first invoke the BHATCH command, this option is not available. By default,

AutoCAD selects the **From Everything on Screen** radio button to create a boundary set from everything visible on the screen. Enabling the **From Everything on Screen** radio button discards the current boundary set, if any, and uses everything visible in the current viewport.

Ray Casting The ray casting controls the way AutoCAD defnes a hatch boundary when you use **Pick Points <** option to select a boundary. Ray casting is only available if the **Island Detection** check box is not selected. If Island Detection check is selected, then AutoCAD performs the hatching of the selected boundary depending on the Style setting (Normal, Outer, or Ignore).

The default option for ray casting is Nearest. AutoCAD expects you to select a point that is inside the boundary and the point must be nearer to the boundary than to any other object.

For example, in Figure 8–14, point A is valid and point B is not. The nearest object to point A is the line that is part of a potential boundary (the square) of which point A is inside. Conversely, point B is nearest a line that part of a potential boundary (the triangle) of which point B is outside. The key word "nearest" means that when AutoCAD begins to look for objects that will be part of boundary, it looks in all directions. With the ray casting option, you can override AutoCAD's nearest (all direction) method of beginning a search for the first object in the process of creating a boundary set. AutoCAD can begin its search in one of four directions, +X, -X, +Y, or -Y.

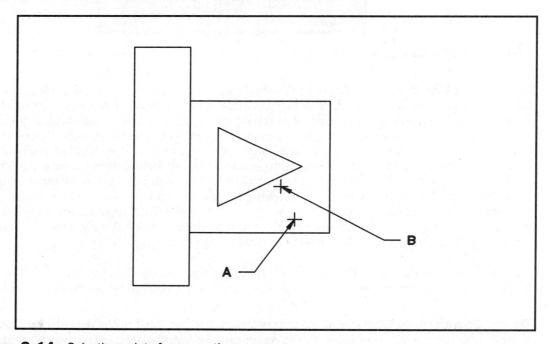

Figure 8–14 Selecting points for ray casting

For example, the square in Figure 8–15 can be the boundary using point B if you have selected the +X direction. Point C can also be used to designate the square (not the rectangle) by using the -X direction. Note that the left side of the square is only part of the line that is the right side of the rectangle. So, when the square is referred to, the left side of its boundary is part of a boundary set. That is, the whole line is in the boundary set and the part that is the left side of the square is part of the boundary. Of course, point A is not a valid point if +Y direction is selected. When AutoCAD begins its search for the object, it encounters the triangle and point A is outside the triangle. Point E can be used to create a boundary for the rectangle using the nearest option. It is inside the boundary and encounters no objects in any direction.

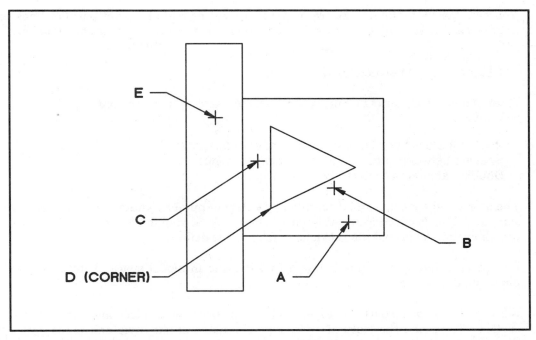

Figure 8-15 Selecting points for ray casting by changing directions

The **Retain Boundaries** check box specifies whether or not the boundary objects will remain in your drawing after hatching is completed. Click the OK button to accept the changes and close the Advanced Options dialog box. Control is returned to Boundary Hatch dialog box.

HATCH Command

Invoke the HATCH command by typing **HATCH** at the "Command:" prompt and pressing [Enter] or spacebar.

    Command: **hatch**
    Pattern (? or name/U,style)<default>: *(hatch pattern name)*

You may use one of the patterns in the ACAD.PAT file by entering its name. See Appendix I for the list of pattern names. Patterns not in the ACAD.PAT file can be in a file with the pattern name followed by a .PAT extension. See Chapter 17 on customizing for how to create and store your own custom hatch patterns.

A list of patterns are displayed by responding as follows:

    Command: **hatch**
    Pattern (? or name/U,style)<default>: **?**
    Pattern(s) to list <*>: [Enter]

Pressing [Enter] lists all patterns in the ACAD.PAT file. Or, you can reply with a name or a combination of characters and wild cards (*, ?, or other wild card) to have certain patterns or groups of patterns listed.

You can specify a simple pattern of parallel lines or two groups of parallel lines (crossing at 90 degrees) at the spacing and angle desired by selecting the **U** option as shown below:

    Command: **hatch**
    Pattern (? or name/U,style)<default>: **u**

After you enter **U**, AutoCAD provides the means to customize the hatch pattern with the following prompts:

    Angle for crosshatch lines <default>:*(specify the angle)*
    Spacing between lines <default>:*(specify spacing)*
    Double hatch area? <default>:*(enter Y or N)*

The angle and spacing can be specified by entering numeric values or by picking two points on the screen. A **Y** or **N** specifies whether double hatching (second family of parallel lines at 90 degrees) is drawn or not. Values of the previous hatch are the defaults.

By giving a line space value followed by XP while in model space, AutoCAD uses an equivalent paper space spacing.

When you specify the pattern name, you have the freedom to select one of the three styles explained earlier. To invoke the Normal style, type the name of the style and press Enter. To invoke the Outermost style, type the name of the pattern followed by a comma (,) and the letter **o**. To invoke the Ignore style, type the name of the pattern followed by a comma (,) and the letter **i**.

Once you specify the type of pattern, and the style, AutoCAD responds with two additional prompts:

    Scale for pattern <default>:
    Angle for pattern <default>:

Each pattern is defined with a real world spacing and with a rotation angle of zero degrees. If necessary, you can change the scale and rotation angle. The rotation angle is given in reference to positive X Axis.

After you choose the pattern scale and rotation angle, AutoCAD prompts:

    Select hatch boundaries or RETURN for direct hatch option:
    Select objects:

Select objects by any of the standard object selection methods or press Enter. When you press Enter, AutoCAD allows you to draw a polyline boundary with a combination of lines and arcs. If necessary, you can retain the polyline, if not AutoCAD hatches the defined boundary without drawing a polyline boundary. This option is useful when you want to hatch certain area of a drawing, but no objects are drawn.

To draw a polyline boundary, press Enter at the Select objects: prompt. AutoCAD prompts:

    Retain polyline? <default>:*(Enter y to retain the hatching boundary or n to discard it after the
        area is hatched)*
    From point: *(specify a start point for the polyline boundary)*
    Arc/Close/Length/Undo/<Next point>: *(specify a point, or enter an option)*

The options are similar to PLINE command explained earlier in Chapter 4. When you've completed the polyline boundary, the HATCH command prompts you to create additional polyline boundaries.

NOTE: The selection of objects for hatching must be done with aware-ness of how each object will affect or be affected by the HATCH com-mand. Complex hatching of large areas can be time consuming. Forgetting to select a vital object can change the whole effect of hatching. You can terminate hatching before it is completed by pressing ⎋.

Hatching Base Point and Angle Different areas hatched with the same (or similar) pattern at the same scale and angle have corresponding lines lined up with each other in adjacent areas. This is because the families of lines were defined in the pattern(s) with the same base point and angle, no matter where the areas to be filled are in the drawing. This causes hatching lines to line up in adjacent hatched areas. But if you wish to offset the lines in adjacent areas, you make the base point in one of the areas different from the base point in the adjacent area. You change the snap base point by using either the SNAP command and the Rotation option or change the system variable called SNAPBASE. This is also useful to improve the look of hatching in any one area.

Changing the SNAPANG system variable or base angle (from the SNAP/Rotate command/option) affects the angles of lines in a hatching pattern. This capability is also possible when responding to the HATCH command's "Angle for pattern <default>:" prompt.

Multiple Hatching When you have finished hatching an area and press ⏎ to repeat the HATCH command, AutoCAD prompts only for the objects to be selected. The optional parameters of pattern, mode, scale, and angle remain unchanged. In order to change any options, you must invoke the HATCH command by typing HATCH at the "Command:" prompt. AutoCAD resumes prompting for the hatch options.

Editing Hatches

The HATCHEDIT command allows you to modify hatch patterns or choose a new pattern for an existing hatch. In addition, it also allows you to change the pattern style of an existing pattern.

The HATCHEDIT command is invoked from the Special Edit flyout located in the Modify toolbar (see Figure 8–16), or at the "Command:" prompt, type HATCHEDIT and press ⏎ or spacebar.

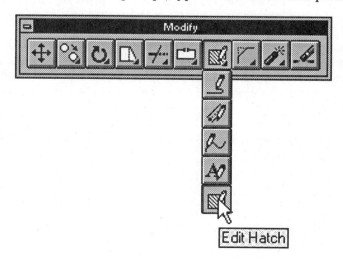

Figure 8–16 Invoke the HATCHEDIT Command from the Modify toolbar

Command:**HATCHEDIT**
Select hatch object:*(select the associative hatch pattern)*

The Hatchedit dialog box appears similar to the one shown in Figure 8–17.

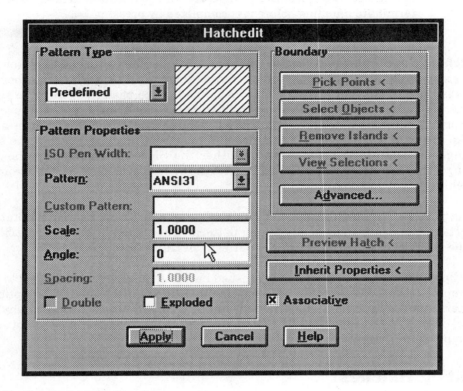

Figure 8–17 Hatchedit dialog box

Select one of the three options, Predefined, User-defined, and Custom from the **Pattern Type** list box. To change the existing pattern with a new one, select one of the predefined patterns by clicking the image tile located in the Pattern Type section of the dialog box. You can also select a new pattern from **Pattern:** list box located in the Pattern Properties section of the dialog box.

If necessary, change the Scale and Angle of the hatch pattern. Click the **Advanced. . .** button to change the pattern style. To inherit properties of an existing hatch pattern, click the **Inherit Properties** button and select an associative hatch pattern. The **Associative** check mark controls whether or not selected hatching will be associative. If this option is selected, the modified hatch pattern is associative.

Once the necessary changes are made in the Hatchedit dialog box, click the **Apply** button to modify the selected hatch pattern.

PROJECT EXERCISE

In this project, you will apply AutoCAD concepts and skills discussed in chapters 2 through 7 to create the mechanical assembly drawing of all three parts drawn as a full section as shown in Figure P8–1.

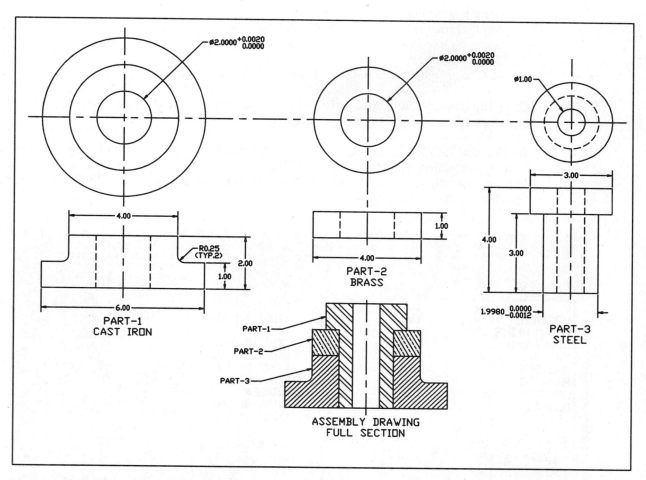

Figure P8–1   Completed project design

> *NOTE:* The step-by-step instructions for this project are designed to provide practice in the concepts presented in chapters 2 through 7. It is not necessarily the most efficient way to draw the design.

STEP 1   Invoke the AutoCAD program from the Windows Program Manager.

STEP 2   Invoke the NEW command from the pull-down menu File or type New at the "Command:" prompt. Enter CH8-PROJ as the name of the drawing file. Make sure ACAD.DWG is selected as the prototype drawing.

STEP 3 Select the UNITS command from the pull-down menu Data to open the DDUNITS dialog box. Set units to decimal with 2 decimal places and degrees to decimal with 2 decimal places.

STEP 4 Invoke the LIMITS command and set the limits as shown.

> Command:**limits**
> on/off/<Lower left corner><0.00,0.00>: `Enter`
> Upper right corner<12.00,9.00>:**24,18**
> Command:**zoom**
> All/Center/Dynamic/Extents/Left/Previous/Vmax/Window/Scale(X/XP)>:**a**

STEP 5 Open the Drawing Aids Dialog box from the pull-down menu Options and set grid to 0.5, snap to 0.25 and turn ON grid and snap.

STEP 6 Invoke the LAYER command from the pull-down menu Data, create layers named border, centerline, object, text, hidden, dimension, and hatch-1, hatch-2, hatch-3 with appropriate colors and linetypes as shown in the dialog box Figure P8–2. Set Layer "border" as the current layer.

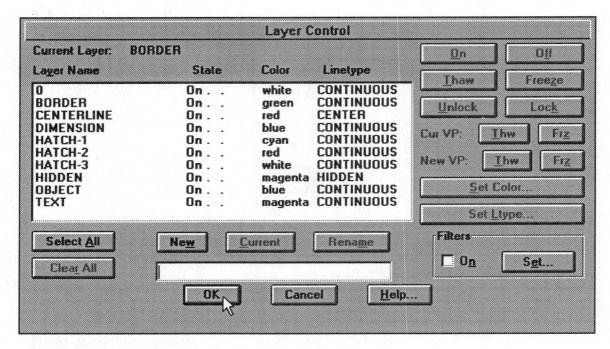

Figure P8–2   Layer dialog box

STEP 7 Invoke the RECTANGLE command from the Draw toolbar to draw the border (23" by 17") as shown in Figure P8–3.

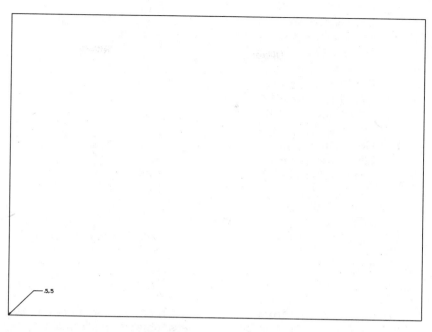

Figure P8–3   Border for mechanical assembly drawing

Command:**rectang**
First corner:**0.5,0.5**
Other corner:**@23,17**

STEP 8   Set Layer "centerline" as the current layer. Invoke the LINE command from the Draw toolbar and draw the center lines 1, 2, 3, and 4 as shown in Figure P8–4.

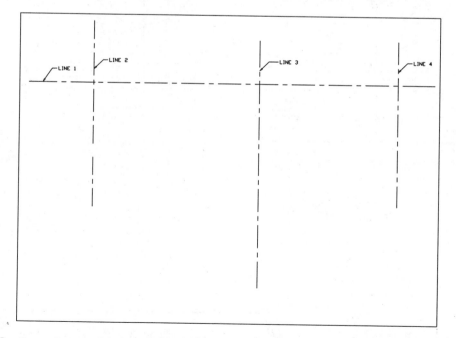

Figure P8–4   Centerlines for the assembly drawing

Command:**line**
From point:**1,13.75** *(line 1)*
To point:**@22<0**
To point: Enter
Command: Enter
LINE From point:**4.5,17** *(line 2)*
To point:**@10<270**
To point: Enter
Command: Enter
LINE From point:**13.5,16** *(line 3)*
To point:**@13.5<270**
To point: Enter
Command: Enter
LINE From point:**21,16** *(line 4)*
To point:**@9<270**

To point: Enter
Command:

STEP 9 Draw the top and front views of part-1, part-2, and part-3 of the design by referring to Figure P8–5 in the appropriate layers "object" and "hidden" .

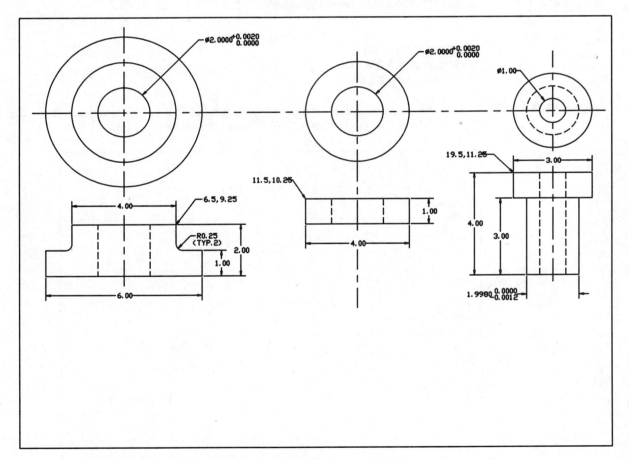

Figure P8–5 Top and front views of part-1, part-2, and part-3

STEP 10   Draw the sectional assembly of part-1, part-2, and part-3 by referring to Figure P8–6.

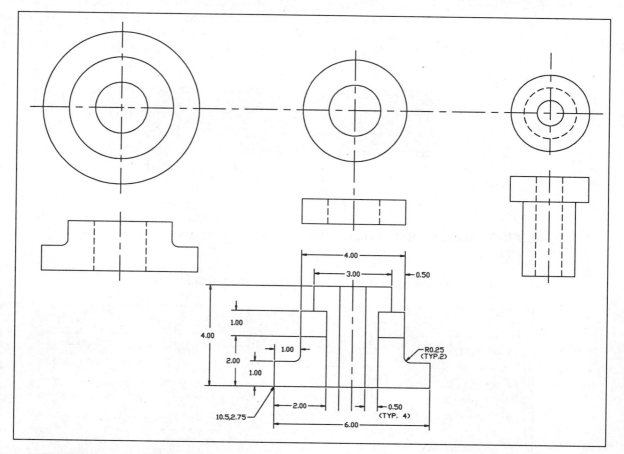

Figure P8–6   Sectional assembly

STEP 11 Set layer "hatch-1" as the current layer. Invoke the BHATCH command from the Draw toolbar (see Figure P8–7). AutoCAD displays the Boundry Hatch dialog box. Set the hatch parameters (hatch pattern: ansi31, pattern scale 1.0, pattern angle 0) as shown in Figure P8–8. Click the **Pick Points** button and select the internal point A and B as shown in Figure P8–9. After selecting point A and B press [Enter] and click the **Apply** button to hatch the selected area.

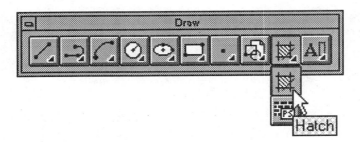

Figure P8–7 Invoke the BHATCH Command from the Draw toolbar

Your drawing should look like as shown in Figure P8–10.

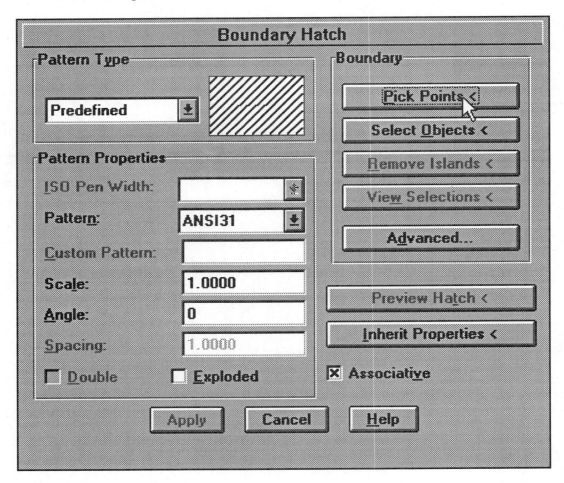

Figure P8–8 Boundary Hatch dialog box

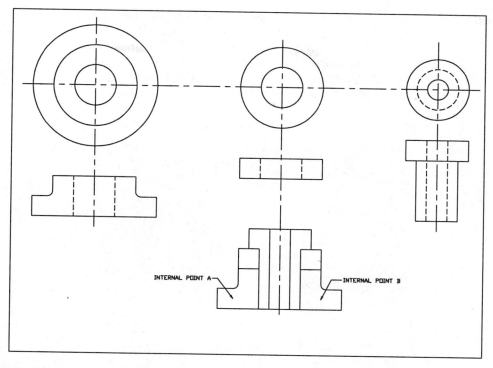

Figure P8–9   Internal points for hatching for Part-1

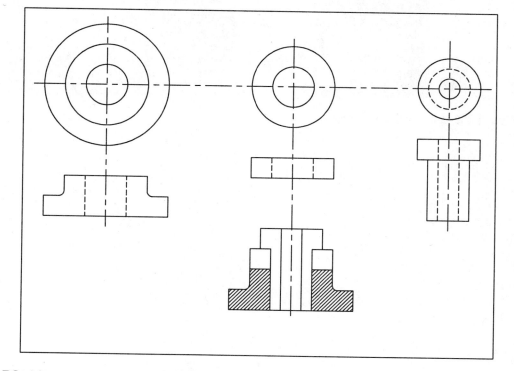

Figure P8–10   Hatching for Part-1 of the assembly section

Step 12   Set Layer "hatch-2" as the current layer. Invoke the BHATCH command again from the Draw toolbar. AutoCAD displays the Boundry Hatch dialog box. Set the hatch parameters (hatch pattern: ansi33, pattern scale 1.0, pattern angle 75) as shown in Figure P8–11. Click the **Pick Points** button and select the internal point C and D as shown in Figure P8–12. After selecting point C and D press [Enter] and click the **Apply** button to hatch the selected area.

Your drawing should look like as shown in Figure P8–13.

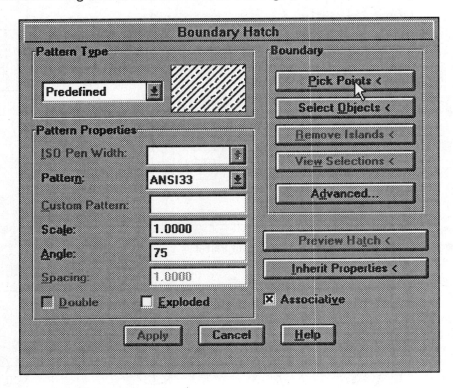

Figure P8–11   Boundary Hatch dialog box

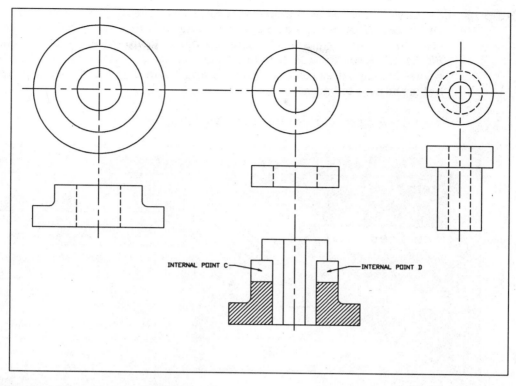

Figure P8–12   Internal points for hatching for Part-2

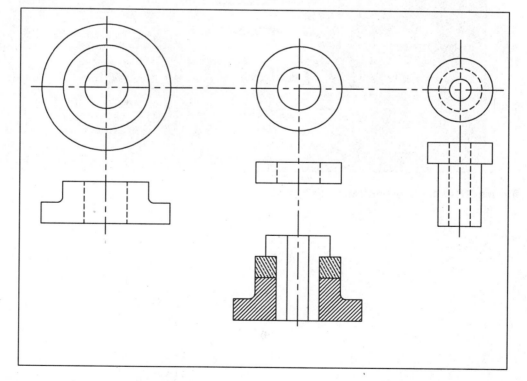

Figure P8–13   Hatching for Part-2 of the assembly section

Step 13 Set Layer "hatch-3" as the current layer. Invoke the BHATCH command again from the Draw toolbar. AutoCAD displays the Boundry Hatch dialog box. Set the hatch parameters (hatch pattern: ansi32, pattern scale 1.0, pattern angle 90) as shown in Figure P8–14. Click the **Pick Points** button and select the internal point E and F as shown in Figure P8–15. After selecting point E and F press Enter and click the **Apply** button to hatch the selected area.

Your drawing should look like as shown in Figure P8–16.

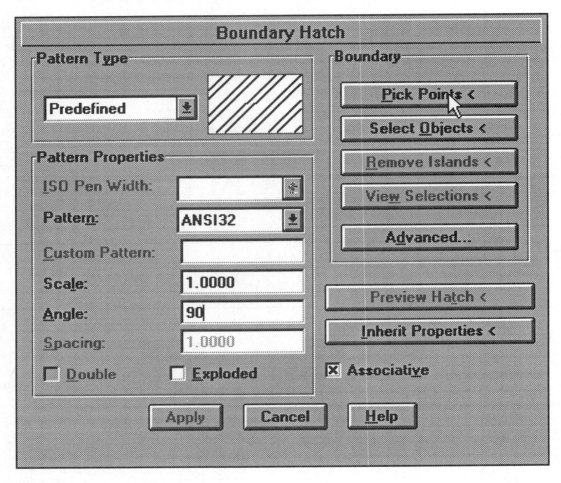

Figure P8–14 Boundary Hatch dialog box

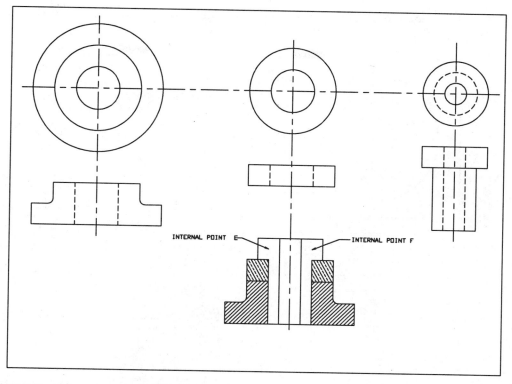

Figure P8–15   Internal points for hatching for Part-3

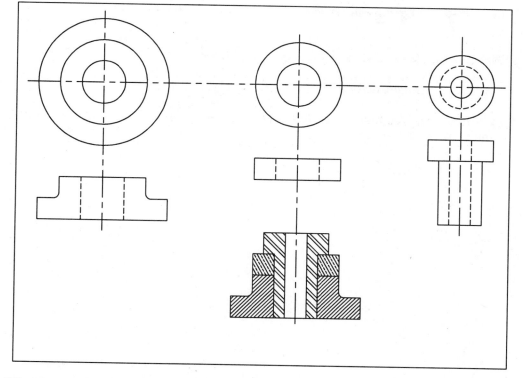

Figure P8–16   Hatching for Part-3 of the assembly section

STEP 14   Complete the drawing by adding dimensions and appropriate text as shown in Figure P8–17.

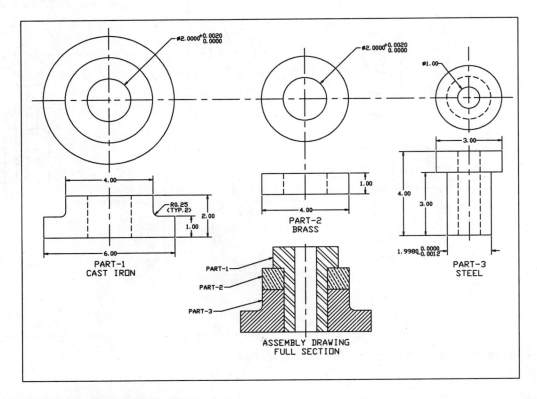

Figure P8–17   Drawing with dimensions

STEP 15   End the drawing by invoking the END command.

Command:**end**

Congratulations. You just successfully applied several AutoCAD concepts in creating a mechanical assembly drawing.

EXERCISES

Exercise 8–1 to 8–3

Create the drawings according to the settings given in the following table:

Settings	Value
1. Units	Decimal
2. LIMITS	
lower left corner	0, 0
upper right corner	17, 11
3. Grid Spacing	0.50
4. Snap Spacing	0.25
5. Text Size	0.125

Exercise 8–1

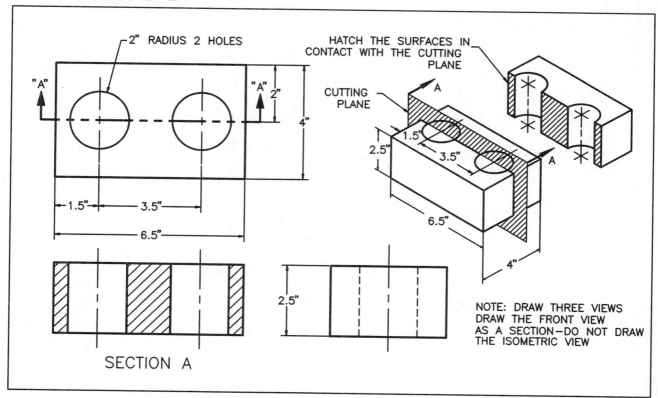

Exercise 8–2

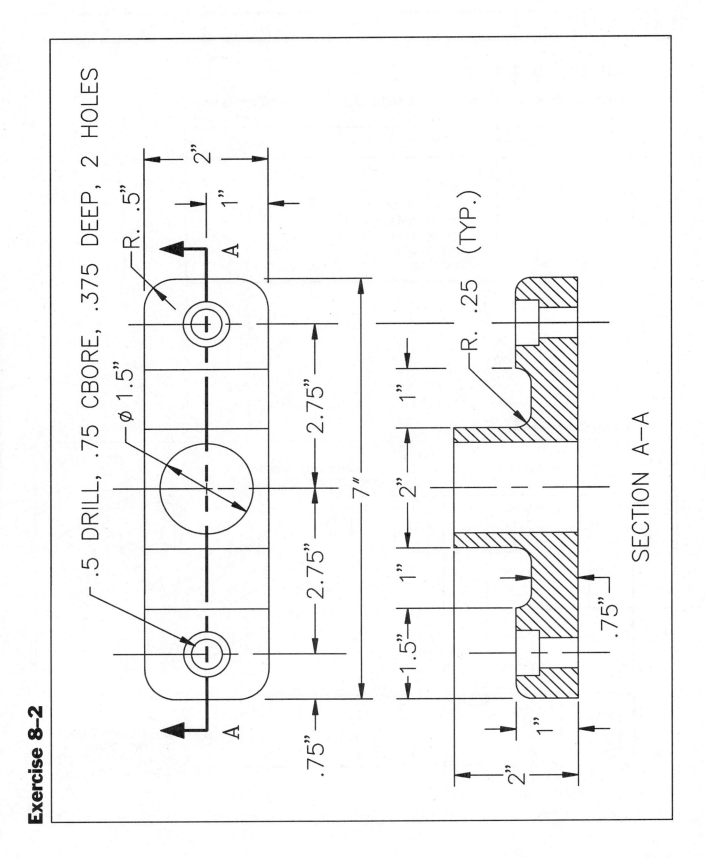

.5 DRILL, .75 CBORE, .375 DEEP, 2 HOLES

R. .5"

ø 1.5"

2"

1"

A

A

7"

2.75"

2.75"

.75"

SECTION A–A

R. .25 (TYP.)

1"

2"

1"

1.5"

.75"

1"

2"

Exercise 8-3

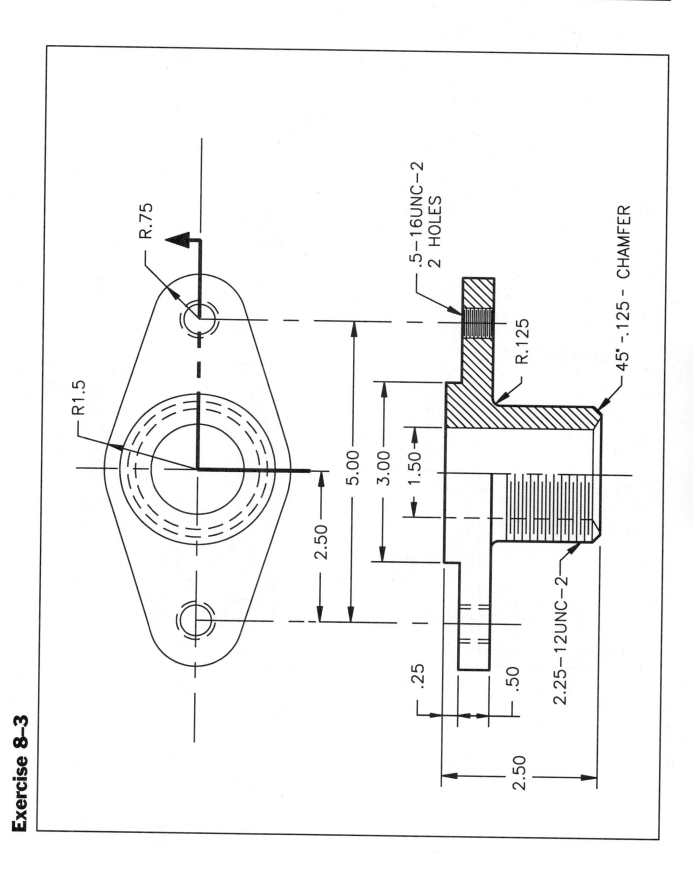

Exercise 8–4 to 8–5

Create the drawings according to the settings given in the following table:

Settings	Value
1. Units	Decimal
2. LIMITS	
lower left corner	0, 0
upper right corner	24, 18
3. Grid Spacing	0.50
4. Snap Spacing	0.25
5. Text Size	0.125

Exercise 8–4

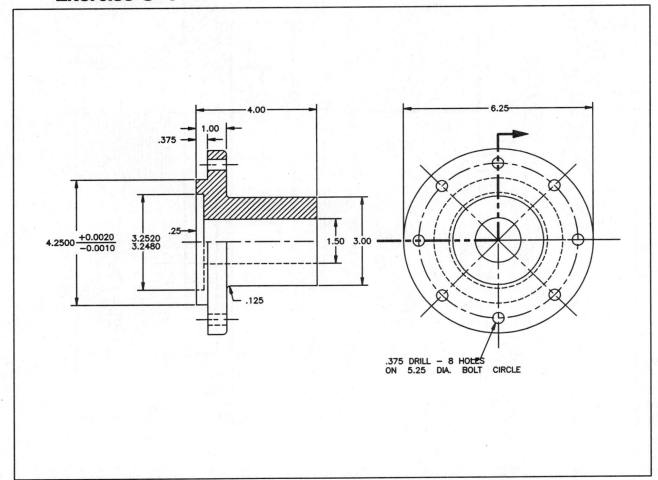

Exercise 8-5

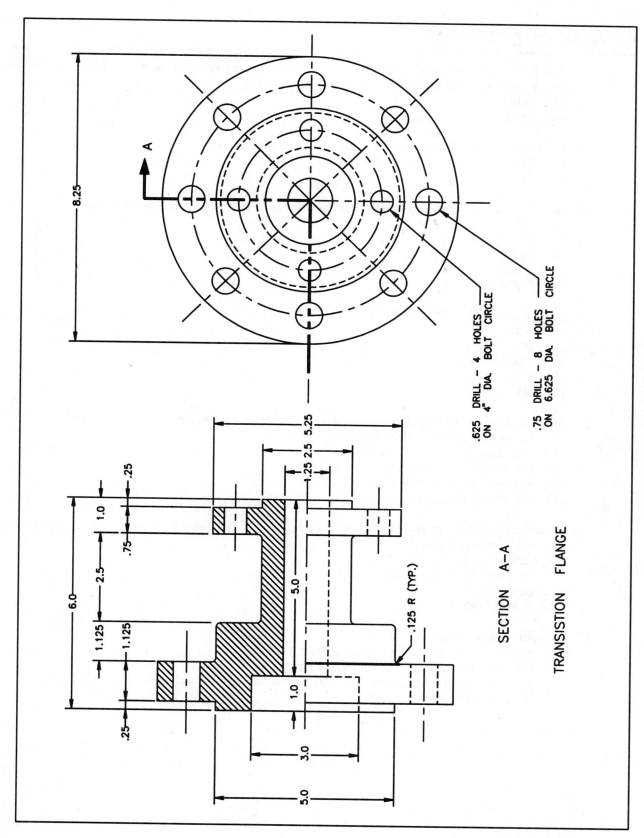

.625 DRILL – 4 HOLES
ON 4" DIA. BOLT CIRCLE

.75 DRILL – 8 HOLES
ON 6.625 DIA. BOLT CIRCLE

SECTION A–A

TRANSISTION FLANGE

REVIEW QUESTIONS

1. The BHATCH command allows you to create an associative hatch pattern which updates when its boundries are modified.
   - (A) True
   - (B) False

2. By default, hatch patterns are drawn at a 45 degree angle.
   - (A) True
   - (B) False

3. All of the following may be used as boundaries for the HATCH command except
   - (A) ARC
   - (B) LINE
   - (C) BLOCK
   - (D) CIRCLE
   - (E) PLINE

4. The following are all valid AutoCAD commands except
   - (A) ANGLE
   - (B) POLYGON
   - (C) BHATCH
   - (D) ELLIPSE
   - (E) MULTIPLE

5. When using the BHATCH command with a named hatch pattern, one can change
   - (A) the color and scale of the pattern
   - (B) the angle and scale of the pattern
   - (C) the angle and linetype of the pattern
   - (D) the color and linetype of the pattern
   - (E) the color and angle of the pattern

6. Boundary hatch patterns inserted with an asterisk "*" preceding the name of the pattern will
   - (A) exclude inside objects
   - (B) ignore inside objects
   - (C) be inserted as individual objects
   - (D) be inserted on layer 0
   - (E) None of the above

7. The AutoCAD hatch feature
   - (A) provides a selection of numerous hatch patterns
   - (B) allows you to change the color and linetype
   - (C) hatches over the top of text when text is contained inside the object to be hatched
   - (D) All of the above

9

BLOCKS AND ATTRIBUTES

INTRODUCTION

AutoCAD's BLOCK command feature is a powerful design/drafting tool. Even though an inserted block is more than one object, the block acts as a single unit when operated on by certain construction and modifying commands like MOVE, COPY, ERASE, ROTATE, ARRAY, and MIRROR. The BLOCK command enables a designer to create an object from one or more objects, save it under a user-determined name, and later place it back into the drawing. When blocks are inserted in the drawing they can be scaled up or down in both or either of the X or Y axes. They can also be rotated as they are inserted on the drawing. Blocks can best be compared with their manual drafting counterpart, the template. You can export a block to become a drawing file outside the current drawing and create a symbol library from which blocks are inserted into other drawings. Like the plastic template, blocks greatly reduce repetitious work.

Using the BLOCK command can save time by not having to draw the same object(s) more than once. Blocks save computer storage by only having to store the object descriptions once. When inserting blocks, you can change the scale and/or proportions of the original object(s).

After completing this chapter, you will be able to:

■ Use the Block, Wblock, Insert and Minsert Commands
■ Define attributes, edit attributes, and control the display of attributes
■ Extract attribute data
■ Use the Divide and Measure Commands
■ Use template and library files to establish drawing standard presets

CREATION OF BLOCKS

When you use the BLOCK command to create a block, AutoCAD refers to this as defining the block. The resulting definition is stored in the drawing data base. The same block can be inserted as many times as needed.

Blocks may comprise one or more objects. The first step in creating blocks is the creation of a block definition. In order to do this, the objects that make up the block must be visible on the screen. That is, the objects that will make up the block definition must have already been drawn so you can select them when prompted to do so during the BLOCK command.

The layer the objects are on comprising the block is very important. Objects that are on layer 0 when the block is created will assume the color and linetype of any future layer on which the block is inserted. Objects on any layer other than 0 when included in the block definition will retain the characteristics of that layer, even when the block is inserted on a different layer. See Figure 9–1 for an example.

Note the warning at the end of Chapter 1 concerning the use of the COLOR command. You should also be careful when using the CHPROP command to change the color or linetype of elements of a block. It is best to keep the color and linetype of blocks and the objects that comprise them in the BYLAYER state.

Examples of some common uses of blocks in various disciplines are shown in Figure 9–2.

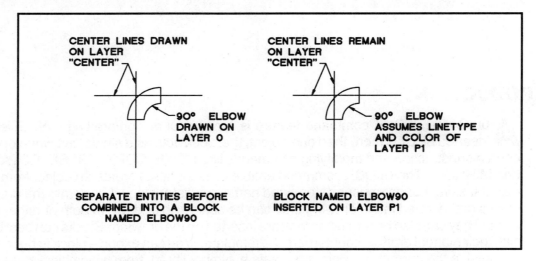

Figure 9–1 Examples of inserting blocks with different formats

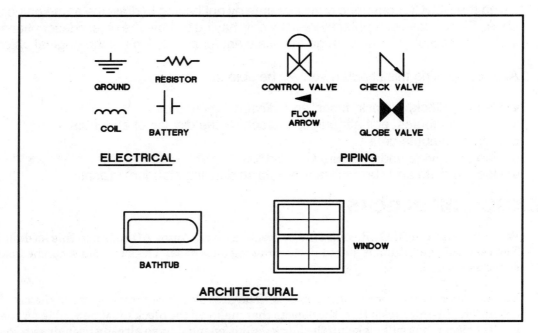

Figure 9–2 Examples of common uses of blocks in various disciplines

BLOCK Command

The BLOCK command is invoked from the Draw toolbar (see Figure 9–3), or at the "Command:" prompt, type **BLOCK** and press Enter or spacebar.

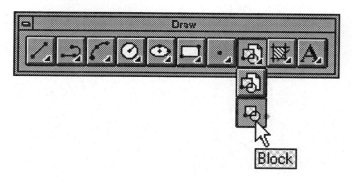

Figure 9–3   Invoke the BLOCK Command from the Draw toolbar

Command: **block**
Block name (or ?): *(block name)*

At this point you can enter a block name up to 31 characters long. The block name may contain letters, digits, and the special characters $ (dollar), - (hyphen), and _ (underscore). All letters are converted to uppercase. If this name has been previously used, AutoCAD prompts:

Block <name> already exists.
Redefine it? <N>

If you accept the default by pressing Enter, the BLOCK command will end without changing anything. Should you respond by entering **Y** (for yes) the block definition with that same name is redefined. Once the drawing is regenerated, any insertion of this block on the drawing with this name redefines to the new symbol.

After the block has been named, AutoCAD prompts:

Insertion base point: *(type a coordinate or pick a point)*

The insertion point specified during the creation of the block becomes the base point for future insertions of this block. It is also the point that the block can be rotated or scaled about during insertion. When determining where to locate the base insertion point it is important to consider what will be on the drawing BEFORE you insert the block. So you must anticipate this preinsertion state of the drawing. It is sometimes more convenient for the insertion point to be somewhere off of the object than on it. Select the point or enter the X and Y coordinate from the keyboard.

After entering the block name and selecting the insertion point the next step is to select the set of objects that will be included in the block. AutoCAD prompts:

Select objects:

At this time you can use any of AutoCAD's object selection methods. Upon selecting the objects that will comprise the new block, AutoCAD confirms the process of creating the block by erasing the objects that make up the definition (all of the objects selected) from the screen. Refer to Figure 9–4 to review the steps for the creation of a Block.

CREATION OF A BLOCK

1. DRAW THE OBJECTS THAT COMPRISE THE BLOCK

2. INVOKE THE BLOCK COMMAND AND RESPOND WITH THE BLOCK NAME.

3. SPECIFY THE INSERTION POINT

4. SELECT THE OBJECTS THAT WILL MAKE UP THE BLOCK

WINDOW

5. TERMINATE THE SELECTION PROCESS BY PRESSING THE ENTER KEY OR THE SPACE BAR

Figure 9–4   Steps for creating a block

1. Draw the objects that comprise the block.
2. Invoke the BLOCK command and respond with a name of your choice.
3. Specify the insertion point. (You may select the insertion point with the pointing device or specify coordinates.)
4. Select the objects that make up the block.

> **NOTE:** It is possible to press Enter out of sequence (before any objects have been selected) and inadvertently create a block without any objects. Just start over again, noting that you will be redefining the "no-objects" block you may have just created.

5. Terminate the selection process by pressing Enter or spacebar.

INSERTING BLOCKS

You can insert previously defined blocks in the current drawing by invoking the DDINSERT or INSERT command. If there is no block definition with the specified name in the current drawing, AutoCAD searches the drives and directories on the path for a drawing of that name and inserts it instead.

> **NOTE:** If blocks were created and stored in a prototype drawing, and you make your new drawing equal to the prototype, those blocks will be in the new drawing ready to insert. Any drawing inserted into the current drawing will bring with it all of its block definitions whether they have been inserted or are only stored as definitions.

DDINSERT Command

The DDINSERT Command is invoked from the Draw toolbar (see Figure 9-5), or at the "Command:" prompt, type DDINSERT and press ⏎Enter or spacebar.

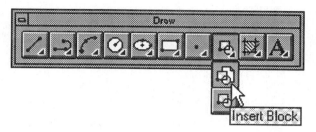

Figure 9–5   Invoke the INSERT Command from the Draw toolbar

Command: **ddinsert**

AutoCAD displays an Insert dialog box similar to the one shown in Figure 9-6.

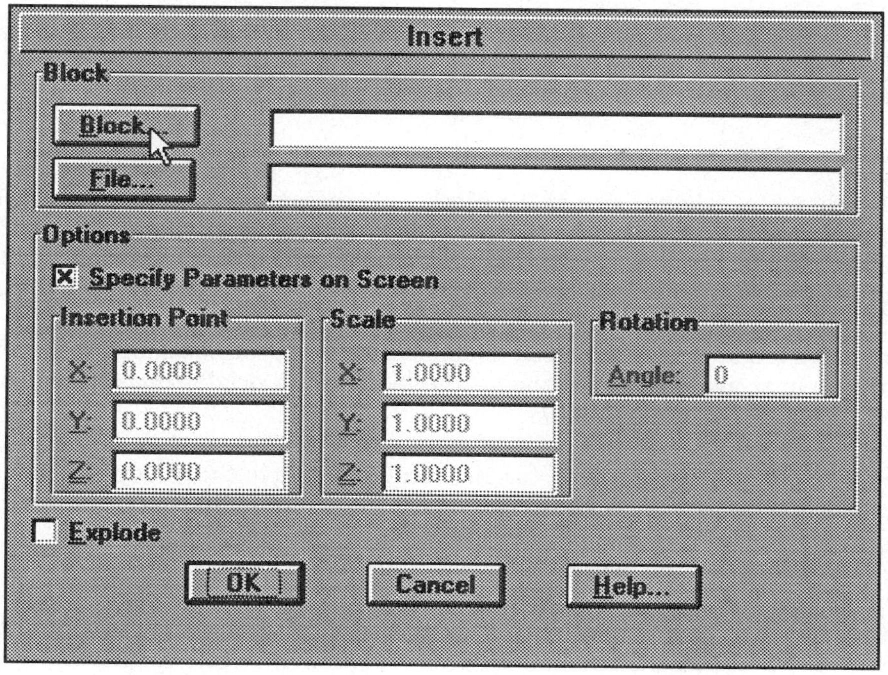

Figure 9–6   The Insert dialog box

Specify a block name in the block edit box or you can click the **Block. . .** button to display a dialog box that lets you select from a list of blocks defined in the current drawing (see Figure 9-7). Select the block you want to insert and click **OK** to close the dialog box.

You can specify the insertion point in terms of X, Y, and Z coordinates, appropriate scale factor and rotation angle in the dialog box. Click the **OK** button and a copy of the specified block is inserted at the designated point in the current drawing to the specified scale and rotation angle. The default scale factor is 1.0 (full scale). You can specify a scale factor between 0 and 1 to insert the block

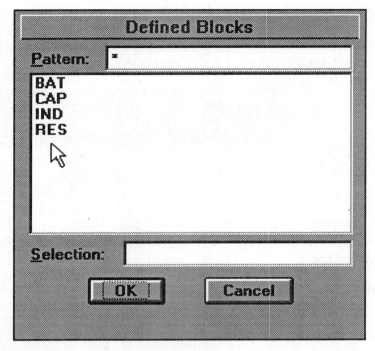

Figure 9-7 Listing of blocks defined in the current drawing

smaller than the original size of the block. If necessary, you can specify different X and Y scale factors for insertion of the block. It is possible to enter a negative value for the X and Y scale factors; this inserts a mirror image of the block about the insertion point. As a matter of fact, if –1 were used for both scale factors, it would "double mirror" the object, the equivalent of rotating it 180 degrees.

The rotation angle causes the block to be inserted at any desired angle. To rotate the block, give a positive or negative angle referencing the block in its original position or drag the block to the correct angle and pick the position.

Instead of specifying the scale factor and rotation angle in the dialog box, you can check ON for the **Specify Parameters on Screen**. AutoCAD in turn prompts you for insertion point, scale factor, and rotation angle. You can place the block at the appropriate insertion point. By dragging, you can place it to the correct angle and scale.

The Explode check box allows you to insert the block as a set of individual objects rather than a single unit. The EXPLODE command is discussed later in this chapter.

To specify a drawing file to insert as a block definition, enter the drawing file name in the File. . . edit box. Or pick the **File. . .** button to display a standard file dialog box and select the appropriate drawing file.

> **NOTE:** The name of the last block inserted during the current drawing session is remembered by AutoCAD. The name becomes the default for subsequent use of the DDINSERT Command.

INSERT Command

The INSERT command is invoked by typing INSERT at the "Command:" prompt and pressing [Enter] or spacebar.

> Command: **insert**
> Block name (or ?): *(block name)*

AutoCAD prompts for the name of the block. Type the name of the existing block. If you are not sure, you can type **?**, and AutoCAD provides you with a list of the available blocks in the current drawing.

Once you type in the appropriate name of the block, AutoCAD prompts:

> Insertion point: *(pick the point)*
> X scale factor <1> / Corner / XYZ: *(type a number or pick a point)*
> Y scale factor (default=X): *(type a number or null response)*
> Rotation angle <0>: *(type a number or pick a point)*

A copy of the specified block is inserted with its defined insertion point located at the designated point in the current drawing to the specified scale at the rotation angle.

NESTED BLOCKS

Blocks can contain other blocks. That is, when using the BLOCK command to combine objects into a single object, one or more of the selected objects may themselves be blocks. And, the blocks selected can have blocks nested within them. There is no limitation to the depth of nesting. You may not, however, use the name of any of the nested blocks as the name of the block being defined. This would mean that you were trying to redefine a block, using its old definition in the new.

Any objects within blocks (as nested blocks) that were on layer 0 when made into a block will assume the color and linetype of the layer on which the block is inserted. If an object (originally on layer 0 when included in a block definition) is in a block that has been inserted on a layer other than layer 0, it will retain the color and linetype of the layer it was on when its block was included in a higher level block. For example, you draw a circle on layer 0 and include it in a block named Z1. Then, you insert Z1 on layer R, whose color is red. The circle would then assume the color of layer R (in this case it will be red). Create another block called Y3 by including the block Z1. If you insert block Y3 on a layer whose color is blue, the block Y3 will retain the current color of layer R (in this case it will be red) instead of taking up the color of blue.

EXPLODE COMMAND

The EXPLODE command causes blocks, hatch patterns and associative dimensioning to be turned into the separate objects from which they were created. It also causes Polylines/Polyarcs and Multilines to separate into individual simple line and arc objects. The EXPLODE command causes 3D Polygon meshes to become 3DFaces, and 3D Polyface meshes to become 3DFaces, and simple line and point objects. When an object is exploded, the new separate objects are created in the space (Model or Paper) of the exploded objects.

The EXPLODE command is invoked from the Explode flyout located in the Modify toolbar (see Figure 9–8) or at the "Command:" prompt, type **explode** and press [Enter] or spacebar.

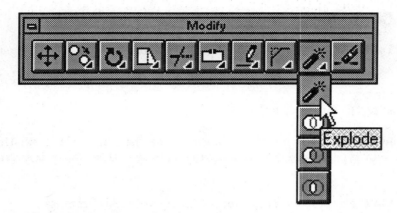

Figure 9-8 Invoke the EXPLODE Command from the Modify toolbar

Command: **explode**
Select objects:

You can use one or more object selection methods. The object selected must be eligible for exploding or an error message will appear. An eligible object may or may not change its appearance when exploded.

Possible Changes Caused by the EXPLODE Command

A Polyline segment having width will revert to a zero-width line and/or arc. Tangent information associated with individual segments is lost. If the Polyline segments have width or tangent information, the EXPLODE command will be followed by the message:

Exploding this polyline has lost (width/tangent) information.
The UNDO command will restore it.

Individual elements within blocks that were on layer 0 when created (and whose color was BYLAYER), but were inserted on a layer with a color different than that of layer 0, will revert to the color of layer zero.

Attributes are special text objects that, when included in a block definition, take on the values (names and numbers) specified at the time the block is inserted. The power and usage of attributes are discussed later in this chapter. To understand the effect of the EXPLODE command on blocks that include attributes, it is sufficient to know that the fundamental object from which an attribute is created is called an attribute definition. It is displayed in the form of an attribute tag before it is included in the block.

An attribute within a block will revert to the attribute definition when the block is exploded and will be represented on the screen by its tag. The value of the attribute specified at the time of insertion is lost. The group will revert to those elements created by the ATTDEF command prior to combining them into a block with the BLOCK command.

In brief, an attribute definition is turned into an attribute when the block in which it is a part is inserted, and conversely, an attribute is turned back into an attribute definition when the block is exploded.

Exploding Blocks with Nested Elements

Blocks containing other blocks and/or polylines are separated for one level only. That is, the highest level block will be exploded, but any nested blocks or polylines will remain blocks and polylines. They in turn can be exploded when they come to the highest level.

Viewport objects in a block definition cannot be turned on after being exploded unless they were inserted in paper space.

Blocks with equal X, Y, and Z scales explode into their component objects. Blocks with unequal X, Y, and Z scales (nonuniformly scaled blocks) might explode into unexpected objects.

> **NOTE:** Blocks inserted with MINSERT command or external references and their dependent blocks cannot be exploded.

MINSERT COMMAND

The MINSERT (multiple insert) command is used to insert blocks in a rectangular array. The total pattern takes the characteristics of a block, except the group cannot be exploded. This command works similar to the rectangular ARRAY command.

The MINSERT command is invoked from the Miscellaneous toolbar (Figure 9–9), or at the "Command:" prompt, type **MINSERT** and press Enter or spacebar.

Figure 9–9   Invoke the MINSERT Command from the Miscellaneous toolbar

```
Command: minsert
Block name (or ?): (name of the block)
Insertion point: (pick the point)
X scale factor <1> / Corner / XYZ: (type a number or pick a point)
Y scale factor (default=X): (type a number or null response)
Rotation angle <0>: (type a number or pick a point)
Number of rows (—) <default>: (specify the number of rows)
Number of columns (III) <default>: (specify the number of columns)
Unit cell or distance between rows (—): (specify the distance between rows)
Distance between columns (III): (specify the distance between columns)
```

The row/column spacing can be specified by the delta-x/delta-y distances between two points picked on the screen. For example, if, in response to the "Distance" prompt, you selected points 2,1 and 6,4 for the first and second points, respectively, the row spacing would be 3 (4-1) and the column spacing would be 4 (6-2).

INSERTING UNIT BLOCKS

Groups of objects often need to be duplicated within a drawing. The BLOCK command earlier showed how AutoCAD makes this task easier. The task of transferring blocks or groups of objects to another drawing is demonstrated in the section on the WBLOCK command. This section covers additional aspects of creating blocks in anticipation of inserting them later with a change in scale factors (sometimes with x and y unequal). This concept is referred to as a "unit block".

Doors and windows are a few of the objects that can be stored as blocks in a symbol library. But, blocks can be used in different ways to suit differing situations. The following examples are offered as procedures that are used without customizing menus or using AutoLISP routines to enhance the process. It should be noted that these procedures may be improved either with customization or possibly with some variations in using standard commands and features. Also, the symbology and names of items are subject to variation.

You can use a variety of symbols to represent windows in an architectural plan view. Horizontal sliding windows may need to be distinguished from single- or double-hung windows, as shown in Figure 9–10. You may also wish to have more than one option as to how you will insert a window. You may wish to use as its insertion point the center of the window sometimes or one of its edges at other times.

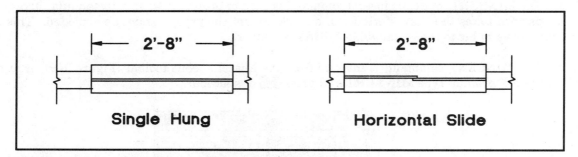

Figure 9–10 Two different windows shown as blocks

Because there are windows of varying widths, you might have to create a separate block for each width. A group of windows might be 1'-0", 1'-6", 2'-0", 2'-8", 3'-0", 3'-4", 4'-0", 5'-4", 6'-0", and 8'-0" and some widths in between. You would have to make a block for each width in addition to the different types. The symbol for the single hung 2'-8"-wide window could be drawn with the Snap set a 0.5 (1/2") to the dimensions shown in Figure 9–11.

The objects in Figure 9–11 could be saved as a block named WDW32 (for a 32"-wide window). This window could be inserted from its corner as shown if you have established that intersection in the wall in which it is to be drawn.

The preceding method requires a separate block for each window width. Another method is to make a drawing of a window in which the X and/or Y dimension is one unit in anticipation of using the final desired dimension as the X and/or Y scale factor during insertion. The following Unit Block symbol for the window can be used for any width window, as shown in Figure 9–12.

This group of objects might be made into a block named WDW1. Then, to use it for a 2'-8" window, the INSERT command is as follows:

```
Command: insert
Block name: wdw1
```

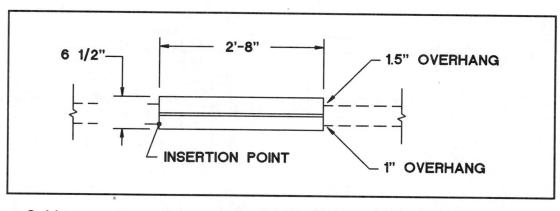

Figure 9–11   Changing the width of a window by changing th X scale factor of a block

> Insertion point: *(select insertion point)*
> X scale factor <1>: **32**
> Y scale factor <default=X>: **1**
> Rotation angle: [Enter]

Note that when you specify a value for the X scale factor, AutoCAD assumes you wish to apply the same value to the Y scale factor, making the resulting shape of the object(s) proportional to the unit block from which it was generated. That is why the Y scale factor defaults to the X scale factor. Therefore, if you wish to insert the block with the X scale factor different from the Y scale factor you must input a Y scale factor even if it is to be a factor of 1. The block WDW1 can be used for any width window by using the desired width (in inches) as the X scale factor and then using 1 as the Y scale factor. Figure 9–13 shows the window inserted in its location with the proper X scale factor. Also shown is the clean-up that can be done with the BREAK command.

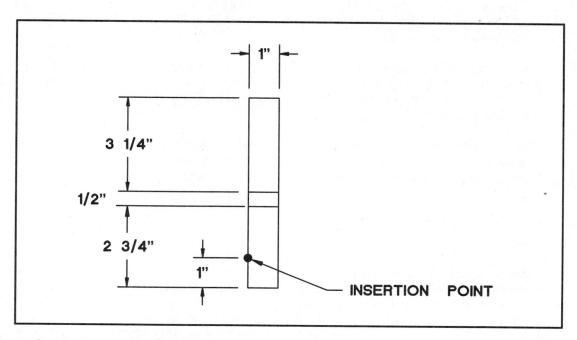

Figure 9–12   Creating a unit block for a window symbol

Blocks and Attributes

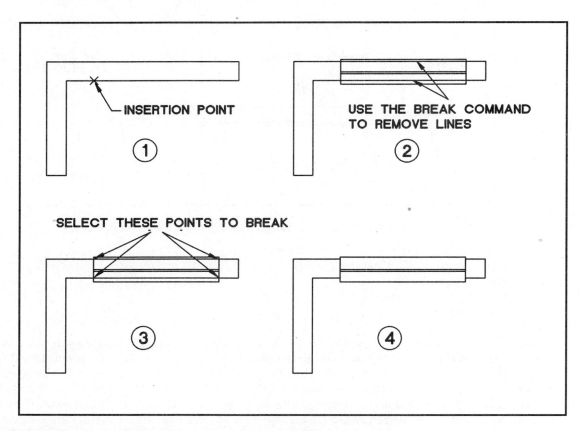

Figure 9–13 Inserting a unit block with a large X scale factor

Another variation on the unit block WDW1 would be to use the same shape for center insertion. It would be drawn the same but the insertion point would be chosen as shown in Figure 9–14. Figure 9–15 shows the window inserted.

Window symbols in plan lend themselves to the one-way scaling unit block application. As demonstrated, they vary only in the X scale and not the Y scale from one size to another. Doors, however, present a special problem when trying to apply the unit block method. A symbol for a 2'-8"-wide door might look like Figure 9–16.

The 2'-8"-wide door is drawn half open or swung at 45 degrees to the wall. Therefore, if you used an approach on the door that was used on the window unit block, some problems are encountered. First, a base block 1-unit wide simplified door symbol would not be practical. Note the Unit Block in Figure 9–17.

The Unit Block in Figure 9–17, if inserted with an X scale factor of 32 and a Y scale factor of 1, would appear as in Figure 9–18.

Even though the 4"-lines that represent the jambs are acceptable, the "door" part of the symbol will not retain its 45-degree swing if not inserted with equal X and Y scale factors. Equal X and Y scale factors present another problem. Using a Y scale factor other than 1 would make the 4"-wide jamb incorrect. Therefore, combining the jambs with the door in the same symbol presents problems that might be impossible to overcome when trying to use a unit block approach to permit one block to be used for all sizes of doors.

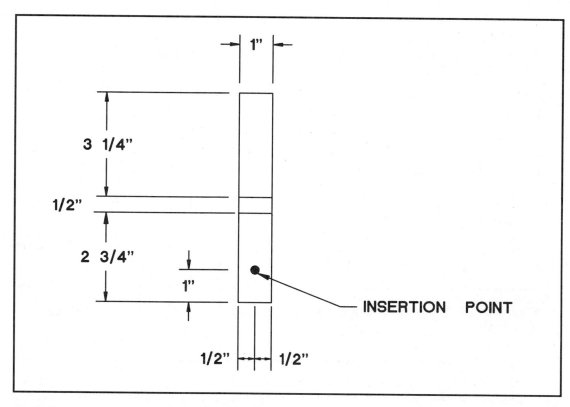

Figure 9–14   Using a unit block with a specified insertion point

Separate Unit Blocks for One Symbol

The solution to the jambs being adaptable to one-way scaling blocks (while the door is not) may be to make these two (jambs and door) into two blocks as shown in Figure 9–19.

Now you can insert the blocks separately as follows (see Figure 9–20):

Command: **insert**
Block name: **jmb**

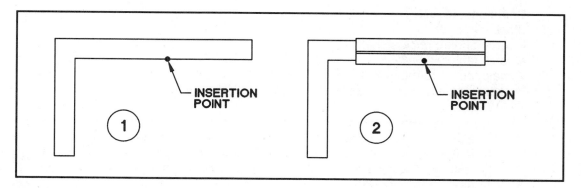

Figure 9–15   The unit block inserted as a window

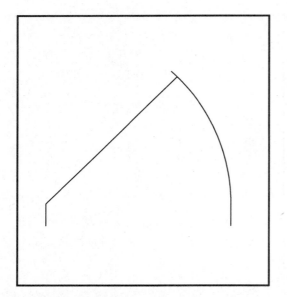

Figure 9–16 Creating a unit block symbol for a door

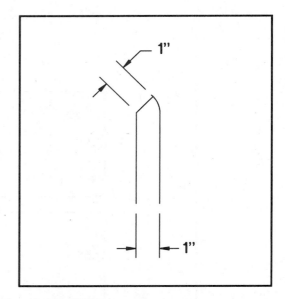

Figure 9–17 Creating a unit block of a door symbol

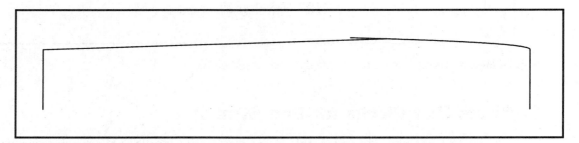

Figure 9–18 A unit block of the door inserted with X and Y scale factors

Insertion point: *(pick a point)*
X scale factor <1>: **32**
Y scale factor <default=X>: **1**
Rotation angle <default>: Enter

Command: **insert**
Block name: **dr**
Insertion point: *(pick a point)*
X scale factor <1>: **32**
Y scale factor <default=X>: Enter
Rotation angle <default>: Enter

> ***NOTE:*** When you intend to apply the concept of the unit block, whether it is to be scaled uniformly (X scale equal to Y scale) or not, be sure that shapes and sizes of all items in the symbol will be correct at their new scale.

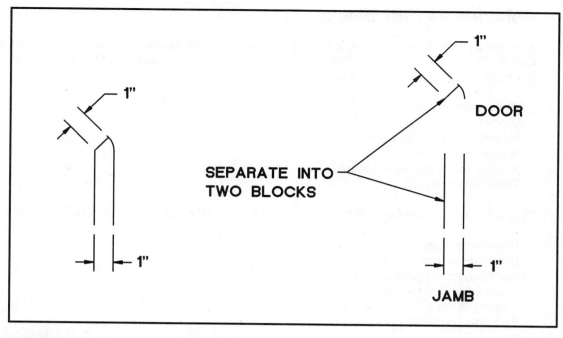

Figure 9–19   Creating one symbol from two unit blocks

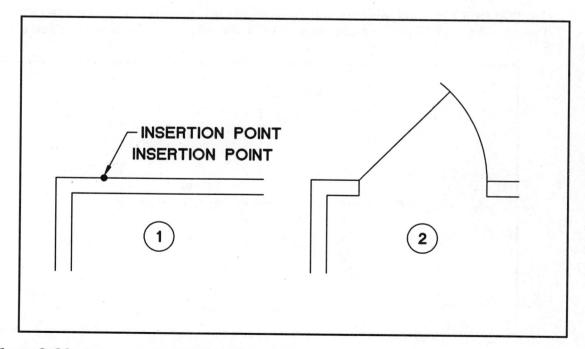

Figure 9–20   Two unit blocks inserted to create one symbol

Blocks and Attributes

Columns as Unit Blocks

Another unit block application is when both X and Y scale factors are changed, but not at the same factor. The column shown in Figure 9-21 is made into a block named COL1 and is inserted for a 10 x 8-wide flange symbol as follows:

Command:**insert**
Block name:**col1**
Insertion point:*(pick point)*
X scale factor <1>:**8**
Y scale factor (default=X>:**10**
Rotation angle:[Enter]

This can also be done for a 16 x 12 column rotated at 90 degrees as shown in Figure 9–22.

Command: **insert**
Block name: **coL1**
Insertion point: *(pick a point)*
X scale factor <1>: **12**
Y scale factor <default=X>: **16**
Rotation angle: **90**

Note the 90-degree rotation. But don't forget that the X and Y scale factors are applied to the block in the respective X and Y directions that were in effect when it was created, not to the X and Y directions after a rotated insertion.

CREATING ONE DRAWING FROM ANOTHER — THE WBLOCK COMMAND

The WBLOCK command permits you to group objects in a manner similar to the BLOCK command. But, in addition, WBLOCK exports the group to a file, which, in fact, becomes a new and separate

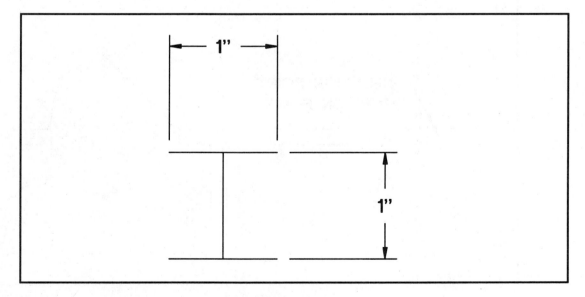

Figure 9–21 Creating a unit block of a column block

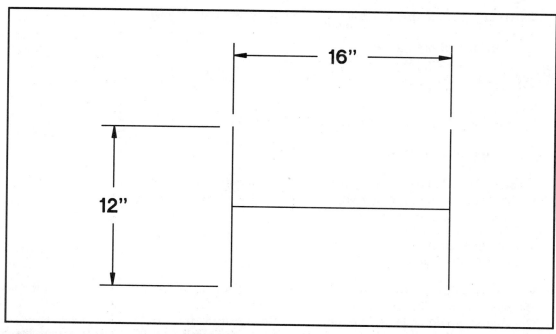

Figure 9–22 The 16 x 12 column symbol inserted and rotated 90 degrees

drawing. The new drawing (created by using the WBLOCK command) might consist of a selected block in the current drawing. Or it might be made up of selected objects in the current drawing. You can even export the complete current drawing to the new drawing file. Whichever of the above you choose to WBLOCK, the new drawing assumes the layers, linetypes, styles, and other environmental items like system variable settings of the current drawing.

The WBLOCK command is invoked by typing **WBLOCK** at the "Command:" prompt and pressing Enter or spacebar.

    Command: **wblock**

The Standard File dialog box appears. Here is where you will provide a drawing name as you do when you begin a new drawing. You should type in only the filename and not the extension. AutoCAD appends the .DWG extension automatically. The name should comply with the operating system requirements of valid characters (maximum of eight in DOS) and should be unique for drawings on the specified directory/path. Otherwise you will get the message:

    "Warning! Drawing (name) already exists. Do you want to replace it with the new drawing?
        <N>."

If you wish to use existing objects in the current drawing to create a new foundation drawing named "Slab1" your response would be as follows:

    Command: **wblock**
    Filename: **slab1**

After providing a valid filename (Slab1 in this case), you will be prompted:

    Block name:

Blocks and Attributes

Optional replies to the "Block name:" prompt include the following:

1. BLOCK (Block name)
2. = (equal sign)
3. * (asterisk)
4. [Enter] (ENTER)

Each of the four options are explained below:

1. Block name: *blockname*

If you had created a block from objects in the current drawing and named it Frame1, you could reply to the "Block name:" prompt with the name of the block as follows:

Command: **wblock**
Filename: **slab1**
Block name: **frame1**

The above sequence would have created a new drawing named "Slab1" that include the objects in the block named "Frame1". It should be noted that when the new drawing is called up for editing, the objects would no longer be combined into one block, but are separate objects, just as they were in the current drawing before being made into the block. In addition, the new drawing "Slab1" would assume the settings of the current drawing from which the block named "Frame1" is being WBLOCKed.

2. Block name: =

If you want to name the new drawing "Frame1", the same as the block you had just created, you would respond as follows:

Command: **wblock**
Filename: **frame1**
Block name: =

The difference between the = response and the previous Slab1 response is that the resulting name of the new drawing will be Frame1 instead of Slab1.

3. Block name: *

If you wished to have the entire current drawing duplicated into a new one (whether or not any objects have been made into a block), you respond as follows:

Command: **wblock**
File name: **slab1**
Block name: *

If existing objects had been made into a block named "Frame1" and it is the only object in the drawing, then responding with the asterisk (*) is similar to the equal sign (=). The asterisk response causes all objects to be written, whether visible or not, and whether in blocks or not.

One advantage of using the WBLOCK with the asterisk (*) response is that when the drawing is written to a file, all of the unused blocks, layers, linetypes, and other unused named objects are not written. That is, the drawing is automatically purged. This means that unused items will not be written to the new drawing file. For example, unused items include block definitions that have not been inserted, noncurrent layers that have no objects drawn on them and styles that are not being used. This can be useful if you just wish to clean up a cluttered drawing, especially one that has had other drawing files inserted into it, each bringing with it various unused named objects.

> 4. Block name: [Enter]

If you do not wish to make a block in the current drawing, you can still make a separate drawing out of selected objects by pressing [Enter] in response to the "Block name:" prompt. You are then be prompted to select the objects to be written to the drawing file. Like the sequence of prompts in the BLOCK command you are also be prompted for an insertion point as shown below:

> Command: **wblock**
> Filename: **slab1**
> Block name: [Enter]
> Insertion point: *(pick a point)*
> Select objects: *(select objects to be written to the new drawing)*

XRef and Model/Paper Space Consideration

XREFS and Model/Paper Space must be considered when using the WBLOCK command. A complete description of Model/Paper Space is found in Chapter 11. A named block (to be written to the new drawing) will be written to model space. An external reference or one of its blocks cannot be WBLOCKed to a file. Using the optional equal (=) response or selecting objects after a [Enter] response to the "Block name:" prompt also writes to model space. When you use the asterisk (*) option, writing the entire drawing to a file, model space objects are written to model space in the new drawing and paper space objects are written to paper space.

BASE COMMAND

The BASE command allows you to establish a base insertion point for the whole drawing in the same manner that you specify a base insertion point when using the BLOCK command to combine elements into a block. The purpose of establishing this base point is primarily so that the drawing can be inserted into another drawing using the INSERT command and having the specified base point coincide with the specified insertion point. The default base point is the origin (0,0,0). You can specify a 2D point and AutoCAD will use the current elevation as the base Z coordinate. Or you can specify the full 3D point. The command sequence is as follows:

> Command: **base**
> Base point <current>: *(specify point)*

ATTRIBUTES

Attributes can be used for automatic annotation during insertion of a block. Attributes are special text objects that can be included in a block definition. Attributes must be defined themselves beforehand and then selected at the proper time during the BLOCK command. This will include the attribute(s) selected in the block definition in a similar manner to other selected objects like lines, circles, arcs and regular text.

The two primary features of Attributes are as follows:

Blocks and Attributes

The first use of attributes permits annotation during insertion of the block to which the attribute(s) are attached. Depending upon how you define the attribute, it appears automatically either with a preset (constant) text string, or it prompts you (or other users) for a string to be written as the block is inserted. This feature permits you to insert each block with a string of preset text or with its own unique string.

The second (perhaps the most important) purpose of attaching attributes to a block is to have extractable data about each block insertion stored in the drawing data base file. Then, when the drawing is complete (or even before) you can use the ATTEXT (short for "attribute extract") command and have attribute data extracted from the drawing and written to a file in a form that data base handling programs can use. You can have as many attributes attached to a block as you wish. As mentioned above, the text string that makes up an attribute can be either constant or user specified at the time of insertion.

A Definition within a Definition

When creating a block you select objects to be included. Objects such as lines, circles, and arcs are drawn by using their respective commands. Normal text is drawn by using the TEXT, DTEXT or MTEXT command.

Similar to drawing objects, attributes must also be drawn before they can be included in the block. It is complicated and requires additional steps to place them in the drawing; AutoCAD calls this procedure "defining the attribute". Therefore, an attribute definition is simply the result of defining an attribute by using the ATTDEF command. The attribute definition is the object that is selected during the BLOCK command. Later, when the block is inserted, the attributes that are attached to it and the manner in which they become a part of the drawing are a result of how you created (defined) the attribute.

Visibility and Plotting

If an attribute is to be used only to store information, then you can, as part of the definition of the attribute, specify whether or not it will be visible. If you plan to use an attribute with a block as a note, label, or call out, you should be alert to the effect of scaling (whether equal or unequal X/Y factors) on the text that will be displayed. The scaling factor(s) on the attribute will be the same as on the block. Therefore, be sure that it will result in size and proportions desired. You should also be aware of the effect of rotation on visible attribute text. Attribute text that is defined as horizontal in a block will be displayed vertical when that block is inserted with a 90-degree angle of rotation.

Note that, like any other object in the drawing, it must be visible on the screen (or would be if the plotted view were the current display) for that object to be eligible for plotting.

Tag, Value, Prompt, and Default

Four components associated with attributes should be understood before attempting a definition. The purpose of each is described as follows:

Tag An attribute definition has a tag just as a layer or a linetype has a name. The tag is the identifier of the attribute definition and is displayed where this attribute definition is located, depicting text size, style and angle of rotation. The tag cannot contain spaces. Two attributes with the same tag should not be included in the same block. Tags appear in the definition only, not after the block is inserted. However, if you explode a block, the attribute value (described herein) changes back into the tag.

If multiple attributes are used in one block, each must have a unique tag in that block. This restriction is similar to each layer, linetype, block, and other named object having a unique name within one drawing. An attribute's tag is its identifier at the time that attribute is being defined, before it is combined with other objects and attributes by the BLOCK command.

Value The value of an attribute is the actual string of text that appears (if the visibility mode is ON) when the block (of which it is a part) is inserted. Whether visible or not, the value is tied directly to the attribute, which in turn, associates it with the block. It is this value that is written to the data base file. It might be a door or window size or, in a piping drawing, the flange rating, weight, or cost of a valve or fitting.

> **NOTE:** When an extraction of attribute data is performed, it is the value of an attribute that is written to a file, but it is the tag that directs the extraction operation to that value. This will be described in detail as part of the ATTEXT command.

Prompt The prompt is what you see when inserting a block with an attribute whose value is not constant or preset. During the definition of an attribute, you can specify a string of characters that will appear in the prompt area during the insertion of the block to prompt you to enter the appropriate value. What the prompt says to you during insertion is what you told it to say when you defined the attribute.

Default You can specify a default value for the attribute during the definition procedure. Then, during insertion of the block, it will appear behind the prompt in brackets; i.e., <default>. It will automatically become the value if Enter is pressed in response to the prompt for a value.

ATTRIBUTE COMMANDS

The four primary commands to manage Attributes are:

1. ATTDEF — Attribute definition
2. ATTDISP — Attribute display
3. ATTEDIT — Attribute edit
4. ATTEXT — Attribute extract

As explained earlier, the ATTDEF command creates an attribute definition, which is an object that is selected during the BLOCK command.

The ATTDISP command controls the visibility of the attributes.

The ATTEDIT command provides a variety of ways to edit without exploding the block.

The ATTEXT command allows you to extract the data from the drawing and have it written to a file in a form that data base handling programs can use as shown in the following:

Blocks and Attributes

DOORS

SIZE	THKNS	CORE	FINISH	LOCKSET	HINGES	INSET
3070	1.750	SOLID	PAINT	PASSAGE	4 X 4	—
3070	1.750	SOLID	VARNISH	KEYED	4 X 4	20 X 20
2868	1.375	HOLLOW	PAINT	PRIVACY	3 X 3	—

ROOM FINISHES

NAME	WALL	CEILING	FLOOR	BASE	REMARKS
LIVING	GYPSUM	GYPSUM	CARPET	NONE	PAINT
FAMILY	PANEL	ACOUSTICAL	TILE	STAIN	STAIN
BATH	PAPER	GYPSUM	TILE	COVE	4'_CERAMIC_TILE
GARAGE	GYPSUM	GYPSUM	CONCRETE	NONE	TAPE_FLOAT_ONLY

You can include an attribute in the WDW Block to record the size of the window. A suggested procedure would be to zoom in near the insertion point and create an attribute definition with a tag that reads WDW-SIZE, as shown in Figure 9–23.

If, during the insertion of the WDW Block, you respond to the prompt for the SIZE attribute with 2054 for a 2'-0" wide × 5'-4" high window, the resulting block object would be as shown in Figure 9–24, with the normally invisible attribute value shown here for illustration purposes. Figure 9–25 shows the result of the attribute being inserted with unequal scale factors.

Even though the value displayed is distorted, the string is not affected when extracted to a data base file for a bill of materials.

To solve the distortion and rotation problem, if you wish to have an attribute displayed for rotational purposes, you can create a block that contains attributes only, or only one attribute. Then it can be inserted at the desired location and rotated for readability to produce the results shown in Figure 9–26.

Attribute definitions would be created as shown in Figure 9–26 and inserted as shown in Figure 9–27.

The insertion points selected would correspond to the midpoint of the outside line that would result from the insertion of the WDW block. The SIZE attributes could be defined into blocks called WDWSIZE and inserted separately with each WDW block, therefore providing both annotation and data extraction.

> **NOTE:** The main caution in having an Attribute Block separate from the symbol (WDW) Block is in editing. Erasing, copying, and moving the symbol Block without the Attribute Block could mean that the data extraction would result in the wrong quantity.

There is another solution to the problem of a visible attribute not being located or rotated properly in the inserted block. If the attribute is not constant, you can edit it independently after the block has been inserted with the ATTEDIT command. It permits changing an attribute's height, position, angle, value, and other properties. The ATTEDIT command is covered in detail later in this

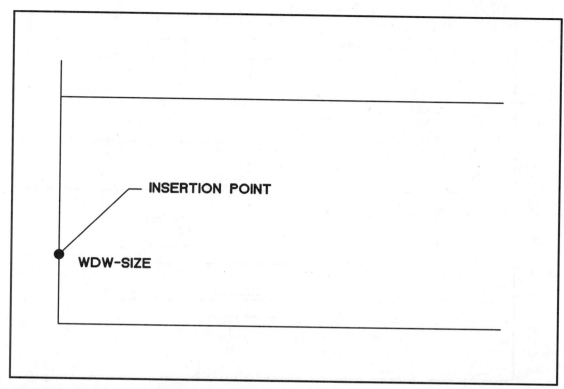

Figure 9–23   Create the attribute definition before defining the block

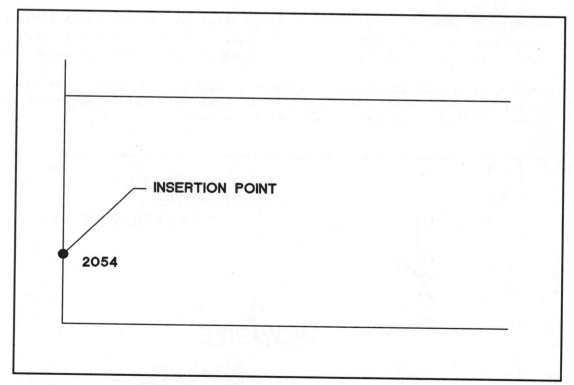

Figure 9–24   The attribute value (2054) visible with the block

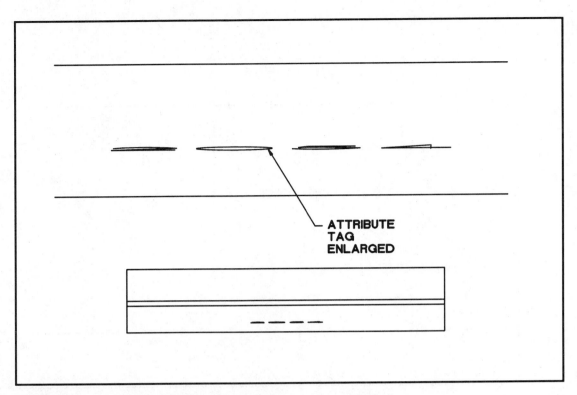

Figure 9–25 The attribute in a block with exaggerated, unequal scale factors

chapter, but it should be noted here that the height editing option applies to the X and Y scales of the text. Therefore, for text in the definition of a block that was inserted with unequal X and Y scale factors, you will not be able to edit its proportions back to equal X and Y scale factors.

Creating an attribute definition is accomplished by using the DDATTDEF command or ATTDEF command. As with the block, defining an attribute must take into consideration the conditions under which the block (to which it is attached) will be inserted.

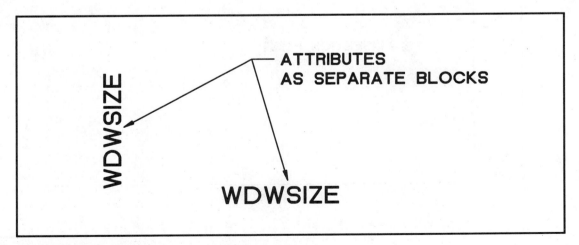

Figure 9–26 Attributes created as separate blocks

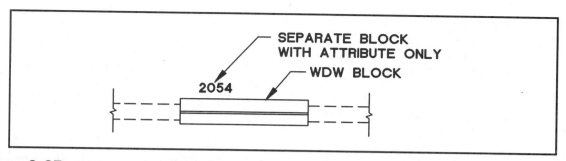

Figure 9–27 Attribute inserted separately from the window block

DDATTDEF Command

The DDATTDEF command is invoked from the Attribute toolbar (see Figure 9–28), or at the "Command:" prompt type DDATTDEF and press [Enter] or spacebar. AutoCAD displays the Attribute Definition dialog box similar to the one shown in Figure 9–29.

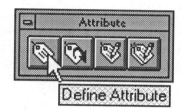

Figure 9–28 Invoke the DDATTDEF Command from the Attribute toolbar

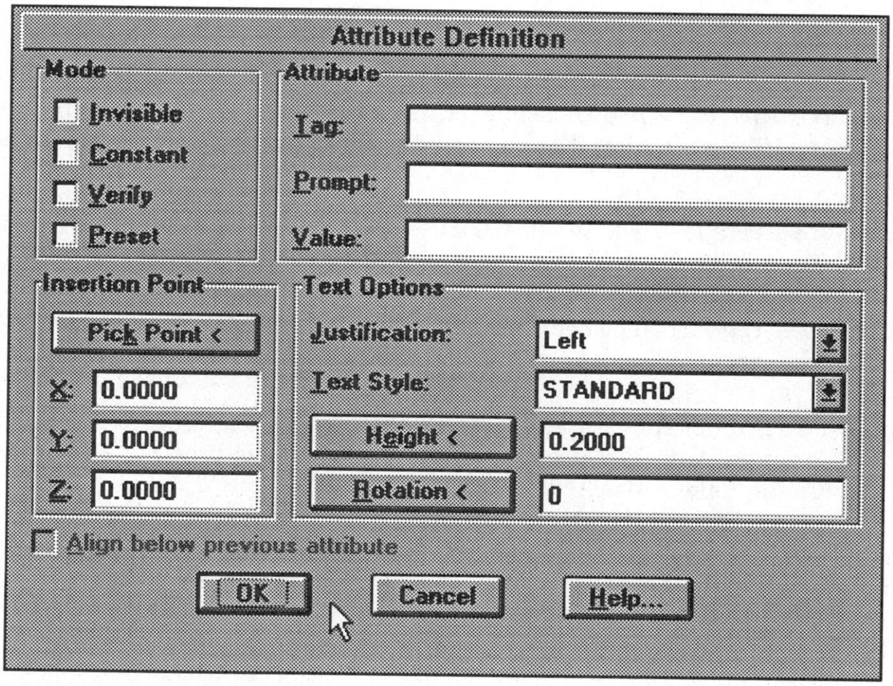

Figure 9–29 Attribute Definition dialog box

Toggle one or more of the available Modes.

Invisible — Setting the Invisible mode to ON causes the attribute value to NOT be displayed when the block insertion is completed. Even if visible, the value will not appear until the insertion is completed. Attributes needed only for data extraction should be invisible to quicken regeneration and keep from cluttering your drawing. You can use the ATTDISP command to override the Invisible mode setting. The Invisible mode being Y does not affect the visibility of the tag in the attribute definition.

Constant — If the Constant mode is set to ON, you must enter the value of the attribute while defining it. That value will be used for that attribute every time the block to which it is attached is inserted. There will be no prompt for the value during insertion and you cannot change the value. You can duplicate an attribute definition, using the COPY command and use it for more than one block. Or you can explode a block and retain one or more of its attribute definitions for use in subsequent blocks.

Verify — If the Verify mode is set to ON, you will be able to verify its value when the block is inserted. For example, if a block with three (nonconstant value) attributes is inserted, once you have completed all prompt/value sequences that have displayed the original defaults, you will be prompted again with the latest values as new defaults, giving a second chance to be sure the values are correct before the INSERT command is completed. Even if you press Enter to accept an original default value, it appears as the second chance default also. If you, however, make a change during the verify sequence, you will not get a third chance, that is, a second verify sequence.

Preset — If the Preset mode is set to ON, the attribute automatically takes the value of the default that was specified at the time of defining the attribute. During a normal insertion of the block, you will not be prompted for the value. You must be careful to specify a default during the ATTDEF command or the attribute value will be blank. A block consisting of only attributes whose defaults were blank and Preset modes were set to ON could be inserted, but would not display anything and cannot be purged from the drawing. The only adverse effect would be that of adding to the space taken in memory. One way to get rid of a nondisplayable block like this is to use a visible entity to create a block with the same name, thereby redefining it to something that can be edited; i.e., erased and subsequently purged.

The Attribute area allows you to set Attribute data. Enter the Attribute's Tag, Prompt, and default Value in the edit boxes.

The Attribute's Tag identifies each occurrence of an attribute in the drawing. The tag can contain any characters except spaces. AutoCAD changes lowercase letters to uppercase.

The Attribute's Prompt appears when you insert a block containing attribute defintion. If you do not specify the prompt, AutoCAD uses the attribute tag as the prompt. If you turn on the Constant mode, the Prompt field is disabled.

The default Value specifies the default attribute value. This is optional, except if you turn on the Constant mode, where the default value needs to be specified.

The Insertion Point area allows you to select a coordinate location for the attribute in the drawing, either by choosing Pick Point to specify the location on the screen or entering coordinates in the edit boxes provided.

The Text Options area allows you to set the Justification, Text Style, Height, and Rotation of the attribute text.

The Align below previous attribute toggle button allows you to place the attribute tag directly below the previously defined attribute. If you haven't previously defined an attribute definition, this option is unavailable.

Click the OK button to define the attribute definition.

After you close the Attribute Definition dialog box, the attribute tag appears in the drawing. Repeat the procedure to define additional attribute definitions.

ATTDEF Command

The ATTDEF command is invoked by typing ATTDEF at the "Command:" prompt and pressing [Enter] or spacebar.

Command: **attdef**
Attribute modes — Invisible:N Verify:N Preset:N
Enter (ICVP) to change, RETURN when done:

The setting of each mode is changed by entering its initial. For example, the Inivisble mode can be changed from "N" to "Y" by entering I. Only one mode can be changed at a time. Once the modes are in the desired status, press [Enter] and the following prompts appears.

Attribute tag: *(enter the tag name)*

If you give a null response, you will get the message:

"Tag cannot be null."

The Attribute tag prompt reappears. The tag can contain any characters except spaces. AutoCAD prompts:

Attribute prompt: *(Enter prompt)*

This option is available if the Constant mode is set to N (no). If you respond by pressing [Enter], the prompt will be the same as the tag.

Default Attribute value: *(enter value or null response)*

The above prompt appears unless the constant mode is set to Y (yes), in which case the prompt will be:

Attribute value: *(enter value)*

In the case above (constant mode set to Y) you will not be prompted for a value during block insertion.

For any value entry (from a default value entry) you can force one or more leading spaces by beginning the string with a backslash (\). A leading backslash (\) can be forced by beginning with two backslashes (\\).

After the above ATTDEF prompts have been answered, you will be prompted to place the tag in the same manner as you would for placing text, except AutoCAD will use the tag in place of the text

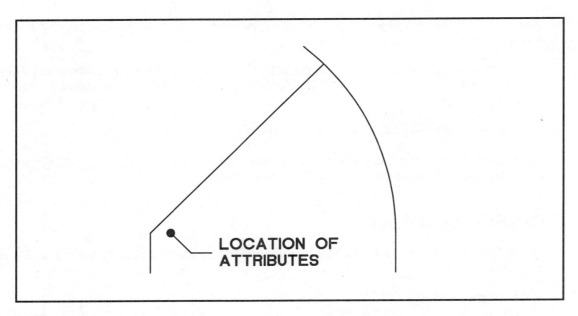

Figure 9–30 Predrawn door with attributes

string. Subsequent attributes can be placed in a manner similar to placing lines of text, using the insertion point and line spacing as left justified, centered, aligned, or right justified lines of text. Simply press [Enter] to invoke a repeating attribute definition.

A predrawn 2'-0"-wide door is made into a block with attributes, as shown in Figure 9–30.

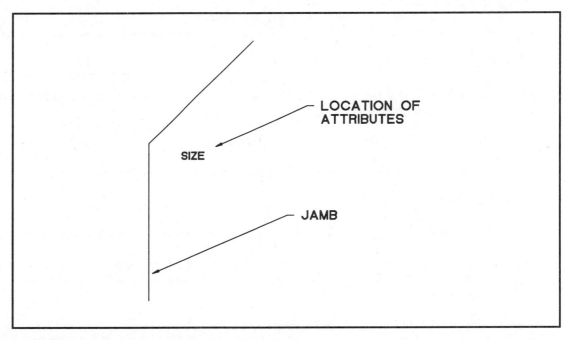

Figure 9–31 Predrawn jamb block with attributes

> **NOTE:** In this example the block is drawn to true size with jambs so it can be inserted with X and Y scale factors equal to 1 (one). But, the attributes will all be invisible, because the door might be inserted at a rotation incompatible with acceptable text orientations. The attributes can also be very small, located at a point that will be easy to find if they must be made visible in order to read (Figure 9–31).

The Attributes are entered as follows (Figures 9–32 and 9–33):

Command: **attdef**
Attribute modes — Invisible:N Constant:N Verify:N Preset:N
Enter (ICVP) to change, RETURN when done: **i**
Attribute modes — Invisible:Y Constant:N Verify:N Preset:N
Enter (ICVP) to change, RETURN when done: **c**
Attribute modes — Invisible:Y Constant:Y Verify:N Preset:N
Enter (ICVP) to change, RETURN when done: [Enter]
Attribute tag: **size**
Attribute value: **26681.375** *for 2'-6" × 6'-8" × 1-3/8"*
Justify/Style/<start point>: *(select point)*
Height <default>: **1/16**
Rotation angle <default>: [Enter]

> **NOTE:** The values given for the various attributes can be written just as any string of text is written. You should note that these strings, when written to a data base handling file, might eventually need to be interpreted as numbers rather than characters. The difference is primarily of concern to the person who will use the data in a data base handling program. So, if you are not familiar with data types such as numeric, character, date, etc., you might wish to consult with someone (or study a book on data bases) if you are entering the values. For example, an architectural distance such as 12'-6 1/2" may need to be written in decimal feet (12.54) without the apostrophe or in decimal inches (150.5) without the inch mark if it is going to be used mathematically once extracted.

Command: [Enter]
Attribute modes — Invisible:Y Constant:Y Verify:N Preset:N
Enter (ICVP) to change, RETURN when done: **c**
Attribute modes — Invisible:Y Constant:N Verify:N Preset:N
Enter (ICVP) to change, RETURN when done: [Enter]
Attribute tag: **matl**
Attribute prompt: **material**
Attribute default value: **mahogany**
Justify/Style/<start point>: *(select point)*
Command: [Enter]

You can continue to define additional attributes in the same manner for the L.H./R.H. SWING, PAINT/VARNISH FINISH, Type of HINGE, Type of LOCKSET, etc. (see Figure 9–34).

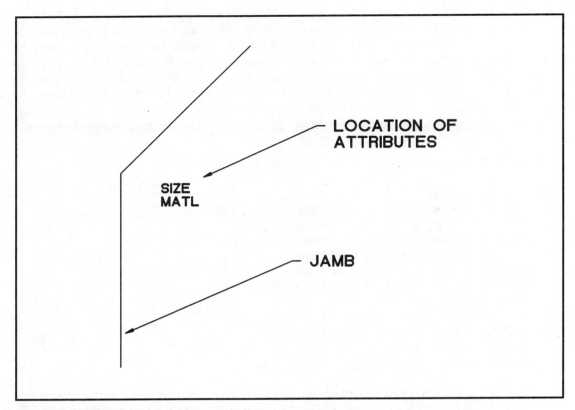

Figure 9–32 Predrawn jamb block with character attributes

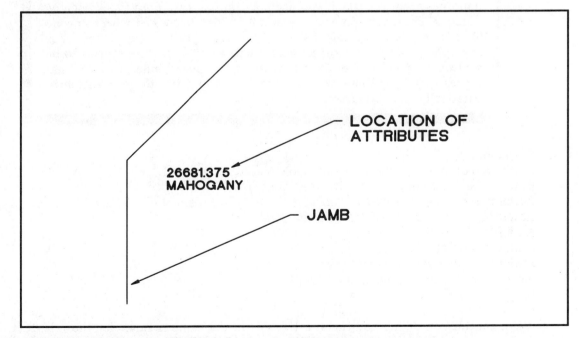

Figure 9–33 Predrawn jamb block with character/numeric attributes defined

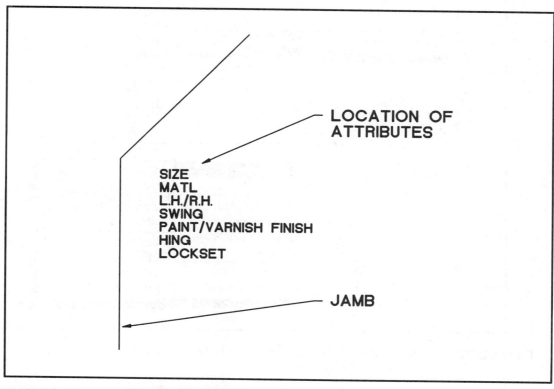

Figure 9–34 Predrawn jamb block with additional attributes defined

Inserting a Block with Attributes

Blocks with attributes may be inserted in the standard manner. If there are any nonconstant attributes you will be prompted to enter the value for each. You may set the system variable called ATTREQ to 0 (zero), thereby suppressing the prompts for attribute values. In this case the values will either be blank or be set to the default values if they exist. You can later use either the DDATTE or ATTEDIT command (described herein) to establish or change values.

You can set the system variable called ATTDIA to a nonzero value and have a dialogue box be displayed for attribute value input.

ATTDISP Command

The ATTDISP command controls the visibility of attributes. Attributes will normally be visible if the Invisible mode is set to N (normal) when they are defined. The ATTDISP command is invoked from the pull-down menu Options (see Figure 9–35), or at the "Command:" prompt type **ATTDEF** and press Enter or spacebar.

   Command: **attdisp**
   Normal/ON/OFF <current value>:

Responding ON makes all attributes visible, OFF makes all attributes invisible. The option Normal displays the attributes as you created them. The system variable called ATTMODE is affected by the ATTDISP setting. If REGENAUTO is ON, changing the ATTDISP setting causes drawing regeneration.

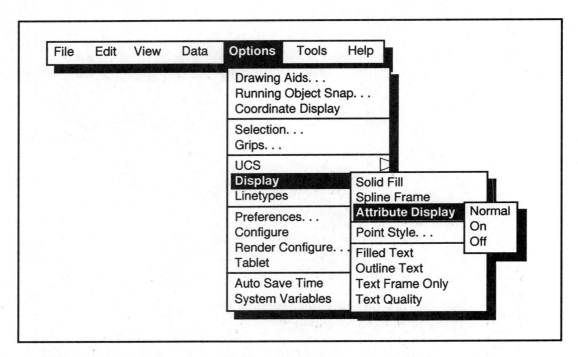

Figure 9–35 Invoke the ATTDISP Command from the pull-down menu Options

Editing Attributes

Unlike other objects in an inserted block, attributes can be edited independently of the block and other attributes. You can, however, edit groups of attributes collectively. This permits you to insert a block with generic attributes, that is, the default values can be used in anticipation of changing them to the desired values later. Or, you can copy an existing block that may need only one or two attribute changes to make it correct for its new location. And, of course, there is always the chance that either an error was made in entering the value or design changes necessitate subsequent changes.

Editing an attribute is accomplished by using the DDATTE command or ATTEDIT command.

DDATTE Command

The DDATTE command is invoked from the Attribute toolbar (see Figure 9–36), or at the "Command:" prompt type DDATTE and press Enter or spacebar.

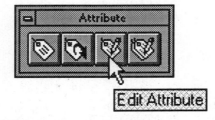

Figure 9–36 Invoke the DDATTE Command from Attribute toolbar

Command: **ddatte**
Select block: *(select the block)*

AutoCAD displays the Edit Attribute dialog box similar to the one shown in Figure 9–37. Selecting objects that are not blocks or blocks that contain no attributes will cause an error message to appear.

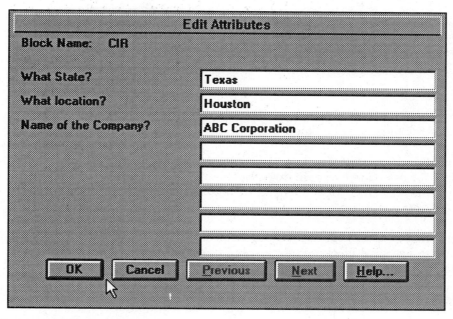

Figure 9–37 Edit Attributes dialog box

The dialog box lists all the attributes defined with values for the selected block. Using the pointing device, you can select values to be changed in the dialog box. Type in the new values and accept the changes by picking the OK button or pressing Enter. Selecting CANCEL button terminates the command, returning all values to their original state.

You can use the DDATTE command to look at the values of a selected attribute without making changes. Or, you can employ repeated editing or repeated inquiry looks at attribute values by modifying the DDATTE command with the MULTIPLE command as follows:

Command: **multiple ddatte**

To change attribute properties such as position, height, and style, use the ATTEDIT command.

ATTEDIT Command

The ATTEDIT command provides a variety of ways to specify attributes to be edited. It also allows various properties of the selected attributes to be edited. It should be noted that attributes with constant values cannot be edited in this manner.

The ATTEDIT command is invoked from the Attribute toolbar (Figure 9–38), or at the "Command:" prompt type **ATTEDIT** and press Enter or spacebar.

Blocks and Attributes

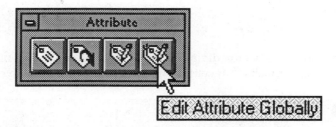

Figure 9–38 Invoke the ATTEDIT Command from Attribute toolbar

Command: **attedit**
Edit Attributes one at a time? <Y>:

Responding **Y** permits you to edit visible attributes individually. You can limit those attributes eligible for selection by specifying block name, tag, or value. In addition to an attribute's value, other properties that can be changed during this one-at-a-time mode include its position, height, and angle of rotation.

Responding **N** permits global (or mass) editing of attributes. Again, you can limit those eligible for editing to specified block name, tag, and value. However, this mode permits editing of attribute values only and no other properties.

After responding **Y** or **N** you will be prompted to specify eligible Attributes as follows:

Block name specification <*>:
Attribute tag specification <*>:
Attribute value specification <*>:

For any attribute to be eligible for editing, the block name, attribute tag, and attribute value must all match the name, tag, and value specified. Use of "*" or "?" wild card characters allows more than one string to match. Pressing Enter in response to the "Block name specification" prompt defaults to the asterisk, which makes all attributes eligible with regard to the block name restriction. Attributes still have to match tag and value responses in order to be eligible for editing.

Global Editing If you responded to the "Edit attributes one at a time? <Y>:" prompt with **N** (no), thereby choosing global editing, and set the block name, tag, and value limitations, the following prompts appear:

Global edit of Attribute values.
Edit only Attributes visible on screen? <Y>

An **N** reply switches AutoCAD to the text window with the following message:

Drawing must be regenerated afterwards.

When the editing for this command is completed (and if AUTOREGEN is ON) a drawing regeneration occurs.

If at the "Edit only Attributes visible on screen? <Y>" prompt, you respond **Y** (or default to **Y** by pressing Enter) you will be prompted as follows:

Select Attributes:

Attributes may now be selected either by picking on the screen or window, crossing, or last method. Eligible attributes are then highlighted and the following prompt appears:

> String to change:
> New string:

> **NOTE:** The changes you specify will affect a group of attributes all at one time. You should take care that unintended changes do not occur.

The responses to "String to change:" cause AutoCAD to search eligible selected attribute strings for matching strings. Each matching string will be changed to your response to "New string:." For example, blocks named WDW20, having tags named SIZE, and values of 2054 (for 2'-0" × 5'-4") can be changed to 2060 by the following sequence:

> String to change: **54**
> New string: **60**

If you did not limit the attributes by block name, tag, and value you might unintentionally change a window whose SIZE is 5440 (for 5'-4" × 4'-0") to 6040.

If you respond to "String to change:" by pressing ⏎Enter, it will cause any response to "New string:" to be placed ahead of all eligible attribute value strings. For example, if you specified only block name WDW20 with an attribute value of 2054 to be eligible for editing, you can make an addition to the value by the following sequence:

> String to change: ⏎Enter
> New string: **dbl hung**

The value 2054 will be changed to read DBL HUNG 2054. You should be sure to add a space behind the G if you do not want the result to be DBL HUNG2054.

Editing Attributes One at a Time If you responded to the "Edit attributes one at a time? <Y>" prompt by pressing ⏎Enter (defaulting to **Y**), and have specified the eligible attributes through the block name, tag, and value sequences, you will be prompted:

> Select Attributes:

You may select attributes by picking them on the screen, or the window, crossing, or last method. The eligible selected attributes with nonconstant values will be marked sequentially with an **X**. The next prompt is as follows:

> Value/Position/Height/Angle/Style/Layer/Color/Next <N>:

Angle is not an option for an attribute defined as fitted text, nor are angle and height options for aligned attributes. Entering any option's initial letter permits a change relative to that option followed by the repeated prompt for the list of options until you default to **N** for the next attribute.

The Value option, if chosen, will prompt you as follows:

> Change or Replace? <R>

Blocks and Attributes

Defaulting to **R** causes the following prompt:

New Attribute value:

Any string entered will become the new value. Even a null response will become a null (blank) value. Entering **C** at the "Change or Replace? <R>" prompt will cause the following prompt to appear:

String to change:
New string:

Responses to these prompts follow the same rules described in the previous section on global editing. In addition to the "Position/Height/Angle" options normally established during attribute definition, you can change those preset properties such as "Style/Layer/Color" with the ATTEDIT command.

ATTEXT Command

Extracting data from a drawing is one of the foremost innovations in CAD. Paper copies of drawings have long been used to communicate more than just how objects look. In addition to dimensions, drawings tell builders or fabricators what materials to use, quantities of objects to make, manufacturers' names and models of parts in an assembly, coordinate locations of objects in a general area, and what types of finishes to apply to surfaces. But, until computers came into the picture (or pictures came into the computer), extracting data from manual drawings involved making lists (usually by hand) while studying the drawing, often checking off the data with a marker. AutoCAD's Attribute feature and the ATTEXT command combine to allow complete, fast, and accurate extraction of (1) data consciously put in for the purpose of extraction, (2) data used during the drawing process, and (3) data that AutoCAD maintains about all objects (blocks in this case).

The CAD drawing in Figure 9–39 shows a piping control set. The seventeen valves and fittings are a fraction of those that might be on a large drawing. Each symbol is a block with attributes attached to it. Values that have been assigned to each attribute tag record the type (TEE, ELL, REDUCER, FLANGE, GATE VALVE, or CONTROL VALVE), size (3", 4", or 6"), rating (STD or 150#), weld (length of weld) and many other vital bits of specific data. Keeping track of hundreds of valves, fittings, and even cut lengths of pipe is a time-consuming task subject to omissions and errors if done manually, even if the drawing is plotted from CAD. Just as important as extracting data from the original drawing is the need to update a list of data when the drawing is changed. Few drawings, if any, remain unchanged. AutoCAD's Attribute feature makes the job fast, thorough, and accurate. An example of some of the blocks with attribute definition is shown in Figures 9–40 to 9–42.

Three examples of blocks as defined and inserted, each attribute having been given a value during the INSERT command. Remember, it is the value that will be extracted in accordance with how the template specifies the tags. Figure 9–43 shows the three blocks inserted with corresponding attribute values in a tabular form. By using the ATTEXT command, a complete listing of all valves and fittings in the drawing can be written to a file as shown in Table 9–1.

The headings above each column in Table 9–1 are for your information only. These will not be written to the extract file by the ATTEXT command. They signify the tags whose corresponding values will be extracted.

When operated on by a data base program, this file can be used to sort valves and fittings by type, size, or other value. The scope of this book is too limited to cover data base applications. But generating a file like Table 9–1 that a data base program can use is the important linkage between

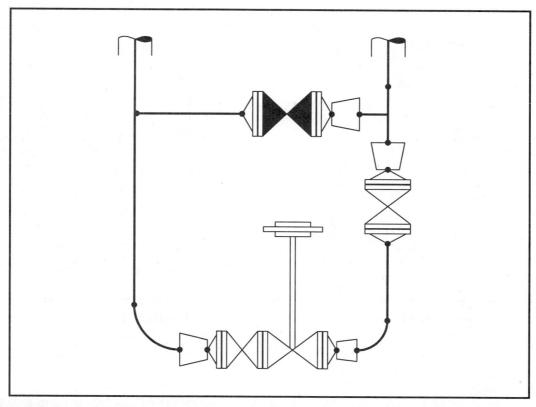

Figure 9–39 Piping control set

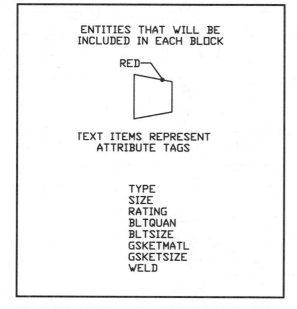

Figure 9–40 Reducer with attribute definition

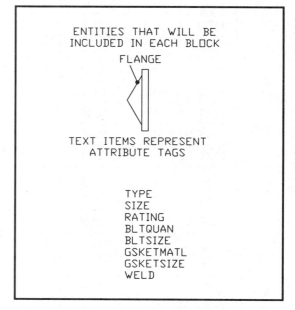

Figure 9–41 Flange with attribute definition

Blocks and Attributes

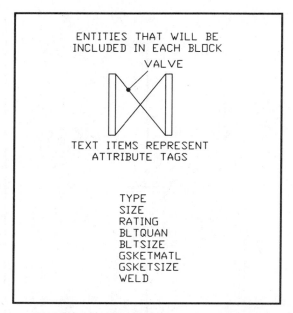

Figure 9–42 Valve with attribute definition

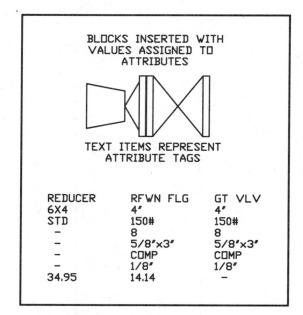

Figure 9–43 Inserted blocks with corresponding attribute values

Table 9–1   A List of Inventory as Specified by the ATTEXT Command and Tags

TYPE	SIZE	RATING	BLTQUAN	BLTSIZE	GSKETMATL	GSKETSIZE	WELD
TEE	6"	STD	¾	¾	¾	¾	62.44
ELL	6"	STD	¾	¾	¾	¾	41.63
ELL	4"	STD	¾	¾	¾	¾	14.14
RED	6X4	STD	¾	¾	¾	¾	34.95
RED	6X4	STD	¾	¾	¾	¾	34.95
RED	6X3	STD	¾	¾	¾	¾	31.81
RED	4X3	STD	¾	¾	¾	¾	25.13
FLG	4"	150#	8	5/8"X3"	COMP	1/8"	14.14
FLG	4"	150#	8	5/8"X3"	COMP	1/8"	14.14
FLG	4"	150#	8	5/8"X3"	COMP	1/8"	14.14
FLG	4"	150#	8	5/8"X3"	COMP	1/8"	14.14
FLG	3"	150#	4	5/8"X3"	COMP	1/8"	11.00
FLG	3"	150#	4	5/8"X3"	COMP	1/8"	11.00
GVL	4"	150#	16	5/8"X3"	COMP	1/8"	¾
GVL	4"	150#	16	5/8"X3"	COMP	1/8"	¾
GVL	3"	150#	8	5/8"X3"	COMP	1/8"	¾
CVL	3"	150#	8	5/8"X3"	COMP	1/8"	¾

computer drafting and computer management of data for inventory control, material takeoff, flow analysis, cost, maintenance and many other applications. The CAD drafter can apply the ATTEXT feature to perform this task.

Files Using the ATTEXT command involves concepts of computer applications other than CAD (although not necessarily more advanced). Some fundamental understanding of the computer's operating system is needed. The operating system is used to manipulate and store files.

Many different types of files or groups of files are involved in using the ATTEXT command.

1. EXE and DLL: AutoCAD program files are being used to perform the Attribute extraction.
2. DWG: The drawing file is a data file that contains the Blocks and their associated Attributes whose values are eligible for extraction.
3. TXT: A template file must be created to tell AutoCAD what type of data to extract.
4. A line editor or word processor is used to create the template file.
5. TXT or DXF: The extraction process creates a FILENAME.TXT file containing the data in accordance with the instructions received from the template file.
6. A set of data base program files usually can operate on the extracted file.

Data Base Extracted data can be manipulated by a data base application program. The telephone directory, a data base, is an alphabetical listing of names, each followed by a first name (or initial), an address, and a phone number. A listing of pipe, valves, and fittings in a piping system can be a data base if each item has essential data associated with it such as its size, flange rating, weight, material of manufacture, product that it handles, cost, location within the system, and many others.

The two elementary terms used in a data base are the record and the field. A record is like one listing in the phone book made up of a name and its associated first name, address, and phone number. The name Jones with its data is one record. Another Jones with a different first name (or initials) is another record. Another Jones with the same first name or initials at a different address is still another record. Each listing is a record. The types of data that may be in a record come under the heading of a field. Name is a field. All the names in the list come under the name field. Address is a field. Phone number is a field. And even though some names may have first names and some may not, first name is a field. It is possible to take the telephone directory that is listed alphabetically by name, feed it into a computer data base program, and generate the same list in numerical order by phone number. You can generate a partial list of all the Joneses sorted alphabetically by the first name. Or you can generate a list of everyone who lives on Elm Street. The primary purpose of the ATTEXT command is to generate the main list that includes all of the desired objects to which the data base program manipulations can be applied.

Creating A Template

The template is a file saved in ASCII format and lists the fields that specify the tags and determine which blocks will have their attribute data extracted. The template must be a file on an accessible path with the extension of .TXT. When you use a text editor or word processor in the ASCII mode, you must add this extension when you name the file.

Field Name The field name must correspond exactly to the attribute tag if you wish for that attribute's value to be extracted. If the attribute tag is called **type**, then there must be a field name in the template called **type**. A field name in the template called **ratings** will not cause a tag name called **rating** to have its values written to the extract file.

Character-numeric The template tells the ATTEXT command to classify the data written to a particular field either as numeric or as character type. Characters (a, b, c, A, #, ", etc.) are always character type, but numbers do not always have to be numeric type. Characters occupy less memory space in the computer. Sometimes numbers, like an address and phone number, are better stored as characters unless they are to be operated on by mathematical functions (addition, subtraction, etc.). The only relative significance of numbers as characters is their order (1 2 3 ....) for sorting purposes by the data base program. Characters (a b c ...) have that same significance. The template contains two elements for each field. The first is the field name. The second is the character-numeric element.

Numbers in strategic spaces in the character-numeric element of the template file specify the number of spaces to allow for the values to be written in the extract file. Others also specify how many decimal places to carry numeric values.

The format is as follows:

fieldname	Nwwwddd	for numeric values with decimal allowance
fieldname	Nwww000	for numeric values without decimal allowance
fieldname	Cwww000	for character values

Each line in the template is one field. The w's and d's are to be filled in with the necessary digits when the template file is created. The order of fields listed in the template does not have to coincide with the order that attribute tags appear in a block. Any group of fields, in any order is acceptable. The only requirement for a block to be eligible for extraction by the ATTEXT command is that there be at least one tag-field match.

A template for the example in Figure 9–42 would be written as follows:

TYPE	C008000
SIZE	C008000
RATING	C006000
BLTQUAN	N004000
BLTSIZE	C010000
GSKETMATL	C006000
GSKETSIZE	C006000
WELD	N006002

> **NOTE:** Word processors add coded characters (often hidden) to files unless specifically set up to write in the ASCII format. These coded characters are not acceptable in the template. Be sure that the text editor or word processor being used is in the proper mode. Also, do not use the [Tab] to line up the second column elements, but key in the necessary spaces, as the [Tab] involves coded characters.

From the extracted file in Table 9–1, a data base program can generate a sorted list whose items correspond to selected values. The procedure (again, to explain would take another book entirely) might list only 3"-flanges, or all 3"-fittings, or all reducers, or any combination of available records required corresponding to tag-field association.

BL:xxxxxx Nonattribute Fields Available If necessary, additional data is also automatically stored with each inserted block. The descriptions of each and the suggested format in a template file is shown below:

BL:LEVEL	Nwww000	(*Block nesting level*)
BL:NAME	Cwww000	(*Block name*)
BL:X	Nwwwddd	(*X coordinate of Block insertion point*)
BL:Y	Nwwwddd	(*Y coordinate*)
BL:Z	Nwwwddd	(*Z coordinate*)
BL:NUMBER	Nwww000	(*Block counter; same for all members of a MINSERT*)
BL:HANDLE	Cwww000	(*Block's handle; same for all members of a MINSERT*)
BL:LAYER	Cwww000	(*Block insertion layer name*)
BL:ORIENT	Nwwwddd	(*Block rotation angle*)
BL:XSCALE	Nwwwddd	(*X scale factor of Block*)
BL:YSCALE	Nwwwddd	(*Y scale factor*)
BL:ZSCALE	Nwwwddd	(*Z scale factor*)
BL:XEXTRUDE	Nwwwddd	(*X component of Block's extrusion direction*)
BL:YEXTRUDE	Nwwwddd	(*Y component*)
BL:ZEXTRUDE	Nwwwddd	(*Z component*)

The comments in the parentheses above are for your information and must not be included in the template file. The first column element is the name of the field, for example "BL:ORIENT." The second column element begins with a C or an N, denoting character or numeric data, respectively. The next three digits denote the width of the field, that is, how many spaces are to be allowed in the extract file for values to be written under this particular field. If the value to be written under this field for any record is too long for the width allowed, AutoCAD truncates the data written, proceeds with the extraction, and displays the following error message:

**Field overflow in record <record number>

The last three digits in the second column element of the field format denote the number of decimal places to which numeric values will be written. Character fields should have zeros in these three places. When fields are specified to be numeric, the attribute values must be numbers, or AutoCAD will display an error message.

You can use one of the two commands available to extract attributes. To extract attribute objects through the attributes extraction dialog box, use the DDATTEXT command. To extract objects at the "Command:" line, use the ATTEXT command.

At the "Command:" prompt type **DDATTEXT** and press Enter. AutoCAD displays the Attribute Extraction dialog box (see Figure 9–44). Select one of the three radio buttons for file format for the extracted Attribute data.

The Comma Delimited Format (CDF) generates a file containing no more than one record for each block reference in the drawing. The values written under the fields in the extract files are separated by commas, with the character fields enclosed in single quotes.

The Space Delimited Format (SDF) writes the values lined up in the widths allowed. It is possible for adjacent mixed fields (characters and numeric) not to have spaces between them. It may be necessary to add dummy fields to provide spaces in these cases.

The AutoCAD Drawing Interchange File format is called DXF. Unlike the DXFOUT command, extraction files generated by the ATTEXT command contain only block reference, attribute, and end-of-sequence objects.

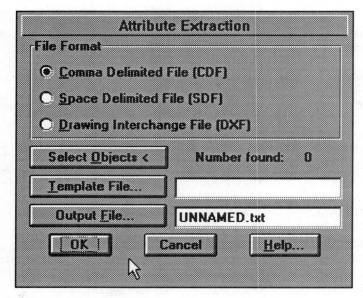

Figure 9–44 The Attribute Extraction dialog box

Specify the Template Filename in the **Template File. . .** edit box if you have selected either CDF or SDF file formats. AutoCAD appends .TXT file type. If you select the DXF file format, the **Template File. . .** button and edit box are disabled.

Specify the Output extract filename in the **Output File. . .** edit box. AutoCAD appends .TXT file type for CDF and SDF file formats and DXX files. DOS permits a filename of *con,* for writing to the screen, or a filename of *prn,* for writing to a printer. In this case, a printer must be connected and ready to print.

Click the **Select Objects<** button. The dialog box will disappear, and AutoCAD allows you to select the Attribute entities. After you have done so, the dialog box reappears, and the number of entities you selected is displayed after the **Number found:** *label.*

ATTEXT command is invoked by typing ATTEXT at the "Command:" and pressing Enter or spacebar.

Command: **attext**
CDF,SDF or DXF Attribute extract (or Entities)? <C>:

Select one of the three options CDF, SDF, or DXF. In addition, you can also select the Entities option that allows you to select the objects for extraction of their attributes. Once selection is complete, the prompt reverts to the CDF, SDF, or DXF prompt without the entities option. Then AutoCAD prompts for template filename and extract filename, respectively.

Duplications The example extract file listed some records whose values in every field were the same. This would serve no purpose in a telephone directory, but in a list of objects in a drawing, it is possible that the only difference between two objects is their location in the drawing. In a bill of materials, the purchasing agent is not concerned with where, but how many duplicate objects there are. If it were essential to distinguish every object, the BL:X, BL:Y, and BL:Z fields could be included in the template to identify each object. Multiple insertions of the same block in the same location could still be distinguished by their BL:HANDLE field if the handles system variable were ON, or by their BL:NUMBER if they were inserted with the MINSERT command.

Also, to the experienced pipe estimator (or astute novice) there are other duplications that are possible if not taken into account. Counting bolts and weld lengths for every fitting and valve could result in twice the quantities required. Mating flanges, each having 4 bolt holes, only require 4 bolts to assemble. An ell welded to a tee likewise requires the specified weld length only once. Therefore, Attribute value quantities associated with corresponding tags should take into account this and similar problems in mating assemblies.

Also, if the same fittings (in the form of blocks with attributes) are shown in more than one view in a drawing, some mechanism should be provided to prevent duplication of quantities in this case. As you can see, advanced features (attributes) that provide solutions to complex problems (data extraction) often require carefully planned implementation.

Changing Objects in a Block Without Losing Attribute Values Sometimes it might be desirable to make changes to the objects within blocks that have been inserted with attributes and have had values assigned to the attributes. Remember that the values of the attributes can be edited with the DDATTE command. But, in order to change the geometry of a block, it normally requires that you explode the block, make the necessary changes, and then redefine the block again. As long as the attribute definitions keep the same tags in the new definition, the redefined blocks that have already been inserted in the drawing will retain those attributes with the original definitions.

Another method of having a new block definition applied to existing blocks is to create a new drawing with the new block definition. This can be done by using the WBLOCK command to create a drawing that conforms to the old definition and then edit that drawing. Or you can start a new drawing with the name of the block that you wish to change.

In order to apply the new definition to the existing block, you can call up the drawing from the OPEN command, and then use the INSERT command with the Block Name: option. For example, if you wish to change the geometry of a block named Part_1, and the changes have been made and stored in a separate drawing with the same name (Part_1), the sequence of prompts is as follows:

```
Command: insert
Block name <default>: part_1=
Block "Part_1" redefined
Regenerating drawing.
Insertion point: Esc
Command:
```

It is not necessary to specify an insertion point or respond to scale factor and rotation angles. Simply inserting the block with the = (equals) behind the name will cause the definition of the drawing to become the new definition of the Block with the same name residing in the current drawing.

DIVIDE AND MEASURE COMMANDS

In this section two additional tools are explained — DIVIDE and MEASURE.

DIVIDE Command

The DIVIDE command causes AutoCAD to divide an object into equal length segments, placing markers at the dividing points. Objects eligible for application of the DIVIDE command are the line, arc, circle, and polyline. Selecting an object other than one of these will cause an error message to appear and you will be returned to the "Command:" prompt.

The sequence of prompts is as follows:

Command: **divide**
Select object to divide: *(select a line, arc, circle, or polyline)*
<Number of segments>/Block:

You may respond with an integer from 2 to 32767, causing points to be placed along the selected object at equal distances, but not actually separating the object. The object snap NODe can snap at the divided points. Logically, there will be one less point placed than the number entered, except in the case of a circle. The circle will have the first point placed at the angle from the center of the current snap rotation angle. A closed polyline will have the first point placed at the first point drawn in the polyline. The total length of the polyline will be divided in the number of segments entered without regard to the length of the individual segments that make up the polyline. An example of a closed polyline is shown in Figure 9–45.

> **NOTE:** It is advisable to set the system variables PDSIZE and PDMODE to values that will cause the points to be visible.

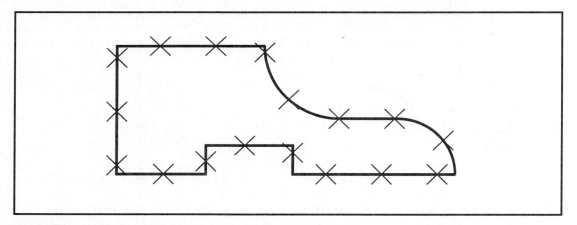

Figure 9–45 The DIVIDE Command as used with a closed polyline

The Block option allows a named block to be placed at the dividing points instead of a point. The sequence of prompts is as follows:

Command: **divide**
Select object to divide: *(select a line, arc, circle, or polyline)*
<Number of segments>/Block: **block** *(or just b)*
Block name to insert: *(enter the name of the block)*
Align block with object? <Y>
Number of segments:

If you respond with **No** or **N** to the "Align block with object?" prompt, all of the blocks inserted will have a zero angle of rotation. If you default to **Yes**, the angle of rotation of each inserted block will correspond to the direction of the linear part of the object at its point of insertion or to that of a line tangent to a circular part of an object at the point of insertion.

MEASURE Command

The MEASURE command causes AutoCAD to divide an object into specified length segments, placing markers at the measured points. Objects eligible for application of the MEASURE command are the line, arc, circle, and polyline. Selecting an object other than one of these will cause an error message to appear and you will be returned to the "Command:" prompt.

The sequence of prompts are as follows:

Command: **measure**
Select object to measure: *(select a line, arc, circle, or polyline)*
<Segment length>/Block:

If you reply with a distance, or show AutoCAD a distance by specifying two points, the object is measured into segments of the specified length, beginning with the closest endpoint from the selected point on the object. The Block option allows a named block to be placed at the measured point instead of a point.

PROJECT EXERCISE

In this project, you will apply AutoCAD concepts and skills discussed in chapter 9 to create the piping flowsheet as shown in Figure P9-1.

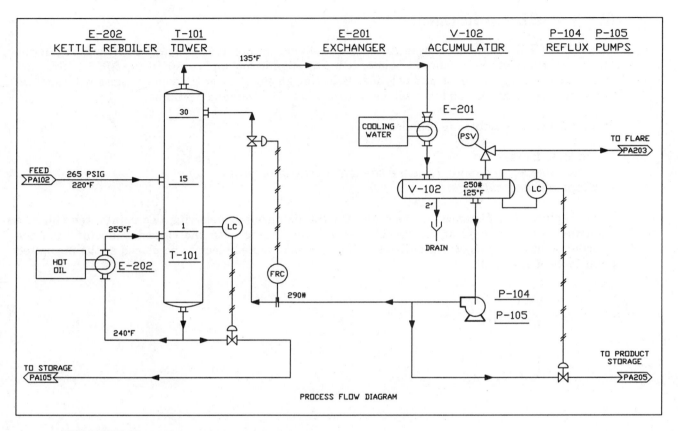

Figure P9–1 Completed project design

NOTE: The step-by-step instructions for this project are designed to provide practice in the concepts presented in chapter 9. It is not necessarily the most efficient way to draw the design.

STEP 1 Invoke the AutoCAD program from the Windows Program Manager.

STEP 2 Invoke the NEW command from the pull-down menu File or type New at the "Command:" prompt. Enter CH9-PROJ as the name of the drawing file. Make sure ACAD.DWG is selected as the prototype drawing.

STEP 3   Select the UNITS command from the pull-down menu Data to open the Units Control dialog box. Set units to decimal and degrees to decimal.

STEP 4   Invoke the LIMITS command and set the limits as shown.

> Command:**limits**
> on/off/<Lower left corner><default>: **0,0**
> Upper right corner<default>:**18,12**
> Command:**zoom**
> All/Center/Dynamic/Extents/Left/Previous/Vmax/Window/Scale(X/XP)>:**a**

STEP 5   Invoke the LAYER command from the pull-down menu Data, create layers named "border", "equipment", "blocks", "text", "pipeline" and "instruments" with appropriate colors and linetype as shown in the dialog box Figure P9–2. Set Layer "border" as the current layer.

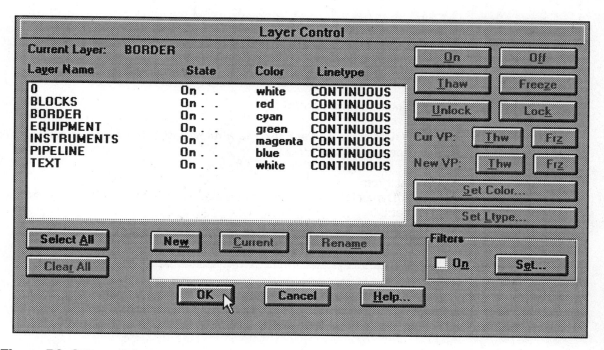

Figure P9–2 Layer dialog box

STEP 6   Invoke the RECTAGLE command from the Draw toolbar to draw the border (17" by 11") as shown in Figure P9–3.

> Command:**rectang**
> First corner:**.5,.5**
> other corner:**@17,11**

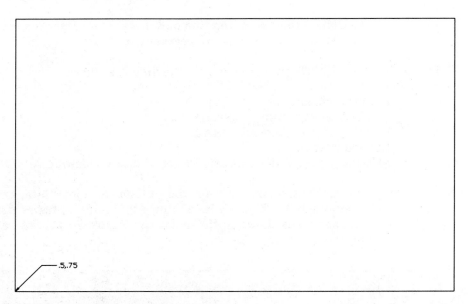

Figure P9–3 Border for piping flowsheet

STEP 7 Set Layer "blocks" as the current layer.

STEP 8 Invoke the ZOOM command and use the window option to zoom in on a small area of the display as shown in Figure P9–4.

> Command:**zoom**
> All/Center/Dynamic/Extents/Left/Previous/Vmax/Window/<Scale(X/XP)>:**window**
> First corner:**3,3**
> Other corner:**6,6**
> Command:

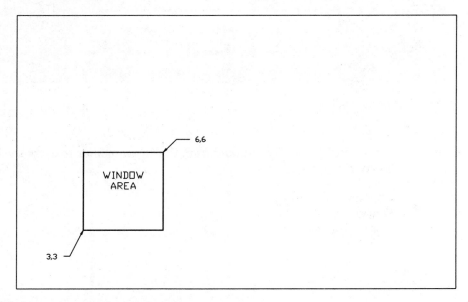

Figure P9-4 Zoom in a portion of the display

STEP 9   Open the Drawing Aids dialog box from the pull-down menu Options and set grid to 0.125, snap to 0.0625 and turn ON grid and snap.

STEP 10   Draw the gate valve as shown in Figure P9–5.

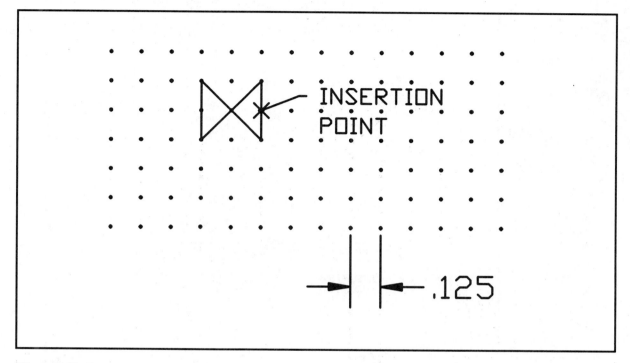

Figure P9–5   The gate valve

STEP 11   Invoke the BLOCK command from the Draw toolbar, as shown in Figure P9–6.

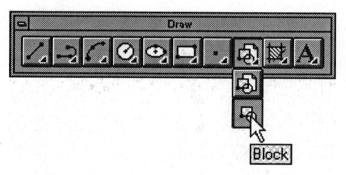

Figure P9–6   Invoke the BLOCK Command from the Draw toolbar

AutoCAD prompts:

Command:**block**
Block name (or ?):**gate** [Enter]
Insertion base point: *(select the insertion point as shown in Figure P9–5)*
Select objects: *(select all the objects that comprise the gate valve)*

STEP 12 Draw the remaining symbols required for the piping flow sheet on the appropriate layers as shown in the Figure P9–7.

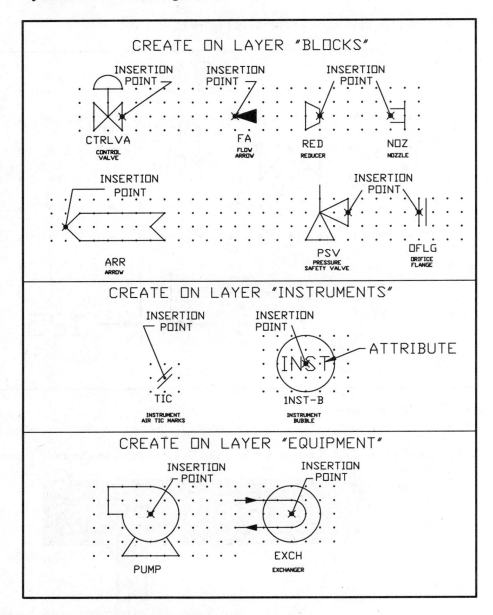

Figure P9–7 Required blocks for the piping flowsheet drawing

Create individual blocks for all the symbols by providing appropriate insertion points and block names (as shown in uppercase letters in Figure P9–7). If necessary, refer to Step 11 for the step-by-step procedure to create a block.

Before you create a block for Instrument Bubble, define an attribute.

Invoke the DDATTDEF command from the Attribute toolbar (Figure P9–8). AutoCAD displays the Attribute Definition dialog box. Set appropriate attributes and the required prompts as shown in Figure P9–9. Click **Pick Point <** button to place the attribute in the center of the instrument bubble as shown in Figure P9–7.

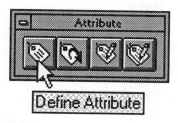

Figure P9–8 Invoke the DDATTDEF Command from the Attribute toolbar

Once you have defined the attribute, create the block for the instrument bubble. Make sure to include the attribute definition as part of the block when selecting objects.

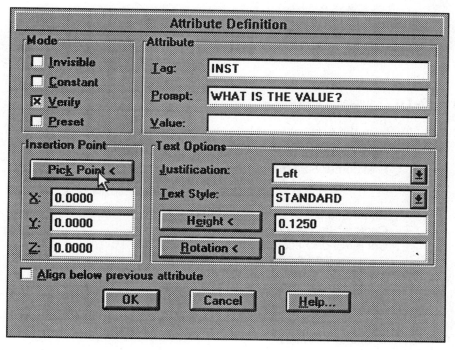

Figure P9–9 Attribute Definition dialog box

STEP 13 Invoke the ZOOM All command to display the entire drawing.

STEP 14 Open the Drawing Aids dialog box from the pull-down menu Options and set grid to 0.25, snap to 0.125 and turn ON grid and snap.

STEP 15 Set Layer "equipment" as the current layer.

STEP 16 Draw the vertical and horizontal vessels, and boxes for the exchangers as shown in Figure P9–10. Following are the prompt sequences to draw the vessels and boxes for the exchangers.

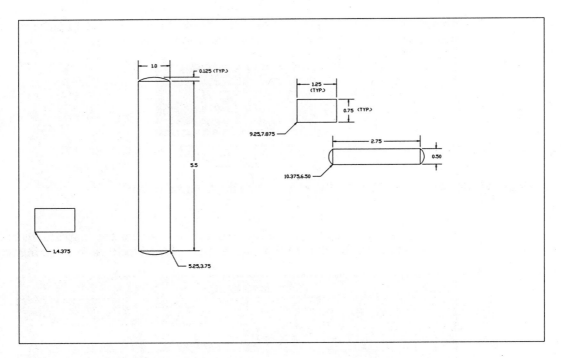

Figure P9–10 Equipment layout

To draw the vertical vessel:

Command:**rectang**
First corner:**5.25,3.75**
other corner:**@-1,5.5**

Command:**arc**
Center/<Start point>:**4.25,3.75**
Center/End/<Second point>:**4.75,3.625**
Endpoint:**5.25,3.75**

Command:**arc**
Center/<Start point>:**5.25,9.25**
Center/End/<Second point>:**4.75,9.375**
Endpoint:**4.25,9.25**

To draw the horizontial vessel:

Command:**rectang**
First corner:**10.375,6.5**
Other corner:**@2.75,0.50**

Command:**arc**
Center/<Start point>:**10.375,7**
Center/End/<Second point>:**10.25,6.75**
Endpoint:**10.375,6.5**

Command:**arc**
Center/<Start point>:**13.125,6.5**
Center/End/<Second point>:**13.25,6.75**

Endpoint:**13.125,7**
Command:

To draw the boxes for the exchangers

Command:**rectang**
First corner:**9.25,7.875**
Other corner:**@1.25,0.75**

Command:**rectang**
First corner:**1,4.375**
Other corner:**@1.25,0.75**
Command:

STEP 17   Insert the exchangers and pump as shown in Figure P9–11 by invoking the INSERT command from the Draw toolbar (Figure P9–12).

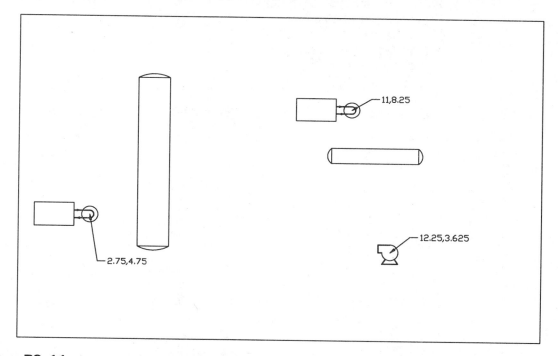

Figure P9–11   Layout with exchanges and pump

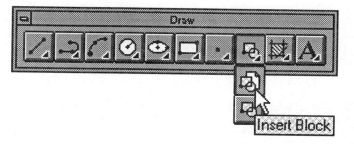

Figure P9–12   Invoke the INSERT Command from the Draw toolbar

Blocks and Attributes

AutoCAD prompts

Command:**insert**
Block name (or ?)<0>:**exch** [Enter]
Insertion point:**2.75,4.75**
X scale factor <1>/ Corner/XYZ: [Enter]
Y scale factor (default=X): [Enter]
Rotation angle <0>: [Enter]

Command:**insert**
Block name (or ?)<exch>: [Enter]
Insertion point:**11,8.25**
X scale factor <1>/ Corner/XYZ: [Enter]
Y scale factor (default=X): [Enter]
Rotation angle <0>: [Enter]

Command:**insert**
Block name (or ?)<exch>:**pump**
Insertion point:**12.25,3.625**
X scale factor <1>/ Corner/XYZ: [Enter]
Y scale factor (default=X): [Enter]
Rotation angle <0>: [Enter]

STEP 18   Similarly insert nozzles as shown in Figure P9–13 by invoking the INSERT command.

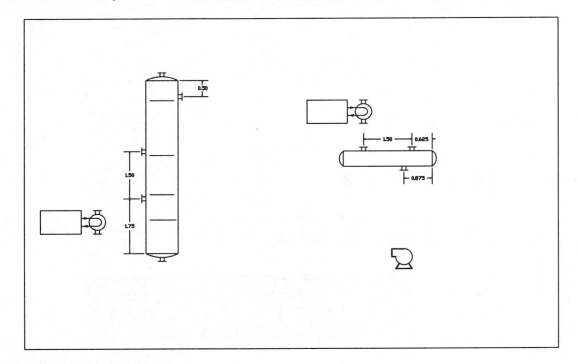

Figure P9–13   Layout with nozzles

STEP 19   Set Layer "pipeline" as the current layer.

STEP 20   Layout the pipelines as shown in Figure P9–14 by invoking the LINE command.

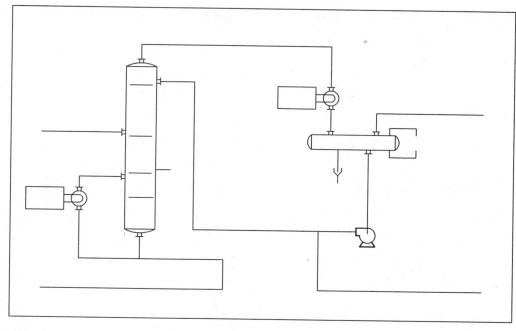

Figure P9–14   Layout with pipelines

STEP 21   Insert the flowsheet symbols at appropriate places as shown in Figure P9–15 by invoking the INSERT command. Make sure to provide appropriate attribute values while inserting the instrument bubble block. After inserting the blocks, use the BREAK command to break out the pipeline passing through the valve symbols.

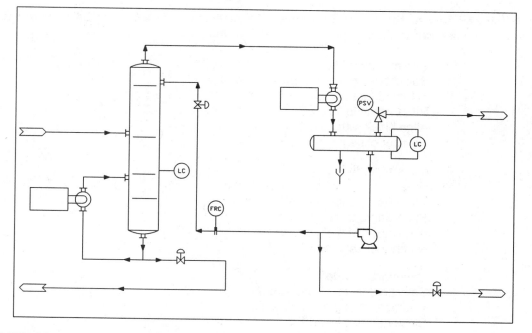

Figure P9–15   Layout with flowsheet symbols

STEP 22 Set Layer "instruments" as the current layer.

STEP 23 Invoke the PLINE command to draw line1, line2, and line3 instrument air lines as shown in Figure P9–16.

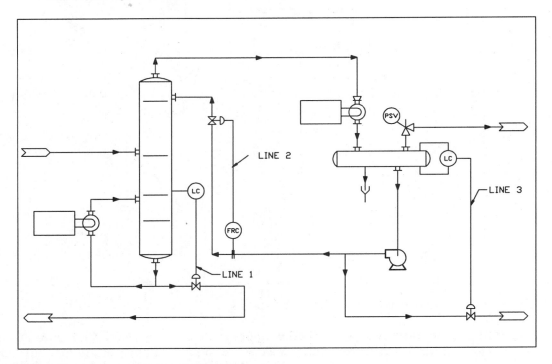

Figure P9–16 Layout with instrument air lines

STEP 24 Invoke the DIVIDE command to insert the block tic on the instrument air lines as shown in Figure P9–17. AutoCAD prompts:

Command:**divide**
Select object to divide:*(select line 1)*
<Number of segments>/Block:**b**
Block name to insert:**tic**
Align block with object? <Y> **n**
Number of segments:**5**

Command:**divide**
Select object to divide:*(select line 2)*
<Number of segments>/Block:**b**
Block name to insert:**tic**
Align block with object? <Y> **n**
Number of segments:**7**

Command:**divide**
Select object to divide:*(select line 3)*
<Number of segments>/Block:**b**
Block name to insert:**tic**
Align block with object? <Y> **n**
Number of segments:**8**

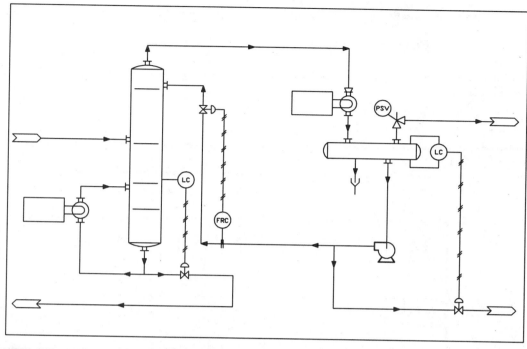

Figure P9–17   Layout with tic marks on the instrument air lines

STEP 25   Set Layer "text" as the current layer.

STEP 26   Invoke the DTEXT command to add the text as shown in Figure P9–18. The larger text height is set to 0.18 and the smaller text height is set to 0.125.

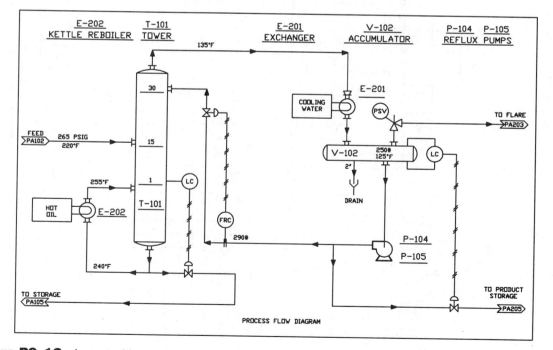

Figure P9–18   Layout with text

STEP 27 End the drawing by typing END at the "Command:" prompt and press [Enter] or spacebar.

Command:**end**

Congratulations. You just successfully applied several AutoCAD concepts in creating a simple schematic drawing.

EXERCISES

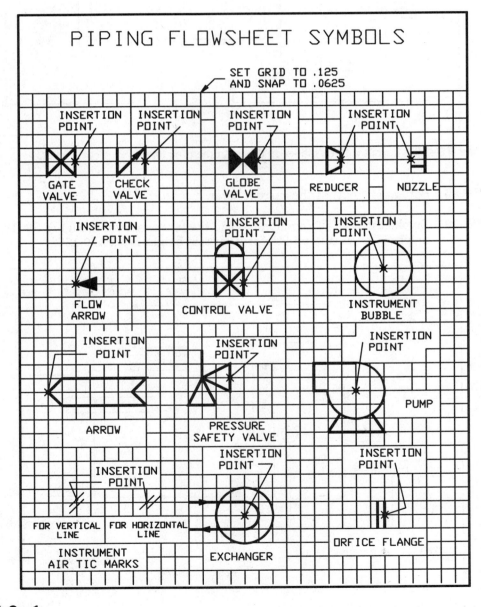

Figure Ex9a–1

Exercise 9–1

Create the drawing according to the settings given in the following table:

Settings	Value
1. Units	Decimal
2. LIMITS	
lower left corner	0, 0
upper right corner	12, 9
3. Grid Spacing	0.500
4. Snap Spacing	0.125
5. Text Size	0.18 Large
	0.125 Small

6. Layers		
Layer Name	Color	Linetype
Blocks	Red	Continuous
Border	Cyan	Continuous
Lines	Yellow	Continuous
Text	Green	Continuous
Equipment	Magenta	Continuous

Create all the required blocks by referring to Figure Ex9a-1. (Set the grid to 0.125 and snap to 0.0625 to draw the symbols.)

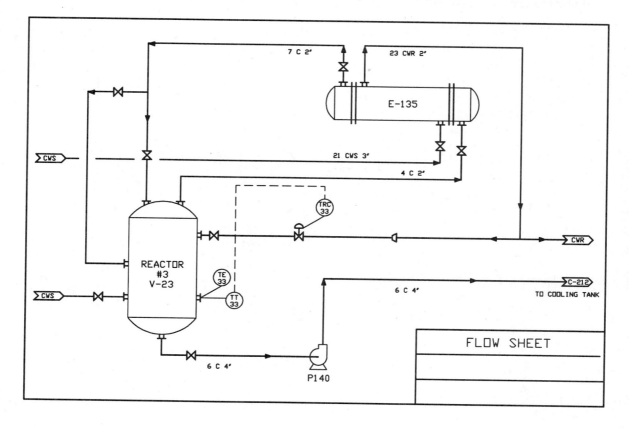

Exercise 9–2

Create the drawing according to the settings given in the following table. Create the instrument bubble block with an attribute tag.

Settings	Value
1. Units	Decimal
2. LIMITS	
lower left corner	0, 0
upper right corner	24, 18
3. Grid Spacing	0.500
4. Snap Spacing	0.125
5. Text Size	0.125

6. Layers

Layer Name	Color	Linetype
Blocks	Red	Continuous
Border	Cyan	Continuous
Lines	Yellow	Continuous
Text	Green	Continuous
Equipment	Magenta	Continuous

Create all the required blocks by referring to Figure Ex9a-1. (Set the grid to 0.125 and snap to 0.0625 to draw the symbols.)

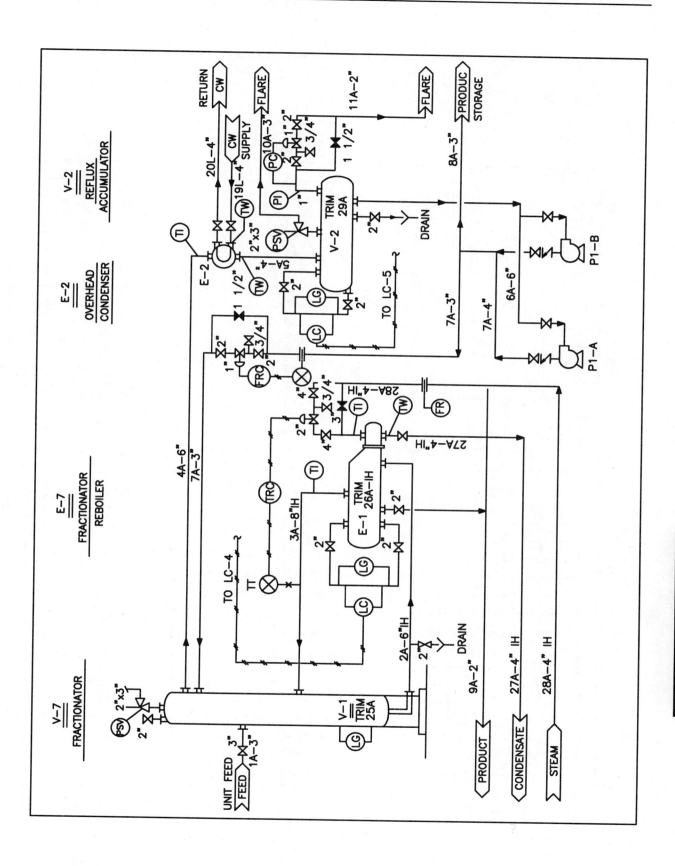

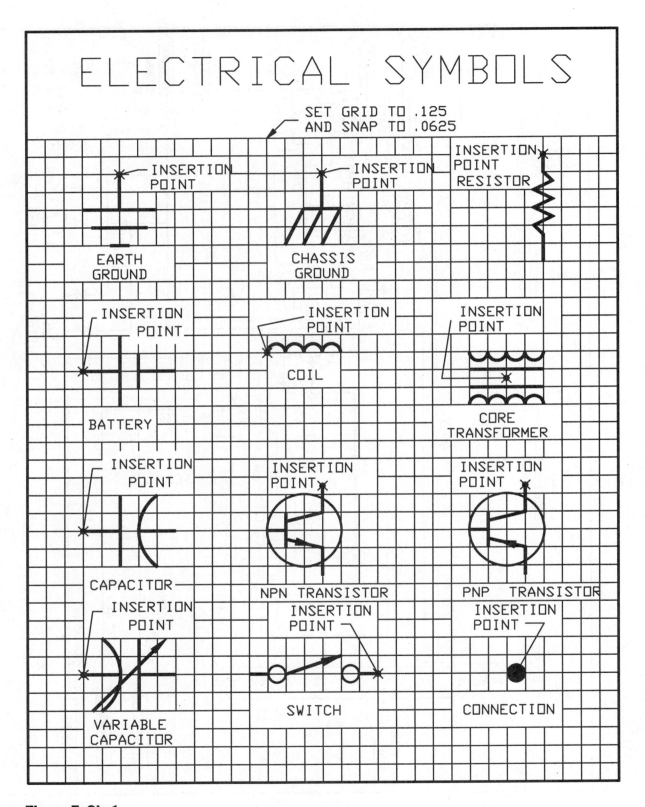

Figure Ex9b–1

Exercise 9–3

Create the drawing according to the settings given in the following table:

Settings	Value
1. Units	Decimal
2. LIMITS	
lower left corner	0, 0
upper right corner	12, 9
3. Grid Spacing	0.500
4. Snap Spacing	0.125
5. Text Size	0.125

6. Layers		
Layer Name	Color	Linetype
Blocks	Green	Continuous
Lines	Yellow	Continuous
Text	Cyan	Continuous
Border	Blue	Continuous

Create all the required blocks by referring to Figure Ex9b-1. (Set the grid to 0.125 and snap to 0.0625 to draw the symbols.)

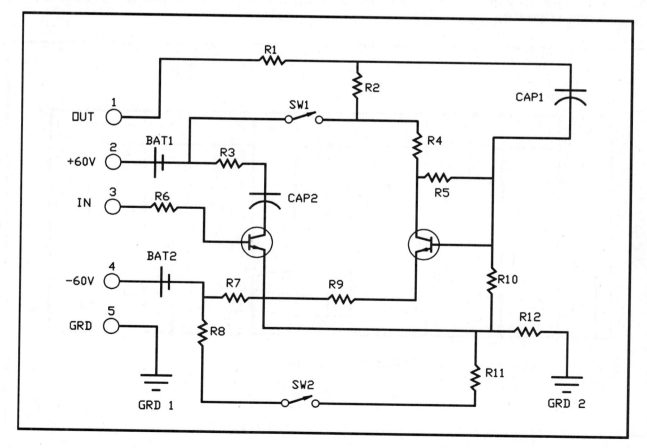

Blocks and Attributes

Exercise 9–4

Create the drawing according to the settings given in the following table. Create all the blocks used in this drawing with an attribute tag.

Settings	Value		
1. Units	Decimal		
2. LIMITS			
lower left corner	0,0		
upper right corner	12,9		
3. Grid Spacing	0.500		
4. Snap Spacing	0.125		
5. Text Size	0.125		
6. Layers			
Layer Name	Color	Linetype	
Blocks	Green	Continuous	
Lines	Yellow	Continuous	
Text	Cyan	Continuous	
Border	Blue	Continuous	

Create all the required blocks by referring to Figure Ex9b-1. (Set the grid to 0.125 and snap to 0.0625 to draw the symbols.)

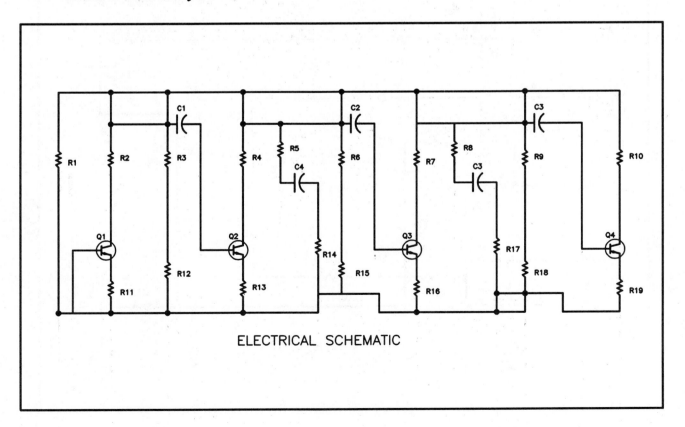

ELECTRICAL SCHEMATIC

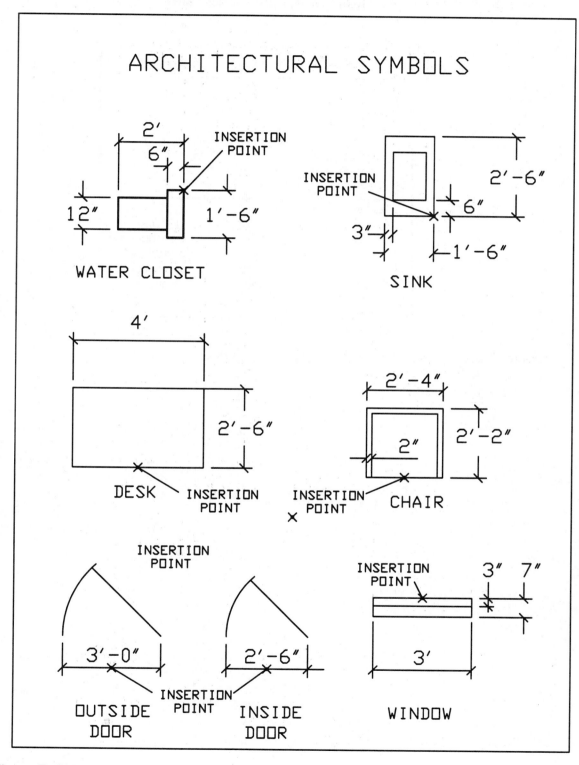

ARCHITECTURAL SYMBOLS

Figure Ex9c–1

Exercise 9–5

Create the drawing according to the settings given in the following table.

Settings	Value		
1. Units	Architectural		
2. LIMITS			
lower left corner	0, 0		
upper right corner	64', 48'		
3. Grid Spacing	1'-0"		
4. Snap Spacing	6"		
5. Text Size	6"		
6. Layers			
<u>Layer Name</u>	<u>Color</u>		<u>Linetype</u>
Border	Blue		Continuous
Floorplan	Cyan		Continuous
Blocks	Green		Continuous
Text	Red		Continuous
Dimension	Magenta		Continuous

Create all the required blocks by referring to Figure Ex9c-1.

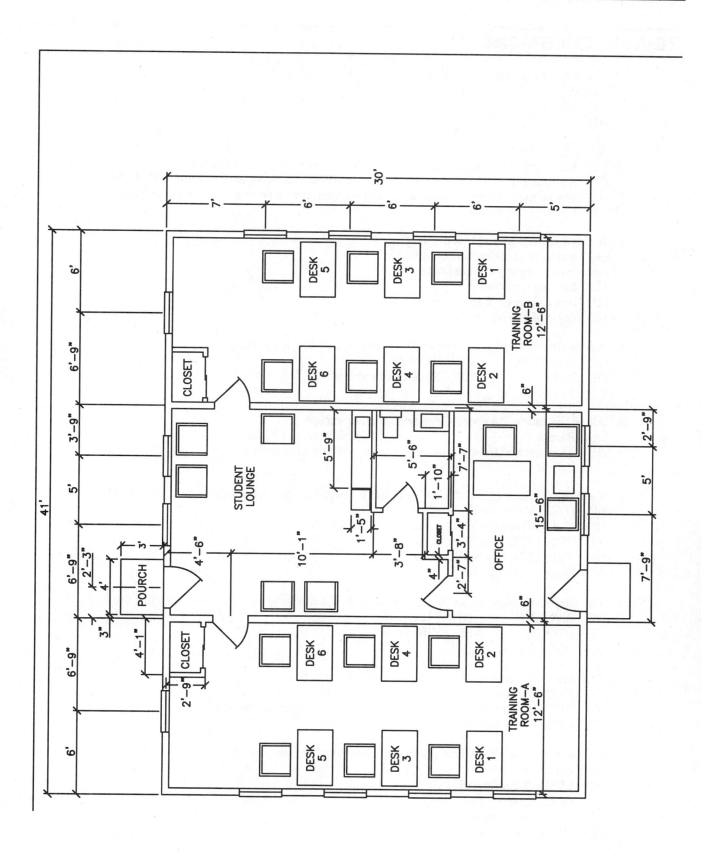

REVIEW QUESTIONS

1. The maximum number of characters for a block name is
    - (A) 8
    - (B) 16
    - (C) 23
    - (D) 31
    - (E) 43

2. A block is
    - (A) a rectangular-shaped figure available for insertion into a drawing
    - (B) a single element found in a block foundation of a building drawing with AutoCAD
    - (C) one or more objects stored as a single object for later retrieval and insertion
    - (D) None of the above

3. A block cannot be exploded if it
    - (A) consists of other blocks (nested)
    - (B) has a negative scale factor
    - (C) has been moved
    - (D) has different X and Y scale factors
    - (E) none of the above

4. A new drawing may be created from an existing block by using
    - (A) WBLOCK
    - (B) NEW
    - (C) BLOCK=
    - (D) SAVEAS
    - (E) None of the above

5. All of the following objects can be exploded except
    - (A) Blocks
    - (B) Associative Dimensions
    - (C) Polylines
    - (D) Minserted Blocks
    - (E) None of the above

6. To insert a block called "Table" and have the block converted into individual objects, type
    - (A) /TABLE for the block name
    - (B) *TABLE for the block name
    - (C) ?TABLE for the block name
    - (D) TABLE for the block name
    - (E) None of the above

7. The command used to write all or just part of a drawing out to a new drawing file is
    - (A) SAVEAS
    - (B) BLOCK
    - (C) DXFOUT
    - (D) FILE
    - (E) WBLOCK

8. To return a block back to its original objects, use the
    - (A) EXPLODE command
    - (B) BREAK command
    - (C) CHANGE command
    - (D) UNDO command
    - (E) STRETCH command

9. To identify a new insertion point for a drawing file, use the
    - (A) BASE command
    - (B) INSERT command
    - (C) BLOCK command
    - (D) WBLOCK command
    - (E) DEFINE command

10. MINSERT places multiple copies of an existing block similar to the command
    - (A) ARRAY
    - (B) MOVE
    - (C) COPY
    - (D) INSERT
    - (E) MIRROR

11. If one drawing is inserted into another drawing and editing operations are to be performed on the inserted drawing, the operator must first
    - (A) use the PEDIT command
    - (B) EXPLODE the inserted drawing
    - (C) UNDO the inserted drawing
    - (D) Select the edited objects with the "Crossing" option
    - (E) None of the above

12. The BASE command
    - (A) can be used to move a Block
    - (B) is a subcommand of PEDIT
    - (C) will accept 3D coordinates
    - (D) allows one to move a dimension baseline
    - (E) None of the above

13. Attributes are associated with
    - (A) objects
    - (B) blocks
    - (C) text
    - (D) layers

14. To merge two drawings, use the command
    - (A) INSERT
    - (B) BIND
    - (C) IGESIN
    - (D) BLOCK
    - (E) WBLOCK

15. The WBLOCK command can be used to create a new block for use
    - (A) in the current drawing
    - (B) in an existing drawing
    - (C) in any drawing
    - (D) only in a saved drawing
    - (E) None of the above

16. The DIVIDE command causes AutoCAD to
    - (A) divide an object into equal length segments
    - (B) divide an object into two equal parts
    - (C) break an object into two objects
    - (D) All of the above

17. One cannot explode
    - (A) polylines containing arcs
    - (B) blocks composed of polylines
    - (C) dimensions incorporating leaders
    - (D) hatch patterns with other than continuous linetypes
    - (E) blocks inserted with different X, Y, and Z scale factors

18. The DIVIDE command will
    (A) place points along a line, arc, polyline or circle
    (B) accept 1.5 as segment input
    (C) place markers on the selected object and break the object
    (D) divide any object into the equal number of segments
    (E) will prompt the operator for the desired PDMODE

19. When using the WBLOCK command to create a new block, one should respond to the block name prompt with
    (A) a block name   (D) a file name
    (B) an equal sign   (E) None of the above
    (C) an asterisk

20. The WBLOCK creates
    (A) a drawing file   (D) an object file
    (B) a collection of blocks (E) None of the above
    (C) a symbol library

21. The MEASURE command causes AutoCAD to divide an object
    (A) into specified length segments
    (B) into equal length segments
    (C) into two equal parts
    (D) All of the above

22. The command used to edit attributes is
    (A) DDATTE   (D) ATTFILE
    (B) EDIT   (E) None of the above
    (C) EDITATT

23. The WBLOCK command
    (A) means "Window Block" and allows for the use of a window to define a block
    (B) allows you to send a previously defined block to file, thus creating a drawing file of the block
    (C) is used in lieu of the INSERT command when the block is made up of only square blocks
    (D) None of the above

24. Attributes are defined as the
    (A) data base information displayed as a result of entering the LIST command
    (B) X and Y values which can be entered when inserting a block
    (C) coordinate information of each vertex found in a triangle created with AutoCAD only if the triangle is stored as a block
    (D) None of the above

25. The Attribute modes Invisible, Constant, and Verify can be toggled on and off by
    (A) typing Y for Yes and N for No
    (B) typing the first letter of each mode
    (C) pressing the function key [F5]
    (D) none of the above

10

EXTERNAL REFERENCES

INTRODUCTION

One of the most powerful time-saving features of AutoCAD is the ability to combine one drawing with another. AutoCAD lets you display or view the contents of as many as 32,000 other drawing files while working in your current drawing file. This feature is provided by the XREF command, short for external reference.

After completing this chapter, you will be able to:

- Attach and detach reference files
- Change the path for reference files
- Use the bind option for XREF command
- Reload the reference file
- Manage external references
- Use the XBIND command — adding dependent symbols to the current drawing

USING EXTERNAL REFERENCES

Prior to Release 11, existing AutoCAD drawings could be combined in only one way: by the INSERT command to insert one drawing into another. When one drawing is inserted into another, the inserted drawing becomes a part of the drawing it is inserted into. The data from the inserted drawing is merged with the data of the current drawing. Once the drawing is inserted, no link or association remains between the original drawing from which the inserted drawing came and the drawing it has been inserted into.

The INSERT command and the XREF command give users a choice of methods in combining existing drawing files. The external reference feature does not make Block insertion of drawings obsolete; users can decide which method is more appropriate for the current application.

When a drawing is externally referenced (instead of inserted as a block), the user can view and object snap to the referenced drawing from the current drawing, but each drawing's data is still stored and maintained in a separate drawing file. The only information in the reference drawing that becomes a permanent part of the current drawing is the name of the reference drawing and its

External References

directory path. If necessary, externally referenced files may be scaled, moved, copied, mirrored, or rotated by using the AutoCAD modify and construct commands. You can control the visibility, color, and linetype of the layers belonging to an external drawing file. This lets you control which portions of the external drawing file are displayed, and how. No matter how complex an external reference drawing may be, it is treated as a single object by AutoCAD. If you invoke the MOVE command and point to one line, for example, the entire object moves, not just the line you pointed to. You cannot explode the externally referenced drawing. All the manipulations performed on an external reference will not affect the original drawing file because an external reference is only an image, however scaled or rotated.

Borders are an excellent example of drawing files that are useful as external reference files. The objects that make up a border will use considerable space in a file, and commonly amount to around 20,000 bytes. If a border is drawn in each drawing file, this would waste a large amount of disk space when you multiply 20,000 bytes by 100 drawing files. If external reference files are used correctly, they can save 2 MB of disk space in this case.

Accuracy and efficient drawing time are other important design features that are enhanced through external reference files. When an addition or change is made to a drawing file that is being used as an external reference file, all the drawings that use the file will reflect the modifications. For example, if you alter the title block of a border, all the drawing files that use that border as an external reference file will automatically display the title block revisions. (Can you imagine accessing 100 drawing files to correct one small detail?) External reference files will save time, and ensure the drawing accuracy required to produce a professional product. Figure 10–1 shows a drawing that externally references four other drawings to illustrate the doorbell detail. In fact, the drawing of the house is referenced twice: one for the right half and a second time for the mirrored left half.

There is a limit of 32,000 external references you can add to a drawing. In practice, this represents an unlimited number. If necessary, you can nest them so that loading one external reference automatically causes another external reference to be loaded. When you attach a drawing file as an external reference file, it is permanently attached until it is detached or bound to the current drawing. When you load the drawing with external references, AutoCAD automatically reloads each external reference drawing file; thus, each external drawing file reflects the latest state of the referenced drawing file.

The XREF command, when combined with the networking capability of AutoCAD, gives the project manager powerful new features to cope with the realities of file management. The project manager instantaneously sees the work of the departments and designers working on aspects of the contract. If necessary, you can overlay a drawing where appropriate, track the progress, and maintain document integrity. At the same time, departments need not lose control over individual designs and details.

XREF'S DEPENDENT SYMBOLS

The symbols that are carried into a drawing by an xref are called "dependent symbols" because they depend on the external file, not the current drawing, for their characteristics. The symbols have arbitrary names and include blocks, layers, linetypes, text styles, and dimension styles.

When you attach an external reference drawing, AutoCAD automatically renames an xref's dependent symbols. AutoCAD forms a temporary name for each symbol by combining its original name with the name of the xref itself. The two names are separated by the vertical bar (I) character. Renaming the symbols prevents the xref's objects from taking on the characteristics of existing symbols in the drawing.

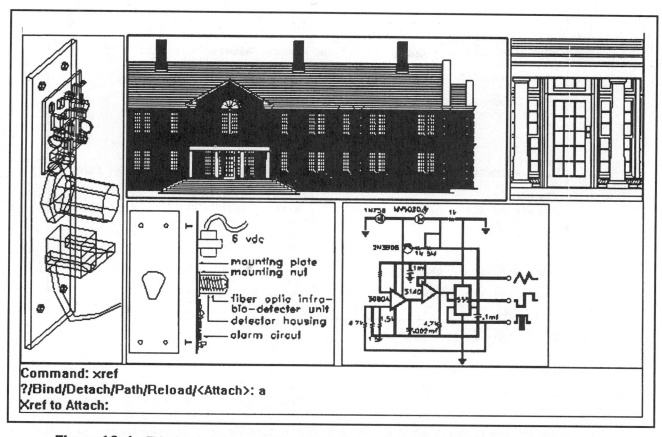

Figure 10–1 This drawing appears to be a single drawing but references four other drawings

For example, you created a drawing called PLAN1 with layers 0, First-fl, Dim, and Text and in addition to blocks Arrow and Monument. If you attach PLAN1 drawing as an external reference file, the layer First-fl will be renamed as PLAN1|First-fl, Dim as PLAN1|Dim, and Text as PLAN1|Text, as shown in Figure 10–2. Blocks Arrow and Monument will be renamed as PLAN1|Arrow and PLAN1|Monument. The only exceptions to renaming are unambiguous defaults like layer 0, and linetype continuous. The information on the layer 0 from the reference file will be placed on the layer 0 of the current drawing. It takes on the characteristics of the current drawing.

This prefixing is carried to nested xrefs. For example, if the external file PLAN1 included an xref named "Title" that has a layer Legend, it would get the symbol name PLAN1|Title|Legend if PLAN1 were attached to another drawing.

This automatic renaming of xref's dependent symbols has two benefits:

1. It allows you to see at a glance which named objects belong to which external reference file.
2. It allows dependent symbols to have the same name in both the current drawing and an external reference, and to coexist without any conflict.

The AutoCAD commands and dialog boxes for manipulating named objects do not let you select xref's dependent symbols. Usually, dialog boxes display these entries using grayed-out text.

External References

```
Command: layer
?/Make/Set/New/ON/OFF/Color/Ltype/Freeze/Thaw/LOck/Unlock: ?

Layer name(s) to list <*>:

     Layer name          State        Color          Linetype
  ─────────────────   ──────────   ─────────────   ──────────────
0                     On           7 (white)       CONTINUOUS
DIM                   On           3 (green)       CONTINUOUS
HIDDEN                On           5 (blue)        HIDDEN
OBJECT                On           7 (white)       CONTINUOUS
PLAN1|CENTER          On           5 (blue)        CONTINUOUS     Xdep: PLAN1

PLAN1|DIM             On           7 (white)       CONTINUOUS     Xdep: PLAN1
PLAN1|OBJECT          On           7 (white)       CONTINUOUS     Xdep: PLAN1
PLAN1|PLAN            On           1 (red)         CONTINUOUS     Xdep: PLAN1
PLAN1|TEXT            On           6 (magenta)     CONTINUOUS     Xdep: PLAN1
TEXT                  On           1 (red)         CONTINUOUS

Current layer: OBJECT

?/Make/Set/New/ON/OFF/Color/Ltype/Freeze/Thaw/LOck/Unlock:
```

Figure 10–2   Attaching an external reference file

For example, you cannot insert a block that belongs to an external reference drawing in your current drawing nor can you make a dependent layer the current layer and begin creating new objects.

You can control the visibility of the layers (ON/OFF, Freeze/Thaw) of an external reference drawing and, if necessary, you can change the color and linetype. When the system variable VISRETAIN is set to 0 (default) any changes you make to these settings, though, apply only to the current drawing session. They are discarded when you end the drawing. If VISRETAIN is set to 1, then the current drawing visibility, color, and linetype for xref dependent layers take precedence. They are saved with the drawing and are preserved during xref reload operations.

There may be times when you want to make your xref data a permanent part of your current drawing. To make an xref drawing a permanent part of the current drawing, use the Bind option of the XREF command. When you use the Bind option, all layers and other symbols, including the data, become part of the current drawing. This is similar to inserting a drawing with the INSERT command.

If necessary, you can make dependent symbols such as layers, linetypes, text styles, and dim styles part of the current drawing by using the XBIND command instead of binding the whole drawing. This allows you to work with the symbol just as if you had defined it in the current drawing.

XREF COMMAND

The XREF command has many options. The XREF command is invoked by typing **XREF** at the "Command:" prompt and pressing [Enter] or spacebar.

Command: **xref**
?/Bind/Detach/Path/Reload/Overlay/<Attach>:

Attach Option

This is the default option of the XREF command. Use it when you want to attach a new external reference file or to insert a copy of the xref file already attached to the current drawing file. When you select this option, AutoCAD displays the **Select file to attach** dialog box as shown in Figure 10–3. Select the appropriate drawing file to attach as a reference file from the dialog box.

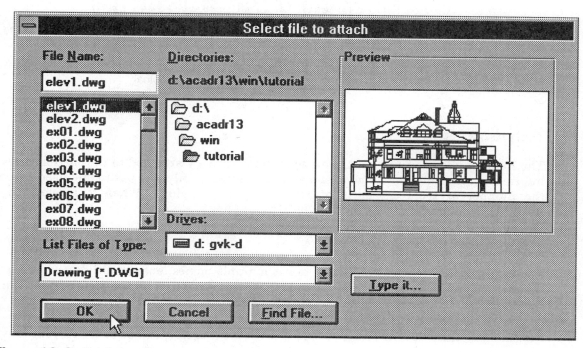

Figure 10–3 The Select file to attach dialog box

AutoCAD prompts for an insertion point, scale, and rotation angle, as described for the INSERT command, earlier in Chapter 9. Before AutoCAD prompts for the insertion point, it checks to see if a standard block of the same name already exists in the drawing, or if it is already been attached as an xref. If a block of the same name already exists, AutoCAD issues an error message and ends the command. If you specify an xref that has already been attached, AutoCAD alerts you to this fact and then prompts for insertion point.

For example, the following command sequence attaches a drawing PLAN1 as an external reference file to the current drawing ELECT-1:

Command: **xref**
?/Bind/Detach/Path/Reload/Overlay/<Attach>: [Enter]
(AutoCAD displays the Select file dialog box, select the PLAN1 drawing file to attach)
Attach Xref PLAN1: **plan1**
PLAN1 loaded.
Insertion point: **0,0**
    X scale factor <1> / Corner / XYZ: [Enter]
    Y scale factor <default=X>: [Enter]
    Rotation angle <0>: [Enter]
Command:

External References

You can also attach an external reference file by selecting the Attach option located in the External Reference toolbar, as shown in Figure 10–4.

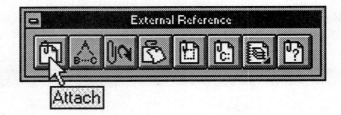

Figure 10–4 Invoke the Attach option from the External Reference toolbar

? Option

The ? option allows you to list the names of xrefs already attached to the current drawing. The information includes the name of the external reference file, the pathname used to load it, and the number of xrefs currently attached to your drawing. When you select this option, AutoCAD prompts:

Xref(s) to list <*>:

You can specify wild card characters to list multiple names, enter multiple names separated by commas, or press Enter in response to the prompt. AutoCAD lists all the xrefs currently attached to the drawing.

For example, the following command sequence lists the xrefs attached to the current drawing:

Command: **xref**
?/Bind/Detach/Path/Reload/Overlay/<Attach>: **?**
Xref(s) to list <*>: Enter

Xref Name	Path	xref typ
PLAN1	\dwg\proj1\plan1	Attach
TITLE	\dwg\title	Attach

Total Xref(s): 2

You can also list the names of external reference files attached to the current drawing by selecting the List option located in the External Reference toolbar, as shown in Figure 10–5.

Figure 10–5 Invoke the List option from the External Reference toolbar

Bind Option

The Bind option allows you to make your xref data a permanent part of the current drawing. This has the same effect as inserting the drawing. When you select this option, AutoCAD prompts:

Xref(s) to bind:

Enter a single xref name, list of names separated by comma, or any valid wild card characters for an xref(s) you want to bind.

When you bind an external reference, it becomes an ordinary block in your current drawing. You insert this block just like any other block. The Bind option also adds the dependent symbols to your drawing, letting you use them as you would any other named objects. In the process, AutoCAD renames the dependent symbols. The vertical bar (|) is replaced with three characters: $, a number, and another $. The number is assigned by AutoCAD to ensure that the named object will have a unique name.

For example, if you bind an xref named Plan1, which has a dependent layer Plan1|First-fl, AutoCAD will try to rename the layer to Plan1$0$First-fl. If there is already a layer by that name in the current drawing, then AutoCAD tries to rename the layer to Plan1$1$First-fl and so on, until there is no duplicate.

If you do not want to bind the entire xref, but only specific dependent symbols (a layer, linetype, block, dim style, or text style), then you can use the XBIND command, explained later in this chapter.

You can also bind external reference files attached to the current drawing by selecting the Bind option located in the External Reference toolbar, as shown in Figure 10–6.

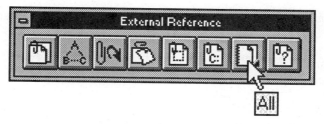

Figure 10–6 Invoke the Bind option from the External Reference toolbar

Detach Option

The Detach option removes an xref from your drawing. If the xref is currently being displayed as part of the current drawing, it disappears when you detach it. When you select this option, AutoCAD prompts:

Xref(s) to detach:

Enter a single xref name, list of names separated by comma, or any valid wild card characters for an xref(s) you want to detach.

You can also detach an external reference file attached to the current drawing by selecting the Detach option located in the External Reference toolbar, as shown in Figure 10–7.

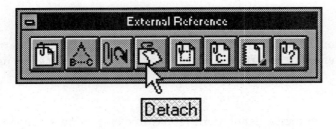

Figure 10–7 Invoke the Detach option from the External Reference toolbar

Path Option

The Path option allows you to change the path to the xref's source file. This is useful when the external drawing file has moved from its original location or been renamed since you first attached it. When you select this option, AutoCAD prompts:

    Edit path for which Xref(s):

Enter a single xref name, a list of names separated by comma, or any valid wild card characters for an xref(s) filename whose path you want to change.

After you enter a name, AutoCAD displays the current pathname of the xref file and prompts you for the new pathname. When you enter a new pathname, AutoCAD tries to locate the file; if it cannot find the file you specified, it discards the new filename and lets you try again. When you have finished changing the specified pathname, AutoCAD automatically reloads (updates) the specified file.

For example, the following command sequence shows steps in changing the path for an external reference file Plan1:

    Command: **xref**
    ?/Bind/Detach/Path/Reload/Overlay/<Attach>: **path**
    Edit path for which Xref(s): **plan1**
    old path: **C:\dwg\proj1\plan1**
    new path: **C:\dwg\proj2\plan1**
    Command:

You can also change the path for an external reference file attached to the current drawing by selecting the Path option located in the External Reference toolbar, as shown in Figure 10–8.

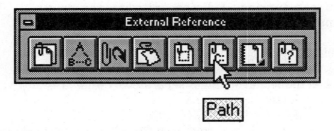

Figure 10–8 Invoke the Path option from the External Reference toolbar

Reload Option

The Reload option allows you to update one or more xrefs any time while the current drawing is in AutoCAD. When you select this option, AutoCAD prompts:

Xref(s) to reload:

Enter a single xref name, a list of names separated by comma, or any valid wild card characters for an xref(s) you want to reload.

When you load a drawing into AutoCAD, it automatically reloads any external references attached. The Reload option has been provided to reread the external drawing from the external drawing file whenever it is desirable to do so from within AutoCAD. The Reload option is helpful in a network environment to get the latest version of the reference drawing while you are in AutoCAD.

You can also reload an external reference file attached to the current drawing by selecting the Reload option located in the External Reference toolbar, as shown in Figure 10–9.

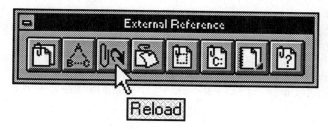

Figure 10–9 Invoke the Reload option from the External Reference toolbar

Overlay Option

The Overlay option allows you to attach a drawing in an overlay status. Unlike an attached xref, an overlaid xref is not included in a drawing when the drawing is itself is attached as an xref or overlaid xref to another drawing. For example, let's say PLAN-A drawing is attached as an overlaid xref to PLAN-B, then in turn PLAN-B drawing is attached as an xref to PLAN-C. You don't see PLAN-A because it is overlaid in PLAN-B, not attached as an xref. Overlaid xrefs are designed for data sharing. When you select this option, AutoCAD displays the **Select file to Overlay** dialog box. Select the appropriate drawing file to attach as an overlay from the dialog box. AutoCAD prompts for an insertion point, scale, and rotation angle, as described for the INSERT command, earlier in Chapter 9.

You can also overlay an external reference file to the current drawing by selecting the Overlay option located in the External Reference toolbar, as shown in Figure 10–10.

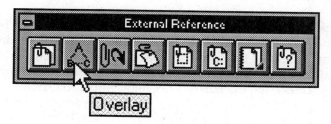

Figure 10–10 Invoke the Overlay option from the External Reference toolbar

External References

XREFCLIP COMMAND

The XREFCLIP command allows you to remove unwanted information from the xref being attached to the current drawing. The TILEMODE system variable must be set to zero to use the XREFCLIP command. If not, AutoCAD provides an option to switch the TILEMODE system variable from one to zero by enabling the paper space. Refer to Chapter 11 for detailed explanation regarding the TILEMODE system variable and paper space.

The XREFCLIP command is invoked from the External Reference toolbar (Figure 10–11) or by typing XREFCLIP at the "Command:" prompt and pressing [Enter] or spacebar. If the TILEMODE system variable is set to 1, then AutoCAD prompts:

Enable Paper Space <Y>: *(press [Enter] or spacebar)*
Xref name: *(specify the name of the drawing to attach as an xref)*
Clip onto what layer? *(enter a name of a nonexistent layer on which to place the clip of the xref)*
First corner of clip box: *(specify the first corner of the clip box)*
Other corner: *(specify the opposite corner of the clip box)*
Enter the ratio of paper space units to model space units...
Number of paper space units <1.0>: *(press [Enter] to accept the default or enter value for the scale factor)*
Number of model space units <1.0>: *(press [Enter] to accept the default or enter value for the scale factor)*
Insertion point for clip: *(specify the insertion point for the lower-left corner of the new viewport object).*

AutoCAD creates a viewport the size of the clip box. The viewport clips the xref, removing from view the portion of the xref outside the viewport.

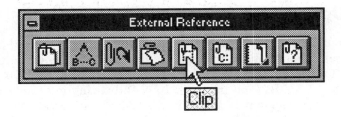

Figure 10–11 Invoke the Clip option from the External Reference toolbar

MANAGEMENT OF EXTERNAL REFERENCES

Several tools are available to help in the management and tracking of external references.

One of the tracking mechanisms is an external ASCII log file that is maintained on each drawing which contains external references. This file, which AutoCAD generates and maintains automatically, has the same name as the current drawing and a file extension .XLG. You can examine the file with any text editor and/or print it. The log file registers each Attach, Bind, Detach, and Reload of each external reference for the current drawing. AutoCAD writes a title block to the log file that contains the name of the current drawing, the date and time, and the operation being performed. Once a log file has been created for a drawing, AutoCAD continues to append to it. The log file is always placed in the same directory as the current drawing.

See Figure 10–12 for a partial listing of the log file entries generated when an external drawing file PLAN1 is attached to the current drawing, ELEC-fl. The log file is maintained only if the XRECTL system variable is set to 1. The default setting for XRECTL system variable is 0.

```
Loading FIG8-2 into Drawing Editor.
Resolving Xref(s).

Xref:  PLAN1 -- (existing)

Resolve Xref PLAN1: plan1

    Update Block symbol table:
    Block update complete.

    Update Ltype symbol table:
    Ltype update complete.

    Update Layer symbol table:
       Overwrite symbol:  PLAN1|FIRST-FL
       Overwrite symbol:  PLAN1|DIM
       Overwrite symbol:  PLAN1|TEXT
    Layer update complete.

    Update Style Symbol table:
       Appending symbol:  PLAN1|STANDARD
```

Figure 10–12   Log file entries generated when an external drawing file is attached to an existing drawing

External references are also reported in response to the ? option of the xref command and the BLOCK command. Because of the external reference feature, the contents of a drawing may now be stored in multiple drawing files. This means that new backup procedures are required to handle drawings linked in external reference partnerships. Three possible solutions are:

1. Make the external reference drawing a permanent part of the current drawing prior to archiving with the Bind option of the XREF command.

2. Modify the current drawing's path to the external reference drawing so that they are both stored in the same directory, then archive them together.

3. Archive the directory location of the external reference drawing with the drawing which references it. Tape backup machines do this automatically.

XBIND COMMAND — ADDING DEPENDENT SYMBOLS TO THE CURRENT DRAWING

The XBIND command lets you permanently add a selected subset of xref's dependent symbols to your current drawing. The dependent symbols include the block, layer, linetype, dim style, and text style. Once the dependent symbol is added to the current drawing, it behaves as if it were created in the current drawing and saved with the drawing when you ended the drawing session. While adding the dependent symbol to the current drawing, AutoCAD removes the vertical bar symbol (|) from each dependent symbol's name, replacing it with three new characters: a $, a number, and another $ symbol.

External References

For example, you might want to use a block that is defined in an external reference. Instead of binding the entire external reference with the Bind option of the XREF command, it is advisable to use the XBIND command. By using the XBIND command, the block and the layers associated with the block will be added to the current drawing. If the block's definition contains reference to an external reference, AutoCAD binds that xref and all its dependent symbols as well. After binding the necessary dependent symbols, you can detach the external reference file.

The XBIND command is invoked by typing **XBIND** at the "Command:" prompt and pressing [Enter] or spacebar.

    Command: **xbind**
    Block/Dimstyle/Layer/Ltype/Style:

Select the type of dependent symbol you want to bind. AutoCAD then prompts for the name(s) of the dependent symbols. Enter a single symbol name, list of names separated by comma, or any valid wild card characters for symbols you want to bind to the current drawing.

The following command sequence shows steps in binding the block arrow from an external reference file Plan1:

    Command: **xbind**
    Block/Dimstyle/Layer/Ltype/Style: **block**
    Dependent Block name(s): **plan1larrow**
    Scanning...
    1 Block(s) bound
    Command:

PROJECT EXERCISE

In this project, you apply AutoCAD concepts and skills discussed in chapter 10 to create the plot plan shown in Figure P10–1.

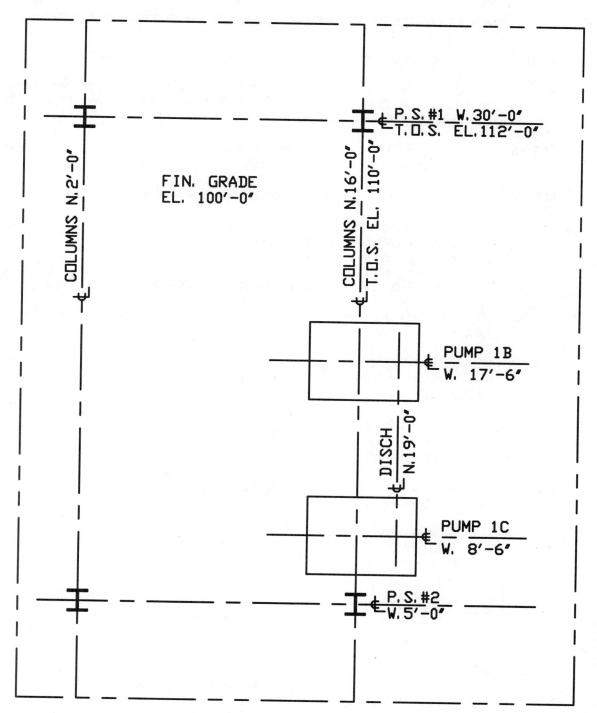

Figure P10–1 Completed project design

> **NOTE:** The step-by-step instructions for this project are designed to provide practice in the concepts presented in chapter 10. It is not necessarily the most efficient way to draw the design. Do not dimension, provided only for reference.

STEP 1   Invoke the AutoCAD program from the Windows Program Manager.

STEP 2   Invoke the NEW command from the pull-down menu File or type New at the "Command:" prompt. Enter "piperack" as the name of the drawing file. Make sure ACAD.DWG is selected as the prototype drawing.

STEP 3   Select the UNITS command from the pull-down menu Data to open the DDUNITS dialog box. Set up units to architectural.

STEP 4   Invoke the LIMITS command and set the limits as shown.

> Command:**limits**
> on/off/<Lower left corner><default>:**0',0'**
> Upper right corner<default>:**28',35'**
> Command:**zoom**
> All/Center/Dynamic/Extents/Left/Previous/Vmax/Window/Scale(X/XP)>:**a**

STEP 5   Open the Drawing Aids Dialog box from the pull-down menu Options and set grid to 1', snap to 6" and turn ON the grid and snap.

STEP 6   Invoke the LAYER command and create layers centerline, object and text with appropriate linetypes and colors. Set layer "centerline" as the current layer. Set the Ltscale factor to 32.

> Command:**ltscale**
> New scale factor <1.0000>:**32**
> Command:

STEP 7   Invoke the LINE command from the Draw toolbar and draw the centerlines as shown in Figure P10–2.

> Command:**line**
> From point:**2',0**
> To point:**@35'<90**
> To point:[Enter]
> Command:**line**
> From point:**0,5'**
> To point:**@23'<0**
> To point:[Enter]
> Command:

Invoke the OFFSET command from the Modify toolbar and offset the vertical line 14' to the right and offset the horizontal line 25' upward.

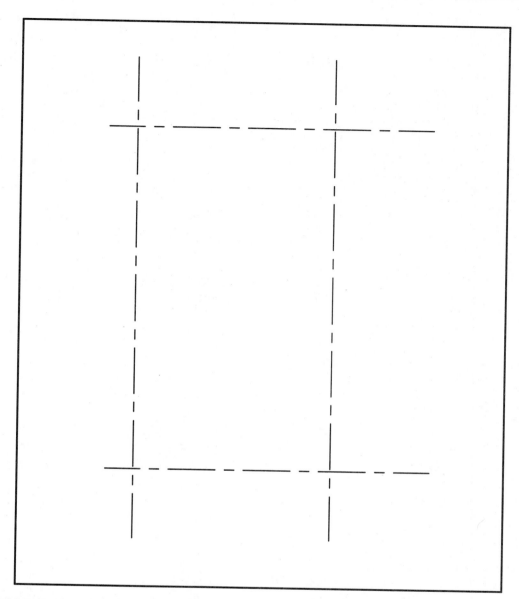

Figure P10–2 Centerlines

STEP 8 Set layer "object" as the current layer and use the PLINE command with the width set to 1" to draw the steel columns at the points shown in Figure P10–3. The steel columns are 12"x 12".

> NOTE: Draw one column then copy it to the other locations. Make sure grid and snap are turned on.

STEP 9 Set layer "text" as the current layer and invoke the DTEXT command to draw in the coordinate callouts as shown in Figure P10–4. Set text height to 4"; this will cause the text to be plotted out 0.125" high when plotted at 0.375" = 12".

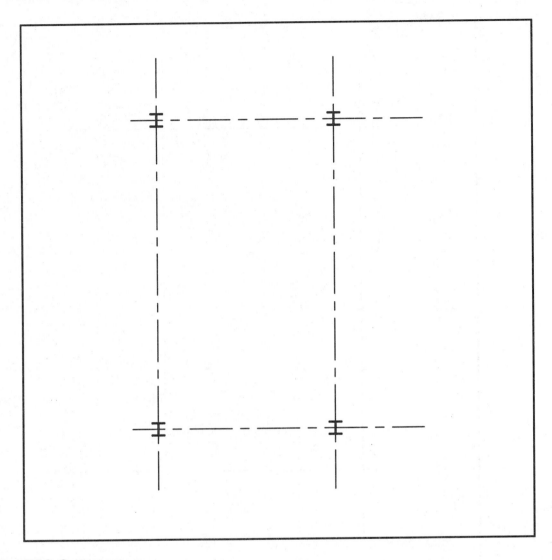

Figure P10–3 Steel columns

STEP 10 End the drawing.

STEP 11 Invoke the NEW command from the pull-down menu File or type New at the "Command:" prompt. Enter "pump" as the name of the drawing file. Make sure ACAD.DWG is selected as the prototype drawing.

STEP 12 Select the UNITS command from the pull-down menu Data to open the DDUNITS dialog box. Set up units to architectural.

STEP 13 Invoke the LIMITS command and set the limits as shown.

> Command:**limits**
> on/off/<Lower left corner><default>:**0',0'**
> Upper right corner<default>:**28',35'**
> Command:**zoom**
> All/Center/Dynamic/Extents/Left/Previous/Vmax/Window/Scale(X/XP)>:**a**

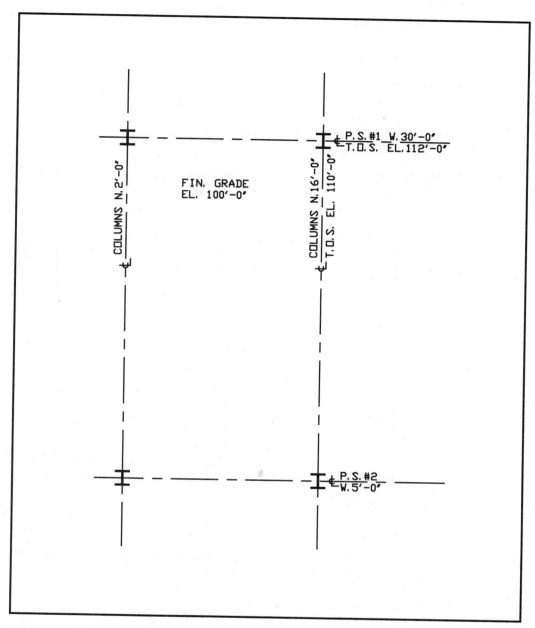

Figure P10–4 Add text to drawing

STEP 14   Open the Drawing Aids dialog box from the pull-down menu Options and set grid to 1', snap to 6" and turn ON the grid and snap.

STEP 15   Invoke the LAYER command and create layers centerline, object and text with appropriate line types and colors. Set layer "centerline" as the current layer. Set linetype scale to "32".

STEP 16   Invoke the LINE command from the Draw toolbar and draw the centerlines as shown in Figure P10–5.

```
Command:line
From point:12'-6",8'-6"
To point:@13'<0
To point:[Enter]
Command:line
From point:19',7'
To point:@12'<90
To point:[Enter]
Command:
```

Invoke the OFFSET command from the Modify toolbar and offset the horizontal centerline 9' upward.

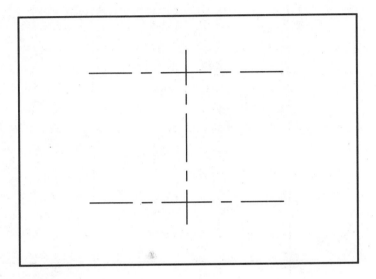

Figure P10–5 Pump centerlines

STEP 17 Set layer "object" as the current layer and use the LINE command to draw the pump foundation as shown in Figure P10–6.

```
Command:line
From point:14'-6",6'-6"
To point:@5'-6"<0
To point:@4'<90
To point:@5'-6"<180
To point:c
Command:

Command:line
From point:14-6",15'-6"
To point:@5'-6"<0
To point:@4'<90
To point:@5'-6"<180
To point:c
Command:
```

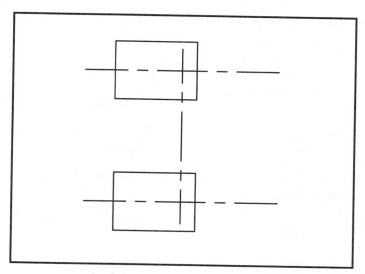

Figure P10–6 Pump foundations

STEP 18 Set layer "text" as the current layer and invoke the DTEXT command from the Draw toolbar to draw in the coordinate callouts as shown in Figure P10–7. Set text height to 4". This will cause the text to be plotted out 0.125" high when plotted at 0.375" = 12".

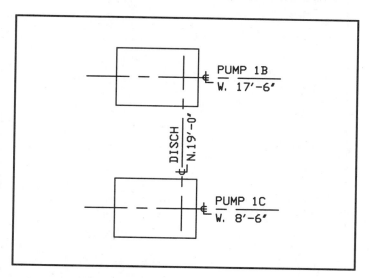

Figure P10–7 Add text to drawing

STEP 19 End the drawing.

STEP 20 Invoke the NEW command from the pull-down menu File or type New at the "Command:" prompt. Enter "border" as the name of the drawing file. Make sure ACAD.DWG is selected as the prototype drawing.

STEP 21 Select the UNITS command from the pull-down menu Data to open the DDUNITS dialog box. Set up units to architectural.

STEP 22   Invoke the LIMITS command and set the limits as shown.

> Command:**limits**
> on/off/<Lower left corner><default>:**-3',-5'**
> Upper right corner<default>:**32',42'**
> Command:**zoom**
> All/Center/Dynamic/Extents/Left/Previous/Vmax/Window/Scale(X/XP)>:**a**

STEP 23   Open the Drawing Aids dialog box from the pull-down menu Options and set grid to 1', snap to 6" and turn ON the grid and snap.

STEP 24   Invoke the LAYER command and create layer border with "phantom" as the line type. Set layer "border" as the current layer. Set linetype scale to "32".

STEP 25   Invoke the LINE command from the Draw toolbar and draw the border line as shown in Figure P10–8.

> Command:**line**
> From point:**0,0**
> To point:**@28'<0**
> To point:**@35'<90**
> To point:**@28'<180**
> To point:**c**
> Command:

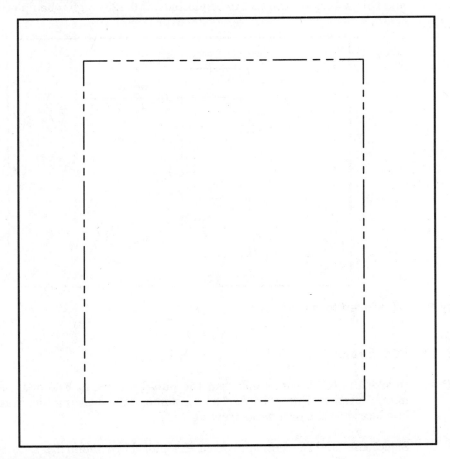

Figure P10–8 Border drawing

STEP 26 Attach the piperack drawing as a reference file to the current drawing. Invoke the XREF command's Attach option from the External Reference toolbar (see Figure P10–9). AutoCAD opens the Select Files to Attach dialog box.

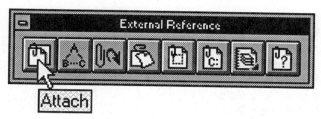

Figure P10–9 Invoke the Attach option from the External Reference toolbar

Command:**xref**
?/Bind/Detach/Path/Reload/Overlay/<Attach>:**a**
Attach Xref:**piperack** *(select the drawing "piperack" to attach)*
Insertion point:**0,0**
X scale factor <1>/corner/XYZ:Enter
Y scale factor(default=X):Enter
Rotation angle <0>:Enter
Command:

After attaching the piperack drawing, your drawing will appear as shown in Figure P10–10.

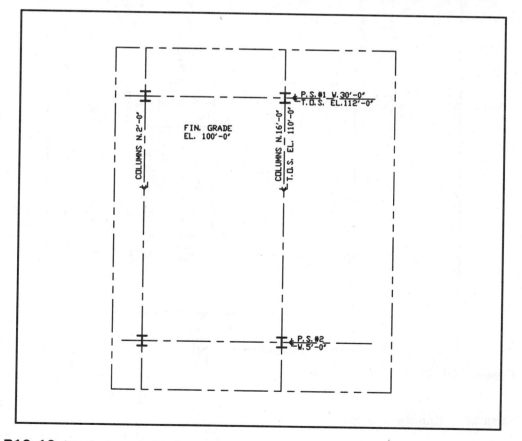

Figure P10–10 Attach piperack drawing

External References

STEP 27 Attach the pump drawing as a reference file to the current drawing. Invoke the XREF command's Attach option from the External Reference toolbar. AutoCAD opens the Select Files to Attach dialog box.

Command:**xref**
?/Bind/Detach/Path/Reload/Overlay/<Attach>:**a**
Attach Xref:**pump** *(select the drawing "pump" to attach)*
Insertion point:**0,0**
X scale factor <1>/corner/XYZ:⌨Enter⌨
Y scale factor(default=X):⌨Enter⌨
Rotation angle <0>:⌨Enter⌨
Command:

After attaching the pump drawing, your drawing will appear as shown in Figure P10–11.

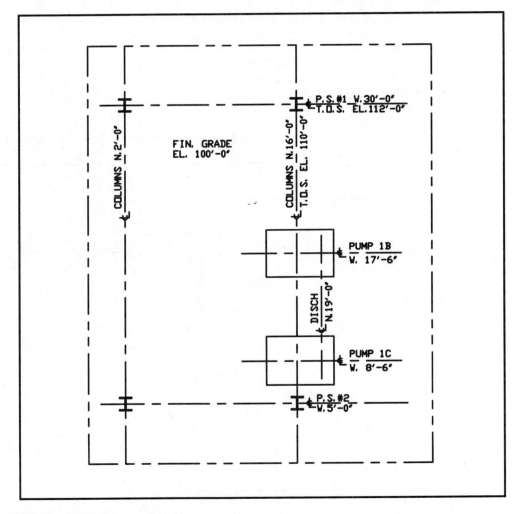

Figure P10–11 Attach pump drawing

Step 28   End the drawing.

Command:**end**

REVIEW QUESTIONS

1. If an externally referenced drawing called "FLOOR.DWG" contains a block called "TABLE" and is permanently bound to the current drawing, the new name of the block is:
   (A) FLOOR0TABLE
   (B) FLOOR TABLE
   (C) FLOOR$$0TABLE
   (D) FLOOR_TABLE
   (E) FLOOR$$$TABLE

2. To make a reference file a permanent part of the current drawing database, use the XREF command with the
   (A) Attach option
   (B) Bind option
   (C) ? option
   (D) Reload option
   (E) None of the above

3. The XREF command is invoked from the toolbar
   (A) Draw
   (B) Modify
   (C) External Reference
   (D) All of the above
   (E) None of the above

4. The Attach option of the XREF command is used
   (A) To bind the external drawing to the current drawing
   (B) To attach a new external reference file
   (C) Reload an external reference drawing
   (D) All of the above

5. The following are the dependent symbols that can be made a permanent part of your current drawing, except
   (A) Blocks
   (B) Dimstyle
   (C) Text Style
   (D) Linetype
   (E) Grid and Snap

External References

CHAPTER

11

DRAWING
ENVIRONMENTS

INTRODUCTION

One of AutoCAD's most useful features is the option to work on your drawing in two different environments, Model Space or Paper Space. You will do most of your drafting and design work in Model Space. You will use Paper Space to arrange, annotate, and plot various views of your model. While Model Space is a 3D environment, Paper Space is a 2D environment for arranging views of your model. Prior to Release 11 the drawings were created entirely in the Model Space.

It does not matter whether you are working on a 2D or 3D model, you will do most of your drawing in Model Space. You will draw in Paper Space when you add standard items like title blocks, tables, and some types of dimensioning or annotation. If necessary, dimensioning and annotation in 3D drawing can be done in Paper Space. But there is no way to view Paper Space other than in plan view. You can draw 3D objects in Paper Space, but with no way to view them, it makes little sense to do so.

After completing this chapter, you will be able to:

- Create viewports—Tiled and Untiled (overlapping)
- Set Tilemode system variable
- Use VPORTS and MVIEW commands
- Use MSPACE and PSPACE commands
- Use VPLAYER (Viewport Layer) command
- Set PSLTSCALE (paper space linetype scaling system variable)
- Dimension in Model Space and Paper Space
- Plot from Model Space and Paper Space

VIEWPORTS

One of the most useful features of AutoCAD is the ability to split the display into two or more separate viewports. Multiple viewports work by dividing your drawing screen into rectangles, making several different drawing areas instead of one. It is like having a multiple zoom lens camera, and each one is used to look at different portions of the drawing. You can have up to 32,000 viewports (or cameras) visible at once. You retain your pull-down menus and "Command:" prompt area.

Each viewport maintains a display of the current drawing independent of the display shown by other viewports. You can simultaneously display a viewport showing the entire drawing, and

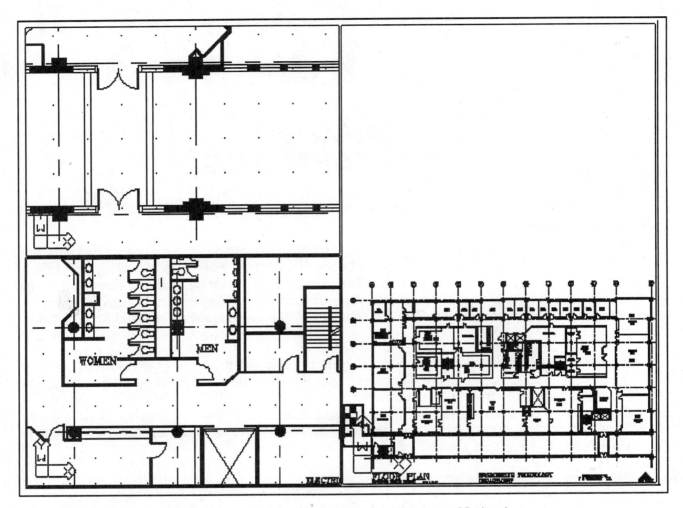

Figure 11-1 Multiple viewports show different parts of the same 2D drawing

another viewport showing a part of the drawing in greater detail. You can draw as well as modify the objects between the viewports. For example, in a 2D drawing, three viewports could be used, two of them to zoom in on two separate parts of the drawing, showing two widely separated features in a great amount of detail on the screen simultaneously; and the third one to show the entire drawing (see Figure 11-1). In a 3D drawing, four viewports could be used to display simultaneously four views of a wire-frame model: top, front, right side, and isometric as shown in Figure 11-2.

You can create and manipulate viewports in two different ways: TILED viewports and UNTILED or overlapping viewports.

TILED Viewports

When the system variable TILEMODE is set to 1 (on), you can divide the graphics area of your display screen into multiple, nonoverlapping (tiled) viewports, as shown in Figures 11-1 and 11-2. You can create the tiled viewports using the VPORTS command.

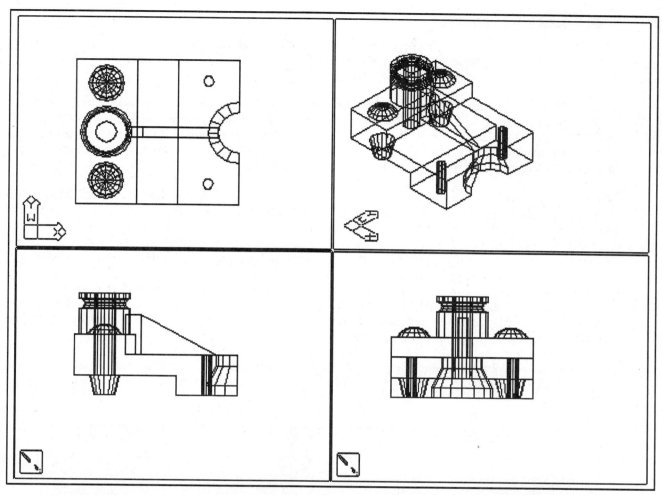

Figure 11-2 Using viewports to show four views simultaneously for a 3D wire-frame model

You can work in only one viewport at a time. This is called the current viewport. You set the current viewport by picking in it with your pointing device. You can even switch viewports in midcommand (except during the ZOOM command). When a viewport is current, its border will be thicker than the other borders. The cross-hairs will appear only in the current viewport; when you move your pointing device outside the current viewport, the cursor appears as an arrow pointer.

Display commands like ZOOM and PAN, and drawing tools like GRID, SNAP, and ORTHO are set independently in each viewport. The most important thing to remember is that the images shown in multiple viewports are multiple images of the same drawing. An object added to or modified in one viewport will affect its image in the other viewports. You are not making copies of your drawing, just putting its image in different viewports.

When you are working in tiled viewports, visibility of the layers is controlled globally in all the viewports. If you turn off a layer, AutoCAD turns it off in all the viewports. AutoCAD also allows you to work only in Model Space environment when you are in tiled viewports.

UNTILED Viewports

If the system variable TILEMODE is set to 0 (off), you can divide the graphics area of your display screen into multiple, overlapping, contiguous, or separated untiled viewports, as shown in Figure 11-3. You can create untiled viewports by using the MVIEW command.

AutoCAD treats untiled viewports like any other object such as lines, arcs, and text. You can use any of the standard AutoCAD modifying and construction commands, such as MOVE, COPY, STRETCH, SCALE, and ERASE, to manipulate the untiled viewports. For example, you can use the MOVE command to grab a viewport and move it around on the screen without affecting other viewports. Viewports can be of any size and located anywhere in Paper Space.

When you are working in untiled viewports, you can switch back and forth between Model and Paper Space by using the MSPACE and PSPACE commands, respectively. When you are in Model Space, you can work in only one viewport at a time, similar to tiled viewports.

When you are working in Paper Space, the cursor cross-hairs span the entire graphics screen and do not change when you position the cursor over a viewport. AutoCAD displays at the bottom of the screen the current environment (MODEL or PAPER) you are currently working in (see Figure 11-3). Double click the image tile to switch back and forth between Model and Paper Space. In addition, AutoCAD displays the Paper Space icon (unless you turned off the icon by using the UCSICON command), as shown in Figure 11-4.

What you draw in Paper Space appears only in untiled viewports. It will disappear if you change over to tiled viewports. What you draw in Model Space will be seen when you switch over to tiled viewports.

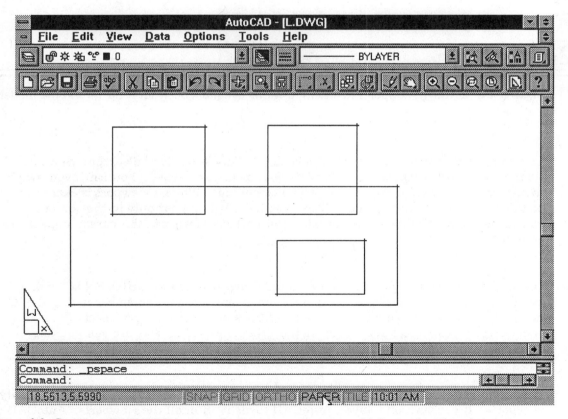

Figure 11-3   When TILEMODE is turned off, you can create multiple overlapping viewports

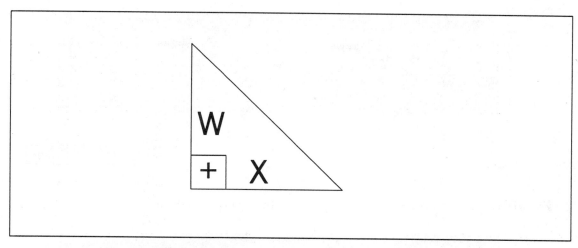

Figure 11-4 The Paper Space icon

You can control the visibility of the layers by viewport, rather than globally, when you are working in untiled viewports Model Space by using the VPLAYER command. This lets you freeze a layer in one viewport while leaving it thawed in another. All the drawing features found in tiled viewports, like the ability to draw from one viewport to another, are possible in this mode. You cannot use MVIEW, VPLAYER, MSPACE, and PSPACE commands unless the TILEMODE variable is set to off (0).

TILEMODE SYSTEM VARIABLE

The TILEMODE system variable allows you to work on either tiled or untiled viewports when the variable is set to on (1) or off (0), respectively. To change the value of the TILEMODE system variable, type TILEMODE at the "Command:" prompt and press [Enter] or spacebar and change the appropriate value.

For example, the following command sequence shows steps to change the TILEMODE system variable from 1 (on) to 0 (off):

```
Command: tilemode
New value for TILEMODE <1>: 0
Command:
```

When you change TILEMODE to 0 (off) in a drawing for the first time, AutoCAD switches to Paper Space, clears the graphics area, and prompts you to create one or more viewports. Since no viewport objects are currently in the drawing, you cannot see your model until you create at least one viewport. Use the MVIEW command to create one or more viewports. If you subsequently toggle TILEMODE to 1 (on) and then to 0 (off) again, AutoCAD displays the Paper Space view that was current before you last turned TILEMODE to 1 (on).

You can also change the Tilemode values by selecting the appropriate icons from the Standard toolbar. To set the Tilemode value to 1, select the Tiled Model Space icon from the Standard toolbar, as shown in Figure 11-5.

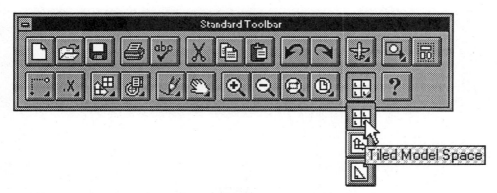

Figure 11-5   Invoke Tiled Model Space from the Standard toolbar

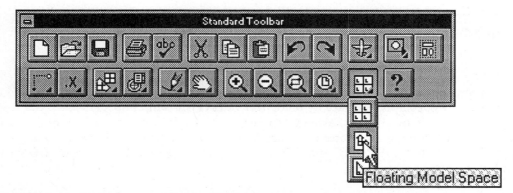

Figure 11-6   Invoke Floating Model Space from the Standard toolbar

To set the Tilemode value to 0 and switch to Model Space, select the Floating Model Space icon from the Standard toolbar, as shown in Figure 11–6.

To set the Tilemode value to 0 and switch to Paper Space, select the Paper Space icon from the Standard toolbar, as shown in Figure 11–7.

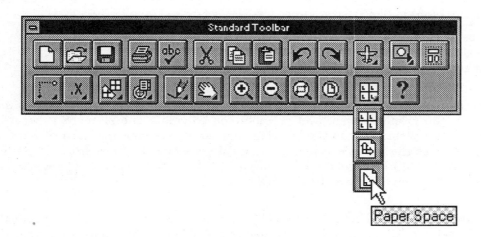

Figure 11-7   Invoke Paper Space from the Standard toolbar

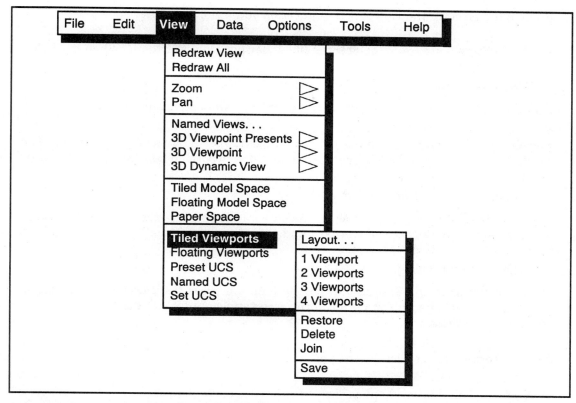

Figure 11-8 Invoke the VPORTS Command from the pull-down menu View

VPORTS (OR VIEWPORTS) COMMAND

The VPORTS (or VIEWPORTS) command creates tiled viewports and can be invoked only when TILEMODE is 1 (on). The VPORTS command offers several options that you can use to build your screen display by adding, deleting, and joining viewports. Invoke the VPORTS command from the pull-down menu View and select the appropriate option (see Figure 11-8), or at the "Command:" prompt type **VPORTS** and press Enter or spacebar.

Command: **vports**
Save/Restore/Delete/Join/SIngle/?/2/<3>/4:

Save Option This option allows you to save the current viewport configuration. The configuration includes the number and placement of active viewports and their associated settings. You can save any number of configurations with the drawing to be recalled at any time. When you select this option, AutoCAD prompts:

?/Name for new viewport configuration:

You can use the same naming conventions to name your configuration that you use for layer names. Instead of providing the name, you can respond with **?** to request a list of saved viewport configurations.

Restore Option This option allows you to redisplay a saved viewport configuration. When you select this option, AutoCAD prompts:

?/Name of viewport configuration to restore:

Provide the name of the viewport configuration you want to restore.

Delete Option This option deletes a named viewport configuration. When you select this option, AutoCAD prompts:

?/Name of viewport configuration to delete:

Provide the name of the viewport configuration you want to delete.

Join Option This option combines two adjoining viewports into a single viewport. The view for the resulting viewport is inherited from the dominant viewport. When you select this option, AutoCAD prompts:

Select dominant viewport <current>:

You can give a null response to show the current viewport as the dominant viewport or you can move the cursor to the desired viewport and press the pick button. Once you identify the dominant viewport, then AutoCAD prompts:

Select viewport to join:

Move the cursor to the desired viewport to join and press the pick button. If the two viewports selected are not adjacent or do not form a rectangle, AutoCAD displays an error message and reissues the prompts.

SIngle Option This option allows you to make the current viewport as the single viewport.

? Option This option displays the identification numbers and screen positions of the active viewports. When you select this option, AutoCAD prompts:

Viewport configuration(s) to list <*>:

To list all save configurations, give a null response. You also can use wild cards to list saved viewport names. All viewports are given an identification number by AutoCAD. This number is independent of any name you might give the viewport configuration. Each viewport is given a coordinate location, in respect to 0.0000,0.0000 as the lower left corner of the graphics area and 1.0000,1.0000 as the upper right corner.

2 Option This option splits the current viewport in half. When you select this option, AutoCAD prompts:

Horizontal/<vertical>:

You can select the Horizontal or Vertical split, as shown in Figure 11-9. Vertical is the default.

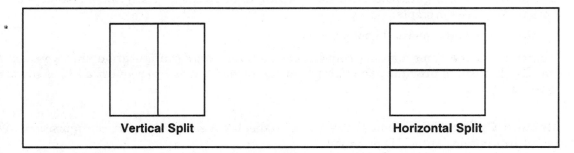

Vertical Split   Horizontal Split

Figure 11-9 Using the 2 option to split a current viewport in half by vertical or horizontal division

Drawing Environments

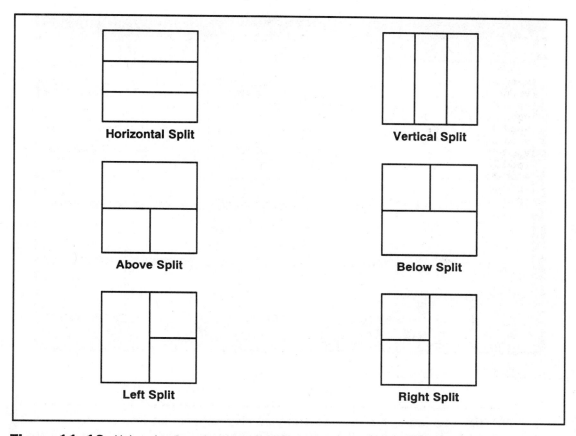

Figure 11-10 Using the 3 option to split a current viewport into various divisions

3 Option This option divides the current viewport into three viewports. This is the default option. When you select this option, AutoCAD prompts:

Horizontal/Vertical/Above/Below/Left/<Right>:

You can select the Horizontal or Vertical option to split the current viewport into thirds by horizontal or vertical division as shown in Figure 11-10. The other options let you split into two small ones and one large one, specifying whether the large is to be placed above, below, left or right (see Figure 11-10).

4 Option This option divides the current viewport into four viewports equal in size both horizontally and vertically, as shown in Figure 11-11.

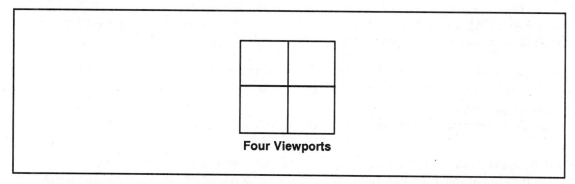

Figure 11-11 Using the 4 option to split a current viewport into four viewports of equal size

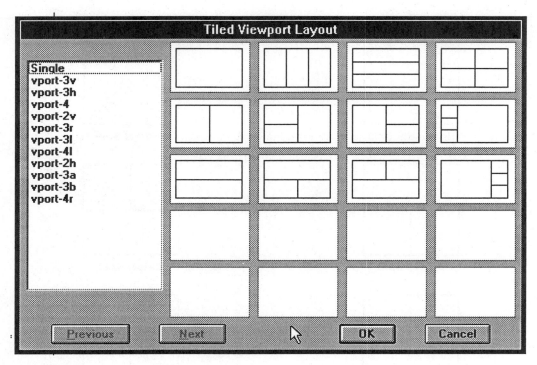

Figure 11-12 Tiled Viewports Layout icon menu

> **NOTE:** You can also select the viewports layout from an icon menu. Select Layout. . . located in the Tiled Viewports submenu from the pull-down menu View to display the Tiled Viewport Layout icon menu. The icon menu is displayed with various options to select layout configuration or tiled viewports (see Figure 11-12).

REDRAWALL AND REGENALL COMMANDS

When you are working in multiple viewports, the REDRAW or REGEN commands will only affect the current viewport. To redraw or regen all the viewports simultaneously use the REDRAWALL or REGENALL commands.

MVIEW COMMAND

The MVIEW command is used to create new untiled viewports, turn their display on or off, and instruct AutoCAD to perform hidden line removal on a viewport's contents during a Paper Space plot. This command can be invoked only when TILEMODE is off (0).

Invoke the MVIEW command from the pull-down menu VIEW and select the appropriate option (see Figure 11-13), or at the "Command:" prompt type **MVIEW** and press ⌷Enter⌷ or spacebar.

    Command: **mview**
    ON/OFF/Hideplot/Fit/2/3/4/Restore/<First Point>: ⌷Enter⌷

First Point Option The First Point option lets you create a single new viewport by providing two diagonal data points. Pick two points to define a rectangular boundary, and the viewport is created to fill that area.

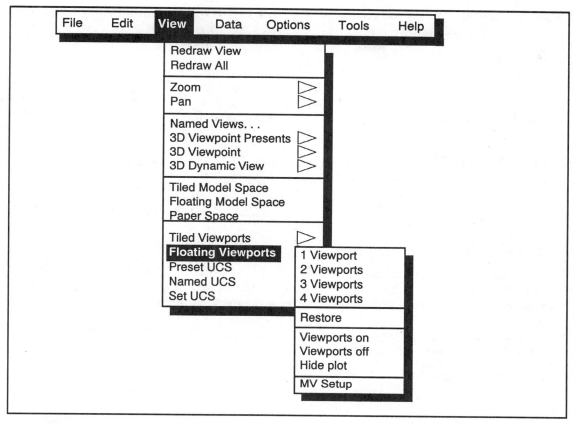

Figure 11-13 Invoke the MVIEW Command from the pull-down menu View

ON Option The ON option turns on a model view inside the viewport. When you create a viewport, the model view is turned on by default. If it is on, AutoCAD automatically regenerates. When you select this option, AutoCAD prompts you to select the viewport to turn it on.

OFF Option The OFF option turns off a model view inside the viewport. This clears the Model Space view and does not regenerate it again until the model view inside the viewport is turned on again. By turning the model view off, you can move, resize, and otherwise Modify the viewport in Paper Space. When you select this option, AutoCAD prompts you to select the viewport to turn off.

Hideplot Option The Hideplot option instructs AutoCAD to turn on or off the hidden line removal on the contents of the selected viewport when plotting in Paper Space. When you select this option, AutoCAD prompts for on or off. Subsequently, AutoCAD prompts you to select the viewport.

Fit Option The fit option creates a single viewport to fill the display. This can be convenient when you simply want the new viewport to fill the available display area.

2 Option The 2 option lets you create two viewports within a rectangular area you specify. When you select this option, AutoCAD prompts:

    Horizontal/<vertical>:

You can divide horizontally or vertically. Vertical is the default.

3 Option The 3 option lets you create three viewports in a rectangular area. When you select this option, AutoCAD prompts:

> Horizontal/Vertical/Above/Below/Left/<Right>:

You can select the Horizontal or Vertical option; AutoCAD creates three viewports stacked on top of each other or side by side. The other options let you create into two small ones and one large one, specifying whether the large is to be placed above, below, left, or right.

4 Option The 4 option lets you create four viewports in a rectangular area, either by specifying the area, or fitting the four viewports to the display.

MSPACE COMMAND

This command lets you switch from Paper Space to Model Space. The TILEMODE system variable must be set to 0 (off) before this command can be used. In order for AutoCAD to switch from Paper Space to Model Space, there must be at least one viewport on and active.

The MSPACE command is invoked from the pull-down menu VIEW, or at the "Command:" prompt type **MSPACE** and press [Enter] or spacebar.

> Command: **mspace**

PSPACE COMMAND

This command lets you switch from Model Space to Paper Space. The TILEMODE system variable must be set to 0 (off) before this command can be used. The PSPACE command is invoked from the pull-down menu VIEW, or at the "Command:" prompt type **PSPACE** and press [Enter] or the spacebar.

> Command: **pspace**

VPLAYER COMMAND

As described earlier, the VPLAYER (short for ViewPort LAYER) command controls the visibility of layers in a single viewport or in a set of viewports. This allows you to select a viewport and freeze a layer in it, while still allowing the contents of that layer to appear in another viewport. See Figure 11-14 in which two viewports contain the same view of the drawing, but in one viewport, the layer containing the dimensioning is on, and in another it is off by using the VPLAYER command. To use the VPLAYER command the system variable TILEMODE must be set to 0 (off).

The VPLAYER command can be invoked from either Model Space or Paper Space. Several options in the VPLAYER command require you to select one or more viewports in which to make your changes. AutoCAD prompts:

> All/Select/<Current>:

To accept the default option, you have to be in Model Space; AutoCAD applies changes in the current viewport. If you opt for the select option and you are in Model Space, AutoCAD temporarily

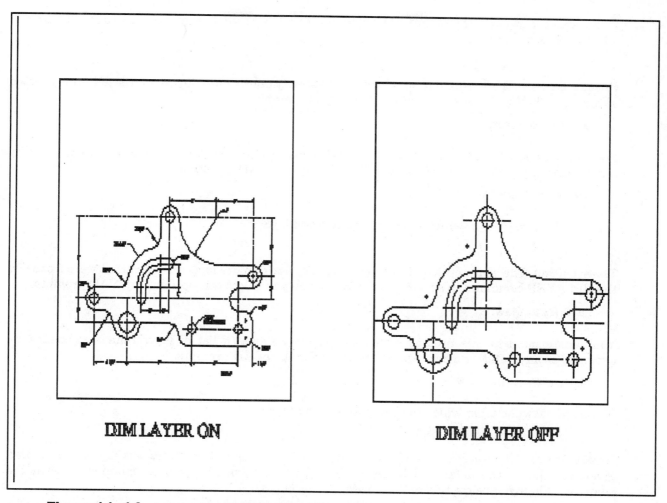

Figure 11-14 A viewport with DIMLAYER ON and DIMLAYER OFF

switches to Paper Space so you can select a viewport. The All option applies your changes to all Paper Space viewports.

If you set your TILEMODE to 1 (on), the global layer settings take precedence over any VPLAYER settings.

The VPLAYER command is invoked by selecting Viewport Layer Controls from the pull-down menu Data, or by typing VPLAYER at the "Command:" prompt and pressing Enter or the spacebar.

Command: **vplayer**
?/Freeze/Thaw/Reset/Newfrz/Vpvisdflt:

? Option The ? option displays the names of layers in a specific viewport that are frozen. When you select this option, AutoCAD prompts:

Select a viewport:

Pick a single viewport. If you are in Model Space, AutoCAD switches temporarily to Paper Space to let you select a viewport.

Freeze Option The Freeze option allows you to specify one or more layers to freeze in the selected viewport. When you select this option, AutoCAD prompts:

>   Layer(s) to freeze:

You can respond to this prompt with a single layer name, a list of layer names separated by commas, or any valid wild card specification. Then AutoCAD prompts:

>   All/Select/<current>:

Select the viewport(s) in which to freeze the selected layers.

Thaw Option The Thaw option allows you to specify one or more layers to thaw that were frozen by the VPLAYER command in specific viewports. When you select this option, AutoCAD prompts:

>   Layer(s) to thaw:

You can respond to this prompt with a single layer name, a list of layer names separated by commas, or any valid wild card specification. Then AutoCAD prompts:

>   All/Select/<current>:

Select the viewport(s) in which to thaw the selected layers.

Reset Option The Reset option allows you to restore the default visibility setting for a layer in a given viewport. The default visibility is controlled by Vpvisdflt option, explained later in the chapter. When you select this option, AutoCAD prompts:

>   Layer(s) to Reset:

You can respond to this prompt with a single layer name, a list of layer names separated by commas, or any valid wild card specification. Then AutoCAD prompts:

>   All/Select/<current>:

Select the viewport(s) in which to reset the selected layers.

Newfrz (New Freeze) Option The New Freeze option allows you to create new layers that are frozen in all viewports. If you create a new viewport, the layers that are created by the Newfrz option will be frozen by default. The layer can be thawed in the chosen viewport by using the Thaw option. When you select this option, AutoCAD prompts:

>   New viewport frozen layer name(s):

You can respond to this prompt with a single layer name or a list of layer names separated by commas.

Vpvisdflt (ViewPort Visibility Default) Option The Viewport Visibility Default option allows you to set a default visibility for one or more existing layers. This default determines the frozen/thawed state of an existing layer in newly created viewports. When you select this option, AutoCAD prompts:

> Layer name(s) to change default viewport visibility:

You can respond to this prompt with a single layer name, a list of layer names separated by commas, or any wild card specification. Then AutoCAD prompts:

> Change default viewport visibility to Frozen/<Thawed>:

You can respond to this prompt with a null response to set the default visibility to thaw or enter **F** to set the default visibility to freeze.

Freezing Layers in Viewports from the Layer Control Dialog Box

If the TILEMODE is off (0), you can freeze layers selectively by viewport from the Layer Control dialog box selected from the pull-down menu Data. This can be done with the options provided in the dialog box (see Figure 11–15).

Select the layer name(s) from the layer name list box. Pick either the Thw or Frz button in the layer control dialog box for the current VP and/or New VP. When a layer is frozen under current VP, a "C" (for current) appears after the layer name in the State Column of the layer list box and a "." appears when it is thawed. If a layer is frozen under New VP, an "N" (for new) appears after the layer name in the State column of the layer list box. A "." appears when it is thawed.

In Figure 11–15 the layers dim, object, and text are frozen in the current viewport. Elevation and Hidden are frozen in all the new viewport objects.

PAPER SPACE LINETYPE SCALING (PSLTSCALE)

Linetype dash lengths are based on the drawing units of the Model or Paper Space in which the objects were created. It can be scaled globally by LTSCALE factor as explained earlier. If you want to display objects in viewports at different scales when Tilemode is set to 0, the linetype objects would be scaled to model space rather than paper space by default. However, by setting paper space linetype scaling (PSLTSCALE) to 1, dash lengths are based on paper space drawing units including the linetype objects that are drawn in model space. For example, a single linetype definition with a dash length of 0.30 and displayed in several viewports with different zoom factors, would be displayed in paper space with dashes of length 0.30, regardless of the scale of the viewpoint in which it is being displayed (PSLTSCALE set to 1).

To set the PSLTSCALE, type PSLTSCALE at the "Command:" prompt and press [Enter] or spacebar. The default value of the PSLTSCALE is 0.

> **NOTE:** When you change PSLTSCALE value to 1, the linetype objects in the viewport are not automatically regenerated. Use the REGEN or REGENALL command to update the linetypes in the viewports.

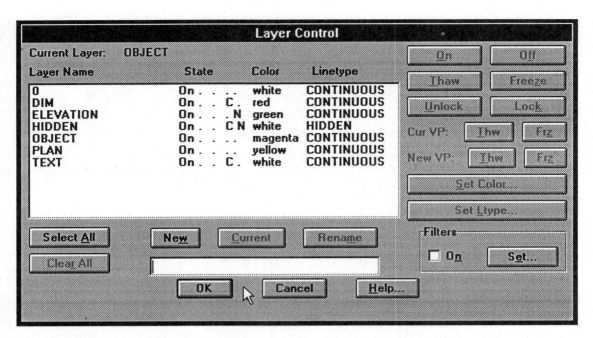

Figure 11-15 Control of layers in viewport from Layer Control dialog box

DIMENSIONING IN MODEL SPACE AND PAPER SPACE

Dimensioning can be done in both Model Space and Paper Space. There are no restrictions on the dimensioning commands by the current mode. It is advisable to draw associative dimensions in Model Space, since AutoCAD places the defining points of the dimension in the space where the dimension is drawn. If the model geometry is modified with commands such as STRETCH, EXTEND, or TRIM, the dimensions are updated automatically. Whereas, if the dimensions are drawn in Paper Space, the Paper Space dimension does not change if the model geometry is modified.

When you do dimensioning in Model Space, the DIMSCALE factor should be set to 0.0. This causes AutoCAD to compute a scale factor based on the scaling between Paper Space and current Model Space viewport. If dimensioning that describes model geometry should be created in Paper Space, then the dimension variable scale factor DIMLFAC should be based on Model Space viewport. It is important that the length scaling must be set to a value that is appropriate for the view being dimensioned.

PLOTTING FROM MODEL SPACE AND PAPER SPACE

In Model Space, the plot is based on how much of the drawing in the current viewport falls within the plot option chosen. In Paper Space, the plot is based on how much of the drawing, including any viewports and their contents, falls within the plot option chosen.

Following are The Ten Golden Steps to be followed to plot a drawing from Paper Space at 1=1 scale after drawing the model in the Model Space to real-world dimensions:

1. Set the LIMITS in Paper Space equal to plotter's maximum available plot area for the given sheet size.

2. After setting the LIMITS, use the ZOOM All Command in Paper Space.

3. Set appropriate GRID and SNAP values (this may be different from the values in the Model Space).

4. Insert a border and title block, if you already have one, at 1=1 scale or attach it as an xref. If not, draw the appropriate border and title on its own layer so you can freeze it as you work on your drawing.

5. Create as many viewports as you need using the MVIEW command on a separate layer for the various views and details you want to plot.

6. If necessary, resize, stretch, and move the viewports to be plotted to match your planned arrangement in the sheet.

7. Enter Model Space and create or modify, drawing your views and details. You can control the layers independently in each viewport by the VPLAYER command.

8. Establish the proper model-to-paper display units scale for each viewport. This can be done with the ZOOM XP Command. Entering a scale factor followed by XP will cause the image to display relative to your Paper Space units. Typing 1/24XP or 0.04167XP (1/24=0.04167) will display an image to a scale of 1/2"= 1'-0", which is the same as 1:24 or 1/24. You determine the ZOOM XP scale factor as a reciprocal of the plot scale that you would use if you plot from Model Space when TILEMODE is set to 1 (on). For example, if you would like to display an image to plot scale 1/4" = 1'-0", then you would enter a scale factor of 1/48 followed by XP to cause the image to display relative to your Paper Space units. See Table 11-1 for factors for the XP option to various plotting scale factors.

After you use ZOOM XP, be careful not to do other ZOOMS in or out in Model Space. Panning is safe and good for fine-tuning the view. The most important thing to remember is that it is the viewport display that is scaled, not the plot.

9. Enter Paper Space. Add any annotations or dimensions that you wish to do in Paper Space. Fill in your title block information.

10. Plot at a scale of 1:1.

> **NOTE:** Partially visible viewports are not plotted. Viewports that have been turned off are not plotted. The "remove hidden lines" option applies only to Model Space objects, and each viewport is processed for hidden lines according to its own Hideplot setting.

Table 11-1 Typical architectural display scaling for Paper Space viewports

Plotting Scale	Display Factors
3" = 1'	ZOOM 1/4XP
3/4" = 1'	ZOOM 1/16XP
1/2" = 1'	ZOOM 1/24XP
3/8" = 1'	ZOOM 1/32XP
1/4" = 1'	ZOOM 1/48XP
1/8" = 1'	ZOOM 1/96XP

EXERCISES

Exercise 11-1

Plot the project drawing from Chapter 4 by displaying the drawing to 3/16" = 1'-0" on Paper Space and plotting to 1=1 (what you see is what you get) on an A-size sheet by following the steps below:

1. Change the TILEMODE system variable from 1 to 0 to get into Paper Space.
2. Set LIMITS in Paper Space for lower left corner to (0,0) and upper right corner to (12,9).
3. Set Grid and Snap to 0.5 and 0.25, respectively.
4. Insert a border and title block (SIZE A), if you already have one, at 1=1 scale or attach it as an xref. If not, draw the appropriate border and title on its own layer so you can freeze it as you work on your drawing.
5. Create a viewport by MVIEW command to a size 7.5" × 4.5".
6. Enter Model Space using the MSPACE command.
7. Set the display of the model by using the ZOOM command to a scale factor of 1/64XP. (DO NOT ZOOM IN OR OUT IN MODEL SPACE AFTER SETTING THE DISPLAY TO THE APPROPRIATE DISPLAY FACTOR.)
8. Enter Paper Space using the PSPACE command.
9. Plot the drawing to a scale of 1=1 on an A-size sheet.

Exercise 11-2

Plot the project drawing from Chapter 3 by displaying the drawing to 1 = 1 on Paper Space and plotting to 1=1 (what you see is what you get) on a C-size sheet. Set LIMITS in Paper Space for lower left corner to (0,0) and upper right corner (22,17). Create a viewport by MVIEW command to a size of 18" × 12" and scale the display to a scale factor of 1XP. Make sure you have an appropriate border and title block, and plot is set to 1=1.

REVIEW QUESTIONS

1. To force a redraw of all visible viewports on the display screen, use
   - (A) REDRAW
   - (B) REDRAWALL
   - (C) ZOOMALL
   - (D) None of the above

2. To set up multiple viewport windows, use
   - (A) VPORT
   - (B) VPORTS
   - (C) VIEWPORT
   - (D) None of the above

3. Paper Space allows
   - (A) display of details at different scales on the same drawing
   - (B) plotting of multiple viewports
   - (C) insertion of such items as title blocks for annotating drawings
   - (D) All of the above

4. To create viewports in Paper Space, use the
   - (A) VPORTS command
   - (B) MVIEW command
   - (C) VPLAYER command
   - (D) PVIEW command
   - (E) None of the above

5. To scale the objects contained in Paper Space viewports, use the ZOOM command along with the
   - (A) All option
   - (B) Extents option
   - (C) XP option
   - (D) Vmax option
   - (E) None of the above

6. Automatic paper space linetype scaling, the ability to scale a linetype in paper space based on the scale of the viewport in which it is scaled, is controlled by the
   - (A) PSPACE system variable
   - (B) LTSCALE system variable
   - (C) SPLTSCALE system variable
   - (D) None of the above

7. While in Paper Space, to make a layer visible in one viewport but invisible in all other viewports, use the
   - (A) LAYER command
   - (B) VPLAYER command
   - (C) MVIEW command
   - (D) VIEWPORTS command
   - (E) None of the above

8. When Tilemode is set to zero, you
   - (A) can go back and forth between Paper Space and Model Space
   - (B) can use the MVIEW command to create viewports
   - (C) can use the VPLAYER command to control the visibility of layers independent of viewports
   - (D) All of the above

9. You can create and manipulate viewports in
   - (A) tiled
   - (B) untiled
   - (C) A and B
   - (D) None of the above

10. The number viewports is limited you to the size of your monitor.
    - (A) True
    - (B) False

12

UTILITY COMMANDS

After completing this chapter, you will be able to:

- Use Geometric Calculator (CAL command) to perform calculations.
- Use the Rename command
- Use the Purge command
- Use the Command modifier — Multiple
- Use the Utility display commands — View, Regenauto, Dragmode, Blipmode, and Toolbar
- Use the Object properties — Color and Linetype commands
- Use the xyz filters
- Use the Shell command
- Use the Files command
- Use the Makepreview command
- Use the Mvsetup command
- Use the Time and Audit commands
- Use the Preference command
- Use the Clipboard commands

GEOMETRIC CALCULATOR (CAL)

The CAL is an on-line calculator that evaluates real, integer, or vector expressions. The CAL command, when entered at the "Command:" prompt (or 'cal transparently when prompted for input) switches you to the calculator mode. When the "Command:" prompt is preceded by the double angle brackets (>>), AutoCAD is awaiting input, which must be in the acceptable calculator format. For example, you can solve a simple algebraic equation by entering the following:

```
Command: cal
Initializing. . .
>>Expression: A=pi*4^2 RETURN
```

causing the following response:

```
50.2655
Command:
```

This sequence might be used to derive the area of a circle with a radius of 4. The variable "A" and the equal sign are not required to arrive at the solution. Entering "pi*4^2" will suffice. However, the "A=" serves to give a user-defined name to a variable (the letter A in this case) so that the result of the equation can be set as the value of the named variable for use later in AutoLISP or in another calculator expression. In the built-in calculator, "pi" has been assigned a preset value of approximately 3.141592654, which is the ratio of a circle's circumference divided by its diameter. The "*" and the "^" are the symbols for multiply and exponent, respectively, as is noted later in the listing of arithmetic operators you may use in calculator expressions.

You may also enter the built-in calculator transparently (while in the middle of another command) as shown during the LINE command:

```
Command: line
From point: 'cal
>>Expression: (mid+end)/2
>>Select object for MID snap: (pick one line)
>>Select object for END snap: (pick other line)
To point: (Enter)
```

See Figure 12–1.

This expression causes AutoCAD to pause while the user selects points by osnapping to a midpoint and endpoint and then using the midpoint between those two points as the starting point of the line to be drawn.

Responses to the ">>Expression:" and other calculator (with leading >>s) prompts vary according to the desired function.

In addition to using CAL (and 'CAL transparently) while in AutoCAD, you can use CAL as an operator within an AutoLISP expression followed by a calculator expression enclosed in double quotes.

CAL can be considered an AutoLISP subroutine with an argument of a calculator expression-string. In the following example, CAL finds the midpoint between two midpoints of parallel and equal length lines 1 and 2 (see Figure 12–2).

```
Command: (setq pt1 (cal "(mid+mid)/2"))
>>Select object for MID snap: (pick one line)
>>Select object for MID snap: (pick other line)
(4.5 5.0 0.0)
```

> **NOTE:** The AutoLISP expression only works if the calculator program has been loaded. This is done as follows:
>
> Command: **(xload "cal")**

Functions available directly or interactively (with AutoLISP) through this programmable calculator include the following:

1. Use expressions similar to common algebra to solve equations.

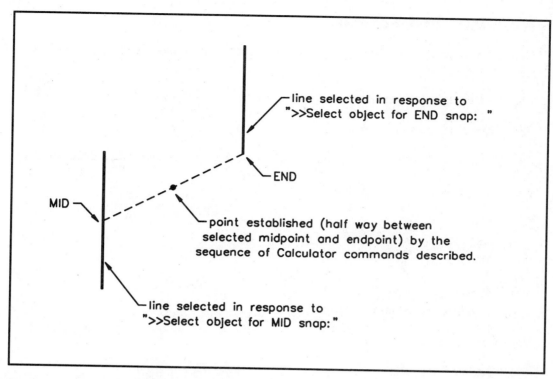

Figure 12-1 Using the CAL Command transparently during the LINE Command

2. Name and store values directly (or indirectly through expressions) to variables for use later in expressions, by AutoLISP or in AutoCAD commands.

3. Derive information about the existing geometry, or use available data to generate or analyze geometric constructs such as points, vectors, components (x,y, & z coordinates) of a point, coordinate systems, and axes.

4. Apply object snap modes.

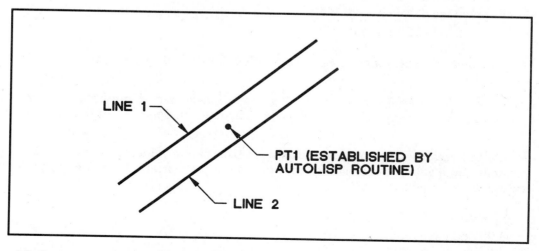

Figure 12-2 CAL finds the midpoint between two other midpoints parallel and equal length lines 1 and 2

Notations and Format

Calculator expressions are entered in a format similar to algebra, known as infix notation. Operational precedences are as follows:

1. Left to right for operators of equal precedence.

2. Parentheses from innermost out.

3. Exponents first; multiplication and division second; addition and subtraction last.

Numeric operators are as follows:

+   add
-   subtract
*   multiply
/   divide
^   raise to power
[] signifies expression

Vector operators are as follows:

+   add vectors
-   subtract vectors
*   multiply a vector by a real number or scaler product of vectors
/   divide a vector by a real number
&   vector product of vectors
[] signifies expression

Point/vector operators and symbols are as follows:

[] encloses point or vector
,   separates coordinate values
<   precedes angle
@   precedes distance
*   denotes WCS (overrides UCS)

Architectural distances may be entered as either feet'-inches" or feet'inches".

Angles may be entered in degrees/minutes/seconds as degrees d, minutes ', seconds ", radians r, or gradians g. Degrees must be entered as 0d if the angle in d/m/s is less than one degree.

Points and vectors are entered by enclosing the coordinate values in square brackets, separated by commas. Zero values can be omitted as long as the commas are there. For example, the following values are valid point/vectors:

[,,] equals [0,0,0]
[8,9,] equals [8,9,0]
[,,7] equals [0,0,7]

Coordinate systems may be entered in the following formats:

system	format	example
polar	=[dist<angle]	[7<45]
cylindrical	=[dist<angle,z]	[3<0.57r,1.0]
spherical	=[dist<angle1,angle2]	[7<30<60]
relative	=[@x,y,z]	[@1.0,2.5,3.75]
WCS	=[*x,y,z]	[*5,6,20]

Conversion of point/vectors between the User Coordinate System and the World Coordinate System can be achieved by the following functions:

W2U converts from the WCS to the UCS
U2W converts from the UCS to the WCS

A point/vector expression may include arithmetic operators as the following example shows:

[4+3<45]
[3<3.14/6,0.5*2]

Other point/vector operators include the following:

sin,asin	sine & arcsine of angle
cos,acos	cosine & arccosine of angle
tang,atan	tangent & arctangent of angle
ln	natural log of the number
log	base-10 log of the number
exp	natural exponent of the number
exp10	base-10 exponent of the number
sqr,sqrt	square & square root
abs	absolute value
round	number rounded to nearest integer
trunc	integer with decimal portion removed
r2d	converts angle in radians to degrees
d2r	converts angle in degrees to radians
pi	quotient of circumference divided by diameter
vec	obtains the vector between two points
vec1	obtains a unit vector between two points

Coordinate values of point/vectors can be obtained singly and in pairs by using one of the following operators:

xyof(point)	returns new point with x and y coordinates of point
xzof(point)	returns new point with x and z coordinates of point
yzof(point)	returns new point with y and z coordinates of point
xof(point)	returns new point with x coordinate of point
yof(point)	returns new point with y coordinate of point
zof(point)	returns new point with z coordinate of point
rxof(point)	returns real that is x coordinate of point
ryof(point)	returns real that is y coordinate of point
rzof(point)	returns real that is z coordinate of point

Cur   The cur command pauses and prompts the user to pick a point with the cursor, using that point in the expression.

@   The @ symbol causes the last point to be used in the expression. This is similar to the relative coordinate method of specifying points.

Object Snap   Using the first three letters of any of the object snap modes in an expression causes AutoCAD to pause and prompt the user for a point subject to the object snap mode specified.

Finding Points You can obtain a point on a line by entering the two end points and either a distance or a scaler value as follows:

pld(pt1,pt2,distance) returns a point that is the given distance from pt1 in the direction of pt2 from pt1

pld([1,2,3], [5,5,3],3.5) obtains pt3, as shown in Figure 12-3.

plt(pt1,pt2,proportion) returns a point that is in the direction of pt2 from pt1; and its distance from pt1 will be the product of the proportion multiplied by the distance between pt1 and pt2

plt(pt1,pt2, 0.5) obtains pt 3, as shown in Figure 12-4.

plt(pt1, pt2, 7/8) obtains pt3, as shown in Figure 12-5.

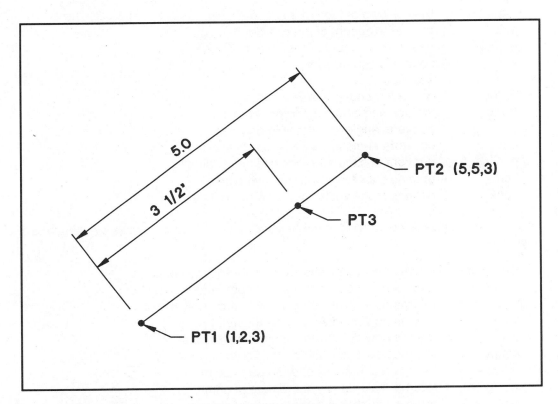

Figure 12-3 Obtaining a point on a line by entering the two end points

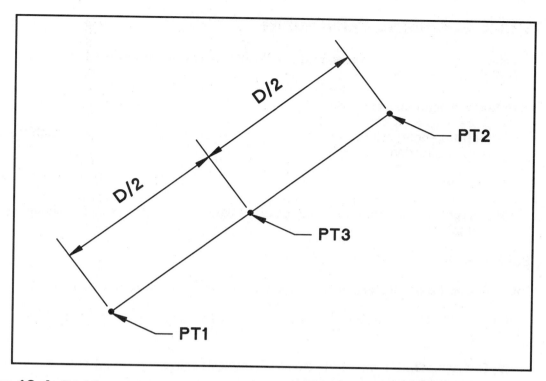

Figure 12–4 Obtaining a point on a line by entering the two end points and a distance

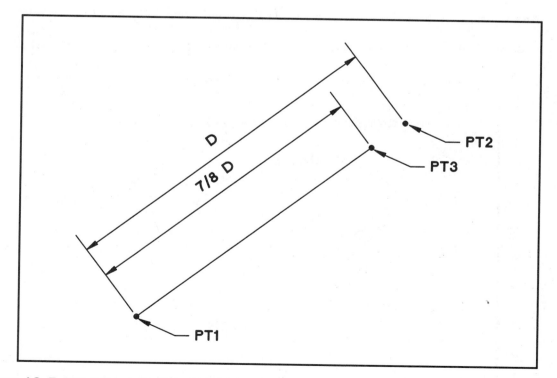

Figure 12–5 Obtaining a point on a line by entering the two end points and a scaler value

Other Geometric Calculations

Special points, vectors, distances, radii, and angles can be derived by using the calculator functions described in this section.

Rotation of a point about an axis.

> **rot(p,origin,angle)** returns the point p rotated ang angle about an axis through the origin in the y direction

See Figure 12–6.

> **rot(p,Axpt1,Axpt2,ang)** returns the point p rotated ang angle about an axis through Axpt1 and Axpt2

See Figure 12-7.

Intersection Point Ille(pt1,pt2) returns the distance between points pt1 and pt2.

> **dpl(pt1,pt2,pt3)** returns the distance (shortest) between point pt1 and a line through pt2 and pt3

> **dpp(pt1,pt2,pt3,pt4)** returns the distance (shortest) between point pt1 and a plane defined by the three points pt2, pt3 and p

Radius Rad pauses for the user to select an arc, circle or 2D polyline arc segment and returns its radius.

Angle Ang(v) returns the angle between the x axis and a line defined by the vector v.

> **ang(pt1,pt2)** returns the angle between the x axis and a line defined by points pt1 and pt2

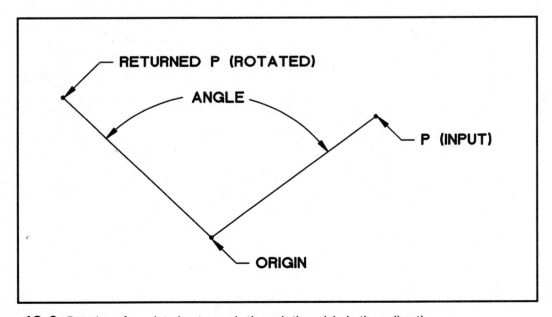

Figure 12–6 Rotation of a point about an axis through the origin in the y direction

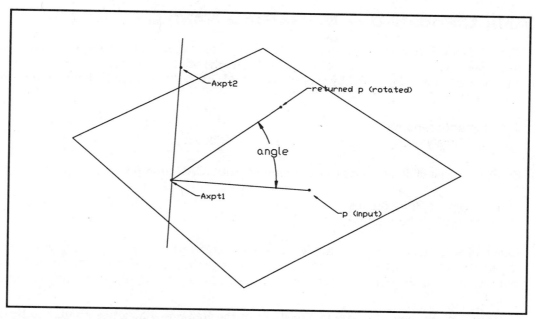

Figure 12–7 Rotation of a point about an axis through Axpt1 and Axpt2

ang(apex,pt1,pt2) returns the angle between lines defined by apex to pt1 and apex to pt2

ang(apex,pt1,pt2,pt3) returns the angle between lines defined by apex to pt1 and apex to pt2 and measured counterclockwise about the axis defined by apex to pt3

Normal Vector

nor returns the normal unit vector (3D) of a selected arc, circle or polyline arc segment

nor(v) returns the normal unit vector (2D) to the vector v

nor(pt1,pt2) returns the normal unit vector (2D) to the line through pt1 and pt2

nor(pt1,pt2,pt3) returns the normal unit vector (3D) to the plane defined by the three points pt1, pt2 and pt3

Shortcut Operations

The shortened version of calculator operators combine operators as follows:

dee	=	dist(end,end)
ille	=	ill(end,end,end,end)
mee	=	(end+end)/2
nee	=	nor(end,end)
vee	=	vec(end,end)
vee1	=	vec1(end,end)

RENAME COMMAND — MANAGING NAMED OBJECTS

The RENAME command allows you to change the names of blocks, dimension styles, layers, linetypes, text styles, views, User Coordinate Systems, or viewport configurations. The RENAME command is invoked by typing **RENAME** at the "Command:" prompt and pressing [Enter] or the spacebar.

    Command: **rename**
    Block/Dimstyle/LAyer/LType/Style/Ucs/VIew/VPort:

Select the type of object option to be renamed. AutoCAD prompts:

    Old (object option) name:
    New (object option) name:

Respond with the old and new names for the object, respectively. Except for the layer named 0 and the linetype named CONTINUOUS, you can change the name of any of the named objects. You can rename external references, which causes AutoCAD to rename all its dependent named objects.

You can also rename the named objects from the Rename dialog box similar to the one shown in Figure 12–8. The dialog box is invoked from the pull-down menu DATA or at the "Command:" prompt type **DDRENAME** and press [Enter] or the spacebar.

    Command: **ddrename**

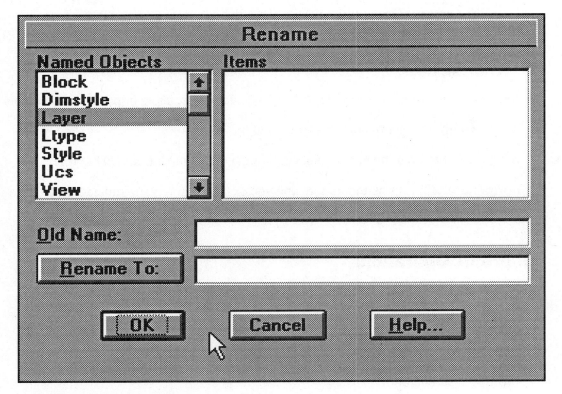

Figure 12–8 The Rename dialog box

In the Named Objects list box, select the object name you want to change. The items list box displays the names of all objects that can be renamed. To change the object's name, pick the name in the items list box or type it into the Old name: edit box. Enter the new name in the Rename To: edit box and pick the **Rename To:** button to update the object's name in the items list box. To close the dialog box, pick the **OK** button.

PURGE COMMAND — DELETING UNUSED NAMED OBJECTS

The PURGE command is used to selectively delete any unused named objects. The PURGE command is invoked from the screen menu DATA or at the "Command:" prompt, type **PURGE** and press Enter or the spacebar.

> Command: **purge**
> Purge unused Blocks/Dimstyles/LAyers/LTypes/SHapes/STyles/APpids/Mlinestyles/All:

Except layer 0, linetype CONTINUOUS, and text style STANDARD, you can purge any or all of the unused named objects by responding to the first prompt with the type of the named objects, or the initial(s) corresponding to the type of the named object or A (for All), respectively. After specifying the type of objects, AutoCAD prompts with the name of all eligible (unused) objects of that type with a default of No as in the following example of unused layers named PLAN and SIDEVIEW:

> Purge layer PLAN? <N>
> Purge layer SIDEVIEW? <N>

You can respond with a **Y** or **Yes** at each object and it will be purged from the drawing or you can press Enter or the spacebar and the object will remain unpurged. If a block has nested blocks, the PURGE command removes the outer block definition only. To remove second, third, or deeper level blocks-within-blocks, you must PURGE the outer one, END the drawing, call it back with the OPEN command, and repeat the process until all depths are purged. It may be that deeper nested blocks are being used elsewhere in the drawing, and that makes them ineligible for PURGING.

Individual shapes are part of a .SHX file. They cannot be renamed, but references to those that are not being used can be purged. Views, User Coordinate Systems, and viewport configurations cannot be purged, but the commands that manage them provide options to delete those that are not being used.

COMMAND MODIFIER — MULTIPLE

MULTIPLE is not a command, but when used with another AutoCAD command, it causes automatic recalling of that command when it is completed. You must enter Esc to terminate this repeating process. An example of using this modifier to cause automatic repeating of the ARC command is as follows:

> Command: **multiple arc**

You can use the MULTIPLE command modifier with any of the Draw, Modify, and Inquiry commands. However, PLOT will ignore the MULTIPLE command modifier.

UTILITY DISPLAY COMMANDS

The Utility display commands include VIEW, REGENAUTO, DRAGMODE, and BLIPMODE.

VIEW Command

The VIEW command allows you to give a name to the display in the current viewport and have it saved as a view. You can recall a view later by using the VIEW command and responding with the name of the view desired. This is useful for moving back quickly to needed areas in the drawing without having to resort to zooms and pans. The VIEW command is invoked by typing **VIEW** at the "Command:" prompt and pressing ⌜Enter⌝ or the spacebar.

```
Command: view
?/Delete/Restore/Save/Window:
```

The options and responses are as outlined in the following sections.

? Option The ? option causes AutoCAD to display a list of named views according to the response to the next prompt:

```
View(s) to list <*>:
```

The default response is the global symbol, the asterisk, which will cause all the named views to be listed. Other typical restrictions of the names can be specified by using whole names or combinations of characters and wild card symbols such as the asterisk and/or the question mark. AutoCAD includes in the list the space (M for Model or P for Paper) in which each view was defined.

Delete Option The Delete option permits deleting specified views according to names or character/ wild card specifications given.

Restore Option The Restore option causes the named view to replace the current display in a manner similar to the combined action of the VPOINT command and the ZOOM Dynamic command.

Model Space views restored to Paper Space are placed in the viewport of your choice by responding to the following prompt:

```
Restoring model space View.
Select viewport:
```

The desired viewport (which must be on and active) can be chosen by picking its border. AutoCAD automatically changes to model space. Restoring a paper space view while working in model space causes AutoCAD to change automatically to paper space. The system variable TILEMODE must be off to restore a paper space view.

Save Option The Save option prompts for a name and saves the display in the current viewport by that name, replacing any view with that name.

Window Option The Window option prompts for two points to specify the diagonally opposite corners of a rectangle, which will be the display used in the same manner as the Save option.

You can also create a new view and restore a view from the View Control dialog box similar to the one shown in Figure 12–9. The View Control dialog box is invoked from the pull-down menu VIEW or at the "Command:" prompt type **DDVIEW** and press Enter or the spacebar.

Command: **ddview**

In the View list box, select the view you want to restore and click on the **Restore. . .** button. To create a new view, click on the **New. . .** button. Another dialog box is displayed. Provide the appropriate name to save it as a view.

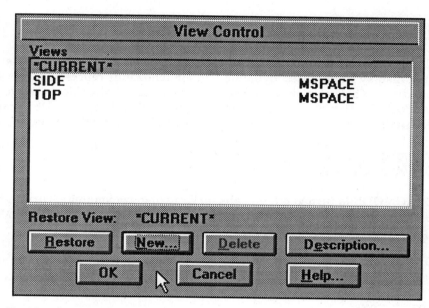

Figure 12–9 The View Control dialog box

REGENAUTO Command

The REGENAUTO command has two settings, ON and OFF. The setting determines whether automatic regeneration occurs when certain commands are completed. Drawing a line or circle on the screen is immediately apparent (unless the current layer is turned off) and does not require regeneration. But, redefining a block or font for a text style can cause regeneration. The REGENAUTO command is invoked by typing **REGENAUTO** at the "Command:" prompt and pressing Enter or the spacebar.

Command: **regenauto**
ON/OFF<current>:

When you turn REGENAUTO off, what you see on the screen may not always represent the current state of the drawing. When changes are made by certain commands the display will be updated only after using the REGEN command. But, waiting time can be avoided as long as you are aware of the status of the display. Turning the REGENAUTO setting back to ON will cause a regeneration. While the REGENAUTO is off and commands requires a regeneration you will be prompted:

About to regen, proceed? <Y>

Responding with **No** will abort the command. Exceptions to this are the ZOOM Vmax command, which does not require a regeneration, and ZOOM All, ZOOM Extents, REGEN, and VIEW Restore, which do require regeneration.

Regeneration during a transparent command will be delayed until a regeneration is performed after that transparent command. The following message will appear:

REGEN QUEUED

DRAGMODE Command

The DRAGMODE command has three settings: on, off, and auto. Certain draw and modify commands display highlighted dynamic (cursor following) representations of the objects being drawn or edited. This can slow down the drawing process if the objects are very complex. Turning the DRAGMODE setting to off turns off dragging. The DRAGMODE command is invoked by typing **DRAGMODE** at the "Command:" prompt and pressing [Enter] or the spacebar.

Command: **dragmode**
ON/OFF/Auto <current>:

When DRAGMODE is turned off, all calls for dragging are ignored. Turning the DRAGMODE on allows dragging by use of the DRAG command modifier. Setting the DRAGMODE to Auto causes dragging wherever possible.

When DRAGMODE is turned off the DRAG command modifier can be used wherever dragging is permitted. For example, during the MOVE prompt you can use the following:

Command: **move**
Select objects: *(select the objects)*
Base point or displacement: *(specify base point)*
Second point of displacement: **drag**

At this point the selected objects follows the cursor movement in highlighted display.

BLIPMODE Command

The BLIPMODE command has two settings: on and off. When the BLIPMODE setting is on, a small cross mark is displayed when points on the screen are picked with the cursor or specified by entering their coordinates. Turning the BLIPMODE setting to OFF prevents the marks from being placed. After editing for a while, the drawing can become cluttered with these blips. They have no effect other than visual reference and can be removed at any time by using the RE-DRAW, REGEN, ZOOM, or PAN commands. Pressing the [F7] key or [Ctrl]+[G] twice (Grid ON/OFF) will also quickly remove the blips. Any other command requiring regeneration causes the blips to be removed. The BLIPMODE command is invoked by typing **BLIPMODE** at the "Command:" prompt and pressing [Enter] or the spacebar.

Command: **blipmode**
ON/OFF<current>: *(specify on or off)*

TOOLBAR Command

The TOOLBAR command is used to display a toolbar at a specific location on the screen and, if necessary, close a toolbar. The TOOLBAR command is invoked by typing **TOOLBAR** at the "Command:" prompt and pressing [Enter] or spacebar. AutoCAD prompts:

Toolbar name (or ALL): *(type the name of the toolbar or type all to display/close all the toolbars)*
Hide/Left/Right/Top/Bottom/Float<Show>:

The **Show** option causes the specified toolbar to be displayed.

The **Hide** option causes the specified toolbar to be closed.

The **Left** option causes the specified toolbar to be docked at the left side of the screen, prompting:

Position<0,0>: *(specify a position or press [Enter])*

The values specify the column and row position relative to a toolbar docking area with the first value being horizontal and the second being vertical.

The **Right** option causes the specified toolbar to be docked at the right side of the screen, prompting:

Position<0,0>: *(specify a position or press [Enter])*

The values specify the column and row position relative to a toolbar docking area with the first value being horizontal and the second being vertical.

The **Top** option causes the specified toolbar to be docked at the top of the screen, prompting:

Position<0,0>: *(specify a position or press [Enter])*

The values specify the column and row position relative to a toolbar docking area with the first value being horizontal and the second being vertical.

The **Bottom** option causes the specified toolbar to be docked at the bottom of the screen, prompting:

Position<0,0>: *(specify a position or press [Enter])*

The values specify the column and row position relative to a toolbar docking area with the first value being horizontal and the second being vertical.

The **Float** option causes the specified toolbar to place anywhere on the screen, prompting:

Position<0.0>: *(specify a position or press [Enter])*

The values specify the column and row position relative to screen coordinates the first value being horizontal and the second being vertical.

The **All** option causes all toolbars to be displayed or closed. You are prompted:

Show/Hide: *(enter s or h)*

Show causes all toolbars to be displayed and Hide causes all toolbars to be closed.

OBJECT PROPERTIES

There are two important properties, color and linetype, that control the appearance of objects. You can specify the color and linetype for the objects to be drawn, with the help of the LAYER command as explained in Chapter 3. You can do the same using the COLOR and LINETYPE commands.

COLOR Command

The COLOR command allows you to specify a color for the objects to be drawn, separate from the layer color. The COLOR command is invoked from the screen menu DATA, or at the "Command:" prompt type **COLOR** and press Enter or the spacebar.

    Command: **color**
    New object color<current>:

The color may be entered as a standard name (red, green, cyan, yellow, magenta, blue, white, or green) or by the number code (1 through 255). Or, you can respond with BYLAYER or BYBLOCK. BYLAYER is the default. If you reply with a standard name or number code, this becomes the current color. All new objects you create are drawn with this color, regardless of which layer is current, until you again set the color to BYLAYER or BYBLOCK. BYLAYER causes the objects drawn to assume the color of the layer on which it is drawn. BYBLOCK causes objects to be drawn in white until selected for inclusion in a block definition. Subsequent insertion of a block that contains objects drawn under the BYBLOCK option causes those objects to assume the color of the layer on which the BLOCK is inserted. You can use the CHANGE command to change the color of existing objects.

> **NOTE:** As noted in Chapter 3, the options to specify colors by both layer and by the COLOR command can cause confusion in a large drawing, especially one containing blocks and nested blocks. You are advised not to mix the two methods of specifying colors in the same drawing.

LINETYPE Command

The LINETYPE command allows you to draw lines with different dash/dot/space combinations. It is used to load linetype definitions from a library or lets you create custom linetypes.

The only objects that linetypes can be applied to are lines, circles, arcs, and 2D polylines. A linetype must exist in a library file and be loaded before you can apply it to an object or layer. Standard linetypes are in the library file called ACAD.LIN and are not loaded with the LAYER command. You have to load the linetype before you assign it to a specific layer.

Linetypes are combinations of dashes, dots, and spaces. Customized linetypes permit "out of line" objects in a linetype such as circles, wavy lines, blocks, and skew segments. All parts of the line must be "on the line."

Dash, dot, and space combinations eventually repeat themselves. For example, a six-unit long dash, followed by a dot between two one-unit long spaces repeats itself according to the overall length of the line drawn and the LTSCALE setting.

Lines with dashes (not all dots) usually have dashes at both ends. AutoCAD automatically adjusts the lengths of end dashes to reach the endpoints of the adjoining line. Intermediate dashes will be the lengths specified in the definition. If the overall length of the line is not long enough to permit the breaks, the line is drawn continuous.

There is no guarantee that any segments of the line fall at some particular location. For example, when placing a center line through circle centers, you cannot be sure that the short dashes will be centered on the circle centers as most conventions call for. To achieve this effect, the short and long dashes have to be created by either drawing them individually or by breaking a continuous line to create the spaces between the dashes. This also creates multiple in-line lines instead of one line of a particular linetype. Or you can use the DIMENSION command Center option to place the desired mark.

Individual linetype names and definitions are stored in one or more files whose extension is .LIN. The same name may be defined differently in two different files. Selecting the desired one requires proper responses to the prompts in the Load option of the LINETYPE command. If you redefine a linetype, loading it with the LINETYPE command will cause objects drawn on layers assigned to that linetype to assume the new definition.

Mastering the use of linetypes involves using the LAYER command, the LINETYPE command, the LTSCALE command and knowing what files contain the linetype definition(s) desired. Also, with the LINETYPE command you can define custom linetypes.

The LINETYPE command is invoked by typing **LINETYPE** at the "Command:" prompt and pressing Enter or the spacebar.

> Command: **linetype**
> ?/Create/Load/Set:

The options and responses are as described in the following sections.

? Option The ? option displays a list of the linetypes in a specified file with graphic descriptions.

> Command: **linetype**
> ?/Create/Load/Set: **?**
> File to list <default>: (Enter *or specify filename)*

You can press Enter to designate the default file or enter the name of another file. Do not add the .LIN extension to the name of the file. AutoCAD assumes this. The display flips to the text screen and lists all the linetypes in a specified file.

Create Option The Create option allows you to create new linetypes and store them in a library file. For a detailed explanation about creating linetypes, see Chapter 17, Customizing AutoCAD.

Load Option The Load option allows you to load explicitly a linetype into your current drawing. Standard linetypes from the library file ACAD.LIN are loaded automatically with the LAYER command Ltype option when the command is selected from the side menu.

Set Option This option allows you to set the current linetype for subsequently drawn objects. If you reply with a standard name, this becomes the current linetype. All new objects you create will be drawn with this linetype, despite which layer is current, until you again set the linetype to BYLAYER or BYBLOCK. BYLAYER is the default. BYLAYER causes the object drawn to

Utility Commands

assume the linetype of the layer on which it is drawn. BYBLOCK causes objects to be drawn in continuous until selected for inclusion in a block definition. Subsequent insertion of a block that contains objects drawn under the BYBLOCK option will cause those objects to assume the linetype of the layer on which the block is inserted. You can use the CHANGE command to change the linetype of existing objects.

> **NOTE:** As noted in Chapter 3, the options to specify linetypes by both layer and by the LINETYPE command can cause confusion in a large drawing, especially one containing blocks and nested blocks. You are advised not to mix the two methods of specifying linetypes in the same drawing.

You can also load linetypes by invoking the LINETYPE command from the screen menu DATA or at the "Command:" prompt type **DDLTYPE** and press Enter or spacebar.

AutoCAD displays the Select Linetype dialog box. Click the Load button. AutoCAD displays the Load or Reload Linetypes dialog box listing all the available linetypes in the current linetype library file. To load all the available linetypes, click the Select All button and click the OK button to close the Load or Reload Linetypes dialog box. AutoCAD loads all the available linetypes.

You can also load the available linetypes from the Layer Control dialog box. Select a layer from the layer list, and click the Set Ltype... button. AutoCAD displays the Select Linetype dialog box. Click the Load button, AutoCAD displays the Load or Reload Linetypes dialog box listing all the available linetypes in the current linetype library file. To load all the available linetypes, click the Select All button and click the OK button to close the Load or Reload Linetypes dialog box. AutoCAD loads all the available linetypes.

DRAWING AID X, Y, AND Z FILTERS—AN ENHANCEMENT TO OSNAP

AutoCAD's filters feature allows you to establish a 2D point by specifying the individual (X and Y) coordinates one at a time in separate steps. In the case of a 3D point you can specify the individual (X, Y, and Z) coordinates in three steps. Or you can specify one of the three coordinate values in one step and a point in another step, from which AutoCAD extracts the other two coordinate values for use in the point being established.

The filters feature is used when being prompted to establish a point, as in the starting point of a line, the center of a circle, drawing a node with the POINT command, or specifying a base or second point in displacement for the MOVE or COPY command, to mention just a few.

> **NOTE:** During the application of the filters feature there are steps where you can input either single coordinate values or points, and there are steps where you can input only points. It is necessary to understand these restrictions and options and when one type of input is more desirable than the other.

When selecting points during the use of filters, you need to know which coordinates of the specified point are going to be used in the point being established. It is also essential to know how to combine object snap modes with those steps that use point input.

The filters feature is actually an enhancement to either the object snap or the @ (last point) feature. Using AutoCAD's ability to establish a point by snapping to a point on an existing object is one of the most powerful features in CAD, and being able to have AutoCAD snap to such an existing point and then filter out selected coordinates for use in establishing a new point adds to that power. Therefore, in most cases, you will not use the filters feature if it is practical to type in all of the coordinates from the keyboard, because typing in all coordinates can be done in a single step. The filters feature is a multistep process, and each step might include substeps; one to specify the coordinate(s) to be filtered out and another to designate the object snap mode involved.

Filters with @

When AutoCAD is prompting for a point, the filters feature is initiated by entering a period followed by the letter designation for the coordinate(s) to be filtered out. For example, if you draw a point starting at (0,0) and use the relative polar coordinate response @3<45 to determine the endpoint, you can use filters to establish another point whose X coordinate is the same X coordinate as the end of the line just drawn. It works for Y and Z coordinates and combinations of XY, XZ, and YZ coordinates also. The following command sequence shows how to apply filter to a line that needs to be started at a point whose X coordinate is the same as the end of the previous line and the Y coordinate is 1.25. The line will be drawn horizontally 3 units long. The sequence is as follows:

> Command: **line**
> From point: **0,0**
> To point: **@3<45**
> To point: Enter

> Command: **line** (*or* Enter)
> From point: **.x**
> of @
> (need YZ): **0,1.25**
> To point: **@3<0**

Entering .x initiates the filters feature. AutoCAD then prompts you to specify a point from which it can extract the X coordinate. The @ (last point) does this. The new line has a starting point whose X coordinate is the same as that of the last point drawn. By using the filters feature to extract the X coordinate, that starting point will be on an imaginary vertical line through the point specified by @ in response to the "of" prompt.

When you initiate filters with a single coordinate (.x in the example above) and respond with a point (@), the prompt that follows asks for a point also. From it (the second point specified) AutoCAD extracts the other two coordinates for the new point.

Even though the prompt is for "YZ," the point may be specified in 2D format as 0,1.25 (the X and Y coordinates) from which AutoCAD takes the second value as the needed Y coordinate. The Z coordinate is assumed to be the elevation of the current coordinate system.

You can use the two-coordinate response to initiate filters, specify a point and then all that AutoCAD requires is a single value for the final coordinate. An example of this follows.

```
Command: line
From point: 0,0
To point: @3<45
To point: [Enter]
```

```
Command: line (or [Enter])
From point: .xz
of @
(need Y): 1.25
To point: @3<0
```

You can also specify a point in response to the prompt "(need Y)" as follows:

(need Y): **0,1.25** *(or pick a point on the screen)*

In this case, AutoCAD uses the Y coordinate of the point specified as the Y coordinate of the new point.

Remember, it is an individual coordinate in 2D (one or two coordinates in 3D) of an existing point that you wish AutoCAD to extract and use for the new point. In most cases you will be object snapping to a point for the response. Otherwise, if you knew the value of the coordinate needed, you would probably type it in from the keyboard.

Filters with Object Snap

Without filters, an object snap (OSNAP) mode establishes a new point to coincide with one on an existing object. With filters, an OSNAP mode establishes selected coordinates of a new point to coincide with corresponding coordinates of one on an existing object.

Extracting one or more coordinate values to be applied to corresponding coordinate values of a point that you are being prompted to establish is shown in the following example. In Figure 12–10, a 2.75" × 7.1875" rectangle has a 0.875"-diameter hole in its center. A board drafter would determine the center of a square or rectangle by drawing diagonals and centering the circle at their intersection. AutoCAD drafters (without filters) could do the same, or might draw orthogonal lines from the

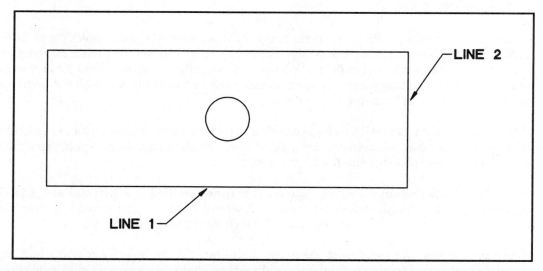

Figure 12–10 Extracting coordinate values to be applied to corresponding coordinate values

midpoint of a horizontal line and from the midpoint of one of the vertical lines to establish a centering intersection. The following command sequence shows steps in drawing a rectangle with a circle in the center using filters.

```
Command: line
From point:  (select point p1)
To point: @2.75<90
To point: @7.1875<0
To point: @2.75<270
To point: c

Command: circle
3P/2P/TTR/<Center point>: .x
of mid
of (select line 1)
(need YZ): mid
of (select line 2)
Diameter/<Radius>: d
Diameter: .875
```

SHELL COMMAND

The SHELL command allows you to execute DOS programs without leaving AutoCAD. You can execute any DOS program as long as there is sufficient memory to execute. The SHELL command is invoked by typing **SHELL** at the "Command:" prompt and pressing [Enter] or the spacebar.

```
Command: shell
OS Command:
```

You can reply with any command that would be a valid response to the operating system's program prompt. When the utility program is finished, AutoCAD takes you back to the "Command:" prompt. If you need to execute more than one DOS program, then give a null response to the "DOS command:" prompt. AutoCAD responds with the following message:

Type EXIT to return to AutoCAD

and then displays the DOS prompt followed by two greater-than signs instead of one, as shown below:

C>>

You can now enter as many DOS commands as you wish. When you are finished, you may return to AutoCAD by typing **EXIT**. It will take you back to the "Command:" prompt.

If there is not enough free memory for the SHELL command, the following message will appear:

Shell error: insufficient memory for command.

Where there is insufficient memory, you can execute the SH command instead of the SHELL command. SH requires less memory than the SHELL command and can be used to access internal DOS commands such DIR, COPY, and TYPE. If the need arises, you can adjust the amount of memory required for the SH and SHELL commands by modifiying the ACAD.PGP file. For additional information, see Chapter 17 on Customizing AutoCAD.

Program Switching with Windows

Under Windows, there is no need for the SHELL command, except for script files, menu macros and AutoLISP routines that were developed under DOS and expect to find the SHELL command. Instead, you can switch from AutoCAD to any other Windows or DOS program with one of the following methods:

Press [Alt]+[Tab] to switch to the program you were most recently using. In most cases, you switch back to the Windows Program Manager.

Hold down [Alt] and press [Tab] repeatedly. Windows displays a dialog box listing a running program. If this is the program you want to switch to, let go of [Alt]; if not, press [Tab] again.

Press [Ctrl]+[Esc] and Windows displays the Task List dialog box (shown in Figure 12–11), which lists the names of all programs currently running under Windows. If the program you want to switch to is not listed (is not running), switch to the Program Manager and launch the application.

If AutoCAD is running in a window smaller than the computer screen, and you can see the other application underneath, simply click on the application's window and it comes to the foreground.

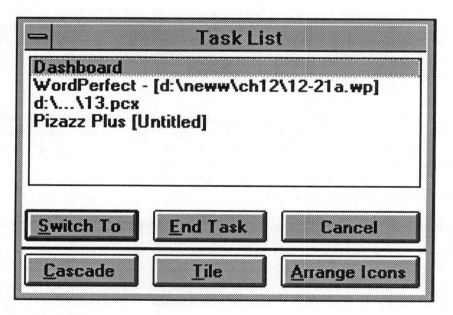

Figure 12–11   Task List dialog box

> **NOTE:** Do not delete the AutoCAD lock files or temporary files created for the current drawing when you are at the operating system prompt. Do not use the CHKDSK command with /F option. Do not run programs that reset the serial I/O ports on the computer.

FILES COMMAND

The FILES command allows you to execute some of the DOS commands while you are in AutoCAD. The DOS commands include listings of files from a specific drive or directory, and enable you to delete, rename, copy or unlock specific files. You can also perform the same operations with the help of the SHELL command.

The FILES command is invoked by typing **FILES** at the "Command:" prompt and pressing [Enter] or the spacebar.

Command: **files**

AutoCAD displays a **File Utilities** dialog box similar to the one shown in Figure 12–12. Select the item for the task you want to perform. Exit is the default option. Each option, except Exit, displays a standard file dialog box that allows you to search for a specific file or group of files, and then perform the necessary action. After you delete, rename, copy, or unlock files, a status message letting you know how many files were changed appears at the bottom of the File Utilities dialog box.

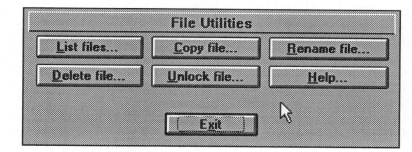

Figure 12–12 The File Utilities dialog box

MAKEPREVIEW Command

The MAKEPREVIEW command is used to make an image for previewing an AutoCAD release 12 (or earlier) drawing. This eliminates the necessity of having to save a drawing in the release 13 format. Once a preview image is made, AutoCAD Release 13 can display a preview image of the drawing in the Open File Select dialog box when the drawing file is selected in the file list box.

The MAKEPREVIEW command is invoked by typing **MAKEPREVIEW** at the "Command:" prompt and pressing [Enter] or spacebar.

AutoCAD creates a .bmp file of the current view in the directory where the drawing is located. AutoCAD automatically creates a preview image if the drawing is saved as AutoCAD Release 13 format.

MVSETUP Command

The MVSETUP command is used to control and set up the view(s) of a drawing, including the choice of standard plotted sheet sizes with a border, scale for plotting on the selected sheet size, and multiple viewports. The MVSETUP is an AutoLISP routine that can be customized to insert any type of border and title block.

Options and associated prompts depend upon whether the TILEMODE system variable is set to ON (1) or OFF (0). When TILEMODE is set to on, Tiled Viewports is enabled. When TILEMODE is set to off, the Floating Viewports menu item is enabled. Other Paper Space related drawing setup options are available.

The MVSETUP command is invoked by typing MVSETUP at the "Command:" prompt and pressing [Enter] or spacebar. AutoCAD prompts depend on the TILEMODE settings.

If TILEMODE is set to 1, then AutoCAD prompts:

Enable paper space?(No/<Yes>): *(press* [Enter] *to enable paper space, and in turn AutoCAD changes the TILEMODE setting to 0, or type n and press* [Enter] *to stay in TILEMODE setting of 1)*

If TILEMODE is set to 0, then AutoCAD prompts:

Align/Create/Scale viewports/Options/Title block/Undo: *(select an option)*

The following is the procedure for setting up the drawing with the TILEMODE is set at 1. AutoCAD prompts:

Enable paper space?(No/<Yes>): *(type n and press* [Enter] *)*
Units type (Scientific/Decimal/Engineering/ Architectural/ Metric): *(select a unit type. Depending on the units selected, AutoCAD lists the available scales. Select one of the available scales or you can even specify custom scale factor)*
Enter the scale factor: *(specify a scale factor)*
Enter the paper width: *(specify the paper width on which the drawing will be plotted)*
Enter the paper height: *(specify the paper height on which the drawing will be plotted)*

AutoCAD sets up the appropriate limits to allow you to draw to full scale and also draws a bounding box enclosing the limits. Draw the drawing to full scale and when you ready to plot, specify the scale mentioned earlier to plot the drawing.

Following is the procedure for setting up the drawing with the TILEMODE is set at 0. AutoCAD prompts:

Align/Create/Scale viewports/Options/Title block/Undo: *(select an option)*

The options are explained in the order that is logical to complete the drawing setup.

Title block The title block option allows you to select appropriate title block. First, AutoCAD lists the available title blocks and prompts to select one of the available title blocks as follows:

0: None
1. ISO A4 Size(mm)
2. ISO A3 Size(mm)
3. ISO A2 Size(mm)
4. ISO A1 Size(mm)
5. ISO A0 Size(mm)
6. ANSI-V Size(in)
7. ANSI-A Size(in)
8. ANSI-B Size(in)
9. ANSI-C Size(in)

10. ANSI-D Size(in)
11. ANSI-E Size(in)
12. Arch/Engineering (24 x 36in)
13. Generic D size Sheet (24 x 36in)

Add/Delete/Redisplay/<Number of entry to load>: *(select one of the available title blocks and press* Enter *, AutoCAD inserts a border and title block, as shown in Figure 12–13, or enter an option)*

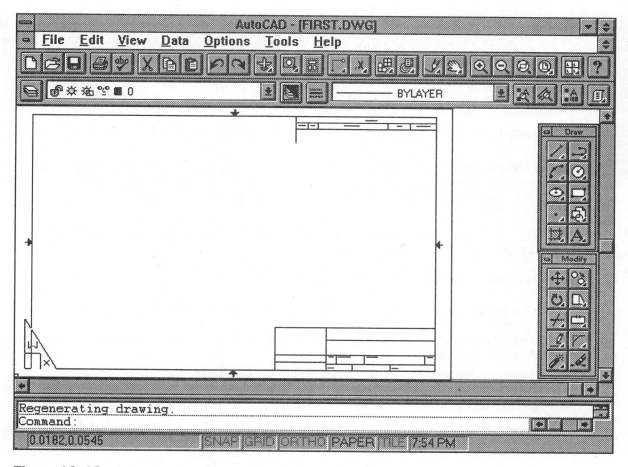

Figure 12–13 Title block and border for ANSI-B Size

The **Add** option allows you to add a title block drawing to the available list.

The **Delete** option allows you to delete an entry from the available list.

The **Redisplay** option redisplays the list of title block options.

Create The Create option allows you to establish viewports. AutoCAD prompts:

Delete objects/Undo/<Create viewports>: *(press* Enter *to create viewports and AutoCAD lists the available viewport layout options or enter an option)*

Available Mview viewport layout options:

0: None
1: Single
2: Std. Engineering
3: Array of Viewports

Redisplay/<Number of entry to load>: *(select one of the available layout options or select an option)*

The **None** selection creates no viewports. The **1** selection creates a single viewports whose size is determined by subsequent prompt. The **2** selection creates a four viewports with preset viewing angle by dividing a specified area into quadrants. The size is determined by subsequent prompt. The **3** selection creates a matrix of viewports along the X and Y axes.

The **Delete objects** option deletes the existing viewports.

The **Undo** option reverses operations performed in the current MVSETUP session.

Scale Viewports   The Scale Viewports option adjusts the scale factor of the objects displayed in the viewports. The scale factor is specified as a ratio of paper space to model space. For example, 1:48 is one paper space unit for 48 model space units (scale for 1/4" = 1'0") .

Options   The Options option lets you establish several different functions that are associated with your layout. AutoCAD prompts:

Set Layer/LImits/Units/Xref: *(enter an option)*

The **Set Layer** option permits you to specify a layer for placing the title block.

The **LImits** option permits you to specify whether or not to reset the limits to drawing extents after the title block has been inserted.

The **Units** option permits you to specify whether sizes and point locations will be translated to inch or millimeter paper units.

The **Xref** option permits you to specify whether the title block is to be inserted or externally referenced.

Align   The Align option causes AutoCAD to pan the view in one viewport so that it aligns with a basepoint in another viewport. Whichever viewport the other point moves to becomes the active viewport. AutoCAD prompts:

Angled/Horizontal/Vertical alignment/Rotate view/Undo: *(select an option)*

The **Angled** option causes AutoCAD to pan the view in a viewport in a specified direction.

The **Horizontal** option causes AutoCAD to pan the view in one viewport, aligning it horizontally with a base point in another viewport.

The **Vertical Alignment** option causes AutoCAD to pan the view in one viewport, aligning it vertically with a basepoint in another viewport.

The **Rotate View** option causes AutoCAD to rotate the view in a viewport around a base point.

The **Undo** option causes AutoCAD to undo the results of the current MVSETUP command.

TIME COMMAND

The TIME command displays the current time and date related to your current drawing session. In addition, you also can find out how long you have been working in AutoCAD. This command uses the clock in your computer to keep track of the time functions and displays to the nearest millisecond using 24-hour military format. The TIME command is invoked by typing **TIME** at the "Command:" prompt and pressing Enter or the spacebar.

        Command: **time**

The following listing is displayed in the text screen followed by a prompt:

        Current time: 11 July 1992 at 11:54:15.340
        Time for this drawing:
        Created: 11 July 1992 at 10:31:12.230
        Last updated: 11 July 1992 at 10:31:12.230
        Total editing time: 0 days 01:23:03:110
        Elapsed timer (on):   0 days 01:23:03:110
        Next automatic save in: 0 days 01:03:17:350
    Display/ON/OFF/Reset:

The first line gives information about today's date and time.

The third line gives information about the date and time the current drawing was initially created. The drawing time starts when you initially begin a new drawing. If the drawing was created by using the WBLOCK command, the date and time is taken into consideration at the time the command was executed.

The fourth line provides information about the date and time the drawing was last updated. This is initially set to the drawing creation time. This is updated each time when you use the END or SAVE command.

The fifth line provides the information about the time you are in AutoCAD. This timer is continuously updated by AutoCAD while you are in the program, excluding plotting and printer plot time. This timer cannot be stopped or reset.

The sixth line provides the information about the stopwatch timer. You can turn this timer ON or OFF and reset to zero. This timer is independent of other functions.

The seventh line provides the information about when the next automatic save will take place.

Display Option The Display option redisplays the time functions with updated times.

ON Option The ON option turns the stopwatch timer to ON, if it is OFF. By default it is ON.

OFF Option The OFF option turns the stopwatch timer to OFF and displays the accumulated time.

Reset Option The RESET option resets the stopwatch timer to zero.

To exit the TIME command, give a null response or [Esc] to the prompt.

AUDIT COMMAND

The AUDIT command is used as a diagnostic tool to correct any errors or defects in the data base of the current drawing. AutoCAD generates an extensive report of the problems and for every error detected, AutoCAD recommends action to correct it.

The AUDIT command is invoked from the screen menu FILE (from MANAGE), or at the "Command:" prompt type **AUDIT** and press [Enter].

    Command: **audit**
    Fix any errors detected? <N>:

If you respond with **Y** or **Yes**, AutoCAD will fix all the errors detected, and display an audit report with the detailed information about the errors detected and fixing them. If you answer with **N** or **No**, AutoCAD will just display a report and will not fix any errors.

In addition, AutoCAD creates an ASCII report file (AUDITCLT System variable should be ON) with the description of problems and the action taken. It will save the file in the current directory, using the current drawing's name with the file extension .ADT. You can use the regular DOS commands TYPE or PRINT to display the report file on the screen or print it on the printer.

OBJECT LINKING AND EMBEDDING (OLE)

Object Linking and Embedding (OLE) is a Microsoft Windows feature that combines various application data into one compound document. AutoCAD Release 13 for Windows has added OLE Client capability to its present Server capability introduced in Release 12. As a client, AutoCAD now permits you to have objects from other Windows applications either embedded or linked into your drawing.

When an object is inserted into an AutoCAD drawing from an application that supports OLE, the object can maintain a connection with its source file. If you insert an embedded object into AutoCAD (client), it is no longer associated with the source (server). If necessary, you can edit the embedded data from inside AutoCAD drawing by using the original application. But at the same time this editing does not change the original file.

Instead, if you insert an object as a linked object in AutoCAD (client), the object remains associated with its source (server). When you edit a linked object in AutoCAD by using the original application, the original file as well as the object inserted in AutoCAD changes.

Linked or embedded objects appear on the screen in AutoCAD and can be printed or plotted using Windows system drivers. If you open the drawing using a DOS or UNIX version of AutoCAD, you do not see the OLE objects.

In AutoCAD Release 13 for Windows, you can make AutoCAD work as a client or as a server.

Let's look at an example of object linking between AutoCAD (server) drawing and Microsoft Write (client). Figure 12–14 shows a drawing of a desk, computer, and chair which contain various attribute values. We are going to link this drawing to a Microsoft Write document.

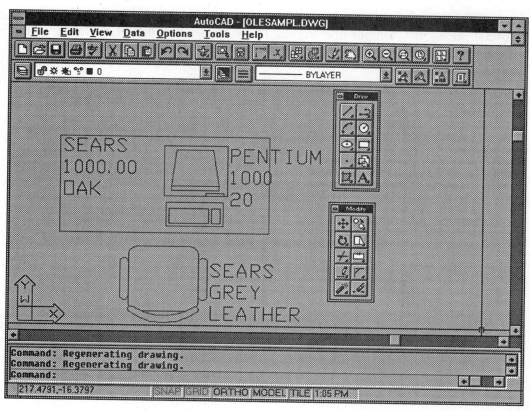

Figure 12–14 Drawing of a desk, computer, and chair with attribute values

From the pull-down menu Edit select the Copy option and AutoCAD prompts to select objects. Select the computer, table, and chair and press Enter. This will copy the selection to the Windows clipboard. Minimize the AutoCAD program.

Invoke the Microsoft Write program from the Program Manager by double clicking the Write program icon from the Accessories group. The Microsoft Write program is displayed, as shown in Figure 12–15. Type one line of sample text, as shown in Figure 12–15.

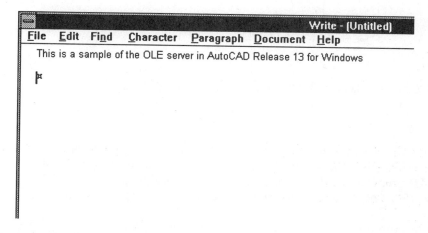

Figure 12–15 Microsoft Write program

From the pull-down menu Edit in Microsoft Write, select Paste Special... and Write displays Paste Special dialog box, as shown in Figure 12–16. Select the Paste Line button. This will insert the AutoCAD drawing object into Microsoft Write, as shown in Figure 12–17.

Figure 12–16   Paste Special dialog box

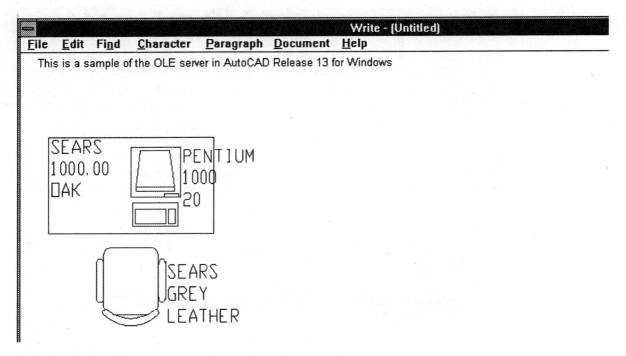

Figure 12–17   Microsoft Write document with AutoCAD drawing

Minimize the Write program and maximize the AutoCAD program (or if AutoCAD program is not open, double click the drawing image in the Write document, and which in turn will launch AutoCAD program with the image drawing open). Edit the values of the attributes in the computer block to 486, 520, 15, which represent a 486 computer with 520MB hard drive and a 15" monitor.

Switch back to the Write program and from the Edit pull-down menu select the Links... option. The Write program will display the Links dialog box, shown in Figure 12–18.

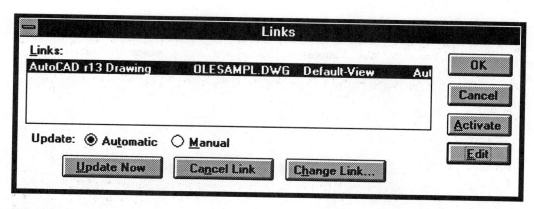

Figure 12–18   Links dialog box

Select the Update Now button and then click the OK button. The image in the Write document is updated, as shown in Figure 12–19.

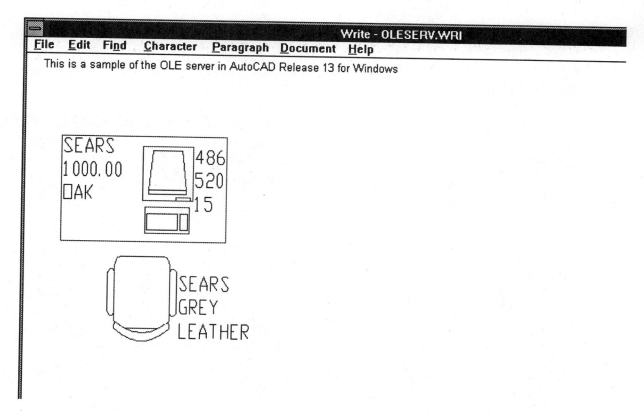

Figure 12–19   AutoCAD drawing updated in the Write document

In the above example, AutoCAD is the server and Microsoft Write is the client.

Alternatively, you can place a linked object into AutoCAD, where AutoCAD is the client and another application is the server. Let's look an example in which AutoCAD is the client and Excel is the server.

From the pull-down menu Edit in AutoCAD, select the Paste Special... option and AutoCAD displays the Paste Special dialog box, as shown in Figure 12–20. Select the Paste Link option radio button and Microsoft Excel 5.0 Worksheet from the list box and click the OK button.

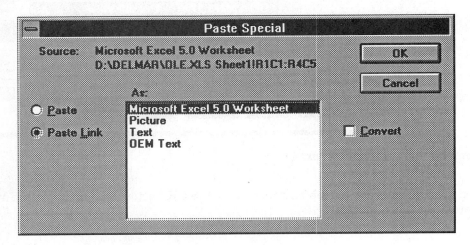

Figure 12–20 Paste Special dialog box

The Excel spreadsheet will be linked to the drawing, as shown in Figure 12–21. AutoCAD is now the client and Microsoft Excel 5.0 is the server.

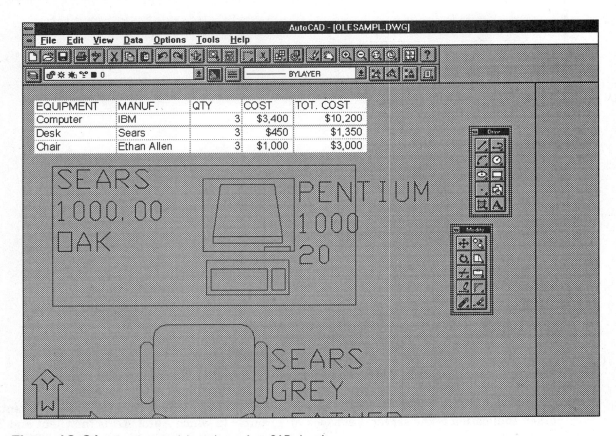

Figure 12–21 Excel spreadsheet in an AutoCAD drawing

To edit the spreadsheet, double click anywhere on the spreadsheet which in turn will launch Excel with the spreadsheet document open. Any changes made to the spreadsheet will be reflected in the drawing. Figure 12–22 shows the changes that were made in the spreadsheet.

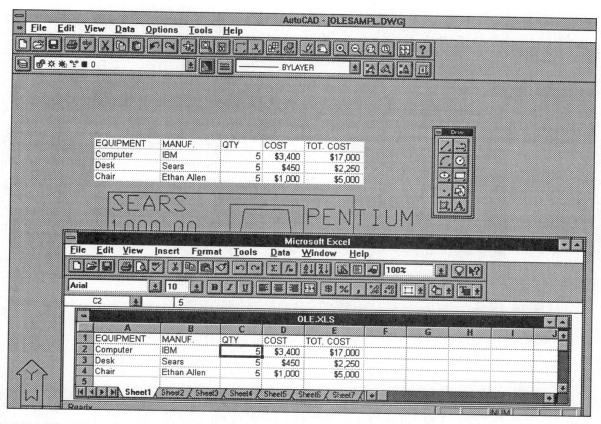

Figure 12–22 AutoCAD drawing showing the changes made in the spreadsheet

Another example of using AutoCAD drawing as the client for both embedding from WORD and linking from EXCEL is illustrated as follows:

Figure 12–23 shows both an AutoCAD screen and an Excel spreadsheet in which the spreadsheet is being used for area calculations. The AREA cells are formulas that calculate the product of the each corresponding WIDTH and LENGTH cells. In turn, the TOTAL cell is the sum of the above AREA cells.

Figure 12–24 shows the same AutoCAD screen and a Word document that was used for typing the GENERAL NOTES which were in turn embedded into the AutoCAD drawing.

Figure 12–25 shows how the cell value in the WIDTH for ROOM1 has been changed, resulting in changes in the AREA and TOTAL cells. Because this object (the spreadsheet consisting of 4 columns and 7 rows including the title) was Paste Linked into the AutoCAD drawing, the linked object automatically reflects the changes.

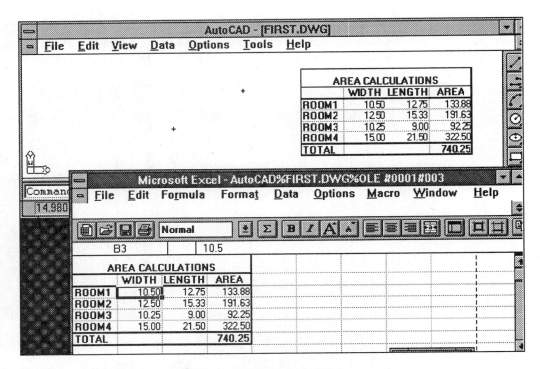

Figure 12–23 AutoCAD drawing screen and an Excel spreadsheet

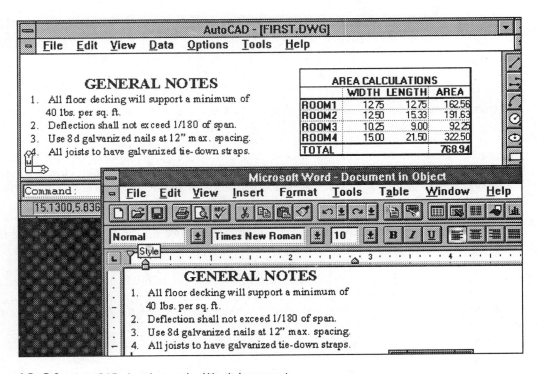

Figure 12–24 AutoCAD drawing and a Word document

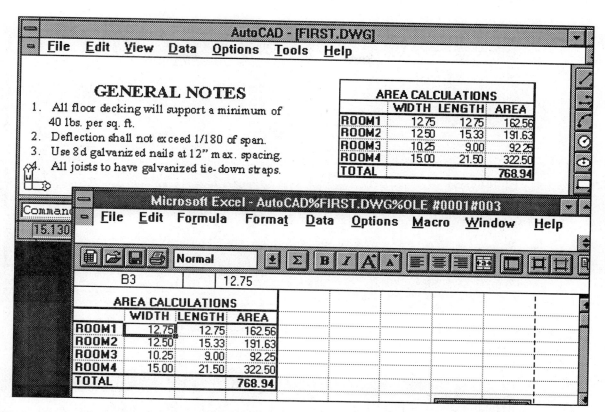

Figure 12-25   Changes shown in the spreadsheet and AutoCAD screen

AUTOCAD PREFERENCES

One of the most common things that AutoCAD users like to do is to change the AutoCAD working environment. The AutoCAD working environment can be changed from the Preferences dialog box. From the pull-down menu Options select Preferences... or at the "Command:" prompt type **PREFERENCES** and press Enter or spacebar. AutoCAD displays the Preferences dialog box, as shown in Figure 12-26.

From the Preferences dialog box, the user can control various aspects of the AutoCAD environment. The Preferences dialog box is divided into five sections, and to make changes to any of the sections, select the name tab from the top of the Preferences dialog box.

System Section   The System section controls the appearance of the AutoCAD graphics window, enables the automatic save feature, and specifies the type of digitizer input. The Font... button displays the Font dialog box. Use this dialog box to specify the font AutoCAD uses for text displayed in the graphics window and text window. The Color... displays the AutoCAD Window Colors dialog box. Use this dialog box to specify colors of elements in the AutoCAD application window.

Environment Section   The Environment section, as shown in Figure 12-27, specifies the directories in which AutoCAD searches for configuration, driver, or menu files. The settings take effect when you close the dialog box. The Memory edit field controls the memory paging. The AutoCAD pager divides the current drawing file into pages, and Windows allocates memory for the pages. When memory becomes full, the pager writes drawing data to disk.

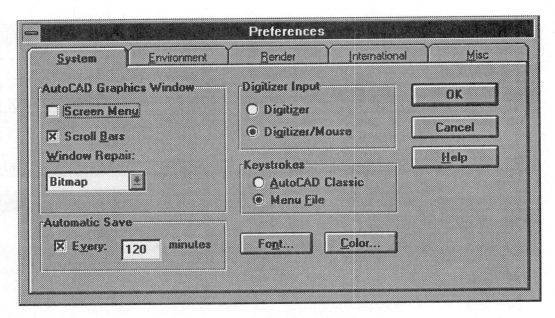

Figure 12-26 Preferences dialog box showing the System section

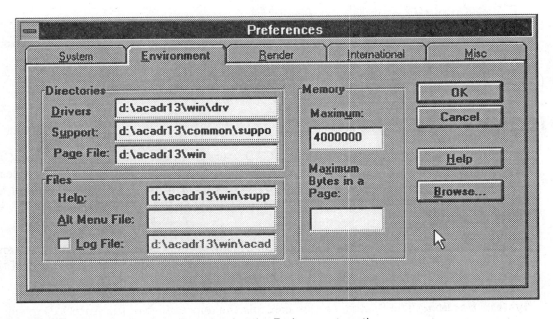

Figure 12-27 Preferences dialog box showing the Environment section

Render Section   The Render section, shown in Figure 12–28, changes your rendering environment. Configuration, face, and page files are placed in the current directory by default. You can designate a directory on a disk drive with plenty of free space.

International Section   The International section, shown in Figure 12–29, specifies international settings and prototype drawing settings.

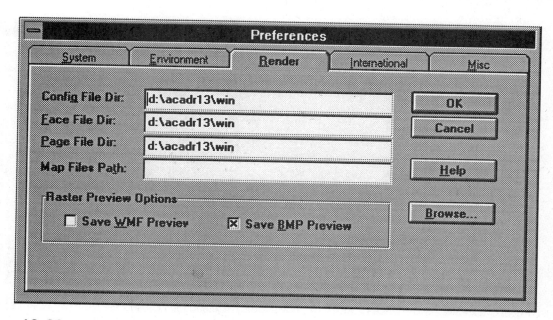

Figure 12–28   Preferences dialog box showing the Render section

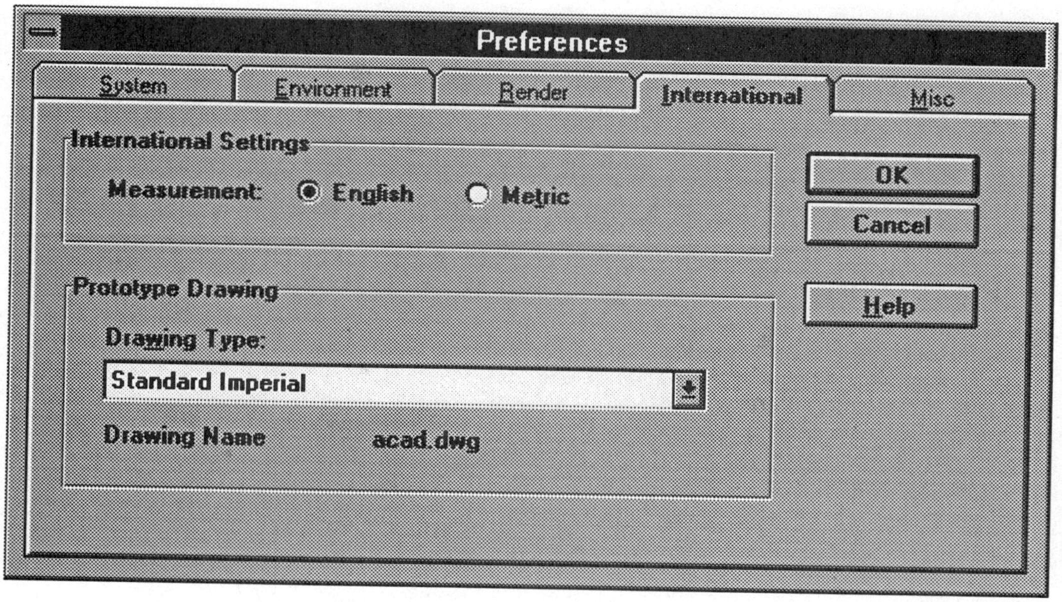

Figure 12–29   Preferences dialog box showing the International section

Misc Section   The Misc section, shown in Figure 12–30, specifies which text editor and font mapping file the MTEXT command uses, and controls the drawing or an application window size on startup. In addition, you can also configure the command line window settings.

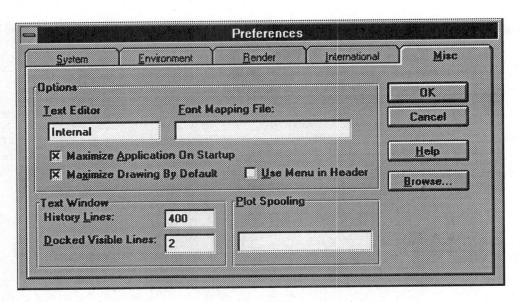

Figure 12–30 Preferences dialog box showing the Misc section

All the changes that are made in the Preferences dialog box are saved in the ACAD.INI file. When AutoCAD is loaded again, all of the changes will be reflected.

REVIEW QUESTIONS

1. All of the following can be renamed using the RENAME command except
   (A) current drawing name   (C) block names
   (B) named Views   (D) text style names

2. The PURGE command can be used
   (A) after an editing session
   (B) at the beginning of the editing session
   (C) at any time during an editing session
   (D) None of the above

3. The following items can be purged from a drawing file except
   (A) text styles
   (B) blocks
   (C) layers
   (D) views
   (E) linetypes

4. The following can be deleted with the PURGE command except
   (A) block not referenced in the current drawing
   (B) linetypes that are not being used in the current drawing
   (C) layer 0
   (D) Named views
   (E) None of the above

5. If the TIME command is not turned off during lunch break, the TIME command will
   (A) include the lunch break time
   (B) exclude the lunch break time
   (C) turn itself off
   (D) automatically subtracts one hour for lunch
   (E) None of the above

6. The VIEW command
   (A) serves a purpose similar to the PAN command
   (B) will restore previously saved views of your drawing
   (C) is normally used on very small drawings
   (D) None of the above

13

SPECIAL FEATURES — SLIDES AND SCRIPTS

INTRODUCTION

Slides are quickly viewable, noneditable views of a drawing or parts of a drawing. There are two primary uses for slides. One is to have a quick and ready picture to display symbols, objects, or written data for information purposes only. The other very useful application of slides is to be able to display a series of pictures, organized in a prearranged sequence for a timed slide show. This is a very useful tool for demonstrations to clients or in a showroom. This feature supplements time-consuming calling up of views required when using the ZOOM, PAN, and other Display commands. The "slide show" is implemented through the SCRIPT command (described later in this chapter).

It should be noted that a slide merely masks the current display. Any cursor movement or editor functions employed while a slide is being displayed affects the current drawing under the slide and not the slide itself.

After completing this chapter, you will be able to:

■ Make and view a slide
■ Create a slide library
■ Create and modify a script file
■ Create Utility commands to use in the script file

MSLIDE — MAKING A SLIDE

The current display can be made into a slide with the MSLIDE command. The current viewport becomes the slide while working in model space. The entire display, including all viewports, becomes the slide when using MSLIDE while working in paper space. The MSLIDE command takes a picture of the current display, and stores it in a file, so be sure it is the correct view. The MSLIDE command is invoked from the pull-down menu TOOLS, or at the "Command:" prompt type **MSLIDE** and press Enter or the spacebar.

Command: **mslide**

The **Create Slide File** dialog box appears as shown in Figure 13–1.

The default is the drawing name, which can be used as the slide filename by pressing [Enter]. Or, you can type any other name, as long as you are within the limitations of the DOS file naming convention. AutoCAD automatically appends the extension .SLD. Only objects that are visible on the screen drawing area (or in the current viewport when in model space) are made into the slide.

If you plan to show the slide on different systems you should use a full-screen view with a high resolution display for creating the slide.

SLIDE LIBRARIES

While in DOS, you can invoke the SLIDELIB command to create a slide library file. The command is as follows:

C:\ACAD>**slidelib** *slidefile <slide-list>*

The SLIDELIB program is used in conjunction with a list of slide filenames. Each slide filename must correspond to an actual slide whose extension is .SLD. The list of filenames is on a separate file, written in ASCII format with each slide filename on a separate line by itself. The filenames in the list may or may not include the .SLD extension, but must include the path (drive and/or directory) for the SLIDELIB command to access the proper file for inclusion in the library.

A file named SLDLIST could read as follows:

```
pic_1
A:pic_2.sld
c:\dwgs\pic_3.sld
b:\other\pic_6
```

Each line represents a slide name, some with extensions, some without. Each one has a different path. When the SLIDELIB command is used (from the DOS prompt) to address this file, all the slides listed will be included in the library that you specify. The paths are not included when used with the SLIDELIB program. If there were a PIC_2.SLD on another path it would not be included or conflict with the one specified for its particular library file. This allows for control of which slides will be used if the same slide filename exists in several drive/directory locations. The SLIDELIB program appends .SLB to the library file it creates from the slide list.

The above listing file can be used to create a library file named ALLPICS.SLB by the following sequence:

C:\ACAD>slidelib allpics <sldlist>

> **NOTE:** The name of the library file does not include the extension .SLB. Also, the less than sign (<) is a DOS function that redirects the names in the file to be used as the list of slides in the library.

VSLIDE — VIEWING A SLIDE

The VSLIDE command displays a slide in the current viewport. The VSLIDE command is invoked from the pull-down menu TOOLS or at the "Command:" prompt type **VSLIDE** and press [Enter] or the spacebar.

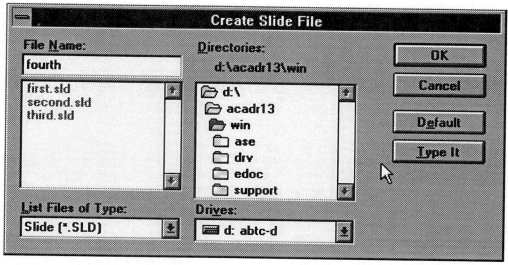

Figure 13-1 Create Slide File dialog box

Command: **vslide**

The **Select Slide File** dialog box appears and you may select the slide to display in the current viewport. If you had stored the slide in a library file and are calling it up for view, you can use the library file keyname followed by the slide name in parentheses. For example, if the slide named PIC_1 (actually stored under the filename pic_1.sld) is in a library file called ALLPICS.SLB, you use the following format:

Command: **vslide**
Slide file <default>: **allpics(pic_1)**

> **NOTE:** The library file only lists the address of each slide. It can be on a path or directory other than that of the slide(s) listed in it. It is not necessary to specify the path in front of the slide name. For example, the ALLPICS.SLB might be on the working directory, while the slide PIC_1 is on drive F in the directory SL1, and the slide PIC_2 is on drive F in the directory SL2. The sequences to call them into view would be as follows:
>
> Command: **vslide**
> Slide file <default>: **allpics(pic_1)**
>
> Command: **vslide**
> Slide file <default>: **allpics(pic_2)**

If the ALLPICS.SLB is on drive F in the subdirectory called SLB, the sequences are as follows:

Command: **vslide**
Slide file <default>: **f:\slb\allpics(pic_1)**

Command: **vslide**
Slide file <default>: **f:\slb\allpics(pic_2)**

SCRIPTS

Of the many means available to enhance AutoCAD through customization, scripts are among the easiest to create. Scripts are similar to the macros that can be created to enhance word processing programs. They permit you to combine a sequence of commands and data into one or two entries. Creating a script, like most enhancements to AutoCAD, requires that you use a text editor to write the Script file (with the extension of .SCR), which contains the instructions and data for the SCRIPT command to follow.

Because script files are written for use at a later time, you must anticipate the conditions under which they will be used. Therefore, familiarity with sequences of prompts that will occur and the types of responses required is necessary to have the script function properly. Writing a script is a simple form of programming.

The Script Text

A script text file must be written in ASCII format. That is, it must not have any embedded print codes or control characters that are automatically written in files when created with a word processor in the document mode. If you are not using the line editor called EDLIN or EDIT (DOS Ver. 5.0 or higher), be sure that you are in the nondocument, programmer, or ASCII mode of your word processor when creating or saving the file. One way to make sure there are no hidden characters in your file is to use the DOS command TYPE or PRINT to display the file. This will reveal such characters.

Each command can occupy a separate line or you can combine several command/data responses on one line. Each space between commands and data is read as an [Enter] just as it does when pressing the spacebar while in AutoCAD. The end of a line of text is also the same as a [Enter].

Spaces and End-of-Lines in Script Files

The following script file contains several commands and data. The commands are GRID, LINE, CIRCLE, LINE, AND CIRCLE again. The data are the response ON, coordinates (such as 0,0 and 5,5) and distances, such as radius 3.

```
GRID ON LINE 0,0 5,5  CIRCLE 3,3 3
LINE 0,5 5,0
CIRCLE 5,2.5 1
```

The first line includes the GRID, LINE, and CIRCLE commands and their response. Note the two spaces after 5,5, which are required to simulate the double [Enter]. Not obvious is the extra space following the 5,0 response in the second LINE command. This extra space and the invisible CR-LF (carriage-return, linefeed) code that ends every line in a text file combine to simulate pressing the spacebar twice. This is necessary, again, to exit the LINE command.

Some text editors automatically remove blank spaces at the end of text lines. To guard against that, an alternative is to have a blank line indicate the second [Enter], as follows:

```
GRID ON LINE 0,0 5,5  CIRCLE 3,3 3
LINE 0,5 5,0

CIRCLE 5,2.5 1
```

Scripts from within the Editor

Invoking a SCRIPT command while in the AutoCAD program is simple. The sequence is as follows:

Command: **script**

The **Select Script File** dialog box appears. The default script file name is the drawing name, which can be used as the script filename by pressing [Enter]. AutoCAD automatically appends the extension .SCR. The commands and responses in the named script file are executed unless terminated by invalid entries or the user presses [Esc] or the [Backspace]. The command name entered becomes the default when the command is completed.

Changing Block Definitions with a Script File

Using a script from DOS to perform a repetitive task is illustrated in the following example. This application also offers some insight on changing the objects in an inserted Block with attributes without affecting the attribute values.

Figure 13–2 shows a group of drawings that all utilize a common block with attribute values in one insertion that are different from the attribute values of those in other drawings. In this case, the border/title block is a block named BRDR. It was originally drawn with the short lines around and outside of the main border line. It was discovered that these lines interfered with the rollers on the plotter and needed to be removed. The BRDR block definition is shown in Figure 13–3. Remember, the insertion of this block has different attribute values in each drawing, such as drawing number, date, title, etc.

You want to change objects in the block but maintain the attribute values as they are, there are two approaches to redefinition. One is to find a clear place in the drawing and insert the block with an asterisk (*). This is the same as inserting and exploding the block. Then, make the necessary changes in the objects and make the revised group into a block with the same block name. This redefines all insertions of blocks with that same name in the drawing. In this case there is only one insertion. You must be careful how any changes to attributes might affect the already inserted block of that name.

The second method is to use the WBLOCK command to place a copy of the block in a file with the same name. This makes a new and separate drawing of the block. Then exit the current drawing, call up the newly created drawing, and make the required changes in the objects and END the drawing that was created by the WBLOCK command. Then you re-enter the drawing in which the block objects need to be changed. You now use the INSERT command and respond with "blockname=" and have the block redefined without losing the attribute values. For example, if the block name is BRDR, the sequence would be as follows:

Command: **insert**
Block name: **BRDR=**
Block BRDR redefined
Regenerating drawing.
Insertion point: [Ctrl] + [C] *(displays *Cancel*)*

The key to the above sequence is the equal sign (=) following the block name. This causes AutoCAD to change the defnition of the block named BRDR to be that of the drawing named BRDR, but maintains the attribute values as long as Attribute definitions remain unchanged.

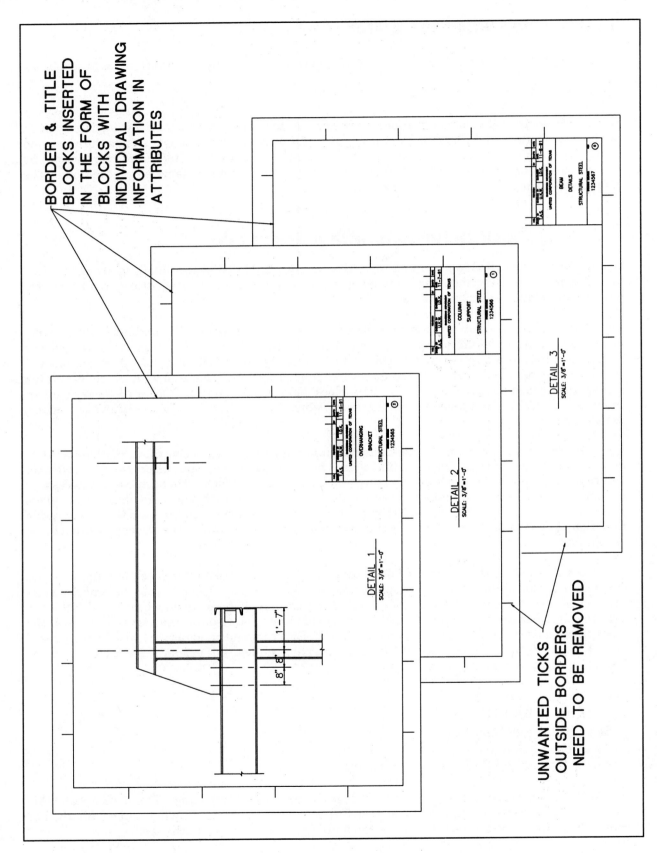

Figure 13—2 Drawings utilizing common block and attribute values that are different from other drawings

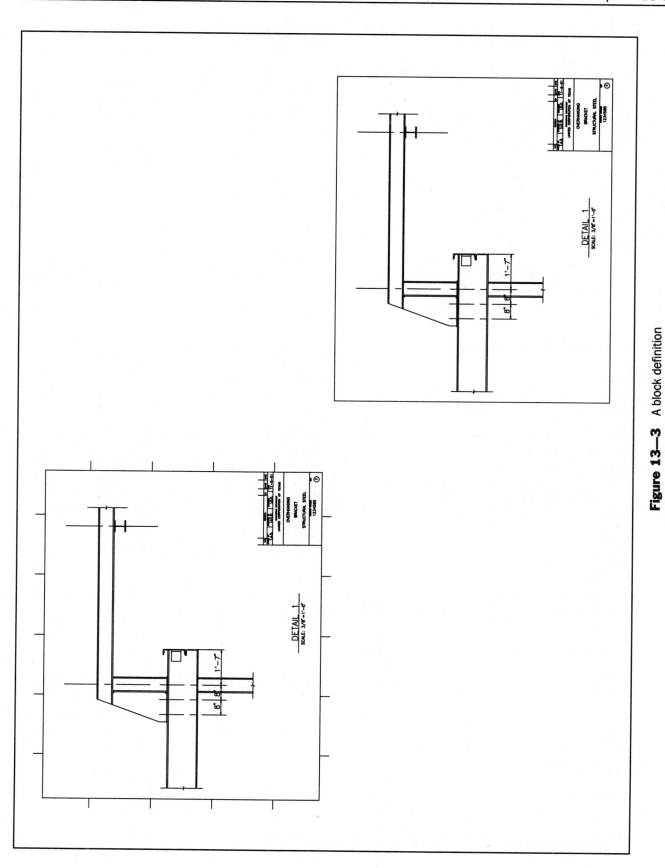

Figure 13—3 A block definition

If the above procedure must be repeated many times, this is where a script file can be employed to automate the process. In the following example, we show how to apply the script to a drawing named PLAN_1. The sequence included an [Enter] as it was described above to be used while in AutoCAD. This expedited the operation by not actually having the block inserted, but only its definition brought into the drawing. Because an [Enter] or [Esc] during the running of a SCRIPT file causes the script to terminate, those keystrokes cannot be in the middle of a script; besides, invoking [Esc] in a SCRIPT command requires using the AutoLISP function "(command)." The script can be written in a file (called BRDRCHNG.SCR for this example) in ASCII format as follows:

```
INSERT
BRDR=
0,0  (the 0,0 is followed by 6 spaces)
ERASE L  (the L is followed by 1 space)
REDRAW
```

Now, from the "Command:" prompt, you can apply the script to drawing PLAN_1 by responding as follows:

Command: **script**

There are several important aspects of the above sequence to be noted.

Line 1–2—This is where you might enter [Esc] if you were not in a SCRIPT command and have the definition of the block named BRDR take on that of the drawing BRDR without having to actually continue with the insertion in the drawing.

Line 3—In this case, 0,0 as the insertion point is arbitrary because the inserted block is going to be erased anyway. Special attention is to given to the six spaces following the insertion point. These are the same as pressing the spacebar or [Enter] six times in response to the "X-scale," "Y-scale," and "Rotation angle" prompts, and the number of spaces ([Enter]s) that follow must correspond to the number of attributes that require responses for values. In this example there were three attributes. Again, the fact that the responses are null is immaterial because this insertion will not be kept.

Line 4—The ERASE L is self-explanatory, but do not forget that after the "L" you must have another space (press the spacebar again) to terminate the object selection process and complete the ERASE command.

Lines 5—The REDRAW command is not really required except to show the user for a second time that the changes have been made before the script ends.

Utility Commands for Script

Following are the Utility commands that may be used within a script file.

DELAY The DELAY command causes the script to pause for the number of milliseconds that have been specified by the delay. A line to delay the script for five seconds would be written as follows:

DELAY 5000

RESUME The RESUME command causes the script to resume running after the user has pressed either [Esc] or the [Backspace] key to interrupt the script. It may be entered as follows:

Command: **resume**

GRAPHSCR and TEXTSCR The GRAPHSCR and TEXTSCR commands are used to flip or toggle the screen to the Graphics or Text mode, respectively, during the running of the script. They are simply entered as a command in the script as follows:

        Command: **graphscr**

or

        Command: **textscr**

These two screen toggle commands can be used transparently by preceding them with an apostrophe.

RSCRIPT The RSCRIPT command, when placed at the end of a script, causes the script to repeat itself. With this feature you can have a slide show run continuously until terminated by `Esc` or a `Backspace`.

A repeating demonstration can be set up to show some sequences of commands and responses as follows:

```
GRID ON
LIMITS 0,0 24,24
ZOOM A
CIRCLE 12,12 4
DELAY 2000
COPY L  M 12,12 18,12 12,18 6,12 12,6 (an extra space at the end)
DELAY 5000
ERASE W 0,0 24,24 (an extra space at the end)
DELAY 2000
LIMITS 0,0 12,9
ZOOM A

GRID OFF
TEXT 1,1 .5 0 THAT'S ALL FOLKS!
ERASE L (an extra space at the end)
RSCRIPT
```

The above script file utilizes the DELAY and the RSCRIPT subcommands. Note the extra spaces where continuation of some actions must be terminated.

The SCRIPT command can be used to show a series of slides as shown in the following sequence:

```
VSLIDE SLD_A
VSLIDE *SLD_B
DELAY 5000
VSLIDE
VSLIDE *SLD_C
DELAY 5000
VSLIDE
DELAY 10000
RSCRIPT
```

The above script uses the asterisk (*) before the slide name prior to the delay. This causes AutoCAD to load the slide, ready for viewing. Otherwise, there would be a blank screen between slides while the next one is being loaded. The RSCRIPT command repeats the slide show.

REVIEW QUESTIONS

1. To load a script file called SAMPLE.SCR, enter the SCRIPT command and type the following name for the script file:
   - (A) SAMPLE
   - (B) SAMPLE.SCR
   - (C) *
   - (D) SCRIPT SAMPLE
   - (E) None of the above

2. The AutoCAD command used for viewing a slide is
   - (A) VSLIDE
   - (B) VIEWSLIDE
   - (C) SSLD
   - (D) SLIDE
   - (E) MSLIDE

3. If a REDRAW is performed while viewing a slide
   - (A) the command will be ignored
   - (B) the current slide will be deleted
   - (C) the current drawing will be displayed
   - (D) None of the above

4. The command used to run a script file is
   - (A) SCRIPT
   - (B) SCRPT
   - (C) SSCRIPT
   - (D) SRUN
   - (E) None of the above

5. A script file is identified by the following extension:
   - (A) .SCR
   - (B) .BAK
   - (C) .DWK
   - (D) .SPT
   - (E) None of the above

6. A slide file is identified by the following extension:
   - (A) .SLD
   - (B) .SCR
   - (C) .SLE
   - (D) .SLU
   - (E) None of the above

7. Slides can be removed from the screen with the command
   - (A) ZOOM ALL
   - (B) REGEN
   - (C) OOPS
   - (D) None of the above

8. The SCRIPT command cannot be used to
   - (A) insert blocks
   - (B) create layers
   - (C) place text
   - (D) create another script file
   - (E) None of the above

CHAPTER

14

AUTOCAD 3D

After completing this chapter, you will be able to:

- Define User Coordinate System
- View in 3D — Vpoint and Dview commands
- Create 3D objects
- Use the Region command
- Use the 3Dpoly and 3Dface commands
- Create Meshes
- Edit in 3D — Align, Rotate3D, Mirror3D, 3Darray, Extending, and Trimming
- Create Solid shapes — Solid box, Solid cone, Solid cylinder, Solid sphere, Solid torus, and Solid wedge
- Create solids from existing 2D objects and regions
- Create solids from revolution
- Create composite solids
- Edit 3D solids — chamfer, fillet, section, slice, and interference
- Obtain mass properties of a solid
- Place multiview on paper space
- Line up orthographic views

WHAT IS 3D?

In 2D drawings you have been working with two axes, X and Y. In 3D drawings, in addition to the X and Y axes, you work with the the Z axis, as shown in Figure 14–1. Plan views, sections, and elevations represent only two dimensions. Isometric, perspective, and axonometric drawings, on the other hand, represent all three dimensions. For example, to create three views of a cube, the cube is simply drawn as a square with thickness. This is referred to as "extruded 2D." Only objects that are extrudable can be drawn by this method. Other views are achieved by rotating the viewpoint or the object, just as if one were physically holding the cube. You can get an isometric or perspective view by simply changing the viewpoint.

Whether you realize it or not, all drawings you have done in previous chapters are created in true 3D. What this means is that with every line, circle, or arc that you have drawn, even if you think you have drawn them in 2D, are really stored with three coordinates. By default, AutoCAD stores the Z value as your current elevation with a thickness of zero. What you think of now as 2D is really only one of an infinite number of views of your drawing in 3D space.

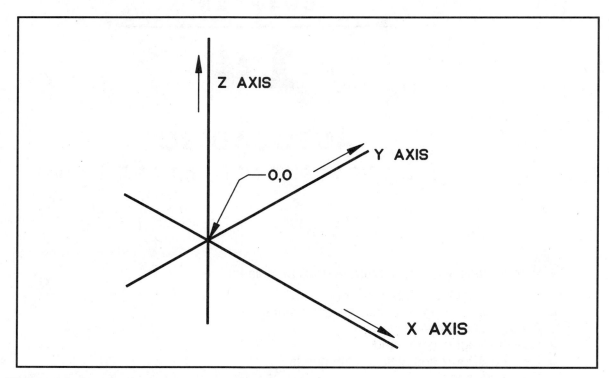

Figure 14–1 The X, Y, and Z axes for 3D drawing

Drawing objects in 3D provides three major advantages:

1. An object is drawn once and then can be viewed and plotted from any angle (viewpoint).

2. A 3D object holds mathematical information, which can be used in engineering analysis such as finite element analysis and computer numerical control (CNC) machinery.

3. Shading and rendering for visualization.

There are two major limitations in working in 3D. Whenever you want to input 3D coordinates whose Z coordinate is different from the current construction plane's elevation, you have to use the keyboard instead of your pointing device. One exception is to osnap to an object not in the current construction plane. The input device (mouse or digitizer) can only supply AutoCAD with two of the three coordinates at a time. Three-dimensional input devices exist but there is no practical support by AutoCAD for them at this time. So, you are limited to using the keyboard. The second limitation is determining where you are in relationship to an object in 3D space.

COORDINATE SYSTEMS

In AutoCAD there are two types of coordinate systems available. One is a single fixed coordinate system called the World Coordinate System and the other is an infinite set of user-defined coordinate systems available through the User Coordinate System.

The **World Coordinate System (WCS)** is fixed and cannot be changed. In this system (when viewing the origin from 0,0,1), the X axis starts at the point 0,0,0 and increases as the point moves to the operator's right; the Y axis starts at 0,0,0 and increases as the point moves to the top of the screen; and finally, the Z axis starts at the 0,0,0 point and gets larger as it comes toward the user.

All drawings from previous chapters are created with reference to WCS. The WCS is still the basic system used in virtually all 2D AutoCAD drawings. However, because of the difficulty in calculating 3D points, the WCS is not suited for many 3D applications.

The **User Coordinate System (UCS)** allows the user to change the location and orientation of the X,Y, and Z axes to reduce the calculations needed to create 3D objects. The UCS command lets you redefine the origin in your drawing, and establish positive X and the positive Y axes. New users think of a coordinate system simply as the direction of positive X and positive Y. But once the directions of X and Y are defined, the direction of Z will be defined as well. Thus, the user only has to be concerned with X and Y. As a result, when you are drawing in 2D, you are also somewhere in 3D space. For example, if a sloped roof of a house is drawn in detail using the WCS, each endpoint of each object on the inclined roof plane must be calculated. On the other hand, if the UCS is set to the same plane as the roof, each object can be drawn as if were in the plan view. You can define any number of UCSs within the fixed WCS and save them, assigning each a user-determined name. But, at any given time only one coordinate system is current and all coordinate input and display is relative to it. If multiple viewports are active, they all share the same current UCS.

Right Hand Rule

The directions of the X,Y, and Z axes change when the UCS is altered, hence, the positive rotation direction of the axes may become difficult to determine. The right hand rule helps in determining the rotation direction when changing the UCS or using commands that require object rotation.

To remember the orientation of the axes, perform the following:

1. Hold your right hand with the thumb, forefinger, and middle finger pointing at right angles to each other, as shown in Figure 14-2.

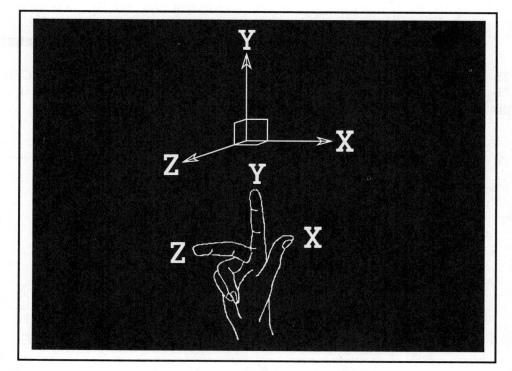

Figure 14–2   The correct hand position when using the right hand rule

2. Consider the thumb to be pointing in the positive direction of the X axis.

3. The forefinger points in the positive direction of the Y axis.

4. The middle finger points in the positive direction of the Z axis.

UCS Icon

The UCS icon provides a visual reminder of how the UCS axes are oriented, where the current UCS origin is, and the viewing direction relative to the UCS XY plane. AutoCAD displays different coordinate system icons in paper space and model space. When model space is current, AutoCAD displays the icon as shown in Figure 14–3 and when paper space is current, AutoCAD displays the icon as shown in Figure 14–3.

The X and Y axis directions are displayed using arrows labeled appropriately, and the Z axis is displayed by the placement of the icon. The icon displays a W in the Y axis arrow if the current UCS is the World Coordinate System, and a (+) appears at the base of the arrows if the icon is placed at the origin of the current coordinate system. When looking straight up or down on the Z plane, the icon seems flat. When viewed at any other angle, the icon looks skewed. The orientation of the Z axis is defined further by the presence or absence of a box at the base of the arrows that create the icon. If the box is visible, you are looking down on the X-Y plane, and if the box is not present, the bottom of the X-Y plane is being viewed. See Figure 14–4 for all the different orientations of the UCS icon.

> **NOTE:** If the viewing angle comes within one degree of the Z axis, the UCS icon will change to a "broken pencil," as shown in Figure 14–5. When this icon is showing in a view, it is recommended that you avoid trying to use the cursor to specify points in that view, because results may be unpredictable.

The display and placement on the origin of the UCS icon is handled by the UCSICON command. The UCSICON command is invoked from the pull-down menu Options, or at the "Command:" prompt type **UCSICON** and press Enter or spacebar.

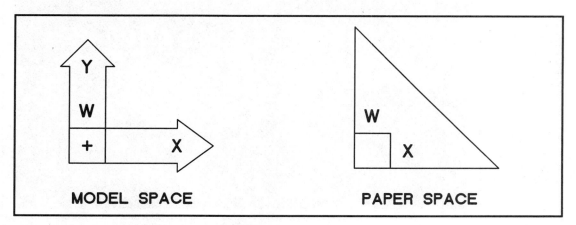

Figure 14–3 The UCS icons for model space and paper space

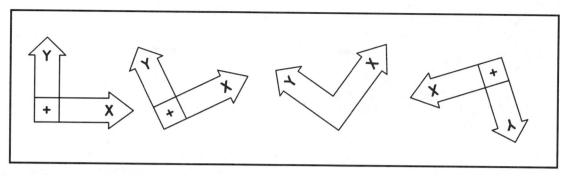

Figure 14-4   The UCS icon in different orientations

Command: **ucsicon**
ON/OFF/All/Noorigin/ORigin <default>:

ON Option The ON option allows you to turn the icon ON if it is OFF in the current viewport.

OFF Option The OFF option allows you to turn the icon OFF if it is ON in the current viewport.

Noorigin Option The Noorigin option tells AutoCAD to display the icon at the lower left corner of the viewport, regardless of the location of the UCS origin. This is like parking the icon in the lower left corner. This is the default setting.

ORigin Option The ORigin option forces the icon to be displayed at the origin of the current coordinate system.

> **NOTE:** If the origin is off screen, the icon is displayed at the lower left corner of the viewport.

All Option The All option determines whether the options that follow affect all of the viewports or just the current active viewport. This option is issued before each and every option if you want to affect all viewports. For example, to turn ON the icon in all the viewports and display the icon on the origin, the following sequence of prompts is displayed:

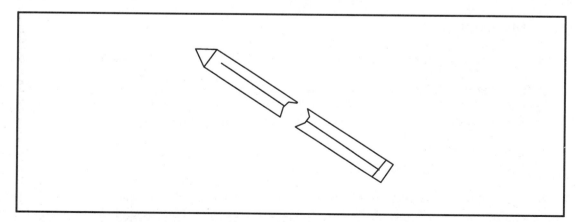

Figure 14-5   The UCS icon becomes a broken pencil when the viewing angle is within one degree of the Z axis

Command: **ucsicon**
ON/OFF/All/Noorigin/ORigin <default>: **all**
ON/OFF/Noorigin/ORigin: **on**
Command: [Enter]

ON/OFF/All/Noorigin/ORigin: **all**
ON/OFF/Noorigin/ORigin: **origin**
Command:

UCS Command

The UCS is the key to almost all 3D operations in AutoCAD, as mentioned earlier. Many commands in AutoCAD are traditionally thought to be 2D commands. They are used effectively in 3D because they are always relative to the current UCS. For example, Rotate only rotates in the direction of X and Y. Therefore, if you wanted to rotate an object in the direction of Z, you would change your UCS so that X or Y is now in the direction what was previously Z. Then you could use the 2D ROTATE command.

The UCS command lets you redefine the origin in your drawing. Broadly, you can define origin by four methods:

1.   Specifying a data point for an origin, a new XY plane by providing three data points, or providing a direction for the Z Axis.

2.   Defining an origin relative to the orientation of an existing object.

3.   Defining an origin by aligning with the current viewing direction.

4.   Defining an origin by rotating the current UCS around one of its axes.

The UCS command is invoked from the pull-down menu VIEW by selecting UCS, from the Standard toolbar, or at the "Command:" prompt type **UCS** and press [Enter] or spacebar.

Command: **ucs**
Origin/ZAxis/3point/OBject/View/X/Y/Z/Prev/Restore/Save/Del/?/<World>:

Origin Option   The Origin option defines a new UCS by shifting the origin of the current UCS, leaving the directions of X,Y, and Z axes unchanged. When you select this option, AutoCAD prompts:

Origin point (0,0,0):

Specify a new origin point relative to the origin of the current UCS, as shown in Figure 14–6.

ZAxis Option   The ZAxis option allows you to define an origin by giving a data point and the direction for the Z axis. AutoCAD arbitrarily, but consistently, sets the direction of the X and Y axes in relation to the given Z axis. When you select this option, AutoCAD prompts:

Origin point (0,0,0):
Point on positive portion of the Z axis <default>:

Specify a data point and the direction for the positive Z axis. If you give a null response to the second prompt, the Z axis of the new coordinate system will be parallel to the previous one. This is similar to using the Origin option.

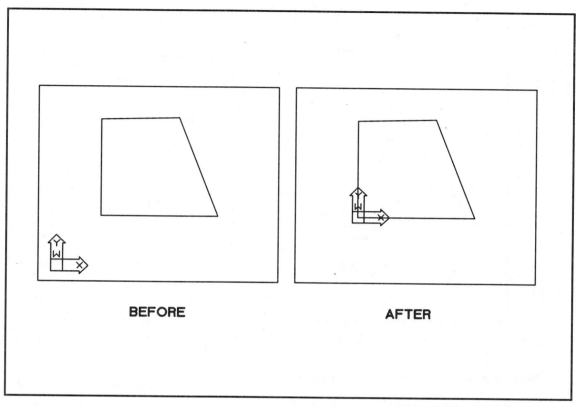

Figure 14–6   Specifying a new origin point relative to the origin of the current UCS

3point Option The 3point option is the easiest and most often used option for controlling the orientation of the UCS. This option allows the user to select three points to define the origin and the directions of the positive X and Y axes. The origin point acts as a base for the UCS rotation, and when a point is selected to define the direction of the positive X axis, the direction of the Y axis is limited because it is always perpendicular to the X axis. When the X and Y axes are defined, the Z axis is automatically placed perpendicular to the XY plane. When you select this option, AutoCAD prompts:

Origin point (0,0,0):
Point on positive portion of the X-axis <default>:
Point on positive-Y portion of the UCS XY plane <default>:

Specify a data point and the direction for positive X and Y axes, as shown in Figure 14–7. The points must not form a straight line. If you give a null response to the first prompt, the new UCS will have the same origin as the previous UCS. If you give a null response to the second or third prompt, then that axis direction will be parallel to the corresponding axis in the previous UCS.

OBject Option The OBject option lets you define a new coordinate system by pointing to an object. The actual orientation of the UCS depends on how the object was created. When the object is selected, the UCS origin is placed at the first point used to create the object (in the case of a line, it will be the closest endpoint; for a circle, it will be the center point of the circle); the X axis is determined by the direction from the origin to the second point used to define the object. And the Z-axis direction is placed perpendicular to the XY plane in which the object sits. Table 14–1 lists locations of the origin and its X axis for different types of objects.

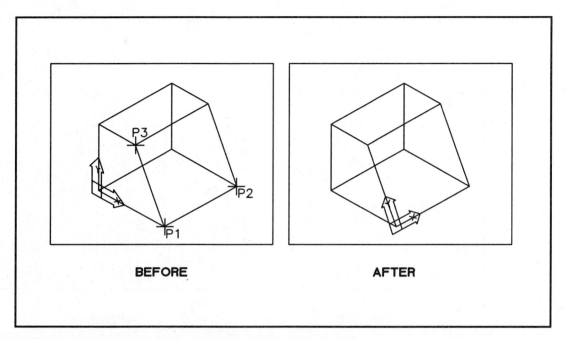

BEFORE   **AFTER**

Figure 14–7   Specifying a pick point and direction for positive X and Y axes with the 3Point Option

When you select this option, AutoCAD prompts:

    Select object to align UCS:

Identify an object to define a new coordinate system, as shown in Figure 14–8.

View Option   The View option places the XY plane parallel to the screen, and makes the Z axis perpendicular. The UCS origin remains unchanged. This method is used mainly for labeling text, which you want to be aligned with the screen rather than with objects.

Table 14–1   Locations of the origin and its X axis for different types of objects

Object	Method of UCS Determination
Line	The nearest endpoint of the pick point becomes the new UCS origin. The new X axis is chosen so that the line lies in the XZ plane of the new UCS.
Circle	The circle's center becomes the new UCS origin, and the X axis passing through the pick point.
Arc	The arc's center becomes the new UCS origin, and the X axis passes through the endpoint of the arc closest to the pick point.
2D Polyline	The Polyline's start point becomes the new UCS origin, with the X axis extending from the start point to the next vertex.
Solid	The first point of the solid determines the new UCS origin, and the X axis lies along the line between the first two points.
Dimension	The new UCS origin is the middle point of the dimension text and the direction of the X axis is parallel to the X axis of the UCS in effect when the dimension was drawn.

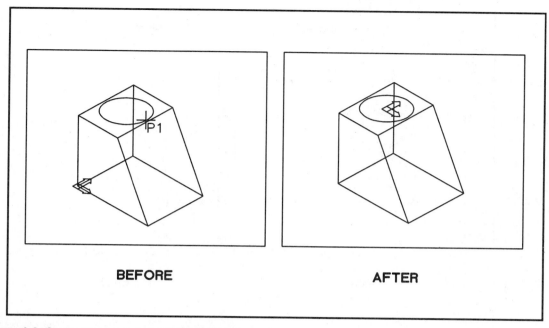

Figure 14–8   Defining a new coordinate system

X/Y/Z Rotation Option The X/Y/Z rotation option lets you define a new coordinate system by rotating the X, Y, and Z axes independently of each other. You can show AutoCAD the desired angle by picking two points or you can enter the rotation angle from the keyboard. In either case, the new angle is specified relative to the X axis of the current UCS. See Figures 14–9, 14–10, and 14–11 for examples in rotating the UCS around X, Y, and Z axes, respectively.

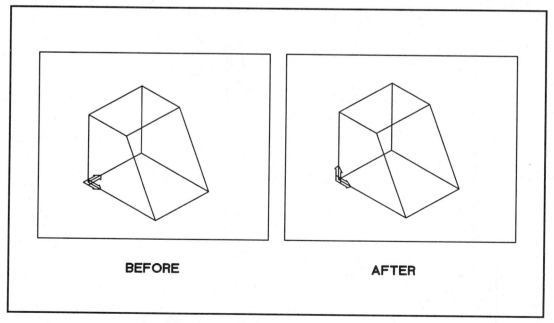

Figure 14–9   Example of rotating the UCS around the X axis

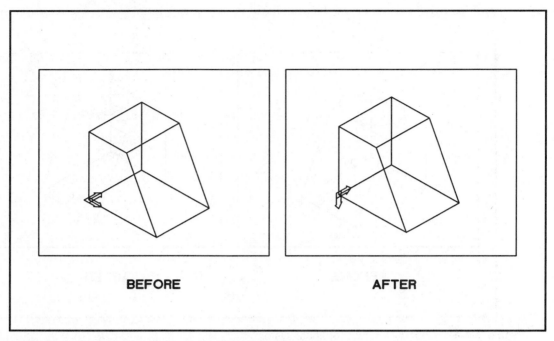

Figure 14–10   Example of rotating the UCS around the Y axis

Previous Option The Previous option is similar to the Previous option of the ZOOM command. AutoCAD saves the last ten coordinate systems in both model and paper space. You can step back through them by using repeated Previous options.

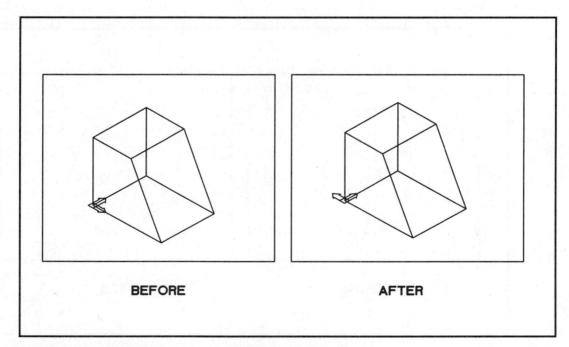

Figure 14–11   Example of rotating the UCS around the Z axis

Restore Option The Restore option allows you to restore any previously saved UCS.

> **NOTE:** You can also restore previously saved UCS by invoking the DDUCS command, which in turn displays a dialog box listing the previously saved UCS.

Save Option The Save option allows you to save the current UCS under a user-defined name.

Delete Option The Delete option allows you to delete any saved UCS.

? Option The ? option lists the name of the UCS you specify, origin, and XYZ axes for each saved coordinate system, relative to the current UCS. To list all the UCS names, accept the default, or you can specify wild cards.

World Option The World option returns the drawing to the WCS.

DDUCSP Command

The DDUCSP command is used to make a preset Coordinate System orientation current. The DDUCSP is invoked from pull-down menu View or at the "Command:" prompt type **DDUCSP** and press [Enter] or spacebar. AutoCAD displays the UCS Orientation dialog box, as shown in Figure 14–12.

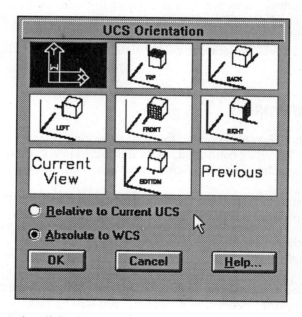

Figure 14–12 UCS Orientation dialog box

The UCS Orientation dialog box displays tiles with standard view from preset orientations from which to select. If you select one of the tiles, the current UCS will be reoriented to align with the displayed view. The orientation will be Relative to Current UCS or Absolute to WCS, depending upon the option selected.

PLAN Command

The PLAN command provides a convenient means of viewing the drawing from plan view. The definition of plan means that you are at positive Z and looking perpendicularly down on X to the right and Y pointing up. You can select the plan view of the current UCS, a previously saved UCS, or the WCS. The PLAN command is invoked from the pull-down menu VIEW by selecting 3D Viewpoint Presets, or at the "Command:" prompt type **PLAN** and press [Enter] or spacebar.

> Command: **plan**
> <Current UCS>/Ucs/World:

Current UCS Option The Current UCS option displays the plan view of the current UCS. This is the default option.

UCS Option The UCS option displays a plan view of a previously saved UCS. When you select this option, AutoCAD prompts for a name of the UCS.

World Option The World option displays the plan view of WCS.

VIEWING IN 3D

Until now, you have been working on the plan view or XY plane. You have been looking down at the plan view from a certain distance along the Z axis. The direction from which you view your drawing or model is called the "viewpoint". You can view a drawing from any point in model space. From your selected viewpoint, you can add objects, modify existing objects, or suppress the hidden lines from the drawing.

The VPOINT and DVIEW commands are used to control viewing of a model from any point in model space.

VPOINT Command

To view a model in 3D, you may have to change the viewpoint. The location of the viewpoint can be controlled by the VPOINT command. The default viewpoint is 0,0,1; i.e., you are looking at the model from 0,0,1 (on the positive Z axis above the model) to 0,0,0 (origin).

The VPOINT command is invoked from the pull-down menu VIEW by selecting 3D Viewpoint, or at the "Command:" prompt type **VPOINT** and press [Enter] or spacebar.

> Command: **vpoint**
> Rotate/<Viewpoint> <current>:

The default method requires you to enter X,Y,Z coordinates from the keyboard. These coordinates establish the viewpoint. From this viewpoint, you will be looking at the model in the space toward the model's origin. For example, a 1,-1,1 setting gives you a –45-degree angle projected in the XY plane and 35.264-degree angle above the XY plane (top, right and front views), looking at the model origin (0,0,0). You can set the VPOINT to any X,Y, and Z location. Table 14–2 lets you experiment with the rotation of 3D objects.

Instead of entering coordinates, give a null response (press [Enter] or spacebar) and a compass and axes tripod appears on the screen, as shown in Figure 14–13.

Table 13-1 Various VPoint Settings for rotating 3D objects

VPOINT Setting	Displayed View(s)
0,0,1	Top
0,0,-1	Bottom
0,-1,0	Front
0,1,0	Rear
1,0,0	Right side
-1,0,0	Left side
1,-1,1	Top, Front, Right side
-1,-1,1	Top, Front, Left side
1,1,1	Top, Rear, Right side
-1,1,1	Top, Rear, Left side
1,-1,-1	Bottom, Front, Right side
-1,-1,-1	Bottom, Front, Left side
1,1,-1	Bottom, Rear, Right side
-1,1,-1	Bottom, Rear, Left side

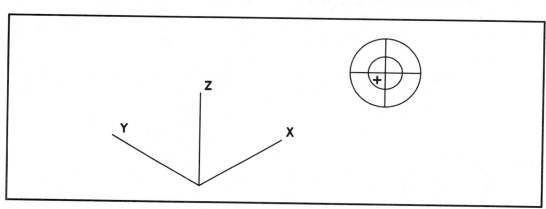

Figure 14–13 The VPOINT Command's compass and axes tripod

The compass, in the upper right of the screen, is a 2D representation of a globe. The center point of the circle being the north pole (0,0,1), the inner circle representing the equator, and the outer circle representing the south pole (0,0,-1), as shown in Figure 14–14.

A small cross is displayed on the compass. You can move the cross using your pointing device. If the cross is in the inner circle, you are above the equator, looking down on your model. If the cross is in the outer circle, you are looking from beneath your drawing, or from the southern hemisphere. By moving the cross, the axes tripod rotates to conform to the viewpoint indicated on the compass. When you achieve the desired viewpoint, press the pick button on your pointing device or press [Enter]. The drawing regenerates to reflect the new vpoint position.

Rotate Option The Rotate option allows you to specify the location of the viewpoint in terms of two angles. The first angle determines the rotation in the XY plane from the X axis (0 degrees) clockwise

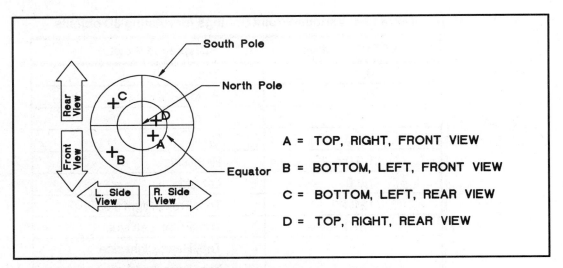

Figure 14–14 Components of the VPOINT command's compass and its poles

or counterclockwise. The second angle determines the angle from the XY plane up or down. When you select the Rotate option, AutoCAD prompts:

Enter angle in X-Y plane from X axis <current>:
Enter angle from X-Y plane <current>:

Specify the angles, and your drawing regenerates to reflect the new VPOINT position.

Viewpoint Presets AutoCAD provides a **Viewpoint Presets** dialog box when you invoke the DDVPOINT command. The dialog box lets you set a 3D viewing direction by specifying an angle from the X axis and an angle from the XY plane. This is similar to using the Rotate option of the VPOINT command.

The DDVPOINT command is invoked from the pull-down menu VIEW by selecting 3D Viewpoint, or at the "Command:" prompt type DDVPOINT and press [Enter] or spacebar.

Command: **ddvpoint**

AutoCAD displays a **Viewpoint Presets** dialog box similar to the one shown in Figure 14–15. Pick viewing angles from the image tile or enter their values in the edit boxes. You specify the view direction relative to the current UCS or the WCS and the viewing angles are updated accordingly. The new angle is indicated by the white arm while the current viewing angle is indicated by the red arm. By clicking the **Set to Plan View** button, you can set the viewing angles to display the plan relative to the selected coordinate system.

> **NOTE:** By default, AutoCAD always places the model to your current VPOINT position in reference to WCS, not the current UCS. If necessary, you can change the system variable WORLDVIEW from 1 (default) to 0, then AutoCAD places the model in reference to UCS for your current VPOINT position. It is recommended that you keep the WORLDVIEW set to 1 (default). Regardless of WORLDVIEW setting, you are always looking through your viewpoint to WCS origin.

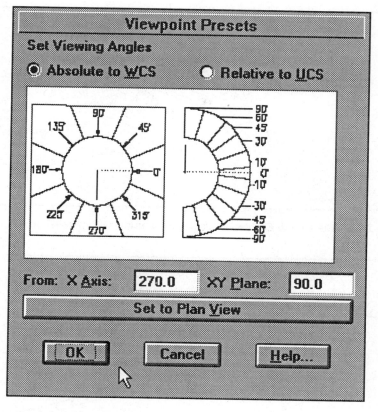

Figure 14–15 The Viewpoint Presets dialog box

DVIEW Command

The DVIEW command is an enhanced VPOINT command. Here you visually move around an object on the screen dynamically viewing selected objects as the view changes. The DVIEW command provides either parallel or perspective views, whereas the VPOINT command provides only parallel views. In the case of a parallel view, parallel lines always remain parallel, whereas in perspective view, parallel lines converge from your view to a vanishing point. Figures 14–16a and 14–16b show parallel and perspective views, respectively, of a model. The viewing direction is the same in each case.

The DVIEW command is invoked from the pull-down menu VIEW by selecting 3D Dynamic View, or at the "Command:" prompt, type **DVIEW** and press Enter or spacebar.

    Command: **dview**
    Select objects:

Select the objects by any of the selection sets used by AutoCAD. All or any part of the objects in the drawing can be selected for viewing during the DVIEW command process, but once you exit the DVIEW command, all objects in the drawing are represented in the new view created. If your drawing is too large to display quickly in the DVIEW display, small portions can be selected and used to orient the entire drawing. The purpose of this is to save time on slower machines and still give dynamic rotation so that you can quickly and effortlessly adjust the view of your object before you begin working with it.

AutoCAD 3D

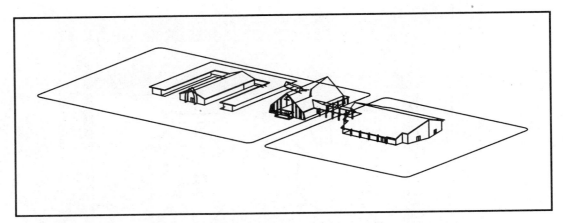

Figure 14–16a   The DVIEW Command displaying a model with parallel projection

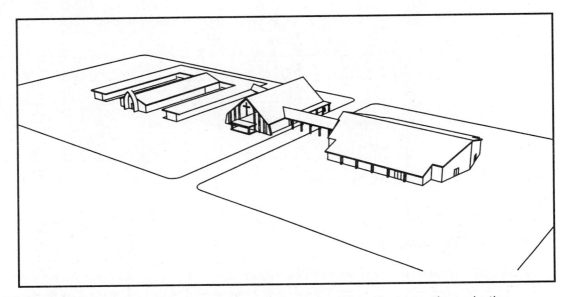

Figure 14–16b   The DVIEW Command displaying the same model with perspective projection

If you give a null response to the "Select objects:" prompt, AutoCAD provides you with a picture of a 3D house. Whatever you do to the 3D house under DVIEW will be done to your current drawing when you exit the DVIEW command.

Each time when you exit the DVIEW command, AutoCAD performs an unconditional regeneration. No matter what the current setting for REGENAUTO is, AutoCAD automatically performs a regeneration.

After selecting the objects, give a null response. AutoCAD prompts with the following options:

CAmera/TArget/Distance/POints/PAn/Zoom/TWist/CLip/Hide/Off/Undo/<eXit>:

CAmera Option   The Camera option is one of the six options that adjust what is seen in the view. When using the Camera option, the drawing is stationary while the camera can move in two directions. It can move up and down (above or below) or it can move around the target to the left or right (clockwise or counterclockwise). When you are moving the camera, the target is fixed.

When you enter the Camera option, AutoCAD prompts:

Toggle angle in/Enter angle from X-Y plane <default>:

You can specify the amount of rotation you want by positioning the graphics cursor in the graphics area. When you move the cursor, you will see the object begin to dynamically rotate vertically and the AutoCAD status line displays a continuous read-out of the new angle. Move the cursor to the desired angle and then press the pick button. Or, you could also type the desired angle from the keyboard. Either way, you have selected an angle of view above or below the target.

Next, AutoCAD prompts for the desired rotation angle of the camera around the target:

Toggle angle from/Enter the angle in the X-Y plane from X axis <default>:

You can move the camera 180 degrees clockwise and 180 degrees counterclockwise around the target. You specify the angle by using the cursor to pick a point on the screen. Or, you could type in the desired angle from the keyboard. Either way, you have selected an angle of view around the target clockwise or counterclockwise.

The toggle angle option allows you to move between two angle input modes.

AutoCAD takes you back to the 12-option prompt of the DVIEW command. When the new angle of view is correct, you exit by giving a null response, or selecting the Exit option. This takes you back to the "Command:" prompt.

When you exit DVIEW, your entire drawing will rotate to the same angle of view as the few objects that you selected.

The following command sequence shows an example of using the CAmera option of the DVIEW command.

Command: **dview**
Select objects: *(select the objects)*
CAmera/TArget/Distance/POints/PAn/Zoom/TWist/CLip/Hide/Off/Undo/<eXit>: **ca**
Toggle angle in/Enter angle from X-Y plane <default>: **45**
Toggle angle from/Enter angle in X-Y plane from X axis <default>: **45**
CAmera/TArget/Distance/POints/PAn/Zoom/TWist/CLip/Hide/Off/Undo/<eXit>: Enter

TArget Option The TArget option is similar to the CAmera option, but in this case, the target is rotated around the camera. The camera remains stationary except for maintaining its lens on the target point. The prompts are similar to the CAmera option. It may seem that there is no difference between the CAmera and TArget options, but there is a difference in the actual angle of view. For instance, if you elevate the camera 75 degrees above the target, you are then looking at the target from the top down. On the other hand, if you raise the target 75 degrees above the camera, you are then looking at the target from the bottom up. The angles of view are reversed. The real difference comes when you are typing in the angles rather than visually picking them.

The following command sequence shows an example of using the TArget option of the DVIEW command.

Command: **dview**
Select objects: *(select the objects)*
CAmera/TArget/Distance/POints/PAn/Zoom/TWist/CLip/Hide/Off/Undo/<eXit>: **ta**

AutoCAD 3D

Toggle angle in/Enter angle from X-Y plane <default>: **75**
Toggle angle from/Enter angle in X-Y plane from X axis <default>: **75**
CAmera/TArget/Distance/POints/PAn/Zoom/TWist/CLip/Hide/Off/Undo/<eXit>: Enter

Distance Option The Distance option creates a perspective projection from the current view. The only information required for this option is the distance from the camera to the target point. Once AutoCAD knows the distance, it will apply the correct perspective. When perspective viewing is on, a box icon appears, as shown in Figure 14–17, in place of the UCS icon on the screen. Some commands (like ZOOM and PAN) will not work while perspective is on. You turn on the perspective just for visual purposes or for plotting.

When you select the Distance option, AutoCAD prompts:

New camera/target distance <default>:

In addition to the prompt, you also see a horizontal bar at the top of the screen. The bar goes from 0x to 16x. These are factor distances times your current distance from the object. Moving the slider cursor toward the right increases the distance between the target and camera, and moving toward the left reduces the distance between the target and camera. The current distance is represented by 1x. For instance, moving the slider cursor to 3x represents the new distance to three times the previous distance. Or, you could also type the desired distance in the current linear units from the keyboard.

The following command sequence shows an example of using the Distance option of the DVIEW command.

Command: **dview**
Select objects: *(select the objects)*
CAmera/TArget/Distance/POints/PAn/Zoom/TWist/CLip/Hide/Off/Undo/<eXit>: **d**
New camera/target distance <default>: **75'**
CAmera/TArget/Distance/POints/PAn/Zoom/TWist/CLip/Hide/Off/Undo/<eXit>: Enter

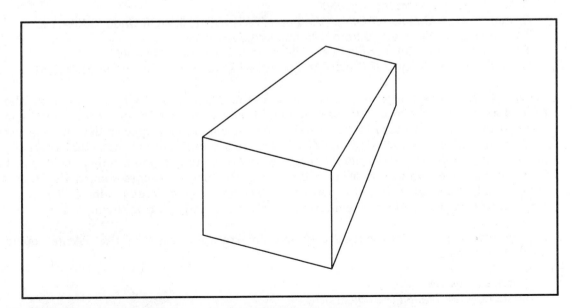

Figure 14–17 The perspective box icon appears when perspective mode is on

Off Option The Off option turns off the perspective view. The following command sequence shows an example of using the Off option of the DVIEW command.

    Command: **dview**
    Select objects: *(select the objects)*
    CAmera/TArget/Distance/POints/PAn/Zoom/TWist/CLip/Hide/Off/Undo/<eXit>: **o**
    CAmera/TArget/Distance/POints/PAn/Zoom/TWist/CLip/Hide/Off/Undo/<eXit>: Enter

> **NOTE:** To turn on the perspective again, select the Distance option and press Enter for all the defaults. There is no option called On to turn on the perspective view.

POints Option The POints option establishes the location of the camera as well as target points. This gives AutoCAD the basic information needed to create the view. The location of the camera and target points must be specified in a parallel projection. If perspective is on, AutoCAD temporarily turns it off while you specify the new location for camera and target points, and then redisplays the image back in perspective.

When you select the POints option, AutoCAD prompts:

    Enter target point:
    Enter camera point:

Specify the target and camera locations. After the locations are defined, the screen shows the new view immediately.

The following command sequence shows an example of using the POints option of the DVIEW command.

    Command: **dview**
    Select objects: *(select the objects)*
    CAmera/TArget/Distance/POints/PAn/Zoom/TWist/CLip/Hide/Off/Undo/<eXit>: **po**
    Enter Target point: *(specify a point)*
    Enter Camera point: *(specify a point)*
    CAmera/TArget/Distance/POints/PAn/Zoom/TWist/CLip/Hide/Off/Undo/<eXit>: Enter

PAn Option The PAn option allows you to view a different location of the model by specifying the pan distance and direction. This option is similar to the regular PAN command. The following command sequence shows an example of using the PAn option of the DVIEW command.

    Command: **dview**
    Select objects: *(select the objects)*
    CAmera/TArget/Distance/POints/PAn/Zoom/TWist/CLip/Hide/Off/Undo/<eXit>: **pa**
    Displacement base point: *(specify a point)*
    Second point: *(specify a point)*
    CAmera/TArget/Distance/POints/PAn/Zoom/TWist/CLip/Hide/Off/Undo/<eXit>: Enter

Zoom Option The Zoom option zooms in to a portion of the model. This option is similar to the regular AutoCAD ZOOM Center command, with the center point lying at the center of the current viewport. This option is controlled by a scale factor value.

AutoCAD 3D

When you select the Zoom option, AutoCAD prompts:

Adjust zoom scale factor <default>:

In addition to the prompt, you also see a horizontal bar at the top of the screen. The slider bar lets you specify a zoom scale factor, with 1x being the current zoom level. Any value greater than 1 increases the size of the objects in the view, while any decimal value less than 1 decreases the size.

> **NOTE:** When the perspective is on, the Zoom option prompts for a lens length rather than a zoom factor, but the effect is similar. The larger the lens size, the closer the object.

TWist Option The TWist option rotates or twists the view. It allows you to rotate the image around the line of sight at a given angle from zero with zero being to the right. The angle is measured counterclockwise.

The following command sequence shows an example of using the TWist option of the DVIEW command.

    Command: **dview**
    Select objects: *(select the objects)*
    CAmera/TArget/Distance/POints/PAn/Zoom/TWist/CLip/Hide/Off/Undo/<eXit>: **tw**
    New view twist <default>: *(select a point)*
    CAmera/TArget/Distance/POints/PAn/Zoom/TWist/CLip/Hide/Off/Undo/<eXit>: [Enter]

CLip Option The CLip option hides portions of the object in view so that the interior of the object can be seen, or parts of the complex object can be more clearly identified.

The CLip option has three suboptions, Back, Front, and Off. The Back suboption eliminates all parts of the object in view that are located beyond the designated point along the line of sight. The Front suboption eliminates all parts of the object in view that are located between the camera and the front clipping plane. The Off suboption turns off front and back clipping.

The following command sequence shows an example of using the CLip option of the DVIEW command.

    Command: **dview**
    Select objects: *(select the objects)*
    CAmera/TArget/Distance/POints/PAn/Zoom/TWist/CLip/Hide/Off/Undo/<eXit>: **cl**
    Back/Front/<Off>: **b**
    On/Off/<Distance from Target> <default>: *(specify the distance or turn on and off the previ-
        ously defined clipping plane)*
    CAmera/TArget/Distance/POints/PAn/Zoom/TWist/CLip/Hide/Off/Undo/<eXit>: [Enter]

Hide Option The Hide option is similar to the regular AutoCAD HIDE command.

Undo Option The Undo option will undo the last DVIEW operation. You use it to step back through multiple DVIEW operations.

eXit Option The eXit option ends the DVIEW command and returns to the "Command:" prompt. It is the default option of the DVIEW command.

CREATING 3D OBJECTS

As mentioned earlier, there are several advantages in drawing objects in 3D, including viewing the model at any angle, automatic generation of standard and auxiliary 2D views, rendering and hidden-line removal; interference checking, and engineering analysis.

AutoCAD supports three types of 3D modeling: wire-frame, surface, and solid.

The wire-frame model consists only of points, lines, and curves that describe the edges of the object. In AutoCAD you can create wireframe model by positioning 2D (planar) objects anywhere in 3D space. In addition, AutoCAD provides additional commands such as 3D polyline and splines to create a wire-frame model.

The surface model is more sophisticated than wire-frame modeling. It defines not only the edges of a 3D object but also its surfaces. AutoCAD's surface modeler defines faceted surfaces using a polygonal mesh. It is possible to create a mesh to a flat or curved surface by locating the boundaries or edges of the surface.

Solid modeling is the easiest type of 3D modeling. Solids are the unambiguous and informationally complete representation of the shape of a physical object. Fundamentally, solid modeling differs from wire-frame or surface modeling in two ways:

1. The information is more complete in the solid model.

2. The method of construction of the model itself is inherently straightforward.

In wire-frame or surface modeling, objects are created by positioning lines or surfaces in 3D space. In solid modeling, you build the model as you would with building blocks. In solid modeling from beginning to the end, you think, draw, and communicate in 3D. One of the main benefits of solid modeling is its ability to be analyzed. You can calculate the mass properties of a solid object, such as its mass, center of gravity, surface area, moments of intertia, etc.

Each modeling type uses a different method for constructing 3D models and each editing method also varies between model types. It is recommended not to mix modeling methods. It is possible in AutoCAD to convert between model types from solids to surfaces and from sufaces to wireframe; however, you cannot convert from wire-frames to surfaces or surfaces to solids.

2D DRAW Commands in 3D Space

You can use most of the Draw commands discussed in previous chapters with a Z coordinate value. But 2D objects such as polylines, circles, arcs, and solids are constrained to the X,Y plane of the current UCS. For these objects, the Z value is accepted only for the first coordinate to set the elevation of the 2D object above or below the current plane. When you pick a point using an osnap mode, it assumes the Z value of the point to which you snapped.

Elevation and Thickness

You can create new objects by first setting up a default elevation or Z value. Subsequently, all the objects drawn assume the current elevation as the Z value whenever a 3D point is expected but you supply only X and Y value. The current elevation is maintained separately in model space and paper space.

Similarly you create new objects with extrusion thickness by presetting a value for the thickness. Subsequently, all the objects drawn, such as lines, polylines, arcs, circles, and solids assume the current thickness and extrude in their Z direction. For example, you can draw a cylinder by drawing a circle with preset thickness, or to draw a cube, simply draw a square with preset thickness.

> **NOTE:** Thickness can be positive or negative. Thickness is in the direction of the Z Axis of 2D objects. For 3D objects that can accept thickness, it is always relative to the current UCS. They will appear oblique if they do not lie in or parallel to the current UCS. If thickness is added to a line drawn directly in the Z direction, it appears that the line extends beyond its endpoint in the positive or negative thickness direction. Text and dimensions ignore the thickness setting.

The elevation and thickness can be set by ELEV command. The ELEV command is invoked by typing **ELEV** at the "Command:" prompt and pressing Enter or spacebar.

```
Command: elev
New current elevation <current>:
New current thickness <current>:
```

Specify the new current elevation and thickness. For example, the following are the command sequences to draw a six-sided polygon at zero elevation with a radius of 2.5 units and a height of 4.5 units and place a cylinder at the center of the polygon with a radius of 1.0 unit at an elevation of 2.0 units with a height of 7.5 units, as shown in Figure 14–18.

```
Command: elev
New current elevation <0.0000>: Enter
New current thickness <0.0000>: 4.5

Command: polygon (draw a polygon with a radius of 2.5 units)
```

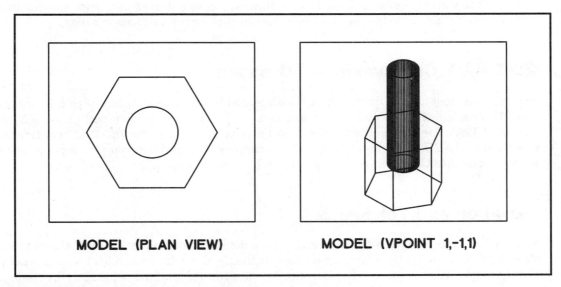

MODEL (PLAN VIEW)   MODEL (VPOINT 1,–1,1)

Figure 14–18 Specifying a new current elevation and thickness

Command: **elev**
New current elevation <0.0000>: **2.0**
New current thickness <0.0000>: **7.5**
Command: **circle** *(draw a circle with a radius 1.0 unit)*

You change the thickness of the existing objects using the CHANGE or CHPROP commands.

REGION Command

The REGION command creates a region object from a selection set of objects. Closed polylines, lines, curves, circular arcs, circles, elliptical arcs, ellipses, and splines are valid selections. Once you create a region, then you can extrude with the EXTRUDE command to make a 3D solid. You can also create a composite region with the UNION, SUBTRACTION, and INTERSECTION commands. If necessary, you can hatch a region with the BHATCH command.

The REGION command is invoked from the Polygon flyout located in the Draw toolbar (Figure 14–19) or at the "Command:" prompt type **region** and press Enter or spacebar.

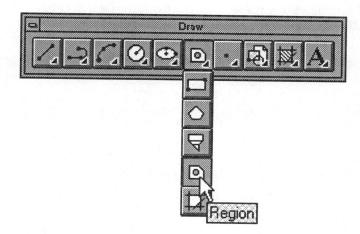

Figure 14–19   Invoke the REGION Command from the Draw toolbar

Command:**region**
Select objects:

Select the objects to create a region. AutoCAD converts closed 2D and planar 3D polylines in the selection set to separate regions and then converts polylines, lines, and curves that form closed planar loops. If more than two curves share an endpoint, the resultant region might be arbitrary. Each object retains its layer, linetype, and color. AutoCAD deletes the original objects after converting them to regions and does not hatch the regions by default.

3DPOLY Command

The 3DPOLY command draws polylines with independent X,Y, and Z axis coordinates. The 3DPOLY command works similar to the PLINE command with a few exceptions. Unlike the PLINE command, 3DPOLY draws only straight line segments without variable width. Editing a 3D

Polyline with the PEDIT command is similar to 2D Polyline, except for some options. 3D Polylines cannot be joined, curve fit with arc segments, or given a width or tangent.

3DFACE Command

When you create a 3D model, it is often necessary to have solid surfaces for hiding and shading. These surfaces are created with the 3DFACE command.

The 3DFACE command creates a solid surface and the command sequence is similar to the SOLID command. Unlike the SOLID command, you can give differing Z coordinates for the corner points of a face, forming a section of a plane in space. Unlike the SOLID command, a 3DFACE is drawn from corner to corner clockwise or counterclockwise around the object (and it does not draw a "bow tie"). A 3D face is a plane defined by either three or four points used to represent a surface. It provides a means of controlling which edges of a 3D face will be visible. You can describe complex, 3D polygons using multiple 3D faces and you can tell AutoCAD which edges you want to be drawn. If you have an object with curved surfaces, then the 3DFACE command is not suitable. One of the mesh commands will be more appropriate, as explained later in the chapter.

The 3DFACE command is invoked from the Surfaces toolbar (Figure 14–20), or at the "Command:" prompt type **3DFACE** and press Enter or spacebar.

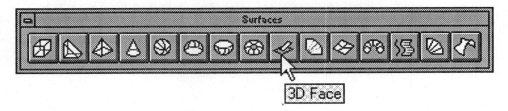

Figure 14–20 Invoke the 3DFACE Command from the Surfaces toolbar

```
Command: 3dface
First point:
```

Specify the first point, and AutoCAD prompts you for the second, third, and fourth points in sequence. Then AutoCAD closes the face from the fourth point to the first point and prompts for the third point. If you give a null response to the third point, AutoCAD closes the 3Dface with three sides and then terminates the command and takes you to the "Command:" prompt.

If you want to draw additional faces in one command sequence, the last two points of the first face becomes the first two points for the second face. And the last two points of the second face becomes the first two points of the third face and so on. You have to be very careful in drawing several faces in one command sequence since AutoCAD does not have an Undo option that works inside the 3DFACE command. A single mistake can cause the entire face to be redrawn. For this reason, it is a good idea to draw 3D faces one at a time.

For example, the following command sequence shows placement of 3D faces, as shown in Figure 14–21.

```
Command:3dface
First point: (select point A1)
Second point: (select point A2)
```

Third point: *(select point A3)*
Fourth point: *(select point A4)*
Third point: *(select point A5)*
Fourth point: *(select point A6)*
Third point: *(select point A7)*
Fourth point: *(select point A8)*
Third point: *(select point A1)*
Fourth point: *(select point A2)*
Third point: Enter

The surface created, as shown in Figure 14–21, required four faces to cover it. Some of the faces are overlapping and this is not acceptable when viewing the object. The 3DFACE command allows face edges to be "invisible." To create an invisible edge, the letter **I** must be entered at the prompt for the first point of the edge to be invisible, and then the point can be entered.

The following command sequence shows placement of 3Dfaces for invisible edges, as shown in Figure 14–21.

Command: **3dface**
First point: *(select point A1)*
Second point: *(select point A8)*
Third point: *(select point A5)*
Fourth point: *(select point A4)*
Third point: *(select point A3)*
Fourth point: *(select point A6)*
Third point: *(select point A7)*
Fourth point: **i** Enter *(select point A8)*
Third point: *(select point A1)*
Fourth point: *(select point A2)*
Third point: *(select point A3)*
Fourth point: *(select point A4)*
Third point: Enter

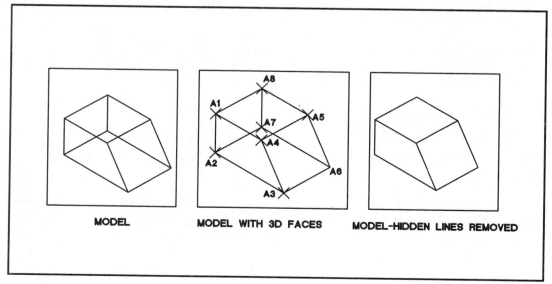

MODEL   MODEL WITH 3D FACES   MODEL–HIDDEN LINES REMOVED

Figure 14–21   Drawing a 3D object with the 3DFACE Command

3DFACE commands ignore the thickness. The SPLFRAME system variable controls the display of invisible edges in 3D faces. If SPLFRAME is set to a nonzero value, all invisible edges of 3D faces are displayed.

Controlling the Visibility of 3D Face The EDGE command allows you to change the visibility of 3D face edges. You can selectively turn ON/OFF the edges. The EDGE command is invoked from the Surfaces toolbar (Figure 14–22) or at the "Command:" prompt type **EDGE** and press [Enter] or spacebar.

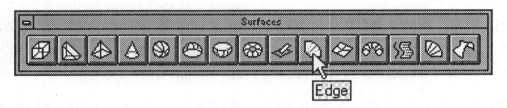

Figure 14–22 Invoke the EDGE Command from the Surfaces toolbar

    Command: **edge**
    Display/<Select edge>:

Select the edges and AutoCAD hides the selected edges. Once you are through selecting the edges, press [Enter] or spacebar to terminate the command sequence.

The **Display** option highlights invisible edges of 3Dfaces so you can change the visibility of the edges. AutoCAD prompts:

    Select/<All>:

The default option displays all the invisible edges. Once the edges are displayed, then AutoCAD allows you to change the status of the visibility.

The **Select** option allows you to selectively identify hidden edges to be displayed. Then, if necessary, you can change the status of the visibility.

Modifying 3D Face The DDMODIFY command allows you to modify a selected 3D face. The DDMODIFY command is invoked by typing DDMODIFY at the "Command:" prompt and pressing [Enter] or spacebar.

    Command: **ddmodify**
    Select object to modify:

Select a 3D face, AutoCAD displays the Modify 3D Face dialog box similar to the one shown in Figure 14–23.

Point 1, Point 2, Point 3, and Point 4 display the vertex coordinates of the selected 3D face. If necessary, you change the vertex coordinates by clicking the appropriate **Pick Point<** button or type coordinates in the appropriate x/y/z edit fields. From the Modify 3D Face dialog box you can also change the color, linetype, and layer of the selected 3D face.

The toggle button located in the Visibility section of the dialog box allows you to change the visibility of the four edges.

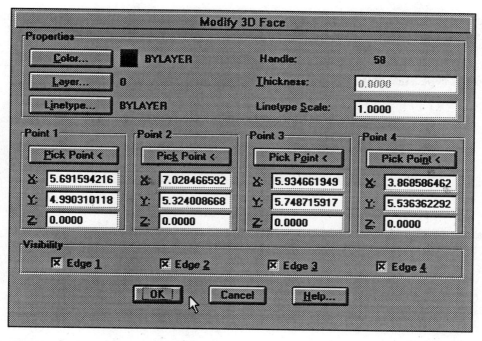

Figure 14–23 The Modify 3D Face dialog box

> **NOTE:** All edges are visible regardless of the visibility setting if the system variable SPLFRAME is set to 1 (On).

CREATING MESHES

A 3D mesh is a single object. It defines a flat surface or approximates a curved one by placing multiple 3D faces on the surface of an object. It is a series of lines consisting of columns and rows. AutoCAD lets you determine the spacing between rows (M) and columns (N).

It is possible to create a mesh to a flat or curved surface by locating the boundaries or edges of the surface. Surfaces created in this fashion are called geometry-generated surfaces. Their size and shape depend on the boundaries used to define them, and the specific formula (or command) used to determine the location of the vertices between the boundaries. AutoCAD provides four different commands to create geometry-generated surfaces, which include RULESURF, REVSURF, TABSURF, and EDGESURF. The differences between these types of meshes depend on the types of objects connecting the surfaces. In addition, AutoCAD provides two additional commands to create polygon mesh: the 3DMESH and PFACE commands. The key to using meshes effectively is to understand the purpose and requirement of each type of mesh and select the appropriate one for the given condition.

3DMESH Command

You can define a 3D polygon mesh by the 3DMESH command. Initially, it prompts you for the number of rows and columns in terms of Mesh M and Mesh N, respectively. Then it prompts for the location of each vertex in the mesh. The product of M times N gives the number of vertices for the mesh.

The 3DMESH command is invoked from the Surfaces toolbar (Figure 14–24) or at the "Command:" prompt type **3DMESH** and press [Enter] or spacebar.

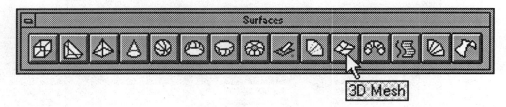

Figure 14–24 Invoke the 3DMESH Command from the Surfaces toolbar

```
Command: 3dmesh
Mesh M Size:
Mesh N Size:
```

Specify an integer value between 2 and 256 for each dimension of the mesh. The points for each vertex must be entered separately, and the M value can be considered the number of lines that will be connected by faces, while the N value is the number of points each line consists of. Vertices may be specified as 2D or 3D points, and may be any distance from each other.

The following command sequence creates a simple 5×4 polygon mesh. The mesh is created between the first point of the first line, the first point of the second line, and so on, as shown in Figure 14–25.

```
Command: 3dmesh
Mesh M Size: 5
Mesh N Size: 4
Vertex (0,0): (select point A1)
Vertex (0,1): (select point A2)
Vertex (0,2): (select point A3)
Vertex (0,3): (select point A4)
Vertex (1,0): (select point B1)
Vertex (1,1): (select point B2)
Vertex (1,2): (select point B3)
Vertex (1,3): (select point B4)
Vertex (2,0): (select point C1)
Vertex (2,1): (select point C2)
Vertex (2,2): (select point C3)
Vertex (2,3): (select point C4)
Vertex (3,0): (select point D1)
Vertex (3,1): (select point D2)
Vertex (3,2): (select point D3)
Vertex (3,3): (select point D4)
Vertex (4,0): (select point E1)
Vertex (4,1): (select point E2)
Vertex (4,2): (select point E3)
Vertex (4,3): (select point E4)
```

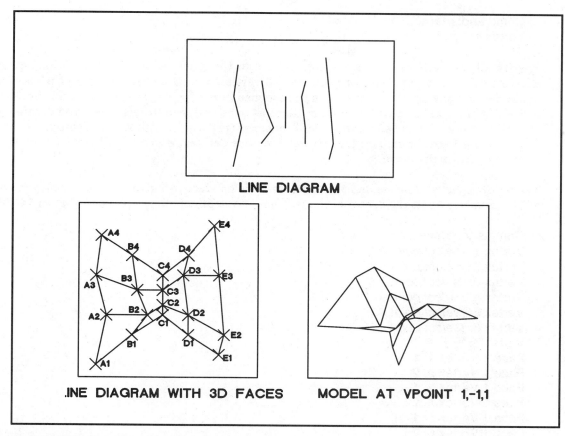

Figure 14-25 Creating a 3D mesh

> **NOTE:** Specifying 3D mesh of any size can be time-consuming and tedious. It is preferable to use one of the geometry-generated surfaces such as the RULESURF, TABSURF, REVSURF, and EDGESURF commands. The 3DMESH command is primarily designed for AutoLISP and ADS applications.

PFACE Command

The PFACE command allows you to construct a mesh of any topology you desire. This command is similar to the 3DFACE command but creates surfaces with invisible interior divisions. You can specify any number of vertices and 3D faces, unlike the other meshes. Producing this kind of mesh lets you conveniently avoid creating many unrelated 3D faces with the same vertices.

AutoCAD first prompts you to pick all the vertex points and then you create your faces by entering the vertex numbers that define their edges.

The PFACE command is invoked by typing PFACE at the "Command:" prompt and pressing Enter or spacebar.

Command: **pface**
Vertex 1:

Specify all the vertices one after another used in the mesh, keeping track of the vertex numbers shown in the prompts. You can specify the vertices as 2D or 3D points and place them at any distance from one another. Enter a null response (press Enter) after specifying all the vertices, then AutoCAD prompts for a vertex number that has to be assigned to each face. You define any number of vertices for each face, and enter a null response (press Enter). AutoCAD prompts for the next face. After all the vertex numbers for all the faces are defined, enter a null reponse (press Enter), and AutoCAD draws the mesh.

The following command sequence creates a simple polyface to a given six-sided polygon with a circle of 1" radius drawn at the center of the polygon at a depth of –2, as shown in Figure 14–26.

Command: **pface**
Vertex 1: *(select point A1)*
Vertex 2: *(select point A2)*
Vertex 3: *(select point A3)*
Vertex 4: *(select point A4)*
Vertex 5: *(select point A5)*
Vertex 6: *(select point A6)*
Vertex 7: Enter
Face 1 Vertex 1: **1**
Face 1 Vertex 2: **2**
Face 1 Vertex 3: **1**
Face 1 Vertex 4: **2**
Face 1 Vertex 5: **1**
Face 1 Vertex 6: **2**
Face 1 Vertex 7: Enter
Face 2 Vertex 1: Enter

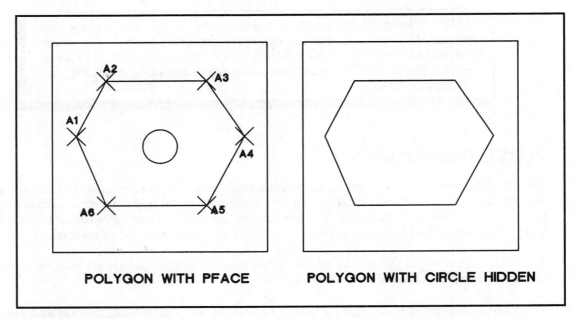

POLYGON WITH PFACE   POLYGON WITH CIRCLE HIDDEN

Figure 14–26 Creating a polyface to a given six-sided polygon with a circle at the center

If necessary, you can make an edge of the polyface mesh invisible by entering a negative number for the beginning vertex of the edge. By default, the faces are drawn on the current layer and color. However, you can create the faces in layers and colors different from the original object. You can assign a layer or color by responding to the prompt:

Face n, Vertex n:

with L for layer or c for color. Then AutoCAD prompts for the name of the layer or color appropriately. It will continue with the prompts for vertex numbers. The layer or color you enter is used for the face you are currently defining and for any subsequent faces created.

> **NOTE:** Specifying the layer or color within the PFACE command does not change object properties for subsequent commands. Specifying PFACE of any size can be time-consuming and tedious. It is preferable to use one of the geometry-generated surfaces such as the RULESURF, TABSURF, REVSURF, and EDGESURF commands. The PFACE command is primarily designed for AutoLISP and ADS applications.

RULESURF Command

The RULESURF command creates a polygon mesh between two objects. The two objects can be lines, points, arcs, circles, 2D polylines, or 3D polylines. If one object is open, such as a line or arc, the other must also be open, too. If one is closed, such as circle, so must the other be. A point can be used as one object, regardless of whether the other is open or closed. But, only one of the objects can be a point.

RULESURF creates an M by N mesh, the value of Mesh M is 2, which is constant. The value of Mesh N can be changed depending on the requirement of the number of faces. This can be done with the help of the system variable SURFTAB1. By default, the SURFTAB1 is set to 6.

The following command sequence shows how to change the value of the SURFTAB1 from 6 to 20:

Command: **surftab1**
New value for SURFTAB1 <6>: **20**

The RULESURF command is invoked from the Surfaces toolbar (Figure 14–27), or at the "Command:" prompt type **RULESURF** and press ⌷Enter⌷ or spacebar.

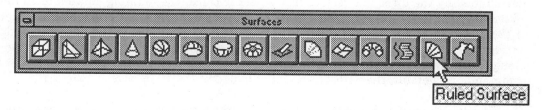

Figure 14–27 Invoke the RULESURF Command from the Surfaces toolbar

Command: **rulesurf**
Select first defining curve:
Select the second defining curve:

Identify the two objects to which a mesh has to be created. See Figure 14–28 in which an arc (A1–A2) and line (A3–A4) were selected and a mesh was created with SURFTAB1 set to 15. Two lines (B1–B2 and B3–B4) were selected and a mesh was created with SURFTAB1 set to 20. A cone was created by drawing a circle at an elevation of 0 and a point (C1) at an elevation of 5, followed by the application of RULESURF with a SURFTAB1 set to 20.

> **NOTE:** When you identify the two objects, make sure to select on the same side of the objects, left or right. If you pick the left side of one of the sides and the right side of the other, you would get a bow-tie effect.

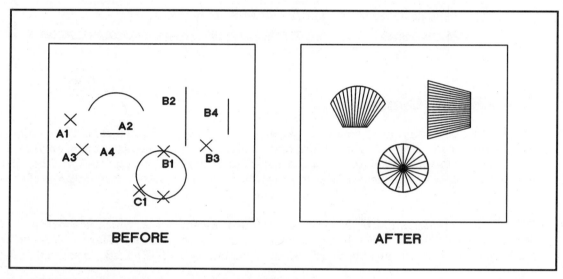

Figure 14–28 Creating ruled surfaces with the RULESURF Command

TABSURF Command

The TABSURF command creates a surface extrusion from an object with a length and direction determined by the direction vector. The object is called the defining curve and can be a line, arc, circle, 2D polyline, or 3D polyline. The direction vector can be a line or open polyline. The endpoint of the direction vector nearest the point picked will be swept along the path curve, describing the surface. Once the mesh is created, the direction vector can be deleted. The number of intervals along the path curve is controlled by the system variable SURFTAB1, similar to the RULESURF command. By default, the SURFTAB1 is set to 6.

The TABSURF command is invoked from the Surfaces toolbar (Figure 14–29), or at the "Command:" prompt type **TABSURF** and press Enter or spacebar.

Figure 14–29 Invoke the TABSURF Command from the Surfaces toolbar

Command: **tabsurf**
Select path curve:
Selection direction vector:

Identify the path curve and then the direction vector. The location at which the direction vector is selected determines the direction of the constructed mesh. The mesh is created in the direction from the selection point to the nearest endpoint of the direction vector. In Figure 14–30, a mesh was created with SURFTAB1 set to 16 by identifying a polyline as the path curve and the line as the direction vector.

> **NOTE:** The length of the 3D mesh is the same as the direction vector.

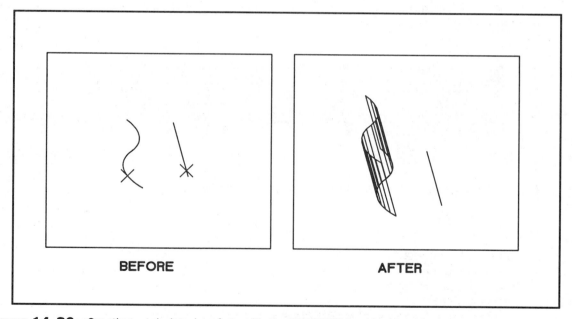

BEFORE   AFTER

Figure 14–30 Creating a tabulated surface with the TABSURF Command

REVSURF Command

The REVSURF command creates a 3D mesh that follows the path defined by a path curve and is rotated around a center line. The object used to define the path curve may be an arc, circle, line, 2D polyline, or 3D polyline. Complex shapes consisting of lines, arcs, or polylines can be joined into one object using the PEDIT command and then you can create a single rotated mesh instead of several individual meshes.

The center line can be a line or polyline that defines the axis around which the faces are constructed. The center line can be of any length and at any orientation. If necessary, you can erase the center line after the construction of the mesh. So, it is recommended that you make the axis longer than the path curve so it is easy to erase after the rotation.

In the case of REVSURF, both the Mesh M size as well as Mesh N are controlled by system variables SURFTAB1 and SURFTAB2, respectively. The SURFTAB1 value determines how many faces are placed around the rotation axis and can be an integer value between 3 and 1024. The SURFTAB2 determines how many faces are used to simulate the curves created by arcs or circles in the path curve. By default, SURFTAB1 and SURFTAB2 are set to 6.

The following command sequence shows how to change the value of the SURFTAB1 from 6 to 20 and SURFTAB2 from 6 to 15:

Command: **surftab1**
New value for SURFTAB1 <6>: **20**

Command: **surftab2**
New value for SURFTAB1 <6>: **15**

The REVSURF command is invoked from the Surfaces toolbar (Figure 14–31), or at the "Command:" prompt type **REVSURF** and press Enter or spacebar.

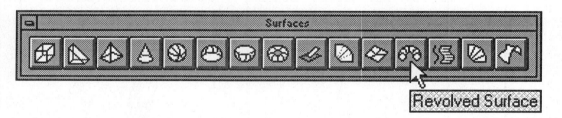

Figure 14–31   Invoke the REVSURF Command from the Surfaces toolbar

Command: **revsurf**
Select path curve:
Select axis of revolution:
Start angle <0>:
Included angle (+=ccw,-=cw) <Full circle>:

Identify the path curve and then the center line for the axis of revolution. For the "Start Angle:" prompt, it does not matter if you are going to rotate the curve 360 degrees (full circle). If you want to rotate the curve only at a certain angle, then provide the start angle in reference to three o'clock (default) and then indicate the angle of rotation in counterclockwise (positive) and clockwise (negative). See Figure 14–32 in which a mesh was created with SURFTAB1 set to 16 and SURFTAB2 set to 12, by identifying a closed polyline as the path curve and the vertical line as the axis of revolution, and then rotated 360 degrees.

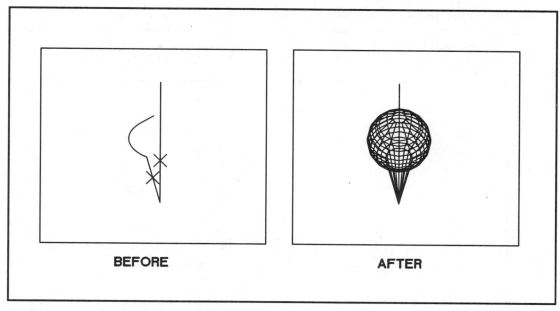

Figure 14–32 Creating a meshed surface with the REVSURF Command

EDGESURF Command

The EDGESURF command allows a mesh to be created with four adjoining sides defining its boundaries. The only requirement for EDGESURF is that it have exactly four sides. The sides can be lines, arcs, or any combination of polylines and polyarcs. Each side must join the adjacent one to create a closed boundary.

In EDGESURF, both the Mesh M size as well as Mesh N can be controlled by system variables SURFTAB1 and SURFTAB2, respectively, just as in REVSURF.

The EDGESURF command is invoked from the Surfaces toolbar (Figure 14–33), or at the "Command:" prompt type in **EDGESURF** and press ⌷Enter⌷ or spacebar.

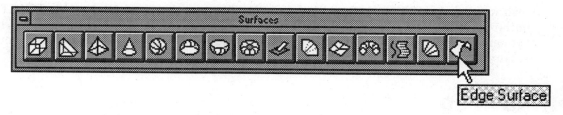

Figure 14–33 Invoke the EDGESURF Command from the Surfaces toolbar

```
Command: edgesurf
Select edge 1:
Select edge 2:
Select edge 3:
Select edge 4:
```

Identify all the four sides in a sequential order. When picking four sides, you must be consistent in picking the beginning of each polyline group. If you pick the beginning of one side and the end of another, the final mesh will cross and look strange. See Figure 14–34 in which a mesh was created with SURFTAB1 set to 25 and SURFTAB2 set to 20 by identifying four sides.

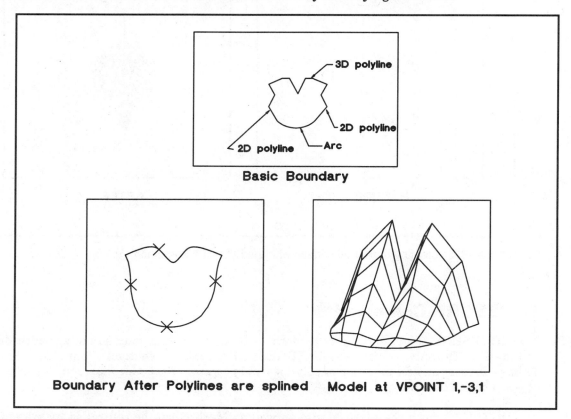

Figure 14–34   Creating a meshed surface with the EDGESURF Command

Editing Polymesh Surfaces

Like blocks, polylines, hatch, and dimensioning, you can also explode a mesh. When you explode a mesh it separates into individual 3D faces. Meshes can also be altered by the PEDIT command similar to editing polylines using the PEDIT command. Most of the options under the PEDIT command can be applied to meshes, except giving width to the edges of the polymesh. For a detailed explanation of the PEDIT command, refer to Chapter 4.

EDITING IN 3D

This section describes how to perform various 3D editing operations, such as aligning, rotating, mirroring, arraying, extending, and trimming.

ALIGN Command

The ALIGN command allows you to translate and rotate objects in 3D space regardless of the position of the current UCS. The move is defined by three source and three destination points.

ALIGN lets you select the objects to move, then subsequently prompts for three source and three destination points. The ALIGN command is invoked from the Rotate flyout located in the Modify toolbar (Figure 14–35), or at the "Command:" prompt type **ALIGN** and press [Enter] or spacebar.

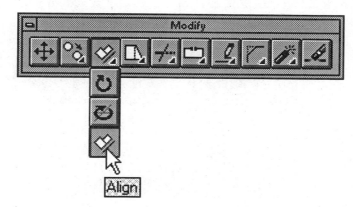

Figure 14–35 Invoke the ALIGN Command from the Modify toolbar

    Command: **align**
    Select objects:

Select the objects to move and press [Enter]. AutoCAD subsequently prompts for three source and three destination points as follows:

    1st source point:
    1st destination point:
    2nd source point:
    2nd destination point:
    3rd source point:
    3rd destination point:

Temporary lines are displayed between the matching pairs of source and destination points. If you enter all six points, the move consists of a translation and two rotations based on the six points. The translation moves the 1st source point to the 1st destination point. The first rotation aligns the line defined by the 1st and 2nd source points with the line defined by the 1st and 2nd destination points. The second rotation aligns the plane defined by the three source points with the plane defined by the three destination points.

Instead of three pairs of points, if you enter two pairs of points, the transformation reduces to a translation from 1st source point to the 1st destination point, and a rotation so that the line passing through the two source points aligns with the line passing through the two destination points. The transformation occurs in either 2D or 3D, depending on your response to the following prompt:

    <2d> or 3d transformation:

If you enter 2d or press [Enter], the rotation is performed in the XY plane of the current UCS. If you enter 3d, the rotation is in the plane defined by the two destination points and the 2nd source point.

If you enter only one pair of points, the transformation reduces to a simple translation from the source to the destination point. This is similar to using the AutoCAD's regular MOVE command without the dynamic dragging.

ROTATE3D Command

The ROTATE3D command lets you rotate an object about an arbitrary 3D axis. The ROTATE3D command is invoked from the Rotate flyout located in the Modify toolbar (Figure 14–36), or at the "Command:" prompt type **ROTATE3D** and press Enter or spacebar.

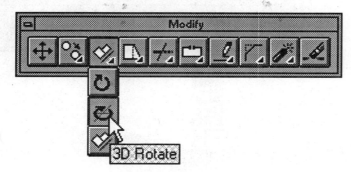

Figure 14–36   Invoke the ROTATE3D Command from the Modify toolbar

> Command: **rotate3d**
> Select objects:

Select the objects to rotate and press Enter, then AutoCAD lists the options for selecting the axis of rotation

> Axis by Entity/Last/View/Xaxis/Yaxis/Zaxis/<2points>:

2points Option The 2points option prompts you for two points. The axis of rotation is the line that passes through the two points and the positive direction is from the first to second point.

Axis by Entity Option The Axis by Entity option lets you select an object and then derives the axis of rotation based on the type of object selected. Valid objects include: line, circle, arc, and pline.

Last Option The Last option uses the last used axis. If there is no last axis, a message is displayed and the axis selection prompt is redisplayed.

View Option The View option prompts you to select a point. The axis of rotation is perpendicular to the view direction and passes through the selected point. The positive axis direction is toward the viewer.

X/Y/Zaxis Option The X/Y/Z option prompts you to select a point. The axis of rotation is parallel to standard axis of the current UCS and passes through the selected point.

Once you have selected the axis of rotation, AutoCAD prompts:

> <Rotation angle>/Reference: *(specify the rotation angle or enter r for reference)*

AutoCAD rotates the selected object(s) to the specified rotation angle. The Reference option allows you to specify the current orientation as reference angle or show AutoCAD the angle by pointing to the two end points of a line to be rotated and then specifying the desired new rotation. AutoCAD automatically calculates the rotation angle and rotates the selected object appropriately.

See Figure 14–37 for an example in rotating the cylinder around Z axis.

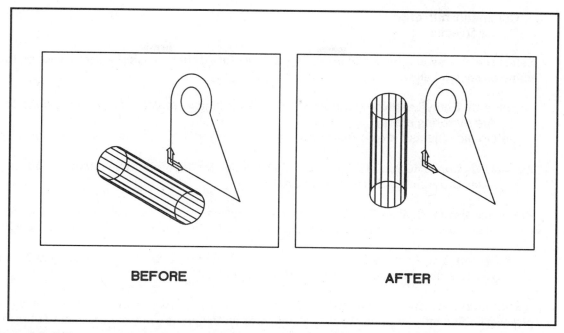

BEFORE   **AFTER**

Figure 14–37   Rotating a cylinder about the Z axis with the ROTATE3D Command

MIRROR3D Command

The MIRROR3D command lets you mirror a selected object about a plane. The MIRROR3D command is invoked from the Copy flyout located in the Modify toolbar (Figure 14–38), or at the "Command:" prompt type **MIRROR3D** and press [Enter].

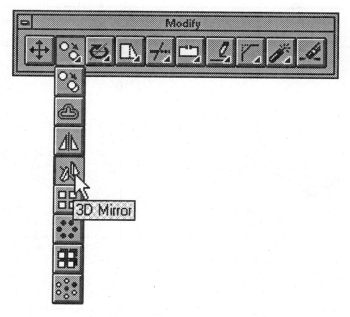

Figure 14–38   Invoke the MIRROR3D Command from the Modify toolbar

AutoCAD 3D

Command: **mirror3d**
Select objects:

Select the objects to mirror and press [Enter], then AutoCAD lists the options for selecting the mirroring plane as shown below:

Plane by Entity/Last/Normal/View/XY/YZ/XZ/<3points>: *(select one of the options to specify the mirroring plane)*
Delete old objects? <No>: *(enter y to delete the objects or n for not to delete the objects)*

3points Option The 3points option prompts you for three points. The mirroring plane is the plane that passes through the three selected points.

Plane by Entity Option The Plane by Entity option lets you select an object and the mirroring plane is aligned with the plane of the object selected. Valid objects include: circle, arc, and pline.

Last Option The Last option uses the last used plane. If there is no last plane, a message is displayed and the plane selection prompt is redisplayed.

Normal Option The Normal option prompts you to select two points. The mirroring plane is the plane specified by a point on the plane and point on the plane's normal (perpendicular to the plane).

View Option The View option prompts you to select a point. The mirroring plane is created perpendicular to the view direction and passes through the selected point.

XY/YZ/XZplane The XY/YZ/XZplane option prompts you to select a point. The mirroring plane is created parallel to standard plane of the current UCS and passes through the selected point.

See Figure 14–39 for an example in mirroring the cylinder aligned with the plane of the object selected (pline).

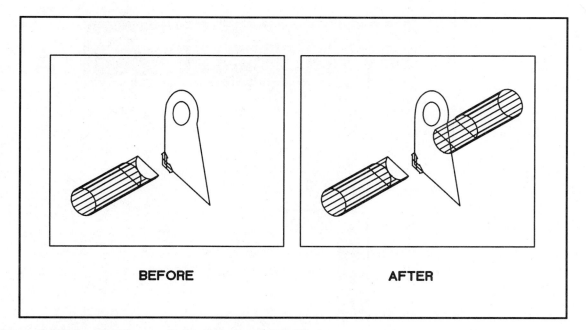

BEFORE   **AFTER**

Figure 14–39 Mirroring a cylinder about a polyline object

3DARRAY Command

The 3DARRAY command is used to make multiple copies of selected objects in either rectangular or polar array in 3D. In the rectangular array, specify the number of columns (X direction), the number of rows (Y direction), the number of levels (Z direction), and the spacing between columns, rows, and levels. In the polar array, specify the number of items to array, the angle that the arrayed objects are to fill, the start point and end point of the axis about which the objects are to be rotated, and whether or not the objects are rotated about the center of the group.

The 3DARRAY command is invoked from the Copy flyout located in the Modify toolbar, or at the "Command:" prompt type **3DARRAY** and press [Enter] or spacebar.

> Command: **3Darray**
> Select objects: *(select the objects to array)*
> Rectangular or Polar array (R/P):

Rectangular Array To generate a rectangular array, enter **R** for rectangular array and AutoCAD prompts:

> Number of rows(---)<1>: *(specify the number of rows or press [Enter] or spacebar)*
> Number of columns(|||)<1>: *(specify the number of columns or press [Enter] or spacebar)*
> Number of levels(...)<1>: *(specify the number of levels or press [Enter] or spacebar)*
> Distance between rows(---)<1>: *(specify a distance)*
> Distance between columns(---)<1>: *(specify a distance)*
> Distance between levels(---)<1>: *(specify a distance)*

Any combination of whole numbers of columns, rows, and levels may be entered. AutoCAD includes the original object in the number you enter. An array must have at least two columns, two rows, or two levels. Specifying one row requires that more than one column be specified, or vice versa. Specifying one level creates a 2D array. Column, row, and level spacing can be different from each other. They can be entered separately when prompted, or you may select two points and let AutoCAD measure the spacing. Positive values for spacing generate the array along positive X, Y, and Z axes. Negative values generate the array along the negative X, Y, and Z axes.

Polar Array To generate a polar array, enter **p** for polar array and AutoCAD prompts:

> Number of items: *(specify the number of items in the array; include the original object)*
> Angle to fill <360>: *(specify an angle or press [Enter] for 360 degrees)*
> Rotate objects as they are copied <Y>: *(enter y to rotate the objects as they are copied or enter n not to rotate the objects as they are copied)*
> Center point of array: *(specify a point)*
> Second point on axis of rotation: *(specify a point for axis of rotation)*

Extending and Trimming in 3D

AutoCAD allows you to extend an object by using AutoCAD's EXTEND command (explained in chapter 3) to any object in 3D space or trim an object to any other 3D space by using AutoCAD's TRIM command (explained in chapter 3), regardless of whether the objects are on the same plane or parallel to the cutting or boundary edges. Before you select an object to extend or trim on 3D space, specify one of the three available projection modes: None, UCS, or View. The **None** option

AutoCAD 3D

specifies no projection. AutoCAD extends/trims only objects that intersect with the boundary/ cutting edge in 3D space. The **UCS** option specifies projection onto the XY plane of the current UCS. AutoCAD extends/trims objects that do not intersect with the boundary/cutting objects in 3D space. The **View** option specifies projection along the current view direction. System variable PROJECMODE allows you to set one of the available projection modes. You can also set the project mode by selecting the Project option available in the EXTEND command.

In addition to specifying the project mode, you also have to specify one of the two available options for Edge. The Edge determines whether the object is extended/trimmed to another object's implied edge, or only to an object that actually intersects it in 3D space. The available options are Extend and No Extend. The **Extend** option extends the boundary/cutting object/edge along its natural path to intersect another object or its implied edge in 3D space. The **No Extend** option specifies that the object is extended/trimmed only to a boundary/cutting object/ edge that actually intersects it in 3D space. System variable EXTEDGE allows you to set one of the available modes. You can also set the Edge by selecting the Edge option available in the EXTEND command.

CREATING SOLID SHAPES

As mentioned earlier, solids are the most informationally complete and least ambiguous of the modeling types. It is easier to edit a complex solid shape than edit wireframes and meshes.

You create solids from one of the basic solid shapes: BOX, CONE, CYLINDER, SPHERE, TORUS, and WEDGE. The user-defined solids can be created by extruding or revolving 2D objects and regions to define a 3D solid. In addition, you can create more complex solid shapes by combining solids together by performing a boolean operation — union, subtraction, and intersection.

Solids can be further modified by filleting and chamfering their edges. AutoCAD provides commands for slicing a solid into two pieces or obtaining 2D cross section of a solid.

Like meshes, solids are displayed as a wire-frame until you hide, shade, or render them. AutoCAD provides commands to analyze solids for their mass properties (volume, moments of inertia, center of gravity, etc.). AutoCAD allows you to export data about a solid object to applications such as NC (numerical control) milling or FEM (finite element method) analysis. If necessary, you can use AutoCAD's EXPLODE command to explode solids into a mesh and wire-frame objects.

> **NOTE:** The system variable ISOLINES controls the number of tessellation lines used to visualize curved portions of the wire-frame. The default value for the ISOLINES is set to 4.

Creating a Solid Box

The BOX command creates a solid box or cube. The base of the box by default is defined parallel to the current UCS. The solid box can be drawn with two options: by providing a center point or by providing a starting corner of the box. The BOX command's Center and Corner options are invoked from Box flyout located in the Solids toolbar (Figure 14–40 and Figure 14–41), or at the "Command:" prompt type **BOX** and press Enter or spacebar.

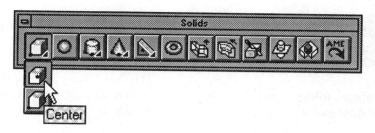

Figure 14–40   Invoke the BOX Command's Center option from the Solids toolbar

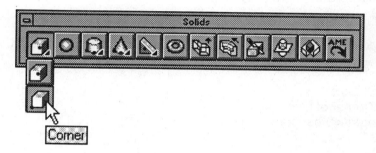

Figure 14–41   Invoke the BOX Command's Corner option from the Solids toolbar

Command: **box**
Center/<Corner of box>:

First, by default you are prompted for the starting corner of the box. Once you provide the starting corner, the box's dimensions can be entered in one of three ways.

The default option lets you create a box by locating the opposite corner of its base rectangle and then its height. The following command sequence defines a box, as shown in Figure 14–42, using the default option:

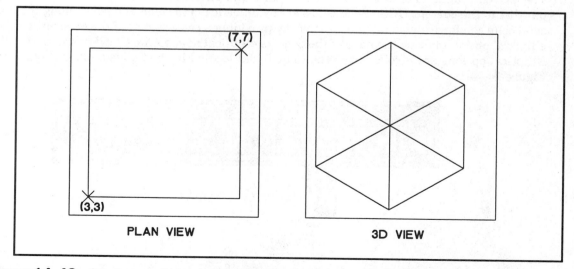

Figure 14–42   Creating a solid box using the default option of the BOX Command

AutoCAD 3D

```
Command: box
Center/<Corner of box>: 3,3
Cube/Length/<Other corner>: 7,7
Height: 4
```

The **Cube** option allows you to create a box in which all edges are of equal length. The following command sequence defines a box using the Cube option:

```
Command: box
Center/<Corner of box>: 3,3
Cube/Length/<Other corner>: c
Length: 3
```

The **Length** option lets you create a box by defining its length, width, and height. The following command sequence defines a box using the Length option:

```
Command: box
Center/<Corner of box>: 3,3
Cube/Length/<Other corner>: l
Length: 3
Width: 4
Height: 3
```

Center Option The Center option allows you to create a box by first locating its center point. Once you locate the center point, a line rubberbands from this point to help you visualize the size of the rectangle. Then AutoCAD prompts you to define the size of the box by entering one of the following options:

```
Cube/Length/<Other corner>:
```

Creating a Solid Cone

The CONE command creates a cone both round and elliptical. By default, the base of the cone is parallel to the current UCS. Solid cones are symmetrical and come to a point along the Z axis. The solid cone can be drawn with two options: by providing a center point of the base or by selecting the elliptical option to draw the base of the cone as elliptical shape. The CONE command's Center and Elliptical options are invoked from the Cone flyout located in the Solids toolbar (Figure 14–43 and Figure 14–44).

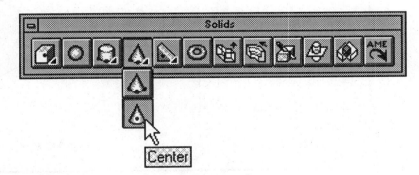

Figure 14–43   Invoke the CONE Command's Center option from the Solids toolbar

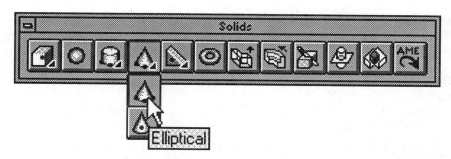

Figure 14-44 Invoke the CONE Command's Elliptical option from the Solids toolbar

Command: **cone**
Elliptical/<Center point>:

By default, AutoCAD prompts you for the center point of the base of the cone and assumes the base to be a circle. Subsequently, you are prompted for radius (or enter **D** for diameter). Enter the appropriate value and then it prompts for the apex/height of the cone. The height of the cone is the default option, and it allows you to set the height of the cone, not the orientation. The base of the cone is parallel to the current base plane; whereas, the apex option prompts you for a point. In turn, it sets the height and orientation of the cone. For example, the following command sequence shows steps in drawing a cone, as shown in Figure 14-45, using the default option:

Command: **cone**
Elliptical/<Center point>: **5,5**
Diameter/<Radius>: **3**
Apex/<Height>: **4**

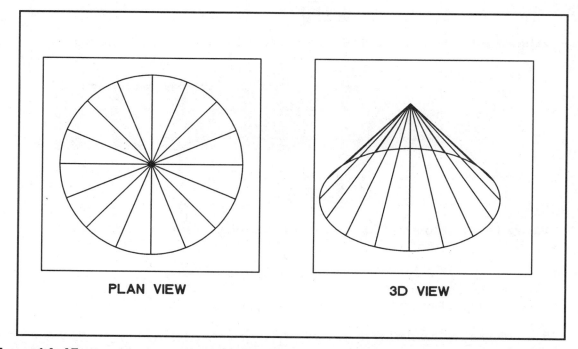

PLAN VIEW   3D VIEW

Figure 14-45 Creating a solid cone using the default option of the CONE Command

Elliptical Option Selecting this option indicates that the base of the cone is an ellipse. The prompts are identical to the regular AutoCAD ELLIPSE command. For example, the following command shows steps in drawing a cone using the Elliptical option:

```
Command: cone
Elliptical/<Center point>: e
<Axis endpoint 1>/Center: 3,3
Axis endpoint 2: 6,6
Other axis distance: 5,7
Apex/<Height>: 4
```

Creating a Solid Cylinder

The CYLINDER command creates a cylinder of equal diameter on each end and similar to an extruded circle or an ellipse. The solid cylinder can be drawn with two options: by providing a center point of the base or by selecting the elliptical option to draw the base of the cylinder as elliptical shape. The CYLINDER command's Center and Elliptical options are invoked from the Cylinder flyout located in the Solids toolbar (Figure 14–46 and Figure 14–47).

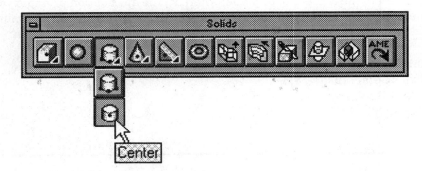

Figure 14–46 Invoke the CYLINDER Command's Center option from the Solids toolbar

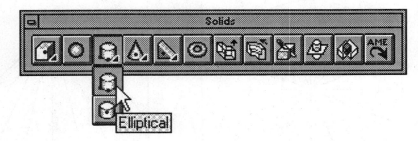

Figure 14–47 Invoke the CYLINDER Command's Elliptical option from the Solids toolbar

```
Command: cylinder
Elliptical/<Center point>:
```

The prompts are identical to those used for a cone. For example, the following command sequence shows steps in drawing a cylinder, as shown in Figure 14–48, using the default option:

Command: **cylinder**
Elliptical/<Center point>: **5,5**
Diameter/<Radius>: **3**
Center of other end/<Height>: **4**

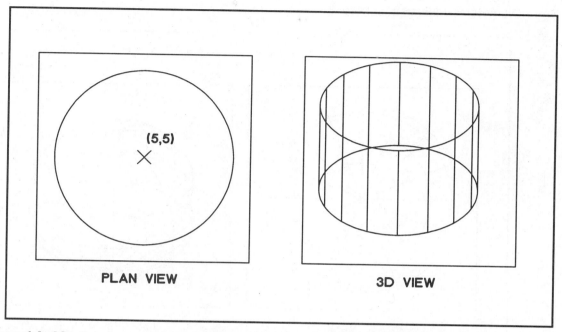

Figure 14–48   Creating a solid cylinder using the default option of the CYLINDER Command

Creating a Solid Sphere

The SPHERE command creates a 3D body in which all surface points are equidistant from the center. The sphere is drawn in such a way that its central axis is coincident with the Z axis of the current UCS. The SPHERE command is invoked from the Solids toolbar (Figure 14–49), or at the "Command:" prompt type **SPHERE** and press Enter or spacebar.

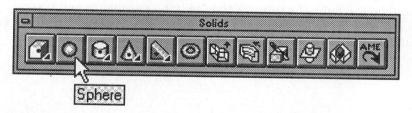

Figure 14–49   Invoke the SPHERE Command from the Solids toolbar

Command: **sphere**
<Center of sphere>:

First, AutoCAD prompts for the center point of the sphere, then you can provide radius or diameter to define a sphere.

For example, the following command sequence shows steps in drawing a sphere, as shown in Figure 14–50:

Command: **sphere**
<Center point>: **5,5**
Diameter/<Radius> of sphere: **3**

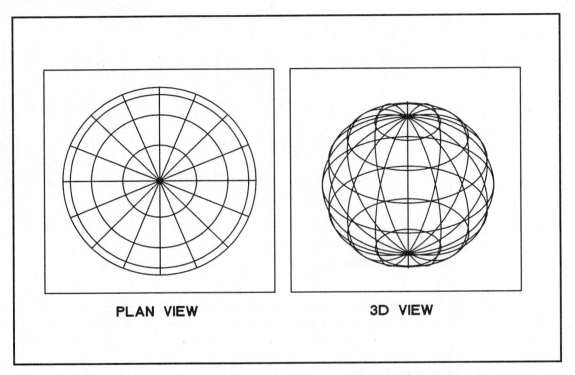

PLAN VIEW   3D VIEW

Figure 14–50   Creating a solid sphere using the default option of the SPHERE Command

Creating a Solid Torus

The TORUS command creates a solid with a donut-like shape. If a torus were a wheel, the center point would be the hub. The torus is created lying parallel to and bisected by the XY plane of the current UCS. The TORUS command is invoked from the Solids toolbar (Figure 14–51), or at the "Command:" prompt type **TORUS** and press ⌷Enter⌷ or spacebar.

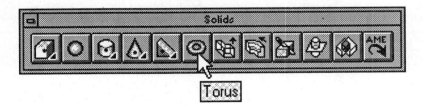

Figure 14–51   Invoke the TORUS Command from the Solids toolbar

Command: **torus**
<Center of torus>:

AutoCAD prompts for the center point of the torus, and then subsequently the diameter or radius of the torus and the diameter or radius of the tube, as shown in Figure 14–52. You can also draw a torus without a center hole as a result of the radius of the tube being greater than the radius of the torus. A negative torus radius would create a football-shaped solid.

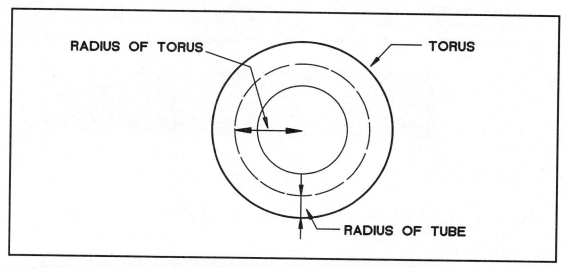

Figure 14–52 Creating a solid torus with a center hole using the TORUS Command

For example, the following command sequence shows steps in drawing a torus, as shown in Figure 14–53:

```
Command: torus
<Center of torus>: 5,5
Diameter/<Radius> of torus: 3
Diameter/<Radius> of tube: 0.5
```

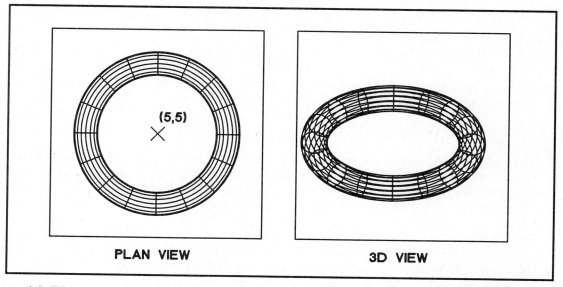

Figure 14–53 Creating a torus by specifying the baseplane and central axis direction using the TORUS Command

Creating a Solid Wedge

The WEDGE command creates a solid like a box that has been a cut in half diagonally along one face. The face of the wedge is always drawn parallel to the current UCS and the sloped face tapering along the Z axis. The solid wedge can be drawn with two options: by providing a center point of the base or by providing starting corner of the box. The WEDGE command's Center and Corner options are invoked from the Wedge flyout located in the Solids toolbar (Figure 14–54 and Figure 14–55).

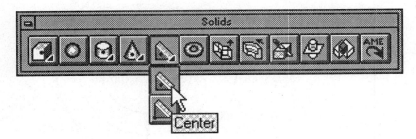

Figure 14–54   Invoke the WEDGE Command's Center option from the Solids toolbar

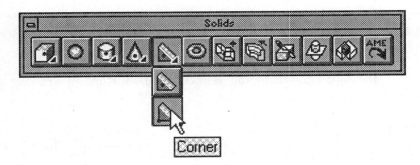

Figure 14–55   Invoke the WEDGE Command's Corner option from the Solids toolbar

> Command: **wedge**
> Center/<corner of wedge>:

First, by default you are prompted for the starting corner of the box. Once you provide the starting corner, then AutoCAD prompts:

> Cube/Length/<corner of wedge>:

The wedge dimensions can be specified by using one of the three options. The **other corner** lets you create a wedge by locating the opposite corner of its base rectangle and then its height. The **Cube** option allows you to create a wedge in which all edges are of equal length. The **Length** option lets you create a box by defining its length, width, and height.

Center Option The Center option allows you to create a wedge first by locating its center point. Once you locate the center point, a line rubberbands from this point to help you visualize the size of the rectangle. Then AutoCAD prompts you to define the size of the box by entering one of the following options:

> Cube/Length/<corner of wedge>:

Creating Solids from Existing 2D Objects (EXTRUDE Command)

The EXTRUDE command creates a unique solid by extruding circles, closed polylines, polygons, ellipses, closed splines, donuts, and regions. Because a polyline can have virtually any shape, the EXTRUDE command allows you to create irregular shapes. In addition, AutoCAD allows you to taper the sides of the extrusion.

> **NOTE:** A polyline must contain at least 3 but not more than 500 vertices and none of the segments can cross each other. See Figure 14–56 for examples that cannot be extruded. If the polyline has width, AutoCAD ignores the width and extrudes from the center of the polyline path. If a selected object has thickness, AutoCAD ignores the thickness.

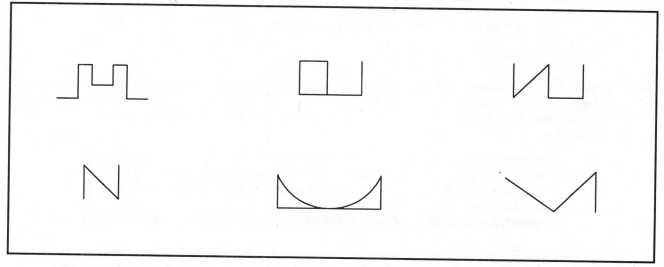

Figure 14–56   Shapes (shown in plan view) that cannot be extruded using the EXTRUDE Command

The EXTRUDE command is invoked from the Solids toolbar (Figure 14–57), or at the "Command:" prompt type **EXTRUDE** and press [Enter] or spacebar.

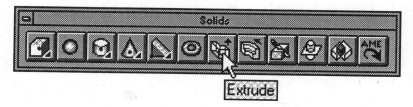

Figure 14–57   Invoke the EXTRUDE Command from the Solids toolbar

Command: **extrude**
Select objects:

Select the objects to extrude (you can select multiple objects in a single use of the command), AutoCAD prompts:

Path/<Height of Extrusion>:

Height of Extrusion Option The Height of Extrusion option (default) allows you to specify the distance for extrusion. Specifying a positive value extrudes the objects along the positive Z axis of the current UCS, and a negative value extrudes along the negative Z axis.

Path Option The Path option allows you to select the extrusion path based on a specified curve object. All the profiles of the selected object are extruded along the chosen path to create solids. Lines, cirles, arcs, ellipses, elliptical arcs, polylines, or splines can be paths. The path should not lie on the same plane as the profile, nor should it have areas of high curvature. The extruded solid starts from the plane of the profile and ends on a plane perpendicular to the path's end point. One of the end points of the path should be on the plane of the profile. Otherwise, AutoCAD moves the path to the center of the profile.

Once you specify the Height of Extrusion and path appropriately, AutoCAD prompts:

Extrusion taper angle <0>:

Specify an angle between -90 and +90 degrees or press Enter or spacebar to accept the default value of 0 degrees. If you specify 0 degrees as the taper angle, AutoCAD extrudes a 2D object perpendicular to its 2D plane as shown in Figure 14–58. Positive angles taper in from the base object. Negative angles taper out.

> **NOTE:** It is possible that a large taper angle or a long extrusion height can cause the object, or portions of the object, to taper to a point before reaching the extrusion height.

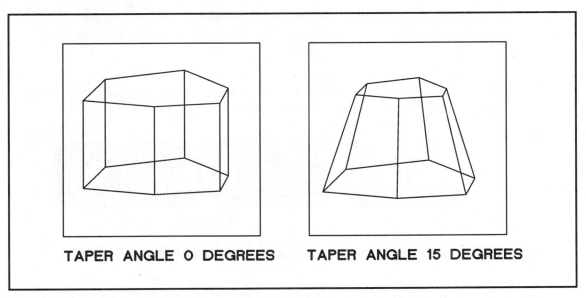

TAPER ANGLE 0 DEGREES   TAPER ANGLE 15 DEGREES

Figure 14–58 Creating a solid with the EXTRUDE Command with (a) 0 degrees and (b) 15 degrees of taper angle

Creating Solids from Revolution (REVOLVE Command)

The REVOLVE command creates unique solid by revolving or sweeping a closed polyline, polygons, circles, ellipses, closed splines, donuts, and regions. Polylines that have crossing or self-intersecting segments cannot be revolved. Only one object can be revolved at any time. The REVOLVE command is similar to the REVSURF command. The REVSURF command creates a surface of revolution, whereas REVOLVE creates a solid of revolution. REVOLVE command provides several options for defining the axis of revolution.

The REVOLVE command is invoked from the Solids toolbar (Figure 14–59), or at the "Command:" prompt type **REVOLVE** and press Enter or spacebar.

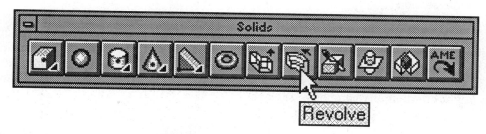

Figure 14–59 Invoke the REVOLVE Command from the Solids toolbar

Command: **revolve**
Select objects:

Select the object to revolve. (You cannot select more than one object.) AutoCAD prompts:

Axis of revolution – Object/X/Y/<Start point of axis>:

Start Point of Axis Option The Start point of axis option (default) allows you to specify two points for start and end points of the axis, and the positive direction of rotation is based on the Right Hand Rule.

Object Option The Object option allows you select an existing line or single polyline segment that defines the axis about which to revolve the object. The positive axis direction is from the closest to the farthest end point of this line.

X Axis Option The X axis option uses the positive X axis of the current UCS as the axis of the revolution.

Y Axis Option The Y axis option uses the positive Y axis of the current UCS as the axis of the revolution.

Once you specify the axis of revolution, AutoCAD prompts:

Angle of revolution <full circle>:

Specify the angle for revolution. The default is for full circle. You can specify any angle between 0 and 360 degrees.

CREATING COMPOSITE SOLIDS

As mentioned earlier in this chapter, you can create a new composite solid or region by combining two or more solids or regions by Boolean operations. While the term "boolean" implies that only two objects can be operated upon at once, AutoCAD lets you select many solid objects in a single boolean command. There are three basic boolean operations that can be performed in AutoCAD. They are as follows:

1. Union

2. Subtraction

3. Intersection

The UNION, SUBTRACTION, and INTERSECTION commands let you select both the solids and regions in a single use of the commands, but solids are combined with solids, and regions combined only with regions. Also, in the case of regions you can make composite regions only with those that lie in the same plane. This means that a single command creates a maximum of one composite solid, but might create many composite regions.

Union Operation

The union is the process of creating a new composite object from one or more original objects. The union operation joins the original solids or regions in such a way that there is no duplication of volume. Therefore, the total resulting volume can be equal or less than the sum of the volumes in the original solids or regions.

The UNION command performs the union operation and is invoked from the Explode flyout located in the Modify toolbar (Figure 14–60), or at the "Command:" prompt type **UNION** and press ⏎ or spacebar.

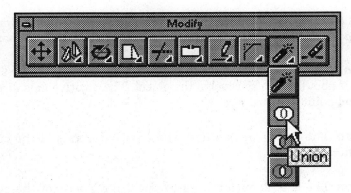

Figure 14–60 Invoke the UNION Command from the Modify toolbar

Command: **union**
Select objects:

Select the objects you want to be unioned. You can select more than two objects at once. The objects (solids or regions) can be overlapping, adjacent, or nonadjacent.

For example, the following command sequence shows steps in creating a composite solid by joining two cylinders, as shown in Figure 14–61:

Command: **union**
Select objects: *(select cylinders A and B and press* Enter *)*

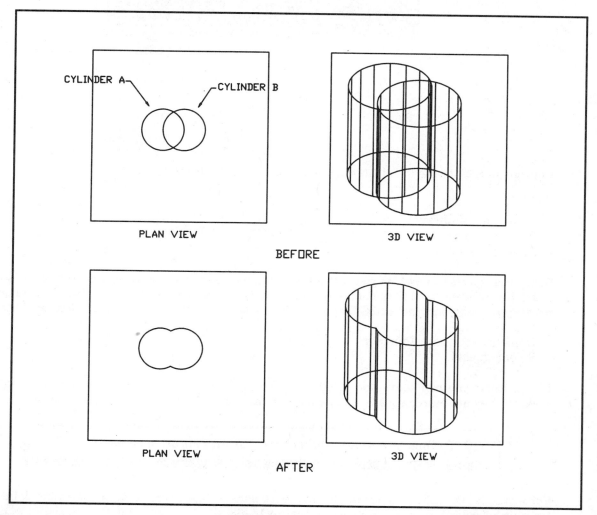

Figure 14–61 Creating a composite solid by joining two cylinders using the UNION Command

Subtraction Operation

Subtraction is the process of forming a new composite object by starting with one object and removing from it any volume that it has in common with a second object. In the case of solids, they are created by subtracting the volume of one set of solids from another set. If the entire volume of the second solid is contained in the first solid, then what is left is the first solid minus the volume of the second solid. However, if only part of the volume of the second solid is contained within the first solid, then only that part that is duplicated in the two solids is subtracted. Similarly, in the case of regions, they are created by subtracting the common area of one set of existing regions from another set.

The SUBTRACT command performs the subtraction operation and is invoked from the Explode flyout located in the Modify toolbar (Figure 14–62), or at the "Command:" prompt type **SUBTRACT** and press Enter or spacebar.

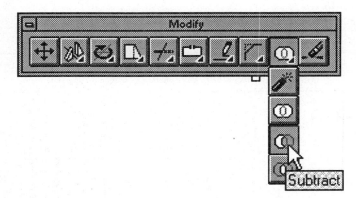

Figure 14–62 Invoke the SUBTRACT Command from the Modify toolbar

Command: **subtract**
Source objects...
Select objects:

Select the objects from which you will subtract other objects. You can select one or more as source objects. If you select more than one, they are automatically unioned. After selecting the source objects, press Enter or spacebar, and AutoCAD prompts you to select the objects to subtract from the source object.

Objects to subtract from them...
Select objects:

If necessary, you can select one or more objects to subtract from the source object. If you select several, they are automatically unioned before they are subtracted from the source object.

> **NOTE:** Objects that are neither solids nor regions are ignored.

For example, the following command sequence shows steps in creating a composite solid by subtracting cylinder B from A, as shown in Figure 14–63.

Command: **subtract**
Select objects: *(select cylinder A and press Enter or spacebar)*
Objects to subtract from them...
Select objects: *(select cylinder B and press Enter or spacebar)*

Intersection Operation

The intersection is the process of forming a composite object from only the volume that is common to two or more original objects. In the case of solids, you can create a new composite solid by calculating the common volume of two or more existing solids. Whereas, in the case of regions, it is done by calculating the overlapping area of two or more existing regions.

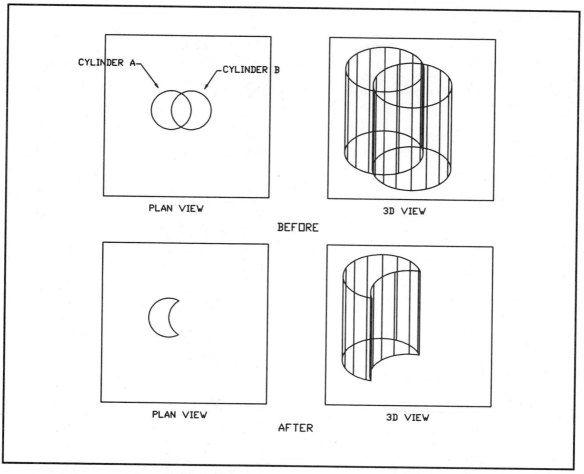

Figure 14–63 Creating a composite solid by subtracting cylinder B from cylinder A using the SUBTRACT Command

The INTERSECT command performs the intersection operation and is invoked from the Explode flyout located in the Modify toolbar (Figure 14–64), or at the "Command:" prompt type **INTER-SECT** and press Enter or spacebar.

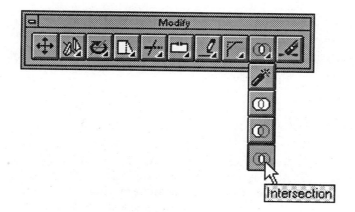

Figure 14–64 Invoke the INTERSECT Command from the Modify toolbar

Command: **intersect**
Select objects:

Select the objects you want intersected. Only two objects can be selected at a time.

For example, the following command sequence shows steps in creating a composite solid by intersecting cylinder A with B, as shown in Figure 14–65:

Command: **intersect**
Select objects: *(select cylinders A and B and press* Enter *or spacebar)*

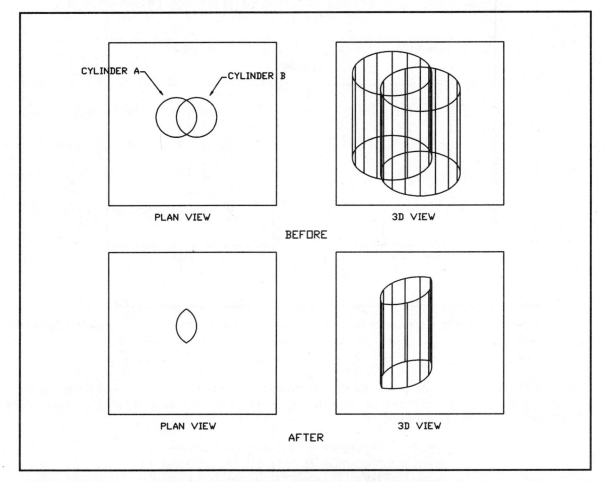

Figure 14–65 Creating a composite solid by intersecting cylinder A with cylinder B using the INTERSECTION Command

EDITING 3D SOLIDS

AutoCAD makes your job a little easier by providing editing tools that include chamfering or filleting the edges, creating a cross section through a solid, creating a new solid by cutting the existing solid and removing a specified side, and creating a composite solid from the interference of two or more solids. If necessary, you can always use the AutoCAD modify and construct commands such as MOVE, COPY, ROTATE, SCALE, AND ARRAY to edit solids.

CHAMFER — Solids

The CHAMFER command (explained in Chapter 3) can also be used to bevel the edges of an existing solid object. The CHAMFER command is invoked from the Modify toolbar, or at the "Command:" prompt type **CHAMFER** and press [Enter] or spacebar.

> Command: **chamfer**
> Polyline/Distances/Angle/Trim/Method/<Select first line>:

Select an edge on a 3D solid. If you pick an edge that is common to two surfaces, AutoCAD highlights one of the surfaces and prompts:

> Next/<OK>:

If this is the surface you want, press [Enter] or spacebar to accept it. If it is not, enter **N** for next to highlight the adjoining surface and then press [Enter] or spacebar. Subsequently, AutoCAD prompts:

> Enter base surface distance <default>: *(specify a distance or press* [Enter] *or spacebar to accept the default)*
> Enter adjacent surface distance <default>: *(specify a distance or press « or spacebar to accept the default)*

Once you provide the chamfer distances, AutoCAD prompts:

> Loop/<Select edge>:

Select the edges of the highlighted surface you want chamfered and then press [Enter] or spacebar. The **Loop** option allows you to select one of the edges on the base surface and AutoCAD automatically selects all edges on the base surface for chamfering.

The following command sequence draws a chamfer for a solid object as shown in Figure 14–66.

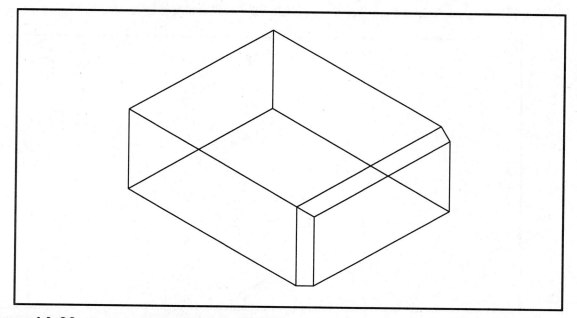

Figure 14–66   Example of chamfering a solid surface

Command: **chamfer**
Polyline/Distances/Angle/Trim/Method/<Select first line>:*(select the edge)*
Next/<OK>: Enter
Enter base surface distance <current>:**0.25**
Enter adjacent surface distance <current>:**0.5**
Loop/<Select edge>: *(select the first edge)*
Loop/<Select edge>: *(select the second edge)*

FILLET — Solids

The FILLET command (explained in Chapter 3) can also be used to round an existing solid object. The FILLET command is invoked from the Modify toolbar, or at the "Command:" prompt, type **FILLET** and press Enter or spacebar.

Command: **fillet**
Polyline/Radius/Trim/<Select first object>:

Select an edge on a 3D solid. If necessary, you can select multiple edges; but you must select the edges individually after specifying the radius for the fillet. AutoCAD prompts:

Enter radius <default>: *(specify a distance for radius or press* Enter *or spacebar to accept the default)*

AutoCAD prompts:

Chain/Radius<Select edge>:

Select additional edges, and once you are through with selection of edges for filleting, press Enter or spacebar to complete the command sequence.

The following command sequence draws a fillet for a solid object as shown in Figure 14–67.

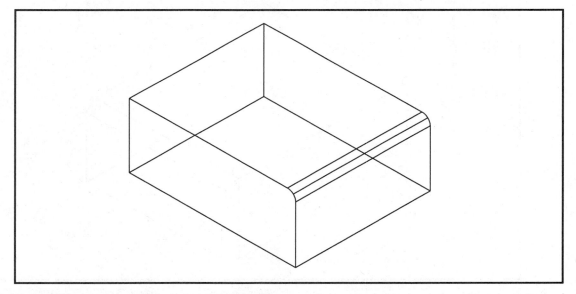

Figure 14–67   Example of filleting a solid surface

Command: **fillet**
Polyline/Radius/Trim/<Select first object>: *(select the solid edge)*
Enter radius<current>:**0.5**
Chain/Radius/<Select edge>: *(select second edge)*
Chain/Radius/<Select edge>: [Enter]

Sectioning Solids

The SECTION command creates a cross section of one or more solids. The cross section is created as one or more unnamed blocks or regions. The block or region is created on the current layer and is inserted at the location of the cross section. If necessary, you can use the MOVE command to move the cross section.

The SECTION command is invoked from the Solids toolbar (Figure 14–68), or at the "Command:" prompt, type **SECTION** and press [Enter] or spacebar.

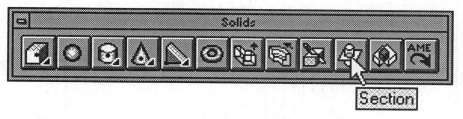

Figure 14–68   Invoke the SECTION Command from the Solids toolbar

Command: **section**
Select objects:

Select the objects from which you want cross section to be generated. After selecting of the objects, press [Enter] or spacebar and AutoCAD prompts to define the sectioning plane:

Section plane by Object/Zaxis/View/XY/YZ/ZX/<3points>:

3points Option The 3points option (default) allows you to define a section plane by locating three points. The first point is the origin, the second point determines the positive direction of the X axis for the section plane, and the third point determines the positive Y axis of the section plane. This option is similar to the 3point option of the AutoCAD UCS command.

Object Option The Object option aligns the sectioning plane with a circle, ellipse, circular or elliptical arc, 2D spline, or 2D polyline segment.

Zaxis Option The Zaxis option defines the section plane by locating its origin point and a point on the Z axis (normal) to the plane.

View Option The View option aligns the section plan with the viewing plane of the current viewport. Specifying a point defines the location of the sectioning plane.

XY Option The XY option aligns the sectioning plane with the XY plane of the current UCS. Specifying a point defines the location of the sectioning plane.

YZ Option The YZ option aligns the sectioning plane with the XY plane of the current UCS. Specifying a point defines the location of the sectioning plane.

ZX Option The ZX option aligns the sectioning plane with the XY plane of the current UCS. Specifying a point defines the location of the sectioning plane.

See Figure 14–69 for a hatched section produced with the SECTION command.

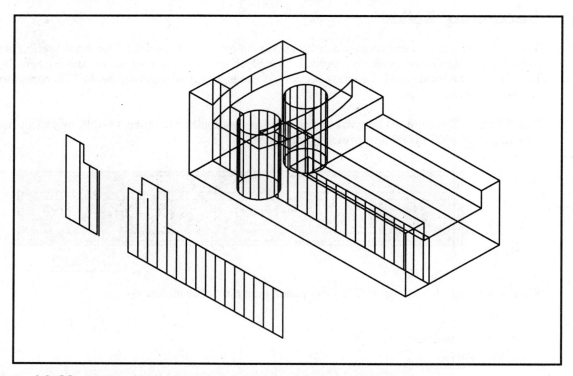

Figure 14–69 Creating a 2D hatched cross-section using the SECTION Command

Slicing Solids

The SLICE command allows you to create a new solid by cutting the existing solid and removing a specified side. If necessary, you can retain both halves of the sliced solids or just the half you specify. The sliced solids retain the layer and color of the original solids.

The SLICE command is invoked from the Solids toolbar (Figure 14–70), or at the "Command:" prompt, type **SLICE** and press Enter or spacebar.

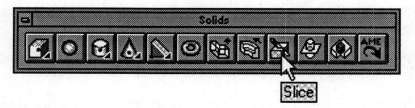

Figure 14–70 Invoke the SLICE Command from the Solids toolbar

Command: **slice**
Select objects:

Select the objects to create a new solid by slicing. After selecting one of the objects, press ⌨Enter or spacebar and AutoCAD prompts to define the slice plane:

Slicing plane by Object/Zaxis/View/XY/YZ/ZX/<3points>;

The options are the same as those of the SECTION command explained earlier in this chapter.

After defining the slicing plane, AutoCAD prompts to indicate which part of the cut solid is to be retained as follows:

Both sides/<Point on desired side of the plane>;

The default option allows you to select with your pointing device the side of the slice that has to be retained in your drawing.

The **Both sides** option allows you to retain both sides of the sliced solids.

Figure 14–71 shows two parts of a solid model that have been cut using the SLICE command and moved apart using the MOVE command.

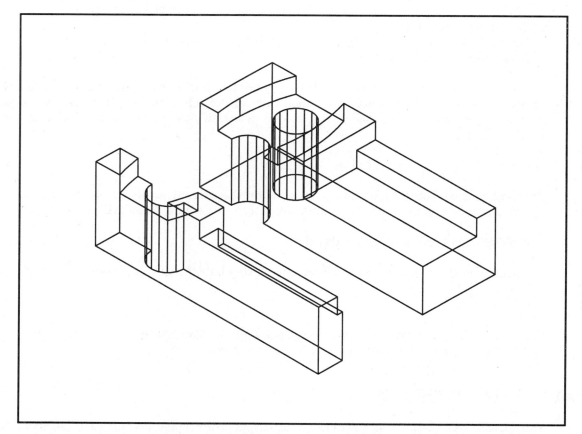

Figure 14–71   Cutting the solid model into two parts using the SLICE Command

Solid Interference

The INTERFERE command checks the interference between two or more solids and creates a composite solid from their common volume.

There are two ways to determine the interference between solids:

1. Select two sets of solids AutoCAD determines the interference between the first and second sets of solids.

2. Select one set of solids instead of selecting two sets of solids, then AutoCAD determines the interference between all of the solids in the set. They are checked against each other.

The INTERFERE command is invoked from the Solids toolbar (Figure 14–72), or at the "Command:" prompt type **INTERFERE** and press Enter or spacebar.

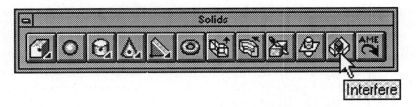

Figure 14–72 Invoke the INTERFERE Command from the Solids toolbar

Command: **interfere**
Select the first set of solids: *(select the first set of solids and press* Enter *or spacebar)*
Select the second set of solids:

The second selection set is optional. Press Enter or spacebar if you do not want to define the second selection set. If the same solid is included in both the selection sets, it is considered part of the first selection set and ignored in the second selection set. AutoCAD highlights all interfering solids and prompts:

Create interference solids? <N>:

Entering **y** creates and highlights new solids on the current layer that is the intersection of the interfering solids. If there are more than two interfering solids, AutoCAD prompts:

Highlight pairs of interfering solids?<N>:

Entering **y**, and if there is more than one interfering pair, AutoCAD prompts:

eXit/<Next pair>:

Pressing Enter cycles through the interfering pairs of solids, and AutoCAD highlights each interfering pair of solids. Enter **x** to complete the command sequence.

MASS PROPERTIES OF A SOLID

The MASSPROP command calculates and displays the mass properties of selected solids and regions. The mass properties displayed for solids are mass, volume, bounding box, centroid, moments of inertia, products of inertia, radii of gyration, and principal moments with corresponding principal directions. The mass properties are calculated based on the current UCS.

The MASSPROP is invoked by typing **MASSPROP** at the "Command:" prompt and pressing [Enter] or spacebar.

    Command: **massprop**
    Select objects:

Select the objects you want displayed as mass properties. The MASSPROP command displays the object mass properties in the text screen as shown in Figure 14–73. AutoCAD prompts:

    Write to file<N>:

If you enter **y**, AutoCAD prompts for a file name and saves the file in an ASCII format.

> **NOTE:** You can also use AutoCAD's LIST and AREA commands to obtain information about individual solid(s) (coordinates) and the area(s) of the solid(s), respectively.

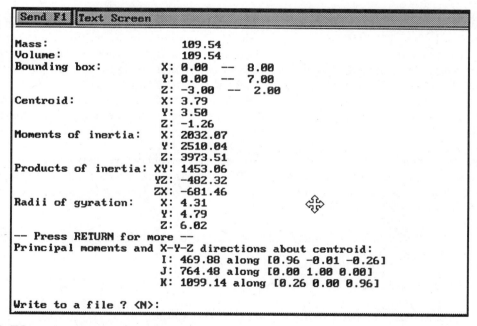

Figure 14–73 The Mass Properties listing

HIDE COMMAND

The HIDE command hides objects or displays in different colors that are behind other objects in the current viewport. Complex models are difficult to read in wire-frame form, and benefit in clarity when the model is displayed with hidden lines removed. HIDE considers circles, solids, traces, wide polyline segments, 3D faces, polygon meshes, and the extruded edges of objects with a thickness to be opaque surfaces hiding objects that lie behind them. The HIDE command remains active only until the next time the display is regenerated. Depending on the complexity of the model, hiding may take from a few seconds to even several minutes.

The HIDE command is invoked from the Render toolbar or at the "Command:" prompt type **HIDE** and press Enter or spacebar.

    Command: **hide**

There are no prompts to be answered. The current viewport goes blank for a period of time, depending on the complexity of the model, and is then redrawn with hidden lines removed temporarily. Hidden line removal is lost during plotting unless you specify that AutoCAD remove hidden lines in the plotting configuration.

PLACEMENT OF MULTIVIEWS ON PAPER SPACE

When you create a 3D model, you can use the powerful capabilities of viewports to display the model from different viewpoints in each viewport and see the model take shape as you draw. Constructing a model is easier when displaying the model in various viewports and you can switch from one port to another while drawing and editing the objects.

The viewports are created by the VPORTS command when TILEMODE is 1 and with the MVIEW command when TILEMODE is 0. For a detailed explanation of creating viewports, refer to Chapter 11. It is recommended that you create four viewports and display the model in accordance with the third-angle projection and isometric view of the model. Third-angle projection requires that the view of the top of the object be placed above the view of the front of the object, and the view of the right side of the object be placed to the right of the front view. First-angle projection is more common in Europe, in which the top view is placed below the front view and the right side is placed on the left.

It is recommended that you create the necessary viewports and display the model from a different viewpoint in each viewport before you start drawing the model. The following are the steps in creating the viewports with appropriate limits for Model Space and Paper Space and setting up the viewpoints when TILEMODE is set to 0.

1. Set LIMITS in Paper Space equal to the plotter's maximum available plot area for the given sheet size.

2. Create a title block, or if you already have one, attach it as an XREF.

3. Create four viewports using the MVIEW command.

4. Enter Model Space and set the appropriate limits for the model to be drawn.

5. Make the top right viewport active and set the viewpoint to 1,-1,1 using the VPOINT command.

6. Make the top left viewport active and make sure it is set to 0,0,1 display.

7. Make the bottom left viewport active and set the viewpoint to 0,-1,0 using the VPOINT command, so that it will display the front view of the model.

8. Make the bottom right viewport active and set the viewpoint to 1,0,0 using the VPOINT command, so that it will display the right side view of the model.

9. Create the model by making the appropriate viewport active. If necessary, scale the model by using the ZOOM XP command.

10. Enter Paper Space. Add any annotations or dimensions while in Paper Space. Fill in your title block information.

11. Plot to a scale of 1:1.

LINING UP ORTHOGRAPHIC VIEWS

Standard drafting practice calls for main orthographic views and auxiliary views to be lined up. It does not matter which projection system is used, the main orthographic views and auxiliary views must be lined up precisely. All the views must be displayed with the same scale (or magnification), and corresponding features between views must line up along the same horizontal or vertical line for orthographic views, or along the same angular line for auxiliary views. This can be done using the ZOOM Center command and the XP option in model space. It works on the principle that if two viewports are the same size and are lined up, then the centers of these viewports are lined up. In model space, if the two different views in those viewports are centered around the same point and are the same scale in relation to paper space, then those views are lined up.

AMECONVERT COMMAND

The AMECONVERT command converts AME solid models drawn from AME Release 2 or 2.1 (provided with AutoCAD Release 12) to AutoCAD solid models. The AMECONVERT command is invoked by typing **AMECONVERT** at the "Command:" prompt and pressing Enter or spacebar.

Command: **ameconvert**
Select objects:

Select solids or regions, AutoCAD converts them to AutoCAD solids. Because of the increased accuracy of the new AutoCAD solid modeler, AME models might look slightly different after conversion.

PROJECT EXERCISE

This project creates the bracket, as shown in Figure P14-1. The bracket is drawn entirely by using AutoCAD Solid Modeling features. By following the steps, you will be able to build the model by using various commands available in AutoCAD Solid Modeling.

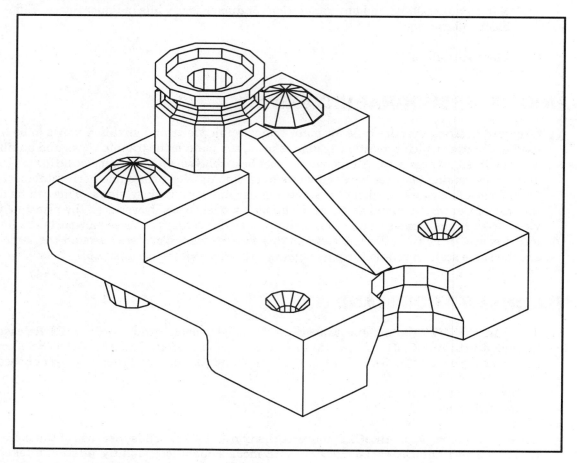

Figure P14–1 Creating a bracket using solid modeling

STEP 1 Begin a new drawing called CH14-PRO.

STEP 2 Set TILEMODE to 0. This automatically places you in paper space.

STEP 3 Set UNITS to 2 decimal places. Set LIMITS to 0,0 and 22,17. ZOOM All.

STEP 4 Create the following layers with appropriate colors and linetypes as shown below:

OBJECT	RED	CONTINUOUS
BORDER	GREEN	CONTINUOUS
DIM	BLUE	CONTINUOUS
VIEWPORTS	CYAN	CONTINUOUS

Set layer BORDER as the current layer.

STEP 5   Draw the border and the title block.

STEP 6   Set layer VIEWPORTS as the current layer. Make four viewports.

>Command: **mview**
>On/OFF/Hideplot/Fit/2/3/4/Restore/<First Point>: **3.5,10**
>Other corner: **9.5,16**
>
>Command: Enter
>On/OFF/Hideplot/Fit/2/3/4/Restore/<First Point>: **11,10**
>Other corner: **17,16**
>
>Command: Enter
>On/OFF/Hideplot/Fit/2/3/4/Restore/<First Point>: **3.5,2.5**
>Other corner: **9.5,8.5**
>
>Command: Enter
>On/OFF/Hideplot/Fit/2/3/4/Restore/<First Point>: **11,2.5**
>Other corner: **17,8.5**

STEP 7   Change to model space.

>Command: **mspace**

Make the upper right viewport current. Set Vpoint to 1,-1,1.

STEP 8   Make the upper left viewport current. Set Grid to 0.5 and Snap to 0.25.

STEP 9   Make the lower left viewport current. Set Vpoint to 0,-1,0.

STEP 10   Make the lower right viewport current. Set Vpoint to 1,0,0.

STEP 11   Set Layer OBJECT as the current layer.

Begin the layout of the drawing by drawing four boxes using the BOX command as follows:

>Command: **box**
>Center/<Corner of box> <0,0,0>: **0,0,-2**
>Cube/Length/<Other corner>: **l**
>Length: **8**
>Width: **7**
>Height: **1**
>
>Command: **box**
>Center/<Corner of box> <0,0,0>: **0,0,-1**
>Cube/Length/<Other corner>: **l**
>Length: **3**
>Width: **7**
>Height: **1**
>
>Command: **box**
>Center/<Corner of box><0,0,0>: **5,0,-3**

Cube/Length/<Other corner>: **l**
Length: **3**
Width: **7**
Height: **1**

Command: **box**
Center/<Corner of box><0,0,0>: **2.5,3.25,-1**
Cube/Length/<Other corner>: **l**
Length: **.75**
Width: **.5**
Height: **2**

The above box constructions form the basic shape of the bracket, as shown in Figure P14-2.

STEP 12   Use the CYLINDER command to create a cylinder as shown below:

Command: **cylinder**
Elliptical/<Center point> <0,0,0>: **1.5,3.5**
Diameter/<Radius>: **1.25**
Center of other end/<Height>: **2**

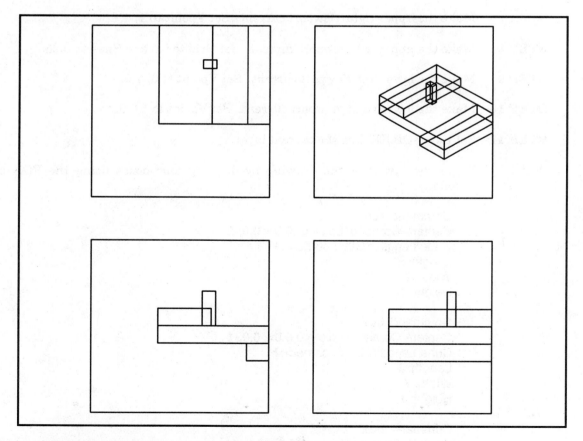

Figure P14–2   Creating the basic shape of the bracket

STEP 13   Use the WEDGE command to create a wedge as shown in Figure P14-3:

> Command: **wedge**
> Center/<Corner of wedge> <0,0,0>: **3.25,3.25,-1**
> Cube/Length/<Other corner>: **l**
> Length: **3.75**
> Width: **.5**
> Height: **2**

STEP 14   Setup a UCS as follows:

> Command:**ucs**
> Origin/ZAxis/3point/OBject/View/X/Y/Z/Prev/Restore/Save/Del/?/<World>:**3**
> Origin point <0,0,0>:*(select point 1 by using object snap ENDpoint as shown in Figure P14–4)*
> Point on positive portion of the x-axis:*(select point 2 by using object snap ENDpoint as shown in Figure P14–4)*
> Point on positive portion of the y-axis:*(select point 3 by using object snap ENDpoint as shown in Figure P14–4)*

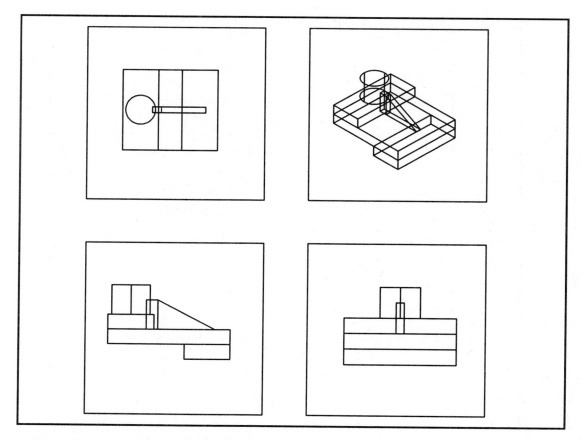

Figure P14–3   Creating the basic shape of the bracket

STEP 15   Draw a polyline to the given coordinates, as shown in Figure P14-5:

> Command: **pline**
> From point: **3.5,2**
> Current line-width is 0.000
> Arc/Close/Halfwidth/Length/Undo/Width/<Endpoint of line>: **@1.0<180**
> Arc/Close/Halfwidth/Length/Undo/Width/<Endpoint of line>: **@0.5<270**
> Arc/Close/Halfwidth/Length/Undo/Width/<Endpoint of line>: **@-0.5,-1**
> Arc/Close/Halfwidth/Length/Undo/Width/<Endpoint of line>: **@0.5<-90**
> Arc/Close/Halfwidth/Length/Undo/Width/<Endpoint of line>: **@1.5<0**
> Arc/Close/Halfwidth/Length/Undo/Width/<Endpoint of line>: **c** [Enter]

STEP 16   Revolve the polyline just created into a solid, as shown in Figure P14-6:

> Command: **revolve**
> Select objects: **l**
> Select object: [Enter]
> Axis of revolution - Object/X/Y/<Start point of axis>: **3.5,2**
> Endpoint of axis: **@2<270**
> Included angle <full circle>: **180**

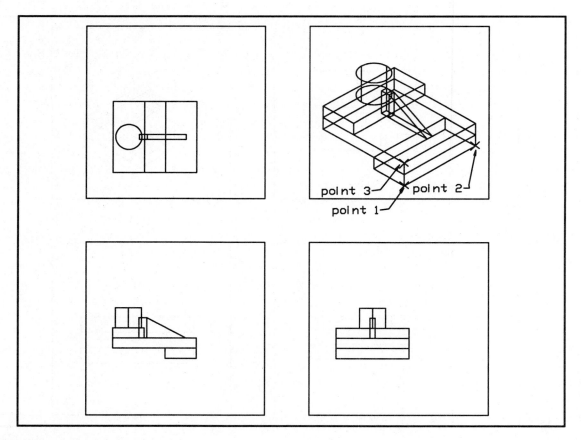

Figure P14—4   Defining a UCS

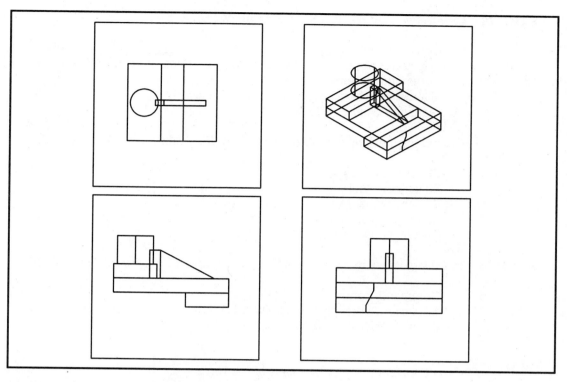

Figure P14–5   Drawing a polyline to specified coordinates

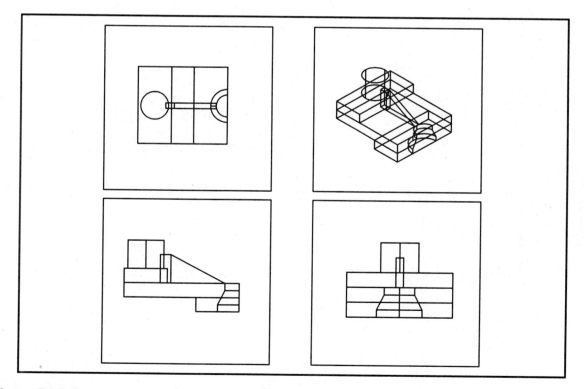

Figure P14–6   Revolving a polyline into a solid

AutoCAD 3D

STEP 17 Create two spheres in reference to the WCS.

> Command: **ucs**
> Origin/ZAxis/3point/Entity/View/X/Y/Z/Prev/Restore/Save/Del/?/<world>: Enter
> Command: **sphere**
> <Center of sphere> <0,0,0>: **1.5,1.125,-0.05**
> Diameter/<Radius of sphere>: **1**

Copy the sphere to a displacement of 0,4.75, as shown in Figure P14-7.

> Command: **copy**
> Select objects: **l**
> Select objects: Enter
> <Base point or displacement>/Multiple: **0,0**
> Second point of displacement: **0,4.75**

STEP 18 Place two cones by using the CONE command, as shown in Figure P14-8.

> Command: **cone**
> Elliptical/<Center point> <0,0,0>: **1.5,1.125,-2**
> Diameter/<Radius>: **0.75**
> Apex/<Height>: **-3**

Copy the cone to a displacement of 0,4.75.

STEP 19 Starting at 0,0,-5, create a box that is $3 \times 7 \times 2$, as shown in Figure P14-9.

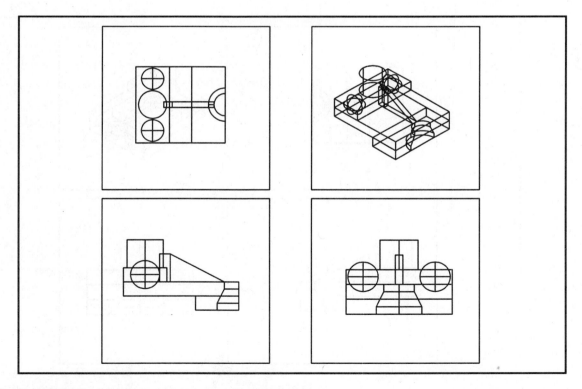

Figure P14–7 Copying a shere to a specified displacement

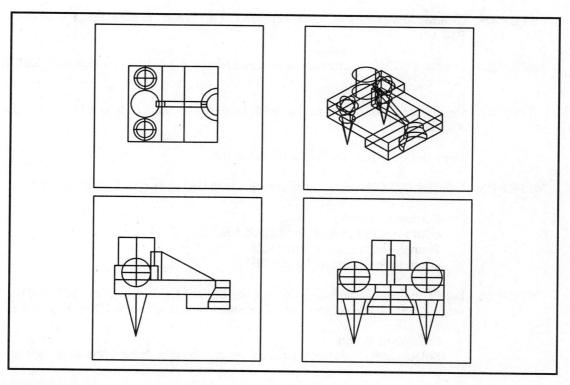

Figure P14–8   Placing two cones using the CONE Command

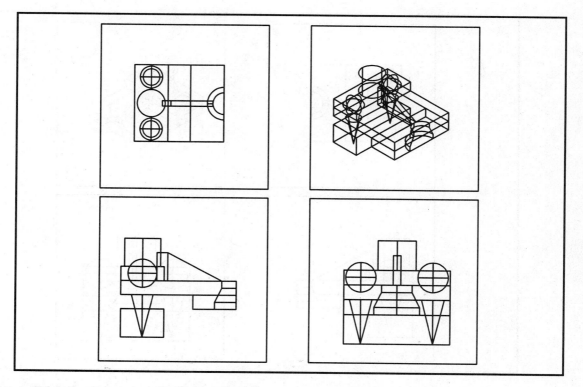

Figure P14–9   Creating a box with starting point 0,0,-5 and dimensions of 3 × 7 × 2

STEP 20   Create a 0.5-radius cylinder, centered at 1.5,3.5,-2, to a height of 4, as shown in Figure P14-10.

STEP 21   Create a cylinder with radius 1, centered at 1.5,3.5,1.75 to a height of 0.25, as shown in Figure P14-11.

STEP 22   Create a cylinder with radius 0.25, centered at 6.5,1.0,-3 to a height of 2, as shown in Figure P14-12.

Copy the cylinder to a displacement of 0,5.

STEP 23   Use the TORUS command to create a torus, as shown in Figure P14-13:

Command: **torus**
<Center of torus> <0,0,0>: **1.5,3.5,1.5**
Diameter/<Radius> of torus: **1.25**
Diameter/<Radius> of tube: **0.25**

STEP 24   Select the connected boxes (except the box that was drawn in Step 19), the wedge, the large cylinder, the spheres, and the cones for use with the UNION command.

Command: **union**
Select objects: *(select the boxes, wedge, large cylinder, spheres, cones and press* Enter *)*

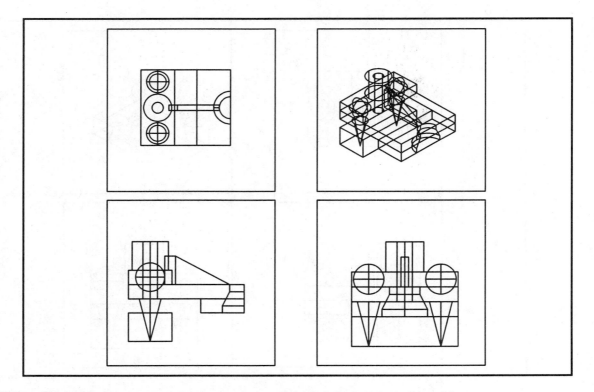

Figure P14–10   Creating a 0.5 cylinder centered at 1.5,3.5,-2 and a height of 4

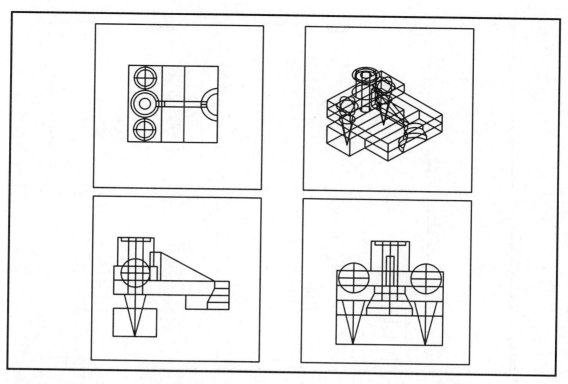

Figure P14–11   Creating a cylinder center at 1.5,3.5,1.75, a height of 0.25, and a radius of 1

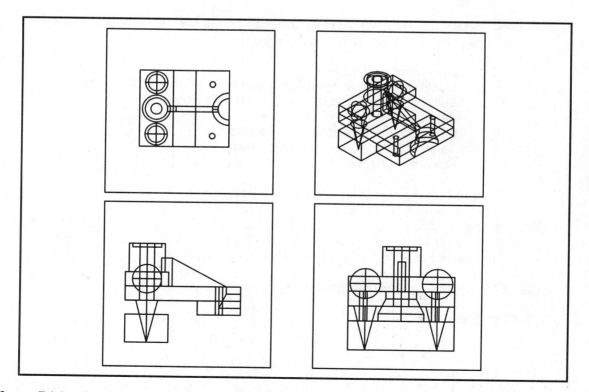

Figure P14–12   Creating a cylinder centered at 6.5,1.0,-3, a height of 2, and a radius of 0.25

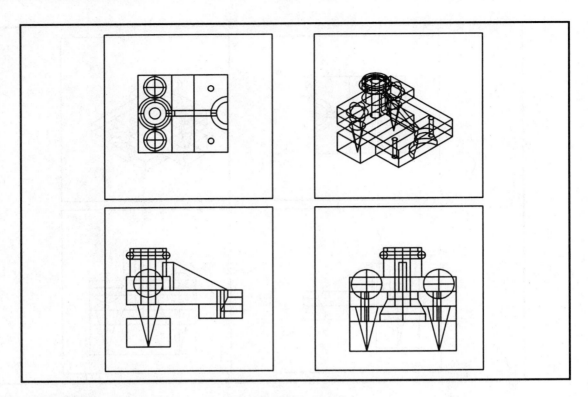

Figure P14–13   Creating a torus using the TORUS Command

STEP 25   Select the resulting solid in response to the first SUBTRACT prompt and then the remaining primitives to be subtracted from it.

> Command: **subtract**
> Select solids and regions to subtract from...
> Select objects: *(select the resulting solid from Step 24)*
> Select objects: ⌨Enter
> Select solids and regions to subtract from...
> Select objects: *(select the remaining primitives)*
> Select objects: ⌨Enter

The drawing should look like Figure P14-14.

STEP 26   Select the faces, as shown in Figure P14-15, for chamfer and fillet. Use the CHAMFER and FILLET commands with 0.25 as the chamfer values and the radii on the respective selected objects. The end result should look as shown in Figure P14-16.

STEP 27   After using the HIDE command, the result is as shown in Figure P14-17.

STEP 28   End the drawing.

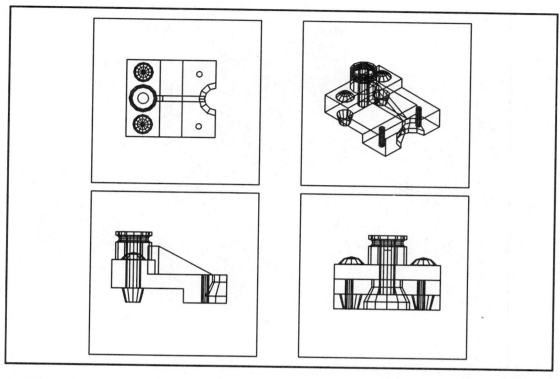

Figure P14–14   Subtracting the primitives from the newly created solid using the SUBTRACT Command

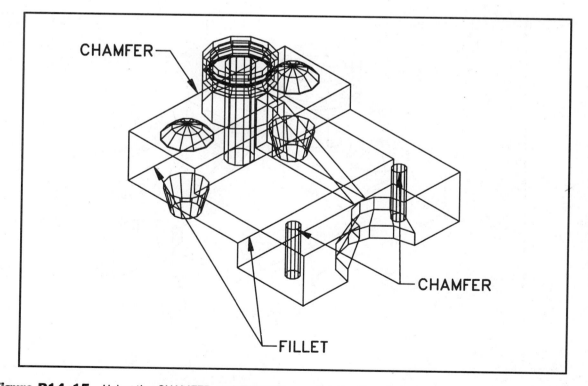

Figure P14–15   Using the CHAMFER and FILLET Commands to chamfer and fillet the faces

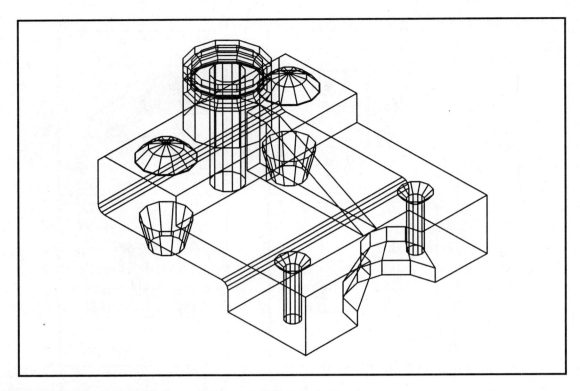

Figure P14–16 The solid after chamfering and filleting the faces

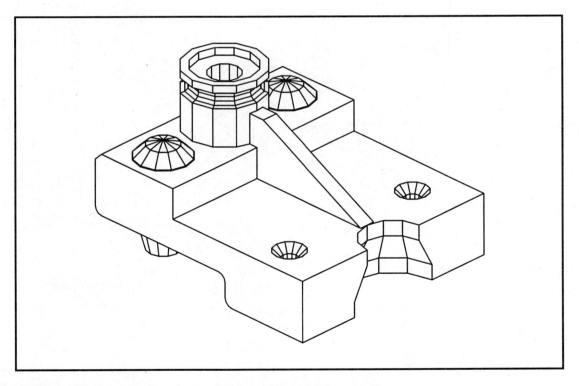

Figure P14–17 The completed solid after using the HIDE Commands

EXERCISES

Exercises 14–1 to 14–5

Layout the objects shown in 3D form. Create the drawings to the given dimension. Display the drawing with VPOINT in four different views. Select the HIDE command for one of the views.

Exercise 14-1

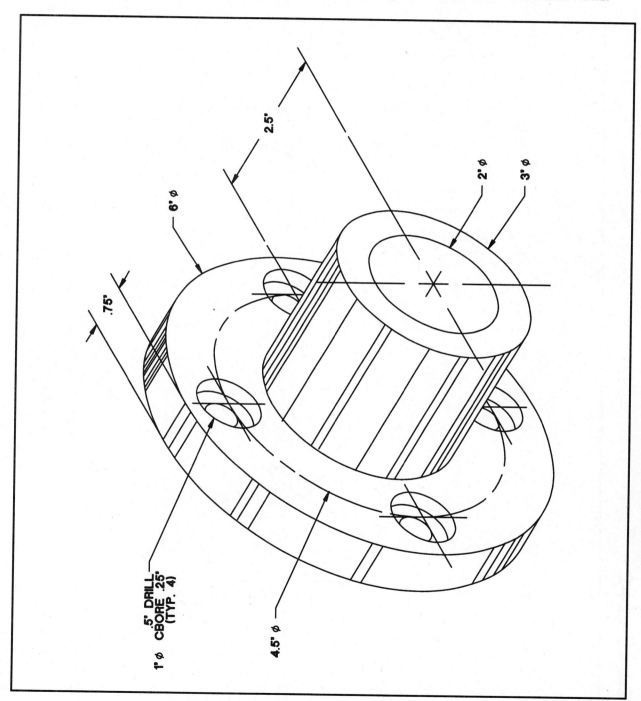

2.5'

6' ⌀

2' ⌀

3' ⌀

.75'

.5' DRILL
1' ⌀ CBORE .25'
(TYP. 4)

4.5' ⌀

AutoCAD 3D

Exercise 14-2

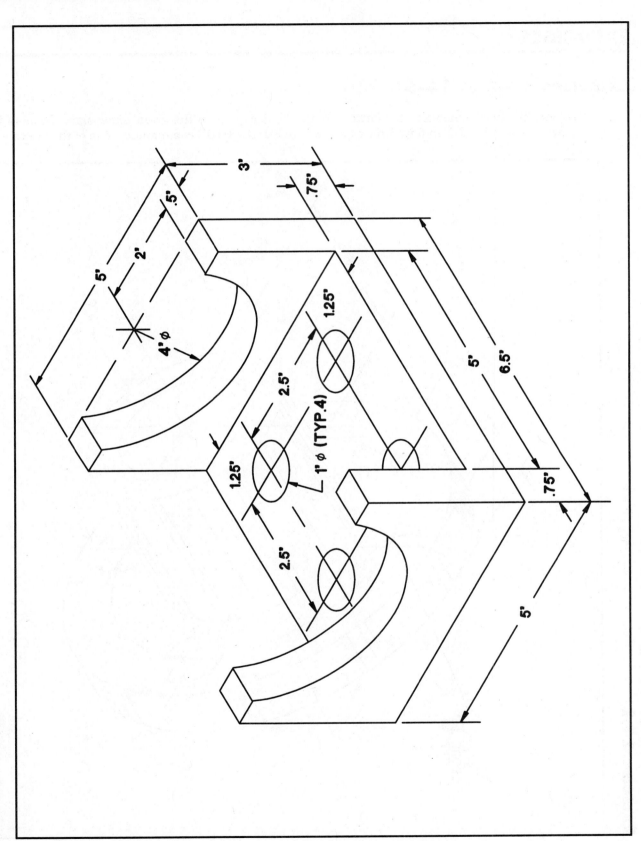

AutoCAD 3D

Exercise 14-3

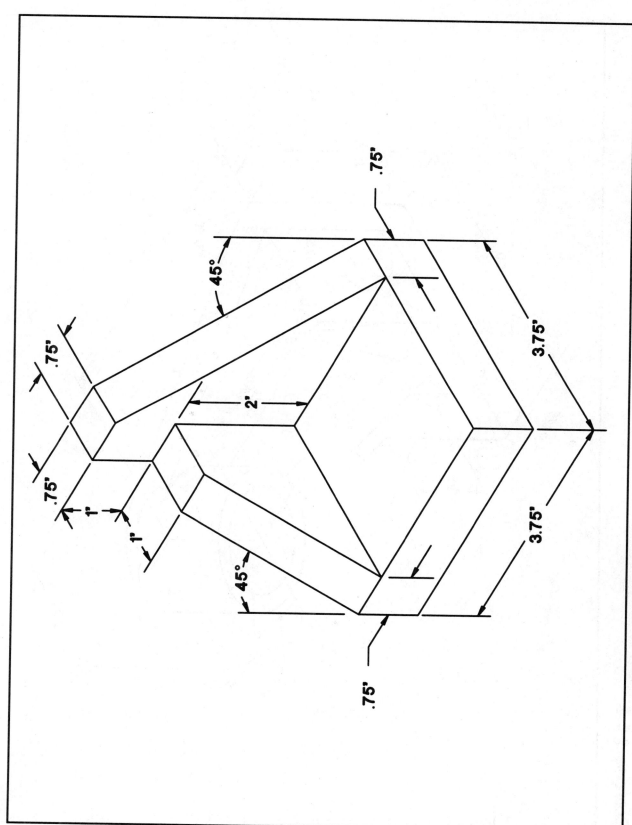

Exercise 14-4

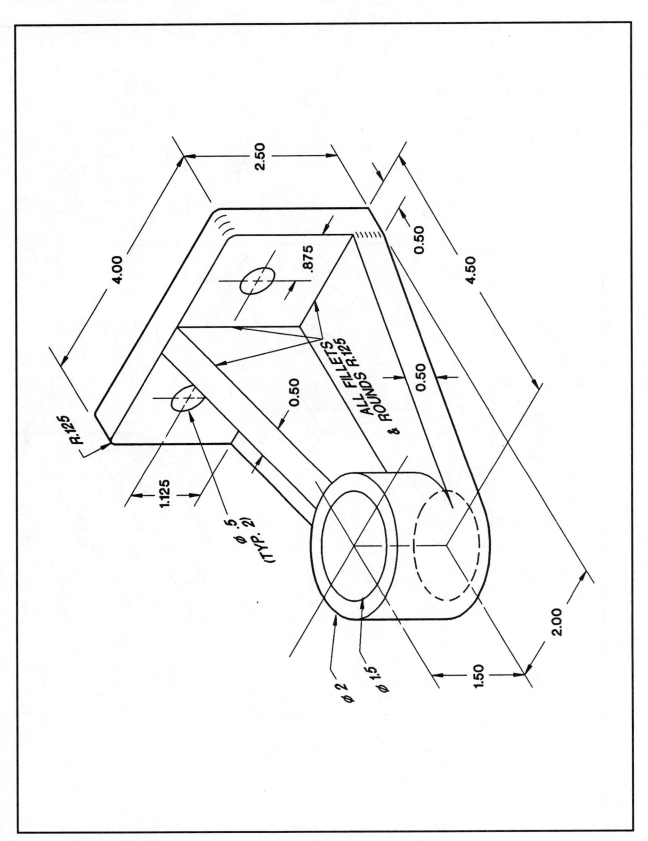

AutoCAD 3D

Exercise 14-5

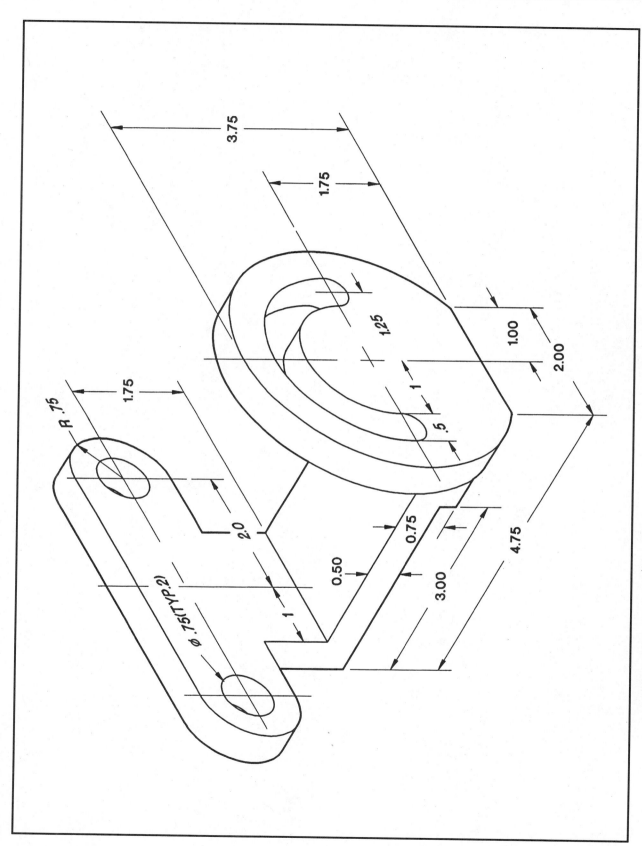

15

RENDERING

INTRODUCTION

Shading or rendering turns your 3D model into a realistic (eye-catching) image. AutoCAD's SHADE command allows you to produce quick shaded models. However, AutoCAD's RENDER gives you more control over the appearance of the final image. You can add lights and control lighting in your drawing and define the reflective qualities of surfaces in the drawing, making objects dull or shiny. You can create the rendered image of your 3D model entirely within AutoCAD.

After completing this chapter, you will be able to:

- Render a 3D model
- Create and modify a light – Ambient, Distant, Point, and Spotlight
- Create and modify a scene
- Create and modify a material
- Save and Replay an image

SHADE COMMAND

The AutoCAD SHADE command lets you produce a shaded picture of the 3D model in the current Viewport. You have little control over lighting. Shade uses a single light that is logically placed just over your right shoulder in the current viewport. The SHADE command is invoked from the Render toolbar (Figure 15–1), or at the "Command:" prompt type **SHADE** and press [Enter] or spacebar.

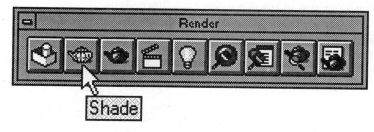

Figure 15–1   Invoke the SHADE Command from the Render toolbar

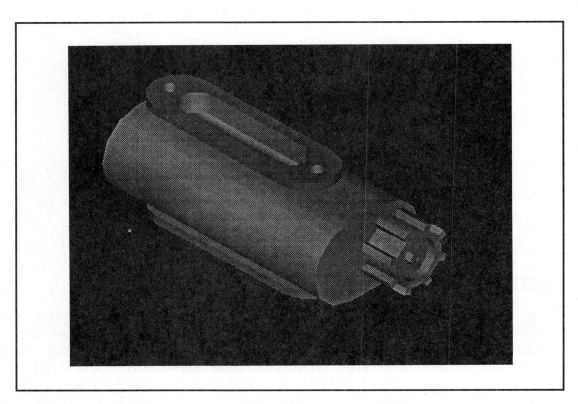

Figure 15–2   A 3D model rendered by AutoCAD   *(Courtesy Autodesk)*

Command: **shade**

There are no prompts to answer. The current viewport goes blank for a period of time. When the entire drawing is being shaded, AutoCAD redraws sections of it on the screen and then reports that the shading is complete.

The shaded image remains until the next regeneration occurs and the original drawing is displayed on the screen. The shaded image can be displayed only on the screen; you can't plot it. You can make a slide by using the MSLIDE command.

AutoCAD's shading is controlled by two system variables, SHADEDGE and SHADEDIF. SHADEDGE defines how your object is shaded in relation to the edges of your model. SHADEDIF allows you to adjust the ratio of ambient light to diffuse light. You may change the way the SHADE command shades your model by changing the system variables SHADEDGE and SHADEDIF.

SHADEDGE allows you to set one of four configurations.

    0   Faces shaded, edges not highlighted
    1   Faces shaded, edges drawn in current background color
    2   Faces not filled, edges in object color
    3   Faces in object color, edges in background color

SHADEDIF allows you to change the ratio of diffuse reflective light to ambient light. In other words, the greater the number in SHADEDIF the greater the difference you see between different surfaces. You can set the SHADEIF value between 0 and 100. The default value is 70.

RENDER

The AutoCAD Render allows you to create realistic models from your AutoCAD drawings. With the AutoCAD Render you may adjust lighting factors, material finishes, and camera placement. All these options allow you a great deal of flexibility. If you wish to take Rendering to its full extent, you may wish to purchase AutoVision or 3D Studio to get the greatest amount of flexibility and photo realism.

The tools available for Rendering allows you to adjust the type and quality of the rendering, setup lights and scenes, and save and replay images. But, you can always use the RENDER command without any other AutoCAD Render setup. By default, Render uses the current view if no scene or selection is specified. If there are no lights specified, the RENDER command assumes a default "over-the-shoulder" distant light source with an intensity of 1.

Invoke the RENDER command by selecting **Render** from the Render toolbar (Figure 15–3), or at the "Command:" prompt type **RENDER** and press Enter or spacebar. AutoCAD displays the Render dialog box as shown in Figure 15–4.

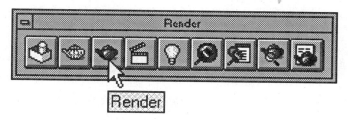

Figure 15–3 Invoke the RENDER Command from the Render toolbar

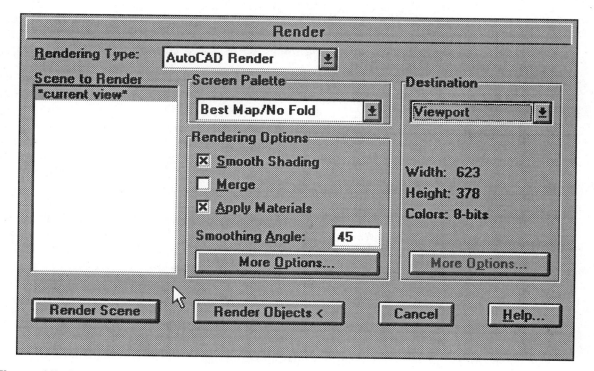

Figure 15–4 Render dialog box

The **Rendering Type** lists the available rendering type, including AutoCAD Render and AutoVision if installed. The default is AutoCAD Render.

The **Screen to Render** lists scenes, including the current view, that you can select for rendering.

The list available in the **Screen Palette** section of the dialog box controls the color map when rendering or replaying an image to viewport using a 256-color combined rendering driver. The options in the list are unavailable if you have configured AutoCAD for a continuous color rendering driver.

Best Map/No Fold Option The Best Map/No Fold option uses a separate color map for rendering and may affect colors 1 to 8 in other viewports depending on the color map used.

Best Map/Fold Option The Best Map/Fold option uses a separate color map for rendering and folds colors above 8. This option also maps colors in the current 256 pallet that most closely match the primary colors 1 to 8 to replace those colors in other viewports.

Fixed ACAD Map Option The Fixed ACAD Map option uses the AutoCAD 256 color map to render drawings in the viewport. While this does not produce the most accurate colors, no flashing occurs when you change to a non-rendering viewport.

AutoCAD provides three options to select in the **Rendering Options** section of the dialog box. You can turn on one or more of the check boxes.

Selection of the **Smooth Shading** option gives objects a smooth appearance. Depending on the object's surfaces and the direction of the scene's lights, smooth shading adds a cleaner, more realistic appearance to a rendering.

Selection of **Merge** option allows you to display multiple renderings in the frame buffer or clear it every time you render. If the Merge check box is selected, the current model is composited with the current image in the frame buffer. To load a background image into the frame buffer, you may either render it or replay the image with Merge check box off. Then you may again render or replay to create a composite.

Selection of **Apply Materials** applies the surface materials you define and attach to an object or ACI in the drawing. If Apply Materials is not selected, all objects in the drawing assume the color, ambient, reflection, and roughness attribute values defined for the *GLOBAL* material. The **Smoothing Angle:** edit field sets the angle at which AutoCAD interprets an edge. The default is 45 degrees and angles greater than 45 degrees are considered edges. For fine tuning Render Quality, click the **More Options. . .** button, AutoCAD displays the AutoCAD Render Options dialog box, as shown in Figure 15–5 for fine tuning the rendering.

The **Destination** section of the dialog box controls the image output setting. There are three options that can be selected from the **Destination list box:** Viewport, Render Window, or File. The **Viewport** selection allows AutoCAD to render to a viewport. The **File** selection renders to a file. When File is selected in the Destination list box, click the **More Options. . .** button to select the file type, setting the colors in the output file and setting the postscript options, if necessary.

When you select the Render Window option, AutoCAD renders the model in a window, as shown in Figure 15–6.

The Open command available from the File pull-down menu in the window allows you to open two types of files: bitmap (.BMP) files and clipboard (.CLP) files. The Save command available from the

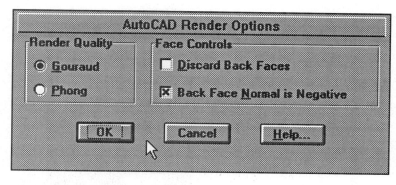

Figure 15–5 AutoCAD Render Options dialog box

File pull-down menu in the window allows you to save an image to a bitmap file. If necessary, you can also use the Print command available from the File pull-down menu to print the image. The Copy command available from the Edit pull-down menu can be used to copy an image from the active render window to the clipboard. The Options command available from the File pull-down menu displays the Render Options dialog box, as shown in Figure 15–7, from which you can select aspect ratios and resolutions for bitmap images.

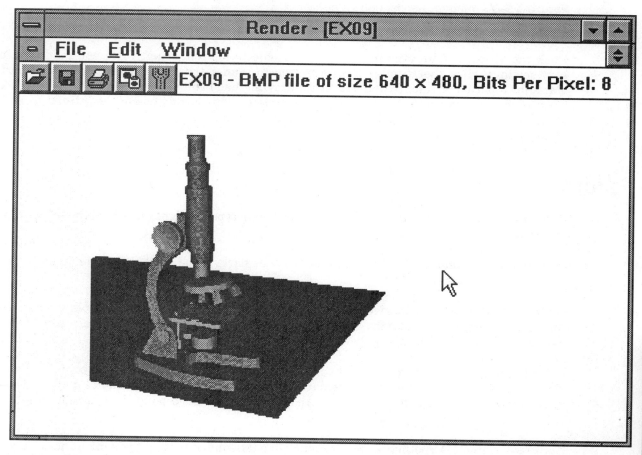

Figure 15–6 Rendering a model in a window

Rendering

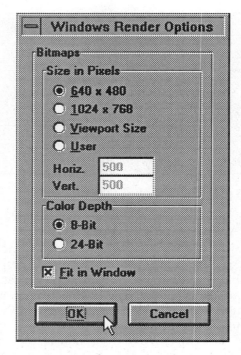

Figure 15–7   Windows Render Options dialog box

Click the **Render Objects<** button to select objects for rendering. Once you made the necessary settings, click the **Render Scene** button to render the scene. The current viewport goes blank for a period of time. When the entire drawing has been rendered, AutoCAD redraws it on the screen and reports that the shading is complete. This is only one of the infinite ways that a 3D model is rendered. To get a more realistic rendered image, you must use lights, cameras, and finishes.

LIGHTS

Render gives you a great deal of flexibility over four types of lights in your renderings. The four different types of lights are:

Ambient Light Ambient light can be thought of as background light that is constant and distributed equally among all objects.

Distant Light Distant light gives off a fairly straight beam of light that radiates in one direction. Another property of Distant light is that its brilliance remains constant, so that an object close to the light receives as much light as a distant object.

Point Light Point light can be thought of as a ball of light. Point lights radiate beams of light in all directions. These lights also have more natural characteristics. Their brilliance may be diminished as the light moves away from its source. An object that is near a point light appears brighter. An object that is farther away will appear darker.

Spotlight AutoCAD Spotlights are very much like the kind of spotlight you might be accustomed to seeing at a theater or auditorium. Spotlights produce a cone of light toward a target that you specify.

To add, delete, or modify a light, invoke the **LIGHT** command from the Render toolbar (Figure 15–8) or at the "Command:" prompt, type **Light** and press Enter or spacebar.

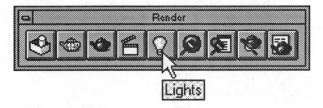

Figure 15–8   Invoke the LIGHT Command from the Render toolbar

AutoCAD displays the Lights dialog box similar to the one shown in Figure 15–9.

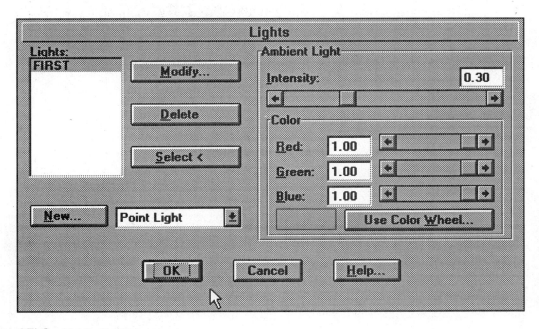

Figure 15–9   Lights dialog box

Creating a New light

Select one of the three available light types from the list box located next to the **New. . .** button. Then, click the **New. . .** button, AutoCAD displays the **New Point Light** dialog box as shown in Figure 15–10, **New Distant Light** dialog box as shown in Figure 15–11, or **New Spotlight** dialog box as shown in Figure 15–12, depending on the type of light selected.

Light Name Type the name of the light in the **Light Name:** edit box. The name must be eight characters or less.

Intensity The slider box located below the **Intensity:** edit box changes the brightness of the light with 0 turning the light off. Distant light intensity values may range from 0 to 1. Point lights have a more complex intensity setting. This setting can be any real number. The factors that control the

Rendering

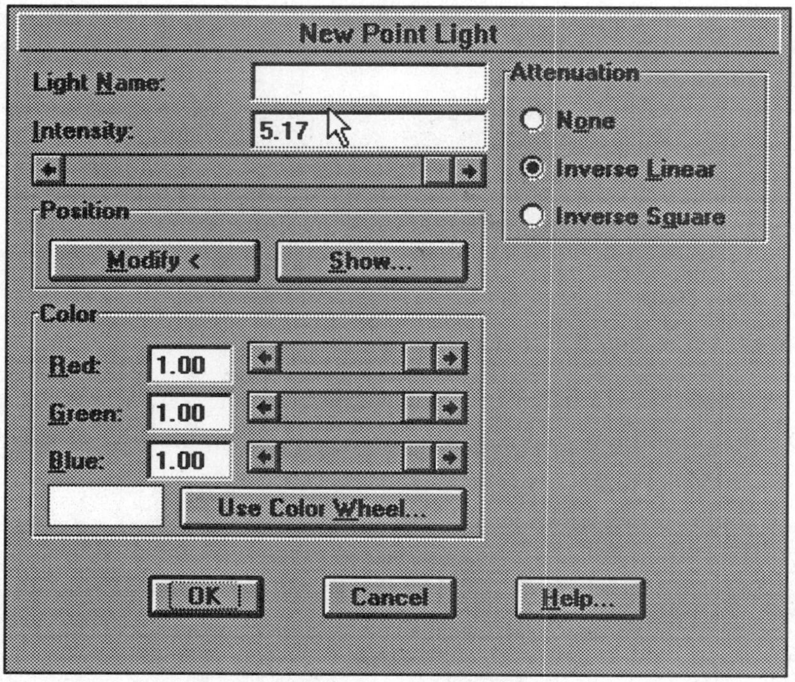

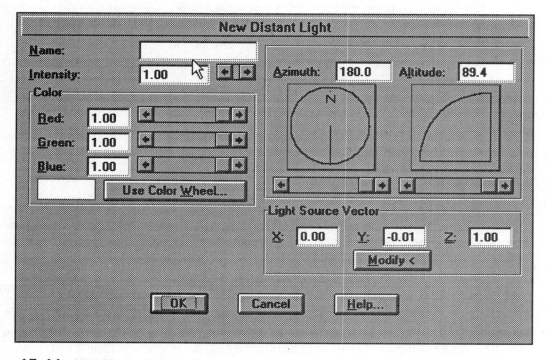

Figure 15–10 New Point Light dialog box

Figure 15–11 New Distant Light dialog box

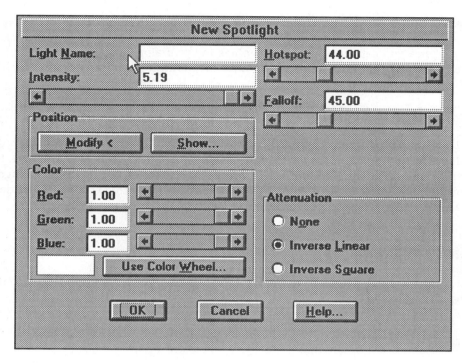

Figure 15–12 New Spotlight dialog box

maximum intensity are the extents of the drawing and the current rate of fall-off. Spotlight Intensity factors are the same as point lights except that the fall-off is always inverse linear.

Position The **Modify<** and **Show. . .** buttons located in the Position section let you modify or look at the X,Y,Z coordinate location of the light and its target.

Color The **Color** section controls the current color of the light. You can use either the Red, Green, and Blue slider bars or the color wheel to set the color.

Attenuation The setting of the attenuation controls how light diminishes over distance. The attenuation applies for both point light as well as spotlight. Select one of the three radio buttons. Selection of **None** sets no attenuation. Objects far from the point light are as bright as objects close to the light. Selection of the **Inverse linear** fall-off decreases the light intensity linearly as the distance increases. For example, an object 10 units away from the light source will be 1/10 as illuminated as an object adjacent to the light source. Selection of **Inverse square** fall-off decreases the light intensity by the inverse of the distance squared. The object that is 10 units away from the light source receives 1/100 the amount of light of an item adjacent to the light source. This function provides rapid fall-off so that a point light can be more localized.

Azimuth and Altitude The **Azimuth and Altitude** edit box located in the New Distant Light dialog box specifies the position of the distant light by using the site-based coordinates. The Azimuth value can be set at any value between -180 to 180. The Altitude can be set at any value between -90 to 90.

Light Source Vector The light source vector displays the light vector that results from the light position you set using Azimuth and Altitude. You can also enter values directly in the edit boxes. AutoCAD updates the corresponding Azimuth and Altitude values.

Rendering

Hotspot and Falloff The **Hotspot and Falloff** edit fields located in the New Spotlight dialog box specifies the angle that defines the brightness cone of light and full cone of light, respectively. Once you set the appropriate values in the dialog box, click the OK button to create a new light. AutoCAD lists the name of the light in the Light list box.

Modifying a Light

First, select the light name from the list box to modify. Then, click the **Modify** button, and AutoCAD displays the appropriate Modify dialog box depending on the light type selected. Make the necessary changes, and click the **OK** button to accept the changes. You cannot change a light type. For example, you cannot make a point light to a distant light. To do so, you must delete the point light and insert a new distant light in the same location.

Delete a Light

First, select the light name from the list box to delete. Then, click the **Delete** button, and AutoCAD deletes the selected light.

Select <

The **Select** < button allows you to select a light from the screen. AutoCAD temporarily dismisses the dialog box while you specify a light on screen using the pointing device. The **Lights** dialog box returns with the selected light highlighted in the Lights list.

Ambient Light

The Ambient Light slider bar allows you to adjust the intensity of the Ambient or background light from a value of (off) to 1 (brightness). The **Color** section controls the current color of the ambient light. You can use either the Red, Green, and Blue slider bars or the color wheel to set the color. Click the **OK** button to accept the changes, and close the **Lights** dialog box.

SCENE

Inserting and adjusting lights allows you to render images from an unlimited number of viewpoints. If necessary, you can save a certain combination of lights and a particular view as a scene, which you can recall at anytime. A scene represents a particular view of the drawing together with one or more lights. Making a scene avoids re-creating a particular set of conditions every time you need to render that image. The VPOINT and DVIEW commands are used to control viewing of a model from any point in model space and the LIGHT command allows you to add/modify one or more lights to the model. The SCENE command allows you to save a scene. You can have an unlimited number of scenes in a drawing.

> **NOTE:** The VIEW command allows you to save a view but doesn't save the lights, whereas the scene can include both the view and the light positions.

To create a scene, invoke the SCENE command from the Render toolbar (Figure 15–13), or at the Command: prompt type **SCENE** and press Enter or spacebar.

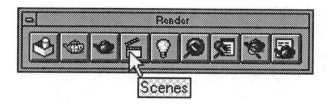

Figure 15–13   Invoke the SCENE Command from the Render toolbar

Command: **scene**

AutoCAD displays the Scenes dialog box similar to the one shown in Figure 15–14.

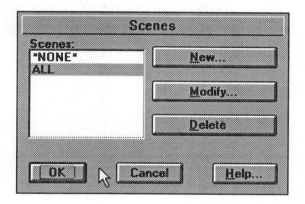

Figure 15–14   Scenes dialog box

New. . .

The **New. . .** option allows you to add a new scene to the current drawing. When you click on **New. . .** from the Scenes dialog box, AutoCAD displays a New Scene dialog box similar to the one shown in Figure 15–15. The same dialog box is displayed when you select the **Modify. . .** button, except the dialog box is entitled Modify Scene.

Scene Name This is the name of the scene. It may be up to eight characters long. You can rename the current scene.

Views The **Views** list box displays the list of views in the current drawing. *CURRENT* is the current view in the active viewport. The active view in the current scene is highlighted. Selecting another view makes it the new view of the scene. You can have only one view in a scene.

Lights The **Lights** list box displays the list of lights in the current drawing. *ALL* is all the lights in the drawing. By selecting *ALL* option, all the lights in the drawing are added to the scene. The lights in the current scene are highlighted. Selecting a non-highlighted light adds that light to the scene. Selecting a highlighted light deselects that light and removes it from the scene.

Rendering

NOTE: You can create a scene with no lights. In this case, the only lighting in the scene is from ambient light.

Modify. . .

The **Modify. . .** option allows you to modify an existing scene. This option invokes the **Modify Scene** dialog box and allows you to add or delete views and lights.

Delete

The **Delete** option deletes a scene from the current drawing.

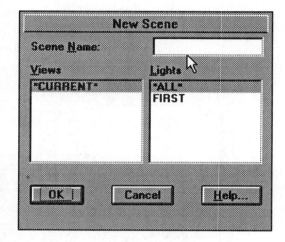

Figure 15–15 New Scene dialog box

MATERIALS

The RMAT command gives you the power to modify the light reflection characteristics of the objects you will render. By modifying these characteristics, you make objects appear rough or shiny. These finish characteristics are stored in the drawing via surface property blocks. The drawing contains one surface property block for each finish you create, an attribute from the name, and AutoCAD color index (ACI) if assigned. You can modify materials by manipulating ambient, diffuse, specular, and roughness factors.

To add, delete, or modify a material, invoke the RMAT command from the Render toolbar (Figure 15–16), or at the "Command:" prompt type **RMAT** and press ⏎ or spacebar.

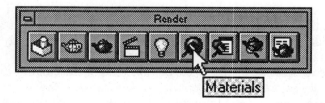

Figure 15–16 Invoke the RMAT Command from the Render toolbar

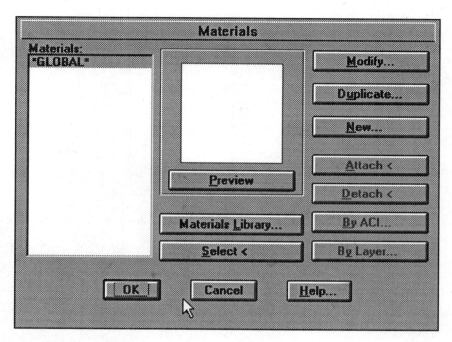

Figure 15–17 Materials dialog box

Command: **rmat**

AutoCAD displays the Materials dialog box similar to the one shown in Figure 15–17.

The **Materials** list box lists the available materials. The default for objects with no other material attached is *GLOBAL*.

Materials Library. . . The **Materials Library. . .** button displays the Materials Library dialog box as shown in Figure 15–18 from which you can select a material.

The **Materials Library** dialog box allows you to import a predefined material from an .MLI materials library into the current drawing. The Materials List box in the dialog box lists the materials currently in the drawing. The Library List box lists the materials available in the library file. If necessary, you can preview a sample of the material selected in the Material list. The sample is applied to a sphere. You can preview only one material at a time. To import materials from the Material Library list box into the current drawing, first select the materials that you want to import from the Material Library list box and then click the **<Import** button. AutoCAD adds the selected materials to the Materials List box. Click the **OK** button to close the Materials Library dialog box, and AutoCAD returns the control to the Materials dialog box.

Select < The **Select<** button temporarily removes the Materials dialog box and displays the graphics area so you can select an object and display the attached material. After you select the object, the Materials dialog box reappears with the method of attachment displayed at the bottom of the dialog box.

Modify < The **Modify <** button allows you to modify a material by displaying the Modify Standard Material dialog box.

Rendering

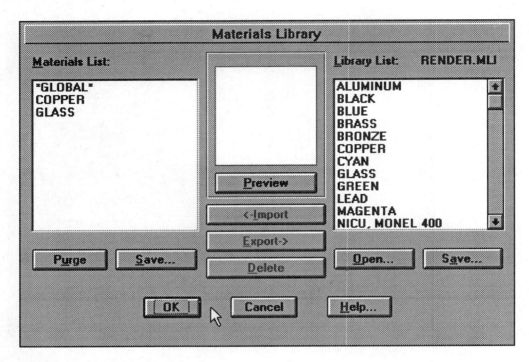

Figure 15–18 Materials Library dialog box

Duplicate The **Duplicate** button duplicates a selected material and displays the New Standard Material dialog box with the Material Name text box. Make the necessary changes, and save the material with a new material name.

New. . . The **New. . .** button allows you to create a new material by displaying the New Standard Material dialog box.

Attach The **Attach** button displays the graphics area so you can select an object and attach the current material to it.

Detach The **Detach** button displays the graphics area so you can select an object and detach the material from it.

By ACI The **By ACI** button displays the Attach by AutoCAD Color Index (ACI) dialog box from which you can select available ACI to attach to a material.

By Layer The **By Layer** button displays the Attach by Layer dialog box from which you can select a layer to attach a material.

Click the **OK** button to accept the changes and close the Materials dialog box.

RENDERING PREFERENCES DIALOG BOX

The Rendering Preferences dialog box has many options that will affect how your model will look. To open the Rendering Preferences dialog box, select **Render** from the Render toolbar (Figure 15-19), or at the "Command:" prompt, type **RPREF** and press ⏎ or spacebar. AutoCAD displays Rendering Preferences dialog box, as shown in Figure 15–20.

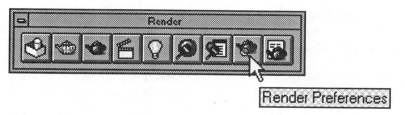

Figure 15–19 Invoke the RPREF Command from the Render toolbar

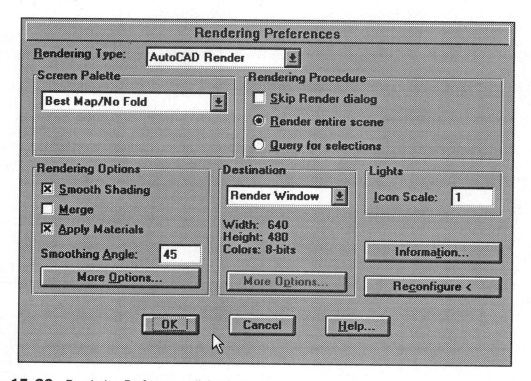

Figure 15–20 Rendering Preferences dialog box

The **Rendering Type** lists the available rendering type, including AutoCAD Render and AutoVision if installed. The default is AutoCAD Render.

The list available in the **Screen Palette** section of the dialog box control the color map when rendering or replaying an image to viewport using a 256-color combined rendering driver. The options in the list is unavailable if you have configured AutoCAD for a continuous color rendering driver.

Best Map/No Fold Option The Best Map/No Fold option uses a separate color map for rendering and may affect colors 1 to 8 in other viewports depending on the color map used.

Best Map/Fold Option The Best Map/Fold option uses a separate color map for rendering and folds colors above 8. This option also maps colors in the current 256 pallet that most closely match the primary colors 1 to 8 to replace those colors in other viewports.

Rendering

Fixed ACAD Map Option The Fixed ACAD Map option uses the AutoCAD 256 color map to render drawings in the viewport. While this does not produce the most accurate colors, no flashing occurs when you change to a non-rendering viewport.

The **Skip Render dialog** check box located in the Rendering Procedure section of the dialog box controls the display of the Render dialog box when you invoke the **RENDER** command.

Select one of the two radio buttons located in the **Rendering Procedure** section of the dialog box that controls the objects that will be selected for rendering by default. The **Render Entire Scene** selection renders all the geometry in a scene and **Query For Selections** prompts to select object to render.

AutoCAD provides three options to select in the **Rendering Options** section of the dialog box. You can turn on one or more of the check boxes. Selection of the **Smooth Shading** gives objects a smooth appearance. Depending on the object's surfaces and the direction of the scene's lights, smooth shading adds a cleaner, more realistic appearance to a rendering.

Selection of **Merge** option allows you to display multiple renderings in the frame buffer or clear it every time you render. If the Merge check box is selected, the current model is composited with the current image in the frame buffer. To load a background image into the frame buffer, you can either render it or replay the image with Merge check box off. Then, you can again render or replay again to create a composite.

Selection of **Apply Materials** applies the surface materials you define and attach to an object or ACI in the drawing. If Apply Materials is not selected, all objects in the drawing assume the color, ambient, reflection, and roughness attribute values defined for the *GLOBAL* material. The **Smoothing Angle:** edit field sets the angle at which AutoCAD interprets an edge. The default is 45 degrees and angles greater than 45 degrees are considered edges. For fine tuning render quality, click the **More Options. . .** button. AutoCAD displays the AutoCAD Render Options dialog box as shown in Figure 15–21 for fine tuning the rendering.

The **Destination** section of the dialog box controls the image output setting. There are two options that can be selected from the **Destination list box:** Viewport or File. The **Viewport** selection allows AutoCAD to render to a viewport. The **File** selection renders to a file. When File is selected in the Destination list box, click the **More Options. . .** button to select the file type, setting the colors in the output file and setting the postscript options, if necessary.

The Lights **Icon Scale:** edit field controls the size of the light blocks in the drawing. Enter a real number to scale the blocks.

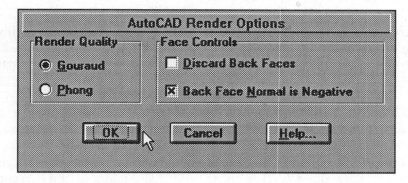

Figure 15–21 AutoCAD Render Options

Click the **Information. . .** button to display information about the current configuration and version of the application you are using.

To reconfigure the rendering device, click the **Reconfigure<** button. AutoCAD provides configuration options to reconfigure the rendering device.

Click the **OK** button to accept the changes, and close the Rendering Preferences dialog box.

SAVE IMAGE

You may save the contents of the frame buffer to a GIF, TIFF, or TGA file format by invoking the SAVEIMG command. The SAVEIMG command is invoked by typing **SAVEIMG** at the "Command:" prompt and pressing ⌜Enter⌝ or spacebar.

> Command: **saveimg**

AutoCAD displays the Save Image dialog box similar to the one shown in Figure 15–22, depending on whether you configured AutoCAD to render to a viewport or to a separate display window.

Image Name and Directory Type the file name and the path in which you want to save the image.

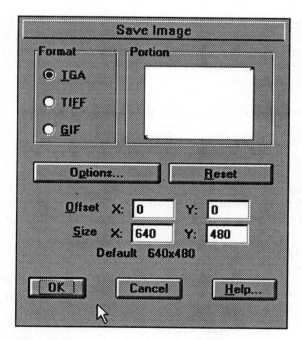

Figure 15–22 Save Image dialog box

Format Choose the file format for the output image. You can save an image in any one of the three industry standard file formats: GIF, TGA, and TIFF.

Portion The portion option lets you save the Active Viewport, drawing area, or full screen when the rendering is configured to render to a viewport. The active viewport option saves the active viewport.

The drawing area option saves the drawing area, excluding the pull-down menu area, screen menu area, and command-prompt area of the drawing. The full screen saves the drawing area including the pull-down menu area, screen menu area, and command-prompt area of the drawing.

REPLAY COMMAND

The REPLAY command allows you to load a GIF, TIFF, or TGA file into the frame buffer for viewing, converting, or using as a background for a composite rendering. Invoke the REPLAY command by typing **REPLAY** at the "Command:" prompt and pressing Enter or spacebar.

Command: **replay**

AutoCAD displays the standard file dialog box. Pick a file or enter a filename. After you select an image file and click OK, an Image Specifications dialog box is displayed.

Image The image tile lets you select a smaller part of the image you want to display. The default size of the image in the image tile reflects the entire display size in pixel measurement with offset set to 0,0 lower left corner of the image. To resize the image, pick two points, one for the lower-left corner and the other one for upper-right corner of the image in the image tile. AutoCAD automatically draws a box to mark the bounds of the reduced image area and updates the values in the X,Y Image Size coordinates.

Screen The screen tile lets you adjust the offset location of the selected, sized image in relation to your screen. The tile displays the size of your screen or your current viewport. To change the offset, select a point in this tile to offset the center of the image to that point. AutoCAD automatically redraws the image size boundaries to mark the new offsets and updates the values in the X,Y Offset coordinates.

Reset Resets the size and offset values to the original values.

STATS

The STATS command gives detailed information on your last rendering. This can be useful for diagnosing problems with your drawing. The STATS command is invoked from the Render toolbar (Figure 15–23), or at the "Command:" prompt, type **STATS** and press Enter or spacebar.

Command: **stats**

Figure 15–23 Invoke the STATS Command from the Render toolbar

AutoCAD displays a statistics dialog box. You can save the information in the Statistics dialog box to a file. To save a file, select the check box and enter a filename.

CHAPTER

16

THE TABLET AND DIGITIZING

INTRODUCTION

The AutoCAD program consists of several major components in the form of program files along with many other supporting files. One major part of the program, the menu (in the form of a filename.MNX file), determines how various devices work with the program. The devices controlled by the menu include the buttons on the pointing device (mouse or tablet puck), the toolbars, pull-down menus, function box keys (not commonly used) and tablet. This chapter covers configuring and using the tablet menu.

First, using the tablet part of any menu requires that the AutoCAD program be installed and configured for the particular make and model of digitizing tablet that is properly connected to the computer.

> *NOTE:* The installation configuration permits using only one digitizing device at a time. Because a mouse and a tablet are both digitizing devices, you must choose between one or the other at any one time. This pre-startup configuration is not to be confused with configuring the installed tablet with the TABLET command while in AutoCAD.

Second, a preprinted template with up to four rectangular menu areas should be used that has properly arranged columns and rows of pick areas within each menu area. Each pick area corresponds to a command or line of programming in the filename.MNX menu file in effect. It is also necessary to set aside a screen area on the tablet if you wish to control the screen cursor with the tablet's puck. See Figure 16–1.

After completing this chapter, you will be able to:

- Configure the tablet menu
- Calibrate the tablet for digitizing

TABLET OPERATION

When a filename.MNX file, digitizing tablet, and overlay have been installed and properly set up to work together, you can use the attached puck on the tablet surface to achieve the following results.

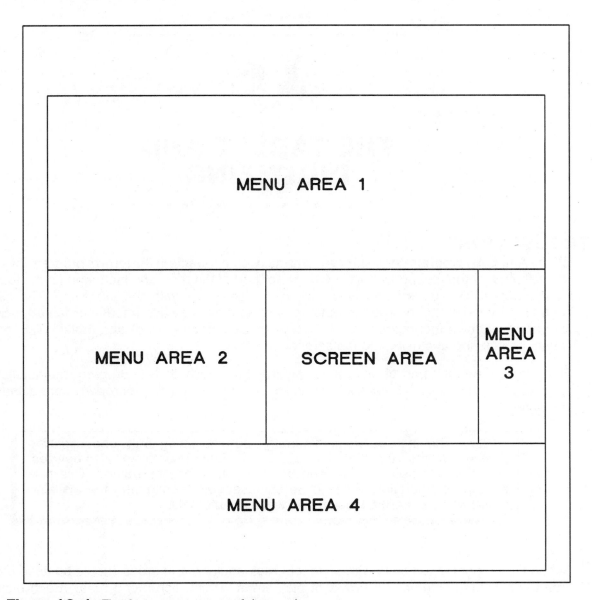

Figure 16-1 The four screen areas of the overlay

Normal operation — The most common usage of a tablet is to allow the user to move the puck and press the pick button while pointing to one of the various commands or symbols on a preprinted overlay and be able to invoke that particular command or initiate a program (perhaps written by users themselves) that will draw that symbol. In addition, when the puck is moved within the overlay's designated screen area, the screen cursor will mimic the puck movement, thereby permitting you to specify points or select objects on the screen.

Mouse movement — Some tablets have an option that causes the puck to emulate mouse type rather than absolute movement. Mouse emulation means that if you pick the puck up off of the tablet surface and move it to another place in the screen area, the screen cursor does not move. The cursor moves only with puck movement while it is on the tablet and in the screen area. Absolute (normal) tablet-puck operation means that, once configured, each point in the tablet's screen area corresponds to only one point on the screen. So, while in the normal mode, if you pick the puck up and put it down at another point in the screen area, the cursor will immediately move to the screen's corresponding point.

Paper copying — By switching the TABLET mode to ON, you can cause points on the tablet to correspond to drawing coordinates rather than screen pixel locations as it does in the Normal or Mouse operations described above. This allows you to fix a drawing (like a map) on the tablet surface, select two points on the map, specify their coordinate locations on the map, after which the puck movement around the map will cause screen cursor movement to correspond to the same coordinates in the computer-generated drawing. Options and precautions for using this feature (referred to as digitizing) are discussed in this chapter.

The ACAD.MNX Tablet Configuration

The intended procedure is to have a preprinted template (the overlay) arranged on a sheet that can be fixed to the tablet. Tablet menu area(s) can then be configured to coincide with the template. Although you could try to configure a bare tablet, it would be difficult to select the required points for rectangular menu areas and also impractical to try and place a template on the tablet after it was configured in such a manner. However, if a tablet has been configured for one template, you can use another template in the same location without reconfiguring as long as the areas are the same. One benefit of this is being able to change from one set of icons/symbols or commands to another set without having to configure again. However, a change in the menu must be made in order to accommodate changes in the template, even if the configuration is the same.

The ACAD.MNX (compiled from ACAD.MNU) menu file supports a multibutton pointing device and the tablet overlay that is provided with the AutoCAD program package. That overlay is approximately 11" × 11" and has four areas for selecting icon/commands and a screen area, as shown in Figure 16-1. The pointing device (the puck furnished with every tablet) usually has three or more buttons (the menu supports up to a ten-button puck or mouse) and the cursor movement on the screen mimics the puck's movement in the tablet's configured screen area.

CUSTOM MENUS

Chapter 17 describes how to customize a menu file. Most of the explanations and examples refer to the screen menu primarily because of its complexity. The same principles of customizing the tablet portion of a menu can be applied.

TABLET Command

The TABLET command is used to switch between digitizing paper drawings and normal command/icon/screen area selecting on a configured overlay. The TABLET command is also used to calibrate a paper drawing for digitizing or to configure the overlay to suit the current menu. The TABLET command is invoked by typing TABLET at the "Command:" prompt and pressing [Enter] or spacebar.

> Command: **tablet**
> Option (ON/OFF/CAL/CFG): [Enter]

CFG (Configuration) Option The CFG option is used to set up the individual tablet menu areas and the screen pointing area. At this time a preprinted overlay should have been fixed to the tablet. Its menu areas should suit the menu you wish to use. The sequence of prompts is as follows:

Command: **tablet**
Option (ON/OFF/CAL/CFG): **cfg**
Enter number of tablet menus desired (0-4) <default>:

Select the number of individual menu areas desired (with a limit of 4). The next prompt asks:

Do you want to realign tablet menu areas? <N>:

If you respond **No** (**N** or press [Enter]), the prompts will skip to selecting rows and columns. If you respond **Yes** (or **Y**), then for each of the menu areas specified you will be prompted to "point and pick" three corners as follows:

Digitize upper left corner of menu area n:
Digitize lower left corner of menu area n:
Digitize lower right corner of menu area n:

The "n" refers to tablet menu areas of the corresponding tablet number in the menu. If the three corners you digitize do not form a right angle (90 degrees), you will be prompted to try again. Individual areas may be skewed on the tablet and with each other, but such an arrangement usually does not provide the most efficient use of total tablet space. Tablet areas should not overlap.

The next prompts are as follows:

Enter the number of columns for menu area n:
Enter the number of rows for menu area n:

Enter the numbers from the keyboard. The area will be subdivided into equal rectangles determined by the row and column values you have entered. If the values you enter do not correspond to the overlay row/column values, the results will be unpredictable when trying to use the tablet. Remember also that the overlay must suit the menu being used.

The standard AutoCAD overlay is installed as follows:

Command: **tablet**
Option (ON/OFF/CAL/CFG): **cfg**
Enter number of tablet menus desired (0-4) <default>: **4**
Do you want to realign tablet menu areas? <N>: **y** *(if required)*

At this time, digitize areas 1 through 4, as shown in Figure 16-2. The values for columns and rows must be entered as follows:

MENU AREA	COLUMN	ROW
1	25	9
2	11	9
3	9	7
4	25	7

The above values are for the ACAD.MNX menu. Other menus may vary. To simplify installing the standard menu tablet, an option called RE-CFG automatically responds with the correct values for columns and rows as long as the areas 1 through 4 are selected in the proper sequence.

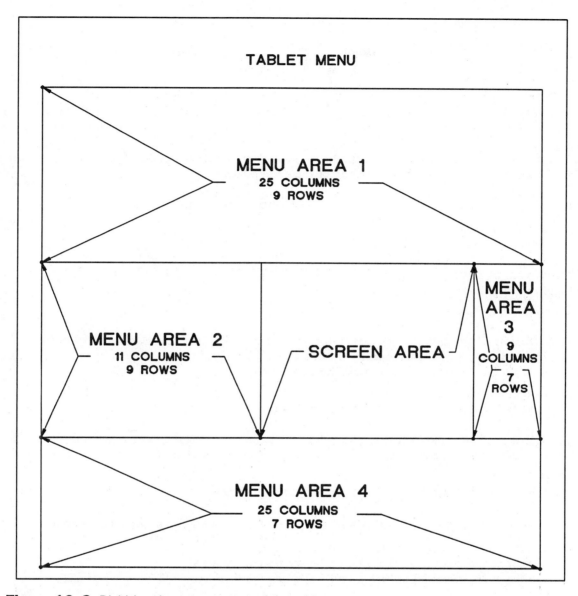

Figure 16-2 Digitizing the screen areas of the tablet menu

Once the tablet menu areas have been configured, you will be prompted to digitize the corners of the screen pointing area. With the overlay that accompanies the standard ACAD.MNX, there is an area set aside for screen pointing. Because there is no command/icon programming associated with the screen pointing area, it is not necessary to specify this particular area. It is, however, positioned for maximum productivity in tablet usage. You may specify a rectangular area anywhere on the tablet, as long as it does not overlap any of the tablet menu areas. On a large (table-sized) tablet, a large screen area may be specified. Too large an area, however, can become tiresome to use. An area about the size of the pad supplied with a mouse (8" × 6") is recommended. The drafting-table-sized tablets are used primarily for digitizing large maps and paper drawings without having to move and recalibrate. The prompts for specifying the screen area are as follows:

Do you want to respecify the Fixed Screen Pointing Area? <N>

If you reply **Yes** (or **Y**), you will be prompted as follows:

Digitize lower left corner of screen pointing area:
Digitize upper right corner of screen pointing area:

ON/OFF Option The default setting of the TABLET mode is OFF. The OFF setting does not incapacitate the tablet as you might think, but means that you are not going to use the tablet for digitizing (making copies of paper drawings). With the TABLET mode set to OFF you may use the tablet to select command/icons in the areas programmed accordingly. You may also use the puck in the screen area of the tablet to control the screen cursor.

In order to digitize paper drawings, you must respond to the prompt as follows:

Command: **tablet**
Option (ON/OFF/CAL/CFG): **on**

Most systems have a toggle key to switch the TABLET mode ON and OFF. With many PCs, the toggle is the function key F10 or Ctrl + T.

CAL Option If the tablet has been calibrated already, the last calibration coordinates will still be in effect. If not, or if you wish to change the calibration (necessary when you move the paper drawing on the tablet), you may respond as follows:

Option (ON/OFF/CAL/CFG): **cal**
Digitize point #1: *(digitize the first known point)*

The point on the paper drawing you select must be one whose coordinates you know. The next prompt asks you to enter the actual paper drawing coordinates of the point you just digitized as follows:

Enter coordinates point #1: *(enter those known coordinates)*

You are then prompted to digitize and specify coordinates for the second known point as follows:

Digitize point #2: *(digitize the second known point)*
Enter coordinates point #2: *(enter those known coordinates)*
Digitize point #3 (or RETURN to end): *(digitize the third known point or press* Enter*)*

An example of a drawing that might be digitized is a map as shown in Figure 16–3.

If for example, the map in Figure 16–3 has been printed on an 11" × 17" sheet and you wish to digitize it on a 12" × 12" digitizer, you can overlay and digitize on half of the map at a time. You may use the coordinates 10560,2640 and 7920,5280 for two calibrating points. But, because the X-coordinates increase toward the left, you must consider them as negative values in order to make them increase to the right. Therefore, in calibrating the map, you may use coordinates –10560,2640 and –7920,5280 to calibrate the first half and coordinates –7920,2640 and –5280,5280 for the second half.

The points on the paper should be selected so that the X values increase toward the right and the Y values increase upward.

Once calibration has been initiated in a particular space (model or paper), turning on the tablet mode must be done while in that particular space.

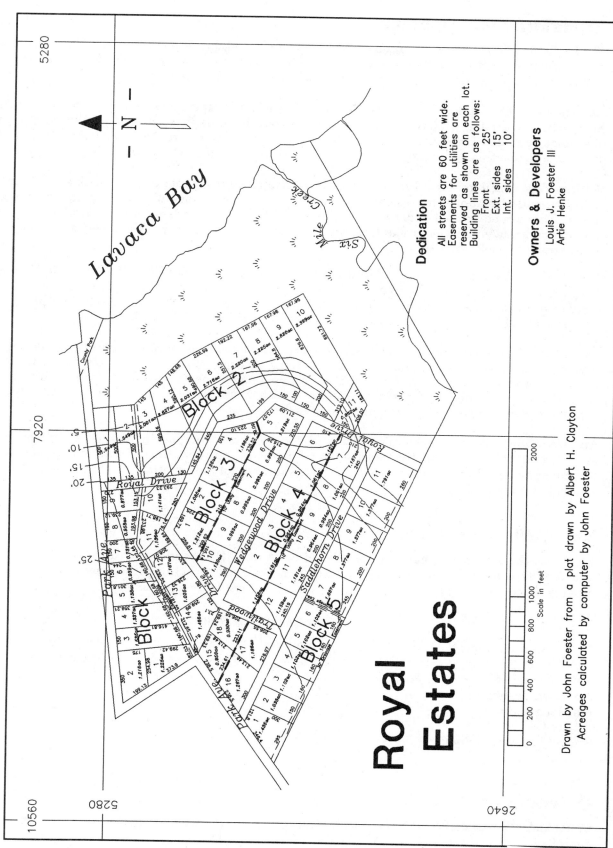

Figure 16-3 An example of a drawing digitized as a map

Transformation Options

Tablet Calibration can be done by one of several transformation methods. These include Orthogonal, Affine, Projective, and Multiple-Point. The method you choose may depend upon the condition of the map/drawing that is to be digitized and the desired accuracy.

Orthogonal This option involves two points. It results in uniform scaling and rotation. The translation is arbitrary. Orthogonal (two point) translation is most suitable for tracing paper drawings that are dimensionally and rotationally (right angles are not skew) accurate. It is advisable to use this option for long, narrow applications (a pipeline, for example).

Affine This option involves three points and can be applied to a paper drawing with scale factors, rotation, and right angle representations that are not to an acceptable accuracy in two dimensions. This can be applied to drawings with parallel lines that are represented parallel, but with x direction scale/y direction scale differential that is out of tolerance. Right angles may not be represented by right angles.

Whether or not you should use the Affine option depends on whether or not those lines that should be parallel are represented by parallel lines on the paper drawing. You can check the report displayed (in the form of a table) when you have digitized at least three points. If the RMS error (described in this section) is small, then the Affine option should be acceptable.

Projective This option involves four points to simulate a translation comparable to a perspective where points from one plane converge while passing through another plane (skew to the first) to one point of view. This option is applicable to copying paper sheets with irregularities that differ from one area to another (known as rubber-sheeting) and parallel lines that are not always represented as parallel. However, lines do project as lines.

Multiple-Point The Multiple-Point option will accept more than four points to be digitized and specified. AutoCAD will use the "least squares" method to optimize the calibration to compensate for imperfections in the paper drawing. The accuracy of this method is proportional to the number of points used.

The Calibration Table

If you use three or more points during calibration, AutoCAD computes the range or error (if any) and reports the results and displays information designed to help you determine if the paper copying process is acceptable. An example of a calibration table follows:

Four Calibration Points

	Orthogonal	Affine	Projective
Transformation type:			
Outcome of fit:	Success	Success	Exact
RMS Error:	143'-6.2"	73'-4.1"	
Standard deviation:	62'-2.7"	1'-7.8"	
Largest residual:	193'-1"	74'-1"	
At point:	2	3	
Second largest residual:	177'-9"	7'-7"	
At point:	3	2	

Outcome of Fit

Cancelled Cancelled occurs only with projective transformations. It indicates the fit has been cancelled.

Exact The number of points used was exactly correct and the transformation defined from them was valid.

Failure Points selected, while the correct number, were probably collinear or coincidental.

Impossible Insufficient points were selected for the transformation type under which "Impossible" is reported.

Success The transformation defined was valid and more points were used than was required.

RMS Error:

If the transformation is reported as a "Success" then the RMS (root mean square) Error is reported. This is the square root of the average of the squares of the distances (called residuals) of each selected point from their respective targets.

Standard Deviation:

This reports the standard deviation of all residuals (the distance each point misses its target).

Point(s)/Residual(s)

The two points whose residuals (see RMS Error: and Standard Deviation) are largest and second largest are reported along with their respective residual values.

TABLET MODE AND SKETCHING

Sketching while in the TABLET mode operates similar to sketching with a mouse or on a tablet with the TABLET mode off. The difference is that the entire tablet surface is used for digitizing while the TABLET mode is on, making the maximum area available for tracing but making the pull-down menus inaccessible.

Editing Sketches

Once sketched lines have been recorded and the SKETCH command has been terminated, you can use regular editing commands (like COPY, MOVE, ERASE) to edit the individual line segments or sketched polylines (discussed next) just as though they had been drawn by the LINE or PLINE command. In the case of sketched polylines, the PEDIT command can be used for editing.

Sketching in Polylines

You can cause AutoCAD to make the created sketch segments into polylines instead of lines by setting the system variable SKPOLY to a nonzero value.

Linetypes in Sketching

You should use the CONTINUOUS linetype while sketching, whether using regular lines or polylines.

CHAPTER

17

CUSTOMIZING AUTOCAD

INTRODUCTION

Off-the-shelf AutoCAD is extremely powerful. But, like many popular engineering and business software programs, it does not automatically do all things for all users. It does (probably better than any software available) permit users to make changes and additions to the core program to suit individual needs and applications. Word processors offer a feature by which you can save a combination of many keystrokes and invoke them at any time with just a few keystrokes. This is known as a macro. Data base management programs (as well as other types of programs) have their own library of users' functions that can also be combined and saved as a user-named, custom designed command. These programs also allow you to create and save standard blank forms for use later to be filled out as needed. Using these features to make your copy of a generic program unique and more powerful for your particular application is known as customizing.

Customizing AutoCAD can include several facets requiring various skill levels. The topics include creating command aliases, linetypes, shapes, hatch patterns, menu customization and command macros. A text editor is required (MS-DOS EDIT.COM or Microsoft Windows NOTEPAD.EXE are examples) in order to customize AutoCAD menus. A macro is a sequence of commands executed by a single user pick from a custom menu. Placing a block into a drawing on a specified layer with predefined attributes such that the operator need not concern themselves as to whether office standards are being maintained, the macro will automatically maintain the office standard allowing the user to concentrate on the specifics of their drafting and design.

After completing this chapter, you will be able to:

- Create Command Aliases
- Create, Modify and Understand AutoCAD's Menu Structure
- Create custom Linetypes, Hatch Patterns and Fonts

EXTERNAL COMMANDS AND ALIASES

AutoCAD allows you to run certain programs without having to exit. These include the internal and external DOS commands, word processors, data base and spreadsheet programs, and many others.

In order to make these external programs possible to use from within AutoCAD, you must first list them with certain specifications in an ASCII file called ACAD.PGP.

As Microsoft Windows is a multi-tasking environment, the External Commands really pertain to the DOS version of AutoCAD. They will work in Windows, but it is much easier to run the applications as separate programs. You can also include aliases in the ACAD.PGP file for regular AutoCAD commands. An alias is nothing but a nickname.

Command aliasing provides an alternate keystroke for invoking a command, not options of the command. The ZOOM command has an option for Window, however you cannot define an alias ZW for ZOOM Window. There is an alias for ZOOM, the letter "Z". Prior to modifying the ACAD.PGP file, it is recommended that you make a backup copy of the file such as XACAD.PGP, so if you make a mistake you can restore the original version. Following is an extract from the ACAD.PGP file.

```
; acad.pgp - External Command and Command Alias definitions
; External Command format:
;    <Command name>,[<DOS request>],<Memory reserve>,[*]<Prompt>,<Return code>

; Examples of External Commands for DOS

CATALOG,DIR /W,0,File specification: ,0
DEL,DEL,        0,File to delete: ,4
DIR,DIR,        0,File specification: ,0
EDIT,EDIT,      0,File to edit: ,4
SH,,            0,*OS Command: ,4
SHELL,,         0,*OS Command: ,4
TYPE,TYPE,      0,File to list: ,0

; Command alias format:
;    <Alias>,*<Full command name>

; Sample aliases for AutoCAD Commands
; These examples reflect the most frequently used commands.
; Each alias uses a small amount of memory, so don't go
; overboard on systems with tight memory.

A,       *ARC
C,       *CIRCLE
CP,      *COPY
DV,      *DVIEW
E,       *ERASE
L,       *LINE
LA,      *LAYER
LT,      *LINETYPE
M,       *MOVE
MS,      *MSPACE
P,       *PAN
PS,      *PSPACE
PL,      *PLINE
R,       *REDRAW
T,       *MTEXT
Z,       *ZOOM
```

The External Commands are defined at the top of the ACAD.PGP file.

The format for a command line is as follows:

<Command name>,<executable>,<Memory reserve>,[*]<Prompt>,<Return code>

An example of lines in an ACAD.PGP file for specifying external commands is as follows:

```
SH,,0, *OS Command: ,0

SHELL,,0, *OS Command: ,0

TYPE,TYPE, 0, File to type: ,0

CATALOG,DIR/W,0, File specification: ,0

DEL,DEL, 0, File to erase: ,0

DIR,DIR, 0, File specification: ,0

EDIT,, 0, File to edit: ,0
```

The command name (to be entered at the "Command:" prompt) should not be the same as an AutoCAD command and should be in uppercase characters.

The executable string is sent to the operative system as the name of a command. It can contain parameters and switches.

The memory amount must contain a number (usually 0). It maintains compatibility with previous versions of AutoCAD.

The prompt (optional) is used to inform the operator if additional input is necessary. If the prompt is preceded by an asterisk (*), then the user's response may contain spaces. The response must be terminated by pressing Enter. Otherwise, pressing the spacebar or Enter will terminate the response.

The return code is a bit-coded specification. The number you specify will represent one or more of the bit-codes. For example, if you specify 3, then bit-codes 1 and 2 will be in effect. If you specify 5, then bit-codes 1 and 4 will be in effect. The values are as follows:

0: Return to text screen.

1: Load DXB file — This causes a file named $cmd.dxb to be loaded into the drawing at the end of the command.

2: Construct block from DXB file — This causes the response to the prompt to become the name of a block to be added to the drawing, consisting of objects in the $cmd.dxb file written by the file command. This code must be used in conjunction with bit-code 1. This may not be used to redefine a previously defined block.

4: Restore text/graphics mode — If this bit-code is included, the mode that you were in (text or graphics) will be returned to when the command is completed; otherwise, you will be in the text mode.

The format to define an alias is as follows:

```
<Alias>,*<Full command name>
```

The abbreviation preceding the comma is the character or characters to be entered at the "Command:" prompt. The asterisk (*) must precede the command you wish invoked. It may be a standard AutoCAD command name, a custom command name that has been defined in and loaded with AutoLISP or ADS, or a display or machine driver command name. Aliases cannot be used in scripts. You can prefix a command in an alias with the underscore that causes a command line version to be used instead of a dialog box, as shown below:

BH, *_BHATCH

MENUS

When you launch the standard version of AutoCAD for Windows, you are presented with the standard menu. Selecting an item from a menu might execute a command, AutoLISP routine, macro or cause another menu to be displayed. Menus are user definable and are created/edited using text editors. Menu files also define the functionality and appearance of the menu area. If you perform an application-specific task on a regular basis that requires multiple steps to accomplish this task, you can place this in a menu macro and have AutoCAD complete all the required processes in a single step while pausing for input if necessary. Menu macros are similar to Script files (files ending with *.SCR). Script files are also capable of executing many commands in sequence but have no decision making capability and cannot pause for interactive user input.

AutoCAD for Windows and DOS supports the following kinds of menus:

- Pull-down and cursor menus
- Screen menus
- Image tile menus
- Pointing device menus
- Tablet menus

AutoCAD for Windows has additional menu functionality as follows:

- Toolbars
- Keyboard Accelerators
- Help Strings and Tool Tips
- Menu Groups

Menu File Types

Prior to AutoCAD Release 13 for Windows, there were two types of menu files, ASCII text file ending with the file extension .MNU and a compiled version of the same file with the extension .MNX . ACAD.MNU file is provided with AutoCAD program and when you launch AutoCAD, if the file ACAD.MNX is not present or if any changes were made to the ACAD.MNU file, AutoCAD automatically compiles and creates a new ACAD.MNX . If you created your own custom menu, for example CUSTOM.MNU, then upon loading the menu, AutoCAD automatically creates CUSTOM.MNX. ACAD.MNU and ACAD.MNX files are still applicable for the DOS and UNIX version of AutoCAD Release 13. Because of the additional functionality of the Windows version of AutoCAD Release 13, a new menu scheme exists.

The following table lists the menu files used by AutoCAD for Windows Release 13 version:

Menu File Type	Description
.MNU	Template menu file, ASCII text
.MNC	Compiled menu file. This binary file contains the command strings and menu syntax that defines the functionality and appearance of the menu.
.MNR	Menu resource file. This binary file contains the bitmaps used by the menu.
.MNS	Source menu file (AutoCAD generated)

AutoCAD Release 13 for Windows comes with two menu files ACAD.MNU and ACADFULL.MNU. These are located in "C:\ACADR13\WIN\SUPPORT" directory, assuming AutoCAD is installed in the C: drive and ACADR13 is the sub-directory. If your location is different, substitute your drive and path location for your case. The ACADFULL.MNU has additional pull-down menus, Draw, Construct, and Modify menus and is intended to ease the transition for AutoCAD 12 users until they become familiar with the Toolbars. The .MNS file is similar in structure to the .MNU file and is automatically created and dynamically updated by AutoCAD when you add new toolbars. The .MNC file compiles when you reload AutoCAD or dynamically update the menu. The .MNR file is automatically created when the .MNS is completed and when buttons on the Toolbars are created, changed or added. The menu resource file .MNR is used for storing bitmaps (*.BMP) for the icons and is a binary file.

When you add toolbar information to the menu, the *.MNS file is the file that is updated. The toolbars are denoted by ***TOOLBARS major section. If you delete the *.MNS file, you will lose the newly created toolbars, because AutoCAD creates a new *.MNS file based on the *.MNU file. If you want to add the toolbars to your *.MNU file, copy the ***TOOLBARS section from your *.MNS file and paste in into your *.MNU file. If you delete your *.MNS file, AutoCAD rebuilds based on the information found in the *.MNU file. AutoCAD has another file that is constantly updated called the ACAD.INI file. Windows applications contain many *.INI files. This is where the initialization and configuration is kept for Windows applications. When you move toolbars and dock menus, the information is read to the ACAD.INI file so when you launch AutoCAD, the menus are located in their new positions. Another new feature in AutoCAD for Windows with respect to flyout menus is that over a period of time, AutoCAD will figure which menu items you use most often, and the items are placed at the top level of the menu.

Menu File Structure

Menus are divided into sections relating to specific menu areas. Menu sections can contain submenus that you can reference and display as needed. The command strings and macro syntax that define the result of a menu selection are called menu macros. The Windows NOTEPAD editor program can only open file size less than 64K in memory. To view the contents of the ACAD.MNU file use the Windows WRITE program which is located in the Accessories group where NOTEPAD is also located. Prior to opening the ACAD.MNU file, copy the file and save it as XACAD.MNU, so if something should happen, you can restore the original. When using Windows WRITE program you will be prompted for conversion of the text. Select the "No Conversion" button. It is important that files remain a text file without any formatting codes.

Following are the major sections in menu files for DOS and Windows versions. (Major sections are denoted by ***):

***BUTTONSn   Pointing device button menu where n is a number from 1 to 4

    ***BUTTONS1 is the normal menu used by a mouse or tablet cursor (puck).

    ***BUTTONS2 holding down `Shift` and pressing the right mouse button or on a three button mouse pressing the middle button activates the menu.

    ***BUTTONS3 holding down `Ctrl` and pressing the right mouse button activates the menu.

    ***BUTTONS4 holding down a combination of `Shift`+`Ctrl` and pressing the right mouse button activates the menu.

***AUXn   Auxiliary device button where n is a number from 1 to 4

***POPn Pull-Down and Cursor menus where n is a number from 0 to 16 (note 0 is used only for cursor menus)

    ***POP0 is the cursor menu which follows the cross-hairs. Pressing `Shift` and left mouse button activates this menu or pressing button #3 on a digitizing puck.

    ***POP1 thru ***POP16 are the pull-down menus. AutoCAD regular menu file does not use all the available pull-down menus.

***SCREEN Screen menu area which slowly and surely is beginning to disappear from AutoCAD for Windows. It may not be supported in future versions.

***IMAGE Image menu tile areas (formerly called ***ICON and will not be supported in the next release of AutoCAD program)

***TABLETn Tablet menu area where n is a number from 1 to 4

    ***TABLET1 thru ***TABLET4 are for the four menu areas of a digitizing tablet.

You can use the find feature of Windows Write to locate the major sections.

Menu system does not have to use all of the above major menu sections. AutoCAD for Windows has additional major sections explained later in the chapter.

Following is the menu code taken from the ACAD.MNU file:

```
***POP1
ID_File      [&File]
ID_New       [&New...\tCtrl+N]^C^C_new
ID_Open      [&Open...\tCtrl+O]^C^C_open
ID_Save      [&Save\tCtrl+S]^C^C_qsave
ID_Saveas    [Save &As...]^C^C_saveas
             [--]
ID_Print     [&Print...\tCtrl+P]^C^C_plot
             [--]
ID_Import    [&Import...]^C^C_import
ID_Export    [&Export...]^C^C_export
ID_Ioopts    [->Op&tions]
ID_Wmfopt     [WMF Op&tions...]^C^C_wmfopts
ID_Psqual     [PostScript &Quality]'_psquality
ID_Psdisp     [PostScript &Display]'_psdrag
              [--]
ID_Psprol     [<-&PostScript Prolog]'_psprolog
              [--]
ID_Mngt       [->&Management]
```

```
ID_Unlock     [&Unlock File...]^C^C_files
ID_Audit      [&Audit]^C^C_audit
ID_Recov      [<-&Recover...]^C^C_recover
              [--]
ID_MRU        [Drawing History]
              [--]
ID_Exit       [E&xit]^C^C_quit
```

POP1 is the major section, which is the <u>F</u>ile or first menu on the menu bar of AutoCAD for Windows. All the words that begin with ID_ are menu tag names. These are specific to AutoCAD for Windows and are discussed later. Labels are enclosed in square brackets []. The ampersand (&) is how you underscore the following letter which allows menu picks with the ALT + "letter" combination, which is common to all Windows programs. The label (or letters between the brackets) is what appears in the pull-down menu. The first label in the menu is what appears on the menu bar as "<u>F</u>ile". All others appear on the menu itself. This is only for POP menus from 1 to 16 and IMAGE menus. The text following the closing bracket is the command macro that AutoCAD will execute.

Looking at this syntax:

```
[&Open...\tCtrl+O]^C^C_open
```

The ^C^C is the cancel command which is followed by the open command. The symbol ^ before the C is a caret which is "Shift + 6" on your keyboard, this combination of characters executes the "ESC" sequence to cancel any previous command. Note that there are two of them. This is because some AutoCAD commands require the user to press Esc twice before canceling a command. After the cancellation, the OPEN command will execute. This is an example of a simple macro.

Menu Macro Syntax

Following is a partial list of the codes you will encounter in menu macros:

Syntax	Description
***	Denotes major sections of the menu
**	Denotes sub-sections located between major sections
[ ]	Menu label
;	Semicolon, equivalent to pressing Enter on the keyboard
space	A space character, equivalent to pressing Enter on the keyboard
\	Pause for user input
'	Issue a command transparently while in another command.
*	Repeat a command until user cancels
+	Allows the long macros to be continued on the next line.

The following example macro will create a layer called "EL_OFFEQ" (Electrical Office Equipment), assign color "RED" and make it the current layer:

```
[EL_OFFEQ]^C^CLAYER;M;EL-EQUIP;C;RED;;;
```

This is the equivalent of typing the LAYER command, selecting the Make option, typing "EL-OFFEQ" as the desired layer name, then selecting the Color option to assign Red color and finally pressing [Enter] three times to exit the command. Selecting this macro will execute all of this in one operation. Use the Make option of the LAYER command in case the layer does not yet exist. If the layer does exist it will become the current layer. Note that there is no space after the ^C^C.

Example of Creating a menu file

Let's go through sequence of steps in creating a menu file incorporating all the facets of menu sections. In order to create the menu file, first create the blocks with attributes shown in Figure 17–1 and save the drawing in your current working directory.

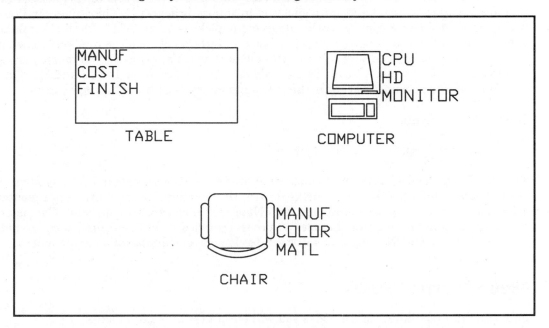

Figure 17-1 Drawing showing the three blocks required to complete the menu exercise

Figure 17–1 shows three blocks: a computer, a table and a chair. Create the objects on LAYER 0 and the attribute definitions on LAYER ATTRIB. Make layer 0 "white" and layer ATTRIB "yellow". Define the attributes as visible and verify. Following is the list of attribute tags with the corresponding block name:

BLOCK NAME	ATTRIBUTE TAG
COMPUTER	CPU
	HD
	MONITOR
TABLE	MANUF
	COST
	FINISH
CHAIR	MANUF
	COLOR
	MATL

Save the blocks as separate drawing files COMP.DWG, CHAIR.DWG and TABLE1.DWG by using the WBLOCK command.

Create a menu system file called TEST.MNU that will insert various items of furniture into a drawing using either a standard set of values or a custom set of values. The purpose of the menu system is to insert the blocks with a single pick from a menu which will automatically create the standard layer for insertion of the block, allow for custom values (if custom option is selected), and set layer 0 as the current layer.

Invoke the AutoCAD program from the Windows file manager. Begin a new drawing and launch Windows NOTEPAD editor from Accessories group. Type the following code and save the file as TEST.MNU in your current working directory.

```
***POP1
**Furniture
[&Furniture]
[->&Standard Furniture]
 [&Computer]^C^C^CATTREQ;0;LAYER;M;EL_OFFEQ;COLOR;1;;;+
INSERT;COMP;\;;\ATTREQ;1;LAYER;SET;0;;
 [&Table]^C^C^CATTREQ;0;LAYER;M;FR_OFF;COLOR;3;;;+
INSERT;TABLE1;\;;\ATTREQ;1;LAYER;SET;0;;
 [<-C&hair]^C^C^CATTREQ;0;LAYER;M;FR_OFF;COLOR;3;;;+
INSERT;CHAIR;\;;\ATTREQ;1;LAYER;SET;0;;
[->Custo&m Furniture]
 [Com&uter]^C^C^CATTDIA;0;LAYER;M;EL_OFFEQ;COLOR;1;;;+
INSERT;COMP;\;;\\\\LAYER;S;0;;ATTDIA;1
 [Tab&le]^C^C^CATTDIA;0;LAYER;M;FR_OFF;COLOR;3;;;+
INSERT;TABLE1;\;;\\\\LAYER;S;0;;ATTDIA;1
 [<-Chai&r]^C^C^CATTDIA;0;LAYER;M;FR_OFF;COLOR;3;;;+
INSERT;CHAIR;\;;\\\\LAYER;S;0;;ATTDIA;1
[--]
[Layer EL_OFFEQ]^C^C^CLAYER;M;EL_OFFEQ;COLOR;1;;;
[Layer FR_OFF]^C^C^CLAYER;M;FR_OFF;COLOR;3;;;
[--]
[Layer 0]^C^C^CLAYER;SET;0;;
```

Get back to the AutoCAD program and load the TEST.MNU menu file by typing MENU at the "Command:" prompt and press Enter or spacebar. The Select Menu File dialog box appears as shown in Figure 17-2.

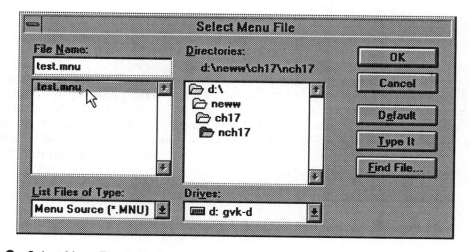

Figure 17-2   Select Menu File dialog box

Select TEST.MNU file from the appropriate drive and directory and click the OK button. TEST.MNU will replace ACAD.MNU. The right mouse button (or [Enter]) on your tablet puck/mouse will not respond to any action because in the TEST.MNU file ***BUTTONS1 major section is not defined. Only pull-down menu Furniture is displayed, as shown in Figure 17–3.

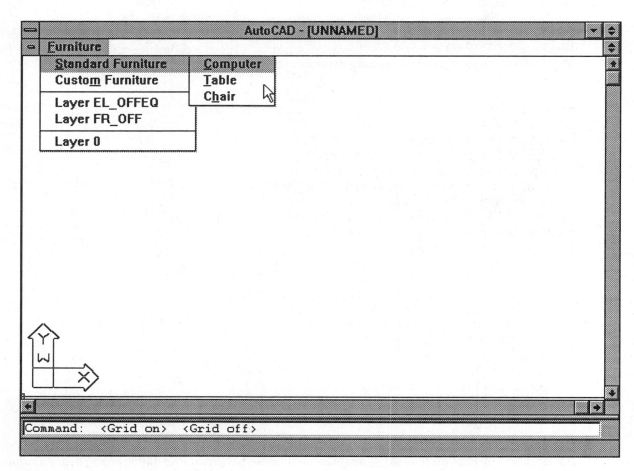

Figure 17–3 Pull-down menu Furniture

To test the menu, select the Computer option from the Standard Furniture cascading menu. AutoCAD prompts for an insertion point and rotation angle. From the Custom Furniture cascading menu, select the Computer option. AutoCAD prompts for the insertion point, rotation angle, and in addition, prompts for 3 attribute values. If you come across an error message, go back to TEST.MNU file and check the syntax and make the necessary changes. Reload the TEST.MNU file and invoke the commands again and make sure it is working properly. Let's examine some of the unique features line-by-line of the TEST.MNU.

***POP1

Indicates that this is a pull-down menu located at position #1.

```
[&Furniture]
```

This is the title that will appear on the menu bar. The ampersand before F will underline the letter "F", allowing the menu to be selected using the "ALT+F" key combination.

```
[->&Standard Furniture]
```

This is the beginning of the cascading menu as noted by "->". The letter "S" will be underscored and "Standard Furniture" will appear as the first item in the "Furniture" pull-down menu.

```
[&Computer]^C^C^CATTREQ;0;LAYER;M;EL_OFFEQ;COLOR;1;;;+
INSERT;COMP;\;;\ATTREQ;1;LAYER;SET;0;;
```

This is the first item available in the cascaded menu. The ^C 's will cancel any previous command. It is advisable to use three ^C combinations because some commands require more that two exits to terminate the command. Following the ^C is ATTREQ, a setvar variable whose function is to control attribute requests. If it has a value of 0, the block will be inserted without prompting for attributes which, in this case, is what we want using standard values. Note the use of the semicolon which is equivalent to pressing [Enter]. Next, the LAYER command is invoked and creates a layer "EL_OFFEQ" and sets the color to "RED" (1 is RED) and followed by three returns to terminate the layer command. The use of the "+" symbol at the end of the line is to allow the code to continue on the next line. There are no spaces between the final return ";" and the "+". The macro continues by invoking the INSERT command and inserts a block called COMP. The first "\" backslash character after the block name is to pause, which allows the user to pick an insertion point. The two semicolons (;;) that follow the backslash character is to accept the default scale factors. The next backslash character is for the user to pick a rotation angle. The setvar variable ATTREQ is reset back to the default value of 1. The final command is to restore layer 0 as the current layer.

```
[->Custo&m Furniture]
[Com&puter]^C^C^CATTDIA;0;LAYER;M;EL_OFFEQ;COLOR;1;;;+
INSERT;COMP;\;;\\\\LAYER;S;0;;ATTDIA;1
```

The above code is for a custom Computer option from the Custom Furniture cascading menu. In the Custom menu, the intent is to allow the operator to insert a block and at the same time allow the user to input non standard values for the attributes of the block. ATTDIA (Attribute Dialog Box), which is a setvar variable, is set to 0. This will disable the Attribute Dialog Box from popping up on the screen. Instead, the user can input attribute values from the "Command:" prompt. The layer command creates "EL_OFFEQ" layer whose color is set to "RED". The "+" is used to allow the continuation of the command on the next line. The INSERT command is invoked and the COMP block is inserted pausing for the user to pick an insertion point. The macro is followed by two semicolons ";;", which accepts the default scale factor. The following four "\\\\" backslash characters is to pause for the operator to pick the rotation angle of the block and input the three attribute values for the block. The final command is to restore layer 0 as the current layer.

NOTE: It is considered good programming practice to reset the setvar variables to its default values.

```
[Layer EL_OFFEQ]^C^C^CLAYER;M;EL_OFFEQ;COLOR;1;;;
[Layer FR_OFF]^C^C^CLAYER;M;FR_OFF;COLOR;3;;;
[--]
[Layer 0]^C^C^CLAYER;SET;0;;
```

The above macros creates new layers if they do not already exist and assigns the appropriate colors. The [--] code draws a line (separator) on the pull-down menu to visually group similar elements together.

Menugroups and Partial Menu Loading

One of the problems with the TEST.MNU file menu is that in order to use it, you have to replace the AutoCAD default menu (ACAD.MNU) and that TEST.MNU is incomplete, containing only one major section. One method around this problem is to rename the major section in TEST.MNU from ***POP1 to ***POP11 and append this menu to AutoCAD's default ACAD.MNU file. Then you can use the all the avilable standard menu commands in addition to using the custom menu. The ACAD.MNU file that comes standard with AutoCAD uses ***POP1 to ***POP10. This has been the traditional approach, which causes rather large menu files just to use the additional functionality. If AutoCAD changes the default menu file, the user will sometimes be forced to make necessary changes to additional functionality to accommodate ACAD.MNU file changes. Windows NOTEPAD can only edit a file less the 64K in size. You would have to use some other editor to append the ***POP11 to the copy of the standard AutoCAD menu. But, AutoCAD Release 13 for Windows provides the ability of partial loading of menus so you can mix and match the functionality of various menus. Changes in one menu will not affect the other menu. AutoCAD achieves this new functionality with addition of a new major section group called ***MENUGROUP. Each menu file can only have one major section called MENUGROUP.

The ***MENUGROUP= major section is how AutoCAD tracks which menus are loaded and referenced. A MENUGROUP string definition can be up to 32 alphanumeric characters (spaces and punctuation marks are not allowed). The ***MENUGROUP= label must proceed all menu definitions that use the name-tag mechanism, which will be covered later. This only applies to AutoCAD Release 13 for Windows and it is not supported by any other platform. Open the TEST.MNU in the NOTEPAD editor and make the following changes and save the file as TEST.MNU to demonstrate partial menu loading.

```
//This is a test menu file and it demonstrates the basic new
//functionality of the new menu name tag syntax.

***MENUGROUP=test
***POP1
**Furniture
ID_Furn [&Furniture]
ID_Furns [->&Standard Furniture]
ID_Comps    [&Computer]^C^C^CATTREQ;0;LAYER;M;EL_OFFEQ;COLOR;1;;;+
INSERT;COMP;\;;\ATTREQ;1;LAYER;SET;0;;
ID_Tables   [&Table]^C^C^CATTREQ;0;LAYER;M;FR_OFF;COLOR;3;;;+
INSERT;TABLE1;\;;\ATTREQ;1;LAYER;SET;0;;
ID_Chairs   [<-C&hair]^C^C^CATTREQ;0;LAYER;M;FR_OFF;COLOR;3;;;+
INSERT;CHAIR;\;;\ATTREQ;1;LAYER;SET;0;;
ID_Furnc [->Custo&m Furniture]
ID_Compc    [Com&uter]^C^C^CATTDIA;0;LAYER;M;EL_OFFEQ;COLOR;1;;;+
INSERT;COMP;\;;\\\\\LAYER;S;0;;ATTDIA;1
```

```
ID_Tablec    [Tab&le]^C^C^CATTDIA;0;LAYER;M;FR_OFF;COLOR;3;;;+
INSERT;TABLE1;\;;\\\\LAYER;S;0;;ATTDIA;1
ID_Chairc    [<-Chai&r]^C^C^CATTDIA;0;LAYER;M;FR_OFF;COLOR;3;;;+
INSERT;CHAIR;\;;\\\\LAYER;S;0;;ATTDIA;1
[--]
[Layer EL_OFFEQ]^C^C^CLAYER;M;EL_OFFEQ;COLOR;1;;;
[Layer FR_OFF]^C^C^CLAYER;M;FR_OFF;COLOR;3;;;
[--]
ID_Lyr0 [Layer 0]^C^C^CLAYER;SET;0;;
```

The text that follows the \\ is considered comment lines by AutoCAD program and is ignored in menu file compilation.

The name tags before the labels in the menu begin with "ID_". This can be any string; however, AutoCAD recommends using "ID_" as part of the string. The other requirement is that name tags be unique. Detailed explanation on how name tags are used is provided later in the chapter. To partial load the menus, invoke Customize Menus... from the pull-down menu Tools. AutoCAD displays the Menu Customization dialog box, as shown in Figure 17–4.

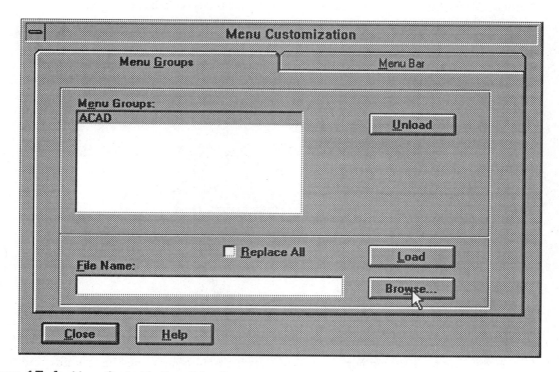

Figure 17–4 Menu Customization dialog box

Select the Browse... button and AutoCAD displays the Select Menu file dialog box. Select the TEST.MNU file from the appropriate drive and directory and click the OK button to close the dialog box. AutoCAD displays the name of the menu file selected in the **File Name:** edit box. Select the Load button. TEST.MNU will be added to the Menu Groups list box. The functionality of the TEST.MNU menu is added to the AutoCAD menu. If the TEST.MNU had Toolbars, then they would have appeared on the screen. To display the TEST.MNU as part of the AutoCAD's menu bar, first select the TEST.MNU from the Menu Groups list box. In turn, select the Menu Bar page, as shown in Figure 17–5. AutoCAD displays the Menu Bar page, as shown in Figure 17–6.

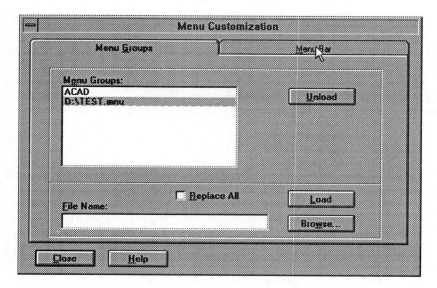

Figure 17–5 Select the Menu Bar page from the Menu Customization dialog box

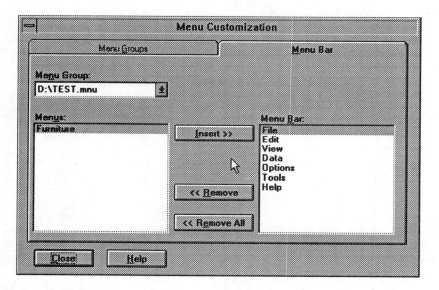

Figure 17–6 Menu Bar page dialog box

The Menu Bar page dialog box shows the Furniture item menu on the left side and the AutoCAD menu bar on the right side. Select Furniture on the left side and Help on the right side and then click the Insert>> button. AutoCAD inserts the Furniture item before the Help item on the right side of the dialog box. Click the Close button to accept the configuration. AutoCAD adds the Furniture menu item to the standard AutoCAD menu bar between the Tools and Help menus, complete with its own functionality, as shown in Figure 17–7.

Partial Menu loading gives you the ability to blend menus together and achieve the functionality as if the menu system were one. Test the menu items from the AutoCAD menu and from the Furniture menu. The system works as if dealing with one menu. To unload the TEST.MNU menugroup, open the Menu Customization dialog box, select the "test" menu group from the Menu Group list box, and then click the Unload button.

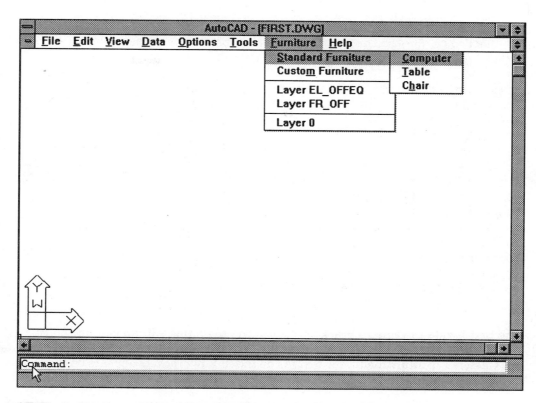

Figure 17–7 Furniture menu item as part of the AutoCAD standard menu

Helpstrings

In the menu file, you can also include help strings that will be displayed in the status bar whenever a command is selected from the pull-down menu. Open the TEST.MNU in the NOTEPAD editor and add the ***HELPSTRINGS section as shown below. Save the file as TEST.MNU to demonstrate the display of help strings.

```
//This is a test menu file it demonstrates the basic new
//functionality of the new menu name tag syntax.

***MENUGROUP=test
***POP1
**Furniture
ID_Furn [&Furniture]
ID_Furns [->&Standard Furniture]
ID_Comps    [&Computer]^C^C^CATTREQ;0;LAYER;M;EL_OFFEQ;COLOR;1;;;+
INSERT;COMP;\;;\ATTREQ;1;LAYER;SET;0;;
ID_Tables   [&Table]^C^C^CATTREQ;0;LAYER;M;FR_OFF;COLOR;3;;;+
INSERT;TABLE1;\;;\ATTREQ;1;LAYER;SET;0;;
ID_Chairs   [<-C&hair]^C^C^CATTREQ;0;LAYER;M;FR_OFF;COLOR;3;;;+
INSERT;CHAIR;\;;\ATTREQ;1;LAYER;SET;0;;
ID_Furnc [->Custo&m Furniture]
ID_Compc    [Com&uter]^C^C^CATTDIA;0;LAYER;M;EL_OFFEQ;COLOR;1;;;+
INSERT;COMP;\;;\\\\LAYER;S;0;;ATTDIA;1
ID_Tablec   [Tab&le]^C^C^CATTDIA;0;LAYER;M;FR_OFF;COLOR;3;;;+
```

```
INSERT;TABLE1;\;;\\\\LAYER;S;0;;ATTDIA;1
ID_Chairc   [<-Chai&r]^C^C^CATTDIA;0;LAYER;M;FR_OFF;COLOR;3;;;+
INSERT;CHAIR;\;;\\\\LAYER;S;0;;ATTDIA;1
[--]
[Layer EL_OFFEQ]^C^C^CLAYER;M;EL_OFFEQ;COLOR;1;;;
[Layer FR_OFF]^C^C^CLAYER;M;FR_OFF;COLOR;3;;;
[--]
ID_Lyr0 [Layer 0]^C^C^CLAYER;SET;0;;


***HELPSTRINGS
ID_Furn [Office Furniture]
ID_Furns [Standard Office Furniture]
ID_Comps [Standard Computer]
ID_Tables [Standard Table]
ID_Chairs [Standard Chair]
ID_Furnc [Custom Office Furniture]
ID_Compc [Custom Computer]
ID_Tablec [Custom Table]
ID_Chairc [Custom Chair]
```

The text inside the square brackets next to the tag name will appear on the Status bar when the command is invoked from the pull-down menu bar. For example, by selecting Computer option from the Custom Furniture menu, the text inside the square brackets appears on the status bar, as shown in Figure 17–8.

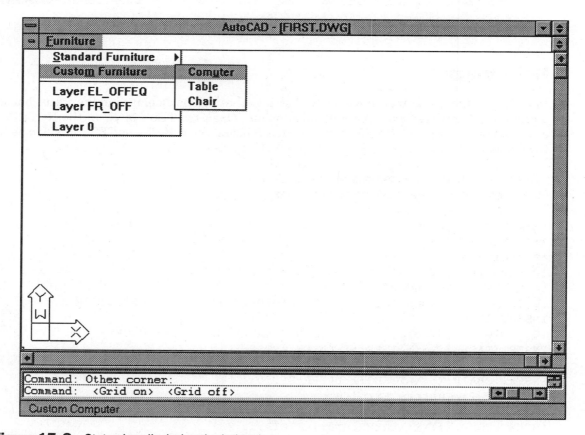

Figure 17–8 Status bar displaying the helpstring

To load the menu with changes, select the Customize Menu... from the pull-down menu Tools. Unload the TEST.MNU file if it is already loaded and then reload the updated file with changes. Select the Browse... button and AutoCAD displays the Select Menu file dialog box. Select the TEST.MNU file from the appropriate directory and click the OK button to close the dialog box. AutoCAD displays the name of the menu file selected in the **File Name:** edit box. Select the Load button. TEST.MNU will be added to the Menu Groups list box. The functionality of the TEST.MNU menu is added to the AutoCAD menu.

To display the TEST.MNU as part of the AutoCAD's menu bar, first select the TEST.MNU from the Menu Groups list box. Then select the Menu Bar page. The Menu Bar page dialog box shows Furniture menu on the left side and AutoCAD menu bar on the right side. Select Furniture item on the left side and Help on the right side and then click the Insert>> button. AutoCAD inserts the Furniture item before the Help item on the right side of the dialog box. Click the Close button to accept the configuration. AutoCAD adds the Furniture menu item to the standard AutoCAD menu bar between the Tools and Help menus, complete with its own functionality. Test the Furniture pull-down menu to see whether the help string appears on the status bar.

Creating and Modifying Toolbars

The easiest way is to create toolbars while you are working in AutoCAD program is to let AutoCAD add the code automatically to the *.MNS file. If you want to add this information to the *.MNU file, copy and paste this information into the *.MNU file, and then delete the *.MNS file. AutoCAD will rebuild the *.MNS file based on the information found in the *.MNU file.

In this section, you will create three new toolbars, as shown in Figure 17–9, as part of the TEST.MNU file: one for custom and standard computers, one for custom and standard tables and finally one for custom and standard chairs. Make sure that the TEST menu file is still partially loaded into the AutoCAD menu.

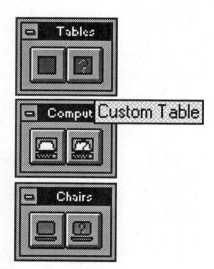

Figure 17–9 Toolbars for custom menu

To create a new toolbar, select Customize Toolbars... from pull-down menu Tools. AutoCAD displays the Toolbars dialog box, as shown in Figure 17–10.

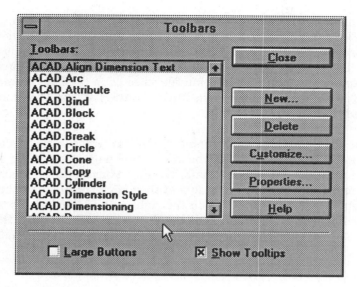

Figure 17–10   Toolbars dialog box

From the Toolbars dialog box, select the <u>N</u>ew... button. AutoCAD displays the New Toolbar dialog box, as shown in Figure 17–11.

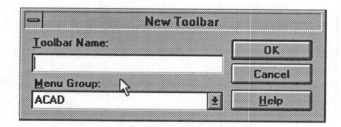

Figure 17–11   New Toolbar dialog box

From the <u>M</u>enu Group: drop down list box, select the test group. In the <u>T</u>oolbar Name: edit box, type Chairs and select the OK button. AutoCAD displays the new toolbar Chairs, as shown in Figure 17–12. If you cannot find the newly created toolbar on the screen, you may have to move the Toolbars dialog box out of the way to find it.

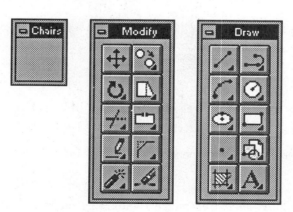

Figure 17–12   Chairs toolbar

To add buttons to the empty Chairs toolbar, click the Customize... button in the Toolbar dialog box. The Customize Toolbars dialog box appears, as shown in Figure 17–13.

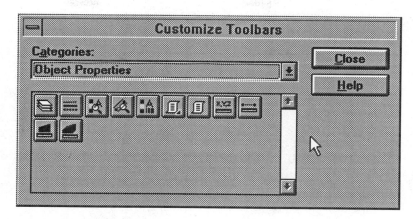

Figure 17–13 Customize Toolbars dialog box

AutoCAD lists various types of button groups in the **Categories:** drop down list box. Select any button from the button groups and, while holding down your left mouse button, drag the outline of the button to the empty Chairs toolbar and release the mouse button. A copy of this button together with its associated code is attached to the toolbar.

Place the cursor on the button located in the Chairs toolbar, and click the right button on your pointing device. AutoCAD displays the Button Properties dialog box, as shown in the Figure 17–14.

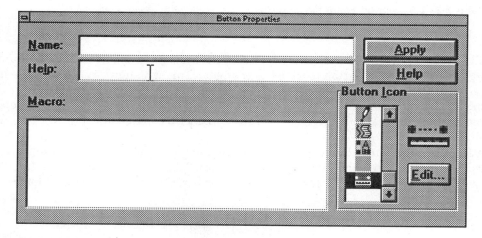

Figure 17–14 Button Properties dialog box

Type Custom Chair in the **Name:** edit box. This is the tooltip that will be displayed when the mouse pointer passes over the button. In the **Help:** edit box, type "Custom Office Furniture". This will be the message that is displayed on the Status bar when the mouse pointer passes over the button. In the Macro: edit section, delete the existing code and replace it with the following code taken from TEST.MNU file created earlier for Custom Chair:

```
^C^C^CATTDIA;0;LAYER;M;FR_OFF;COLOR;3;;;INSERT;CHAIR;\;;\\\\LAYER;S;0;;ATTDIA;1
```

Do not add "+" in the macro. While this will work for the POP menus, it will not work in the Button Property dialog box. Remember that spaces and semicolons are considered returns by AutoCAD. You may now wish to edit the Button Icon by clicking the Edit... button located in Button Properties dialog box. AutoCAD displays Button Editor dialog box as shown Figure 17–15.

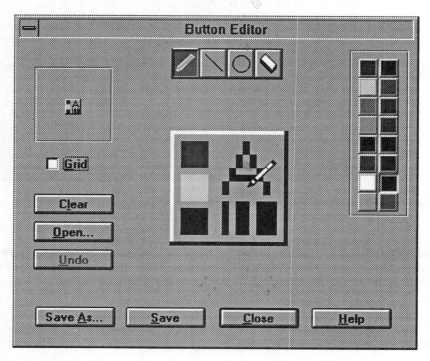

Figure 17–15   Button Editor dialog box

Make necessary changes to the icon by using the tools provided in Button Editor dialog box. Select the Save or Save As... button to save the changes. This will allow you to save the icon as a BITMAP (files with the *.BMP extension). Click the Close button to return to the Button Properties dialog box. For the changes to take effect, select the Apply button from the Button Properties dialog box. Once again AutoCAD will save the changes to the TEST.MNS file.

Repeat the procedure to add another button to the Chairs toolbar, adding a chair as standard furniture. Make sure to copy the appropriate code from the TEST.MNU file. In addition, create two more toolbars; one called Tables and the other called Computers, as shown in the Figure 17–16.

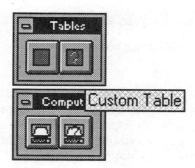

Figure 17–16   Table and Computer Toolbars

Let's look at an example of creating a flyout toolbar called Office Furniture as shown in Figure 17–17. In order to create a flyout toolbar, we need to reference existing toolbars.

Figure 17–17   Flyout toolbar

The Office Furniture toolbar will include three flyout icons, namely Computers, Chairs, and Tables. The Computers flyout will include macros for Standard Computer, and Custom Computer. Similarly, Chairs and Tables flyout will include Standard Chair and Custom Chairs and Standard Table and Custom Table, respectively.

To create a new toolbar, select Customize Toolbars... from pull-down menu Tools, AutoCAD displays the Toolbars dialog box. From the Toolbars dialog box select the New... button. AutoCAD displays New Toolbar dialog box.

From the **Menu Group:** drop down list box select the test group. In the **Toolbar Name:** edit box, type Office Furniture and select the OK button. AutoCAD displays the new toolbar Office Furniture. If you cannot find the newly created toolbar on the screen, you may have to move the Toolbar dialog box out of the way to find it. To add buttons to the empty Office Furniture toolbar, click the Customize... button in the Toolbar dialog box. AutoCAD displays the Customize Toolbars dialog box. From the dialog box Categories drop-down list box, select the Custom option. AutoCAD provides a choice of two types of buttons: a standard button and a flyout button, as indicated by the small block triangle in the lower right corner of the button, as shown in Figure 17–18.

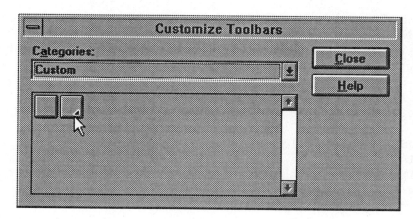

Figure 17–18   Flyout button box

Select the flyout button and drag it to the Office Furniture toolbar. Place two additional flyout buttons in the Office Furniture toolbar. Move your mouse pointer to the Office Furniture toolbar and right click on the left button. The Flyout Properties dialog box appears, as shown in Figure 17–19.

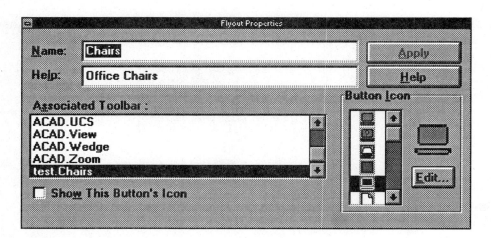

Figure 17–19 Flyout Properties dialog box

In the **Name:** edit box, type Computers. In the **Help:** edit box, type "Office Computers". From the Associated Toolbar drop-down list select test.Computer and then select the Apply button. Repeat this process for the Tables and Chairs. Make sure the check box for Show this Button's icon is turned off in the Flyout Properties dialog box. If it is set to on, then AutoCAD will not allow swapping of the icons to reflect the last toolbar icon selected. Once all the flyout buttons are defined, close the Toolbars dialog box.

Select Customize Menus... from the pull-down menu Tools, unload the TEST menugroup, and then reload the updated test menugroup. Add the Furniture menu bar item before the AutoCAD help menu from the Menu Bars page. Various toolbars will be displayed on the screen. Select the various buttons from the newly created toolbars and verify that the associated macros work.

When you created the toolbars, AutoCAD adds all descriptions of the toolbars to the TEST.MNS file under a major section called ***TOOLBARS. AutoCAD creates and maintains the *.MNS files. You can add the ***TOOLBARS section to your *.MNU template file. From the Program Manager Accessories Group start the NOTEPAD editor program and open the TEST.MNS file. From the TEST.MNS file select the ***TOOLBARS major section and paste it into the TEST.MNU file. You can have multiple copies of the NOTEPAD editor open at the same time. Following is the line-by-line listing of the code of the TEST.MNU file after button bars are added:

```
//This is a test menu file it demonstrates the basic new
//functionality of the new menu name tag syntax.

***MENUGROUP=test
***POP1
**Furniture
ID_Furn [&Furniture]
ID_Furns [->&Standard Furniture]
ID_Comps    [&Computer]^C^C^CATTREQ;0;LAYER;M;EL_OFFEQ;COLOR;1;;;+
INSERT;COMP;\;;\ATTREQ;1;LAYER;SET;0;;
ID_Tables   [&Table]^C^C^CATTREQ;0;LAYER;M;FR_OFF;COLOR;3;;;+
INSERT;TABLE1;\;;\ATTREQ;1;LAYER;SET;0;;
ID_Chairs   [<-C&hair]^C^C^CATTREQ;0;LAYER;M;FR_OFF;COLOR;3;;;+
INSERT;CHAIR;\;;\ATTREQ;1;LAYER;SET;0;;
ID_Furnc [->Custo&m Furniture]
```

```
ID_Compc      [Com&uter]^C^C^CATTDIA;0;LAYER;M;EL_OFFEQ;COLOR;1;;;+
INSERT;COMP;\;;\\\\LAYER;S;0;;ATTDIA;1
ID_Tablec     [Tab&le]^C^C^CATTDIA;0;LAYER;M;FR_OFF;COLOR;3;;;+
INSERT;TABLE1;\;;\\\\LAYER;S;0;;ATTDIA;1
ID_Chairc     [<-Chai&r]^C^C^CATTDIA;0;LAYER;M;FR_OFF;COLOR;3;;;+
INSERT;CHAIR;\;;\\\\LAYER;S;0;;ATTDIA;1
[--]
[Layer EL_OFFEQ]^C^C^CLAYER;M;EL_OFFEQ;COLOR;1;;;
[Layer FR_OFF]^C^C^CLAYER;M;FR_OFF;COLOR;3;;;
[--]
ID_Lyr0 [Layer 0]^C^C^CLAYER;SET;0;;


***HELPSTRINGS
ID_Furn [Office Furniture]
ID_Furns [Standard Office Furniture]
ID_Comps [Standard Computer]
ID_Tables [Standard Table]
ID_Chairs [Standard Chair]
ID_Furnc [Custom Office Furniture]
ID_Compc [Custom Computer]
ID_Tablec [Custom Table]
ID_Chairc [Custom Chair]


***TOOLBARS
**COMPUTER
ID_Computer      [_Toolbar("Computer", _Floating, _Show, 200, 100, 0)]
ID_Layers        [_Button("Standard Computer", ICON2580.bmp,
ICON_32_LAYERS)]^C^C^CATTREQ;0;LAYER;M;EL_OFFEQ;COLOR;1;;;INSERT;COMP;\;;\ATTREQ;1;LAYER;S
ET;0;;
ID_Layers_0      [_Button("Custom Computer", ICON7216.bmp,
ICON_32_LAYERS)]^C^C^CATTDIA;0;LAYER;M;EL_OFFEQ;COLOR;1;;;INSERT;COMP;\;;\\\\LAYER;S;0;;AT
TDIA;1


**TABLES
ID_Tables_0      [_Toolbar("Tables", _Floating, _Show, 200, 200, 0)]
ID_StandardComputer [_Button("Standard Table", ICON1629.bmp,
ICON499.bmp)]^C^C^CATTREQ;0;LAYER;M;FR_OFF;COLOR;3;;;INSERT;TABLE1;\;;\ATTREQ;1;LAYER;SET;
0;;
ID_CustomComputer [_Button("Custom Table", ICON5498.bmp,
ICON8877.bmp)]^C^C^CATTDIA;0;LAYER;M;FR_OFF;COLOR;3;;;INSERT;TABLE1;\;;\\\\LAYER;S;0;;ATTD
IA;1


**CHAIRS
ID_Chairs        [_Toolbar("Chairs", _Floating, _Show, 200, 300, 0)]
ID_StandardTable [_Button("Standard Chair", ICON2854.bmp,
ICON5060.bmp)]^C^C^CATTREQ;0;LAYER;M;FR_OFF;COLOR;3;;;INSERT;CHAIR;\;;\ATTREQ;1;LAYER;SET;
0;;
ID_CustomTable [_Button("Custom Chair", ICON665.bmp,
ICON4474.bmp)]^C^C^CATTDIA;0;LAYER;M;FR_OFF;COLOR;3;;;INSERT;CHAIR;\;;\\\\LAYER;S;0;;ATTDI
A;1


**OFFICE_FURNITURE
**TB_OFFICE_FURNITURE
```

```
                    [_Toolbar("Office Furniture", _Floating, _Show, 200, 400, 0)]
ID_                 [_Flyout("Computer", ICON8617.bmp, ICON_32_BLANK, _OtherIcon,
test.COMPUTER)]
ID__0               [_Flyout("Tables", ICON3090.bmp, ICON_32_BLANK, _OtherIcon,
test.TABLES)]
ID__1               [_Flyout("Chairs", ICON9328.bmp, ICON_32_BLANK, _OtherIcon,
test.CHAIRS)]
```

Make sure you save the TEST.MNU file. If you deleted the TEST.MNS file without copying the ***TOOLBARS section to the TEST.MNU file, you will lose the newly created toolbars. During the process of adding new toolbars, it is always recommended to copy the ***TOOLBARS sections to the *.MNU file. Remember, if there is no *.MNS file, AutoCAD creates it for you based on the *.MNU template file.

You can manually create ***TOOLBARS section of code into your TEST.MNU file, but let AutoCAD do the job and then copy it into the *.MNU template file. Let's examine some of the unique features of line-by-line code of the TEST.MNU in the ***TOOLBARS section.

***TOOLBARS
> Defines the major section for toolbars.

**COMPUTER
> Menu subsection

```
ID_Computer [_Toolbar("Computer", _Floating, _Show, 200, 100, 0)]
```

> ID_Computer
> > Tagname by which the item on the menu is referenced.

> _Toolbar
> > Identifies that the menu is dealing with a toolbar definition.

> "Computer"
> > Name that appears above the Toolbar

> _Floating
> > Indicates that the Toolbar is floating and not docked. Possible values are _Top, _Bottom, _Left,_Right or _Floating. The underscore character in front of the keywords is not required, however is used for the International versions of AutoCAD. The keywords are not case sensitive.

> _Show
> > Visibility keyword, available options include _Show or _Hide

> 200, 100, 0
> > The first number is the distance in pixels from the left edge of the screen. The second number is the distance in pixels from the top edge and the final number is the number of rows in the toolbar.

```
ID_Layers    [_Button("Standard Computer",ICON2580.bmp,ICON_32_LAYERS)]macro
```

> ID_Layers
> > Tagname by which this item on the menu is referenced.

_Button
>   Identifies that the menu is dealing with a button definition.

"Standard Computer"
>   This is the tooltip text that is displayed when the mouse pointer passes over the button.

ICON2580.bmp
>   ID of the small icon (16x16) bitmap

ICON_32_LAYERS
>   ID of the large icon (32x32) bitmap

macro
>   Command sequence required to complete the macro.

Flyout section of the menu

```
**TB_OFFICE_FURNITURE
       [_Toolbar("Office Furniture", _Floating, _Show, 200, 400, 0)]
ID_    [_Flyout("Computer", ICON8617.bmp, ICON_32_BLANK, _OtherIcon,
test.COMPUTER)]
ID__0 [_Flyout("Tables", ICON3090.bmp, ICON_32_BLANK, _OtherIcon,
test.TABLES)]
ID__1 [_Flyout("Chairs", ICON9328.bmp, ICON_32_BLANK, _OtherIcon,
test.CHAIRS)]


 [_Toolbar("Office Furniture", _Floating, _Show, 200, 400, 0)]
```

The toolbar menu item is the same as the toolbar description explained above.

```
ID_    [_Flyout("Computer", ICON8617.bmp, ICON_32_BLANK, _OtherIcon,
test.COMPUTER)]
```

ID_
>   Tagname by which the item on the menu is referenced.

Flyout
>   Identifies that the menu is dealing with a flyout definition

"Computer"
>   Tooltip text that is displayed when the mouse pointer passes over the button.

ICON8617.bmp
>   ID of the small icon (16x16) bitmap

ICON_32_BLANK
>   ID of the large icon (32x32) bitmap

_OtherIcon
>   Has two possible values _OtherIcon or _OwnIcon. The OtherIcon value allows the button to switch icons and displays the last icon selected. The OwnIcon value will not permit this switching.

Accelerator Keys

AutoCAD for Windows Release 13 supports user defined accelerator keys. Add the following major section (***ACCELERATORS) to the TEST.MNU file.

```
***ACCELERATORS
ID_Comps   [SHIFT+"F1"]
ID_Tables  [SHIFT+"F2"]
ID_Chairs  [SHIFT+"F3"]
ID_Lyr0    [SHIFT+"L"]
```

The first item is the name tag followed by the accelerator key combination included in the brackets. Type the keyboard combination (for example: [Shift]+[F1]), the menu item identified by ID_Comps will be executed. The accelerator key combination will not work if the menu is partially loaded as part of the ACAD.MNU. Only when the menu is loaded in place of AutoCAD's menu will these key combinations work.

Apart from including macros, you can also include AutoLISP (refer to Chapter 18) code in the menus or have the menu macros load and run AutoLISP applications.

DIESEL

As mentioned earlier, a macro is a string of commands that AutoCAD executes when the menu item is selected. You can also add AutoLISP in a macro and call an AutoLISP routine from a macro. AutoCAD provides a macro language alternative to AutoLISP, called DIESEL. DIESEL is an acronym for Direct Interpretively Evaluated String Expression Language. The subject of DIESEL is beyond the scope of this book, but lets go through an example to see the application of DIESEL. DIESEL allows you to customize the AutoCAD status line through the use of a setvar variable MODEMACRO and it also allows modification of the appearance of pull-down menus. DIESEL, while it is a macro language and similar in style to AutoLISP, does not have the power and flexibility of AutoLISP.

The simplest use of DIESEL is through the MODEMACRO setvar variable. At the AutoCAD "Command": prompt type MODEMACRO and press [Enter] or spacebar. AutoCAD prompts:

```
New value for MODEMACRO, or . for none <"">:Captain CAD
```

Type in a text string as shown in the above example and press [Enter]. AutoCAD displays the text string in the status bar, as shown in Figure 17–20.

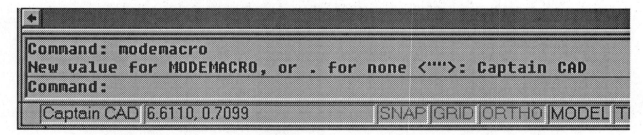

Figure 17–20   Display of the text string in the status bar

To return to the default value, type MODEMACRO at the "Command:" prompt and press [Enter] or spacebar. Type in a single period to the prompt and press [Enter] or spacebar. The status bar returns to the default settings.

In another example, a string with arguments is provided in response to the MODEMACRO prompt:

```
New value for MODEMACRO, or . for none <"">:LAYER = $(getvar,clayer)
```

AutoCAD gets the current layer name and displays it in the status bar, as shown in Figure 17–21.

DIESEL expressions can also be placed as part of the menus.

Figure 17–21   Display of the current layer name in the status bar

Tablet Menus

The previous explanations and examples of the menu customization can be applied to customizing the tablet menu area. One problem not encountered in a tablet menu is that of the display. The brackets that enclose nonactive items will not be visible except to someone who is reading the filename.MNU file from which the filename.MNX was compiled.

The main concern in customizing the tablet part of the menu is in placing the programming lines in the right order and in the right area so they will correspond to the preprinted overlay that will be configured on the tablet for use with the menu.

A menu may have up to four tablet areas. They will have the headings of ***TABLET1, ***TABLET2, ***TABLET3, and ***TABLET4. The first program line following a heading will correspond to the configured overlay's upper left column/row rectangle. Subsequent program lines will correspond the rectangle to the right in the same row as its predecessor until the end of the row is reached. Then the next program line will be on the extreme left rectangle of the next row. For example, a tablet menu area with 12 program lines might be in any one of the six following arrangements:

1	2	3	4	5	6	7	8	9	10	11	12

1	2	3	4	5	6
7	8	9	10	11	12

1	2	3	4
5	6	7	8
9	10	11	12

1	2	3
4	5	6
7	8	9
10	11	12

1	2
3	4
5	6
7	8
9	10
11	12

1
2
3
4
5
6
7
8
9
10
11
12

If there are more rectangles specified in the tablet configuration than there are program lines, the extras will be nonactive when picked. If there is an excess of program lines in the menu, they will, of course, not be accessible.

DIALOG CONTROL LANGUAGE

AutoCAD Release 12 introduced programmable dialog boxes and this feature is continued in AutoCAD Release 13. Programming dialog boxes requires a thorough knowledge of AutoLISP and/ or C/C++. The description of the Dialog Box is a text file known as a DCL (Dialog Control Language) file. The DCL file is a description of the various parts of the Dialog and elements the Dialog contains. The following is an example of a DCL file.

```
cesdoor : dialog
{
    label = "CESCO Doors";
    : row
    {
        : radio_cluster
```

```
        {
          key = "thick";
          : boxed_radio_column
          {
            label = "Thickness";
            : radio_button
            {
              key = "t1";
              label = "1\"";
              value = "1";
            }
            : radio_button
            {
              key = "t2";
              label = "2\"";
            }
            : radio_button
            {
              key = "t4";
              label = "4\"";
            }
          }//boxed radio column - Thickness
        }//radio cluster - Thick
        : radio_cluster
        {
          key = "hinge";
          : boxed_radio_column
          {
            label = "Hinge";
            spacer;
            : radio_button
            {
              key = "rt";
              label = "Right";
            }
            : radio_button
            {
              key = "lt";
              label = "Left";
              value = "1";
            }
            spacer;
          }//boxed radio column - Hinge location
        }//radio_cluster - Hinge
      }// row - top
      : row
      {
        : radio_cluster
        {
          key = "opng";
          : boxed_radio_column
          {
            label = "Open";
```

Customizing AutoCAD

```
        width = 9;
        : radio_button
        {
           key = "in";
           label = "In";
        }
        : radio_button
        {
           key = "out";
           label = "Out";
           value = "1";
        }
     }//boxed radio column - Opening
  }//radio_cluster - opng
  : radio_cluster
  {
     key = "hand";
     : boxed_radio_column
     {
        label = "Handles";
        : radio_button
        {
           key = "hndl2";
           label = "2";
           value = "1";
        }
        : radio_button
        {
           key = "hndl3";
           label = "3";
        }
     }//boxed radio column - Number of handles
  }//radio_cluster - hand
}//row - 2nd row
spacer_1;
ok_cancel;
}
```

When AutoCAD is loaded into memory, it automatically loads two files; ACAD.DCL and BASE.DCL. These files contain various attributes upon which you can build your dialogs. Each element (:radio_button for example) contains a key—key = "hndl3". These keys are the name to which AutoLISP and C/C++ refer to retrieve values from and act upon. Figure 17–22 shows a sample dialog box.

Selecting the OK button causes AutoLISP or C/C++ to read the various keys to determine which values the user selected and pass the results to the calling program. When writing programs that utilize dialog boxes, a certain portion of the code is dedicated to reading and responding to the dialog box (apart from the DCL file describing the dialog box itself). This provides the user with a more detailed view of all the inputs and can be used to limit the user inputs to the program. Dialog boxes can utilize radio buttons, toggle boxes, horizontal and vertical sliders, list boxes, edit boxes, buttons, image tiles, and more to enhance the front end to any program requiring user input.

A complete discussion of programming dialog boxes is beyond the scope of this book. Refer to AutoCAD's Customization Guide for more details.

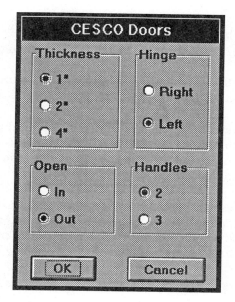

Figure 17–22 Sample dialog box

EXERCISES

1. What extension must a file have when writing a custom menu?

2. How many menus may be active simultaneously?

3. What AutoCAD command sequence will activate a menu written as a file named XYZ.MNU?

4. Under the ***BUTTONS menu, which program line corresponds to the second button on the mouse/puck?

5. Placing three blank spaces in a menu program line is equivalent to what action from the keyboard?

6. What is the purpose of the caret " ^ " in a menu program line?

7. What is the purpose of the "^C" at the beginning of a menu program line?

8. Create a menu file to include a program line that will draw a rectangle whose opposite corners are points whose coordinates are 1,1 and 5,2.

9. Create a menu file to include a program line that will draw a circle whose diameter is 2 units and center is a point whose coordinates are 3,3.

10. Create a menu file to include a program line that will array the previous circle in a polar array every 30 degrees with the center of the array at a point whose coordinates are 4,3.

11. Create a menu file to include a program line that will permit a line-arc-line continuation starting at point 1,1 with user picks for second, third, and fourth points.

12. Write lines that set UNITS as follows:

    a. Decimal to four-place display.

    b. Architectural to 1/8"-display.

    c. Each of the above to include a mechanism to return to the graph screen.

HATCH PATTERNS

Certain concepts about hatch patterns should be understood before learning to create one.

1. Hatch patterns are made up of lines or line segment\space combinations. There are no circles or arcs available in hatch patterns like there are in shapes and fonts (which will be covered next).

2. A hatch pattern may be one or more series of repeated parallel lines or repeating dot or line segment/space combinations. That is, each line in one so-called family is like every other line in that same family. And each line has the same offset and stagger (if a segment/space combination) relative to its adjacent sibling as every other line.

3. One hatch pattern can contain multiple families of lines. One family of lines may or may not be parallel to other families. With properly specified base points, offsets, staggers, segment/space combinations, lengths, and relative angles, you can create a hatch pattern from multiple families of segment/space combinations that will display repeated closed polygons.

4. Each family of lines is drawn with offsets and staggers based on its own specified base point and angle.

5. All families of lines in a particular hatch pattern will be located (base point), rotated, and scaled as a group. These factors (location, angle of rotation, and scale factor) are determined when the hatch pattern is loaded by the HATCH command and used to fill a closed polygon in a drawing.

6. The pattern usually can be achieved by different ways of specifying parameters.

Hatch patterns are created by including their definition in a file whose extension is .PAT. This can be done by using a line editor such as EDLIN (EDIT in DOS 6.xx) or a word processor in the nondocument (or programmer) mode which will save the text in ASCII format. Your hatch pattern definition can also be added to the ACAD.PAT file. You can also create a new file specifically for a pattern.

Each pattern definition has one header line giving the pattern name/description and a separate specification line describing each family of lines in the pattern.

The header line has the following format:

```
*pattern-name[,description]
```

The pattern name will be the name for which you will be prompted when using the HATCH command. The description is optional and is for use only by someone reading the .PAT file to be able to identify the pattern. The description has no effect nor will it be displayed while using the HATCH command. The leading asterisk denotes the beginning of a hatch pattern.

The format for a line family is as follows:

```
angle, x-origin, y-origin, delta-x, delta-y [,dash-1, dash-2...]
```

The brackets "[]" denote optional segment/space specifications used for noncontinuous line families. Note also that any text following a semicolon (;) is for comment only and will be ignored. The angle, origins, and deltas are mandatory (even if their values are zero) in all definitions.

An example of continuous lines that are rotated at 30 degrees and separated by 0.25 units is as follows (see Figure 17–23):

```
*P30, 30 degree continuous
30, 0,0, 0,.25
```

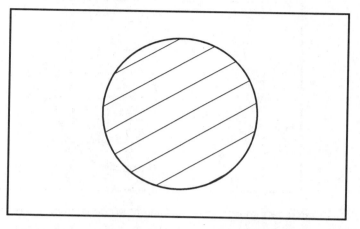

Figure 17–23 A hatch pattern with continuous lines rotated at 30 degrees and separated by 0.25 unit

The 30 specifies the angle.

The first and second zero specify the coordinates of the origin.

The third zero, though required, is meaningless for continuous lines.

The 0.25 specifies the distance between lines.

A pattern of continuous lines crossing at 60 degrees to each other could be written as follows (see Figure 17–24):

```
*PX60,x-ing @ 60
30, 0,0, 0,.25
330, 0,0, 0,.25
```

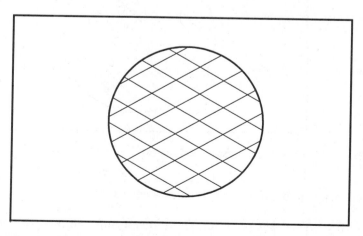

Figure 17–24 A hatch pattern with continuous lines crossing at 60 degrees to each other 0.25 unit

A pattern of lines crossing at 90 degrees, but having different offsets is as follows (see Figure 17–25):

```
*PX90, x-ing @ 90 w/ 2:1 rectangles
0, 0,0, 0,.25
90, 0,0, 0,.5
```

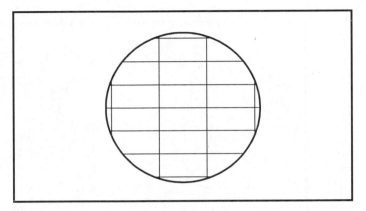

Figure 17–25 A hatch pattern with lines crossing at 90 degrees having different offsets

Note the effect of the delta-y. It is the amount of offset between lines in one family. Hatch patterns with continuous lines do not require a value (other than zero) for delta-x. Orthogonal continuous lines also do not require values for the x-origin unless used in a pattern that includes broken lines.

To illustrate the use of a value for the y-origin, two parallel families of lines can be written to define a hatch pattern for steel as follows (see Figure 17–26):

```
*steel
45, 0,0, 0,1
45, 0,.25, 0,1
```

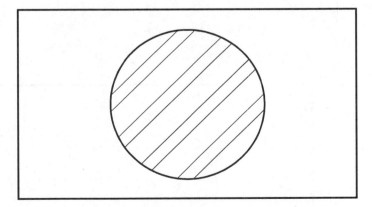

Figure 17–26 Defining a hatch pattern for steel

Three concepts are worthy of note in the above example.

1. If the families were not parallel, then specifying origins other that zero would not serve a purpose.

2. Parallel families of lines should have the same delta-y offsets. Different offsets would serve little purpose.

3. Most importantly, the delta-y is at a right angle to the angle of rotation, but the y-origin is in the y direction of the coordinate system. The steel pattern as written above would fill a polygon, as shown in Figure 17–27. Note the dimensions when used with no changes to the scale factor of 1.0 or rotation angle of zero.

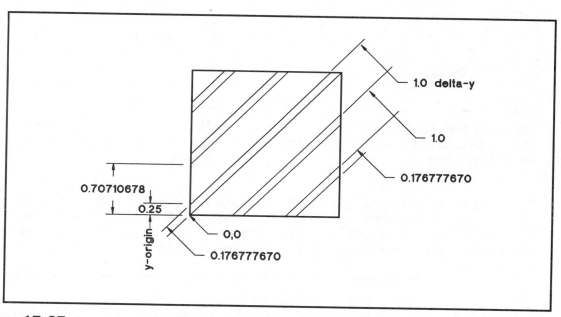

Figure 17–27 The steel hatch pattern with the delta-y at a right angle to the angle of rotation and the y-origin in the y direction of the coordinate system

Custom Hatch Patterns and Trigonometry

The dimensions in the hatch pattern resulting from a 0.25 value for the delta-y of the second line family definition may not be what you expected, as shown in Figure 17–28. If you wished to have a 0.25 separation between the two line families (see Figure 17–29), then you must either know enough trigonometry/geometry to predict accurate results or else put an additional burden on the user to reply to prompts with the correct responses to achieve those results. For example, you could write the definition as follows:

```
*steel
0, 0,0, 0,1
0, 0,.25, 0,1
```

In order to use this pattern as shown the user will have to specify a 45-degree rotation when using it. This will maintain the ratio of 1 to .25 between the offset (delta-y) and the spacing between families (y-origin). However, if you wish to avoid this inconvenience to the user, but still wish to have the families separated by .25, you can write the definition as follows:

```
*steel
45, 0,0, 0,1
45, 0,.353553391, 0,1
```

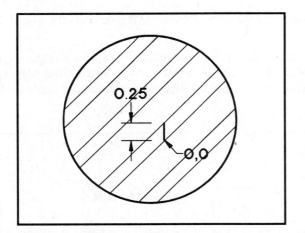

Figure 17–28 Hatch pattern dimensions resulting from a 0.25 value for the delta-y of the second line family definition

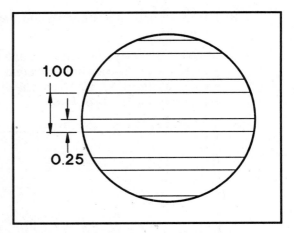

Figure 17–29 The steel hatch pattern defined with a 0.25 separation between the two line families

The value for the y-origin of .353553391 was obtained by dividing .25 by the sine (or cosine) of 45 degrees, which is .70710678. The x-origin and y-origin specify the coordinates of a point. Therefore, setting the origins of any family of continuous lines merely tells AutoCAD that the line must pass through that point. See Figure 17–30 for the trigonometry used.

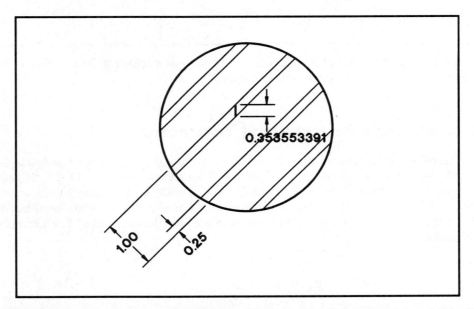

Figure 17–30 The steel hatch pattern defined with a 45 degree rotation to maintain a 1:25 offset ratio

For families of lines that have segment/space distances, the point determined by the origins can tell AutoCAD not only that the line passes through that point, but that one of the segments will begin at that point. A dashed pattern can be written as follows (see Figure 17–31):

```
*dashed
0, 0,0, 0,.25, .25,-.25
```

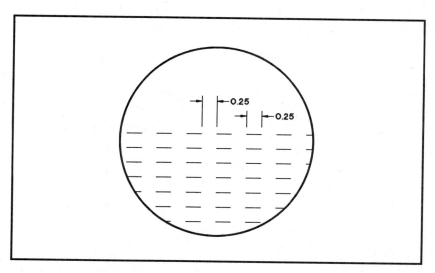

Figure 17-31   Writing a dashed pattern

Note that the value of the x-origin is zero, thus causing the dashes of one line to line up with the dashes of other lines. Staggers can be produced by giving a value to the x-origin as follows (see Figure 17-32):

```
*dashstagger
0, 0,0, .25,.25, .25,-.25
```

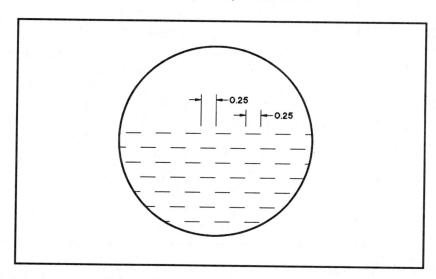

Figure 17-32   Writing a staggered dash pattern

In a manner similar to defining linetypes, you can cause lines in a family to have several lengths of segments and spaces (see Figure 17-33).

```
*simple
0, 0,0, 0,.5
90, 0,0, 0,1, .5,-.5
```

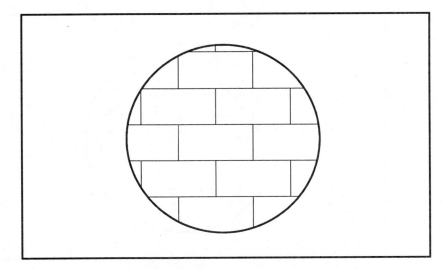

Figure 17–33 A pattern with several lengths of segments and spaces

A similar, but more complex hatch pattern, could be written as follows (see Figure 17–34):

```
* complex
45, 0,0, 0,.5
-45, 0,0, 0,1.414213562, 0,1.41421356
```

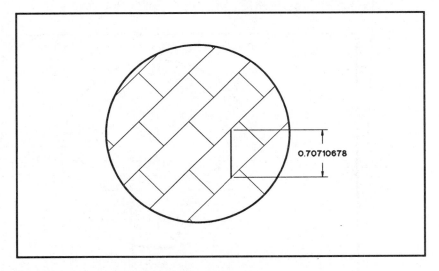

Figure 17–34 A pattern with more complex hatch patterns

Repeating Closed Polygons

Creating hatch patterns with closed polygons requires planning. For example, a pattern of 45/90/45-degree triangles, as shown in Figure 17–35, should be started by first extending the lines, as shown in Figure 17–35a. Extend the construction lines through points of the object parallel to other lines of the object. Note the grid that emerges when you use the lines and distances obtained to determine the pattern.

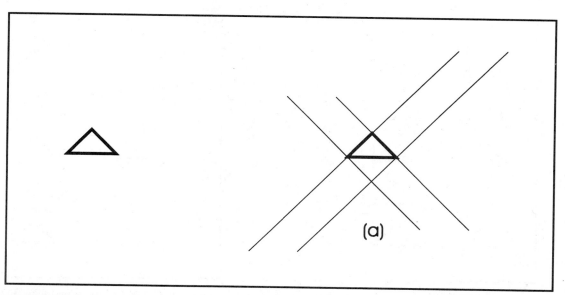

Figure 17–35 Closed polygons

It is also helpful to sketch construction lines that are perpendicular to the object lines. This will assist you in specifying segment/space values.

In the example, two of the lines are perpendicular to each other, thus making this easier. Figures 17–36 through 17–39 illustrate potential patterns of triangles. Once the pattern is selected, the grid, and some knowledge of trigonometry, will assist you in specifying all of the values in the definition for each line family.

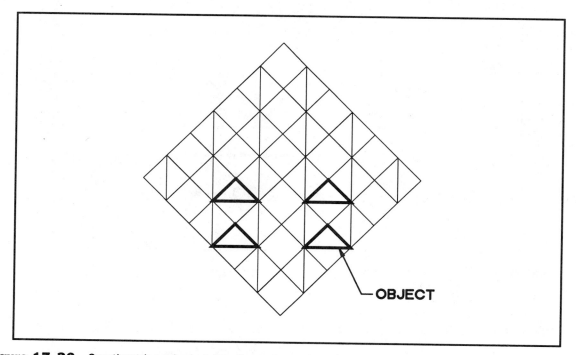

Figure 17–36 Creating triangular hatch patterns — method #1

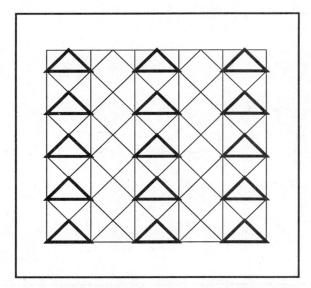

Figure 17–37 Creating triangular hatch patterns — method #2

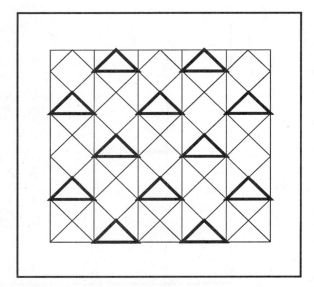

Figure 17–38 Creating triangular hatch patterns — method #3

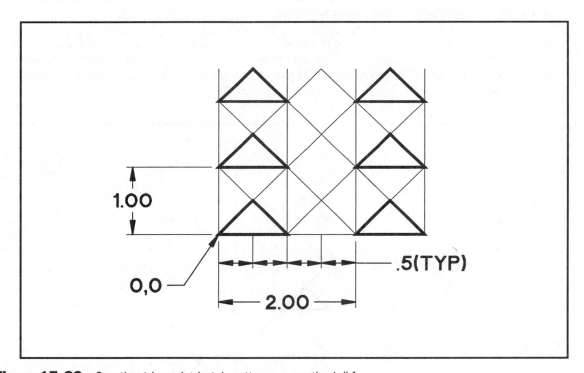

Figure 17–39 Creating triangular hatch patterns — method #4

For pattern PA the horizontal line families can be written as follows (see Figure 17–40):

```
0, 0,0, 0,1, 1,-1
```

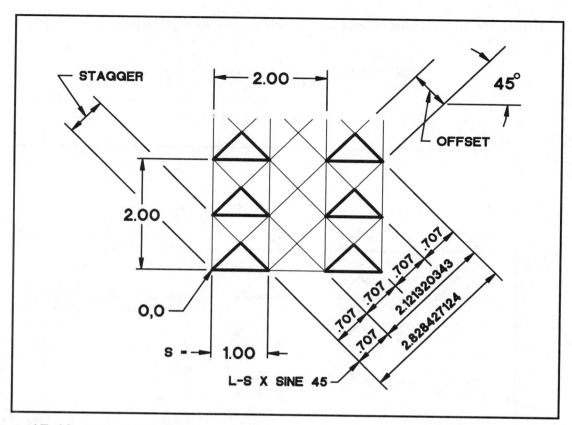

Figure 17–40 Triangular patterns

The specifications for the 45-degree family of lines can be determined by using the following trigonometry:

```
sin 45 degrees = 0.70710678
S = 1
L = S times sin 45 degrees
L = 1 times sin 45 degrees = 0.70710678
```

Note that the trigonometry function is applied to the hypotenuse of the right triangle. In the example the hypotenuse is 1 unit. A different value would simply produce a proportional result, i.e., a hypotenuse of .5 would produce an L = S times 0.70710678 = 0.353553391. The specifications for the 45-degree family of lines could be written as follows:

```
45, 0,0 0.70710678,0.70710678, 0.70710678,-2.121320343
angle,origin,offset,  stagger,            segment,      space
```

For the 135-degree family of lines, the offset, stagger, segment, and space have the same values (absolute) as the 45-degree family. Only the angle, the x-origin and the sign (+ or -) of the offset or stagger may need to be changed.

The 135-degree family of lines could be written as follows:

```
135, 1,0,  -0.70710678,-0.70710678, 0.70710678,-2.121320343
```

Putting the three families of lines together under a header could be written as follows, and as shown in Figure 17–41.

```
*PA,45/90/45 triangles stacked
0, 0,0, 0,1, 1,-1
45, 0,0 0.70710678,0.70710678, 0.70710678,-2.121320343
135, 1,0,  -0.70710678,-0.70710678, 0.70710678,-2.121320343
```

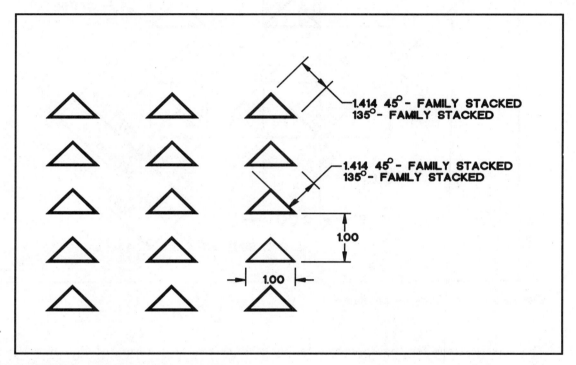

Figure 17–41 Triangular patterns families

Noting the "could be written" in the above statement tells you that there may be other ways to write the definitions. As an exercise, write the descriptions using 225 degrees instead of 45 degrees and 315 instead of 135 for the second and third families, respectively. As a hint, you determine the origin values of each family of lines from the standard coordinate system. But, to visualize the offset and stagger, orient the layout Grid so that the rotation angle coincides with the zero angle of the coordinate system. Then the signs and the values of delta-x and delta-y will be easier to establish along the standard plus for right/up and negatives for left/down directions.

Examples of two hatch patterns, PB and HONEYCOMB, follow.

The PB pattern can be written as follows, and as shown in Figure 17–42.

```
*PB, 45/90/45 triangle staggered
0, 0,0, 1,1, 1,-1
45, 0,0, 0,1.414213562, 0.70710678,0.70710678
135, 0,0, 0,1.414213562, 0.70710678,0.70710678
```

Note that this alignment simplifies the definitions of the second and third families of lines over the PA pattern.

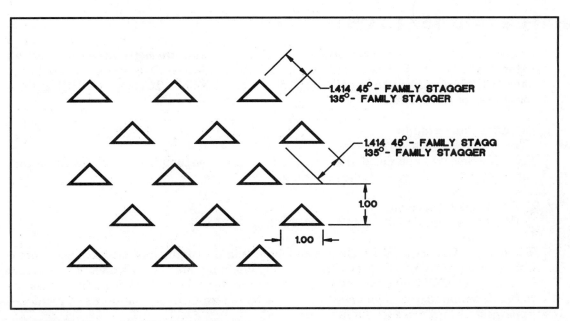

Figure 17–42   Example of the PB hatch pattern

The Honeycomb pattern can be written as follows, and as shown in Figure 17–43.

```
*HONEYCOMB
90, 0,0, 0,1, 0.577350264,-1.154700538
330, 0,0, 0,1, 0.577350264,-1.154700538
30, 0.5,-0.288675135, 0,1, 0.577350264,-1.154700538
```

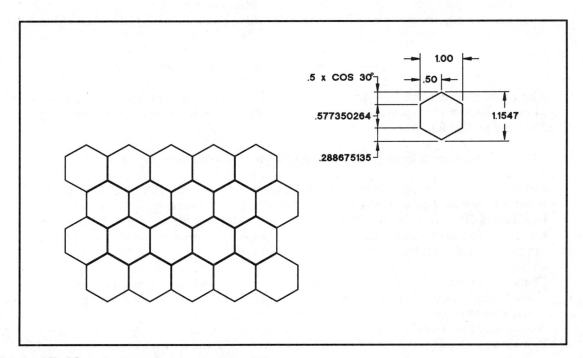

Figure 17–43   Example of the honeycomb pattern

SHAPES AND TEXT FONTS

Shapes and fonts are written in the same manner and are both stored in files with .SHP file extensions. The .SHP files must be compiled into .SHX files. This section covers how to create and save .SHP files and how to compile .SHP files into .SHX files. To compile a .SHP file into a .SHX file for shapes or fonts, enter:

Command: **compile**

From the Select Shape File dialog box, select the file to be compiled. If the file has errors they will be reported; otherwise, you will be prompted:

Compilation successful
Output file name .SHX contains nnn bytes

The main difference between shapes and fonts is in the commands used to place them in a drawing. Shapes are drawn by using the SHAPE command and fonts are drawn using commands that insert text, such as TEXT or DIM. Whether or not an object in a .SHP/.SHX file can be used with the SHAPE command or as a font character is partly determined by whether its shapename is written in uppercase or lowercase (explained herein).

Each shape or character in a font in a .SHP or .SHX file is made up of simplified objects. These objects are simplified lines, arcs, and circles. The reason they are referred to as simplified is because in specifying their directions and distances, you cannot use decimals or Architectural units. You must use only integers or integer fractions. For example, if the line distance needs to be equal to 1 divided by the square root of 2 (or .7071068), the fraction 70 divided by 99 (which equals .707070707) is as close as you can get. Rather than call the simplified lines and arcs "objects," we will refer to them as "primitives."

Individual shapes (and font characters) are written and stored in ASCII format. .SHP/.SHX files may contain up to 255 SHAPE-CHARACTERS. Each SHAPE-CHARACTER definition has a header line as follows:

*shape number, defbytes, shapename

The codes that describe the SHAPE-CHARACTER may take up one or more lines following the header. Most of the simple shapes can be written on one or two lines. The meaning of each item in the header is as follows:

The shape number may be from 1 to 255 with no duplications within one file.

Defbytes is the number of bytes used to define the individual SHAPE-CHARACTER, including the required zero that signals the end of a definition. The maximum allowable bytes in a SHAPE-CHARACTER definition is 2000. Defbytes (the bit-codes) in the definition are separated by commas. You may enclose pairs of bit-codes within parentheses for clarity of intent, but this does not affect the definition.

The shapename should be in uppercase if it is to be used by the SHAPE command. Like a block name is used in the BLOCK command, you enter the shapename when prompted to do so during the SHAPE command. If the shape is a character in a font file, you may make any or all of the shapename characters lowercase, thereby causing the name to be ignored when compiled and stored in memory. It will serve for reference only in the .SHP file for someone reading that file.

Pen Movement Distances and Directions

The specifications for pen movement distances and directions (whether the pen is up or down) for drawing the primitives that will make up a SHAPE-CHARACTER are written in bit-codes. Each bit-code is considered one defbyte. Codes 0 through 16 are not DISTANCE-DIRECTION codes, but special instructions-to-AutoCAD codes that will be explained after DISTANCE-DIRECTION codes.

DISTANCE-DIRECTION codes have three characters beginning with a zero. The second character specifies distance. More specifically, it specifies vector length, which may be affected by a scale factor. Vector length and scale factor combine to determine actual distances. The third character specifies direction. There are 16 standard directions available through use of the DISTANCE-DIRECTION bit-code (or defbyte). Vectors of 1 unit in length are shown in the 16 standard directions in Figure 17–44.

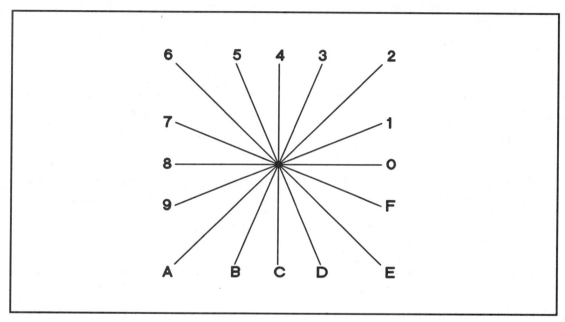

Figure 17–44   DISTANCE-DIRECTION bit-codes

Directions 0, 4, 8, and C are equivalent to the default 0, 90, 180, and 270 degrees, respectively. Directions 2, 6, A, and E are 45, 135, 225, and 315 degrees, respectively. But, the odd-numbered direction codes are NOT increments of 22.5 degrees, as you might think. They are directions that coincide with a line whose delta-x and delta-y ratio are 1 unit to 2 units. For example, the direction specified by code 1 is equivalent to drawing a line from 0,0 to 1,.5. This equates to approximately 26.56505118 degrees (or the arctangent of 0.5). The direction specified by code 3 equates to 63.434494882 degrees (or the arctangent of 2) and is the same as drawing a line from 0,0 to .5,1.

Distances specified will be measured on the nearest horizontal or vertical Axis. For example, 1 unit in the 1 direction specifies a vector that will project 1 unit on the horizontal Axis. Three units in the D direction will project 3 units on the vertical Axis (downward). So the vector specified 1 unit in the 1 direction will actually be 1.118033989 units long at an angle of 26.65606118 degrees and the vector specified 3 units in the D direction will be 3.354101967 units long at an angle of 296.5650512 degrees. See Figure 17–45 for examples of specifying direction.

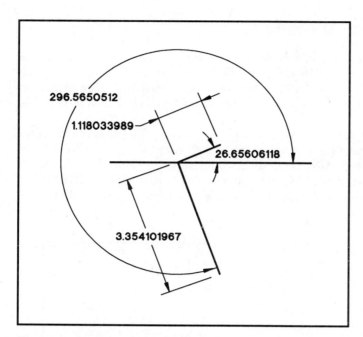

Figure 17–45 Specified distances

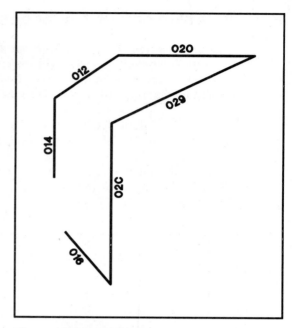

Figure 17–46 DISTANCE-DIRECTION vector specifying codes

To illustrate the DISTANCE-DIRECTION vector specifying codes, the following example is a definition for a shape called "oddity" that will draw the shape shown in Figure 17–46.

```
*200,7,ODDITY
014,012,020,029,02C,016,0
```

To draw the shape named oddity, you would first load the shape file that contains the definition and then use the SHAPE command as follows:

Command: **shape**
Name (or ?): **oddity**
Starting point: *(specify a point)*
Height <default>: *(specify a scale factor)*
Rotation angle <default>: *(specify a rotation angle)*

> **NOTE:** An alternative to standard DISTANCE-DIRECTION codes is to use Codes 8 and 9 to move the pen by paired (delta-x,delta-y) ordinate displacements. This is explained in the Special Codes section below.

Special Codes

Special codes may be written in decimal or hexadecimal. You may specify a special code as 0 through 16 or as 000 through 00E. A three-character defbyte with two leading zeros will be interpreted as a hexadecimal special code. A Code 10 is a special code in decimal. However, 010 is equivalent to decimal 16. But more importantly, it will be interpreted by AutoCAD as a DIS-TANCE-DIRECTION code with a vector length of 1 and a direction of 0. The hexadecimal equivalent to 10 is 00A. The code functions are as follows.

Code 0: End of Shape The end of each separate shape definition must be marked with the Code 0.

Codes 1 and 2: Pen Up and Down The "PEN DOWN" (or DRAW) mode is on at the beginning of each shape. Code 2 turns the DRAW mode off or lifts the pen. This permits moving the pen without drawing. Code 1 turns the DRAW mode on.

Note the relationship between the insertion point specified during the SHAPE command and where you wish the object and its primitives to be located. If you wish for AutoCAD to begin drawing a primitive in the shape at a point remote from the insertion point, then you must lift the pen with a Code 2 and move the pen (with the proper codes) and then lower the pen with a Code 1. Movement of the pen (directed by other codes) after a "PEN DOWN" Code 1 is what causes AutoCAD to draw primitives in a shape.

Codes 3 and 4: Scale Factors Individual (and groups of) primitives within a shape can be increased or decreased in size by integer factors as follows: Code 3 tells AutoCAD to divide the subsequent vectors by the number that immediately follows the Code 3. Code 4 tells AutoCAD to multiply the subsequent vectors by the number that immediately follows the Code 4.

CAUTION!

Scale factors are cumulative. The advantage of this is that you can specify a scale factor that is the quotient of two integers. A two-thirds scale factor can be achieved by a Code 4 followed by a factor of 2 followed by a Code 3 followed by a factor of 3. But, the effects of scale factor codes must be reversed when they are no longer needed. They do not go away by themselves. Therefore, at the end of the definition (or when you wish to return to normal or other scaling within the definition) the scale factor must be countered. For example, when you wish to return to the normal scale from the two-thirds scale, you must use Code 3 followed by a factor of 3 followed by a Code 4 followed by a factor of 2. There is no law that states you must always return to normal from a scaled mode. You can, with Codes 3 and 4 and the correct factors, change from a two-thirds scale to a one-third scale for drawing additional primitives within the shape. You should ALWAYS, however, return to the normal scale at the end of the definition. A scale factor in effect at the end of one shape will carry over to the next shape.

Codes 5 and 6: Saving and Recalling Locations Each location in a SHAPE definition is specified relative to a previous location. However, once the pen is at a particular location, you can store that location for later use within that SHAPE definition before moving on. This is handy when an object has several primitives starting or ending at the same location. For example, a wheel with spokes would be easier to define by using Code 5 to store the center location, draw a spoke, and then use Code 6 to return to the center.

Storing and recalling locations are known as pushing and popping them, respectively, in a stack. The stack storage is limited to four locations at any one time. The order in which they are popped is the reverse of the order in which they were pushed. Every location pushed must be popped.

More pushes than pops will result in the error message:

    Position stack overflow in shape nnn

More pops than pushes will result in the error message:

    Position stack underflow in shape nnn

Code 7: Subshape One shape in a .SHP/.SHX file can be included in the definition of another shape in the same file by using the Code 7 followed by the inserted shape's number.

Codes 8 and 9: X-Y Displacements Normal vector lengths range from 1 to 15 and can be drawn in one of the 16 standard directions unless you use a Code 8 or Code 9 to specify X-Y displacements. A Code 8 tells AutoCAD to use the next two bytes as the X and Y displacements, respectively. For example, 8, (7,-8) tells AutoCAD to move the pen a distance that is 7 in the X direction and 8 in the Y direction. The parentheses are optional for viewing effects only. After the displacement bytes, specifications revert to normal.

Code 9 tells AutoCAD to use all following pairs of bytes as X-Y displacements until terminated by a pair of zeros. For example: 9,(7,-8),(14,9),(-17,3),(0,0) tells AutoCAD to use the three pairs of values for displacements for the current mode and then revert to normal after the (0,0) pair.

Code 00A: Octant Arc Code 00A (or 10) tells AutoCAD to use the next two bytes to define an arc. It is referred to as an octant (an increment of 45 degrees) arc. Octant arcs start and end on octant boundaries. Figure 17–47 shows the code numbers for the octants. The specification is written in the following format:

    `10, radius. (-)OSC`

The radius may range from 1 to 255. The second byte begins with zero and specifies the direction by its sign (clockwise if negative, counterclockwise otherwise), the starting octant (S) and the number of octants it spans (C) which may be written as 0 to 7 with 0 being 8 (a full circle). Figure 17–48 shows an arc drawn with the following codes:

    `10,(2,-043)`

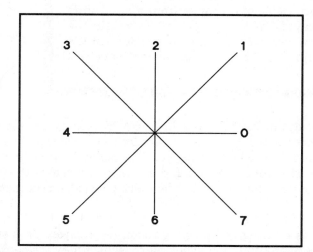

Figure 17–47 Code numbers for octants

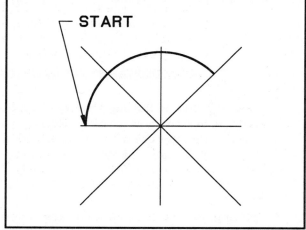

Figure 17–48 A arc drawn with code 10,(2, -043)

The arc has a radius of 2, begins at octant arc 4, and turns 135 degrees or 3 octants clockwise.

Code 00B: Fractional Arc Code 00B (11) can be used to specify an arc that begins and ends at points other that the octants. The definition is written as follows:

$$11,\text{start-offset, end-offset, high-radius, low-radius, (-)OSC}$$

Start and end offsets specify how far from an octant the arc starts and ends. The high-radius, if not zero, specifies a radius greater than 255. The low-radius is specified in the same manner as the radius in a Code 10 arc, as are the starting octant and octants covering specifications in the last byte. The presence of the negative also signifies a clockwise direction.

The units of offset from an octant are a fraction of 1 degree times 45 divided by 256, or approximately .17578125 degrees. For example, if you wish to specify the starting value near 60 degrees the equation would be:

$$\text{offset} = (60-45)*(256/45) = 85.333333$$

So the specification value would be 85.

To end the arc at 102 degrees the equation would be:

$$\text{offset} = (102-90)*(256/45) = 68.2666667$$

So the specification value would be 68.

To draw an arc with a radius of 2 that starts near 60 degrees and ends near 102 degrees, the specifications would be as follows:

$$11,(85,68,0,2,012)$$

The last byte (012) specifies the starting octant to be 1 (45 degrees) and the ending octant to be 2 (90 degrees).

Codes 00C and 00D: Bulge-Specified Arc Codes 00C and 00D (12 and 13) are used to specify arcs in a different manner from octant codes. Codes 00C and 00D call out bulge factors to be applied to a vector displacement. The effect of using Code 00C or 00D involves specifying the endpoints of a flexible line by the X-Y displacement method and then specifying the bulge. The bulge determines the distance from the straight line between the endpoints and the extreme point on the arc. The bulge can range from −127 to 127. The maximum/minimum values (127 or −127) define a 180-degree arc, or half circle. Smaller values define proportionally smaller-degree arcs. That is, an arc specified some value, say x, will be x times 180 divided by 127 degrees. A bulge value of zero will define a straight line.

Code 00C precedes a single bulge defined arcs while 00D precedes multiple arcs. This is similar to the way Codes 008 and 009 work on X-Y displacement lines. Code 00D, like 009, must be terminated by a 0,0 byte pair. You can specify a series of bulge arcs and lines without exiting the Code 00D by using the zero bulge value for the lines.

Code 00E: Flag Vertical Text Command Code 00E (14) is only for dual-orientation text font descriptions, where a font might be used in either horizontal or vertical orientations. When Code 00E is encountered in the SHAPE definition, the next code will be ignored if the text is horizontal.

Text Fonts

Text fonts are special SHAPE files written for use with AutoCAD TEXT drawing commands. The shape numbers should correspond to ASCII codes for characters. Table 17-1 shows the ASCII codes.

Codes 1 through 31 are reserved for special control characters. Only Code 10 (line feed) is used in AutoCAD. In order to be used as a font, the file must include a special shape number, 0, to describe the font. Its format is as follows:

```
*0,4,fontname
above, below, modes, 0
```

"Above" specifies the number of vector lengths that uppercase letters extend above the baseline, and "below" specifies the number of vector lengths that lowercase letters extend below the baseline. A modes byte value of zero (0) defines a horizontal (normal) mode and a value of two (2) defines dual-orientation (horizontal or vertical). A value of 2 must be present in order for the special Code 00E (14) to operate.

Standard AutoCAD fonts include special shape numbers 127, 128, and 129 for the degrees symbol, plus/minus symbol, and diameter dimensioning symbol, respectively.

The definition of a character from the TXT.SHP file is shown below. Note that the number 65 corresponds to the ASCII character that is an uppercase "A." The name "uca" (for uppercase a) is in lowercase to avoid taking up memory. As an exercise, you can follow the defbytes to see how the character is drawn.

```
*65,21,uca
2,14,8,(-2,-6),1,024,043,04D,02C,2,047,1,040,2,02E,14,8,(-4,
-3),0
```

The above character definition starts by lifting the pen. A font containing the alphanumeric characters must take into consideration the spaces between characters. This is done by having similar starting and stopping points based on each character's particular width.

CUSTOM LINETYPES

Linetype definitions are stored in files with a .LIN extension. Approximately 40 standard linetype definitions are stored for use in the acad.line file. The definitions are in ASCII format and the definitions can be edited or you can add new ones of your own by using either a text editor in the non-document mode or by using the Create option of the Linetype command. Or, you can save new or existing linetype definitions in another filename.lin file.

Simple linetypes consist of series of dashes, dots, and spaces. Their definitions are considered the in-line pen-up/pen-down type. Complex linetypes have repeating "out-of-line" objects, such as text and shapes, along with the optional in-line dashes, dots, and spaces. These are used in mapping/surveying drawings for such things as topography lines, fences, utilities, and many other descriptive lines. Instrumentation/control drawings use many lines with repeating shapes also to indicate graphically the purpose of each line.

Each linetype definition in a file comprises two lines. The first line must begin with an asterisk, followed by the linetype name, and an optional description in the following format:

```
*ltname,description
```

Table 17-1 ASCII Codes for Text Fonts

Code	Character	Code	Character	Code	Character
32	space	64	@	96	left apostrophe
33	!	65	A	97	a
34	" double quote	66	B	98	b
35	#	67	C	99	c
36	$	68	D	100	d
37	%	69	E	101	e
38	&	70	F	102	f
39	' apostrophe	71	G	103	g
40	(	72	H	104	h
41	)	73	I	105	i
42	*	74	J	106	j
43	+	75	K	107	k
44	, comma	76	L	108	l
45	- hyphen	77	M	109	m
46	. period	78	N	110	n
47	/	79	O	111	o
48	0	80	P	112	p
49	1	81	Q	113	q
50	2	82	R	114	r
51	3	83	S	115	s
52	4	84	T	116	t
53	5	85	U	117	u
54	6	86	V	118	v
55	7	87	W	119	w
56	8	88	X	120	x
57	9	89	Y	121	y
58	: colon	90	Z	122	z
59	; semicolon	91	[	123	{
60	<	92	\ backslash	124		vertical bar
61	=	93	]	125	}
62	>	94	^ caret	126	~ tilde
63	?	95	_ underscore		

Codes 1 to 31 are for control characters, only one of which is used in AutoCAD text fonts.

Customizing AutoCAD

The second line gives the alignment and description by using proper codes and symbols in the following format:

    alignment,patdesc-1,patdesc-2,...

A simple linetype definition for two dashes and a dot, called DDD, could be written as follows:

    *DDD,___ ___ . ___ ___ . ___ ___ .
    A,.75,-.5,.75,-.5,0,-.5

The linetype name is DDD. A graphic description of underscores, spaces, and periods follow. The dashes are given as .75 (positive for pen down) in length separated by spaces of -.5 (negative for pen up) in length with the 0 specifying a dot. No character other than the A should be entered for the alignment as it is the only one applicable at this time. This type of alignment causes the lines to begin and end with dashes (except for linetypes with dots only).

The complex linetype definitions include a descriptor (enclosed in square brackets) in addition to the alignment and dash/dot/space specification. A shape descriptor will include the shape name, shape file, and optional transform specification as follows:

    [shapename,filename,transform]

A text descriptor will include the actual text string (in quotes), the text style, and optional transform specification as follows:

    ["string",textstyle,transform]

Transform specifications (if included) can be one or more of the following:

    A=##   Absolute rotation
    R=##   Relative rotation
    S=##   Scale
    X=##   X offset
    Y=##   Y offset

The ## for rotation is in decimal degrees (plus or minus) and for scale and offset in decimal units.

The following example of an embedded shape in a line for an instrument air line (with repeating circles) could be written as follows:

    *INSTRAIR, ___ [CIRC] ___ [CIRC] ___
    A,2.0,-.5,[CIRC,ctrls.shx],-.5

If the ctrls.shx file contains a proper shape description of the desired circle, it will be repeated in the broken line (with spaces on each side) when applied as the INSTRAIR linetype. If the scale of the circle needed to be doubled in order to have the proper appearance, it could be written as follows:

    *INSTRAIR, ___ [CIRC] ___ [CIRC] ___
    A,2.0,-.5,[CIRC,ctrls.shx,S=2],-.5

The following example of an embedded text string in a line for a storm sewer (with repeating SSs could be written as follows:

```
*STRMSWR,____ SS ____ SS ____
A,3.0,-1.0,["SS",simplex,S=1,R=0,X=0,Y=-0.125],-1.0
```

CUSTOMIZING AND PROGRAMMING LANGUAGE

There are various other topics with respect to the customization of AutoCAD, some of which are beyond the scope of this book. AutoCAD provides a programming language called AutoLISP (refer to Chapter 18 for Introduction to AutoLISP). AutoLISP is a structured programming language similar in a number of ways to other programming languages. However, it is an interpreted language. Because it is an interpreted language you can type an AutoLISP statement at the command prompt in AutoCAD and AutoCAD will execute it. AutoLISP code is created with a text editor. A compiled language (AutoCAD supports a number of these too) is first converted into object code (this is called the compiling process) or machine language and then linked with various other compiled object code modules (this is called the linking process) to form an executable file. The executable file is then loaded into memory and executed. C/C++ and ARx (AutoCAD Runtime Extension) are examples of compiled programming languages and require additional software to create their executable files.

REVIEW QUESTIONS

1. The purpose of the ACAD.PGP file is to
   (A) allow other programs to be accessed while editing a drawing
   (B) enable shape files to be compiled
   (C) store system configurations
   (D) serve as a "file manager" for system variables
   (E) None of the above

2. The standard AutoCAD screen menu
   (A) is stored in a file named ACAD.MNU
   (B) can be viewed using the DOS TYPE command
   (C) contains the screen menu items found in the AutoCAD screen menus
   (D) All of the above

3. In an AutoCAD menu file, a semicolon contained in a menu item will tell the computer to
   (A) prompt the user for input
   (B) press Enter
   (C) press Ctrl
   (D) None of the above

4. AutoCAD menu files are stored with what type of file extension?
   (A) DWG   (D) MNO
   (B) DXF   (E) None of the above
   (C) MNU

5. When developing screen menus, the information you would like to see displayed in the screen menus should be
   (A) typed in uppercase letters only
   (B) enclosed with brackets
   (C) longer than four characters but shorter than ten characters
   (D) All of the above

6. How many characters between brackets will display in a screen menu?
   (A) 6   (C) 10
   (B) 8   (D) 4

7. What symbology signifies the heading of a menu device such as a digitizer or tablet area?
   (A) ****   (C) **S
   (B) ***   (D) None of the above

8. What is the purpose of the backslash "\" in a menu line?
   (A) Pause for user input   (C) Press Enter
   (B) Terminate a command   (D) None of the above

9. What file defines external commands and their parameters?
   (A) ACAD.DWK   (C) ACAD.PGP
   (B) ACAD.MNX   (D) ACAD.LSP

18

AUTOLISP

INTRODUCTION

This chapter will cover the fundamental concepts of the AutoLISP programming language. Included are writing, storing, and loading .LSP files, the concepts of variables and expressions, the LIST, custom functions, and file handling.

After completing this chapter, you will be able to:
- Grasp fundamental concepts of the AutoLISP programming language
- Decipher program files written by others
- Establish a basis for more advanced programming

In Version 2.1 (Release 6) in May, 1985, Autodesk first introduced its embedded programming language. It provided on board computational power for the operator while in AutoCAD. It also permitted true programming routines to be used by way of menu devices, including interactive functions to receive input from the operator in the form of keyboard entries and screen picks for use in the routine. In January, 1986, Version 2.18 included a full implementation of user-defined functions and custom commands, which added a whole new world of open architecture (meaning you can customize the program to suit your needs) to AutoCAD.

Loading AutoLISP Into Your Drawing

You do not have to learn how to write AutoLISP programs in order to be able to use them. AutoLISP programs are available from several sources. They are in the form of filename.LSP files. AutoCAD comes with program files that are ready to load and use in your drawing.

An AutoLISP file named RECTANG.LSP (which facilitates drawing a square or rectangle) can be loaded for use during the current editing session by using the AutoLISP function called load as follows:

Command: **(load "rectang")**

Note the following:

1. The use of the parentheses distinguishes AutoLISP functions and routines. This is especially important when using a function such as "load" for which there is an AutoCAD command of the same name.

2. You should not include the .LSP extension. AutoCAD appends it automatically.

3. You may also specify a path if necessary. For example, if the RECTANG.LSP file is on the A: drive in a directory called Lisp the following response can be used:

Command: **(load "a:/lisp/rectang")**

Note the use of the nonstandard forward slashes to specify the directory path.

Expressions And Variables

Expressions in AutoLISP should be understood before getting into variables. The simplest application of AutoLISP is to evaluate an equation by just typing it in and pressing Enter. Of course, you must enter the equation in the proper format, which is somewhat different from ordinary algebraic notation. It involves a format that is unique among those used in other more popular computer programming languages. For example, if you wish to add 5 and 3, simply enter the following expression:

Command: **(+ 5 3)**

The integer 8 will be displayed in the prompt area. That is, AutoLISP evaluates the expression and returns the integer 8. Throughout this lesson, the word "return" will be used to describe the result of an evaluation. Another expression:

Command: **(+ 5 3 1 99)**

returns the integer 108.

Four things are worthy of note regarding these expressions and returns.

1. When AutoCAD sees an open parenthesis (unless responding to a prompt to enter text), it knows that it is entering an AutoLISP expression to be evaluated. The AutoLISP evaluator remains in effect until it encounters the closing parenthesis that is the mate of the first open parenthesis.

2. AutoLISP uses prefix notation, which means that expressions begin with the operator (after the opening parenthesis, of course). In the above examples, the plus sign (+) is the arithmetic operator. The operator tells AutoLISP what operation to perform on the items that follow. The items that follow the operator are known as the arguments.

3. As you can see by the second example, the plus operator can have more than the usual two arguments to which an algebraic plus sign is restricted.

4. Elements in an AutoLISP expression are separated by one or more spaces. Multiple adjoining spaces (unlike spaces in a menu line) are considered as one space in an AutoLISP routine.

Variables as Symbols and Symbols that Should Not Vary Just as algebra uses letter names for the unknown-at-the-time values in an equation, AutoLISP utilizes symbols as variables, whose name you may select during the writing of the program. In algebra, for example, as sequence might be written as follows:

	ALGEBRA		AutoLISP
	a = 3		(setq a 3)
	b = 7		(setq b 7)

therefore

| | a + b = 10 | | (+ a b) returns 10 |

and

| | ab = 21 | | (* a b) returns 21 |

Assigning Names   Three reasons for assigning names are as follows:

1. Expressions

   Pi is the name for 3.14159 and so forth.

2. Variables

   A variable is an expression whose value is not known when originally written into the program. Variables will take on some value after the program has been called into use. The value of the variable is usually determined by some operation on some other value which the user has been prompted to enter while the program is in progress.

3. Custom-Defined Functions

   AutoCAD permits users to create and name a customized function and then use it in AutoCAD in a manner similar to a standard AutoCAD command.

Terminology And Fundamental Concepts

LISTS, OPERATORS, ARGUMENTS, TYPES, PARENTHESES, the EXCLAMATION POINT, and the concept of the FUNCTION-LIST comprise the basis of AutoLISP.

LISTs   Practically everything in AutoLISP is a list of some sort or another. Functions are usually represented as a list of expressions enclosed in parentheses. For example, (+ 1 2.0) is an AutoLISP function with three elements in it, the "+", the "1," and the "2.0." Other lists may be established by applying a function called LIST or by applying the single quote, such as '(1 2 3.0 a "b").

Operators and ARGUMENTS   Arguments are those items in a function-list on which the operator operates. For example, in the function-list (+ 1 2), the operator is (+) and the ARGUMENTs are "1" and "2."

TYPES   Arguments are classified by their TYPE. The ARGUMENTS in the example (+ 1 2) are of the type called INTEGER. In the function-list (+ 1.0 2.0), the ARGUMENTs are of the TYPE called REAL, signifying a real number.

The Parentheses   The primary mechanisms for entering and leaving AutoLISP and entering expressions within AutoLISP are the open and closed parentheses.

AutoLISP

CAUTION!

For every open parenthesis "(" there must be a closed parenthesis ")." If AutoCAD encounters a condition where the closed parentheses are one fewer than the open ones, the prompt will display the following:

1>

The above is caused most often by the need for one closed parenthesis. A display of 3> could indicate the need of three closed parentheses. The problem is usually remedied by just entering the specified number of closed parentheses. This type of error message can also be caused by having an odd number of double quotation marks inside of an AutoLISP expression, in which case one double quotation mark must be entered, followed by the required number of closed parentheses, in order to eliminate the error message in the prompt area. Further examination will usually reveal that the program line needs to be corrected to prevent the message from recurring.

The Exclamation Point   A leading exclamation point in response to a prompt is another mechanism of entering AutoLISP. This tells AutoCAD that the symbol that follows the exclamation point is an AutoLISP variable that has been set equal to some value and that AutoCAD should use the value of the variable as a response to the prompt.

The above terms and concepts are explained in detail with examples in the sections that follow.

Functions   The first function-list to be introduced involves three expressions: the operator SETQ, the variable that we have arbitrarily named "x," and the REAL number 2.5. Within this function SETQ will perform a special operation on the variable "x" and the REAL number 2.5. SETQ is probably AutoLISP's most common function. It means "set equal." By using SETQ as the first of three expressions, you will set the second expression equal to the third. We are accustomed to performing this operation by the conventional expression "x = 2.5." But as you will see in the example below, in order to write "x equals 2.5" in AutoLISP you must write in a special format "SET x EQUAL 2.5." It is done by writing three expressions in parentheses with the first being the operator SETQ, the second being "x," and the third being the value to which the variable named "x" is to be equal, for example:

Command: **(setq x 2.5)**

Having x = 2.5, or more properly, to have SET x EQUAL 2.5 is necessary only if you wish to use the value of the REAL number 2.5 later by just entering its name "x." If you have entered "(setq x 2.5)" at the "Command:" prompt earlier, then any time during that current editing session you may re-enter AutoLISP right from the keyboard by using ! before the name of the value in response to a prompt for some REAL number. If the prompt is asking for a name of something (like a layer name, which requires responding with something called a string variable), then trying to use a variable that has been set equal to a REAL number will cause an error message. The use of ! is another method of entering AutoLISP directly from the keyboard or in a string of custom menu commands and responses.

For example, you have created a unit block named UB and wish to INSERT it with a scale factor of 2.5. The sequence of prompts and responses would be as follows:

Command: **insert**
Block name (or ?): **ub**
Insertion point: *(pick an insertion point)*
X scale factor <1> / Corner / XYZ: **!x**

Note at this point that the use of the name "x" and the fact that it is being applied to the "X scale" is purely coincidental.

By using the ! in front of the "x," you will have the value of x (or 2.5 in this case) used as a response to the prompt asking for the X scale.

This example is not very efficient. Entering !x appears to take only two key strokes, where entering 2.5 takes three. If that were true, you would save a key stroke. But, because entering the exclamation point ! requires the shift key, it is a double stroke requiring both hands. Along with the x it is actually less convenient than entering 2.5, which has three one-hand strokes. Additionally, the characters "2," ".," and "5" are all accessible on AutoCAD's tablet overlay while the ! is not. Entering 2.5 will, however, give the same accuracy as entering 2.50000000000000.

> ***NOTE:*** If x has not previously been set equal to a value, then entering !x will return "nil." Believe it or not, advanced programming does make use of the "nil." Normally, variables and expressions retain their names and values only during the current editing session. They are lost when a drawing is ended. At the beginning of each session they must be re-established. But even this problem of saving variable values from one session to another can be addressed by a custom program.

Naming And Setqing The Value Of An Expression Suppose the value you wish to enter is 1 divided by the square root of 2. This could be written as 0.7071068 depending on the accuracy desired. Now compare three key strokes using AutoLISP versus nine or 10 from the keyboard or tablet. Not only will a variable having a short name (and having been set equal to that value) save time in entering, but it will decrease the probability of errors in both reading and keying-in a long string of characters, for example:

Command: **(setq x 0.7071068)**

If the value 0.7071068 is needed in response to a prompt, simply enter !x. Programming begins to appear both expedient and practical.

> **CAUTION!**
>
> You may respond with .7071068 outside AutoLISP, but while in AutoLISP, you must use some value (even if zero) on both sides of the decimal point. Expressions beginning or ending with a dot (.) have another special meaning.

Before leaving this example, additional power of AutoLISP can be seen in a demonstration of using an expression within an expression within an expression. Two other AutoLISP operators will be introduced at this time. They are the SQRT and the "/" functions. The SQRT returns the square root of the argument following (it must be only one ARGUMENT and must be a nonnegative REAL

AutoLISP

number). The "/" function requires two ARGUMENTS and returns the quotient of the first divided by the second, for example:

Command:**(sqrt 2)**

The above returns 1.414213562373...... You may now use this value as follows:

Command: **(setq y (sqrt 2))**

This does two things. It sets y equal to the expression that follows, which is the square root of 2, and returns 1.414213562.

Having entered the above routine you may operate on y as follows:

Command: **(/ 1.0 y)**

This expression will return the quotient of 1 divided by the value of y, which was previously set equal the square root of 2. Therefore, the expression evaluates to 0.7071068.

Using an AutoLISP function in this fashion neither sets values nor gives them names. It is of little use later but does return (display in the prompt area) the result of the prescribed computation for immediate viewing. Sometimes this is handier than picking up a hand-held calculator.

A two step use of AutoLISP could be written as follows:

Command: **(setq y (sqrt 2))**
Command: **(setq x (/ 1 y))**

The first step sets y equal to the square root of 2. The second step sets x equal to the inner expression, which uses the "/" operator (for division) and returns the value of 1 divided by the value of y. This two step sequence involves four operators (SQRT, /, and SETQ twice). It names y and sets it equal to the square root of 2. It names x and sets it equal to the reciprocal of y.

Instead of the above two-step routine, a simpler one-step routine is as follows:

Command: **(setq x (/ 1 (sqrt 2)))**

So in one step you can name an expression "x" and set it equal to the reciprocal of the square root of 2. It allows you to now respond to any prompt for a REAL number and apply this value by simply entering !x. This saves time and insures 14 decimal place accuracy, which is what CAD is all about in the first place— speed and accuracy.

Example

At the "Command:" prompt enter the following expression:

Command: **(setq a 1 b 2 c 99 d pi e 2.5)**

This expression is a function-list using the operator SETQ. Note the opening and closing parentheses that distinguish it as an individual expression. Unlike the (+...) function that performs a single operation of as many ARGUMENTs as you wish to furnish, the (setq...) must have pairs of

ARGUMENTs. SETQ operates on each pair of ARGUMENTs individually. After entering the above, you may have AutoLISP evaluate equations by entering them as follows:

Command: **(setq x (+ a b))** *(returns 3)*
Command: **(setq y (- a c))** *(returns -98)*
Command: **(setq z (* b d))** *(returns 6.283185308)*
Command: **(setq q (/ c e))** *(returns 39.6)*

Perform the following exercises.

1. Name and give values to variables corresponding to the following algebraic equations.
   a = 4
   b = 7
   c = a × b
   d = b² *with 2 as exponent*
   e = √a² + b² *square root of a squared plus b squared*

Exercises from the Keyboard

Line After first drawing a random line (with the snap mode off), establish variables for the points p1 and p2 as follows (see Figure 18–1). Type in **(setq p1 (getpoint))**. Use the OSNAP mode Endpoint to pick one end of the line. Type in **(setq p2 (getpoint))** and use the OSNAP mode Endpoint to pick the other endpoint of the line. Do not be alarmed that the prompt area is blank. When the points have been returned, record the X and Y coordinates on paper for use in the following exercises. For example, if (1.2345 6.7890 0.0000) is returned for p1, enter the following:

Command: **(setq X1 1.2345)** *returns 1.2345*
Command: **(setq Y1 6.7890)** *returns 6.7890*

> ***Note:*** Enter the numbers you obtain, not 1,2345 and 6,789 from the example!

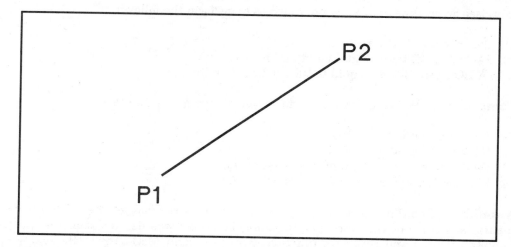

Figure 18–1 The line for writing a routine

Write in from keyboard routines to perform the following:

1. Set "dx" equal to the horizontal distance between p1 and p2.
2. Set "dy" equal to the vertical distance between p1 and p2.
3. Set "d" equal to the distance between p1 and p2.
4. Set "a" equal to the angle between p1 and p2 in radians.

Circle After first drawing a random circle (with the snap mode off), set variables to the center "c" of the circle and to one point "p" on the circle (see Figure 18–2). Write routines to perform the following:

1. Set "r" equal to the radius of the circle.
2. Set "d" equal to the diameter of the circle.
3. Set "p" equal to the perimeter of the circle.
4. Set "a" equal to the area of the circle.

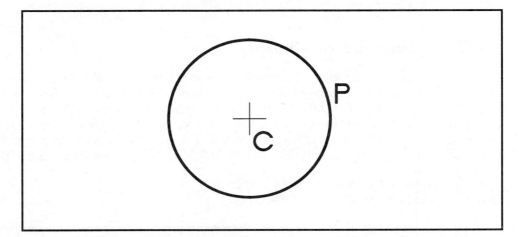

Figure 18–2 The circle for writing a routine

Arc Establish endpoints p1 and p2 and the center "c" of the arc (see Figure 18–3) as in the exercises on the line above. Write routines to perform the following:

1. Set "r" equal to the radius of the arc.
2. Set "lc" equal to the chord length of the arc.
3. (A DOOZIE) Set "la" equal to the arc length of the arc.

Computation Write routines to perform the following (see Figure 18–4):

1. If a = 1 and b = 2, then find c.
2. If b = 2 and c = 3, then find a.
3. Find the area of the triangle for question 1.
4. Find the area of the triangle for question 2.

According to Ben Shneiderman in his preface to Dan Friedman's "The Little LISPer," "The fundamental structure of the LISP programming language was derived from the abstract notions of lambda calculus and recursive function theory by John McCarthy. His goal was to produce a programming language with a powerful notation for defining and transforming functions. Instead

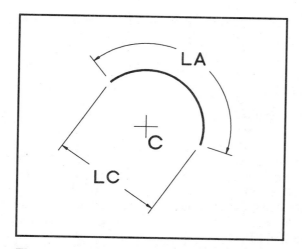

Figure 18-3 The arc for writing a routine

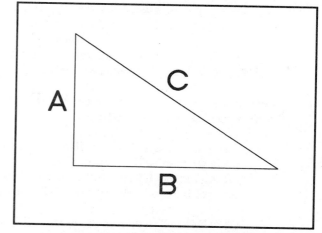

Figure 18-4 The triangle for writing a routine

of operating on numeric quantities, LISP was designed to manipulate abstract symbols, called atoms, and combinations of symbols, called lists. The expressive power was recognized by a small number of researchers who were primarily concerned with difficult symbolic manipulation problems in artificial intelligence."

Translating an algebraic word problem into a true algebraic expression demands a certain symbol classification and list processing also. Many algebra students can learn the process of solution to an algebraic expression (or at least memorize the procedures) once it is in the proper structure, but suffer a complete impasse when asked to "interpret" the word problem into that proper structure.

Words in a sentence or paragraph have characteristics similar to AutoLISP functions or expressions. Verbs act on subjects like subroutines act on variables and expressions. The conjunction "and" joins phrases like the "+" joins real numbers. A phrase like "out of here" has the subphrase "of here" in it.

THE LIST

TYPEs of ARGUMENTs

While an ARGUMENT is defined in part by *The American Heritage Dictionary* as "A quarrel; contention," it also is defined under the heading of math as "The independent variable of a function." AutoCAD's Programmer's Reference consistently describes the variables upon whose value the function value depends as ARGUMENTs.

The LIST in AutoLISP is an ARGUMENT When is a LIST NOT a LIST? As mentioned earlier, almost every function in AutoLISP is some form of a LIST. The AutoLISP interpreter operates on LISTs as they occur in a routine or program. The AutoLISP expression (setq x (/ 1 (sqrt 2))) is a LIST. To the AutoCAD lisp interpreter it is a LIST to be evaluated according to the operator "SETQ." Likewise, (/ 1 (sqrt 2)) and (sqrt 2) are a sublist and subsublist, respectively, to be evaluated. But none of these would be considered as the type of defined LIST (known as LIST to the TYPE function) that some of the AutoLISP function-lists, like (CAR <list>), normally require as their ARGUMENT. The LISTs that are acceptable ARGUMENTs to these certain functions might be looked upon as special LISTs within lists. They must take on a special format in order to satisfy the main function-list as the required ARGUMENT(s).

AutoLISP function-lists that require LISTs as one of their ARGUMENTs include the CAR, CADR, LAST, LENGTH, NTH, and REVERSE functions.

Whenever an AutoLISP function-list requires a LIST as one of its ARGUMENTs, then you must use one of the following procedures:

1. You may use the function-list that has as its operator the function called LIST. This function-list is written in the format (list <expr>...) as described in AutoCAD's Programmer's Reference. Typing in (list 1.0 2.0) will return (1.000000 2.000000). But more importantly, it will satisfy the requirements of this special LIST when needed for data input. Other function-lists (such as the one with the operator SQRT) most likely will NOT satisfy the special requirement of an ARGUMENT that must be of the TYPE called LIST.

2. If you must respond within AutoLISP with the special form of LIST required, writing (list 1.0 2.0) every time becomes laborious (like writing 3.14159 and so forth when the use of pi will do). Therefore, it is convenient to use the SETQ function and write:

   (setq p (list 1.0 2.0))

The name "p" is strictly arbitrary in this case. Any unique variable name you would like to use will suffice. Then whenever your routine requires you to respond with a point whose X and Y coordinates are 1.0 and 2.0, respectively, you may respond with "p" within AutoLISP or "!p" directly from the keyboard while in AutoCAD. Try this exercise for an illustration of the above. The default limits of 0,0 and 12,9 as in the ACAD.DWG will be helpful. Type in at the "Command:" prompt the following:

   Command:**(setq p (list 1.0 2.0))**
   ((1.000000 2.000000) will be displayed)
   Command: **line**
   From point: **(list 6.0 7.0)**
   To point: **!p**

Creating A LIST

As explained earlier in this chapter, the (list <expr>..) function-list is often used under restrictive conditions. For example, using it as a response to some commands requiring a 2D point, the "<expr>..." part of the overall expression must be "<expr> <expr>" where both <expr>'s are REAL numbers.

Remember that an INTEGER can be entered in AutoLISP and AutoCAD will translate it into a REAL number under certain conditions. For a 3D point, the form of the response must be "<expr> <expr> <expr>." Using "<real> <real>," "<real> <int>," or "<int> <int>" may be considered as proper responses to a prompt for the starting point of a 2D line. This coincides with the type of entry required for a point even while NOT in AutoLISP.

For example, the following are considered appropriate while in AutoCAD:

   Command: **line**
   From point: **1.5, .7081068**

or
From point: **3.1415, 5**
or
From point: **1, 1**

A similar mixture of REALs and INTEGERs is evident in the following example from within AutoLISP:

Command: **line**
From point: **(list 1.5 0.7071068)**
or
From point: **(list pi 5)**
or
From point: **(list 1 1)**

Note two subtle differences! (Not the parentheses, because they are not subtle.) First, from within AutoLISP, any REAL number must begin with an INTEGER, NOT a decimal point.

Second, the two expressions comprising the list within each function are separated by a space, as in the last examples (within AutoLISP) instead of a comma, as in the first examples (not in AutoLISP).

A LIST That Doesn't Look Like A LIST   Once a symbol (name of your choice) has been SETQed (set equal) to a LIST by the (setq <sym> (list <expr> <expr>...)) function, then that symbol becomes a defined LIST. It will evaluate to that (<expr> <expr>...) for use as a response within AutoLISP or out of AutoLISP by using the ! prefix. For example, entering (setq p1 (list 2.0 3.0)) returns (2.0000 3.0000). Using the TYPE command, as in entering (TYPE p1), will return "LIST." It will work for the following response to the LINE command:

From point: **!p1**

But if (setq p1 (list 2.0 "z")) has been entered as the prior routine instead of (setq p1 (list 2.0 3.0)), the above sequence will NOT accept !p1 as a valid response, even though (TYPE p1) still returns "LIST." Its ARGUMENT, (<expr> <expr>..), as a LIST is not (<real> <real>..) as points require.

Before you even considered programming in AutoLISP, you were using LISTs. If, in response to the "From point:" prompt, you entered "2,3.75" from the keyboard (or any form of "real,real," "real,integer," or "integer, integer") then you used a LIST. Even if you had entered "x1,2.5" or "3,y" you would have been using a LIST. But you would have found out that even though it was in a similar format, the elements of the entry were not of the proper classification. Once you understood that AutoCAD rejected anything except certain classifications of elements, you learned to work using that knowledge (or went back to the drawing board, literally!).

A disguised use of the LIST input is when you pick a point on the screen. AutoCAD defines that pick as a LIST in the proper format, (x-coordinate,y-coordinate), and enters it for you. It is a LIST in the acceptable format.

Association LIST   The following:

((a 097) (b 098) (c 099) (d 100)....(x 120) (y 121) (z 122))

is a LIST, but it is a very special LIST.

Each expression in the LIST similarly has two expressions enclosed in parentheses (making them each a LIST themselves) with the first being a lowercase letter, and the second being an INTEGER.

What makes the last LIST special is that it satisfies the requirements of an ASSOCIATION LIST. It may be used (like other qualified association lists) as an ARGUMENT in the AutoLISP function ASSOC. It takes the form of (assoc <item> <alist>).

EXERCISES

Determine if the evaluation results below satisfy the requirements of the expression of the TYPE LIST. If not, explain why.

a. 1 , 2
b. 1 2
c. (12)
d. (1 2)
e. (1.0 2)
f. (1.0 2.0)
g. ((1 2))
h. ((1 2)
i. (1 .2)
j. (1.0 0.2)
k. (1.0 2.0 3.0 x)
l. (1.0 2.0x3.0)
m. (* 2 4)
n. (-2 -4)

PAUSING FOR USER INPUT

There are very few AutoCAD commands that begin and end by just entering the command name. Except for END, REGEN, REDRAW, OOPS, UNDO, and the like, most commands pause for user input before they are completed. You can include this interactive capability in your AutoLISP routines through several input functions. The exercises in this section will introduce two such functions, (getpoint...) and (getreal...). The (getpoint) function pauses for input of a point (either from the keyboard or a pick on the screen) and returns that point in the form of a LIST of two REALs. The (getreal) function pauses for user input of a REAL number and returns that REAL number.

AutoLISP Functions — The Command Function

The function-list (command <args>...) provides a method of invoking an AutoCAD command from within AutoLISP. It is usually the culmination of the routine. The <args> are written in the same sequence as if entered from the keyboard from the AutoCAD. The AutoCAD command name that follows the (command ...) function must be enclosed in quotation marks as in the following example:

```
(setq p1 (list 1.0 1.0))
(setq p2 (list 2.0 2.75))
(command "line" p1 p2 "")
```

The above sequence, when included in an AutoLISP routine, will draw a line from 1,1 to 2,2.75.

Note that the double-double quotation mark is the equivalent of pressing [Enter] while in AutoLISP. It is referred to as the null STRING (""). It simulates pressing the spacebar.

In the (command ...) function-list, the arguments that are AutoCAD entries are enclosed within quotation marks while AutoLISP symbols and expressions are NOT. One of the notable differences is illustrated in responding to a prompt for an angle. Remember, AutoLISP requires radians while AutoCAD normally uses degrees (unless the UNITS are set for angle input to be in radians). For this illustration certain symbols were named and SETQed to values as shown below:

> (setq ublkname "UB1")
> (setq inspt (list 2.0 2.0))
> (setq xscal 2.5)
> (setq yscal 2.5)
> (setq ang 90)

Then a routine could be written in two different ways with the same results, as follows:

> (command "insert" ublkname inspt xscal yscal ang)
> or
> (command "insert" "UB1" "2,2" "2.5" "" "90")

Although angular responses to normal AutoLISP functions must be in radians, this is an angular response while temporarily back in the AutoCAD screen and therefore must be 90 for degrees.

The first program line uses AutoLISP symbols as responses to the INSERT command that the (command ...) function invoked. The second line uses AutoCAD equivalents of the same responses. In the latter, the responses must be enclosed within quotation marks. This use of the quotation marks is different from their use to mark characters as a STRING type of ARGUMENT in function-lists other than the (command ...) function.

Two subtle lessons can be gotten from the above.

1. The use of quotation marks returns you to AutoCAD types of responses.

2. The double-double quotation marks (null STRING) is used to cause the Y scale factor to default to the X scale factor. This would not be appropriate if the Y scale needed to be different, of course. Using the null STRING in this manner is equivalent to returning to the AutoCAD screen, striking the spacebar, and then returning back to AutoLISP.

The Pause Symbol

During a (command...) function you can cause a pause if you wish to allow the user to have input during that particular AutoCAD command that you have called up. This is done by using the pause symbol in lieu of a variable or a fixed value where a particular response is required. For example, in the above program line you could have allowed the user to input a name and an angle:

> (command "insert" pause inspt xscal yscal pause)
> *or*
> (command "insert" pause "2,2" "2.5" "" pause)

Symbology Used In This Chapter To Describe Functions

The function descriptions in this section include the operator (+ or −, for example), and the elements (ARGUMENTs) that must (or may) follow the operator. If the ARGUMENT(s) following the

AutoLISP

operator in the description are enclosed with angle <> brackets only, then those ARGUMENTs must follow the operator and must be of the TYPE specified. An ARGUMENT in square [ ] brackets following the operator (not necessarily immediately) is optional. When an ARGUMENT is followed by an ellipsis "...," then the operator will accept multiple ARGUMENTs of the type specified.

ELEMENTARY FUNCTIONS

(+ <number> <number>...)

This function returns the sum of the <number>s. There may be any quantity of <number>s.

(- <number> <number>...)

This function returns the difference of the <number>s. There may be any quantity of <number>s.

(* <number> <number>...)

This function returns the product of any quantity of <number>s.

(\ <number> <number>...)

This function returns the quotient of the first <number> divided by the second <number>, and if there are more than two ARGUMENTs, the quotient of the first and second will be divided by the third and so on.

Rules Of Promotion Of An Integer To A Real

As noted in the Reference Manual, INTEGERs may range from –32768 to 32767, depending on the platform. Adding or multiplying INTEGERs whose sum or product exceeds 32767 (or is less than –32768) will not provide an acceptable result.

1. If any ARGUMENT in one of the functions is entered as an INTEGER and that INTEGER is outside the integer limits, then the result is not usable.

2. If all of the number ARGUMENTs entered are INTEGERs, then the result will be an INTEGER, and if that result is outside the INTEGER limits, the result will be subject to error.

3. If any of the ARGUMENTs is entered as a REAL (and none is an INTEGER exceeding the INTEGER limits), then the result will be a REAL without limits.

More Elementary Functions

(1+ <number>) and (1– <number>)

These functions are just different methods of writing (+ <number> 1) and (- <number> 1), respectively. For example:

(1+ 7) returns 8
(1– 7) returns 6

(abs <number>)

This function returns the absolute value of the <number>. For example:

(abs (- 4 7)) returns 3

(ascii <string>)

This function returns the ASCII value of the first character of the <string>. For example:

> (ascii "All") returns 65
> (ascii "a") returns 97
> (ascii "B") returns 66

(chr <number>)

This function returns the character (as a one-character STRING) whose ASCII code is <number>. For example:

> (chr 65) returns "A"
> (chr 97) returns "a"
> (chr 100) returns "d"

(eval <expr>)

This function returns the result of evaluating <expr>, where <expr> is any LISP expression. For example:

> (setq z 6)
> (setq q 'z)
> (eval z) returns 6
> (eval q) returns 6

(exp <number>)

This function returns e raised to the <number> power (natural antilog). It returns a REAL. For example:

> (exp 1.0) returns 2.718282
> (exp -0.2) returns 0.818730753

(expt <base> <power>)

This function returns <base> raised to the specified <power>. If both ARGUMENTs are INTEGERs, the result is an INTEGER; otherwise, the result is a REAL. For example:

> (expt 3 4) returns 81

(log <number>)

This function returns the natural log of <number> as a REAL. For example:

> (log 3.74) returns 1.32175584
> (log 1.025) returns 0.024692613

(sqrt <number>)

This function returns the square root of <number> as a REAL. For example:

> (sqrt 16) returns 4.000000
> (sqrt 2.0) returns 1.414213562

(type <item>)

This function returns the TYPE of <item>, where TYPE is one of the following (as an atom):

> REAL   floating point numbers

FILE	file descriptors
STR	strings
INT	integer
SYM	symbol
LIST	lists (and user functions)
SUBR	internal AutoLISP functions
PICKSET	AutoCAD selection sets
ENAME	AutoCAD entity names
PAGETB	Function paging table

Trigonometry

(sin <angle>)

This function returns the sine of <angle>, where <angle> is expressed in radians.

(cos <angle>)

This function returns the cosine of <angle>, where <angle> is expressed in radians. For example:

(cos 1) returns .540302306
(sin (/ pi 2)) returns 1.00000

(atan <num1> [<num2>])

If only <num1> is present, then (atan ...) returns the angle (in radians) whose tangent is <num1>. If <num1> and <num2> are present, then (atan ...) returns the angle whose tangent is the dividend of <num1> divided by <num2>. For example:

(atan 0.75) returns 0.643501109
(atan 1.0 2.0) returns 0.463647609

LIST HANDLING FUNCTIONS

(list <expr>...)

This function has expression(s) as its ARGUMENTs. It is included in this section because it is the function that creates the LISTs that the other functions in this section require as ARGUMENTs.

(list ...)

This function takes any number of expressions and makes them into a LIST. For example:

(list 1 1) returns (1 1)

Remember! A created LIST is enclosed in parentheses.

A specific application of the (list ...) function is to combine two or three REALs in the format required by a function whose ARGUMENT is <pt> which is a 2D or 3D point. The point is a special form of a LIST.

For example:

(setq p1 (list 1.0 1.0))
(setq p2 (list 2.0 2.0))

allows the following:

$$\text{(setq a (angle p1 p2)) returns 0.785398163}$$

but

$$\text{(setq p1 (list "you" 1.0))}$$
$$\text{(setq p2 (list 2.0 2.0))}$$

followed by

$$\text{(setq a (angle p1 p2)) returns}$$
$$\text{error: bad point value}$$

(angle <pt1> <pt2>)

This function returns the angle (in radians) between the base line of angle zero and the line from pt1 to pt2.

(distance <pt1> <pt2>)

This function returns the distance in decimal units from pt1 to pt2. If the UNITS are set to Architectural and the distance between two points is 6'-3", the (distance ...) function will return 75.000000.

(polar <pt> <angle> <distance>)

This function returns a point. It can be one of the most useful tools in the AutoLISP tool kit. The ARGUMENTs must be of the proper TYPE. The <pt> must evaluate to a LIST of two REALs. The <angle> and <distance> are each a REAL. The value of the <angle> is in radians.

(osnap <pt> <mode-string>)

This function returns a point. It allows Osnapping to a point while in AutoLISP. Like the (polar ...) function, it returns a point in the form of a LIST of two or three REALs. For example, if a circle has been drawn using p1 and p2 in the 2P method as follows:

$$\text{(setq p1 (list 1.0 3.0))}$$
$$\text{(setq p2 (list 4.0 3.0))}$$
$$\text{(command "circle" "2P" p1 p2)}$$

then

$$\text{(command "line" "0,0" (setq c (osnap p1 "center")) "")}$$

returns (2.5 3.0) or the LIST or two REALs representing the center of the circle as the endpoint of the line.

(inters <pt1> <pt2> <pt3> <pt4> [<onseg>])

This function returns a point. It can be used for the following:

1. To determine if two nonparallel lines intersect.

2. If they intersect, the location of that point.

3. If they do not intersect, where they would intersect if one or both were extended until they intersected.

If the optional <onseg> ARGUMENT is present and is nil, the lines will be considered infinite in length and the function will return a LIST of three REALs designating that intersection point.

If the optional <onseg> ARGUMENT is not present or is not nil, then their intersection must be on both segments in order for a point to be returned; otherwise, the function will return nil.

CAR, CDR, And Combinations

CAR and CDR are the primary functions that select and return element(s) of a LIST. Unlike the (angle ...) function and (distance ...) function, these functions will operate on a LIST comprised of elements of any TYPE. The elements can be atoms or LISTs within the LIST. The atoms can be REALs, INTEGERs, STRINGs, or symbols. The ARGUMENT to the CAR and CDR functions can even be a LIST of mixed types of elements. These were the foundation functions designed to analyze a LIST of symbols (which is what language is). In AutoLISP, these functions break down points into coordinates. For example:

(setq p1 '(1.0 2.0)) returns (1.0 2.0)

then

(car p1) returns 1.0, a real

but

(cdr p1) returns (2.0), a list

Note the parentheses enclosing 2.0.

If

(setq L1 (list 1.0 2.0))

and

(setq L2 (list L1 3.0))

then

(car L2) returns (1.0 2.0), a list

Here is a LIST within a LIST. Or in the function-list (setq L2 (list L1 3.0)), L1 is a LIST within a LIST within a function-list.

The above expression is not used very often in AutoLISP, but its capability is worthy of note.

(car <list>) returns the first element of <list>.

(cdr <list>) returns <list> without the first element.

The TYPE of the return of the (car <list>) function depends upon the TYPE of the first element.

If

(setq L (list 1.0 2.0))

then

(car L) returns 1.0, a real

If

(setq L (list 1 2.0))

then

(car L) returns 1, an integer

If

(setq L (list "1" 2))

then

(car L) returns "1," a string

If the symbol "a" evaluates to nil and

(setq L (list a 2))

then

(car L) returns the symbol "a"

but, if

(setq a 1.0)

and

(setq L (list a 2.0))

then

(car L) returns 1.0, a real

While (car <list>) can return any type of expression, (cdr <list>) always returns a LIST. The return may not look like a LIST, but its TYPE will be a LIST (even if nil). For example:

(setq L1 (1.0 2.0))

(cdr L1) returns (2.0), a LIST

Remember, the parentheses designate the LIST and (car L1) returns 1.0, a REAL; so, how can the LIST (2.0) be used as a REAL? By using the combination of:

(car (cdr L1))

which is the same as

(car (2.0)) which returns 2.0, a REAL

Note how (car <list>) breaks the first expression out of the <list> and returns it evaluated to its type.

So while (car <list>) and (cdr <list>) operate on the same LIST, (cdr <list>) always returns a LIST. Consider:

(setq L1 (list 1.0)) returns (1.0), a LIST

(car L1) returns 1.0, a REAL

and

(cdr L1) returns nil;

it is the null LIST

or the same as (list ( ))

If

$$\text{(setq L1 (list 1.0 2.0))}$$

then

$$\text{(car L1) returns 1.0}$$

$$\text{(cdr L1) returns (2.0)}$$

and

$$\text{(car (cdr L1)) returns 2.0}$$

A short cut for the above is:

$$\text{(cadr <list>)}$$

or

$$\text{(cadr L1) which returns 2.0, a REAL}$$

CADR is one of several short forms of combinations of CAR and CDR.

REMEMBER!

$$\text{(car <list>) may return any type}$$

$$\text{(cdr <list>) is a LIST}$$

The short forms of CAR and CDR begin with "C" and end with "R." The characters between will be either an "A" or a "D" and will determine the sequence of combined CAR(s) and CDR(s). Some short forms are shown below:

CAAR	(car (car <list>))
CDDR	(cdr (cdr <list>))
CADR	(car (cdr <list>))
CDAR	(cdr (car <list>))

Any form that begins with "CA" will return an expression.

Any form that begins with "CD" will return a LIST.

All CARs and CDRs represented by "A's" and "D's" in such forms as CADAR and CDDAR, however deep, must have LISTs as their individual ARGUMENTs.

For example:

If

$$\text{(setq L1 (list (1.0 2.0) 3.0)) returns ((1.0 2.0) 3.0)}$$

$$\text{(car L1) returns (1.0 2.0), a LIST}$$

$$\text{(cdr L1) returns (3.0), also a LIST}$$

(list (1.0 2.0) 3.0) makes a LIST out of the LIST (1.0 2.0) and the atom 3.0. That is why the (car L1) returned a LIST, even though 3.0 is a REAL in the LIST "L1," (cdr <list>) always returns a LIST.

The first element of L1 is (1.0 2.0) and when removed from ((1.0 2.0) 3.0), then (3.0) remains. And that is the function of (cdr L1), to return a LIST with its first element removed.

So

(caar L1)

is the same as

(car (car L1)) and returns 1.0, a REAL

but

(cdar L1)

which is the same as

(cdr (car L1)) returns (2.0), a LIST

Because 2.0 and 3.0 are not first elements, in order to return their values as REALs, they must first be returned as the first elements of a LIST as follows:

(cadar L1)

means

(car (cdr (car L1))) and returns 2.0

and is the same as

(car (cdr (1.0 2.0)))

and the same as

(car (2.0))

and

(cadr L1)

means

(car (cdr L1)) and returns 3.0

or

(car (3.0))

CAR and CADR Mainly for Graphics

(car ...) and (cadr ...) are the primary functions for accessing the X and Y coordinates of a point in AutoCAD. Remember if:

(setq L1 (list 1.0 2.0))

is entered,

(cdr L1) returns the not-so-useful LIST (2.0)

but by using

(cadr L1)

which means

$$(car (cdr L1))$$

in the following manner

$$(cadr L1) \text{ returns } 2.0$$

which is no longer a LIST but a REAL.

Review

All forms of the CAR-CDR combination that begin with "CA" will return the first expression. All forms that begin with "CD" will return a LIST.

For graphics applications, LISTs represent the X and Y coordinates of a 2D point and the X, Y, and Z coordinates of a 3D point. Therefore, the more useful CAR-CDR combination forms are as follows:

in a 2D point

```
(setq p2d (list 1.0 2.0))
(car p2d) returns 1.0 the X coordinate
(cadr p2d) returns 2.0 the Y coordinate
(caddr p2d) returns nil
```

in a 3D point

```
(setq p3d (list 1.0 2.0 3.0))
(car p3d) returns 1.0 the X coordinate
(cadr p3d) returns 2.0 the Y coordinate
(caddr p3d) returns 3.0 the Z coordinate
(cdr p2d) returns (2.0) a LIST
```

and

```
(cdr p3d) returns (2.0 3.0), a LIST
```

neither of which is very useful unless the programmer wishes to project all of the 3D points on the Y-Z plane.

(last <list>) returns the last expression in the <list>. While (last <list>) can be used to return the Y coordinate of a 2D point and the Z coordinate of a 3D point, it is not recommended for that purpose. Because there might be an erroneous return, it is recommended that (cadr <list>) be used for the Y coordinate and (caddr <list>) for the Z coordinate.

(cons <new first element> <list>) returns the <first new element> and <list> combined into a new LIST, as in the following:

```
(setq a 2.0)
(setq b 3.0)
(setq L1 (list a b))
(cons 1.0 L1) returns (1.0 2.0 3.0)
```

(cons ...) will also return what is known as a "dotted pair" when there is an atom in place of the <list> ARGUMENT, as in the following:

```
(cons 1.0 2.0) returns (1.000000 . 2.000000)
```

This special form of LIST requires less memory than ordinary LISTs.

(length <list>) returns the number of elements in <list> as in the following:

> (setq L1 (list "you" (1.0 2.0) 3.0))
> returns ("you" (1.0 2.0) 3.0)
> (length L1) returns 3
> (length (car L1)) returns nil because (car L1) is an atom
> (length (cdr L1)) returns 2
> (length (cadr L1)) returns 2
> (length (caddr L1)) returns nil

If

> (setq L1 (list "you" (1.0) 2.0))
> (length L1) returns 3
> (length (cadr L1)) returns 1

(nth <n> <list>) returns the "nth" element of <list>.

(Zero is the first element.) For example:

> (setq L1 (list "you" (1.0 2.0) 3))
> (nth 0 L1) returns "you," a STRING
> (nth 1 L1) returns (1.0 2.0), a LIST
> (nth 2 L1) returns 3, an INTEGER
> (nth 0 (cadr L1)) returns 1.0, a REAL
> (nth 1 (cadr L1)) returns 2.0, a REAL
> (nth 3 L1) returns nil

(reverse <list>) returns the <list> with the elements in reverse order, as in the following example:

> (setq L1 (list (1.0 2.0) 3.0))
> (reverse L1) returns (3.0 (1.0 2.0))
> (reverse (car L1)) returns (2.0 1.0)

TYPE CHANGING FUNCTIONS

In order for the AutoCAD operator, AutoCAD, and AutoLISP to properly communicate between each other (and within each internally), data is constantly exchanged. Of the different data TYPEs (as classified by AutoLISP) there are three TYPEs of data that may be stored as one TYPE, but need to be communicated as another TYPE. These are the INTEGER, the REAL, and the STRING.

Some AutoLISP functions are designed to take data of one TYPE as their ARGUMENT and return that data as another TYPE. The basic outline below, Figure 18–5, shows the functions and the TYPEs that they are designed to translate from and to.

(angtos <angle> [<mode> [<precision>]]) takes <angle> input as a REAL in radians and returns a STRING in the form determined by <mode>. The value of <mode> and its corresponding format is as follows:

ANGTOS MODE	FORMAT
0	Degrees
1	Degrees/Minutes/Seconds
2	Grads
3	Radians
4	Surveyor's Units

AutoLISP

		FROM		
		INTEGER	REAL	STRING
TO	INTEGER	(FIX)	FIX	ATOI
	REAL	FLOAT	(FLOAT)	ATOF
	STRING	ITOA	ANGTOS	
			RTOS	

Figure 18–5 The basic translation for communication between AutoCAD and AutoLisp

For example:

If

(setq p1 (1.0 1.0))
(setq p2 (2.0 2.0))
(setq a (angle p1 p2)) returns 0.78539816

then

(angtos a 0) returns "45"
(angtos a 1) returns "45.000000"
(angtos a 2) returns "45d0'0.0000""
(angtos a 3) returns "0.78539816r"
(angtos a 4) returns "N 45d0'0.0000 W""

The optional <precision> determines the decimal places to be displayed.

(atof <string>) takes a <string> and returns a REAL. For example:

(atof "3.75") returns 3.750000
(atof "4") returns 4.000000

(atoi <string>) takes a <string> and returns an INTEGER. For example:

(atoi "3.75") returns 3
(atoi "4") returns 4

(itoa <int>) takes an <integer> and returns a STRING. For example:

(itoa 33) returns "33"
(itoa -4) returns "-4"

The (rtos <number> [<mode> [<precision>]]) function takes a REAL input and returns a STRING in the form determined by <mode>. The value of <mode> and its corresponding format is as follows:

RTOS MODE	FORMAT
1	Scientific
2	Decimal
3	Engineering
4	Architectural
5	Arbitrary Fractional Units

The optional <precision> determines the decimal places to be displayed.

(fix <number>) takes a REAL or INTEGER and returns an INTEGER. For example:

(fix 4) returns 4
(fix 4.25) returns 4

(float <number>) takes a REAL or INTEGER and returns a REAL. For example:

(float 4) returns 4.000000
(float 4.25) returns 4.250000

INPUT FUNCTIONS

The INPUT functions cause a program to pause for user input of a particular TYPE and return data in the format of a specified TYPE.

The optional [<prompt>] in all (get ...) functions allows the programmer to display the <prompt> message in the prompt area on the screen. It will be demonstrated in the first (get ...) function description.

> **NOTE:** The (getvar ...) function is NOT a function for user input.

> **CAUTION!**
> For all (get ...) functions, the user input CANNOT be in the form of an AutoLISP function.

(getangle [<pt>] [<prompt>]) will return an angle in radians between two points, the first of which may be the optional [<pt>] in the function. Note the option of either selecting two points or inputting the first point into the AutoLISP function and selecting the second point. This method is used in the (getdist ...) and the (getorient ...) functions and will be referred to in their descriptions. For example:

(setq a (getangle "PICK TWO POINTS: "))

will pause for the user to input 2 points, either of which may be typed in on the keyboard (as in 1'2,3'6-1/2 if in the Architectural UNITS mode), or picked on the screen. If the response to the above (getangle ...) function were 1,1 and 2,2 then the function would return 0.785398. Or if

(setq p1 (list 14.0 42.5))

then

(setq a (getangle p1 "PICK SECOND PT: "))

will use p1 for the first point and pause for the user to input the second point from the keyboard or on the screen.

If

(setq p1 (list 1 1))

and

$$(\text{setq a (getangle p1 "PICK SECOND PT: ")})$$

and 2,2 were entered, it would return 0.785398.

```
                          CAUTION!

Unlike the (angle ...) function, the angle returned by the (getangle ...)
function is affected by a change in the ANGBASE system variable.  If the
ANGBASE were changed from 0 degrees to 45 degrees, the above
(getangle p1 ...) function with a response of 2,2 would return 0.000000.
(See the (getorient ...) function description.)
```

(getcorner <pt> [<prompt>]) returns a point selected during the pause. As the user places the cursor for selection, a rectangle is displayed with the <pt> as one corner of the rectangle and the cursor location as the diagonally opposite corner.

(getdist [<pt>] [<prompt>]) returns the distance between two points in the same manner and with the same options as the (getangle ...) function returns an angle. The return will be a REAL. If the UNITS are set to Architectural a length of 3'-6 1/2" would be returned as 42.500000.

(getint [<prompt>]) pauses for an INTEGER input and returns that INTEGER.

(getkword [<prompt>]) pauses for user input of a keyword that must correspond to a word on a LIST set up by the (initget ...) function prior to using the (getkword ...) function. If the response is not appropriate then AutoCAD will retry. This function prevents a program from terminating prematurely due to the wrong type of data being input by mistake, and gives the user another chance. It also permits returning a STRING by just inputting initial letters. For example:

```
(initget 1 "SET Make New")
(setq g (getkword "LAYER CHOICES? (SET, M, or N): "))
```

AutoCAD will reject any response that does not comprise the initial uppercase characters of the options in the list set by (initget ...). The response may also include any and all of the lowercase characters in the STRING, but nothing in addition to the characters of any of the options. The responses that are valid to the above example are: SET, M, Ma, Mak, Make, N, Ne, and New, with any of the preceding in uppercase.

```
(initget 1 "SET MaKe New")
(getkword)
```

will accept "m" because the "K" was preceded by a lowercase "a."

```
(initget 1 "SET MAke New")
(getkword)
```

will not accept "m," but will accept "ma," "mak," or "make," but not "makeup."

(getorient [<pt>] [<prompt>]) will pause for the user to input two points, and will return an angle in radians between two points.

The point selection options are the same as the (getangle ...) function. Unlike the (getangle ...) function, the (getorient ...) function is not affected by an ANGBASE system variable change. It will return an angle determined by the line connecting the two input points. The angle will be measured between that line and the zero East baseline regardless of the ANGBASE setting.

(getpoint [<pt>] [<prompt>]) pauses for input of a point (either from the keyboard or a pick on the screen), and returns that point in the form of a LIST of two REALs.

The optional <pt>, if used, will cause a rubberband line from <pt> to the placement of the cursor until a pick is made.

(getreal [<prompt>]) pauses for user input of a REAL number and returns that REAL number.

(getstring [<cr>] [<prompt>]) pauses for keyboard characters to be entered and returns them as a STRING. It is not necessary to enclose the input in quotation marks. AutoLISP will do that automatically. The optional <cr>, if present and not nil, will permit the STRING to have blank spaces. The STRING must be terminated by striking [Enter]. Otherwise, if <cr> is present and nil, striking the spacebar will terminate the entry.

(initget [<bits>] [<string>]) offers the programmer a one-time control of the user's response to the next (get ...) function, and that (get ...) function only.

This only means that any time control is needed for a (get ...) function, a new (initget ...) function must precede it.

The type of control that is offered by the (initget ...) function is as follows:

1. The program can be set up to reject responses of a certain unwanted type or value (without terminating the program) and offer the user a second chance to enter an acceptable response.
2. The program can be made to accept points outside of the limits even when LIMCHECK is on.
3. The program can be made to return 3D points rather than 2D points.
4. Dashed lines can be used when drawing a rubberband or a box.
5. The program can be made to accept a STRING when the (get ...) function normally requires a specific TYPE such as POINT or REAL.

The controls offered by using the <bits> option are shown in Figure 18–6. The <bits> may be a sum of whichever values in Figure 18–6 correspond to the controls desired for the next (get ...) function. For example:

```
(setq p1 (list 0 0))
(initget 9)
(setq d (getdist p1 "SECOND POINT: "))
```

The bits in the above line are a sum of 1 (rejects null input) and 8 (allows input outside limits). This will allow the second point to be outside the limits even if the LIMITS mode is ON. It also will not accept a null return.

CONDITIONAL AND LOGIC FUNCTIONS

AutoLISP's conditional and logic functions allow the user to have a program test certain conditions and proceed according to the result of those tests. Or, by using the WHILE function, a programmer's LOOP situation will allow iteration of a changing variable between the extents of a specified range.

BITS VALUE	MEANING
1	REJECTS NULL INPUT
2	REJECTS ZERO VALUES
4	REJECTS NEGATIVE VALUES
8	ALLOWS INPUT OUTSIDE LIMITS
16	RETURNS 3D POINTS RATHER THAN 2D
32	USES DASHED LINES FOR RUBBERBAND/BOX

Figure 18–6 The controls offered by the Bits option

The symbol "T" is used when an expression is needed that will never evaluate to nil.

(if <testexpr> <thenexpr> [<elseexpr>]) evaluates the <testexpr>. If the <textexpr> does not return nil, then the function returns the evaluation of the <thenexpr>. If the optional <elseexpr> is present and the <testexpr> evaluates to nil, then the function returns the evaluation of the <elseexpr>. Otherwise, the function returns nil. For example:

```
(setq q (getint "ENTER QUANTITY FROM 1-99: " ))
(if (< q 10)
    (setq c q)
    (setq c (fix (/ q 10)))
)
```

This program will take a number (from user input) and test to see if it is less than 10. If so, it will SETQ the symbol "c" to that number. If it is 10 or greater, it will divide the number by 10 and SETQ "c" to the whole number of the result, such as 37 becomes 3.7 becomes 3.

(cond (<test1> <result1> ...) ...) accepts any number of ARGUMENTs. The first item in each list is evaluated, and when one returns not nil, the following expressions in that list are evaluated and the function returns the value of the last expression. For example, a routine could be written to return the angle of a line to be only in the first or fourth quadrants, regardless of how it was originally selected. Note the four possibilities shown in Figure 18–7.

We will not consider the four ortho directions N, E, S, or W, in this example. If an angle is returned that was determined by the function (setq a (angle p1 p2)), then it could be in one of four quadrants. Then to assure that no matter which angle was set by p1-p2, the function would return an angle in the first or fourth quadrant. For example:

```
(setq a (angle p1 p2))
(cond
    ((and (> a pi) (< a (* 3 (/ pi 2)))) (setq a (- a pi))
    ((and (> a (/ pi 2)) (< a pi)) (setq a (+ a pi))
)
```

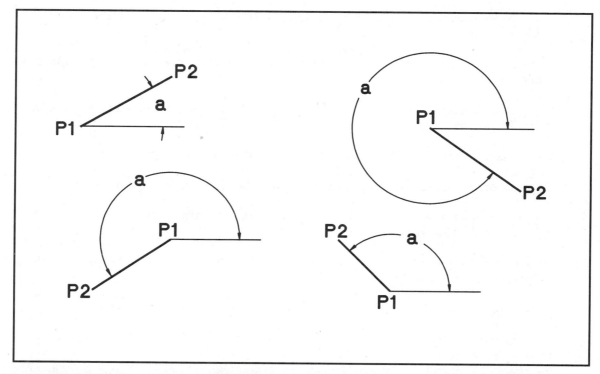

Figure 18–7   Conditional and logic function return possibilities

The (while <testexpr> <expr>...) function evaluates the <textexpr>, and if not nil, evaluates the following expressions and then repeats the procedure again with the <testexpr>.

This repetition continues until the <textexpr> evaluates to nil and then the function returns the evaluation of the <lastexpr>.

Test Expressions

The (if ...), (cond ...), and (while ...) functions normally use one of the logic functions as the <textexpr>. For example, the following program line was previously entered:

> (setq a 10.0)
> (if (null a) (setq a 6.0))

This sequence will not change the value of the symbol "a" because the evaluation of the expression (null a) is "nil." Therefore, the following expression will not be evaluated. Had "a" not been previously SETQed, the expression (null a) would evaluate to "T" (for TRUE), and the expression following would be evaluated and would have SETQed the symbol "a" to 6.0.

(= <atom> <atom> ...) returns T if all of the <atom>s evaluate to the same thing.

(/= <atom1> <atom2>) returns T if <atom1> is "not equal to" <atom2>. It is nil otherwise.

(< <atom> <atom> ...) returns T if each <atom> is "less than" the <atom> to its right. It is nil otherwise.

(<= <atom> <atom> ...) returns T if each <atom> is "less than or equal to" the <atom> to its right. It is nil otherwise.

(> <atom> <atom> ...) returns T if each <atom> is "greater than" the <atom> to its right. It is nil otherwise.

(>= <atom> <atom> ...) returns T if each <atom> is "greater than or equal to" the <atom> to its right. It is nil otherwise.

(and <expr>...) returns T if all <expr>s return T. It is nil otherwise.

(boundp <atom>) returns T if <atom> has a value bound to it. It is nil otherwise.

(eq <expr1> <expr2>) returns T if <expr1> and <expr2> are identical and are bound to the same object. It is nil otherwise.

(equal <expr1> <expr2>) returns T if <expr1> and <expr2> evaluate to the same thing. It is nil otherwise.

(not <expr>) returns T if <expr> is nil. Otherwise the function returns nil.

(null <item>) returns T if <item> is bound to nil. The function returns nil otherwise.

(or <expr>...) returns T if any of the <expr>s evaluate to something that is not nil. Otherwise the function returns nil.

EXERCISES

1. Identify the atoms in the following expressions:
   (if (not (null dfr)) (setq dfr (rtos rad)) (setq dfr "0"))

Write the AutoLISP expression equivalent to the following:

2. $a = 1$
3. $b = 2.0$
4. $c = a$
5. $d = 1 + 2$
6. $e = \sqrt{2}$
7. $f = 1 + b^2$
8. $g = 7 + 9 + 3 + 7$
9. $h = (3 + 5 + 6) + 7$
10. $i = (7 \quad 3) + (4 - (6 \quad 3))$
11. $j = 3 (7 + 6)$
12. $k = 3 + (7 \times 6)$
13. $l = 5 - (7 + 2)$
14. $m = \sin\ 0.75$
15. $n = \cos\ 1.75$
16. $o = \sin\ (pi \div 2)$
17. $p = $ absolute value of a
18. $q = x^3$
19. $r = \tan^{-1}((3\ pi) + 4)$

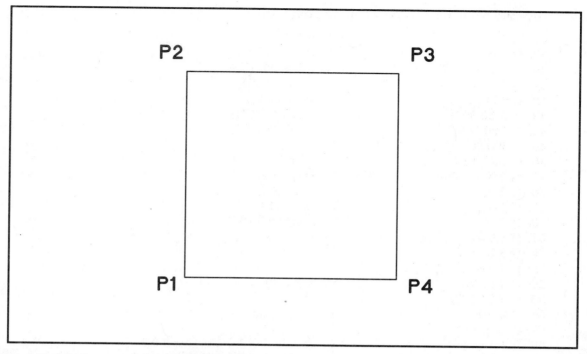

Figure Ex18–1   The rectangle for writing expressions

In the rectangle shown in Figure Ex18–1, write the expressions that evaluate to the following:

20. the vertical distance between p1 and p3
21. the distance between p1 and p3
22. the horizontal distance between p2 and p4
23. the distance between p1 and p4
24. p2 in terms of p1 and p3
25. p3 in terms of p2 and p4
26. the sum of the four sides (perimeter)
27. the area enclosed by the four sides
28. the area of a triangle whose vertices are p1, p2, and p3
29. the angle between lines from p1 to p3 and from p1 to p4

Answer the following:

30. In (setq L1 (list 1.0 2.0)) what is (car L1)?
31. In (setq L2 (list 3.0 4.0)) what is (cdr L2)?
32. In (setq L3 (list 5.0 6.0)) what is (cadr L3)?

Example: (setq L5 (list 1.0 '(2.0 (3.0 4.0)) 5.0))

In the above example, write the combination of car and cdr that will return the following from the LIST L5:

33. 1.0
34. 2.0
35. 3.0
36. 4.0
37. 5.0

Give the evaluations of the following expressions:

38. (+ 1.0 2.0)
39. (+ 3 4)
40. (+ 5 6.0)
41. (- 7 6)
42. (- 8 9)
43. (+ 1 20 300)
44. (- 1 20 300)
45. (- 300 20 1)
46. (- 30000 1.0)
47. (+ 30000 30000)
48. (* 1 2)
49. (* 1.0 2.0)
50. (* 3 4)
51. (* 5.0 6)
52. (* 1 2 3)
53. (* 4 4 6.0)
54. (* 7 8000)
55. (* 8.0 9000)
56. (* 3 pi)
57. (* pi pi)
58. (/ 2.0 1.0)
59. (/ 2.0 1)
60. (/ 2 1)
61. (/ 1 2)
62. (/ 3 2)
63. (/ 3.0 2)
64. (/ 3 2.0)

65. (/ 1.0 2)
66. (/ 40000 2)
67. (/ 2 40000)
68. (abs (+ 4 2))
69. (abs (- 4 2))
70. (ascii "ABC")
71. (ascii "aBC")
72. (chr 66)
73. (chr 98)
74. (expt 3 2)
75. (expt 2 3)
76. (sqrt 9)
77. (sqrt (* 2 8))
78. (type 1)
79. (type pi)
80. (type 3.0)
81. (type T)
82. (sin 0)
83. (cos (/ pi 2))
84. (atan 1)
85. (angle (list 1.0 1.0) (list 2.0 2.0))
86. (angle (list 2.0 1.0) (list 0.0 1.0))
87. (distance (list 1.0 1.0) (list 3.5 1.0))
88. (distance (list 6.0 5.0) (list 2.0 2.0))
89. (polar (list 1.0 1.0) 0 2.0)
90. (polar (list 2.0 3.0) pi 1)
91. (inters (list 0.0 0.0) (list 3.0 3.0) (list 3.0 0.0) (list 0.0 3.0))

CUSTOM COMMANDS AND FUNCTIONS

(defun ...) and (defun C: ...)

This is an AutoLISP function called DEFUN that will create a custom-designed function. Its format is:

(defun <sym> <argument list> <expr>...).

The DEFUN function operates in a manner similar to the SETQ function. SETQ names a variable and sets it equal to a value. DEFUN names a new function so that when its name is entered in a routine, it will evaluate to the subsequent expression(s). In addition, it allows variables to be operated on by the function by entering the name of that defined function followed by a variable or group of variables.

The customizing power of this feature cannot be emphasized enough. What this means to the programmer is that when a routine has been worked out in AutoLISP, the entire routine can be given a name. Then when the routine needs to be used again, the programmer simply enters the name of the routine. This makes it a user-defined or custom-defined function.

The name of a custom-defined function can also be entered while in AutoCAD or it can be included in a MENU STRING by entering its name enclosed in parentheses.

In addition to having a one-word entry perform the task of many lines of programming, there is an optional feature that makes the custom-defined function even more effective. The user can define the custom function to perform the prescribed task on a dummy variable in the definition and then enter the defined function followed by some real variable later and have the task performed on the REAL variable. The dummy variables are listed in the <argument list>.

Arguments And Local Symbols

Every custom-defined function and command must include the parentheses used to enclose the ARGUMENTs. Even if there are no ARGUMENTs or local symbols (which means the opening and closing parentheses would be empty), those opening and closing parentheses must follow the user-designated function name. Remember, however, that ARGUMENTs (the dummy variables) are not permitted in custom commands using the "C:FNAME" format. The following forms are examples of how function and command definitions may be written:

(defun fname ( )...def exprs...)	no ARGUMENTs or local symbols
(defun C:FNAME ( )...def exprs...)	no ARGUMENTs or local symbols
(defun fname (/ x y z)...def exprs...)	three local symbols only
(defun C:FNAME (/ x y z)...def exprs...)	three local symbols only
(defun fname (a b)...def exprs...)	two ARGUMENTs only
(defun fname (a b / x y z)...def exprs...)	two ARGUMENT and three local symbols

---

CAUTION!

If the ARGUMENTs enclosing parentheses are inadvertently omitted, AutoLISP will take whatever is in the first parentheses of the definition expressions and try to use them as ARGUMENTs and/or local symbols. This will naturally not operate as expected and result in an error message. Therefore, include parentheses as shown, even if empty.

Also, within the <argument list> optional local symbols may be listed (after the slash) to name symbols to be used within the function definition only, without having any effect on the same symbol name outside the defined function. This form of creating a defined function is for use within AutoLISP and cannot be entered without the enclosing parentheses. An added feature, to be discussed later, will allow the same user-defined function to be invoked in the same manner as AutoCAD commands. That is, with the added feature, they can be entered from the keyboard or in the menu without parentheses and then recalled immediately afterward by simply striking Enter.

Defined Functions And Commands

When one starts to delve into custom programs in many graphic applications, one of the first geometric-trigonometric stumbling blocks to overcome is the use of radians to measure angles. AutoCAD is no exception. Even if the use of radians is second nature to someone, using degrees seems to be first nature with almost all designer-drafters. The main problem is in converting from one to the other. This is often necessary because AutoCAD uses degrees in the screen and radians in AutoLISP. Therefore, one of the first AutoLISP routines introduced in articles and books on AutoLISP is one that converts the value of an angle in degrees to its value in radians. The second routine is usually one that converts from radians back to degrees. The usual name for the degrees-to-radians function is an abbreviation called dtr. The dtr function is written as follows:

```
(defun dtr (a)
   (* pi (/ a 180.0))
)
```

From the format:

```
(defun <sym> <argument list> <expr>...)
```

dtr is the symbol (<sym>), "a" is the only ARGUMENT in the ARGUMENT list, and the expression (<expr>) is:

```
(* pi (/ a 180.0)).
```

While (/ a 180.0) is an expression, it resides within the expression "(* pi (/ a 180.0))," and is not considered one of the separate "<expr>" expressions in the form:

```
(defun <sym> <argument list> <expr>...)
```

The "<expr>... " indicates there is no limit to the number of expressions possible in a defined function. While this is a very minor point, it may help in understanding what an expression is and how AutoLISP looks at them.

Writing a Defined Function

The dtr function may be typed in from the keyboard while in the AutoCAD screen as follows:

Command: **(defun dtr (a) (* pi (/ a 180.0)))**

This function may be used and applied to any real number in the following manner:

Command: **(dtr 90.0)**
(returns 1.570796327)
        or
Command: **(dtr 180.0)**
(returns 3.141592654)
        or
Command: **(dtr 7.5)**
(returns 0.130899694)

While entering the above from the keyboard will define the dtr function for use at any time during the current editing session, the definition will be lost when the drawing is ENDed. Although writing this routine is fairly simple, it is still not very economical. There is a better way.

Writing And Storing a Defined Function

Usually, any function that needs to be defined in one drawing will be useful enough to warrant saving the definition for instant re-use later in any drawing without having to type it in repeatedly.

Therefore, defined functions may be saved for loading into a drawing. By using a text editor or word processor in the programmer mode, the custom programmer can create a file having the file extension of .LSP, and then type in the routine. The example below is similar to the first example, only with a slight variation in format. It is as follows:

Filename: **ANGLE.LSP**

```
(defun dtr (a)              ;degrees to radians
    (* pi (/ a 180.0))      ;pi times "a" divided by 180
    )                       ;leave function definition
```

The indentation is permissible in writing a defined function in a FILENAME.LSP file (unlike the program lines in a FILENAME.MNU file). It is even desirable in order to be able to easily identify the distinct elements and subelements of the function definition. The value of this procedure will become more evident with more elaborate definitions. The closing parenthesis, on a line by itself, is lined up with the opening parenthesis. This is an example of how indentation coincides with the depth of nesting of expressions.

In the last example, remarks have been written to the right, following semicolons. AutoLISP ignores anything on a line following a semicolon.

Function Names   The name of the file may or may not be the same as any of the function names it includes. It may even be the same as a function in another file, although that would not be logical. Uniqueness of names is critical within a group of named items, such as files, functions, variables, drawings on one directory, etc. But in most cases it is not a problem to duplicate names across groups, such as having a FILENM1.LSP and a FILENM1.DWG and a FILENM1.SHP at the same time along with defining a custom function as follows:

```
(defun filenm1 (.....
```

Duplication in this case is not only acceptable, but sometimes desirable in coordinating a group of specially named custom files and functions that are all in a single enhancement program being used for a singular purpose.

Loading a Defined Function   As mentioned earlier in this chapter, custom-defined functions must be written into a FILENAME.LSP file in order to be saved and usable later. Once a custom-defined function is stored in that file, the user must load the file in order to use it. For example, the file named ANGLE.LSP has been created to store the custom-defined function named dtr as follows:

Filename: **ANGLE.LSP**

```
(defun dtr (a)              ;degrees to radians
    (* pi (/ a 180.0))      ;pi times a divided by 180
    )                       ;leave function definition
```

In order to make dtr usable, the user must invoke the AutoLISP function named LOAD. It has the format of:

```
(load <filename>)
```

with <filename> being a STRING without the extension of .LSP. Therefore, the filename must be enclosed within quotations as follows:

```
(load "angle")
```

CAUTION!

The user is advised to be aware of the distinction between the AutoLISP function "load" and the AutoCAD command "load". The AutoCAD command named "LOAD" is used to load FILENAME.SHP (shape) files and is entered without the parentheses in the following manner:

Command: **LOAD**

The AutoLISP function named "load" is used to load FILENAME.LSP (AutoLISP) files and is entered with the parentheses in the following manner:

Command: **(load "angle")**

The above sequence will make the custom-defined function named dtr usable in the current editing session. The user must be careful when trying to load .LSP files from some other drive or directory. If the file named ANGLE.LSP is stored on the directory named "LISPFILE" then the format would be as follows:

Command: **(load "/lispfile/angle")**

Special note should be made of the forward slash versus the backslash. The filename is a STRING and a leading backslash in a STRING is itself a special control character used in conjunction with other code characters for specific operations on the STRING. Note that in order to have a backslash read as a backslash in a STRING, there must be a double backslash. Therefore, the forward slash is recommended in designating a directory path in PC-DOS/MS-DOS.

Drive specifications can also be included in the AutoLISP LOAD function format as follows:

Command: **(load "a:angle")**

or

Command: **(load "a:/lispfile/angle")**

The last entry may be used if the ANGLE.LSP file is in the lispfile directory on the A: drive.

If the custom programmer has created custom-defined functions in a file called "ACAD.LSP" and that file is accessible when a drawing is edited, AutoCAD will "load" that file automatically. Only functions that might be used in all drawings should be included in that file if it is created.

SIN And COS, But Not TAN! Sometimes designer-drafters wish to determine some distances in the all-powerful right triangle (from which trigonometry is derived) by using the opposite and adjacent sides instead of the hypotenuse. So why doesn't AutoLISP have the TAN (tangent) function in addition to the SIN and COS? First of all, an angle is defined in *Webster's New Collegiate Dictionary* as "...a measure of the amount of turning necessary to bring one line or plane into coincidence with or parallel to another." Two special cases exist in computing the tangent of an angle, one of which causes a problem that the sine and cosine do not cause. When two lines exist, it is assumed that they must have length and therefore have a nonzero value. When considering the sine or cosine of an angle, the hypotenuse is always one of the existing nonzero lines. And in the sine and cosine of any angle the hypotenuse is always the divisor. So, even if the opposite side (in the case of the sine) or the adjacent side (in the case of the cosine) turn out to be zero, the worst that can happen is that the function will result in zero. In the case of the tangent where the divisor is the adjacent side, if it is zero, the result approaches infinity and is therefore not valid for use within the program. This occurs, of course, at 90 degrees.

The other special case is where the angle is zero and the tangent is zero. Zero may be a valid entry, where infinity cannot be. This problem does not occur in the sine and cosine functions because the results of either range from 1 to 0 to -1 and back to 1. All results within this range are valid for use within programs.

An approach to arriving at the tangent is possible by using existing AutoLISP functions named SIN and COS. The tangent can be expressed as the quotient of the sine divided by the cosine. But here again is the possibility of the divisor being zero because the cosine of 90 degrees is just that. If used for specific purposes where it is known that the value of the adjacent side involved is nonzero, then a custom-defined function that will return the tangent of an angle (along with a radians-to-degrees function) might be included in the ANGLE.LSP file as follows:

Filename: **ANGLE.LSP**

```
(defun dtr (a)              ;degrees to radians
   (* pi (/ a 180.0))       ;pi times a divided by 180
)                           ;leave function definition

(defun rtd (b)              ;radians to degrees
   (* 180.0 (/ b pi))       ;180 times b divided by pi
)                           ;leave function definition

(defun tan (c)              ;tangent
   (/ (sin c) (cos c))      ;sine divided by cosine
)                           ;leave function definition
```

Defined AutoLISP Commands   AutoCAD's programming features allow the creation of custom-defined AutoLISP commands with two characteristics similar to regular AutoCAD commands.

1. AutoLISP commands can be entered from the keyboard or within a menu string by just entering the name of the custom command without having to enclose it in parentheses.

2. If a particular AutoLISP command was the last command used, then striking Enter will recall that same command for immediate use.

> **NOTE:** AutoLISP commands cannot operate on external variables (ARGUMENTs) of an <argument list>. However, local symbols are allowed.

Writing An AutoLISP Function   The format used in creating an AutoLISP command is as follows:

(defun C:CMDNAME </ local symbols> <expr>...)

where "CMDNAME" may be a name of your choice and can duplicate the name of an existing AutoCAD command or function, if your purpose is to override that command with a definition of your own.

WHAT IS THE DATA BASE?

The file that stores information about the drawing includes TABLES and BLOCK sections that include data associated with linetype, layer, style (for text), view, UCS, viewport, and Blocks. These are accessible through the (tblnext...) and (tblsearch...) functions.

The ENTITIES section contains data associated individually with each entity in the drawing. There are functions that point to the entity data and that can use or manipulate that data.

Entity Names, Entity Data, And Selection Sets

Information is continually being updated during an editing session. An ongoing record is being kept for each new, modified, or deleted entity. The information or data concerning each entity is stored at some particular location in the drawing file. (This location is not to be confused with its X, Y, and Z coordinates.)

AutoLISP gains access to an entity's data through its entity name, which points to the location of the entity's data within the drawing file. The entity name is the address of that entity's data. You must grasp the concepts of entity name and entity data and be able to distinguish between the two.

Entity Name Functions

Entity name functions evaluate to an item whose DATA TYPE is called an AutoCAD entity name. An entity name can be used as a response when an AutoCAD command prompts you to "Select object:."

The (entnext [<ename>]) function, if performed with no ARGUMENTs, returns the entity name of the first nondeleted entity in the data base. If (entnext...) is performed with an entity name (which we will arbitrarily call en1 for illustration purposes) as the ARGUMENT, it returns the entity name of the first nondeleted entity that follows en1 in the data base.

Walking Through The Data Base

Certain functions can search through the data base. The (entlast) function returns the entity name of the last nondeleted main entity in the data base. It may be used to return the entity name of a new entity that has just been added by a previous (command...) function.

The (entsel [<prompt>]) function returns a LIST which has the entity name as the first element and the point by which the entity was selected as the second element. Note that the second element (a point) is a LIST itself. For example:

```
Command: line
From point: 1,1
to point: 4,4
to point: Enter
Command: (setq es (entsel "Select an Entity: "))
Select an Entity: 2.5,2.5
returns (<Entity name: 60000018> (2.5 2.5 0.0))
```

While the evaluation of (entsel...) is a LIST and not an AutoCAD entity name, its first element is an entity name, obtainable by using the following:

Command: **(car es)**
returns <Entity name: 60000018>,
an entity name

Note that the address of the above entity is displayed in hexadecimal form "60000018" and is different for each different entity name. It will also differ from one editing session to the next for the same entity.

Point data is also obtainable by:

Command: **(cadr es)**
returns (2.5 2.5 0.0),
a LIST

and the X-coordinate is obtainable by:

Command: **(caadr es)**
returns 2.5,
a REAL

Note that:

Command: **(cdr es)**
returns ((2.5 2.5 0.0)),

which is a LIST whose only element is also the LIST (2.5 2.5 0.0).

The (handent <handle>) function returns the entity name associated with the specified handle. This more advanced concept will not be covered within the scope of this section. It is noteworthy, however, that the (handent...) function does assist in the problem of entities changing their names from one editing session to the next.

Entity Data Functions

These functions have entity names as their ARGUMENTs.

ENTGET Function   The primary entity data function is (entget <ename>). This function returns a LIST of entity data describing <ename> in that special format called an ASSOCIATION LIST.

Data Types For Data Base Functions   Before continuing with detailed descriptions of the entity data functions and even before introducing selection sets, it would be convenient to discuss certain DATA TYPES which AutoLISP has set aside especially for use when accessing the data base. Some of the concepts used in this discussion of DATA TYPES will not be described in detail until later in this section. Therefore, the student will probably wish to refer back later for review after studying those concepts.

In a manner similar to INTEGERs, REALs, STRINGs, and LISTs, the special DATA TYPES called AutoCAD selection sets and AutoCAD entity names can be used as ARGUMENTs required by

AutoLISP

certain AutoLISP functions. It should be noted that the special functions designed to operate on these DATA TYPES can operate on them only. For example:

Having performed the following:

>   (setq en1 (entnext))
>   (setq ss1 (ssget "w" '(0 0) '(12 9))
>   (setq od1 (list 1.0 2.0))
>   (setq od2 "HELLO")

then

>   (setq ed1 (entget en1))

and

>   (setq en2 (ssname ss1 0))

are valid entries.

But

>   (setq ed2 (entget od1))

and

>   (setq ed3 (entget od2))

are not valid. The reason for the above valid and nonvalid entries are because en1 is an AutoCAD entity name which is the required DATA TYPE for an ARGUMENT to the (entget...) function, while od1 and od2 are other DATA TYPES and not valid as ARGUMENTs. Od1 is a LIST and od2 is a STRING.

Similarly, ss1 is a special DATA TYPE called AutoCAD selection set and is valid as an ARGUMENT to the (ssname...) function.

Further study will show that the (ssname...) function returns a value in the form of that special DATA TYPE called AutoCAD entity name. Therefore, if the above entries had been performed, then the following:

>   (setq ed4 (entget (ssname ss1 0)))

is a valid entry, returning the data (as an ASSOCIATION LIST) about the first entity in the drawing file that is included in a window whose corners are 0,0 and 12,9. Even if no entities had been found, and the above operation returned nil, the operation would still have been proper, having had the required DATA TYPE as an ARGUMENT to the (entget...) function.

Back To Entget For an example let's say a newly created drawing had as the first entries, the following:

```
Command: line
From point: 1,1
To point: 4,4
To point: Enter

Command: line
From point: 1,4
To point: 4,1
To point: Enter
```

then:

(setq L1 (entget (entnext))

returns ((-1 . <Entity name: 60000018>) (0 . "LINE") (8 . "0") (10 1.0 1.0 0.0) (11 4.0 4.0 0.0) (210 0.0 0.0 1.0))

and

(setq L2 (entget (entlast))

or

(setq L2 (entget (entnext L1))

returns ((-1 . <Entity name: 60000030>) (0 . "LINE") (8 . "0") (10 1.0 4.0 0.0) (11 4.0 1.0 0.0) (210 0.0 0.0 1.0))

Also note the syntax in the following example:

Having entered:

(setq en1 (entnext))

and

(setq en2 (entlast))

then

(setq L1 (entget en1))

returns the same as

(setq L1 (entget (entnext)))

and

(setq L2 (entget en2))

returns the same as

(setq L2 (entget (entlast)))

or

(setq L2 (entget (entnext L1)))

This is to emphasize that the entity names en1 and en2 are only addresses (or pointers) to where the data associated with the entities are located within the drawing file. The data list itself is gotten through the (entget...) function, which must have that address or entity name as its ARGUMENT.

The ASSOCIATION LIST

Once the concepts of <ename>s and <elist>s are understood and the throes of creating those first routines to extract them are survived, the custom programmer must now deal with how to make use of the results.

The (assoc <item> <alist>) function is the primary mechanism used to extract specific data associated with a selected entity. In order to store data in an organized, efficient, and economical fashion, each common group of data is assigned what is called a GROUP CODE. That GROUP CODE is simply an INTEGER. For example, for a line, its starting point is a GROUP CODE 10 and its layer a GROUP CODE 8.

Using the first entity in the previous example, then you may enter the following sequence:

Command: **(setq ed1 (entget (entnext)))**

returns the ASSOCIATION LIST we saw earlier, which we will display as follows:

```
((-1 . <Entity name:60000018>)
  (0 . "LINE")
  (8 . "0")
  (10 1.0 1.0 0.0)
  (11 4.0 4.0 0.0)
  (210 0.0 0.0 1.0)
)
```

Dotted Pairs   The first and last parentheses enclose the ASSOCIATION LIST. The other matched pairs of parentheses each enclose LISTs, each comprising a specific GROUP CODE INTEGER as the first element followed by its associated value. In the case of the GROUP CODE 8, its value is the STRING "0," which is the name of the layer that this entity is on. Likewise, the value of the GROUP CODE 0 is the entity type which is the STRING "LINE." Note that these two sublists have a period between the GROUP CODE and its associated value (separated by spaces). This is a special list called a dotted pair, which requires less memory in storage. For economy, AutoCAD uses these dotted pairs where feasible. Some GROUP CODES, like the starting point, may be in the more common form of the LIST, such as (10 1.0 1.0 0.0) with the GROUP CODE as the first element followed by the X, Y, and Z coordinates, respectively.

GROUP CODES are broken down in accordance with the following tables:

GROUP CODE RANGE	FOLLOWING VALUE
0 – 9	STRING
10 – 59	FLOATING-POINT
60 – 79	INTEGER
210 – 239	FLOATING-POINT
999	COMMENT (STRING)

GROUP CODE	VALUE TYPE
0	Identifies the start of an entity, table entry, or file separator. The text value that follows indicates which.
1	The primary text value for an entity.
2	A name, Attribute tag, Block name, etc.
3–4	Other textual or name values.
5	Entity handle expressed as a hexadecimal string.
6	Linetype name (fixed).
7	Text style name (fixed).
8	Layer name (fixed).
9	Variable name identifier (used only in HEADER section of the DXF file).

10	Primary point (start point of a Line or Text entity, center of a circle, etc.).
11–18	Other points.
39	This entity's thickness if nonzero (fixed).
40–48	Floating-point values (text height, scale, etc.).
49	Repeated value — multiple 49 groups may appear in one entity for variable length tables (such as the dash lengths in the LTYPE table).
50–58	Angles.
62	Color number (fixed).
66	"Entities follow" flag (fixed).
70–78	Integer values, such as repeat counts, modes.
210,220,230	X, Y, and Z components of extrusion direction.
999	Comments

Extracting Data From a LIST

```
((-1 . <Entity name:60000018>)
  (0 . "LINE")
  (8 . "0")
  (10 1.0 1.0 0.0)
  (11 4.0 4.0 0.0)
  (210 0.0 0.0 1.0)
)
```

If the above list had been SETQed to the variable named ed1 then examples of the (assoc...) function would be as follows:

Command: **(assoc 0 ed1)**
returns (0 . "LINE")

Command: **(assoc 8 ed1)**
returns (8 . "0")

Command: **(assoc 10 ed1)**
returns (10 1.0 1.0 0.0)

The above results are LISTs. The first two are dotted pairs. In order to extract data from these, the following may be entered:

Command: **(cdr (assoc 0 ed1))**
returns "LINE,"
a STRING

Command: **(cdr (assoc 8 ed1))**
returns "0,"
also a STRING

AutoLISP

but

Command: **(cdr (assoc 10 ed1))**
returns (1.0 1.0 0.0),
a LIST

Therefore, in order to extract the X coordinate, enter:

Command: **(cadr (assoc 10 ed1))**
returns 1.0,
a REAL

Note how CDR returns the second element of a dotted pair as an atom while it requires CADR to return the second element of an ordinary LIST as an atom. CDR applied to an ordinary LIST returns a LIST (unless it is applied to a single element LIST).

Other Entity Data Functions

The (entdel <ename>) function deletes the entity specified by <ename> from the drawing or restores the entity previously deleted during the current editing session.

The (entmod <elist>) updates the data base information for the entity specified. Using this function in conjunction with the AutoLISP (subst...) function is a convenient method of making specific changes to selected entities.

The (entupd <ename>) function is used for more advanced handling of Block and Polyline subentities. The student is referred to the AutoLISP Programmer's Reference for use of this function.

Selection Sets

A selection set is a collection of entity names. It is the programmer's equivalent to a group of entities selected by one or more of the optional methods of selecting objects from the screen. Except that, by using the selection set functions, certain entities not visible on the screen may even be included in the group. It should be emphasized that a selection set comprises the entity names of the entities in the group. The selection set can be used in response to any AutoCAD command where selection by "Last" is valid. It also is a valid ARGUMENT to selection set functions that supply entity names to the (entget) function, which then returns entity data in the form of an ASSOCIATION LIST.

The (ssget [<mode>] [<pt1> [<pt2>]]) function returns the selection set and prompts something like <Selection set: 1>. This indicates that the selection set contains one or more entities. If no objects meet the selection method, then nil would be returned.

The <mode>, if included, determines by what method the selection process is made. The "W," "L," "C," or "P" correspond to the window, last, crossing, or previous selection modes. Examples are as follows:

(ssget)	Asks the user for entity selection with one or more standard options.
(ssget "W" '(2 2) '(8 9))	Selects the entities inside the window from 2,2 to 8,9.
(ssget "L")	Selects last entity added to the data base.

(ssget "C" '(0 0) '(5 3))	Selects the entities crossing the box from 0,0 to 5,3.
(ssget "P")	Selects the most recently selected objects.
(ssget '(1.0 1.0))	Selects the entity passing through the point 1,1.
(ssget "X" <filter-list>)	Selects the entities matching the "filter-list."

SSGET Filters The (ssget "X" <filter-list>) function provides a method of scanning the entire drawing file and selecting the entities having certain values associated with specified GROUP CODES. This function is used in conjunction with the (cons...) function. Note that while the (ssget...) function returns a group of entity names, it scans a group of ASSOCIATION LISTS (the drawing file, that is). So, the filter will be constructed in a manner that can be tested against entity data. Examples are as follows:

> (ssget "X" (list (cons 0 "CIRCLE")))

returns a selection set consisting of all the circles in the drawing.

> (ssget "X" (list (cons 8 "0")))

returns all entities on layer "0."

> (ssget "X" (list (cons 0 "CIRCLE") (cons 8 "0")))

returns all circles on layer "0."

The student should note at this time that the (ssget "X"...) function only selects from main entities. Special methods must be used to gain data about subentities such as attributes and Polyline vertices.

The (sslength <ss>) function returns an integer containing the number entities in selection set <ss>. For example:

> (setq sset (ssget "L"))
> (sslength sset)

returns 1.

The (ssname <ss> <index>) returns the entity name of the <index>'th element of selection set <ss>. The first element begins with number 0. For example, let's say that (setq sset (ssget)) results in five items:

> (setq en1 (ssname sset 0))
> returns the first entity.
> (setq en3 (ssname sset 2))
> returns the third entity.

The (ssadd [<ename> [<ss>]]) function without ARGUMENTs constructs a selection set with no members. If performed with a single entity name ARGUMENT, it constructs a new selection set containing that single entity name. If performed with an entity name and a selection set, it adds the named entity to the selection set.

The (ssdel <ename> <ss>) function deletes entity name <ename> from selection set <ss>.

The (ssmemb <ename> <ss>) function tests whether entity name <ename> is a member of selection-set <ss>.

Advanced ASSOCIATION LIST And (Scanning) Functions

Examples of the (assoc <item> <alist>) have been demonstrated previously in this section. It will now be used in our custom-designed command.

The (subst <newitem> <olditem> <list>) function searches <list> for <olditem>, and returns a copy of <list> with <newitem> substituted in every place where <olditem> occurred.

Two sample routines are listed below. The TSAVE routine redefines the REDRAW command and then uses a time-checking part to cause the newly defined REDRAW command to invoke a SAVE command after a predetermined time has passed. The PARAB routine draws a parabola.

Saved in the file named TSAVE.LSP:

```
;——————————————————Autosave——————————————————
(defun S::STARTUP ( )
        (command "undefine" "redraw")
        (setq savetime 0.25)
)

(defun C:TSAVE ( )
        (setq temptime (getreal "ENTER INTERVAL OF TIME IN MINUTES FOR SAVING: "))
        (setq savetime (/ temptime 60.0))
)

(defun C:REDRAW ( )
    (if (null cdate1)
        (setq cdate1 (decihr (getvar "cdate"))))
    (setq cdate2 (decihr (getvar "cdate")))
    (if (or (> (- cdate2 cdate1) savetime)
        (> cdate1 cdate2)
        )
        (progn
                (setq tempex (getvar "expert"))
                (setvar "expert" 2)
                    (command "save" "c:backup")
                (setq cdate1 cdate2)
                (setvar "expert" tempex)
          )
      )
        (command ".redraw")
)

(defun decihr (dt / hms dh dm ds hd)
        (setq hms (* (- dt (fix dt)) 10000.0))
        (setq dh (/ (fix hms) 100.0))
        (setq dm (/ (- dh (fix dh)) 0.6))
        (setq ds (/ (- hms (fix hms)) 36.0))
        (setq hd (+ (fix dh) dm ds))
)
```

Saved in the file named PARAB.LSP:

----------------------------- PARABOLA --

```
(defun c:parab ( )
    (setq point1 (getpoint "ENTER POINT: " ))
    (setq number (getint "ENTER ITERATIONS: "))
    (setq i (getreal "ENTER INCREMENTS: "))
    (setq p1 point1 p (car point1) counter 0)
    (while (< counter number)
        (setq p2
            (list
                (+ (car point1) i)
                (+ (cadr point1) (* 2.0 (sqrt (* p i))))
            )
        )
    (command "line" p1 p2 "")
    (setq p1 p2 counter (1+ counter) i (+ i i))
    )
)
```

AUTOCAD DEVELOPMENT SYSTEM (ADS)

The AutoCAD Development System (ADS) is a programming interface that, like AutoLISP, permits you to write or use applications for AutoCAD in high-level languages such as C. The applications are loaded in a similar manner to AutoLISP. AutoLISP is more appropriate for smaller applications, while ADS makes use of an extensive, powerful, and more complex library of programming functions. ADS, because of the large library, demands more of your system. ADS is not stand-alone, but tied to AutoLISP, and therefore, is not a good substitute for simpler tasks that can be so easily implemented with AutoLISP.

AutoLISP

REVIEW QUESTIONS

1. To load the LISP file "SETUP" into the current AutoCAD drawing, type in the following at the "Command:" prompt
   - (A) "SETUP"
   - (B) LOAD SETUP
   - (C) (LOAD "SETUP")
   - (D) (LOAD SETUP)
   - (E) None of the above

2. The command used to easily select and load AutoLISP and ADS routines is
   - (A) APPLOAD
   - (B) LOAD
   - (C) DBLIST
   - (D) ADS
   - (E) None of the above

3. What does the (cadr L) function do?
   - (A) Returns the first element of list L
   - (B) Returns the second element of list L
   - (C) Returns the third element of list L
   - (D) None of the above

4. What does the (atan N) function do?
   - (A) Returns the angle whose tangent is N
   - (B) Draws a line tangent to the last object drawn
   - (C) Draws a line parallel to the last object drawn
   - (D) None of the above

5. What does the (/ A B) function do?
   - (A) Returns the quotient of A divided by B
   - (B) Returns the quotient of B divided by A
   - (C) Returns the remainder of A divided by B
   - (D) Returns the remainder of B divided by A
   - (E) None of the above

6. In (+ a 7), the + is called?
   - (A) operand
   - (B) operator
   - (C) symbol
   - (D) None of the above

7. The following are the data types, except
   - (A) REAL
   - (B) INTEGER
   - (C) STRING
   - (D) STORAGE
   - (E) SYMBOL

8. If (setq a 7), what does (list 4 a) return?
   - (A) The list (4 7)
   - (B) The list (7 4)
   - (C) The list (11)
   - (D) None of the above

9. What does (/ 3 7) return?
   - (A) 10
   - (B) 0 (zero)
   - (C) 4
   - (D) None of the above

10. The expression to add 7 and 3 is
   - (A) (7+3)
   - (B) (+ 7 3)
   - (C) (7 3 +)
   - (D) None of the above

A

HARDWARE AND
SOFTWARE INTRODUCTION

INTRODUCTION

The configuration of your CAD system is a combination of the hardware and software you have assembled to create your system. There are countless PC configurations available on the market. The goal for a new computer user should be to assemble a PC workstation that does not block future software and hardware upgrades. This section lists the essential hardware required to run AutoCAD Release 13 for Windows.

RECOMMENDED CONFIGURATION

The configuration recommended by Autodesk for a personal computer CAD workstation include the following:

1. IBM compatible personal computer with an Intel 386SX, Intel 486, Pentium processor or compatible.

2. Math Coprocessor 80387: (On 80486, the coprocessor is an integral part of the chip.)

3. Memory: Minimum of sixteen megabytes of random access memory (RAM). One megabyte contains the 640K of conventional memory.

4. Drives: A hard disk with at least 40 megabyte of free space, 40MB of disk swap space (minimum), and a 1.2 megabyte, 5 1/4-inch floppy drive or a 720K or 1.44MB, 3 1/2-inch floppy drive.

5. Video display and Windows-supported display adapter.

6. MS-DOS or PC-DOS Operating System: Version 5.0 or later.

7. Windows 3.1 running in enhanced mode or Windows for Workgroups version 3.1 or later.

8. Microsoft's Win32S version 1.20 or later (Autodesk supplies this with the installation).

Appendix A

9. Input Devices: Digitizing tablet or mouse.

10. Plotters and Printers.

PERSONAL COMPUTER

AutoCAD for DOS runs only on 386, 486, and Pentium-compatible computers. The 386 computers come in various classes with differing processor speeds, including the following:

1. 386SX (speeds 16MHz through 25 MHz)

2. 386DX (speeds 16MHz through 33MHz)

3. 486SX (speeds 16MHz through 33MHz)

4. 486DX (speeds 25MHz through 100 MHz)

5. Pentium (speeds 60MHz through 100MHz)

Select the one that best suits your workload. If you are planning to do large drawings then it is worthwhile buying a 486 (33MHz or 50MHz speeds) or Pentium. If you are not sure if AutoCAD is for you, or if you cannot spend a lot on a CAD workstation, then select a 486DX-based computer. Prices for 486DX (25MHz) and 486 (33MHz) stations with 8MB of RAM range from under $800 to $1200 depending on the manufacturer. This does not include software and peripherals such as plotters and laser printers.

The central processing unit (CPU) is the heart of your personal computer. The job of the CPU is to process the interaction of instructions and data involved with your PC, and it is responsible for the majority of the work. The CPU coordinates the data from the "input" devices (keybord, digitizer, etc.) and generates the appropriate data through the output devices (monitor, plotters).

The central processing unit is controlled by the operating system software. Equally important is the PC memory. While the operating system is responsible for processing all the data involved with your PC, the memory provides storage for program instructions and data until it is ready to be processed.

Math Coprocessor

AutoCAD requires a math coprocessor chip. This chip plugs into a socket reserved for this chip in the central processing unit. This chip increases the speed of the central processing unit's computations dramatically. Tests indicate that the performance improvement that results from this addition to the central processing unit justifies the comparatively low cost.

If you purchase a computer with a 486DX or Pentium chip, then the math chip circuitry is included. Computers using the 386 or 486SX chip require a separate, matched math chip.

Memory

To run AutoCAD for Windows, your computer must be equipped with at least 16MB of RAM. "Random access" means that the operating system has direct access to the data it needs. The storage locations can be filled (written to) and refilled (written over) as the CPU processes data. It is important to remember that RAM is temporary memory. The data is stored as long as the CPU has power. Once the electrical power is turned off, the data is erased from the storage locations.

The second type of computer memory is Read-Only Memory (ROM). Read-only memory is used to store data required by the CPU to perform processing functions. The information can be "read" by the CPU programs and carried out. However, new data cannot be written to ROM. It is not lost when the power is turned off.

Drives

As we have discussed, data that is input to your personal computer is present in RAM for the length of time that your computer has power. To make future retrieval possible, data must be stored on some form of magnetic media. The two types of magnetic media storage devices we discuss are hard disks and floppy disks.

Both hard disks and floppy disks are examples of direct access storage devices. Through them the central processing unit is able to go directly to the stored data regardless of the location on the magnetic media. The central processing unit uses electronic read/write heads to create and read magnetic fields on a specially coated disk.

Hard Disks The hard disk is the primary data storage device of your personal computer. The magnetic hard disk read/write heads are in a sealed unit to protect against dust contamination. Sealing the units allows the read/write heads to fly just above the disk surface yielding greater density and access rates. The hard disk accesses data at a range from 9 milliseconds to 80 milliseconds. High performance is 20 milliseconds or faster, while 80 milliseconds is considered extremely slow.

AutoCAD may be run with a 40-megabyte hard disk, but a larger capacity is advised, at least 100MB. In choosing a powerful personal computer, you will obtain a faster response time and the ability to work with many large program files and data files.

Floppy Disks Floppy disks are commonly available in low density and high density and in 5 1/4" and 3 1/2" sizes. Low-density 5 1/4" floppy disks are capable of storing 360K (kilobytes) of data and 3 1/2" low-density diskettes can store 720K of information. The high-density 5 1/4" floppy disks have a data storage capacity of 1.2MB (megabytes), while the 3 1/2" high-density diskettes can store 1.4MB of information.

An advantage to using floppy disks is that they are removable and easily transportable. They can be used to transfer program and data files from one computer to another. For those reasons, floppy disks are the standard means of software and data distribution. While floppy disks operate approximately 20 times slower than hard drives, they are most valuable when used to "back up" data located on the hard disk.

Video Display and Adapter

As with any graphics program for PC CAD systems, AutoCAD requires a video adapter capable of displaying graphics information. A video adapter is an integrated circuit board which plugs into the mother board and generates signals to drive a monitor. When mounted in place, a socket (known as a port) will be accessible on the exterior of the computer for plugging in the monitor. AutoCAD supports a number of display options, ranging from low-priced monochrome setups to high resolution color units. Some of the video display controllers can be used in combination to give a two-screen display.

Appendix A

"Resolution" is the degree of graphic detail the board can provide. Both the monochrome and the color screen resolution are measured by the number of horizontal and vertical dots, called picture elements (or pixels), that the screen can display.

In selecting your graphics adapter board, you should be aware that general prices increase with the number of colors and resolution. Since the monitor must match the graphics board resolution and output specifications, the monitor price will increase or decrease proportionally, depending upon the graphics board you choose. As a minimum, select a VGA graphics adapter which has a resolution of 640 x 480 and displays 16 colors. However, SuperVGA (800 x 600 resolution and 256 colors) is not much more expensive but displays a clearer picture.

DOS: The Operating System

DOS (short for Disk Operating System) is an extremely elaborate program, and without it, none of your other programs will work. The operating system directs all the internal workings of the CPU by performing these important functions:

1. Governs the stream of data to and from the central processing unit and all other hardware associated with the computer system.

2. Defines the commands and directs the arithmetic/logic section to perform any calculations that are required.

3. Interacts with the random access memory to access instructions of the programs stored there.

4. Provides the utility to format your disk storage.

5. Provides the utility to read and write to the disk drives.

6. Gives you the ability to control and manage your data files through the system commands.

7. Provides the utility to keep and see the directory of your data files.

8. Allows you to check the amount of free space available for data storage.

The DOS operating system is available from three vendors: Microsoft (MS-DOS), IBM (PC-DOS), and Novell (DR-DOS). Microsoft writes the original program; IBM licenses the program from Microsoft; and Novell writes its own copy of the Microsoft version.

Windows: The Operating Environment

Windows is the name of the operating environment that runs on top of DOS. Windows provides the graphical user interface, device independence, and lets you run more than one program at a time.

The graphical user interface (or "GUI," for short) consists of the windows, icons, scroll bars, menu bar, button bar and other graphical elements you see on the Windows screen. The GUI lets you use the mouse to control most aspects of a software program, including selecting commands, resizing windows, clicking on icons, and drawing.

Device independence means that all software applications running under Windows use the same device drivers, such as for the display, the mouse, and the printer. Under DOS, AutoCAD uses its own collection of device drivers; under Windows, AutoCAD uses the Windows device driver.

The multi-tasking and task switching feature of Windows lets you be more productive. "Multi-tasking" means that Windows can run more than one program at a time, unlike DOS which runs just one program at a time. "Task switching" means that you can quickly switch from task to task (or from one program to another).

At time of writing, Microsoft supplies three versions of Windows. Windows v3.1 is the most common version in use. Windows for Workgroups add networking support, allowing computers to share files and printers. Windows NT is different enough that it runs AutoCAD too slowly for production work.

Windows for Workgroups is only recommended if your office needs a peer-to-peer network and most of your computers remain in Windows most of the time (Windows for Workgroups no longer works as a network when your computer runs DOS). Windows NT is not recommended at all unless you have the NT version of AutoCAD.

Input Devices

AutoCAD supports several input device configurations. Data may be entered through the keyboard, the mouse, or a digitizing tablet.

Keyboard The keyboard is one of the primary input methods. It can be used to enter commands and responses.

Mouse The mouse is used with the keyboard as a tracking device to move the cross-hair on the screen. This method is fast and far surpasses the keyboard for positioning the screen cross-hair.

The mouse is equipped with two or more buttons. The left button is the pick button, and the other buttons can be programmed to perform any of the AutoCAD commands.

Digitizer The digitizer is another means of input supported by AutoCAD but is not well supported by Windows. Hence, Autodesk provides a "mole" mode that lets the mouse and digitizer work at the same time in Windows while AutoCAD is running.

The digitizing tablet is a flat, sensitized electromechanical device that can recognize the location of the tablet cursor. The tablet cursor moves over the surface of the digitizing tablet causing a corresponding movement of the screen cursor.

Another use of the digitizing tablet is to overlay a tablet menu, configured to enter commands when they are selected by placing the cross-hairs of the puck at the corresponding digitizer coordinates. This process automates any AutoCAD command options that are represented on the menu, and eliminates the use of the keyboard except to enter an occasional command value.

The tablet cursor (puck) may have from four to 16 buttons. Except for the first button, the current menu can be programmed to cause the remaining buttons to perform any of the regular AutoCAD commands. The first button is always the "pick" button.

Plotters and Printers

AutoCAD supports several types of output devices for producing hard copies of drawings. The most common devices are the thermal plotter, pen plotter, inkjet printer, and the laser printer.

Appendix A

Thermal Plotters The thermal plotter heats up the drawing paper, changing the color to black to create a hard copy of the drawing. The resolution of the output, which is measured in dots per inch (dpi), may range from a low-quality (100 dpi) product to medium-quality (400 dpi) product.

Pen Plotters The pen plotter draw continuous lines on the paper. The drawing pen is driven by vector commands that correspond to the X and Y coordinates on the drawing paper. Drawing media varies between mylar, vellum, and bond. The pens used in such plotters also vary in size and quality, thus affecting the drawing resolution. Resolution is typically between the equivalent of 1,000 and 2,000 dpi.

Pen plotters come in all shapes and sizes, and over the years pen plotters have improved in the areas of speed, accuracy, and price. The pen plotter is an established favorite for those who demand clear line and shape definition. Although prices vary on the different types of pen plotters, it is possible to get a good desktop pen plotter in the area of $2000. Contact your dealer to find out if a particular model is supported.

Inkjet Printers AutoCAD supports the ability to generate a hard copy of your drawing with an inkjet printer, either in black-white or in color. Inkjet printers form characters and graphics by squirting ink onto standard paper. Inkjet printers provide the most inexpensive means for color printing. They are generally used to provide rough draft hard copies for graphics and text data. They are an excellent and cost-effective way to produce check plots in A-, B-, and C-size.

Laser Printers Laser printers are the newest printing device on the CAD market. They deliver a low-cost, medium- to high-resolution hard copy that can be driven from a personal computer. Laser printers boast resolutions from 300 dpi to 1200 dpi and printing speeds of about 4-12 pages per minute (ppm) for text and one to two pages per minute for graphics.

As with any raster device, laser printers require a vector-to-raster conversion to generate most graphics. AutoCAD can plot design files on laser printers that support the HP LaserJet PCL and PostScript graphic output languages. The cost of laser printers ranges from under $1000 to over $12,000, yet the increase in resolution makes the price a good investment for many serious CAD users.

Configuring AutoCAD for Windows

Installing and configuring your system is a vital part of getting AutoCAD to function properly. Autodesk covers this portion with great detail and accuracy in the *Installation and Performance Guide* provided with your software.

Installing AutoCAD on your system by use of the SETUP command will create several directories and subdirectories on your system. Below is a list of these directories and the general files found in them.

\ACADR13\WIN	AutoCAD executable and other related files
\ACADR13\WIN\SAMPLE	Sample AutoCAD drawings
\ACADR13\WIN\SUPPORT	AutoCAD support files
\ACADR13\WIN\ADS	Library for ADS, and sample ADS programs
\ACADR13\WIN\ASE	files related to database linkage
\ACADR13\WIN\DRV	AutoCAD driver files
\ACADR13\COMMON\SUPPORT	support files common to DOS & Windows version
\ACADR13\COMMON\SAMPLE	sample files common to DOS & Windows version
\ACADR13\COMMON\FONTS	fonts files common to DOS & Windows version
\ACADR13\COMMON\ADS	ADS files common to DOS & Windows version

INTRODUCTION

Most AutoCAD users soon become acquainted with certain computer files and learn the DOS and Windows commands necessary to perform some operations on these files. Some of the more important DOS commands, such as DIR, COPY, ERASE, RENAME, etc., are made convenient through AutoCAD's FILES Command; users can also access the Windows File Manager directly while in AutoCAD.

DOS (DISK OPERATING SYSTEM)

It is possible that a drafter might create a drawing, save, and plot it without ever putting it on a floppy disk or tape. This would be rare indeed, unless the drawing or the time it took to create it were of so little value that its loss (perhaps due to a hard disk crash) could be ignored. It is a rare AutoCAD user who does not save work periodically on a floppy disk or tape during and at the end of the session.

Some DOS commands are easier to use while not in AutoCAD. For example, to copy a file while in AutoCAD, you must type in the filename for the source and then the filename for the target directory. Copying one or two files in this fashion is not a great inconvenience. Copying more than just a few files, though, might become tedious.

Some recommendations for easier file handling will be offered during the following sections. Some of the DOS-related features, commands, and terms that are useful to the operator are listed as follows:

COPY	Copies one or more files to another drive and directory
RENAME	Changes the name of one or more files
ERASE	Erases one or more files
FORMAT	Prepares a new diskette for DOS
MKDIR or MD	Creates a subdirectory
CHDIR or CD	Changes to another subdirectory
DIR	Lists the names of files in the current subdirectory

The symbol \	Represents the root directory; also, separates the names of subdirectories
The symbol *	Represents any file name
The symbol :	Represents a drive name
The symbol .	Represents the current subdirectory
The symbol ..	Represents the parent subdirectory

Disk(ette)

Floppy disks are the media on which software is distributed. The software is in the form of files. There are aspects of the storage of data on diskettes, such as sectors, partitions, binary sequences, hexadecimals, etc., that are not necessary to learn in order to be able to use sophisticated and powerful CAD graphics programs. Large software packages (including AutoCAD Release 13) are now distributed on CD-ROM, which can store 680MB of information. Once properly formatted, a diskette is simply addressed by the name of the drive in which it is inserted.

Usually, floppy disk drives are labeled drive A and (if there is a second floppy drive) drive B. Important uses of the floppy disk are:

1. Safe backup storage of files.

2. Transfer of files from one computer to another.

3. Temporary repository of files in the floppy drive for support or editing without copying them onto the fixed disk.

Fixed disks or hard drives, like floppy disks, store software in the form of files. Like their name says, they are fixed and not removable for the purpose of transferring files to another computer. Their main advantage is in their large capacity, being that of hundreds of diskettes. Fixed drives are usually labelled drive C and (if a second fixed drive is installed) drive D. The fixed drive is where the AutoCAD program files are stored. Because of the risk of fixed disk failure (beyond recoverability of files), all important files on a fixed disk should also be stored on floppy disks or backup tapes. These backup files differ from the files that are sometimes created by programs automatically and have the file extension of .BAK. Backup files that are copied to floppy disks for the purpose of safekeeping usually have the same name and file extension as the file they back up.

Files

File specifications (or filespec) include the drive label, the filename and an optional extension. The directory path is sometimes included when accessing a file. The drive label and directory path do not always have to be included, as will be explained later.

A file contains data and is stored under a particular filename. The filename may also include an extension. The data may be a simple two-line batch file, a 10-page letter, or a large encrypted and compiled executable program like AutoCAD's ACAD.EXE file or one of your larger drawing files with the file extension of .DWG. When DOS commands operate on a file, they usually operate on the whole file as a unit. Programs like AutoCAD, line editors, word processors, and data base manipulators (which are all program files themselves) create or open data files, edit, and close them. Being able to create files and knowing how and when to address them are skills necessary to do advanced file editing and manipulating. One application, for example, is if you wish to do programming in AutoLISP.

DRIVES AND DIRECTORIES

Drives and directories are established for the purpose of storing files. The combination of a floppy drive and a fixed drive is like a warehouse with a railroad loading dock attached. DOS and Windows are the warehouse manager and, when properly instructed, does the following:.

1. DOS handles the files into and out of storage.

2. DOS and Windows take you to a program file that can operate on a data file. (Reading, editing, and printing are all done by using a program file.)

3. DOS and Windows then take you to that data file and open it for you to read, edit, or print a copy of the file.

4. DOS closes the file when you are through and takes you to another set of program and data files.

Windows accesses the file management function through DOS; Windows just gives a prettier and more user-friendly facade to the arcane DOS commands.

The main warehouse is the fixed drive. You may have the manager (DOS or Windows) store all the files in the open space commonly known as the "root directory". But when enough files start to fill the root directory, it becomes unwieldly. Just listing all the files causes the screen to fill and scroll. It is difficult to locate and identify particular files. Therefore, DOS can create storerooms in the warehouse called "subdirectories". This conveniently allows you to store a group of related files apart from other groups of files. A subdirectory may even have its own subsubdirectories, like storerooms within the storerooms in the warehouse.

It is advisable to keep the root directory (the area of the warehouse outside of all storerooms) as free as possible. Only the needed DOS command files and batch files (to be explained later) should be stored in the root directory. All other data and program files should be stored in subdirectories created especially for them. It is also advisable to use short names for the subdirectories. They will have to be typed in from the keyboard as part of the path to files. Keep them as short as possible and still have them identifiable. If you have created a directory named AutoLISP, you will be surprised how quickly you will get tired of typing in "AutoLISP," or even "LISP" (if you have given the directory one of those names), every time you type in the path to your file. You will soon get used to remembering that "AL" or just "L" is the name of the directory that your files are stored in. However, if most of your file manipulations are done with the help of a utility program such as Norton Utilities, PCTOOLS, XTREE, or Windows Manager, then longer, more recognizable directory names will probably be advantageous.

The floppy drive is like a railroad loading dock. The floppy disk inserted in the drive is like a railroad car parked at the loading dock. It is accessible through the label for the drive it is in.

It is possible, though not as commonly done as on the fixed drive, to create subdirectories on the floppy disk while it is parked in the floppy drive. These subdirectories are like storerooms and rooms in the main warehouse. They stay with that diskette and when it leaves the dock (the floppy drive) the subdirectories go with it. A new car (floppy diskette) brings its own rooms (subdirectories) with it if they have been created previously by DOS.

As an experienced AutoCAD operator you will soon learn your way around drives and directories to get to appropriate files. The most common arrangement is to have the computer start up (boot up) with the floppy drive door open. The computer, after memory check, looks at drive A (floppy) first, finds it inaccessible, redirects itself to the fixed drive, looking for the disk operating system in a trio of boot files called IO.SYS, MSDOS.SYS, and COMMAND.COM. Then, when the boot up is complete, the computer is automatically logged onto the fixed drive (usually labeled "C") and a prompt appears which includes the "C>". Failure to keep the A drive (floppy) open during boot up will cause a message to appear regarding a "nonsystem disk..." (unless the A drive contains a diskette with the three boot files on it). If that were the case, a prompt would appear having "A>" in it, indicating that you were logged onto the A drive. It would be your current drive until the time you invoked the DOS command to change drives.

Should the "nonsystem disk..." message appear, simply open the floppy drive door and press any key. The redirection to drive C: should proceed without further problems.

Changing Drives

To change from one drive to another simply enter the new drive letter followed by a colon. For example, while on drive A the prompt reads:

A:\>

After typing in the "C:" the prompt reads:

A:\>C:

After pressing [Enter], the prompt changes to:

C:\>

You are now logged onto drive C. It is your current drive. Reversing the above: C:\>A: produces A:\> and logs you back on drive A, the floppy drive.

To change drives with the Windows File Manager, click on the appropriate drive icon (see Figure B-1). To change to the C: drive, click on the drive icon next to "c". To change back to the A: drive, click on the drive icon next to "a".

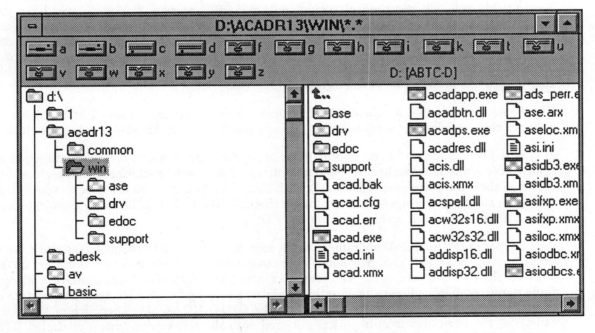

Figure B-1   Change drives with the Windows File Manager by clicking on the appropriate drive icon

Logging Onto a Drive and Directory

The importance of being logged onto a particular drive and directory depends on the type of file you are operating with. As mentioned before, some files just contain data to be operated upon by other programs. These data files are letters, drawings, and lists of items such as a phone list or bill of materials. Other files are, of course, the programs themselves.

If you decide to delve into customizing AutoCAD, one of the first files you become involved with is the MENU file (whose extension is .MNU). It is an excellent example of a data file that while being created or edited is a data file, but when completed becomes a program file. Students should note with care which drive and directory they are currently logged onto and which drive and subdirectory the program and data files are on at the time a command is invoked. It is possible that four different locations (drives and directories) could be involved at the same time during one command.

As mentioned previously, diskettes and fixed disks are addressed through their drive label. To access or operate on a file stored on a floppy disk in drive A (and drive A is not the current drive) the user must prefix the file specification with "A:." For example:

C:\>TYPE A:MYNEW.LSP

In order for the DOS command called TYPE to operate on the file called MYNEW.LSP, you must address MYNEW.LSP through its drive label followed by a colon if you are not logged onto drive A. If you are logged onto drive A you may address the file without using the drive label prefix as follows:

A:>TYPE MYNEW.LSP

Three things must be taken into consideration concerning drives when operating on files.

1. **Current Drive** — You need to know which drive you are presently logged onto.

2. **Source and Target Drives** — You need to know the drive(s) where the source file and the target are. For instance, in using the DOS COPY command, the source is where the file is stored before the command is used and the target is where the new copy of the file will reside.

3. **Internal or External DOS Command** — It is advisable to study the list of the particular DOS commands you will be using in order to know if they are internal or external commands. For example, the DOS commands COPY and TYPE are internal commands. They reside within the COMMAND.COM program file and can be invoked from any directory while logged on any drive because COMMAND.COM was loaded into RAM when the machine was booted up.

First the Rule! (Path Makes an Exception)

The DOS command PRINT is an external command. It requires access to the program file called PRINT.COM. In versions of DOS prior to 3.0, it can only be invoked when the directory that it is stored on is the current directory of its drive. The commands with the extension of .COM, .EXE, and .BAT are accessed in a similar manner.

In DOS version 3.0 or later, files on drives other than the current one can be accessed in an easier fashion than before. If the computer environment has previously been set up with a "path" to the .COM, .EXE, or .BAT files, then they can be invoked from directory other than their own. For example, PRINT.COM is on the directory named DOS. When the computer is booted up, enter the following:

PATH=\DOS

Then while in the ACAD directory you may simply enter:

PRINT MYNEW.MNU

and DOS will go to the DOS subdirectory and use the PRINT command to print the file on the ACAD directory named MYNEW.MNU.

The "PATH=" entry is best included in the AUTOEXEC.BAT file.

By studying carefully and understanding the following examples, the novice can apply the same approach to other file handling procedures and programs, including his/her own custom programs that involve file handling. Even the moderately experienced DOS user can get into some procedural habits that might be improved upon.

Paths are used by Windows and must be set in DOS before entering Windows.

Example No. 1

> Objective: *(Print the file named MYNEW.LSP)*
> Current drive: **A:**
> Current directory: *(Root directory of drive A:)*
> Drive where MYNEW.LSP is stored: **C:**
> Directory where MYNEW.LSP is stored: **\LISP**
> Drive where PRINT.COM is stored: **C:**
> Directory where PRINT.COM is stored: **\DOS**

Entering the following will work under one condition:

A:\>C:PRINT C:\LISP\MYNEW.LSP

Even though the path to the file is correct, the path to the DOS command PRINT works only if (when you changed from drive C:), the PATH= \DOS\ has been entered previously. Otherwise, if you had been in the root directory or in the \LISP directory when you left drive C (by entering **A:** to get to drive A), then the path "C:" to PRINT.COM would not work.

Example No. 2

> Objective: *(Print the file named MYNEW.LSP)*
> Current drive: **C:** *(changed from Example No. 1)*
> Current directory: **\LISP** *(changed from Example No. 1)*
> Drive where MYNEW.LSP is stored: **C:**
> Directory where MYNEW.LSP is stored: **\LISP**
> Drive where PRINT.COM is stored: **C:**
> Directory where PRINT.COM is stored: **\DOS**

Entry No.1

C>CD\DOS

This logs you onto the DOS directory where the program file called PRINT.COM is stored. It is an external DOS command.

Entry No. 2

  C:\>PRINT \LISP\MYNEW.LSP

This will work now.

Review Files may be accessed through their paths no matter which drive and directory you are logged onto. The drive specifier and/or directory path may be omitted when you are logged onto the same drive and/or directory as the file you are accessing.

Using external DOS commands requires one of three things. One option is to be logged on the same directory as the DOS program file for that command. Another option is if you are on another drive, then the drive on which the DOS command program file is stored must have as its current directory the one on which the DOS program file is stored (this applies to older versions of DOS with or without the PATH= entry). The third option is to have entered a "PATH=" command so that DOS will seek out the .COM, .EXE, or .BAT file from any directory.

The Exceptional Path

The following example is a method of using external DOS commands from a directory other that the one on which they are stored. This shows how to set up a path to their directory. Care must be taken in doing this. If the computer environment has already had a path set up to include other directories, then arbitrarily using the DOS command called PATH might nullify the other preset paths. It is best to include the path to external DOS commands with the path to other necessary directories in the PATH command in the AUTOEXEC.BAT file as mentioned previously. An example would be as follows:

  Objective: *(Provide access to files in the ACADDWG directory, certain digitizer files in the*
      DIGI directory, and to the external DOS commands in the DOS directory.)
  Context: **PATH=C:\ACADDWG;\DIGI;\DOS;**

Because the DOS command PATH is an internal command, the above can be entered from any directory or drive.

CAUTION!
In using the above setting, it should be noted that duplicate filenames in different directories might cause a problem. Under the circumstances this is not likely, but if a drawing were named PRINT.DWG, then trying to use the DOS command named PRINT from some other directory, DOS might try to access the PRINT.DWG file instead of the PRINT.COM file. Because of the different extensions, this may not happen, but extension differences may not prevent DOS from trying to use a wrong file in other cases. When DOS looks for a file by the path route, it looks in the directories in the order that they are placed after the PATH command. In the above example, the ACADDWG directory will be searched first, the DIGI second, and the DOS last.

Appendix B

DIRECTORY COMMANDS

While logged onto the root directory of drive C:, the prompt should show only the "C>" or "C:\>" without any subdirectory name displayed. It would be advisable to type in **CD** to be sure that you are on the root directory. Depending on the boot up parameters for the prompt, it is possible for you to be logged on a subdirectory and not have it show in the prompt area. Under certain prompt parameter settings, if you were logged onto the subdirectory named "ACAD" on drive C, the prompt might display "C:\ACAD>".

Making Directories

You may use the MKDIR or MD command to create a new directory as a branch of any directory, including the root directory. A subdirectory called MENU is created as follows:

C:\>MD \MENU

In Windows, you create a new subdirectory with the **File | Create Directory** command (select the **File** command from the menu bar, then select the **Create Directory** item from the menu). Windows displays the **Create Directory** dialog box (see Figure B–2).

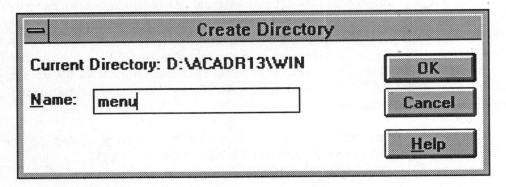

Figure B–2 The Create Directory dialog box

This creates a subdirectory called "MENU" to the root directory, shown as \. This only creates the subdirectory, and does not log you onto it. Another command is used for that purpose.

> **NOTE:** Note the use of the "\" (backslash) for specifying a directory. Any time you are logged onto a directory other than the root directory or the one whose path you wish to specify, you must prefix the name of the target directory with the \ symbol. The root directory is the "NO NAME" directory, therefore when specifying a path to it from some other directory, you must use the \ symbol without a directory name.

For simplicity, from here on, directories and subdirectories will primarily be referred to as just directories. The distinction between directories and subdirectories is primarily technical and not critical as long as one learns the correct path to any file.

Searching Directories

It is useful to be able to display on the screen a list of all the files that are stored on a directory. This is accomplished using the DOS command called DIRECTORY or DIR. This command displays the files and directories created as a part of the particular directory you are searching. A search of the root directory can be entered as follows:

C:\>**DIR**

The following might be displayed:

```
Volume in drive C has no label
Directory of C:\
COMMAND     COM         23456     1-23-88
DOS                     <DIR>     1-23-88
AUTOEXEC    BAT           128     2-13-88
ACAD        BAT            28     3-21-88
ACAD                    <DIR>     3-21-88
PIPESTAR                <DIR>     4-12-88
SIDEKICK                <DIR>     4-30-88
```

After having used the MD\MENU command, the DIR command would display:

```
C:\> DIR
    Volume in drive C has no label
    Directory of C:\
COMMAND     COM         23456     1-23-88
DOS                     <DIR>     1-23-88
AUTOEXEC    BAT           128     2-13-88
ACAD        BAT            28     3-21-88
ACAD                    <DIR>     3-21-88
PIPESTAR                <DIR>     4-12-88
SIDEKICK                <DIR>     4-30-88
MENU                    <DIR>     (the current date)
```

In Windows, the File Manager always displays the list of subdirectories in the left window. The right window displays the files and subdirectories in the current directory (see Figure B–1).

An additional convenience of the DIR command is to be able to list the files across the screen in a wide fashion. This is done by adding a "/W" to the DIR command:

C:\>**DIR/W**

The display would be as follows:

```
C> DIR
    Volume in drive C has no label
    Directory of C:\
COMMAND COM       [DOS]           AUTOEXEC BAT      ACAD BAT
[PIPESTAR]        [SIDEKICK]      [MENU]            [ACAD]
```

The sizes and dates of files are not displayed when the "/W" parameter is added to the DIR command. Another handy feature is the "/P" either with or without the "/W" following the DIR command. The "/P" causes the scrolling to pause each time the screen is filled with a display of the list of files and directories. Of course, it is only needed when the list is larger than the screen can display.

In Windows, select the **View | Name** command (or click on the icon) to show just filenames in the File Manager (see Figure B–3).

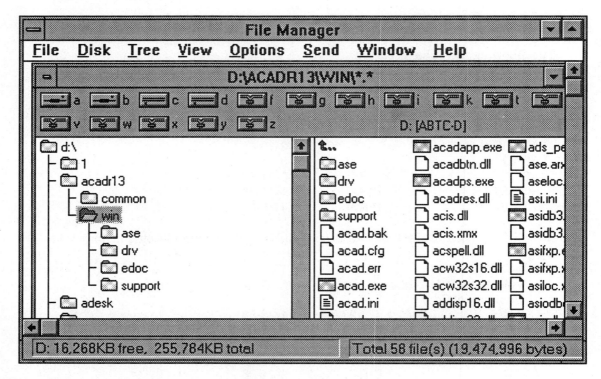

Figure B–3   The Windows File Manager displaying just filenames

To show filenames and other details, select **View | Partial Details** (or click on the icon). The File Manager displays the **Partial Details** dialog box (see Figure B–4). Select the details you want displayed by clicking on the check box.

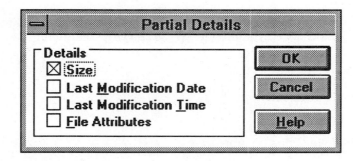

Figure B–4   The Partial Details dialog box

To display all details about files, click on **View | All Details**. The File Manager displays the size, date and time of creation, and attributes next to each filename.

When a directory has been created there are two unnamed hidden files created at the same time. Their presence is indicated by the "." and the ".." symbols displayed when the DIR command is used. These are of no special concern to the average operator. An effort to delete them, however, might play havoc with DOS so they are best left alone.

Changing Directories

Logging onto another directory on the same drive is done by using the DOS command called CHDIR or CD. It requires the "\" (backslash) prefix in the following manner:

C:\>**CD \MENU**

This will log you onto the directory called MENU.

In Windows, to change to a different subdirectory, click on its name in the File Manager. To display all sub-subdirectories, double-click on the name of the subdirectory. A quicker way to display all subdirectories is to select **Tree | Expand All** (see Figure B–5). If your computer's hard drive has many subdirectories, this may take a while as Windows reads all subdirectories.

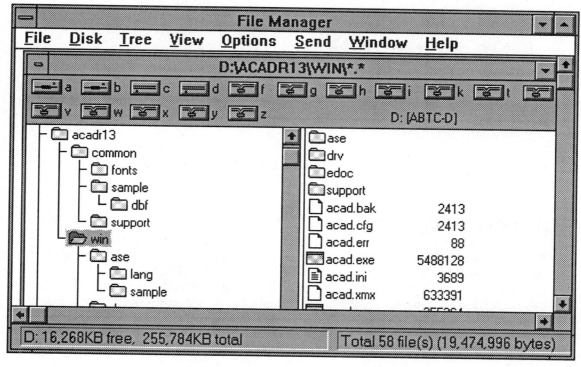

Figure B–5   Double-click on a subdirectory name to display the sub-subdirectories

Getting Back to the Root Directory

Because the root directory has no name, enter the following:

C>**CD **

This will return you to the root directory.

Drive and Directory Specifiers

It is possible (but not advisable at this time) to create a subdirectory inside the MENU directory. It may be done in three different ways depending upon which is the current drive and directory. This example is for the purpose of illustrating the use of the (:) symbol for the drive specifier and the (\) symbol for the directory specifier.

Example No. 3

Objective: *(Create a subdirectory named LISPMENU to the directory named MENU which is itself a subdirectory of the root directory of drive C.)*
Current drive: **A** *(same as Example No. 1)*
Current directory: \ *(same as Example No. 1)*

Enter the following:

A>MD C:\MENU\LISPMENU

Example No. 4

Objective: *(Same as Example No. 3)*
Current drive: **C** *(changed from Example No. 3)*
Current directory: \ *(changed from Example No. 3)*

Enter the following:

C>MD \MENU\LISPMENU

In Windows, create sub-directories in the same way as described above. Make sure that you have clicked on the name of the parent directory first.

FORMATTING THE DISK

Before you can write information onto a new disk, you must prepare the diskette so that you can store information. This can be done by a program called FORMAT.COM. The formatting program is located on your DOS directory. You only need to format a disk once. Log into the directory that has the FORMAT program or, if you have a path for the directory that has the FORMAT program, then you can type the command at any DOS prompt.

Example No. 5

Current drive: **C**
Current directory: *(Root directory)*
Drive where FORMAT.COM is stored: **C:**
Disk to be formatted is in drive A

A suggested sequence would be as follows:

C:>format a:

The following message will appear:

Insert new diskette for drive A:
and strike ENTER when ready

Insert a new diskette and press Enter. You will see the message:

Formatting...

The message may differ, depending on the version of MS-DOS your computer is running. After a while the following message appears:

Format complete
Format another (Y/N):

If you want to format another disk, take out the newly formatted disk and replace it with another new disk. Then press **Y** and Enter. If you do not want to format another disk, press **N** and Enter to terminate the program. Remember, you only have to format a disk once, even if you erase the information on it.

> **NOTE:** To format a low-density diskette (360KB), you have to add switch /4 to the format command as shown below:
>
> **C:>format a:/4**

In Windows, select the **Disk | Format Disk** item from the menu bar. The File Manager displays the **Format Disk** dialog box, as shown in Figure B–6. Select the name of the drive to format (A: or B:), capacity of diskette (360KB, 1.2MB, 720KB, or 1.44MB).

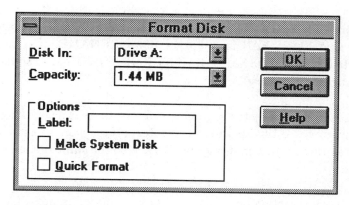

Figure B–6 The Format Disk dialog box

RENAMING FILES

An example of operating on a file with DOS while in the root directory is to RENAME a file. Each time a drawing is called into AutoCAD, it creates a backup file of the drawing before any changes are made. For example, you have previously created and ended a drawing named "XMPL." It is saved as a file with the name XMPL.DWG. At the begining of any subsequent editing session, AutoCAD creates a temporary file named XMPL.BAK. Should you use the SAVE or END commands during the subsequent editing session, XMPL.BAK becomes a permanent file. If you had QUIT the editing session without saving during the session, the XMPL.BAK file would have been abandoned. Each time you SAVE during the session, the drawing in its current status will be poised to replace the previous .BAK file. It will actually be kept as a third file in a temporary state, ready to take the place of the .BAK file. So before you use the SAVE command, be sure that you will not want to go back to the drawing in the status it was in when re-editing began.

There is a way to get back to the drawing in its status one SAVE prior to the last SAVE or END command. This requires renaming the .BAK file. AutoCAD drawings must, of course, have the extension of .DWG in order to edit them. So if you wish to use the XMPL.BAK file as a drawing, you must change the extension from .BAK to .DWG. But, there already exists a file named XMPL.DWG. DOS will not let you name or rename a file when one already exists with the same name ON THE SAME DRIVE AND DIRECTORY. Therefore, when renaming the .BAK file, you must also change the filename to something unique on that directory.

Example No. 6

Current drive: **C**
Current directory: **\DRAWINGS**
Drive where XMPL.BAK is stored: **C:**
Directory where XMPL.BAK is stored: **\DRAWINGS**
Existing XMPL.DWG is on same path as XMPL.BAK

A suggested sequence would be as follows:

C>**RENAME XMPL.BAK XMPL2.DWG**

The above entry suggests two things you have just studied. One, you are logged onto the same drive and directory that XMPL.BAK is stored on. Two, RENAME must be an internal DOS command. The only way to RENAME the XMPL.BAK file XMPL.DWG is to first delete the existing XMPL.DWG file from the current directory.

Another thing is suggested by the sequence. That is, there is no existing file named XMPL2.DWG on the current directory. If the drawing in its latest status were in such bad shape as to not be worth saving, then deleting it and renaming the .BAK with the same filename is one way to keep the same drawing name.

Note in the following section on using the DOS command named COPY on files, the caution about losing an existing file on a directory. DOS prevents this in the use of the RENAME command.

Examples of using the RENAME command from other locations are as follows:

Example No. 7

Current drive: **C:**
Current directory: \ *(root directory)*
Drive where XMPL.BAK is stored: **C:**
Directory where XMPL.BAK is stored: **\DRAWINGS**
Existing XMPL.DWG is on same path as XMPL.BAK

A suggested sequence would be as follows:

C>RENAME \DRAWINGS\XMPL.BAK XMPL2.DWG

Note that the path is only given to the file's old name. It is not necessary to prefix the new name with the drive and directory specifiers. You can send a copy of a file to another location and change the name at the same time in the COPY command. The RENAME command does not leave a copy of the file under its old name as the COPY command does.

Another sequence would be required if the file were in a subdirectory of another directory.

Example No. 8

Current drive: **A:**
Current directory: \ *(root directory)*
Drive where XMPL.BAK is stored: **C:**
Directory where XMPL.BAK is stored: **\ACAD\DRAWINGS**

(Note that \DRAWINGS is a subdirectory of \ACAD)

A suggested sequence would be as follows:

A:\>RENAME C:\ACAD\DRAWINGS\XMPL.BAK XMPL2.DWG

As you can see, having to specify drives and directories in the path to a file can influence two things in using DOS commands:

1. If many file operations are required, try to keep required directory specifying to a minimum by either changing to the directory of the file or by limiting the depth of subdirectories.

2. Keep directory names as short as possible.

In Windows, click on the filename you want to change and use the **File | Rename** command. File Manager displays the **Rename** dialog box with the file's name (see Figure B–7). Type the different file name and click on the **OK** button.

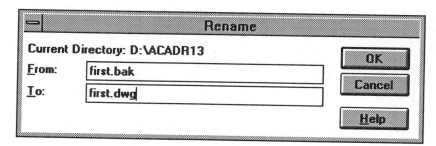

Figure B–7   The Rename dialog box

COPYING FILES

It is sometimes necessary to copy files from one location to another. Unlike the RENAME command this involves different drives and/or directories. The only case where a file can be copied to its same drive and directory is if the name is changed in the process. This produces two identical files with different names.

One occasion to copy a file would be if you created a custom menu on a directory containing a word processor, and wished to transfer it to the ACAD directory for use in AutoCAD. This is not the most efficient way to write and test programs, but it does illustrate the DOS command called COPY.

Example No. 9

> Objective: *(Copy the file named TRIAL.MNU from the directory called WRDPRCSR to the directory called ACAD)*
> Current drive: **C:**
> Current directory: \ *(root directory)*

A suggested sequence would be as follows:

> C:\>**COPY\WRDPRCSR\TRIAL.MNU \ACAD\TRIAL.MNU**

Example No. 10

> Objective: *(Same as Example No. 11)*
> Current drive: **C:**
> Current directory:**\WRDPRCSR**

A suggested sequence would be as follows:

> C:\>**COPY TRIAL.MNU \ACAD\TRIAL.MNU**

Example No. 11

> Objective: *(Same as Example No. 11)*
> Current drive: **C:**
> Current directory: **\ACAD**

A suggested sequence would be as follows:

> C:\>**COPY \WRDPRCSR\TRIAL.MNU**

Note the permissible omission of the target altogether.

In Windows, you copy a file by dragging the filename from one subdirectoy to another; there is no need to type any filenames. To drag a filename:

1. Move the mouse pointer over the filename.

2. Press the left mouse button and hold down the button.

3. In addition, hold down Ctrl.

4. Move the cursor to the other subdirectory and let go of the mouse button.

The File Manager displays the **Confirm Mouse Operation** dialog box to confirm the copy operation (see Figure B–8). Click the **OK** button.

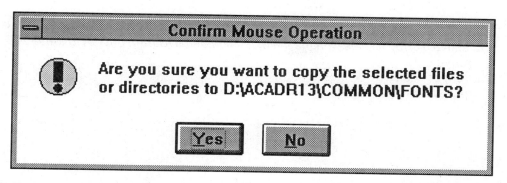

Figure B–8   The Confirm Mouse Operation dialog box

To move a file, don't hold down ⌨Ctrl; just hold down the mouse button.

Copying Between Drives

Another common need for copying files is between floppy drives and fixed drives. This also facilitates transferring files from one computer station to another.

Example No. 12

> Objective: *(Copy the file named TRIAL.MNU from a floppy disk in drive A to the ACAD directory on the fixed drive.)*
> Current drive: **C:**
> Current directory: \ *(root directory)*

A suggested sequence would be as follows:

> C:\>**COPY A:TRIAL.MNU \ACAD\TRIAL.MNU**

Example No. 13

> Objective: *(Same as Example No. 14)*
> Current drive: **A:**
> Current directory: \ *(root directory)*

A suggested sequence would be as follows:

> A:\>**COPY TRIAL.MNU C:\ACAD\TRIAL.MNU**

Example No. 14

> Objective: *(Same as Example No. 14)*
> Current drive: **C:**
> Current directory: **\ACAD**

A suggested sequence would be as follows:

> C:\>**COPY A:TRIAL.MN**

Example No. 15 (Use of the global symbol "*")

Objective: *(Copy all files with the file extension of .MNU from drive A to the ACAD directory on drive C.)*
Current drive: **C:**
Current directory: **\ACAD**

A suggested sequence would be as follows:

C>COPY A:*.MNU

Example No. 16 (Use of the global symbol "*")

Objective: *(Copy all files on drive A to the ACAD directory on drive C.)*
Current drive: **C:**
Current directory: **\ACAD**

A suggested sequence would be as follows:

C>COPY A:*.*

or

C>COPY A:.

As you can see, like in programming, DOS commands can be made easier with a little planning.

In Windows, there are two ways to copy a file between drives.

Method 1   The first method is to:

Drag the filename to one of the disk icons at the top of the File Manager. To copy the file, simply drag the file; to move the file, hold down [Shift] while dragging.

Method 2   The second method is to open a second file window, then drag the file.

1. Double-click on the other drive icon.

2. The select the **Windows | Tile Horizontally** command. This displays the files of two disk drives in the File Manager (see Figure B–9).

3. To copy the file, drag the file from one drive's subdirectory to the other drive's subdirectory.

or

3. To move the file, hold down [Shift] while dragging.

SELECTING A GROUP OF FILES – WINDOWS

There are two ways to select a group of files in the File Manager. To select a consecutive group of filenames, click on the first name of the group. Then press [Shift] and click on the last name in the group. The File Manager highlights the group.

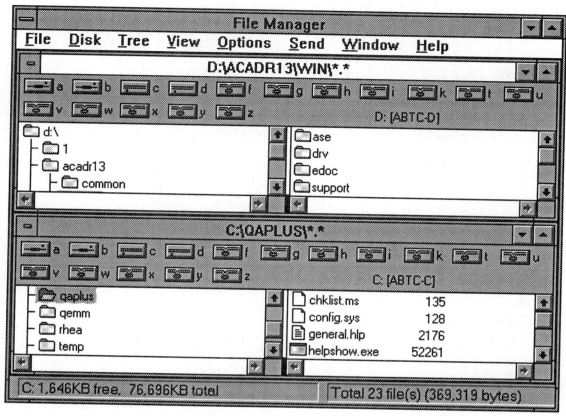

Figure B–9   The File Manager displaying the files of two disk drives

To select a nonconsecutive group of filenames, click on the first filename. Then hold down ⎡Ctrl⎤. Now click on the other filenames you want to select. When done, let go of ⎡Ctrl⎤.

You can now move or copy the group of files.

DELETE A FILE OR GROUP OF FILES

The storage space on a disk is limited and all of it may eventually be occupied by files. Therefore, it is sometimes necessary to delete files you no longer need. The built-in command ERASE and its shorter form DEL can delete a single file or a group of files. Both commands do exactly the same thing and work the same way. You can use whichever command you prefer.

Example No. 17

Objective: *(Delete the file XMPL.BAK.)*
Current drive: **C:**
Current directory: \ *(root directory)*
Drive where XMPL.BAK is stored: **C:**
Directory where XMPL.BAK is stored: **\ACAD\DRAWINGS**

(Note that \DRAWINGS\ is a subdirectory of \ACAD\)

A:\>ERASE C:\ACAD\DRAWINGS\XMPL.BAK

Example No. 18

Objective: *(Delete all the files with extension .BAK in drive A.)*
Current drive: **C:**
Current directory: \ *(root directory)*

A suggested sequence would be as follows to delete the files:

C:\>ERASE A:*.BAK

Example No. 19

Objective: *(Delete all the files in the directory DWG.)*
Current drive: **C:**
Current directory: **c:\DWG**

A suggested sequence would be as follows to delete the files:

C:\DWG>ERASE *.*

or

C:\DWG>ERASE .

The following message will appear:

Are you sure (Y/N)?

You must answer **Y** if you want DOS to continue. Otherwise, the operation is terminated without further action.

In Windows, select a file (or group of files, as noted above), then press ⌐. The File Manager displays the **Delete** dialog box, as shown in Figure B–10.

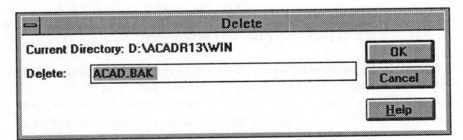

Figure B–10 The Delete dialog box

DOS REFERENCE BOOKS

A variety of books are available that discuss the MS DOS operating system. It is suggested that you read any one of the available books for detailed information about the operating system and system management.

APPENDIX

C

QUICK REFERENCE OF KEY-IN COMMANDS

COMMANDS

Command (Aliases)	Explanation	Options	Toolbar	Pull-Down Menu
'About	Displays a dialog box with the AutoCAD version and serial numbers, a scrolling window with the text of the *acad.msg* file, and other information.			TYPE IN
Acisin	Imports an ACIS file.			File
Acisout	Exports AutoCAD solid objects to an ACIS file.			File
Align	Moves and rotates objects to align with other objects.		Modify	
Ameconvert	Converts AME solid models to AutoCAD solid objects.			TYPE IN
Aperture	Regulates the size of the object snap target box.	Select (1-50 pixels) to increase or reduce size of box.		TYPE IN
Appload	Loads AuotLISP, ADS, and ARX applications.			Tools
Arc (A)	Draws an arc of any size.	A Included angle. C Center point. D Starting direction. E Endpoint. L Length of chord. R Radius. S Start point. ⏎ Continues arc from endpoint of line or arc.	Draw	

(Reprinted with permission from Autodesk Inc.)

Command (Aliases)	Explanation	Options	Toolbar	Pull-Down Menu
Area	Calculates the area of a polygon, pline, or a circle.	A Sets add mode. S Sets subtract mode. E Calculates area of the circle or pline selected.	Object Properties	
Array	Copies selected objects in circular or rectangular pattern.	P Polar (circular) arrays about a center point. R Rectangular arrays objects in horizontal rows and vertical columns.	Modify	
Attdef	Creates an Attribute Definition that assigns (tags) textual information to a Block.	I Regulates visibility. C Regulates constant/variable mode. V Regulates verify mode. P Regulates preset mode.	Attribute	
Attdisp	Regulates the visibility of Attributes in the drawing.	ON Makes all Attribute tags visible. OFF Makes all Attributes invisible. N Normal visibility set individually.		Options
Attedit	Permits the editing of Attributes.		Attribute	
Attext	Extracts Attribute information from a drawing.	C CDF comma-delimited format. D DXF format. S SDF format. E Select objects.		TYPE IN
Attredef	Redefines a block and updates associated attributes.		Attribute	
Audit	Performs drawing integrity check while in AutoCAD.	Y Fixes errors encountered. N Reports, but does not fix errors.		File
Base	Defines the origin point for insertion of one drawing into another.			TYPE IN
Bhatch	Fills an automatically defined boundary with a hatch pattern through the use of dialog boxes. Also, allows previewing and repeated adjustments without starting over each time.		Draw	
Blipmode	Turns blip markers on and off.			Options
Block	Makes a compound object from a group of objects.	? Lists names of defined Blocks.	Draw	
Boundary	Creates a Polyline of a closed boundary.			TYPE IN
Box	Creates a three-dimensional solid box.		Solids	

Command (Aliases)	Explanation	Options		Toolbar	Pull-Down Menu
Break	Breaks out (erases) part of an object or splits it into parts.	F	Allows you to reselect the first point again.	Modify	
Cal	Evaluates mathematical and geometric expressions.				Tools
Cancel [Esc]	Cancels the current command.				
Chamfer	Makes a chamfer at the intersection of two lines.	D P	Sets chamfer distance. Chamfers all intersections of a pline figure.	Modify	
Change	Makes changes in the location, size, orientation, and other properties of selected objects. This command is very helpful for editing text.	P E C LA LT F	Changes properties of objects. Elevation Color Layer Linetype Thickness	Modify	
Chprop	Makes changes in the properties of selected objects.	C LA LT T	Color Layer Linetype Thickness		TYPE IN
Circle (C)	Draws a circle of any size. Default is center point and radius.	2P 3P D TTR R	Two endpoints on diameter. Three points on circle. Enters circle diameter. Tangent, Tangent, Radius Enter radius	Draw	
Color 1. Red 2. Yellow 3. Green 4. Cyan 5. Blue 6. Magenta 7. White	Sets color for objects by name or number. Also sets color to be by block or layer.	number name BYBLOCK BYLAYER	Sets color by number. Sets a color by name. Retains color of Block. Uses color of layer.		Data
Compile	Compiles shape and font files.				Tools
Cone	Creates a three-dimensional solid cone.			Solids	
Config	Displays options in the text window to reconfigure the video display, digitizer, plotter, and operating parameters.				Options
Copy (CP)	Makes one or more copies of selected objects.	M	Makes more than one copy of the selected object.	Modify	

Command (Aliases)	Explanation	Options	Toolbar	Pull-Down Menu
Cylinder	Creates a three-dimensional solid cylinder.		Solids	
Dblist	Makes a listing of every object in the drawing data base.			TYPE IN
Ddattdef	Displays a dialog box that creates an Attribute Definition object for textual information to be associated with a Block Definition.		Attribute	
Ddatte	Edits Attributes via a dialog box.		Attribute	
Ddattext	Displays a dialog box that extracts data from a drawing. Available formats are DXF, CDF, SDF, or selected objects.			File
Ddchprop	Displays a dialog box that modifies the color, layer, linetype, and thickness of selected objects.			TYPE IN
Ddcolor	Sets color for new objects.		Object Properties	Data
Ddedit	Edits text and Attributes via a dialog box.		Attributes	
'Ddemodes	Sets current layer, linetype, elevation, and text style via a dialog box.			Data
'Ddgrips	Allows you to enable grips and set their colors and size via a dialog box.			Options
'Ddim	Controls dimensioning through a series of dialog boxes. See also DIM.		Dimensioning	Data
Ddinsert	Displays a dialog box that inserts a copy of a previously drawn part or a drawing file into a drawing, and lets you set an insertion point, scale, rotate, or explode the part. See also Insert.		Draw	
'Ddlmodes	Sets layer properties via a dialog box.		Object Properties	Data
Ddltype	Loads and sets linetypes.		Object Properties	Data
Ddmodify	Controls object properties.		Standard	

Command (Aliases)	Explanation	Options	Toolbar	Pull-Down Menu
'Ddosnap	Displays a dialog box for setting running Osnaps for the Endpoint, Midpoint, Center, Node, Quadrant, Intersection, Insertion, Tangent, From, ApplInt, Nearest, and Quick object snap modes. Also, lets you set the size of the cross-hair target box aperture. See also Osnap.		Standard	Options
Ddtype	Specifies the display mode and size of point objects.			Options
'Ddrename	Displays a dialog box that renames text styles, layers, linetypes, Blocks, views, User Coordinate Systems, viewport configurations, and dimension styles. See also Rename.			Data
'Ddrmodes	Allows drawing aids to be set via a dialog box.			Options
'Ddselect	Displays a dialog box that sets object selection modes, the size of the pickbox, and the object sort method.			Options
Dducs	To control the User Coordinate System via a dialog box.		Standard	View
Dducsp	Selects a preset User Coordinate System.		Standard	View
'Ddunits	Displays a dialog box that sets coordinate and angle display formats and precision. See also Units.			Data
Ddview	Creates and restores views.		Standard	View
Ddvpoint	Sets the three-dimensional viewing direction.		Standard	View
Delay	Sets timing for a sequence of commands used in a script file.			TYPE IN
Dim	Accesses dimensioning mode.		Dimensioning	
Dist	Determines distance between two points.		Object Properties	
Divide	Places markers along selected objects, dividing them into a specified number of parts.	B Sets a specified Block as a marker.	Draw	

Command (Aliases)	Explanation	Options		Toolbar	Pull-Down Menu
Doughnut (Donut)	Draws a solid circle or a ring with a specified inside and outside diameter.			Draw	
Dragmode	Allows control of the dynamic specification (dragging) feature for all appropriate commands.	ON OFF A	Honors drag requests when applicable. Ignores drag requests. Sets Auto mode: drags whenever possible.		TYPE IN
Dtext	Enters text on the display as it is typed in.	See Text command for options.		Draw	
Dview (DV)	Defines parallel or visual perspective views dynamically.	CA CL D H OFF PA PO TA TW U X Z	Selects the camera angle relative to the target. Sets front and back clipping planes. Sets camera-to-target distance, turns on perspective. Removes hidden lines on the selection set. Turns perspective off. Pans drawing across the screen. Specifies the camera and target points. Rotates the target point about the camera. Twists the view around your line of sight. Undoes a Dview subcommand. Exits the Dview command. Zooms in/out, or sets lens length.	Standard	View
Dxbin	Inserts specially coded binary files into a drawing.				File
Dxfin	Loads a drawing interchange file.				File
Dxfout	Writes a drawing interchange file.	B E 0–16	Writes binary DXF file. Outputs selected entities only. Floating point precision.		File
Edge	Changes the visibility of three-dimensional face edges.			Surfaces	
Edgesurf	Constructs a 3D Polygon mesh approximating a Coons surface patch (a bicubic surface interpolated between four adjoining edges).			Surfaces	
Elev	Sets elevation and extrusion thickness for entities to be drawn in 3D drawings.				TYPE IN

Command (Aliases)	Explanation	Options		Toolbar	Pull-Down Menu
Ellipse	Draws ellipses using any of several methods.	C	Selects center point.	Draw	
		R	Selects rotation rather than second Axis.		
		I	Draws isometric circle in current isoplane.		
End	Exits after saving the updated drawing.				TYPE IN
Erase (E)	Deletes objects from the drawing.			Modify	
Explode	Changes a block or polyline back into its original objects.			Modify	
Extend	Extends a line, arc, or polyline to meet another object.	U	Undoes last extension.	Modify	
Extrude	Creates unique solid primitives by extruding existing two-dimensional objects.			Solids	
Files	Performs disk file utility tasks.				File
Fill	Determines if solids, traces, and wide polylines are automatically filled.	ON	Solids, traces and wide polylines filled.		TYPE IN
		OFF	Solids, traces, and wide polylines outlined.		
Fillet	Constructs an arc of specified radius between two lines, arcs, or circles.	P	Fillets an entire Polyline. Sets fillet radius.	Modify	
		R	Sets fillet radius.		
Filter	Creates lists to select objects based on properties.			Standard	
Gifin	Imports GIF-format raster-image file.				File
Graphscr [F2]	Flips to the graphics display on single-screen systems. Used in command scripts and menus.				TYPE IN
Grid [F7] On/Off toggle	Displays a Grid of dots, at desired spacing, on the screen.	ON	Turns Grid on.	Status bar	
		OFF	Turns Grid off.		
		S	Locks Grid spacing to Snap resolution.		
		A	Sets Grid aspect (differing X-Y spacings).		
		number	Sets Grid spacing (0=use Snap spacing).		
		number X	Sets spacing to multiple of Snap spacing.		

Command (Aliases)	Explanation	Options		Toolbar	Pull-Down Menu
Group	Creates a named selection set of objects.			Standard	
Hatch	Creates cross-hatching and pattern-filling.	name	Uses hatch pattern name from library file.		TYPE IN
		U	Uses simple user-defined hatch pattern.		
		?	Lists selected names of available hatch patterns.		
		NAME and U can be followed by a comma and a hatch style from the following list:			
		I	Ignores internal structure.		
		N	Normal style: turns hatch lines off and on when internal structure is encountered.		
		O	Hatches outermost portion only.		
Hatchedit	Modifies an existing associative hatch block.			Modify	
"Help or '?	Displays a list of valid commands and data entry options or obtains help for a specific command or prompt.	To get a set of Help modes use [Esc] and [F2] for flip screen.		Help	Help
Hide	Regenerates a 3D visualization with hidden lines removed.			Render	
Id	Displays the coordinates of a point selected on the drawing.			Object Properties	
Insert	Inserts a copy of a block or Wblock complete drawing into the current drawing.	fname	Loads fname as block.	Draw	
		fname=f	Creates block fname from file f.		
		*name	Retains individual part objects.		
		C	(as reply to X scale prompt) Specifies scale via two points.		
			(Corner specification of scale)		
		XYZ	(as reply to X scale prompt) Readies Insert for X,Y, and Z scales.		
		~	Displays a File Dialog box.		
		?	Lists names of defined blocks.		

Command (Aliases)	Explanation	Options		Toolbar	Pull-Down Menu
Interfere	Finds the interference of two or more solids and creates a composite solid from their common volume.			Solids	
Intersect	Creates composite solids or regions from the intersection of two or more solids or regions.			Modify	
Isoplane `Ctrl` + `E`	Changes the location of the isometric cross-hairs to left, right and top plane.	L R T (Return)	Left plane. Right plane. Top plane. Toggle to next plane.		TYPE IN
Layer (LA)	Allows for creation of drawing layers and assigning color and linetype properties.	C F LT M N ON OFF S T ? L U	Sets layers to color selected. Freezes layers. Sets specified layers to linetype. Makes a layer the current layer, creating it if necessary. Creates new layers. Turns on layers. Turns off layers. Sets current layer to existing layer. Thaws layers. Lists specified layers and their associated colors, linetypes, and visibility. Lock Unlock	Object Properties	Data
Lengthen	Lengthens an object.			Modify	
Light	Manages lights and lighting effects.			Render	
Limits	Sets up the drawing size.	2 points ON OFF	Sets lower left/upper right drawing limits. Enables limits checking. Disables limits checking.		Data
Line (L)	Draws straight lines of any length.	(Return) C U	(as reply to "From point:") Starts at end of previous line or arc. (as reply to "To point:") Closes polygon. (as reply to "To point:") Undoes segment.	Draw	

Command (Aliases)	Explanation	Options		Toolbar	Pull-Down Menu
Linetype	Defines, loads, and sets the linetype.	?	Lists a linetype library.		TYPE IN
		C	Creates a linetype definition.		
		L	Loads a linetype definition.		
		S	Sets current object linetype. Set suboptions:		
		name	Sets object linetype name.		
		BYBLOCK	Sets floating object linetype.		
		BYLAYER	Uses layer's linetype for objects.		
		?	Lists specified loaded linetypes.		
List	Provides data base information for objects that are selected.			Object Properties	
Load	Loads a file of user-defined shapes to be used with the Shape command.	?	Lists the names of loaded Shape files.		Data
Logfileoff	Closes the log file opened by LOGFILEON.				Options
Logfileon	Writes the text window contents to a file.				Options
Ltscale	Regulates the scale factor to be applied to all linetypes within the drawing.				TYPE IN
Massprop	Calculates and displays the mass properties of regions or solids.			Object Properties	Assist
Matlib	Imports and exports materials to and from a library of materials.				Tools
Measure	Inserts markers at measured distances along a selected object.	B	Uses specified block as marker.	Draw	
Menu	Loads a menu into the menu areas (screen, pull-down, tablet, and button).				Tools
Menuload	Loads partial menu files.				TYPE IN
Menuunload	Unloads partial menu files.				TYPE IN

Command (Aliases)	Explanation	Options		Toolbar	Pull-Down Menu
Minsert	Inserts multiple copies of a block in a rectangular array.	fname	Loads fname and forms a rectangular array of the resulting block.	Draw	
		fname=f	Creates block fname from file f and forms a rectangular array.		
		?	Lists names of defined Blocks.		
		C	(as reply to X scale prompt) Specifies scale via two points (Corner specification of scale).		
		XYZ	(as reply to X scale prompt) Readies Mini-sert for X,Y, and Z scales.		
		~	Displays a File dialog box.		
Mirror	Reflects selected objects about a user-specified Axis, vertical, horizontal or inclined.			Modify	
Mirror3D	Creates a mirror image copy of objects about a plane.			Modify	
Mledit	Edits multiple parallel lines.			Modify	
Mlstyle	Defines a style for multiple parallel lines.				Data
Move (M)	Moves selected objects to another location in the drawing.			Modify	
Mslide	Creates a slide of what is displayed on the screen.				Tools
Mspace (MS)	Switches to Model Space from Paper Space.			Status bar	View
Mtext	Creates paragraph text.			Draw	
Mtprop	Changes paragraph text properties.				TYPE IN
Multiple	Allows the next command to repeat until canceled.				TYPE IN

Command (Aliases)	Explanation	Options		Toolbar	Pull-Down Menu
Mview	Sets up and controls viewports.	ON	Turns selected viewport(s) on. Causes model to be regenerated in the selected viewport(s).	Standard	View
		OFF	Turns selected viewport(s) off. Causes model to not be displayed in the selected viewport(s).		
		Hideplot	Causes hidden lines to be removed in selected viewport(s) during Paper Space plotting.		
		Fit	Creates a single viewport to fit the current Paper Space view.		
		2	Creates two viewports in specified area or fit to the current Paper Space view.		
		4	Creates four equal viewports in specified area or fit to the current Paper Space view.		
		Restore	Translates viewport configurations saved with the Vports command into individual viewport objects in Paper Space.		
		<point>	Creates a new viewport within the area specified by two points.		
Mvsetup	Sets up the specifications of a drawing				Tools
New	Creates a new drawing.			Standard	File
Offset	Reproduces curves or lines parallel to the one selected.	number T	Specifies offset distance. Through: allows specification of a point through which the offset curve is to pass.	Modify	
Oops	Recalls last set of objects previously erased.			Modify	
Open	Opens an existing drawing.			Standard	File
Ortho F8	Restricts cursor to vertical or horizontal use.	ON	Forces cursor to horizontal or vertical use.	Status bar	
		OFF	Does not constrain cursor movement.		

Command (Aliases)	Explanation	Options	Toolbar	Pull-Down Menu
Osnap	Allows for selection of precise points on existing objects.	CEN Center of arc or circle. END Closest endpoint of arc or line. INS Insertion point of Text/ Block/Shape. INT Intersection of line/arc/circle. MID Midpoint of arc or line. NEA Nearest point of arc/circle/ line/point. NOD Node (point) NON None (off) PER Perpendicular to arc/line/circle. QUA Quadrant point of arc or circle. QUI Quick mode (first find, not closest). TAN Tangent to arc or circle.	Object Snap	
'Pan (P)	Moves the display window.		Standard	View
Pcxin	Imports a PCX-format raster image file.			File
Pedit (2D)	Permits editing of 2D polylines.	C Closes to start point. D Decurves, or returns a spline curve to its control frame. F Fits curve to Polyline. J Joins to Polyline. O Opens a closed Polyline. S Uses the Polyline vertices as the frame for a spline curve (type set by SPLINETYPE). U Undoes one editing operation. W Sets uniform width for Polyline. X Exits Pedit command. E Edits vertices. B Sets first vertex for Break. G Go (performs Break or Straighten operation). I Inserts new vertex after current one. M Moves current vertex. N Makes next vertex current. P Makes previous vertex current. R Regenerates the Polyline. S Sets first vertex for Straighten. T Sets tangent direction for current vertex. W Sets new width for following segment. X Exits vertex editing, or cancels Break/Straighten.	Modify	

Command (Aliases)	Explanation	Options	Toolbar	Pull-Down Menu
Pedit (3D)	Allows editing of 3D polylines.	C Closes to start point. D Decurves, or returns a spline curve to its control frame. O Opens a closed polyline. S Uses the polyline vertices as the frame for a spline curve (type set by SPLINETYPE). U Undoes one editing operation. X Exits Pedit command. E Edits vertices. During vertex editing: B Sets first vertex for Break. G Go (performs Break or Straighten operation). I Inserts new vertex after current one. M Moves current vertex. N Makes next vertex current. P Makes previous vertex current. R Regenerates the Polyline. S Sets first vertex for Straighten. X Exits vertex editing, or cancels Break/Straighten.	Modify	
Pedit (Mesh)	Allows editing of 3D polygon meshes.	D Desmooth-restores original mesh. M Opens (or closes) the mesh in the M direction. N Opens (or closes) the mesh in the N direction. S Fits a smooth surface as defined by SURFTYPE. U Undoes one editing operation. X Exits Pedit command. E Edits Mesh vertices. D Moves down to previous vertex in M direction. L Moves left to previous vertex in N direction. M Repositions the marked vertex. N Moves to next vertex. P Moves to previous vertex. R Moves right to next vertex in N direction. RE Redisplays the polygon mesh. U Moves up to next vertex in M direction. X Exits vertex editing.	Modify	
Pface	Creates a 3D mesh of arbitrary complexity and surface characteristics.			TYPE IN

Command (Aliases)	Explanation	Options	Toolbar	Pull-Down Menu
Plan	Puts the display in plan view (Vpoint 0,0,1) relative to either the current UCS, a specified UCS, or the WCS.	C Establishes a plan view of the current UCS. U Establishes a plan view of the specified UCS. W Establishes a plan view of the WCS.		View
Pline (PL)	Draws 2D Polylines.	H Sets new half-width. U Undoes previous segment. W Sets new line width. [Enter] Exits Pline command. C Closes with straight segment. L Segment length (continues previous segment). A Switches to arc mode. In arc mode: A Included angle. CE Center point. CL Closes with arc segment. D Starting direction. L Chord length, or switches to line mode. R Radius. S Second point of three-point arc.	Draw	
Plot (Print)	Plots a drawing to a plotting device or a file.		Standard	File
Point	Draws single points on the drawing.		Draw	
Polygon	Creates regular polygons with the specified number of sides indicated.	E Specifies polygon by showing one edge. C Circumscribes around circle. I Inscribes within circle.	Draw	
Preferences	Customizes the AutoCAD settings.			Options
Psdrag	Controls the appearance of an imported PostScript image that is being dragged (that is, positioned and scaled) into place by the PSIN command.	0 Only the image's bounding box is displayed as you drag it into place. 1 The rendered PostScript image is displayed as you drag it into place.		File
Psfill	Fills 2D Polyline outlines with PostScript fill patterns defined in the AutoCAD PostScript support file (acad.psf).			TYPE IN
Psin	Imports Encapsulated PostScript (EPS) files.			File

Command (Aliases)	Explanation	Options	Toolbar	Pull-Down Menu
Psout	Exports the current view of your drawing to an Encapsulated Postscript (EPS) file.			File
Pspace (PS)	Switches to Paper Space.		Status bar	View
Purge	Removes unused Blocks, text styles, layers, linetypes, and dimension styles from the drawing.	A Purges all unused named objects. B Purges unused Blocks. D Purges unused dimstyles. LA Purges unused layers. SH Purges unused shape files. ST Purges unused text styles. LT Purges linetypes.		Data
Qsave	Saves the drawing without requesting a filename.		Standard	File
Qtext	Enables text objects to be identified without drawing the test detail.	ON Quick text mode on. OFF Quick text mode off.		Options
Quit	Exit AutoCAD.			File
Ray	Creates a semi-infinite line.		Draw	
Rconfig	Reconfigures the rendering setup.			Options
Recover	Attempts to recover damaged or corrupted drawings.			File
Rectang	Draws a rectangular polyline.		Draw	
Redefine	Restores a built-in command deleted by Undefine.			TYPE IN
Redo	Reverses the previous command if it was U or Undo.		Standard	
'Redraw (R)	Refreshes or cleans up the current viewport.		Standard	View
'Redrawall	Redraws all viewports.		Standard	View
Regen	Regenerates the current viewport.			TYPE IN
Regenall	Regenerates all viewports.			TYPE IN
Regenauto	Controls automatic regeneration performed by other commands.	ON Allows automatic regens. OFF Prevents automatic regens.		TYPE IN
Region	Creates a region object from a selection set of existing objects.		Draw	

Command (Aliases)	Explanation	Options	Toolbar	Pull-Down Menu
Reinit	Allows the I/O ports, digitizer, display, plotter, and PGP file to be reinitialized.			TYPE IN
Rename	Changes the names associated with text styles, layers, linetypes, blocks, views, UCSs, viewport configurations, and dimension styles.	B Renames block. D Renames dimension style. LA Renames layer. LT Renames linetype. S Renames text style. U Renames UCS VI Renames view. VP Renames viewport configuration.		TYPE IN
Render	Creates a realistically shaded image of a three-dimensional wire frame or solid model.		Render	Tools
Renderunload	Unloads the AuotCAD Render application from your system's memory.			TYPE IN
Rendscr	Redisplays the last rendering created using RENDER.			TYPE IN
Replay	Displays a GIF, TGA, or TIFF image.			Tools
'Resume	Resumes an interrupted command script.			TYPE IN
Revolve	Creates a solid by revolving a two-dimensional object about an axis.		Solids	
Revsurf	Creates a 3D polygon mesh approximating a surface of revolution, by rotating a curve around a selected Axis.		Surfaces	
Rmat	Manages rendering materials.		Render	Tools
Rotate	Rotates existing objects to the angle selected.	R Rotates with respect to reference angles.	Modify	
Rotate3D	Moves objects about a three-dimensional axis.		Modify	
Rpref	Sets rendering preferences.			Tools
Rscript	Restarts a command script from the beginning.			TYPE IN
Rulesurf	Creates a 3D polygon mesh approximating a ruled surface between two curves.		Surfaces	

Command (Aliases)	Explanation	Options	Toolbar	Pull-Down Menu
Save	Updates the current drawing file without exiting the Drawing Editor.		Standard	File
Saveas	Same as SAVE, but also renames the current drawing.			File
Saveasr12	Saves the current drawing in AutoCAD Release 12 format.			TYPE IN
Saveimg	Saves a rendered image to a file.			Tools
Scale	Changes the size of existing objects to selected scale factor.	R Resizes with respect to reference size.	Modify	
Scene	Manages scenes in model space		Render	Tools
Script	Executes a command script.			Tools
Section	Uses the intersection of a plane and solids to create a region.		Section	
Select	Groups objects into a selection set for use in subsequent commands.			TYPE IN
'Setvar	Allows you to display or change the value of system variables.	? Lists specified system variables.		TYPE IN
Shade	Shades model in the current viewport.		Render	
Shape	Draws predefined shapes.	? Lists available Shape names.		TYPE IN
Shell	Allows access to other programs while running AutoCAD.			TYPE IN
Sketch	Allows freehand sketching.	C Connect: restarts sketch at endpoint. E Erases (backs up over) temporary lines. P Raises/lowers sketching pen. Q Discards temporary lines, remains in Sketch. R Records temporary lines, remains in Sketch. X Records temporary lines, exits Sketch. Draws line to current point.	Draw	
Slice	Slices a set of solids with a plane.		Solids	

Command (Aliases)	Explanation	Options		Toolbar	Pull-Down Menu
Snap [F9]	Allows for precision alignment of points.	number ON OFF A R S	Sets snap resolution. Aligns designated points. Does not align designated points. Sets aspect (differing X-Y spacing). Rotates Snap Grid. Selects style, standard or isometric.	Status bar	
Solid	Creates filled-in polygons.			Draw	
Spell	Checks spelling in a drawing.			Standard	Tools
Sphere	Creates a three-dimensional solid sphere.			Solids	
Spline	Creates a quadratic or cubic spline (NURBS) curve.			Draw	
Splinedit	Edits a spline object.			Modify	
Stats	Displays rendering statistics.				Tools
Status	Displays drawing setup.				Data
Stlout	Stores a solid in ASCII or binary file.				File
Stretch	Allows you to move a portion of a drawing while retaining connections to other parts of the drawing.			Modify	
Style	Sets up named text styles, with various combinations of font, mirroring, obliquing, and horizontal scaling.	?	Lists specified currently defined text styles.		Data
Subtract	Creates a composite region or solid by subtracting the area of one set of regions from another and subtracting the volume of one set of solids from another.			Modify	
Tablet	Allows for configuration of a tablet menu or digitizing of an existing drawing.	ON OFF CAL	Turns tablet mode on. Turns tablet mode off. Calibrates tablet for use in the current space.		Options
Tabsurf	Creates a polygon mesh approximating a general tabulated surface defined by a path and a direction vector.			Surfaces	

Command (Aliases)	Explanation	Options		Toolbar	Pull-Down Menu
Text	Enters text on the drawing.	J	Prompts for justification options.	Draw	
		S	Lists or selects text style.		
		A	Aligns text between two points, with style-specified width factor; AutoCAD computes appropriate height.		
		C	Centers text horizontally.		
		F	Fits text between two points, with specified height; AutoCAD computes an appropriate width factor.		
		M	Centers text horizontally and vertically.		
		R	Right-justifies text.		
		BL	Bottom Left.		
		BC	Bottom Center.		
		BR	Bottom Right.		
		ML	Middle Left.		
		MC	Middle Center.		
		MR	Middle Right.		
		TL	Top Left.		
		TC	Top Center.		
		TR	Top Right.		
'Textscr [F1]	Flips to the text display on single-screen systems. Used in command scripts and menus.				TYPE IN
Tiffin	Imports a TIFF-format raster-image file.				File
Time	Indicates total elapsed time for each drawing.	D	Displays current times.		Data
		ON	Starts user elapsed timer.		
		OFF	Stops user elapsed timer.		
		R	Resets user elapsed timer.		
Tolerance	Creates geometric tolerances.			Dimensioning	
Torus	Creates a donut-shaped solid.			Solids	
Trace	Creates solid lines of specified width.			Draw	
Treestat	Displays information on the drawing's current spatial index, such as the number and depth of nodes in the drawing's database. Use this information with the TREEDEPTH system variable setting to fine-tune performances for large drawings.				TYPE IN
Trim	Deletes portions of selected entities that cross a selected boundary edge.	U	Undoes last trim operation.	Modify	

Command (Aliases)	Explanation	Options		Toolbar	Pull-Down Menu
U	Reverses the effect of the previous command.			Standard	
UCS	Defines or modifies the current User Coordinate System.	D	Deletes one or more saved coordinate systems.	Standard	View
		E	Sets a UCS with the same extrusion direction as that of the selected object.		
		O	Shifts the origin of the current coordinate system.		
		P	Restores the previous UCS.		
		R	Restores a previously saved UCS.		
		S	Saves the current UCS.		
		V	Establishes a new UCS whose Z Axis is parallel to the current viewing direction.		
		W	Sets the current UCS equal to the WCS.		
		X	Rotates the current UCS around the X Axis.		
		Y	Rotates the current UCS around the Y Axis.		
		Z	Rotates the current UCS around the Z Axis.		
		ZA	Defines a UCS using an origin point and a point on the positive portion of the Z Axis.		
		3	Defines a UCS using an origin point, a point on the positive portion of the X Axis, and a point on the positive Y-portion of the X plane.		
		?	Lists specified saved coordinate systems.		
Ucsicon	Controls visibility and placement of the UCS icon, which indicates the origin and orientation of the current UCS. The options normally affect only the current viewport.	A	Changes settings in all active viewports.		Options
		N	Displays the icon at the lower-left corner of the viewport.		
		OR	Displays the icon at the origin of the current UCS if possible.		
		ON	Enables the coordinate system icon.		
Undefine	Deletes the definition of a built-in AutoCAD command.				TYPE IN

Command (Aliases)	Explanation	Options		Toolbar	Pull-Down Menu
Undo	Reverses the effect of multiple commands, and provides control over the Undo facility.	number	Undoes the number most recent commands	Standard	
		A Auto:	controls treatment of menu items as Undo groups.		
		B Back:	undoes back to previous Undo mark.		
		C Control:	enables/disables the Undo mark.		
		E End:	terminates an Undo group.		
		G Group:	begins sequence to be treated as one command.		
		M Mark:	places marker in Undo file (for back).		
Union	Creates a composite region or solid.			Modify	
Units	Selects coordinate and angle display formats and precision.				Data
'View	Saves the current graphics display and space as a named view, or restores a saved view and space to the display.	D	Deletes named view.		View
		R	Restores named view to screen.		
		S	Saves current display as named view.		
		W	Saves specified window as named view.		
		?	Lists specified named views.		
Viewports or Vports	Divides the AutoCAD graphics display into multiple viewports, each of which can contain a different view of the current drawing.	D	Deletes a saved viewport configuration.		View
		J	Joins (merges) two viewports.		
		R	Restores a saved viewport configuration.		
		S	Saves the current viewport configuration.		
		S1	Displays a single viewport filling the entire graphics area.		
		2	Divides the current viewport into viewports.		
		3	Divides the current viewport into three viewports.		
		4	Divides the current viewport into four viewports.		
		?	Lists the current and saved viewport configurations.		
Viewres	Adjusts the precision and speed of circle and arc drawing on the monitor.				Options

Appendix C

Command (Aliases)	Explanation	Options		Toolbar	Pull-Down Menu
Vplayer	Sets viewport visibility for new and existing layers.	?	Lists layers frozen in a selected viewport.		Data
		Freeze	Freezes specified layers in selected viewport(s).		
		Thaw	Thaws specified layers in selected viewport(s).		
		Reset	Resets specified layers to their default visibility.		
		Newfz	Creates new layers that are frozen in all viewports.		
		Vpvisdflt	Sets the default viewport visibility for existing layers.		
Vpoint	Selects the viewpoint for a 3D visualization.	R	Selects viewpoint via two rotation angles.		View
		(Return)	Selects viewpoint via compass and axes tripod.		
		x,y,z	Specifies viewpoint.		
Vslide	Displays a previously created slide file.	file	Views slide.		Tools
		*file	Preloads next Vslide you will view.		
Wblock	Creates a Block as a separate drawing.	name	Writes specified Block Definition.		File
		=	Block name same as file name.		
		*	Writes entire drawing.		
		(Return)	Writes selected objects.		
Wedge	Creates at three-dimensional solid with a tapered sloping face.			Solids	
Xbind	Permanently adds a selected subset of an Xref's dependent symbols to your drawing.	Block	Adds a Block.	External Reference	
		Dimstyle	Adds a dimstyle.		
		Layer	Adds a layer.		
		Ltype	Adds a linetype.		
		Style	Adds a style.		
Xline	Creates an infinite line.			Draw	
Xplode	Breaks a compound object into its component objects.				TYPE IN

Command (Aliases)	Explanation	Options		Toolbar	Pull-Down Menu
Xref	Allows you to work with other AutoCAD drawings without adding them permanently to your drawing and without altering their contents.	Attach	Attaches a new Xref or inserts a copy of an Xref that you have already attached.	External Reference	
		Bind	Makes an Xref a permanent part of your drawing.		
		Detach	Removes an Xref from your drawing.		
		Path	Allows you to view and edit the filename AutoCAD uses when loading a particular Xref.		
		Reload	Updates one or more Xrefs at any time, without leaving and re-entering the Drawing Editor.		
		?	Lists Xrefs in your drawing and the drawing associated with each one.		
Xrefclip	Inserts and clips an xref			External Reference	
'Zoom (Z)	Enlarges or reduces the display area of a drawing.	number	Multiplier from original scale.	Standard	View
		numberX	Multiplier from current scale.		
		number XP	Scale relative to Paper Space.		
		A	All		
		C	Center		
		D	Dynamic Pan Zoom		
		E	Extents ("drawing uses")		
		L	Lower left corner		
		P	Previous		
		V	Virtual screen maximum		
		W	Window		
3Dface	Draws 3D plane sections.	I	Makes the following edge invisible.	Surfaces	
3Dmesh	Defines a 3D polygon mesh (by specifying its size in terms of M and N) and the location of each vertex in the mesh.			Surfaces	
3Dpoly	Creates a 3D Polyline.	C	Closes the Polyline back to the first point.	Draw	
		U	Undoes (deletes) the last segment entered.		
		(Return)	Exits 3Dpoly command.		

DIMENSIONING COMMANDS

Command	Explanation
Dimaligned	Aligns dimension parallel with objects.
Dimangular	Draws an arc to show the angle between two nonparallel lines or three specified points.
Dimbaseline	Continues a linear dimension from the baseline (first extension line) of the previous or selected dimension.
Dimcenter	Draws a circle/arc center mark or center lines.
Dimcontinue	Continues a linear dimension from the second extension line of the previous dimension.
Dimdiameter	Dimensions the diameter of a circle or arc.
Dimedit	Edits dimensions.
Dimexit	Returns to the normal command mode.
Dimhorizontal	Generates a linear dimension with a horizontal dimension line.
Dimoblique	Adjusts obliquing angle of a linear associative dimension's extension lines.
Dimordinate	Creates ordinate point associative dimensions.
Dimoverride	Overrides a subset of the dimension variable settings associated with selected dimension objects.
Dimradius	Dimensions the radius of a circle or arc, with an optional center mark or center lines.
Dimstyle	Switches to a new text style.
Dimtedit	Allows repositioning and rotation of text items in an associative dimension without affecting other dimension subentities.
Dimtrotate	Allows specification of a rotation angle for the text items of several associative dimensions at one time.
Dimvertical	Generates a linear dimension with a vertical dimension line.
Leader	Draws a line with an arrowhead placement of dimension text.

DIMENSIONING VARIABLES

Name	Description	Type	Default
DIMALT	Alternate Units.	Switch	Off
DIMALTD	Alternate Units Decimal Places.	Integer	2
DIMALTF	Alternate Units Scale Factor.	Scale	25.4
DIMALTTD	Alternate Units Tolerance Value.	Integer	2
DIMALTTZ	Toggles Suppression of Zeros for Tolerance Values.	Integer	0
DIMALTU	Sets Unit Format for Alternate Units.	Integer	2
DIMALTZ	Toggles Suppression of Zeros for Alternate Values.	Integer	0
DIMAPOST	Alternate Units Text Suffix.	String	None
DIMASO	Associative Dimensioning.	Switch	On
DIMASZ	Arrow Size.	Distance	0.18
DIMAUNIT	Angle Format.	Integer	0
DIMBLK	Arrow Block.	String	None
DIMBLK1	Separate Arrow Block 1.	String	None
DIMBLK2	Separate Arrow Block 2.	String	None
DIMCEN	Center Mark Size.	Distance	0.09
DIMCLRD	Dimension Line Color.	Color number	BYBLOCK
DIMCLRE	Extension Line Color.	Color number	BYBLOCK
DIMCLRT	Dimension Text Color.	Color number	BYBLOCK
DIMDEC	Decimal Place for Tolerance Values.	Integer	4
DIMDLE	Dimension Line Extension.	Distance	0.0
DIMDLI	Dimension Line Increment.	Distance	0.38
DIMEXE	Extension Line Extension.	Distance	0.18
DIMEXO	Extension Line Offset.	Distance	0.0625
DIMFIT	Placement of Text and Arrowheads.	Integer	3
DIMGAP	Dimension Line Gap.	Distance	0.09
DIMJUST	Controls Horizontal Text Position.	Imteger	0
DIMLFAC	Length Factor.	Scale	1.0
DIMLIM	Limits Dimensioning.	Switch	Off
DIMPOST	Dimension Text Suffix.	String	None
DIMRND	Rounding Value.	Scaled distance	0.0
DIMSAH	Separate Arrow Blocks.	Switch	Off
DIMSCALE	Dimension Feature Scale Factor.	Switch	1.0
DIMSD1	Suppresses First Dimension Line.	Switch	Off
DIMSD2	Suppresses Second Dimension Line.	Switch	Off
DIMSE1	Suppress Extension Line 1.	Switch	Off
DIMSE2	Suppress Extension Line 2.	Switch	Off
DIMSHO	Show Dragged Dimension.	Switch	On

Name	Description	Type	Default
DIMSOXD	Suppress Outside Dimension Lines.	Switch	Off
DIMSTYLE	Dimension Style.	Name	*UNNAMED
DIMTAD	Text Above Dimension Line.	Switch	Off
DIMTDEC	Tolerance Values.	Integer	4
DIMTFAC	Tolerance Text Scale Factor.	Scale	1.0
DIMTIH	Text Inside Horizontal.	Switch	On
DIMTIX	Text Inside Extension Lines.	Switch	Off
DIMTM	Minus Tolerance Value.	Scaled distance	0.0
DIMTOFL	Text Outside, Force Line Inside.	Switch	Off
DIMTOH	Text Outside Horizontal.	Switch	On
DIMTOL	Tolerance Dimensioning.	Switch	Off
DIMTOLJ	Tolerance Dimensioning Justification.	Integer	1
DIMTP	Plus Tolerance Value.	Scaled distance	0.0
DIMTSZ	Tick Size.	Distance	0.0
DIMTVP	Text Vertical Position.	Scale	0.0
DIMTXSTY	Dimension Text Style	String	Standard
DIMTXT	Text Size.	Distance	0.18
DIMUNIT	Sets Unit Format.	Integer	2
DIMUPT	User Positioned Text.	Switch	Off
DIMZIN	Zero Suppression.	Integer	0

OBJECT SELECTION

Object selection option	Meaning
point	Selects one object that crosses the small pick box. If no object crosses the pick box and Auto mode has been selected, this designated point is taken as the first corner of a Crossing or Window box
Multiple	Allows selection of multiple objects using a single search of the drawing. The search is not performed until you give a null response to the "Select objects:" prompt
Window	Selects all objects that lie entirely within a window
WPolygon	Selects objects that lie entirely within a polygon shaped selection area
Crossing	Selects all objects that lie within *or cross* a window
CPolygon	Selects all objects that lie within and crossing a polygon shaped selection area
Fence	Selects all objects that cross a selection fence line
BOX	Prompts for two points. If the seocnd point is to the right of the first point, selects all objects inside the box (like 'Window'). Otherwise, selects all objects within or crossing the box (like "Crossing")
AUto	Accepts a point, which can select an object using the small pick box. If the point you pick is in an empty area, it is taken as the first corner of a Box (see above)
ALL	Selects all entities in the drawing except entities on frozen or locked layers
Last	Selects the most recently drawn object that is currently visible
Previous	Selects the previous selection set
Add	Establishes Add mode to add following objects to the selection set
Remove	Sets Remove mode to remove following objects from the selection set
SIngle	Sets single selection mode. As soon as one object (or one group of objects via Window/Crossing box) is selected, the selection set is considered complete and the editing command uses it without further user interaction
Undo	Undoes (removes objects last added)

D

AUTOCAD MENUS

(See figures on the following pages)

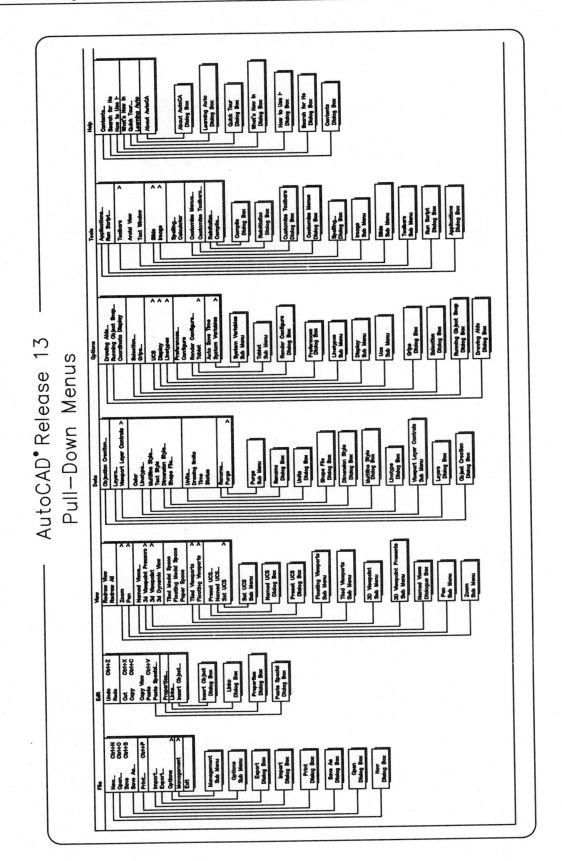

AutoCAD® Release 13
Pull-Down Menus

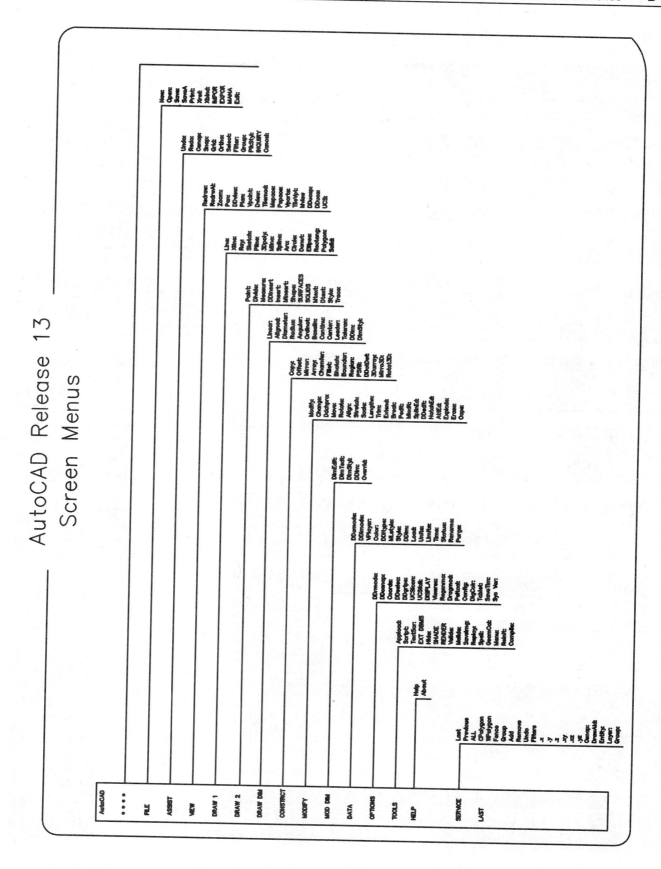

AutoCAD Release 13
Screen Menus

AutoCAD for Windows Release 13 Toolbars

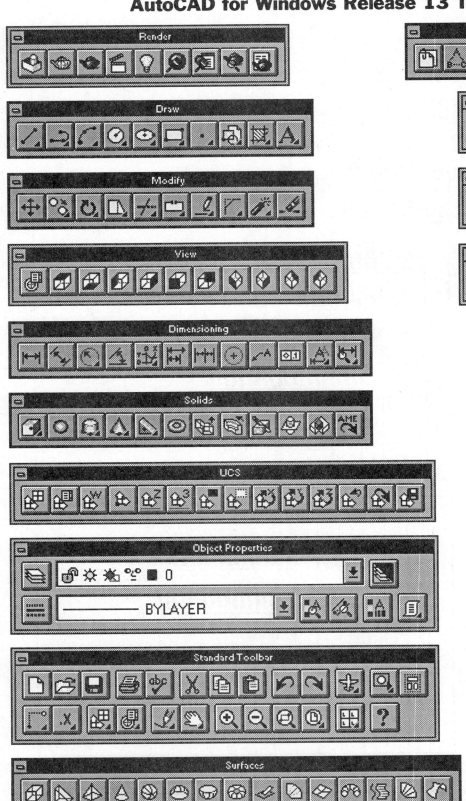

E

FILE TYPES USED
BY AUTOCAD

The following table shows different file types used by AutoCAD programs.

File type	File description
.ads	ADS applications file
.adt	Audit report file
.bak	Drawing file backup
.bdf	VESA font file
.bkn	Emergency backup file incremented sequentially to next unique name
.cfg	Configuration file
.dcc	Dialogue color control file (DOS only)
.dce	Dialogue box error report
.dcl	Dialogue Control Language description file
.dfs	Default file settings file (created by *mvsetup.lsp*)
.dwg	Drawing file
.dxb	Binary drawing interchange file
.dxf	Drawing interchange file (ASCII or binary)
.dxx	Attribute extract file (DXF format)
.eps	Encapsulated PostScript file
.err	Report generated listing errors if AutoCAD crashes
.exp	ADS executable files (DOS only)
.flm	Filmroll file (for AutoShade)
.hlp	Help file
.hdx	Help index file
.igs	IGES interchange file

File type	File description
.lin	Linetype library file
.lsp	AutoLISP program library file
.mat	Materials file (AME)
.mnl	AutoLISP functions associated with a menu file
.mnu	Menu source file
.mnx	Compiled menu file
.msg	Message file
.old	Original version of converted drawing file
.pat	Hatch pattern library file
.pcp	Plot configuration parameters file
.pfb	PostScript font file
.pgp	Program parameters file
.plt	Plot output file
.ps	PostScript file
.psf	PostScript support file
.pwd	Login file
.scr	Command script file
.shp	Shape/font definition source file
.shx	Compiled Shape/font file
.slb	Slide library file
.sld	Slide file
.txt	Attribute extract or template file (CDF/SDF format)
.unt	Units file
.xlg	External references log file
.xmx	Exteral message file

APPENDIX

F

ERROR MESSAGES

INTRODUCTION

The most common error messages you are likely to see when using AutoCAD are the result of invalid input. The following are some of the messages you will see while working in AutoCAD:

Invalid input
Point or option keyword required
Requires numeric distance or two points.
Invalid

The above messages appear if you enter wrong information. In most cases, the prompt for the required input is repeated, and you can try again.

Disk Full Handling

When there is insufficient disk space on the drive containing the drawing file, AutoCAD displays the following message:

<Disk almost full>

If you see the above message, you have three choices:

1. End or Quit the drawing immediately.

2. Use the FILES command and delete some of the unwanted files from the drive that contains the drawing file.

3. Try changing the option under the UNDO command to None and it will free up some space in your drive.

Disaster Handling

AutoCAD updates the drawing data base after each command that adds, deletes, or changes anything in the drawing. The drawing data base is thus always up-to-date when the user begins a new command. If, for some reason, AutoCAD encounters a problem during execution of a command and cannot continue, one of the following messages is displayed:

Internal error *(followed by lot of numbers)*

or

Fatal error

Usually, an additional short message is displayed giving an error code. Following this, AutoCAD displays:

AutoCAD cannot continue, but any changes to your drawing made up to the start of the last command can be saved. Do you want to save your changes? <Y>

If you answer **Y** or hit [Enter], AutoCAD writes the drawing data base to disk before exiting. If this operation is successful, the following message will appear:

Drawing file successfully saved

If AutoCAD terminates with an internal error or fatal error, it tries to record diagnostic information concerning the error in the file ACAD.ERR. When reporting problems to Autodesk, the user should always include a printout of this file.

AutoCAD identifies drawing files saved after a crash. AutoCAD refuses to edit such files until they are loaded with Recover damaged drawing option. Refer to Appendix G for additional information about recovery of a damaged drawing.

G

RECOVERY OF DAMAGED DRAWINGS

INTRODUCTION

Sometimes, often through no fault of your own, an AutoCAD drawing becomes damaged or corrupted. To help repair damaged drawings, AutoCAD provides the RECOVER and AUDIT commands.

THE RECOVERY COMMAND

The RECOVER Command allows the user to recover a damaged drawing. Once the name has been given, the procedure is automatic, and the drawing is loaded. Block definitions, text fonts, linetypes, etc. are checked for invalid information (resulting from hardware problems, power surge, user error, software bug, etc.). Warning messages are displayed from the recovery and audit procedure to help the user in validation and correction. The output from the audit is also written to a log file. It puts this report file in the same directory as the current drawing, using the current drawing's name with the file extension .ADT.

Unfortunately, there are cases when the drawing is so badly damaged or corrupted that the drawing recovery will not be successful.

THE AUDIT COMMAND

You can also use the AUDIT command while you are in AutoCAD, as a diagnostic tool in examining a drawing to determine if it is valid, and optionally to correct errors. For every error detected, AutoCAD recommends action to correct it. It also generates a report and places it in the current directory under the current drawing's name with the file extension .ADT. To invoke the command, type **AUDIT** at the "Command:" prompt:

    Command: **audit**
    Fix any errors detected? <N>:

By answering **Y**, AutoCAD reports the number of errors, gives a detailed description of the errors and recommendations for fixing the errors. If you answer **N**, then AutoCAD will report the errors, but will not fix them at the same time.

APPENDIX

H

SYSTEM VARIABLES

T his is a complete listing of the AutoCAD system variables. Each variable has an associated type: integer, real, point, or text string. These variables can be examined and changed (unless read-only) by means of the SETVAR command and AutoLISP's (getvar and setvar) functions. Many of the system variables are saved across editing sessions; as indicated in the table, some are saved in the drawing itself, while others are saved in the AutoCAD general configuration file, ACAD.CFG.

Variable	Default Setting	Type	Saved in	Explanation
ACADPREFIX	" "	String	Read Only	The directory path, if any specified by the ACAD environment variable, with path separators appended if necessary (read-only).
ACADVER		String		This is the AutoCAD version number, which can only have values like "12" or "12a" (read-only). Note that this differs from the DXF file $ACADVER header variable, which contains the drawing data base level number.
AFLAGS	0	Integer		Attribute flags bit-code for ATTDEF command (sum of the following): 1 = Invisible 2 = Constant 4 = Verify 8 = Preset
ANGBASE	0	Real	Drawing	Angle 0 direction (with respect to the current UCS).
ANGDIR	0	Integer	Drawing	1 = clockwise angles, 0 = counterclockwise (with respect to the current UCS).
APERTURE	10	Integer	Config	Object Snap target height, in pixels (default value = 10).
AREA		Real		True area computed by Area, List, or Dblist (read-only).

(Reprinted with permission from Autodesk Inc.)

Variable	Default Setting	Type	Saved in	Explanation
ATTDIA	0	Integer	Drawing	1 causes the INSERT command to use a dialog box for entry of attribute values; 0 to issue prompts.
ATTMODE	1	Integer	Drawing	Attribute display mode (0 = off, 1 = normal, 2 = On).
ATTREQ	1	Integer	Drawing	0 assumes defaults for the values of all attributes during Insert of Blocks; 1 enables prompts (or dialog box) for Attribute values, as selected by ATTDIA.
AUDITCTL	0	Integer	Config	Controls whether an *.adt* log file (audit report file) is created. 0 = Disables (or prevents) the writing of *.adt* log files 1 = Enables the writing of *.adt* log files by the AUDIT command
AUNITS	0	Integer	Drawing	Angular units mode (0 = decimal degrees, 1 = degrees/minutes/seconds, 2 = grads, 3 = radians, 4 = surveyor's units).
AUPREC	0	Integer	Drawing	Angular units decimal places.
BACKZ	0.0000	Integer	Drawing	Back clipping plane offset for the current viewport, in drawing units. Meaningful only if the back clipping bit in VIEWMODE is on. The distance of the back clipping plane from the camera point can be found by subtracting BACKZ from the camera-to-target distance (read-only).
BLIPMODE	1	Integer	Drawing	Marker blips on if 1, off is 0.
CDATE		Real		Calendar date/time (read-only)
CECOLOR	"BY-LAYER"	String	Drawing	Current object color (read-only).
CELTSCALE	1	Real	Drawing	Sets the current global linetype scale for objects.
CELTYPE	"BY-LAYER"	String	Drawing	Current object linetype (read-only).
CHAMFERA	0.0000	Real	Drawing	First chamfer distance.
CHAMFERB	0.0000	Real	Drawing	Second chamfer distance.
CHAMFERC	0.0000	Real	Drawing	Sets the chamfer length.
CHAMFERD	0.0000	Real	Drawing	Sets the chamfer angle.
CHAMMODE	0	Integer		Sets the input method by which AutoCAD creates chamfers. 0 = Requires two chamfer distances 1 = Requires one chamfer length and an angle.
CIRCLERAD	0.0000	Real	Drawing	Sets the default circle radius. To specify no default, enter 0 (zero).
CLAYER	"0"	String	Drawing	Sets the current layer (read-only).

Variable	Default Setting	Type	Saved in	Explanation
CMDACTIVE		Integer		Bit-code that indicates whether an ordinary command, transparent command, script, or dialog box is active (read only). It is the sum of the following: 1 = Ordinary command is active 2 = Ordinary command and a transparent command are active 4 = Script is active 8 = Dialog box is active
CMDDIA	1	Integer	Config	1 = Use dialog boxes for PLOT commands; 0 = don't use dialog boxes for PLOT command.
CMDECHO	1	Integer		When the AutoLISP (command) function is used, prompts and input are echoed if this variable is 1, but not if it is 0.
CMDNAMES		String		Displays in English the name of the command (and transparent command) that is currently active. For example: LINE'ZOOM indicates that the ZOOM command is being used transparently during the LINE command.
CMLUUST	0	Integer		Specifies multiline justification. 0 = Top 1 = Middle 2 = Bottom
CMSCALE	1.0000	Real	Config	Controls the overall width of a multiline.
CMSTYLE		String	Config	Sets the name of the multiline style that AutoCAD uses to draw the multiline.
COORDS	1	Integer	Drawing	If 0, coordinate display is updated on point picks only. If 1, display of absolute coordinates is continuously updated. If 2, distance and angle from last point are displayed when a distance or angle is requested.
CVPORT	2	Integer	Drawing	The identification number of the current viewport.
DATE		Real		Julian date/time (read-only)
DBMOD		Integer		Bit-code that indicates the drawing modification status (read-only). It is the sum of the following: 1 = Entity database modified 2 = Symbol table modified 4 = Database variable modified 8 = Window modified 16 = View modified
DCTCUST		String	Config	Displays the current custom spelling dictionary path and file name.
DCTMAIN		String	Config	Displays the current main spelling dictionary file name.

Variable	Default Setting	Type	Saved in	Explanation
DELOBJ	1	Integer	Drawing	Controls whether objects used to create other objects are retained or deleted from the drawing database. 0 = Objects are deleted. 1 = Objects are retained.
DIASTAT		Integer		Dialog box exit status. If 0, the most recent dialog box was exited via "CANCEL." If 1, the most recent dialog box was exited via "OK" (read-only).
DIMxxx		Assorted	Drawing	All the dimensioning variables are also accessible as system variables.
DISTANCE	0.0000	Real		Distance computed by DIST command (read-only).
DONUTID	0	Real		Default donut inside diameter, can be zero.
DONUTOD		Real		Default donut outside diameter. Must be non-zero. If DONUTID is larger than DONUTOD, the two values are swapped by the next command.
DRAGMODE	2	Integer	Drawing	0 = no dragging, 1 = on if requested, 2 = auto.
DRAGP1	10	Integer	Config	Regen-drag input sampling rate
DRAGP2	25	Integer	Config	Fast-drag input sampling rate
DWGCODEPAGE		String	Drawing	Drawing code page. This variable is set to the system code page when a new drawing is created, but otherwise AutoCAD doesn't maintain it. It should reflect the code page of the drawing and you can set it to any of the values used by the SYSCODEPAGE system variable or "undefined." It is saved in the header.
DWGNAME		String		Drawing name as entered by the user. If the user-specified a drive/directory prefix, it is included as well (read-only).
DWGPREFIX		String		Drive/directory prefix for drawing (read-only).
DWGTITLED		Integer		Bit-code that indicates whether the current drawing has been named. (read-only) 0 = The drawing hasn't been named 1 = The drawing has been named
DWGWRITE		Integer		Controls the initial state of the read-only toggle in the OPEN command's "Open Drawing" standard file dialog box. 0 = Opens the drawing for reading only 1 = Opens the drawing for reading and writing. The default is 1
ELEVATION	0.0000	Real	Drawing	Current 3D elevation, relative to the current UCS for the current space.

Variable	Default Setting	Type	Saved in	Explanation
ERRNO		Integer		Code for errors caused by on-line programs such as AutoLISP and ADS applications.
EXPERT	0	Integer		Controls the issuance of certain "are you sure?" prompts, as indicated next.
				0 = Issues all prompts normally.
				1 = Suppresses "About to regen, proceed?" and "Really want to turn the current layer off?"
				2 = Suppresses the preceding prompts and Block's "Block already defined. Redefine it?" and Save/Wblock's "A drawing with this name already exists. Overwrite it?"
				3 = Suppresses the preceding prompts and those issued by linetype if you try to load a linetype that is already loaded or create a new linetype in a file that already defines it.
				4 = Suppresses the preceding prompts and those issued by "Ucs Save" and "Vports Save" if the name you supply already exists.
				5 = Suppresses the preceding prompts and those issued by "Dim Save" and "Dim Override" if the dimension style name you supply already exists (the entries are redefined).
				When a prompt is suppressed, EXPERT, the operation in question, is performed as though you had responded **Y** to the prompt. In the future, values greater than 5 may be used to suppress additional safety prompts. The setting of EXPERT can affect scripts, menu macros, AutoLISP, and the command functions. The default value is 0.
EXTMAX		3D point	Drawing	Upper right drawing uses extents. Expands outward as new objects are drawn; shrinks only by ZOOM All or ZOOM Extents. Reported in World coordinates for the current space (read-only).
EXTMIN		3D point	Drawing	Lower left drawing uses extents. Expands outward as new objects are drawn; shrinks only by ZOOM All or ZOOM Extents. Reported in World coordinates for the current space (read-only).
FACETRES	0.5	Real	Drawing	Adjust smoothness of shaded and hidden line-removed objects.
FFLIMIT	0	Integer	Config	Limits numbers of PostScript and TrueType fonts in memory.
FILEDIA	1	Integer	Config	1 = Use file dialogue boxes if possible; 0 = do not use file dialog boxes unless requested via ~ (tilde).
FILLETRAD	0.0000	Real	Drawing	Fillet radius.

Variable	Default Setting	Type	Saved in	Explanation
FILLMODE	1	Integer	Drawing	Fill mode on if 1, off if 0.
FONTALT	" "	String	Config	Specifies alternate font.
FONTMAP		String	Config	Specifies font mapping file.
FRONTZ	0.0000	Real	Drawing	Front clipping plane offset for the current viewport, in drawing units. Meaningful only if the front clipping bit in VIEWMODE is On and the Front clip not at eye bit is also ON. The distance of the front clipping bit from the camera point can be found by subtracting FRONTZ from the camera-to-target distance (read-only).
GRIDMODE		Integer	Drawing	1 = Grid on for current viewport, X and Y.
GRIDUNIT		2D point	Drawing	Grid spacing for current viewport, X and Y.
GRIPBLOCK	0	Integer	Config	Controls the assignment of grips in blocks. 0 = Assigns grip only to the insertion point of the block. 1 = Assigns grips to entities within the block
GRIPCOLOR	5	Integer (1–255)	Config	Color of nonselected grips; drawn as a box outline.
GRIPHOT	1	Integer (1–255)	Config	Color of selected grips; drawn as a filled box.
GRIPS	1	Integer	Config	Allows the use of selection set grips for the Stretch, Move, Rotate, Scale, and Mirror modes. 0 = Disables grips. 1 = Enables grips. To adjust the size of the grips, use the GRIPSIZE variable to adjust the effective pick area used by the graphics cursor when you snap to a grip, use the GRIPSIZE system variable
GRIPSIZE	3	Integer (1–255)	Config	The size in pixels of the box drawn to display the grip.
HANDLES	0	Integer	Drawing	If 0, entity handles are disabled, if 1, handles are on (read-only).
HIGHLIGHT	1	Integer		Object selection highlighting on if 1, off if 0.
HPANG		Real		Default hatch pattern angle.
HPDOUBLE	0	Integer		Default hatch pattern doubling for "U" user-defined patterns. 0 = Disables doubling 1 = Enables doubling
HPNAME	" "	String		Default hatch pattern name. Up to 34 characters, no spaces allowed. Returns " " if there is no default. Enter . (period) to set no default.
HPSCALE		Real		Default hatch pattern scale factor. Must be nonzero.

Variable	Default Setting	Type	Saved in	Explanation
HPSPACE		Real		Default hatch pattern line spacing for "U" user-defined simple patterns. Must be nonzero.
INSBASE		3D point	Drawing	Insertion base point (set by BASE command) expressed in UCS coordinates for the current space.
INSNAME	" "	String		Default block name for DDINSERT or INSERT. The name must conform to symbol naming conventions. Returns " " if there is no default. Enter . (period) to set no default.
ISOLINES		Real		Stores the end angle of the last arc entered.
LASTANGLE	0	Real		The end angle of the last arc entered, relative to the XY plane of the current UCS for the current space (read-only).
LASTPOINT	0.0000, 0.0000, 0.0000	3D point		The last point entered, expressed in UCS coordinates for the current space. Referenced by @ during keyboard entry.
LENSLENGTH	50.0000	Real	Drawing	Length of the lens (in millimeters) used in perspective viewing, for current viewport (read-only).
LIMCHECK	0	Integer	Drawing	Limits checking for the current space. On if 1, off if 0.
LIMMAX	12,000, 9,000	2D point	Drawing	Upper right drawing limits for the current space, expressed in World coordinates.
LIMMIN	0.0000, 0.0000	2D point	Drawing	Lower-left drawing limits for the current space, expressed in World coordinates.
LOCALE	"en"	String		Displays the ISO language code of the current AutoCAD version.
LOGINNAME		String		Displays the user's name as configured or input when AutoCAD is loaded (read-only).
LTSCALE	1.000	Real	Drawing	Linear units mode (1 = scientific, 2 = decimal, 3 = engineering, 4 = architectural, 5 = fractional).
LUNITS	2	Integer	Drawing	Linear units decimal places or denominator.
LUPREC	4	Integer	Drawing	Sets linear units decimal places.
MAXACTVP	16	Integer		Maximum number of viewports to regenerate at one time (read-only).
MAXSORT	200	Integer	Config	Maximum number of symbol/file names to be sorted by listing commands. If the total number of items exceeds this number, then none of the items are sorted (dflt. val=200).
MENUCTL	1	Integer	Config	Controls the page switching of the screen menu. 0 = Screen menu doesn't switch pages in response to keyboard command entry. 1 = Screen menu switches pages in response to keyboard command entry.

Variable	Default Setting	Type	Saved in	Explanation
MENUECHO	0	Integer		Menu echo/prompt control bits (sum of the following): 1 = Suppresses echo of menu items (^P in a menu item toggles echoing). 2 = Suppresses printing of system prompts during menu. 4 = Disables ^P toggle of menu echoing. The default value is 0 (all menu items and style prompts are displayed).
MENUNAME	"Acad"	Integer	Drawing	The name of the currently loaded menu file. Includes a drive/path prefix if you entered it (read-only).
MIRRTEXT	1	Integer	Drawing	Mirror reflects text if nonzero, retains text direction if 0.
MODEMACRO		String		Allows you to display a text string in the status line, such as the name of the current drawing, time/date stamp, or special modes. You can use MODEMACRO to display a simple string of text, or use special text strings written in the DIESEL macro language to have AutoCAD evaluate the macro from time to time and base the status line on user-selected conditions.
MTEXTED	" "	String	Config	Sets the name of program to use for editing mtext objects.
OFFSETDIST	0.0000	Real		Sets the default offset distance. If you enter a negative value, it defaults to Through mode.
ORTHOMODE	0	Integer	Drawing	Ortho mode on if 1, off if 0.
OSMODE	0	Integer	Drawing	Object Snap modes bit-code (sum of the following): 1 = Endpoint 2 = Midpoint 4 = Center 8 = Node 16 = Quadrant 32 = Intersection 64 = Insertion 128 = Perpendicular 256 = Tangent 512 = Nearest 1024 = Quick
PDMODE	0	Integer	Drawing	Point entity display mode.
PDSIZE	0.0000	Real	Drawing	Point entity display size.
PELLIPSE	0	Integer	Drawing	Controls the ellipse type created with ELLIPSE. 0 = Creates a true ellipse object. 1 = Creates a polyline representation of an ellipse.
PERIMETER		Real		Perimeter computed by Area, List, or Dblist (read-only).

Variable	Default Setting	Type	Saved in	Explanation
PFACEMAX	4	Integer		Maximum number of vertices per face (read-only).
PICKADD	1	Integer	Config	Controls additive selection of objects 0 = Disables PICKADD. The most recently selected objects, either by an individual pick or windowing, become the selection set. Previously selected objects are removed from the selection set. You can add more objects to the selection set, however by holding down Shift while selecting. 1 = Enables PICKADD. Each object you select, either individually or by windowing, is added to the current selection set. To remove objects from the selection set, hold down Shift while selecting.
PICKAUTO	1	Integer	Config	Controls automatic windowing when the Select objects: prompt appears 0 = Disables PICKAUTO. 1 = Allows you to draw a selection window (both window and crossing window) automatically at the Select objects: prompt.
PICKBOX	10	Integer	Config	Object selection target height, in pixels.
PICKDRAG	0	Integer	Config	Controls the method of drawing a selection window 0 = You draw the selection window by clicking the mouse at one corner, and then at the other corner. 1 = You draw the selection window by clicking at one corner, holding down the mouse button, dragging, and releasing the mouse button at the other corner.
PICKFIRST	1	Integer	Config	Controls the method of object selection so that you can select objects first, and then use an edit/inquiry command. 0 = Disables PICKFIRST 1 = Enables PICKFIRST
PICKSTYLE	3	Integer	Drawing	Controls group selection and associative hatch selection.
PLATFORM		String		Read-only message that indicates which version of AutoCAD is in use. This is a string such as one of the following: Microsoft Windows Sun4/SPARCstation 386 DOS Extender DECstation Apple Macintosh Silicon Graphics Iris Indigo

Variable	Default Setting	Type	Saved in	Explanation
PLINEGEN	1	Integer	Drawing	Sets the linetype pattern generation around the vertices of a 2D Polyline. When set to 1, PLINEGEN causes the linetype to be generated in a continuous pattern around the vertices of the polyline. When set to 0, polylines are generated with the linetype to start and end with a dash at each vertex. PLINEGEN doesn't apply to polylines with tapered segments.
PLINEWID	0.0000	Real	Drawing	Default polyline width. It can be zero.
PLOTID		String	Config	Changes the default plotter, based on its assigned description.
PLOTROTMODE	1	Integer	Drawing	Controls orientation of plots.
PLOTTER		Integer	Config	Changes the default plotter, based on its assigned integer (0-maximum configured). You can create up to 29 configurations.
POLYSIDES	8	Integer		Default number of sides for the POLYGON command. The range is 3–1024.
POPUPS	1	Integer		1 if the currently configured display driver supports dialog boxes, the menu bar, pull-down menus, and icon menus. 0 if these Advanced User Interface features are not available (read-only).
PROJMODE	1	Integer	Config	Sets the current Projection mode for Trim or Extend operations.
PSLTSCALE	0	Integer	Drawing	Controls paper space linetype scaling. 0 = No special linetype scaling. 1 = Viewport scaling governs linetype scaling.
PSPROLOG		String	Config	Assigns a name for a prologue section to be read from the *acad.psf* file when using the PSOUT command.
PSQUALITY		Integer	Config	Controls the rendering quality of PostScript images and whether they are drawn as filled objects or as outlines. A zero setting disables PostScript image generation and a nonzero setting enables PostScript generation. Positive setting: Sets the number of pixels per AutoCAD drawing unit for the PostScript resolution. Negative setting: Still sets the number of pixels per drawing unit, but uses the absolute value. Causes AutoCAD to show the PostScript paths as outlines and doesn't fill them.
QTEXTMODE	0	Integer	Drawing	Quick text mode on if 1, off if 0.
RASTERPREVIEW	0	Integer	Drawing	Controls whether drawing preview images are saved with the drawing.

Variable	Default Setting	Type	Saved in	Explanation
REGENMODE	1	Integer	Drawing	Regenauto on if 1, off if 0.
RE-INIT		Integer		Reinitializes the I/O ports, digitizer, display, plotter, and *acad.pgp* file using the following bit codes. To specify more than one reinitialization, enter the sum of their values, for example, 3 to specify both digitizer port (1) and plotter port (2) reinitialization. 1 = Digitizer port reinitialization 2 = Plotter port reinitialization 4 = Digitizer reinitialization 8 = Display reinitialization 16 = PGP file reinitialization (reload)
RIASPECT	0.0000	Real		Changes the image aspect ratio for imported raster images.
RIBACKG	0	Integer		Specified the backgroup color number for imported raster images.
RIEDGE	0	Integer		Controls the edge detection feature: 0 = Disables edge detection. 1-255 = Sets the threshold for RIEDGE detection.
RIGAMUT	256	Integer		Controls the number of colors GIFIN, PCXIN, and TIFFIN use when they import a color image.
RIGREY	0	Integer		Imports an image as a gray-scale image.
RITHRESH	0	Integer		Controls importing an image based on luminance (brightness).
SAVEFILE		String	Config	Current auto-save filename (read-only).
SAVENAME		String		The filename you save the drawing to (read-only).
SAVETIME	120	Integer	Config	Automatic save interval, in minutes (or 0 to disable automatic saves). The SAVETIME timer starts as soon as you make a change to a drawing, and is reset and restarts by a manual SAVE, SAVEAS, or QSAVE. The current drawing is saved to *auto.sv$*.
SCREENBOXES		Integer	Config	The number of boxes in the screen menu area of the graphics area. If the screen menu is disabled (configured off), SCREENBOXES is zero. On platforms that permit the AutoCAD graphics window to be resized or the screen menu to be reconfigured during an editing session, the value of this variable might change during the editing session (read-only).
SCREENMODE		Integer	Config	A (read-only) bit code indicating the graphics/text state of the AutoCAD display. It is the sum of the following bit values: 0 = text screen is displayed 1 = graphics mode is displayed 2 = dual-screen display configuration

Variable	Default Setting	Type	Saved in	Explanation
SCREENSIZE		2D point		Current viewpoint size in pixels, X and Y (read-only).
SHADEDGE	3	Integer	Drawing	0 = faces shaded, edges not highlighted. 1 = faces shaded, edges drawn in background color. 2 = faces not filled, edges in object color. 3 = faces in entity color, edges in background color.
SHADEDIF	70	Integer	Drawing	Ratio of ambient to diffuse light (in percent of ambient light).
SHPNAME	" "	String		Default shape name. Must conform to symbol naming conventions. If no default is set, it returns a " ". Enter . (period) to set no default.
SKETCHINC	0.1000	Real	Drawing	Sketch record increment.
SKPOLY	0	Integer	Drawing	Sketch generates lines if 0, polylines if 1.
SNAPANG	0	Real	Drawing	Snap/Grid rotation angle (UCS-relative) for the current viewport.
SNAPBASE	0.0000, 0.0000	2D point	Drawing	Snap/Grid origin point for the current viewport (in UCS XY coordinates).
SNAPISOPAIR	0	Integer	Drawing	Current isometric plane (0 = left, 1 = top, 2 = right) for the current viewport.
SNAPMODE	0	Integer	Drawing	1 = Snap on for current viewport; 0 = Snap off.
SNAPSTYL	0	Integer	Drawing	Snap style for current viewport (0 = standard, 1 = isometric).
SNAPUNIT	1.0000, 1.0000	2D point	Drawing	Snap spacing for current viewport, X and Y.
SORTENTS		Integer	Config	Controls the display of objects sort order operations using the following codes. To select more than one, enter the sum of their codes, for example, enter 3 to specify codes 1 and 2. The default, 96, specifies sort operations for plotting and PostScript output. 0 = Disables SORTENTS 1 = Sort for object selection 2 = Sort for object snap 4 = Sort for redraws 8 = Sort for MSLIDE slide creation 16 = Sort for REGENs 32 = Sort for plotting 64 = Sort for PostScript output

Variable	Default Setting	Type	Saved in	Explanation
SPLFRAME	0	Integer	Drawing	If = 1: – the control polygon for spline fit Polylines is to be displayed. – only the defining mesh of a surface fit polygon mesh is displayed (the fit surface is not displayed). – invisible edges of 3D faces are displayed. If = 0: – does not display the control polygon for spline fit Polylines. – displays the fit surface of a polygon mesh, not the defining mesh. – does not display the invisible edges of 3D faces.
SPLINESEGS	8	Integer	Drawing	The number of line segments to be generated for each spline patch.
SPLINETYPE	6	Integer	Drawing	Type of spline curve to be generated by Pedit Spline. The valid values are: 5 = quadratic B-spline 6 = cubic B-spline
SURFTAB1	6	Integer	Drawing	Number of tabulations to be generated for Rulesurf and Tabsurf. Also mesh density in the M direction for Resurf and Edgesurf.
SURFTAB2	6	Integer	Drawing	Mesh density in the N direction for Revsurf and Edgesurf.
SURFTYPE	6	Integer	Drawing	Type of surface fitting to be performed by Pedit Smooth. The valid values are: 5 = quadratic B-spline surface 6 = cubic B-spline surface 8 = Bezier surface
SURFU	6	Integer	Drawing	Surface density in the M direction.
SURFV	6	Integer	Drawing	Surface density in the N direction.
SYSCODEPAGE		String	Drawing	Indicates the system code page specified in *acad.xmf* (read-only). Codes are as follows: ascii dos932 dos437 iso8859–1 dos850 iso8859–2 dos852 iso8859–3 dos855 iso8859–4 dos857 iso8859–5 dos860 iso8859–6 dos861 iso8859–7 dos863 iso8859–8 dos864 iso8859–9 dos865 mac-roman dos869
TABMODE	0	Integer		Controls the use of tablet mode. 0 = Disables tablet mode 1 = Enables tablet mode

Variable	Default Setting	Type	Saved in	Explanation
TARGET	0.0000, 0.0000, 0.0000	3D point	Drawing	Location (in UCS coordinates) of the target (look-at) point for the current viewport (read-only).
TDCREATE		Real	Drawing	Time and date of drawing creation (read-only)
TDINDWG		Real	Drawing	Total editing time (read-only)
TDUPDATE		Real	Drawing	Time and date of last update/save (read-only)
TDSURTIMER		Real	Drawing	User elapsed timer (read-only)
TEMPPREFIX	" "	String		This variable contains the directory name (if any) configured for placement of temporary files, with a path separator appended if necessary (read-only).
TEXTEVAL	0	Integer		If = 0, all responses to prompts for text strings and Attribute values are taken literally. If = 1, text starting with "(" or "!" is evaluated as an AutoLISP expression, as for nontextual input. Note: The DTEXT command takes all input literally, regardless of the setting of TEXTEVAL.
TEXTSIZE	0.2000	Real	Drawing	The default height for new text objects drawn with the current text style (meaningless if the style has a fixed height).
TEXTSTYLE	"STANDARD"	String	Drawing	This variable contains the name of the current text style (read-only).
THICKNESS	0.0000	Real	Drawing	Current 3D thickness.
TILEMODE	1	Integer	Drawing	1 = Release 10 compatibility mode (uses Vports) 0 = Enables Paper Space and Viewport entities (uses MVIEW).
TOOLTIPS	1	Integer	Config	Controls the display of Tool Tips.
TRACEWID	0.0500	Real	Drawing	Default trace width.
TREEDEPTH		Integer	Drawing	A 4-digit (maximum) code that specifies the number of times the tree-structured spatial index may divide into branches, hence affecting the speed in which AutoCAD searches the database before completing an action. The first two digits refer to the depth of the model space nodes, and the second two digits refer to the depth of paper space nodes. Use a positive setting for 3D drawings and a negative setting for 2D drawings.
TREEMAX	10000000	Integer	Config	Limits memory consumption during drawing regeneration.
TRIMMODE	1	Integer		Controls whether AutoCAD trims selected edges for chamfers and fillets.

Variable	Default Setting	Type	Saved in	Explanation
UCSFOLLOW	0	Integer	Drawing	The setting of UCSFOLLOW is maintained separately for both spaces and can be accessed in either space, but the setting is ignored while in Paper Space (it is always treated as if set to 0).
UCSICON	0	Integer	Drawing	The coordinate system icon bit-code for the current viewport (sum of the following): 1 = On – icon display enabled 2 = Origin – if icon display is enabled, the icon floats to the UCS origin if possible.
UCSNAME	" "	String	Drawing	Name of the current coordinate system for the current space. Returns a null string if the current UCS is unnamed (read-only).
UCSORG	0.0000, 0.0000, 0.0000	3D point	Drawing	The origin point of the current coordinate system for the current space. This value is always returned in World coordinates (read-only).
UCSXDIR	1.0000, 0.0000, 0.0000	3D point	Drawing	The X direction of the current UCS for the current space (read-only).
UCSYDIR	0.0000, 1.0000, 0.0000	3D point	Drawing	The Y direction of the current UCS for the current space (read-only).
UNDOCTL	1	Integer		A (read-only) code indicating the state of the UNDO feature. It is the sum of the following values: 1 = set if UNDO is enabled 2 = set if only one command can be undone 4 = set if Auto-group mode is enabled 8 = set if a group is currently active
UNDOMARKS		Integer		The (read-only) number of marks that have been placed in the UNDO control stream by the UNDO command's Mark option. The Mark and Back options are unavailable if a group is currently active.
UNITMODE	0	Integer	Drawing	0 = Displays fractional, feet and inches, and surveyor's angles as previously. 1 = Displays fractional, feet and inches, and surveyor's angles in input format.
VIEWCTR		3D point	Drawing	Center of view in current viewport, expressed in UCS coordinates (read-only).
VIEWDIR		3D point	Drawing	The current viewport's viewing direction expressed in World coordinates. This describes the camera point as a 3D offset from the TARGET point (read-only).

Variable	Default Setting	Type	Saved in	Explanation
VIEWMODE	0	Integer	Drawing	Viewing mode bit-code for the current viewport (read-only). The value is the sum of the following: 1 = perspective view active 2 = front clipping on 4 = back clipping on 8 = UCS follow mode 16 = Front clip not at eye. If On, the front clip distance (FRONTZ) determines the front clipping plane. If Off, FRONZ is ignored and the front clipping is set to pass through the camera point (i.e., vectors behind the camera are not displayed). This flag is ignored if the front clipping bit (2) is off.
VIEWSIZE		Real	Drawing	Height of view in current viewport, expressed in drawing units (read-only).
VIEWTWIST	0	Real	Drawing	View twist angle for the current viewport (read-only).
VISRETAIN	1	Integer	Drawing	If = 0, the current drawing's On/Off, Freeze/Thaw, color, and linetype settings for Xref-dependent layers take precedence over the Xref's layer definition. If = 1, these settings don't take precedence.
VSMAX		3D point		The upper right corner of the current viewport's virtual screen, expressed in UCS coordinates (read-only).
VSMIN		3D point		The lower left corner of the current viewport's virtual screen, expressed in UCS coordinates (read-only).
WORDDUCS	1	Integer		If = 1, the current UCS is the same as the WCS. If = 0, it is not (read-only).
WORLDVIEW	1	Integer	Drawing	Dview and Vpoint command input is relative to the current UCS. If this variable is set to 1, the current UCS is changed to the WCS for the duration of a DVIEW or VPOINT command. Default value = 1.
XREFCTL	1	Integer	Config	Controls whether .xlg files (external reference log files) are written. 0 = Xref log (.xlg) files not written 1 = Xref log (.xlg) files written

I

HATCH & FILL
PATTERNS

. . . .

INTRODUCTION

AutoCAD supports two types of hatch pattern: vector patterns and PostScript fill patterns. Vector patterns are made of straight lines and dots; they are defined in the Acad.Pat pattern file. You can create custom hatch patterns or purchase patterns created by third-party vendors. You place a hatch pattern with the HATCH or BHATCH commands.

PostScript fill patterns are made by the PostScript PDL (page description language); they are defined in the Acad.Psf file. To create a custom fill pattern, you need to know PostScript programming. You place a fill pattern with the PSFILL command.

The 53 hatch patterns and 11 PostScript fills supplied with the AutoCAD package are shown on the following pages.

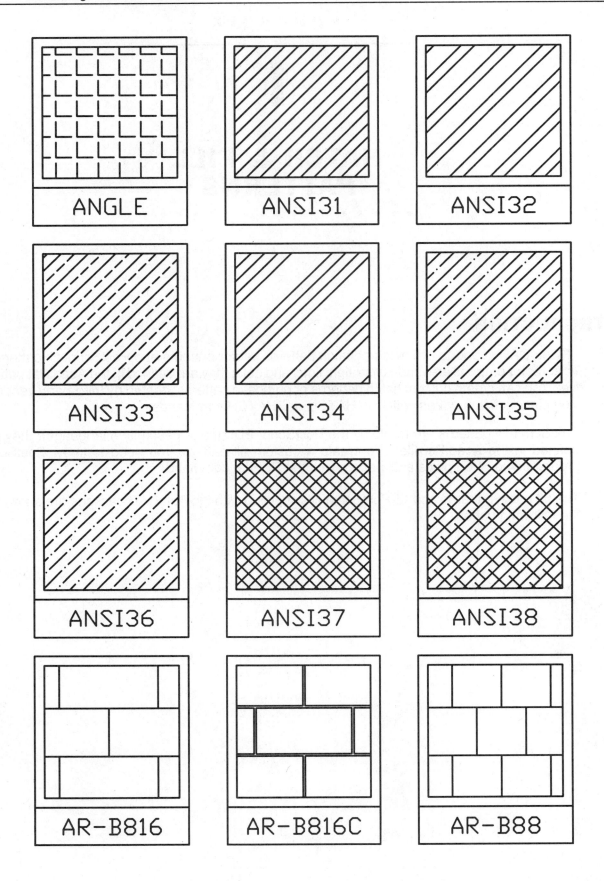

AR-BRELM

AR-BRSTD

AR-CONC

AR-HBONE

AR-PARQ1

AR-RROOF

AR-RSHKE

AR-SAND

BOX

BRASS

BRICK

BRSTONE

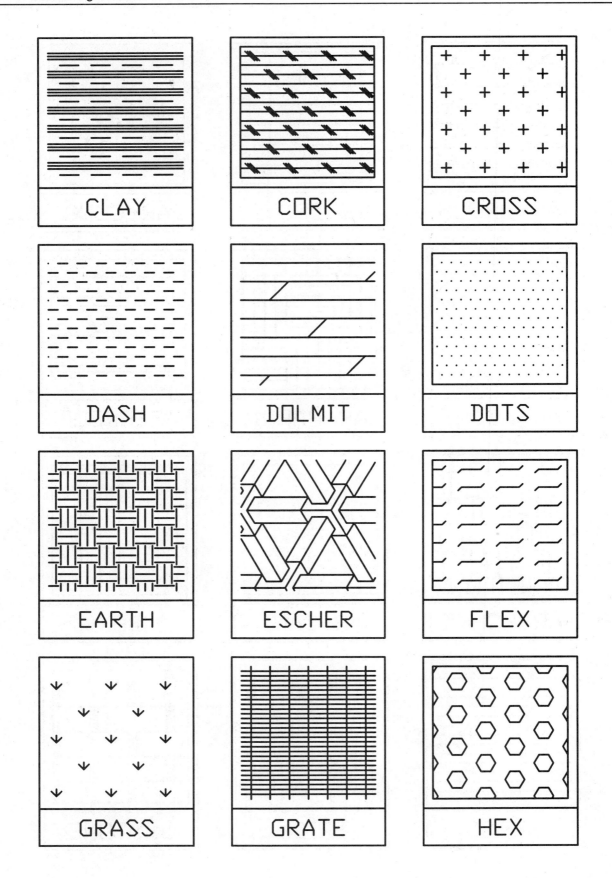

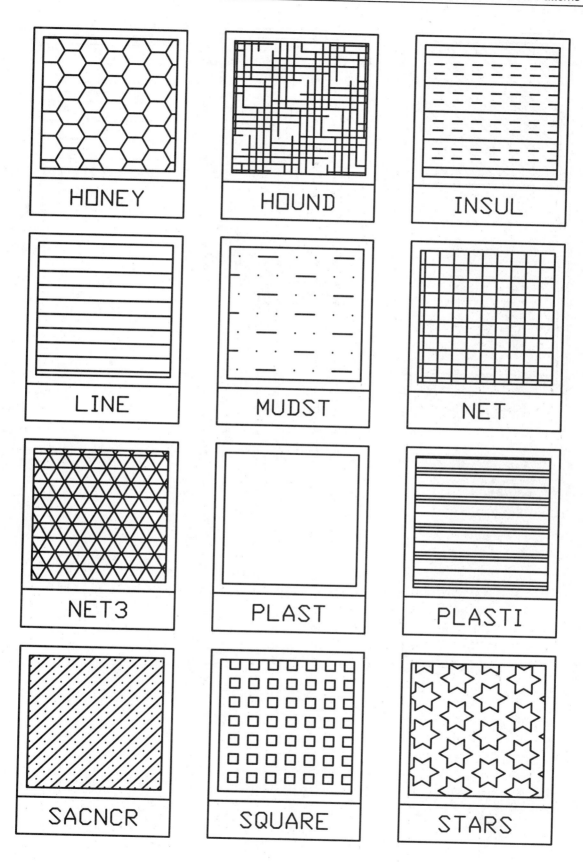

HONEY

HOUND

INSUL

LINE

MUDST

NET

NET3

PLAST

PLASTI

SACNCR

SQUARE

STARS

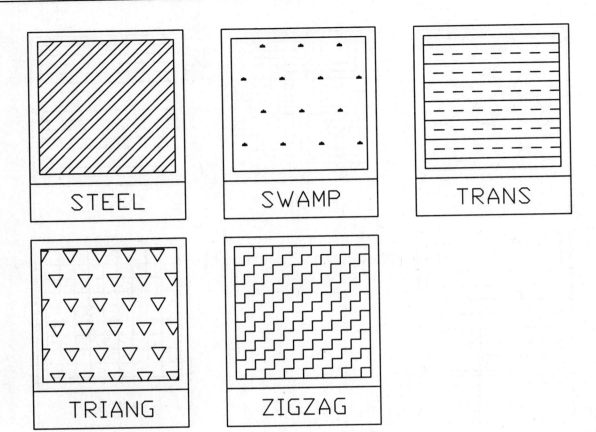

POSTSCRIPT FILL PATTERNS

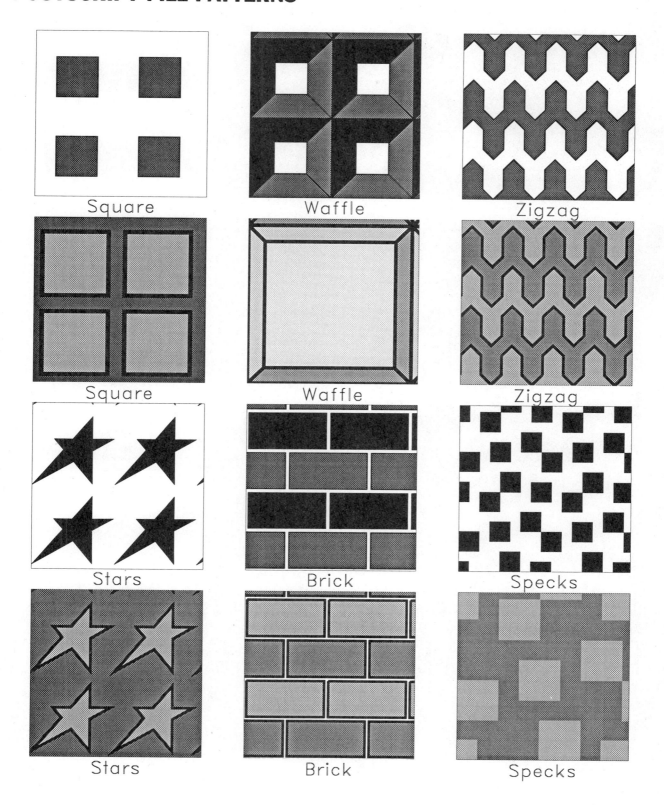

Square   Waffle   Zigzag

Square   Waffle   Zigzag

Stars   Brick   Specks

Stars   Brick   Specks

APPENDIX

J

FONTS

INTRODUCTION

AutoCAD works with two type of text fonts: the original SHX-format font files and PFB PostScript font files. The AutoCAD package includes 17 SHX text fonts, five SHX symbol fonts, and 16 PFB text fonts, as shown on the following pages.

USING SHX AND PFB FILES

Other SHX font files are available from third-party developers. In addition, AutoCAD can use PostScript fonts from any source, many of which are included free with other software packages. Postscript fonts are usually stored in the \Psfonts subdirectory.

AutoCAD does not store text fonts in the drawing file. Instead, the DWG file references SHX font definition files stored elsewhere on the hard drive. Thus, if you receive a drawing from another AutoCAD system, you might have to tell AutoCAD where to find the font files on your system.

PostScript fonts placed in an AutoCAD drawing have two anomilies: the fonts are unfilled; the fonts are drawn 30% too small. To compensate for the reduced size, specify a text height 50% higher.

Appendix J

STANDARD TEXT FONTS

FAST FONTS

TXT   ABCDEFGHIJKLMNOPQRSTUVWXYZ 1234567890

MONOTXT   ABCDEFGHIJKLMNOPQRSTUVWXYZ 1234567890

SIMPLEX FONTS

ROMANS   ABCDEFGHIJKLMNOPQRSTUVWXYZ 1234567890

SCRIPTS   *ABCDEFGHIJKLMNOPQRSTUVWXYZ* 1234567890

GREEKS   ABXΔEΦΓHIϑKΛMNOΠΘPΣTΥVΩΞΨZ 1234567890

DUPLEX FONTS

ROMAND   ABCDEFGHIJKLMNOPQRSTUVWXYZ 1234567890

COMPLEX FONTS

ROMANC   ABCDEFGHIJKLMNOPQRSTUVWXYZ 1234567890

ITALICC   *ABCDEFGHIJKLMNOPQRSTUVWXYZ 1234567890*

SCRIPTC   *ABCDEFGHIJKLMNOPQRSTUVWXYZ 1234567890*

GREEKC   ABXΔEΦΓHIϑKΛMNOΠΘPΣTΥVΩΞΨZ 1234567890

TRIPLEX FONTS

ROMANT   **ABCDEFGHIJKLMNOPQRSTUVWXYZ 1234567890**

ITALICT   ***ABCDEFGHIJKLMNOPQRSTUVWXYZ 1234567890***

STANDARD TEXT FONTS

GOTHIC FONTS

GOTHICE

GOTHICG

GOTHICI

SYMBOL FONTS

A B C D E F G H I J K L M N O P Q R S T U V W X Y Z
a b c d e f g h i j k l m n o p q r s t u v w x y z

SYASTRO

SYMAP

SYMATH

SYMETEO

SYMUSIC

STANDARD TEXT FONTS

POSTSCRIPT FONTS

CIBT.PFB   ABCDEFGHIJKLMNOPQRSTUVWXYZ 1234567890

COBT.PFB   ABCDEFGHIJKLMNOPQRSTUVWXYZ 1234567890

EUR.PFB   ABCDEFGHIJKLMNOPQRSTUVWXYZ 1234567890

EURO.PFB   ABCDEFGHIJKLMNOPQRSTUVWXYZ 1234567890

PAR.PFB   ABCDEFGHIJKLMNOPQRSTUVWXYZ 1234567890

ROM.PFB   ABCDEFGHIJKLMNOPQRSTUVWXYZ 1234567890

ROMB.PFB   ABCDEFGHIJKLMNOPQRSTUVWXYZ 1234567890

ROMI.PFB   ABCDEFGHIJKLMNOPQRSTUVWXYZ 1234567890

SAS.PFB   ABCDEFGHIJKLMNOPQRSTUVWXYZ 1234567890

SASB.PFB   ABCDEFGHIJKLMNOPQRSTUVWXYZ 1234567890

SASBO.PFB   ABCDEFGHIJKLMNOPQRSTUVWXYZ 1234567890

SASO.PFB   ABCDEFGHIJKLMNOPQRSTUVWXYZ 1234567890

SUF.PFB   ABCDEFGHIJKLMNOPQRSTUVWXYZ 1234567890

TE.PFB   ABCDEFGHIJKLMNOPQRSTUVWXYZ 1234567890

TEB.PFB   ABCDEFGHIJKLMNOPQRSTUVWXYZ 1234567890

CYRILLIC FONTS

CYRILLIC   АБВГДЕЖЗИЙКЛМНОПРСТУФХЦЧШЩ 123456789(

CYRILTLC   АБЧДЕФГХИЩКЛМНОПЦРСТУВШЖЙЗ 123456789(

APPENDIX

K

LINETYPES

INTRODUCTION

Linetypes are defined by the ACAD.LIN file. In addition to the continuous linetype, the AutoCAD program comes with the 24 linetypes shown on the next page. You can add custom linetypes to the ACAD.LIN file.

Before you can use a linetype in a drawing, it must be loaded with the LINETYPE command. Set the linetype scale with the LTSCALE command; set independent linetype scaling in paper space with the PSLTSCALE system variable; control the generation of linetype along a polyline with the PLINEGEN system variable.

Appendix K

STANDARD LINETYPES

BORDER

BORDER2

BORDERX2

CENTER

CENTER2

CENTERX2

DASHDOT

DASHDOT2

DASHDOTX2

DASHED

DASHED2

DASHEDX2

DIVIDE

DIVIDE2

DIVIDEX2

DOT

DOT2

DOTX2

HIDDEN

HIDDEN2

HIDDENX2

PHANTOM

PHANTOM2

PHANTOMX2

INDEX

Program switching with Windows,
12-22, 12-22(*Fig. 12-11*)
Prototype drawings, 2-5
PSFILL, 7-20
PSIN, 7-18
   PSDRAG, 7-18
   PSQUALITY, 7-18
PSLTSCALE, 11-15
PSOUT, 7-19–7-20
PSPACE, 1-20, 11-12
Pull-down menus, 1-7, 1-7(*Fig. 1-9*),
   1-9–1-10, 1-9(*Fig. 1-11*),
   1-10(*Fig. 1-12*), D-2
PURGE, 3-31, 12-11

Q
QTEXT, 5-44
Quick Tour help window, 1-19,
   1-19(*Fig. 1-25*)
QUIT, 2-35–2-36, 2-36(*Fig. 2-33*)

R
Radio buttons, 1-14, 1-14(*Fig. 1-17*)
Radius dimensioning, 6-16–6-17
RAY, 5-1, 5-3, 5-3(*Fig. 5-2*)
RECTANGLE, 2-22, 2-22(*Fig. 2-21*)
Rectangular array, 3-46–3-47, 14-41
Rectangular coordinates
   absolute, 2-24–2-26
   relative, 2-26–2-27
REDO, 1-29, 5-55, 5-55(*Fig. 5-61*)
REDRAW, 2-62–2-63, 2-63(*Figs.
   2-67* and *2-68*)
REDRAWALL, 11-10
REGEN, 2-63
REGENALL, 11-10
REGENAUTO, 2-63, 12-13–12-14
REGION, 14-23
Relative
   polar coordinates, 2-27–2-28
   rectangular coordinates, 2-26–
   2-27
RENAME, 3-31, 12-10–12-11,
   12-10(*Fig. 12-8*)
RENDER, 15-3–15-6, 15-3(*Figs.
   15-3* and *15-4*), 15-5(*Figs. 15-5
   and 15-6*)
Rendering, 1-29, 15-1–15-18
   preferences dialog box, 15-14–
   15-17
REPLAY, 15-18
Report format, 2-12
RESUME, 13-8
Revolution
   solid of, 14-53
   surface of, 14-33
REVOLVE, 14-53, 14-53(*Fig. 14-59*)
   Object option, 14-53

Start point of axis option, 14-53
   X axis option, 14-53
   Y axis option, 14-53
REVSURF, 14-33–14-35, 14-34(*Fig.
   14-31*), 14-35(*Fig. 14-32*)
Right hand rule, 14-3–14-4, 14-3(*Fig.
   14-2*)
RMAT, 15-12–15-14, 15-12(*Fig.
   15-16*), 15-13(*Fig. 15-17*),
   15-14(*Fig. 15-18*)
RPREF, 15-14–15-17, 15-15(*Figs.
   15-19* and *15-20*)
ROTATE, 1-28, 4-38–4-40, 4-38(*Fig.
   4-52*), 4-39(*Fig. 4-53*)
   Reference Angle option, 4-38–
   4-40, 4-39(*Fig. 4-54*)
ROTATE3D, 14-38, 14-38(*Fig.
   14-36*), 14-39(*Fig. 14-37*)
RSCRIPT, 13-9
RULESURF, 14-31–14-32,
   14-31(*Fig. 14-27*), 14-32(*Fig.
   14-28*)

S
SAVE, 2-2, 2-34, 2-35(*Fig. 2-32*),
   2-36(*Fig. 2-33*)
SAVEAS, 2-2, 2-34–2-35
SAVEIMG, 15-17–15-18, 15-17(*Fig.
   15-22*)
SAVETIME system variable, 2-34
Saving and quitting, 2-34–2-36
SCALE, 4-40–4-41, 4-40(*Fig. 4-55*),
   4-41(*Fig. 4-56*)
   Reference Scale option, 4-41,
   4-41(*Fig. 4-57*)
Scaling annotations and symbols,
   7-6, 7-6(*Table 7-1*)
SCENE, 15-10–15-12, 15-11(*Figs.
   15-13* and *15-14*), 15-12(*Fig.
   15-15*)
Screen, 1-3–1-8, 1-3(*Fig. 1-2*)
   command window, 1-7–1-8,
   1-8(*Fig. 1-10*)
   drawing window, 1-3
   pull-down menu, 1-7, 1-7(*Fig. 1-9*)
   status bar, 1-4
   title bar, 1-4
   toolbars, 1-4–1-6
Screen menu, 1-10–1-11, 1-10(*Fig.
   1-13*), 1-11(*Fig. 1-14*), D-3
SCRIPT, 13-5, 13-8
Script files, 13-4
   changing block definitions with,
   13-5–13-8
   spaces and end-of-lines in, 13-4
   text, 13-4
   utility commands for, 13-8–13-9
   from within AutoCAD, 13-5

SECTION, 14-61–14-62, 14-61(*Fig.
   14-68*), 14-62(*Fig. 14-69*)
SELECT, 2-38
Selection sets, 18-44–18-45
SERVICE menu, 1-11
SETVAR, 2-5, 2-14, 5-50–5-52
SHADE, 15-1–15-2, 15-1(*Fig. 15-1*),
   15-2(*Fig. 15-2*)
   SHADEDGE, 15-2
   SHADEDIF, 15-2
SHAPE-CHARACTER, 17-44
Shapes, 17-44–17-49
   DISTANCE-DIRECTION codes,
   17-45–17-46, 17-45(*Fig. 17-44*),
   17-46(*Figs. 17-45* and *17-46*)
   SHAPE, 1-30, 17-44
   special codes, 17-46–17-49,
   17-48(*Figs. 17-47* and *17-48*)
SHELL, 12-21–12-22
SIN, 18-36–18-37
SKETCH, 5-31–5-33, 5-31(*Fig. 5-43*)
Sketching, 5-30–5-31
   in TABLET mode, 16-9
SLICE, 14-62–14-63, 14-62(*Fig.
   14-70*), 14-63(*Fig. 14-71*)
SLIDELIB, 13-2
Slides, 1-28, 13-1
   MSLIDE, 13-1–13-2
   SLIDELIB, 13-2
   VSLIDE, 13-2–13-3
SNAP, 1-20, 2-47–2-48, 2-47(*Fig.
   2-46*)
   Aspect option, 2-48
   OFF option, 2-48
   ON option, 2-47
   Rotate option, 2-48
   Style option, 2-48, 2-48(*Fig. 2-47*)
SOLID, 1-22, 4-6–4-9, 4-7(*Figs. 4-6
   and 4-7*), 4-8(*Figs. 4-8* and *4-9*),
   4-9(*Fig. 4-10*)
Solid models/shapes, 14-42
   composite solids, 14-54–14-58
   editing, 14-58–14-64
SPELL, 5-38–5-40, 5-39(*Figs. 5-48
   and 5-49*)
Spell checking, 5-38
SPHERE, 14-47–14-48, 14-47(*Fig.
   14-49*), 14-48(*Fig. 14-50*)
SPLINE, 1-31, 5-26–5-27, 5-26(*Fig.
   5-41*)
Spline curves, 5-26
   editing, 5-27
SPLINEDIT, 5-27–5-30, 5-28(*Fig.
   5-42*)
   Close option, 5-29
   Exit option, 5-30
   Fit Data option, 5-28–5-29
   Move Vertex option, 5-29–5-30